Guide to
First Edition Prices
2002/3

Guide to

First Edition Prices 2002/3

Edited by
R.B. Russell

Tartarus Press

Guide to First Edition Prices, 2002/3, edited by R.B. Russell
Published by The Tartarus Press, November 2001, at:
Coverley House, Carlton, Leyburn, North Yorkshire, DL8 4AY

Book printed and bound by the Atheneum Press Ltd., Tyne and Wear

ISBN 1 872621 58 9

Copyright © 2001 R.B. Russell/Tartarus Press

Wherever possible each value in this *Guide* has been checked against copies of the book offered for sale in the last year. The greatest care has been taken to ensure that the information included in the guide is accurate, but the editor cannot be held accountable for any losses that may occur as a result of the information contained herein. The prices represent the perceived average prices as contained in advertisements of bookdealers, prices paid at auction for books, and with reference to reputable guides credited in the introduction.

INTRODUCTION

This is the fourth edition of the Tartarus Press *Guide to First Edition Prices*. It contains suggested values for over 25,000 sought-after books by over 500 authors. For the majority of these authors we provide a full bibliography of their writings.

The values of books are governed in theory by the law of supply and demand. A rare book will have little value if it is not sought after by collectors, and conversely a book printed in a run of several thousands can still be worth a great deal if there are more collectors eager to acquire a copy than there are copies available. There will always be exceptions, of course, but the fact that a famous author's piece of embarrassing juvenilia may be worth a great deal more than their classic works of more mature years is because their first efforts were usually printed in small numbers, and there are many enthusiasts who would like to own a copy of every book by that author.

First editions are sought after because they represent a book in the state in which it was first published. Despite the fact that later editions may tidy up typographical errors or contain important revisions, collectors will usually prefer the first editions. Some reprints *are* collected, if they contain important additional matter, for example illustrations by a collectable artist, and where appropriate they are included in this *Guide*.

The single point which causes the widely-varying prices asked for apparently the same volume is condition. Simply put, collectors prefer to have their books in as smart a condition as possible, and will pay more for a book if it is in as close a condition to its newly-published state as possible. The importance of the dust wrapper cannot be over-emphasised, as the most extreme variations in price are usually between books offered with and without their original dust wrappers. Some books almost never appear for sale in a mint state, and when they do a premium can be asked for by a dealer. It is hard to believe, but a small nick or crease can half the value of some books. Inscriptions by previous owners (unless famous), notes in margins etc, will further decrease the value of a book. So take care of them!

The prices asked by dealers for first editions seem to have increased a great deal in the last few years. In previous editions of this *Guide* the values suggested were the prices asked by the average provincial bookdealer selling a title to a collector. The advent of the Internet has given provincial dealers on the most obscure and unvisited parts of the globe many thousands of potential customers. They are astute enough to realise that they can now ask the highest prices for the books they offer. The vastly increased number of books on offer to any one collector with access to the Internet has levelled out the values of unfashionable and reprinted books, but at the top end of the market prices have risen greatly. Some very rare books are now being offered in wonderful condition, but mind-boggling prices are often being asked.

An important issue that many dealers have asked me to point out is that this *Guide* represents the prices that a dealer might charge a collector, not the price at which they would necessarily buy books for their own stock. My own personal experience is that a dealer will often offer the vendor a quarter of the re-sale value of an ordinary book. For a large number of very indifferent titles the proportion will be considerably less. However, a very desirable and expensive book will often be bought for much nearer its eventual re-sale value. Anyone offering a book for sale should remember that there is nothing wrong with a dealer attempting to make an honest profit. Most dealers choose their profession out of a love of books, but they would not be there to sell you the books if they could not make a living.

The rate of appreciation in the value of collectable first editions is impossible to predict, but it should be remembered that copies in poor condition, acquired for little, will have little re-sale value. If you can afford it, it is always a better investment to buy a fine copy. Advertisements for investment opportunities always carry the caveat (usually in smaller print than this) that prices may go down as well as up.

Please remember that this is only a guide. Limitations of space make it impossible to comment adequately on the complexities of different "states", variant bindings etc. If in any doubt, especially if you are about to make an expensive purchase, please do consult author-specific bibliographies which will give much more detailed information. If in doubt, ask the bookdealer! Although I am grateful to the many people who have helped me to compile this *Guide*, as editor I must assume all responsibility for any errors which, inevitably, may have crept in. I welcome any suggestions, corrections etc at the publisher's address. A criticism of all previous editions has been the omission of certain authors. We will never be able to do justice to every collectable author, but a number of new entries suggested by dealers and collectors are again included in this edition. As ever, suggestions for new entries for future editions of the *Guide* are welcomed.

No one can learn the tricks of the book trade overnight. This *Guide* does not explain how to become a bookdealer, or how to get one step ahead of the trade. It is unlikely that it will help anyone make their fortune, and no one person can be an expert on all of the titles listed here. I have only been able to compile the *Guide* thanks to the experience of the countless bookdealers who have advertised books for sale over the last few years. I would additionally like to acknowledge the specific help of the following: John Abrahamson, The Margery Allingham Society, Mike Ashley, Chris Barker, Mike Berro, Dr Glen Cavaliero, Shelley Cox, Clarissa Cridland, Richard Dalby, David Downes, Nicholas Granger-Taylor, Norman Gates, Clive Harper, Malcolm Henderson, Susan Hill, Lawrence Knapp, Rick Loomis, Edward Mendelson, Gary Morris & the Compton-Burnett Cabal, Rosalie Parker, Timothy Parker Russell, Ryan Roberts, Colin Smythe, Colin Scott-Sutherland, Ed Seiler, David Tibbetts, David Tibet and Mark Valentine.

NOTES

Entries are listed alphabetically by author, then chronologically by publication. Where two values are given the first is for a book with a dust wrapper and the second for a copy without a dust wrapper. If there is only one price quoted it is for a book without a dustwrapper. All books are assumed to be very good for their age. Before 1920 books are given a single value because the survival of dust wrappers from before this time is so rare that it is very difficult to value them. Limited editions are noted simply as *x copies*. If it

is signed it is assumed that it was the author who did the signing, unless noted otherwise. If a book was re-issued under a new title then it is listed under the original title but noted thus: *ditto*, as *Starship*, Criterion (U.S.), 1959 . £60/£20 If a book was issued pseudonomously then a note follows the date, ie. (pseud. 'Fred Smith')

REFERENCES

Ahern, Allen and Patricia, *Collected Books, A Guide to their Values, 1998 Edition*, Putnam's, 1997.

Bédé, Jean-Albert, & Edgerton, William B., eds., *Columbia Dictionary of Modern European Literature*, Columbia University Press, 1980.

Breese, Martin, *Breese's Guide to Modern First Editions*, 2000, Breese Books, 1999.

Browning, D.C. (editor), *Everyman's Dictionary of Literary Biography*, Everyman, 1970.

Cole, Michael (editor), *Annual Register of Book Values, Modern First Editions*, The Clique. (various editions)

Connolly, Joseph, *Modern First Editions*, Orbis, 1993.

Cooper, John, & Pike, B.A., *Detective Fiction: The Collector's Guide*, Scolar Press, 1994 (second edition).

Hamer, Martin, *The Hamer Comic Annual Guide*, Hamer 20th Century Books, 2000.

Jackson, Crispin (editor), *Collecting Children's Books*, Book and Magazine Collector, 1995.

Ousby, Ian (editor), *The Cambridge Guide to Literature in English*, Guild Publishing, 1989.

Ward, K. Anthony, *First Editions, A Field Guide*, Scolar Press, 1994.

Woodcock, George, *20th-Century Fiction*, Macmillan, 1983.

The Book and Magazine Collector, various issues.

INDEX OF AUTHORS

RICHARD LE
  GALLIENNE
URSULA LE GUIN
ROSAMOND LEHMANN
ELMORE LEONARD
GASTON LEROUX
DORIS LESSING
C.S. LEWIS
NORMAN LEWIS
WYNDHAM LEWIS
DAVID LINDSAY
DAVID LODGE
JACK LONDON
E.C.R. LORAC
H.P. LOVECRAFT
PETER LOVESEY
MALCOLM LOWRY
ROSE MACAULAY
GEORGE MACDONALD
ROSS MACDONALD
IAN McEWAN
JOHN McGAHERN
ARTHUR MACHEN
COLIN MACINNES
ALASTAIR MACLEAN
LOUIS MACNEICE
NORMAN MAILER
THOMAS MANN
KATHERINE MANSFIELD
CAPTAIN FREDERICK
  MARRYAT
NGAIO MARSH
W. SOMERSET
  MAUGHAM
ARTHUR MILLER
HENRY MILLER
ABRAHAM MERRITT
A.A. MILNE
GLADYS MITCHELL
MARGARET MITCHELL
NAOMI MITCHISON
MARY RUSSELL
  MITFORD
NANCY MITFORD
NICHOLAS MONSARRAT
BRIAN MOORE
WILLIAM MORRIS
JOHN MORTIMER
IRIS MURDOCH
VLADIMIR NABOKOV
SHIVA NAIPAUL
V.S. NAIPAUL
VIOLET NEEDHAM
KAY NIELSEN
PATRICK O'BRIAN
EDNA O'BRIEN
FLANN O'BRIEN
LIAM O'FLAHERTY
EUGENE O'NEILL
JOE ORTON
GEORGE ORWELL
JOHN OSBORNE
WILFRED OWEN
THOMAS LOVE
  PEACOCK
MERVYN PEAKE
ELLIS PETERS
HAROLD PINTER
SYLVIA PLATH
EDGAR ALLAN POE

BEATRIX POTTER
EZRA POUND
ANTHONY POWELL
JOHN COWPER POWYS
LLEWELYN POWYS
T.F. POWYS
TERRY PRATCHETT
ANTHONY PRICE
J.B. PRIESTLEY
V. S. PRITCHETT
MARCEL PROUST
BARBARA PYM
ELLERY QUEEN
JONATHAN RABAN
ARTHUR RACKHAM
ANN RADCLIFFE
ARTHUR RANSOME
FORREST REID
RUTH RENDELL
JEAN RHYS
ANNE RICE
FRANK RICHARDS
W. HEATH ROBINSON
SAX ROHMER
FREDERICK ROLFE
  (BARON CORVO)
J.K. ROWLING
RUPERT *see Mary Tourtel*
SALMAN RUSHDIE
VITA SACKVILLE-WEST
SAKI
J.D. SALINGER
SARBAN
SIEGFRIED SASSOON
THE SAVOY
DOROTHY L. SAYERS
PAUL SCOTT
ANNA SEWELL
TOM SHARPE
GEORGE BERNARD
  SHAW
MARY SHELLEY
M.P. SHIEL
NEVIL SHUTE
ALAN SILLITOE
GEORGES SIMENON
EDITH SITWELL
OSBERT SITWELL
SACHEVERELL SITWELL
CLARK ASHTON SMITH
STEVIE SMITH
C.P. SNOW
ALEXANDER
  SOLZHENITSYN
MURIEL SPARK
STEPHEN SPENDER
GERTRUDE STEIN
JOHN STEINBECK
COUNT ERIC STENBOCK
ROBERT LOUIS
  STEVENSON
BRAM STOKER
TOM STOPPARD
DAVID STOREY
GILES LYTTON
  STRACHEY
MONTAGUE SUMMERS
GRAHAM SWIFT
A.J.A. SYMONS
JULIAN SYMONS

W.M. THACKERAY
PAUL THEROUX
DYLAN THOMAS
EDWARD THOMAS
FLORA THOMPSON
COLIN THUBRON
JAMES THURBER
J. R. R. TOLKIEN
MARY TOURTEL
WILLIAM TREVOR
ANTHONY TROLLOPE
BARRY UNSWORTH
JOHN UPDIKE
FLORENCE UPTON
ALISON UTTLEY
JULES VERNE
GORE VIDAL
KURT VONNEGUT
LOUIS WAIN
ALFRED WAINWRIGHT
A.E. WAITE
EDGAR WALLACE
MINETTE WALTERS
REX WARNER
SYLVIA TOWNSEND
  WARNER
EVELYN WAUGH
MARY WEBB
DENTON WELCH
FAY WELDON
H. G. WELLS
MARY WESLEY
REBECCA WEST
EDITH WHARTON
DENNIS WHEATLEY
PATRICK WHITE
T.H. WHITE
WALT WHITMAN
OSCAR WILDE
CHARLES WILLIAMS
TENNESSEE WILLIAMS
HENRY WILLIAMSON
A.N. WILSON
ANGUS WILSON
R.D. WINGFIELD
JEANETTE WINTERSON
WISDEN CRICKETERS'
  ALMANACKS
P.G. WODEHOUSE
TOM WOLFE
VIRGINIA WOOLF
JOHN WYNDHAM
THE YELLOW BOOK

APPENDIX
CHINUA ACHEBE
W. HARRISON
  AINSWORTH
LOUISA MAY ALCOTT
RICHARD HARRIS
  BARHAM
WILLIAM BECKFORD
THOMAS BEWICK
R.D. BLACKMORE
WILLIAM BLAKE
ROLF BOLDREWOOD
GEORGE BORROW
JAMES BOSWELL
JOHN BUNYAN
FANNY BURNEY

ROBERT BURNS
ROBERT BURTON
SAMUEL BUTLER
ERSKINE CHILDERS
SAMUEL TAYLOR
  COLERIDGE
WILLIAM CONGREVE
STEPHEN CRANE
W.H. DAVIES
THOMAS DE QUINCEY
CHARLES M. DOUGHTY
EDWARD FITZGERALD
JOHN GAY
OLIVER GOLDSMITH
NADINE GORDIMER
KENNETH GRAHAME
JOHN GRAY
GEORGE and WEEDON
  GROSMITH
E.T.A. HOFFMANN
HEINRICH HOFFMANN
W.H. HUDSON
THOMAS HUGHES
SHIRLEY JACKSON
LIONEL JOHNSON
SAMUEL JOHNSON
BEN JONSON
NIKOS KAZANTZAKIS
CHARLES KINGSLEY
CHARLES LAMB
MATTHEW GREGORY
  LEWIS
ANITA LOOS
EDWARD BULWER
  LYTTON
RICHARD MARSH
Rev. C.R. MATURIN
HERMAN MELVILLE
JOHN MILTON
MICHAEL MOORCOCK
BILL NAUGHTON
BARONESS ORCZY
JOHN POLIDORI
ALEXANDER POPE
MARIO PUZO
THOMAS PYNCHON
CHARLES READE
SAMUEL RICHARDSON
CHRISTINA ROSSETTI
DANTE GABRIEL
  ROSSETTI
PHILIP ROTH
SIR WALTER SCOTT
RONALD SEARLE
PETER SHAFFER
PERCY BYSSHE
  SHELLEY
EDMUND SPENSER
LAURENCE STERNE
WALLACE STEVENS
HARRIET BEECHER
  STOWE
WILLIAM STYRON
ELIZABETH TAYLOR
COLIN WILSON
LEONARD WOOLF
WILLIAM BUTLER
  YEATS

This is an aid to identifying some of the alternative names which writers sometimes use.

Alternative Name	Usual Name
352087 A/C Ross	T.E. Lawrence
Abhavananda	Aleister Crowley
Ashdown, Clifford	R. Austin Freeman
Ashe, Gordon	John Creasey
Aston, James	T.H. White
Axton, David	Dean Koontz
Bachman, Richard	Stephen King
Bassetto	George Bernard Shaw
Bell, Acton	Anne Brontë
Bell, Currer	Charlotte Brontë
Bell, Ellis	Emily Brontë
Beynon, John	John Wyndham
Bishop, George Archibald	Aleister Crowley
Blake, Nicholas	C. Day Lewis
Blayre, Christopher	E. Heron-Allen
Box, Edgar	Gore Vidal
Boz	Charles Dickens
Bryan, Michael	Brian Moore
Burke, Leda	David Garnett
C.3.3.	Oscar Wilde
Camberg, Muriel	Muriel Spark
Carnac, Carol	E.C.R. Lorac
Carr, H.D.	Aleister Crowley
Carr, Jolyon	Ellis Peters
Catherall, Arthur	'BB'
Chaucer, Daniel	Ford Maddox Ford
Cherry	Benjamin Disraeli
Clerk, N.W.	C.S. Lewis
Coffey, Brian	Dean Koontz
Comte de Fénix	Aleister Crowley
Comus	R.M. Ballantyne
Cooke, M.E.	John Creasey
Cooke, Margaret	John Creasey
Cousins, Sheila	Graham Greene (with Ronald Matthews)
Coyle, William	Thomas Keneally
Credo	John Creasey
Davison, Lawrence H.	D.H. Lawrence
Deane, Norman	John Creasey
Derry Down Derry	Edward Lear
Dixon, Carter	John Dickson Carr
Douglas, Michael	Michael Crichton
Douglass, G. Norman	Norman Douglas
Doyle, John	Robert Graves
Dwyer, Deanna	Dean Koontz
Dwyer, K.R.	Dean Koontz
Dwyer, K.R.	Dean Koontz
Earle, William	Captain W.E. Johns
Early, Jon	Captain W.E. Johns

Eastway, Edward	Edward Thomas
Fairbairn, Roger	John Dickson Carr
Farran, Richard M.	John Betjeman
Father Tuck	Louis Wain
Felcamps, Elise	John Creasey
Firth, Violet M.	Dion Fortune
Flying Officer 'X'	H.E. Bates
Frazer, Robert Caine	John Creasey
French, Paul	Isaac Asimov
Furey, Michael	Sax Rohmer
Gaunt, Graham	Jonathan Gash
Gaunt, Jonathan	Jonathan Gash
Gentleman of the University of Cambridge, A	Aleister Crowley
Gill, Patrick	John Creasey
Grand Orient	A.E. Waite
Grimalkin	Louis Wain
H.B.	Hillaire Belloc
Halliday, Michael	John Creasey
Hamilton, Clive	C.S. Lewis
Hammond, Ralph	Hammond Innes
Harris, John Beynon	John Wyndham
Harris, Johnson	John Wyndham
Haycraft, Anna	Alice Thomas Ellis
Hill, John	Dean Koontz
Hockaby, Stephen	Gladys Mitchell
Hogarth, Charles	John Creasey
Hope, Brian	John Creasey
Hudson, Jeffery	Michael Crichton
Hueffer, Ford Maddox	Ford Maddox Ford
Hueffer, H. Ford	Ford Maddox Ford
Hughes, Colin	John Creasey
Hunt, Kyle	John Creasey
Jones, Edith	Edith Wharton
Kell, Joseph	Anthony Burgess
Kerouac, John	Jack Kerouac
Khan, Khaled	Aleister Crowley
Kittycat	Louis Wain
Leander, Richard	Louis Wain
Lear, Peter	Peter Lovesey
Lee, William (Willy)	William S. Burroughs
Lincoln, Geoffrey	John Mortimer
Lucas, Victoria	Sylvia Plath
Lutiy, the late Major Lutiy	Aleister Crowley
Macdonald, John Ross	Ross Macdonald
Macdonald, John	Ross Macdonald
Mahatma Guru Sri Parahamsa Shivaji	Aleister Crowley
Mallowan, A.C.	Agatha Christie
Malone, Louis	Louis Macniece
Mann, James	John Harvey
Manton, Peter	John Creasey
Mara, Bernard	Brian Moore
March, Maxwell	Margery Allingham
Markham, Robert	Kingsley Amis
Marric, J.J.	John Creasey

Marsden, James	John Creasey
Master Therion	Aleister Crowley
Mattheson, Rodney	John Creasey
McClure, S.S.	Willa Cather
Millar, Kenneth	Ross Macdonald
Mitchell, James Leslie	Lewis Grassic Gibbon
Moorland, Dick	Reginald Hill
Morgan, Claire	Patricia Highsmith
Morton, Anthony	John Creasey
Myles na gCopaleen	Flann O'Brien
Nabokoff-Sirin, Vladamir	Vladimir Nabokov
Nichols, Leigh	Dean Koontz
Norden, Charles	Lawrence Durrell
Normyx	Norman Douglas
North, Anthony	Dean Koontz
O'Casey, Brenda	Alice Thomas Ellis
Paige, Richard	Dean Koontz
Palinurus	Cyril Connolly
Pargeter, Edith	Ellis Peters
Peeslake, Gaffer	Lawrence Durrell
Perdurabo, Frater	Aleister Crowley
Ramal, Walter	Walter de la Mare
Ranger, Ken	John Creasey
Redfern, John	Ellis Peters
Reed, Eliot	Eric Ambler
Reid, Desmond	Michael Moorcock
Reilly, William K.	John Creasey
Rich, Barbara	Robert Graves (with Laura Riding)
Richards, Hilda	Frank Richards
Riley, Tex	John Creasey
Ruell, Patrick	Reginald Hill
Seymour, Alan	S. Fowler Wright
Siluriensis, Leolinus	Arthur Machen
Somers, Jane	Doris Lessing
Sparks, Timothy	Charles Dickens
St John Cooper, Henry	John Creasey
St. E. A. of M. & S	Aleister Crowley
Steele, V.M.	Dion Fortune
Stuart, Ian	Alistair Maclean
Temple, Paul	Francis Durbridge
Titmarsh Mr M.A.	W.M. Thackeray
Torre, Malcolm	Gladys Mitchell
Traherne, Michael	'BB'
Underhill, Charles	Reginald Hill
Verey, Rev. C.	Aleister Crowley
Vine, Barbara	Ruth Rendell
Warddel, Nora Helen	E. Heron-Allen
West, Owen	Dean Koontz
Westmacott, Mary	Agatha Christie
Wilson, John Burgess	Anthony Burgess
Wingrave, Anthony	S. Fowler Wright
Wolfe, Aaron	Dean Koontz
York, Jeremy	John Creasey
Young, Collier	Robert Bloch

ANTHONY ABBOT
(b.1893 d.1952)

The pseudonym of Fulton Oursler, whose Thatcher Colt novels are examples of the Golden Age of detective fiction.

Thatcher Colt Novels
About the Murder of Geraldine Foster, Covici Friede (U.S.), 1930 . . . . £250/£65
ditto, as *The Murder of Geraldine Foster*, Collins Crime Club, 1931 . . . . . . £25/£10
About the Murder of the Clergyman's Mistress, Covici Friede (U.S.), 1931 . . . . £200/£40
ditto, as *The Crime of the Century*, Collins Crime Club, 1931 . . . . £25/£10
About the Murder of the Night Club Lady, Covici Friede (U.S.), 1931 . . . . . . £200/£40
ditto, as *The Murder of the Night Club Lady*, Collins Crime Club, 1932 . . . . . . £25/£10
About the Murder of the Circus Queen, Covici Friede (U.S.), 1932 . . . . £200/£40
ditto, as *The Murder of the Circus Queen*, Collins Crime Club, 1933 . . . . . . £25/£10
About the Murder of a Startled Lady, Farrar & Rinehart (U.S.), 1935 . . . . . £200/£40
ditto, as *Murder of a Startled Lady*, Collins Crime Club, 1936 . . . . £25/£10
About the Murder of a Man Afraid of Women, Farrar & Rinehart (U.S.), 1937. . . . . £200/£40
ditto, as *Murder of a Man Afraid of Women*, Collins Crime Club, 1937 . . . . . . £25/£10
The Creeps, Farrar & Rinehart (U.S.), 1939 £125/£20
ditto, as *Murder at Buzzards Bay*, Collins Crime Club, 1940 . . . . £25/£10
The Shudders, Farrar & Rinehart (U.S.), 1943 . . . .
. . . . £125/£20
ditto, as *Deadly Secret*, Collins Crime Club, 1943 . .
. . . . £25/£10

PETER ABRAHAMS
(b.1919)

Peter Abrahams left South Africa in 1939 when he was twenty years of age, but the impact of the South African system on him has been such that with one exception all his work has been set in Africa and deals with racial conflict, oppression, economic injustice, and social and political deprivation.

Novels
Song of the City, Crisp, London, 1945 . . £75/£20
Mine Boy, Crisp, London, [1946] . . . £50/£15
ditto, Knopf (U.S.), 1955 (wraps) £20
The Path of Thunder, Harper (U.S.), 1948 . £75/£25
ditto, Faber, 1952 . . . . £35/£10
Wild Conquest, Harper (U.S.), 1950 . . £25/£10

ditto, Faber, 1951 . . . . £35/£10
A Wreath for Udomo, Knopf (U.S.), 1956 . £25/£10
ditto, Faber, 1956 . . . . £35/£10
A Night of Their Own, Knopf (U.S.), 1965 . £25/£10
ditto, Faber, 1965 . . . . £25/£10
This Island Now, Faber, 1966 . . . . £25/£10
ditto, Knopf (U.S.), 1967 . . . . . . £25/£10

Short Stories
Dark Testament, Allen & Unwin, 1942 . . £75/£15

Verse
A Blackman Speaks of Freedom, Durban, 1942 (wraps) £250

Others
Return to Goli, Faber, 1953 . . . . . £25/£10
Tell Freedom: Memories of Africa, Knopf (U.S.), 1954 . . . . £35/£10
ditto, Faber, 1954 . . . . £35/£10
Jamaica: An Island Mosaic, Her Majesty's Stationery Office, 1957 . . . . . . £40/£15

J.R. ACKERLEY
(b.1896 d.1967)

For many years Ackerley was literary editor of *The Listener*. *My Father and Myself* is considered by many to be his masterpiece.

Novel
We Think the World of You, The Bodley Head, 1960 .
. . . . £125/£25
ditto, Ivan Obolensky (U.S.), 1961 . . . £100/£20

Poetry
Cambridge Poets 1914-1920, Heffers, 1920 (ed. E. Davison) . . . . £100/£25
Poems by Four Authors, Bowes & Bowes, 1923 . .
. . . . £175
Micheldever and Other Poems, McKelvie, 1972 (350 numbered copies, wraps) £300

Other Titles
The Prisoners of War: A Play in Three Acts, Chatto & Windus, 1925. . . . . £75/£35
ditto, Chatto & Windus, 1925 (wraps) . . . £45
Hindoo Holiday: An Indian Journey, Chatto & Windus, 1932. . . . . £175/£75
ditto, Viking (U.S.), 1932 . . . . . £25/£10
ditto, Chatto & Windus, 1952 (revised edition). . .
. . . . £30/£10
My Dog Tulip: Life with an Alsatian, Secker & Warburg, 1956 . . . . £50/£15
ditto, Fleet Publishing Corp (U.S.), 1965 (expanded edition) . . . . £15/£5

My Father and Myself, The Bodley Head, 1968 . .
. . . . £25/£10
ditto, Coward-McCann (U.S.), 1969 . . . £20/£5
E.M. Forster: A Portrait, McKelvie, 1972 (wraps) .
. . . . £10
The Letters of J.R. Ackerley, Duckworth, 1975 .
. . . . £15/£5
My Sister and Myself, Hutchinson, 1982 . £15/£5

Edited by Ackerley
Escapers All, The Bodley Head, 1932 . . £20/£5

PETER ACKROYD
(b.1949)

A wide-ranging and versatile writer, Ackroyd is best known as a novelist and biographer. His life of T.S. Eliot won the Whitbread and Heinemann Awards for 1984, and his monumental biography of Dickens is much acclaimed.

Novels
The Great Fire of London, Hamish Hamilton, 1982 .
. . . . £250/£30
The Last Testament of Oscar Wilde, Hamish Hamilton, 1983 . . . . £75/£15
ditto, Harper & Row (U.S.), 1983 . . . £20/£5
Hawksmoor, Hamish Hamilton, 1985 . . £125/£20
ditto, Harper & Row (U.S.), 1985 . . . £45/£10
Chatterton, Hamish Hamilton, 1987. . . . £25/£5
ditto, Hamish Hamilton, 1987 (150 signed copies, glassine d/w) . . . . . . £65/£45
ditto, Grove Press (U.S.), 1988 . . . . £20/£5
First Light, Hamish Hamilton, 1989. . . . £25/£5
ditto, Grove Weidenfeld (U.S.), 1989 . . £20/£5
English Music, Hamish Hamilton, 1992 . . £15/£5
ditto, London Limited Editions, 1992, (150 signed, numbered copies, glassine d/w). . . . £50/£35
ditto, Knopf (U.S.), 1992 . . . . . . £15/£5
ditto, The Franklin Library, 1992 (full leather, signed, limited edition) £30
The House of Doctor Dee, Hamish Hamilton, 1993 .
. . . . £15/£5
Dan Leno and the Limehouse Golem, Sinclair-Stevenson, 1994 . . . . £15/£5
ditto, as *The Trial of Elizabeth Cree*, Doubleday (U.S.) 1995 . . . . £10/£5
Milton in America, Sinclair-Stevenson, 1996 . £10/£5
ditto, Doubleday (U.S.), 1997 . . . . £10/£5
The Plato Papers, Chatto & Windus, 1999 . £10/£5

Verse
Ouch, The Curiously Strong Vol IV No.2 1971, (xeroxed copies, sheets, usually in stapled wraps) .
. . . . £200
London Lickpenny, Ferry Press, 1973, (26 signed copies of edition of 500, illustrated card wraps) £150

ditto, Ferry Press, 1973, (474 unsigned copies of edition of 500, illustrated card wraps) . . . £35
Country Life, Ferry Press, 1978, (324 signed copies of edition of 350, card wraps) £50
ditto, Ferry Press, 1978, (26 signed copies of edition of 350, with additional holograph poem, card wraps) .
. . . . £225
The Diversions of Purley, Hamish Hamilton, 1987 .
. . . . £25/£10

Biography
Ezra Pound and His World, Thames & Hudson, 1980
. . . . £20/£5
ditto, Scribners, 1980 . . . . £15/£5
T.S. Eliot, Hamish Hamilton, 1984 . . . £20/£5
ditto, Simon & Schuster, 1984 . . . . £15/£5
Dickens, Sinclair-Stevenson, 1990 . . . £20/£5
ditto, London Limited Editions, 1990, (150 signed copies, glassine d/w). . . . . . £50/£40
ditto, HarperCollins (U.S.), 1990. . . . £15/£5
Blake, Sinclair-Stevenson, 1995 . . . . £15/£5
ditto, Knopf (U.S.), 1996 . . . . . . £10/£5
The Life of Thomas More, Chatto & Windus 1998 .
. . . . £10/£5
ditto, Doubleday (U.S.), 1998 . . . . £10/£5

Miscellaneous
Notes for a New Culture: An Essay on Modernism, Vision Press, 1976 . . . . . . £100/£25
ditto, Barnes & Noble (U.S.), 1976 . . . £100/£25
Dressing Up, Transvestism and Drag: The History of an Obsession, Thames & Hudson, 1979 . £45/£20
ditto, Simon & Schuster, 1979 . . . . £30/£10
Dickens' London: An Imaginative Vision, Headline, 1987 (introduced by Peter Ackroyd) . . . £15/£5
Introduction to Dickens, Sinclair-Stevenson, 1991 .
. . . . £20/£5
ditto, Ballantine (U.S.), 1992 (wraps) . . . £5
London, A Biography, Chatto & Windus 2000 . £15/£5

DOUGLAS ADAMS
(b.1952 d.2001)

Author of *The Hitch-Hiker's Guide To The Galaxy* and related science fiction silliness, the *Hitchhikers* adventures were first heard on the radio, became books, and were then televised.

Novels
The Hitch-Hiker's Guide To The Galaxy, Pan, 1979 (wraps) £10
ditto, Arthur Barker, n.d. [1980] (first hardback edition) . . . . £100/£20
ditto, Harmony (U.S.), 1980 . . . £35/£10
The Restaurant At The End Of The Universe, Pan, 1980 (wraps) £5

ditto, Arthur Barker, 1980 (first hardback edition) . .
. . . . £75/£15
ditto, Harmony (U.S.), 1980 . . . . . . £20/£15
Life, The Universe and Everything, Pan, 1982   £5
ditto, Arthur Barker, 1982 (first hardback edition) . .
. . . . £75/£15
ditto, Harmony (U.S.), 1982 . . . . . £20/£15
So Long, And Thanks For All The Fish, Pan, 1984
. . . . £20/£5
ditto, Harmony (U.S.), 1985 . . . . . . £10/£5
The Hitch-Hiker's Guide To The Galaxy: A Trilogy in Four Parts, Heinemann, 1986 . . . . £20/£5
ditto: A Trilogy in Five Parts, Heinemann, 1995 . .
. . . . £10/£5
Dirk Gently's Holistic Detective Agency, Heinemann, 1987 . . . . £15/£5
ditto, Simon & Schuster (U.S.), 1987 . . £10/£5
The Long Dark Tea-Time Of The Soul, Heinemann, 1988 . . . . £10/£5
ditto, Simon & Schuster (U.S.), 1988 . . £10/£5
Mostly Harmless, Heinemann, 1992 . . . £10/£5
ditto, Harmony (U.S.), 1992 . . . . . £10/£5
Starship Titanic, Harmony Books (U.S.), 1997 (with Terry Jones) . . . . £10/£5

Others
The Meaning of Liff, Pan, 1983 (with John Lloyd, wraps). £5
ditto, Harmony (U.S.), 1984 . . . . . £10/£5
The Hitch-Hiker's Guide To The Galaxy: The Original Radio Scripts, Pan, 1985 (wraps) . £10
ditto, Harmony (U.S.), [c.1985] £10
Last Chance To See ..., Heinemann, 1990 (with Mark Carwardine) . . . . £10/£5
ditto, Harmony (U.S.), 1992 . . . . . £10/£5
The Deeper Meaning of Liff, Pan, 1990, (with John Lloyd). . . . . £10/£5
ditto, Harmony (U.S.), 1990 . . . . . . £10/£5
Doctor Who - Pirate Planet, Titan Books, 1994 (wraps) £5

RICHARD ADAMS
(b.1920)

The classic *Watership Down* won the Guardian Award and Carnegie Medal. Much of Adams' best work is concerned with man's cruelty to animals. The first issue of *The Girl in a Swing* was withdrawn through fear of libel, and among the changes made was the name of the heroine.

Watership Down, Rex Collings, 1972 . . £450/£75
ditto, Macmillan (U.S.), 1972 . . . . £45/£10
ditto, Penguin, 1976 (first illustrated edition, in slipcase) . . . . £50/£15
ditto, deluxe illustrated edition (limited to 250 signed, numbered copies, slipcase) . . . . . £600/£500

Shardik, Allen Lane, 1974 . . . . . £15/£5
ditto, Simon & Schuster (U.S.), [1974] . . £10/£5
Plague Dogs, Allen Lane, 1977 . . . £10/£5
ditto, Knopf (U.S.), 1978 . . . . . . £10/£5
The Girl in a Swing, Allen Lane, 1980 (withdrawn first issue with 'Kathe Geutner') . . . . £50/£15
ditto, Knopf (U.S.), 1980 (withdrawn issue) £40/£15
*ditto, Allen Lane, 1980 (second issue, revised edition, with 'Karin Förster'). . . . . . £10/£5
ditto, Knopf (U.S.), 1980 (revised edition) . £10/£5
The Iron Wolf and Other Stories, Allen Lane, 1980 .
. . . . £10/£5
ditto, as The Unbroken Web: Stories & Fables, Crown (U.S.), 1980 . . . . £10/£5
The Legend of Te Tuna, Sylvester & Orphanos, 1982
. . . . £15/£5
ditto, Sidgwick & Jackson, 1986 . . . £10/£5
Maia, Viking, 1984 . . . . . . £10/£5
ditto, Knopf (U.S.), 1985 . . . . . . £10/£5
The Bureaucrats, Viking Kestrel, 1985 . . £10/£5
Traveller, Knopf (U.S.), 1988 . . . . £10/£5
ditto, Hutchinson, 1988 . . . . . . £10/£5
Tales from Watership Down, Hutchinson, 1996 £10/£5
ditto, Knopf (U.S.), 1996 . . . . . . £10/£5

Verse
The Tyger Voyage, Cape, 1976 . . . . . £15/£5
ditto, Knopf (U.S.), 1976 . . . . £10/£5
The Ship's Cat, Cape, 1977 . . . . . £10/£5
ditto, Knopf (U.S.), 1977 . . . . £10/£5

Non Fiction
Nature Through the Seasons, Kestrel, 1975 (with Max Hooper) . . . . £10/£5
ditto, Simon & Schuster (U.S.), 1975 . . . £10/£5
Nature Day and Night, Kestrel, 1978 (with Max Hooper) . . . . £10/£5
ditto, Viking (U.S.), 1978. . . . . . . £10/£5
Voyage Through the Antarctic, Allen Lane, 1982 (with Ronald Lockley). . . . . . . £10/£5
ditto, Knopf (U.S.), 1983 . . . . £10/£5
The Nature Diary, Viking, 1985 . . . £10/£5
Day Gone By, Hutchinson, 1988 . . . . £10/£5
ditto, Knopf (U.S.), 1991 . . . . £10/£5

CHAS ADDAMS
(b.1912 d.1988)

An American cartoonist with a dark sense of humour, who is best known for the 'Addams Family'

Cartoons
Drawn and Quartered, Random House (U.S.), 1942 .
. . . . £75/£35
ditto, Hamish Hamilton, 1943 . . . . £65/£25
Addams and Evil, Random House (U.S.), 1947 . .
. . . . £60/£25

ditto, Hamish Hamilton, 1947 . . . . £60/£25
Monster Rally, Simon & Schuster (U.S.), 1950. . .
. . . . £60/£25
ditto, Hamish Hamilton, 1951 . . . . £50/£20
Homebodies, Simon & Schuster (U.S.), 1954 £60/£25
ditto, Hamish Hamilton, 1954 . . . . £50/£20
Nightcrawlers, Simon & Schuster (U.S.), 1957. . .
. . . . £60/£25
ditto, Hamish Hamilton, 1957 . . . . £50/£20
Black Maria, Simon & Schuster (U.S.), 1960 £60/£25
ditto, Hamish Hamilton, 1960 . . . . £50/£20
The Penguin Charles Addams, Penguin, 1962 (wraps)
. . . . £10
The Groaning Board, Simon & Schuster (U.S.), 1964.
. . . . £40/£15
ditto, Hamish Hamilton, 1964 . . . . £40/£15
The Chas Addams Mother Goose, Windmill Books/
Harper (U.S.), 1967 . . . . . . £40/£15
ditto, Collins, 1967 . . . . . . £40/£15
My Crowd, Simon & Schuster (U.S.), 1970. £40/£15
ditto, Tom Stacey, 1971 . . . . . £40/£15
Favourite Haunts, Simon & Schuster (U.S.), 1976 .
. . . . £30/£10
ditto, W.H. Allen, 1977 . . . . . £30/£10
Creature Comforts, Simon & Schuster (U.S.), 1981 .
. . . . £25/£10
ditto, Heinemann, 1981 . . . . . £25/£10
The Addams Family Album, Hamish Hamilton, 1991
(wraps) £5
The World of Chas Addams, Hamish Hamilton, 1992.
. . . . £15/£5

Others
Afternoon in the Attic by John Kobler, Dodd, Mead
(U.S.), 1950 . . . . £15/£5
Dear Dead Days: A Family Album, Putnam (U.S.),
1959 . . . . £40/£15
ditto, Hamlyn, [1960] . . . . . . £25/£10

JAMES AGEE
(b.1909 d.1955)

U.S. poet, novelist, journalist, film critic, and social
activist, Agee led an unorthodox, hard-driving life
that resulted in an early death.

Reportage
Let Us Now Praise Famous Men, Houghton Mifflin
(U.S.), 1941 (with Walker Evans) . . £2,000/£250
A Way of Seeing, Viking, 1965 (with Helen Levitt) .
. . . . £200/£50

Poetry
Permit Me Voyage, Yale Univ. Press (U.S.), 1934 . .
. . . . £500/£75

Collected Poems, Houghton Mifflin (U.S.), 1968 . .
. . . . £45/£15

Novels
The Morning Watch, Houghton Mifflin (U.S.), 1951 .
. . . . £100/£15
A Death in the Family, Obolensky (U.S.), 1957 (first
issue 'walking' for 'waking' on p.80) . . £125/£20
ditto, Obolensky (U.S.), 1957 (second issue) £45/£10
ditto, Gollancz, 1958 . . . . . . £65/£20

Others
Agee on Film, vol. 1, Obolensky (U.S.), 1958 . . .
. . . . £100/£25
ditto, vol. 2, Obolensky (U.S.), 1960. . . £60/£15
Letters of James Agee to Father Flye, Braziller, 1962
. . . . £50/£15
Four Early Stories, Cummington Press (U.S.), 1964
(285 copies) . . . . £250/£175
The Collected Short Prose of James Agee, Houghton
Mifflin, 1968 . . . . £40/£10

ROBERT AICKMAN
(b.1914 d.1981)

British short story writer, critic, lecturer and novelist.
He edited *The Fontana Book of Great Ghost Stories*
between 1964 and 1972.

Short Stories
We Are For the Dark - Six Ghost Stories, Cape, 1951
(with Elizabeth Jane Howard) . . . £350/£125
Dark Entries, Collins, 1964 . . . . . £250/£100
Powers of Darkness, Collins, 1966 . . £250/£100
Sub Rosa, Gollancz, 1968 . . . . . £175/£100
ditto, Gollancz, 1968 (40 signed copies). . £300/£200
Cold Hand in Mine, Gollancz, 1975 [1976] £90/£50
ditto, Scribners (U.S.), 1975 [1977] . . . £25/£10
Tales of Love and Death, Gollancz, 1977 . £100/£45
Painted Devils: Strange Stories, Scribner (U.S.), 1979
. . . . £40/£10
Intrusions: Strange Tales, Gollancz, 1980 . £80/£50
Night Voices: Strange Stories, Gollancz, 1985 .
. . . . £35/£10
The Wine-dark Sea, Arbor House (U.S.), 1988. . .
. . . . £20/£10
ditto, Mandarin, 1990 (wraps) £5
The Unsettled Dust, Mandarin, 1990 (wraps) . £10
The Collected Strange Stories, Tartarus/Durtro, 1999
(2 vols) . . . . £125/£75

Novels
The Late Breakfasters, Gollancz, 1964 . . £100/£45
ditto, Portway, 1978 . . . . . . £20/£10
The Model, Arbor House (U.S.), 1987 . . . £15
ditto, Robinson, 1988 . . . . £15

Canals
Know Your Waterways, Coram, [1955] (wraps)   £10
ditto, Coram, [1956]   . . . . . .   £25/£10
The Story of Our Inland Waterways, Pitman, 1955   .
. . . .   £25/£10

Autobiography
The Attempted Rescue, Gollancz, 1966   . .   £150/£75
The River Runs Uphill, Pearson, 1986   . .   £20/£10

ALAIN-FOURNIER
(b.1886 d.1914)

Alain-Fournier was the pen name of Henri Fournier, author of one novel, *Le Grand Meaulnes*, published in France in 1913. Often translated into English as *The Wanderer* or *The Lost Domain*, it is a classic novel of a lost childhood love.

The Wanderer, Houghton Mifflin (U.S.), 1928 (translated by Françoise Delisle)   . . .   £75/£25
ditto, Constable, 1929   . . . . . .   £50/£15
Towards the Lost Domain: Letters from London, 1905, Carcanet, 1986 (edited and translated by W.J. Strachan)   . . . . £15/£5
Le Grand Meaulnes and Miracles, Tartarus Press, 1999   . . . .   £25/£10

ALASTAIR
(b.1887 d.1969)

Pseudonym for Hans Henning Voight, an illustrator who owes a great debt to Aubrey Beardsley, but succeeds in offering a decadent style all of his own.

Books illustrated by Alastair
Forty-Three Drawings by Alastair (with a note of Exclamation by Robert Ross), John Lane, 1914 (500 copies) £750
Poèms pour Pâques, by Loïs Cendré, privately printed, 1915 (printed anonymously by 'Celui qui aime l'amour', 7 illustrations). £200
The Sphinx, by Oscar Wilde, John Lane, 1920 (1,000 copies, 10 illustrations) £200
Carmen, by Prosper Mérimée, Verlag Rascher (Zurich), 1920 (50 copies on Japon paper, 12 illustrations) £750
ditto, Verlag Rascher (Zurich), 1920 (ordinary edition of 450 copies, 12 illustrations) £200

Die Buchse der Pandora, by Frank Wedekind, George Muller Verlag (Munich), [1921] (12 illustrations)   .
. . . .   £100
Erdgeist, by Frank Wedekind, George Muller Verlag (Munich), [1921] (12 illustrations). . . .   £100
Die Rache einer Frau, by Barbey d'Aurevilly, (Vienna), 1924 (9 illustrations). £100
Sebastian van Storck, by Walter Pater, Im Avalun Verlag (Vienna), 1924 (480 copies, 8 illustrations)   .
. . . .   £200
ditto, John Lane, 1927, (1050 copies, 8 illustrations, of which one is signed in pencil by the artist)   .   £200
ditto, Propyläen Verlag (Frankfurt), 1974 (facsimile reprint of, 1924 edition, limited to 400 copies, 8 illustrations) £50
Salome, by Oscar Wilde, G. Crès (Paris) 1922 (9 illustrations) £75
ditto, G. Crès (Paris), 1922 (100 copies on Imperial Japon paper, 9 illustrations). £500
Fifty Drawings, by Alastair, Alfred A. Knopf (U.S.), 1925 (1025 copies in box)   . . . .   £300/£200
Red Skeletons, by Harry Crosby, Editions Narcisse (Paris), 1927 (ordinary edition of 337 copies, 9 illustrations) £500
ditto, Editions Narcisse (Paris), 1927, (33 copies on Imperial Japon paper, 9 illustrations) . . . £1,000
The Fall of the House of Usher, by Edgar Allan Poe, Editions Narcisse (Paris), 1928 (1 copy only on old Japon paper containing the original drawings, 5 illustrations) £20,000
ditto, Editions Narcisse (Paris), 1928 (307 copies, 5 illustrations) £750
L'Anniversaire de L'Enfant, by Oscar Wilde, Black Sun Press (Paris), 1928 (9 illustrations)   . .   £200
The Birthday of the Infanta, by Oscar Wilde, Black Sun Press (Paris), 1928 (100 copies, as above but text in English, 9 illustrations, slipcase).   £1,250/£1,000
Manon Lescaut, by Abbé Prévost, John Lane, 1928 (1850 copies, 11 illustrations) £75
ditto, privately printed for Rarity Press, 1933 (a very poor reprint of the above, 11 illustrations). .   £30
Les Liaisons Dangereuses, by Choderlos de Laclos, Black Sun Press (Paris), 1929 (2 vols, edition of 15 sets on Japon paper, 7 illustrations). . .   £2,500
ditto, Black Sun Press (Paris), 1929 (ordinary edition of 1005 sets, 7 illustrations)   . . . . .   £250/£150
ditto, privately printed for William Godwin (U.S.), 1933 (as *Dangerous Acquaintances*, a very poor reprint of Vol. 1 of above edition) £30
Alastair: Illustrator of Decadence, Thames & Hudson (U.S.), 1979   . . . .   £45/£20

Verse
Das Flammende Tal, Hyperion Verlag (Munich), 1920 (680 copies) £450

CECIL ALDIN
(b.1870 d.1925)

A British comic illustrator in the 1890s, Aldin later became a successful sporting artist.

Children's

Spot, An Autobiography, Houlston, 1894 (14 illustrations) £125
Wonderland Wonders, by Rev. John Isabell, Home Words, 1895 (frontispiece and 19 illustrations, also contributions by Louis Wain) £75
Two Little Runaways, by James Buckland, Longman, 1898 . . . . £80
Every-Day Characters, Kegan, Paul, Trench, Trubner & Co., 1898 . . . . £450
A Cockney in Arcadia, by Harry Spurr, George Allen, 1899 (28 illustrations by Aldin and John Hassall) £80
Two Well-Worn Shoe Stories, Sands, 1899 . . £225
Ten Little Puppy Dogs, Sands, [1902] . . . £200
A Sporting Garland, Sands, 1902 . . . . £700
Faithful Friends, Blackie, 1902 . . . . . £100
Bubble and Squeak, by P. Robinson, Isbister, 1902 . . . . £350
A Dog Day, or The Angel in the House, by Walter Emanuel, Heinemann, 1902 (28 illustrations) £125
The House Annual, Gale & Palden, 1902 . . £80
The Young Folks Birthday Book, Hills, 1902 . £50
The Snob: Some Episodes In a Mis-spent Youth, by Walter Emanuel, Lawrence & Bullen, 1904 (19 colour plates) £125
A Gay Dog: The Story of a Foolish Year, by Walter Emanuel, Heinemann, 1905 (24 colour plates) £150
The Dogs of War, by Walter Emanuel, Bradbury Agnew, [1906] £125
The Happy Annual, Heinemann, 1907 (with John Hassall) £75
Old Christmas, by Washington Irving, Hodder & Stoughton, 1908 (27 colour plates, 6 b/w plates) £150
Farm Friends for Little Folk, Blackie, 1908 . £100
The Playtime Picture Books, Lawrence & Jellicoe, 1909 (series) . . . . £175 each
Pussy and Her Ways, Henry Frowde/Hodder & Stoughton, [1909] £200
Doggie and His Ways, Henry Frowde/Hodder & Stoughton, [1909] £200
The Black Puppy Book, Henry Frowde/Hodder & Stoughton, [1909] £225
The White Puppy Book, Henry Frowde/Hodder & Stoughton, [1909] £225
The White Kitten Book, Henry Frowde/Hodder & Stoughton, [1909] (11 colour plates) . . . £225
Pickles, A Puppy Dog's Tale, Henry Frowde/Hodder & Stoughton, [1909] (24 colour illustrations) . £350
Rough and Tumble, Henry Frowde/Hodder & Stoughton, [1909] £350
Field Babies, Henry Frowde/Hodder & Stoughton, [1910] (24 colour plates) £200

The Twins, Henry Frowde/Hodder & Stoughton, [1910] (24 full-page colour plates) £325
The Red Puppy Book, Henry Frowde/Hodder & Stoughton, [1910] (12 colour plates) . . . £200
My Pets, Henry Frowde/Hodder & Stoughton, [1910] £100
An Old-Fashioned Christmas Eve, by Washington Irving, Hodder & Stoughton, 1910 . . . . £50
An Old-Fashioned Christmas Day, by Washington Irving, Hodder & Stoughton, 1910 . . . . £50
The Posthumous Papers of the Pickwick Club, by Charles Dickens, Chapman & Hall/Lawrence & Jellicoe, 1910 (2 vols, vol. I with 13 colour plates, vol. II with 11 colour plates) £225
My Book of Doggies: Stories and Pictures for Little Folk, Blackie, [1910] £100
Puppy Tails, by Richard Waylett, Lawrence & Jellicoe, [1910]. £125
Farm Babies, by May Byron, Henry Frowde/Hodder & Stoughton, [1911] (24 full-page colour illustrations) £300
Farmyard Puppies, Henry Frowde/Hodder & Stoughton, [1911] (12 colour illustrations) . £150
Merry and Bright, Henry Frowde/Hodder & Stoughton, [1911] (24 full-page colour illustrations) £350
Mac: A Story of a Dog, Henry Frowde/Hodder & Stoughton, [1912] £350
The Mongrel Puppy Book, Henry Frowde/Hodder & Stoughton, [1912] (12 colour plates) . . . £200
Black Beauty, by Anna Sewell, Jarrold, [1912] (18 colour plates). £100
White-Ear and Peter: The Story of a Fox and a Fox-Terrier, by Neils Heiberg, Macmillan, 1912 (16 colour plates). £200
Cecil Aldin's Happy Family, by May Byron, Henry Frowde/Hodder & Stoughton, [1912] (6 parts, illustrated in colour) . . . . . . £75 each
ditto, Henry Frowde/Hodder & Stoughton, [1912] (single volume edition) £100
Cecil Aldin's Merry Party, by May Byron, Henry Frowde/Hodder & Stoughton, [1913] (6 parts, illustrated in colour) . . . . . . £75 each
ditto, Henry Frowde/Hodder & Stoughton, [1913] (single volume edition) £100
My Dog, by Maurice Maeterlinck, Allen, 1913 (6 colour plates). £100
Zoo Babies, by G.E. Farrow, Henry Frowde/Hodder & Stoughton, 1913 . . . . £125
The Merry Puppy Book, Milford, 1913 (36 colour plates). £275
The Underdog, by Sidney Trist, Animals' Guardian, 1913 (4 illustrations). £75
Cecil Aldin's Rag Book, The Animals' School Treat, by Clifton Bingham, Dean: 'Rag Book' series No. 70, [1913] (24 colour illustrations) £175
The Bobtail Puppy Book, Henry Frowde/Hodder & Stoughton, [1914] £225

Jack and Jill, by May Byron, Henry Frowde/Hodder &
Stoughton, [1914] £325
The Dog Who Wasn't What He Thought He Was, by
Walter Emanuel, Raphael Tuck, [1914] (24 colour
plates). £325
Animal Revels, by May Byron, Henry Frowde/Hodder
& Stoughton, [c.1914] £100
Animal Frolics, by May Byron, Henry Frowde/Hodder
& Stoughton, [1914]. £100
Mouflou, by Ouida, T.C. & E.C. Jack, 1915 . £100
The Cecil Aldin Painting Books, Lawrence & Jellicoe,
[1915]. £125
Jock and Some Others, by Richard Waylett, Gale &
Polden, [1916] (16 full-page colour illustrations, 15
b/w) £250
The Merry Party, Humphrey Milford, [1918] . £150
Bunnyborough, Humphrey Milford, [1919] . £275
ditto, Eyre & Spottiswoode, 1946 (15 colour plates) .
. . . . £75/£25
Gyp's Hour of Bliss, by Gladys Davidson, Collins,
1919 . . . . £200
The Great Adventure, Humphrey Milford, [1920] (17
colour plates). £225
Cecil Aldin Letter Books, Humphrey Milford, [1920] .
. . . . £100
Us, Humphrey Milford, [1922] £150
An Artist's Models, H. F & G Witherby, 1930 . £100
Dogs of Character, Eyre & Spottiswoode, 1927 £100
A Dozen Dogs Or So, by P.R. Chalmers, Eyre &
Spottiswoode, 1927 (13 colour plates) . . . £125
ditto, Eyre & Spottiswoode, 1927 (13 colour plates,
250 copies, signed by Aldin and Chalmers) . £350
Sleeping Partners: A Series of Episodes, Eyre &
Spottiswoode, [1929] (20 colour plates) . . £250
Jerry: The Story of an Exmoor Pony, by Eleanor E.
Helme and Nance Paul, Eyre & Spottiswoode, [1930]
(11 full-page b/w illustrations) £50
An Artist's Model, Witherby, 1930 (20 colour plates) .
. . . . £200
Mrs Tickler's Caravan, Eyre & Spottiswoode, 1931 .
. . . . £50
Lost, Stolen or Strayed, by Marion Ashmore, Eyre &
Spottiswoode, 1931 (30 b/w illustrations and colour
frontispiece) £50
Flax, Police Dog, by Svend Fleuron, Eyre &
Spottiswoode, [1931] (10 b/w illustrations) . £45
Forty Fine Ladies, Eyre & Spottiswoode, 1929 £130
The Bunch Book, by James Douglas, Eyre &
Spottiswoode, 1932 (51 b/w illustrations and coloured
frontispiece) £45
The Joker, and Jerry Again, by Eleanor E. Helme and
Nance Paul, Eyre & Spottiswoode, 1932 . £45
The Cecil Aldin Book, Eyre & Spottiswoode, 1932 (8
colour plates and 95 b/w illustrations) . . £45
Scarlet, Blue and Green, by Duncan Fife, Macmillan,
1932 (5 colour plates, 7 half-tone and 25 b/w
illustrations) £75
His Apologies, by Rudyard Kipling, Doubleday Doran
(U.S.), 1932 . . . . £45

Dogs of Every Day, by Patrick Chalmers, Eyre &
Spottiswoode, 1933 (12 full-page mono plates) £75
Who's Who in the Zoo, Eyre & Spottiswoode, 1933 (4
colour plates and 35 full-page b/w illustrations) £50
Hotspur the Beagle, by John Vickerman, Constable,
1934 . . . . £50
Just Among Friends, Eyre & Spottiswoode, 1935 £175
How to Draw Dogs, John Lane: The Bodley Head,
1935 . . . . £150
Smuggler's Gallows, by William E.S. Hope, Eyre &
Spottiswoode, 1936 . . . . £20
Hunting Scenes, Eyre & Spottiswoode, 1936 . £175

Others
Old Inns, Heinemann, 1921 (16 plates) . . . £100
Old Manor Houses, Heinemann, 1923 (12 plates) £65
Time I Was Dead: Pages from my Autobiography,
Eyre & Spottiswoode, 1934. . . . . £60

RICHARD ALDINGTON
(b.1892 d.1962)

Richard Aldington, poet, novelist and literary scholar,
is probably best known for being one of the first three
Imagist poets, along with Ezra Pound and H.D.

Novels
Death of a Hero, Chatto & Windus, 1929 . £150/£40
ditto, Covici, Friede (U.S.), 1929. . . . £75/£20
ditto, Babou & Kahane (Paris), 1930 (first
unexpurgated edition, 300 copies, 2 vols, tissue d/w).
. . . . £200/£165
The Colonel's Daughter. A Novel, Chatto & Windus,
1931 . . . . £20/£5
ditto, Chatto & Windus, 1931 (210 signed, numbered
copies) £125
ditto, Doubleday (U.S.), 1931 . . . . £20/£5
Stepping Heavenward, - A Record, Orioli (Florence),
1931 (808 signed, numbered copies) . . £64/£45
ditto, Chatto & Windus, 1931 . . . . £25/£5
All Men are Enemies: A Romance, Chatto & Windus,
1932 . . . . £20/£5
ditto, Chatto & Windus, 1933 (110 signed copies) £100
ditto, Doubleday (U.S.), 1933 . . . . £20/£5
Women Must Work, Chatto & Windus, 1934 £20/£5
ditto, Doubleday (U.S.), 1934 . . . . £20/£5
Very Heaven, Heinemann, 1937. . . . £15/£5
ditto, Doubleday (U.S.), 1937 . . . . £15/£5
Seven Against Reeves: A Comedy-Farce, Heinemann,
1938 . . . . £15/£5
ditto, Doubleday (U.S.), 1938 . . . . £15/£5
Rejected Guest, Viking (U.S.), 1939. . . £20/£5
ditto, Heinemann, 1939 . . . . . £25/£5
The Romance of Casanova: a Novel, Duell, Sloan, and
Pearce (U.S.), 1946 . . . . . . £15/£5
ditto, Heinemann, 1946 . . . . . £15/£5

Short Stories

Roads to Glory, Chatto & Windus, 1930 . £65/£15

ditto, Chatto & Windus, 1930 (360 numbered copies) .
. . . . £90

ditto, Doubleday (U.S.), 1931 . . . . £30/£10

Two Stories, Elkin Mathews & Marrot, 1930 (530 signed, numbered copies) . . . . £100/£75

At All Costs, Heinemann, 1930 . . . . £15/£5

ditto, Heinemann, 1930 (275 signed, numbered copies)
. . . . £75

Last Straws, Hours Press (Paris), 1930 (500 numbered copies out of 700) £100

ditto, Hours Press (Paris), 1930 (200 signed, numbered copies out of 700) £2000

Soft Answers, Chatto & Windus, 1932 . . . £20/£5

ditto, Chatto & Windus, 1932 (110 signed copies) £90

ditto, Doubleday (U.S.), 1932 . . . . £20/£5

Verse

Images (1910-1915), The Poetry Bookshop, 1915 (wraps). £200

ditto, as *Images Old and New*, Four Seas Company (U.S.), 1916 (wraps). £75

The Love of Myrrhine and Konallis And Other Prose Poems, The Clerk's Press (U.S.), 1917 (40 copies, wraps). £250

ditto, Pascal Covici (U.S.), 1926 (150 signed copies) .
. . . . £75/£45

ditto, Pascal Covici (U.S.), 1926 (unsigned copies) .
. . . . £25/£5

Reverie, A Little Book of Poems for H.D., The Clerk's Press (U.S.), 1917 (50 copies, wraps) . . . £150

Images of War, Beaumont Press, 1919 (30 numbered, signed copies, in box) £400

ditto, (50 copies on cartridge paper numbered 31 to 80)
. . . . £200

ditto, (120 unsigned copies on hand-made paper, numbered 81 to 200). £75

ditto, Allen & Unwin, 1919 . . . . . £20

ditto, Four Seas Company (U.S.), 1921 (wraps) £65

Images of Desire, Elkin Mathews/Riverside Press, 1919 (signed, numbered, wraps) . . . £95

Images, The Egoist Ltd, 1919 (wraps) . . . £45

War and Love (1915-1918), Four Seas Company (U.S.), 1919 . . . . £45

The Berkshire Kennet, Curwen Press, 1923 (50 copies, wraps). £150

Collected Poems 1915-1923, Allen & Unwin, 1933 .
. . . . £35/£15

Exile and Other Poems, Allen & Unwin, 1923 (750 copies) £50

A Fool i' the Forest: a Phantasmagoria, Allen & Unwin, 1924 . . . . £15/£5

Hark the Herald, Hours Press (Paris), 1928 (100 numbered, signed copies) £300

The Eaten Heart, Hours Press (Paris), 1929 (200 numbered, signed copies) £300

ditto, Chatto & Windus, 1933 . . . . £20/£10

Movietones: Invented and Set Down by Richard Aldington, 1928-1929, privately printed, 1932 (10 copies) £7,500

Love and the Luxembourg, Covici, Friede (U.S.), 1930 (475 signed copies, slipcase) . . . . £45/£25

ditto, as *A Dream in the Luxembourg*, Chatto & Windus, 1930 (308 signed copies) . . . £45/£25

The Poems of Richard Aldington, Doubleday (U.S.), 1934 . . . . £15/£5

Life Quest, Chatto & Windus, 1935 . . . . £15/£5

ditto, Doubleday (U.S.), 1935 . . . . . £10/£5

The Crystal World, Heinemann, 1937 . . . £10/£5

Others

Literary Studies and Reviews, Allen & Unwin 1924 .
. . . . £10/£5

Voltaire, Routledge, 1925 . . . . . . £10/£5

ditto, Dutton (U.S.), 1924. . . . . . £10/£5

French Studies and Reviews, Allen & Unwin, 1926 .
. . . . £10/£5

ditto, Dial Press (U.S.), 1926 . . . . . £10/£5

D.H. Lawrence: An Indiscretion, University of Washington Book Store (U.S.), 1927 (wraps) . £25

ditto, as *D.H. Lawrence*, Chatto & Windus, 1930 (250 signed copies) . . . . . . £45/£25

Remy de Gourment. A Modern Man of Letters, University of Washington Book Store (U.S.), 1928 (wraps) £25

Balls and Another Book for Suppression, Lahr, 1930 (100 copies, wraps) £45

Balls, privately printed, 1932 (99 + copies, single folded sheet) £200

The Squire Heinemann, 1934 . . . . . £2,750

D.H. Lawrence: a Complete List of His Works, Together with a Critical Appreciation, Heinemann, [1935?] . . . . £35/£10

Artifex: Sketches and Ideas, Chatto & Windus, 1935 .
. . . . £20/£5

ditto, Doubleday, 1935 . . . . . . £15/£5

W. Somerset Maugham, An Appreciation, Doubleday (U.S.), 1939 (wraps). £25

Life for Life's Sake, A Book of Reminiscences, Viking (U.S.), 1941 . . . . £40/£20

The Duke, Being an Account of the Life and Achievments of the 1st Duke of Wellington, Viking (U.S.), 1943 . . . . £10/£5

ditto, as *Wellington*, Heinemann, 1946 . . £10/£5

Jane Austen, Ampersand Press (U.S.), 1948 £45/£20

Four English Portraits 1801-1851, Evans, 1948 . .
. . . . £15/£5

The Strange Life of Charles Waterton, Evans, 1949 .
. . . . £20/£5

ditto, Duell, Sloan & Pearce (U.S.), 1949 . . £15/£5

D.H. Lawrence: An Appreciation, Penguin, 1950 (wraps) £5

ditto, as *D.H. Lawrence, Portrait of a Genius, But ...*, Heinemann, 1950 . . . . . . £25/£10

Pinorman: Personal Recollections of Norman Douglas, Pino Orioli, and Charles Prentice, Heinemann, 1954 . . . . £15/£5

Ezra Pound & T.S. Eliot - A Lecture, The Peacocks Press, 1954 (350 signed, numbered copies, glassine d/w) . . . . £75/£65

ditto, The Peacocks Press, 1954 (10 trial copies, azure paper, signed) £250

A.E. Housman & W.B. Yeats: Two Lectures, The Peacocks Press, 1955 (350 copies of 360, glassine d/w) . . . . £75/£65

Lawrence L'Imposteur: T.E. Lawrence, the Legend and the Man, Amiot-Dumont (Paris), 1954 £35/£10

ditto, as *Lawrence of Arabia: A Biographical Enquiry,* Collins, 1955 . . . . . . £50/£20

Introduction to Mistral, Heinemann, 1956 . £15/£5

ditto, Southern Illinois Univ. Press (U.S.), 1960 £10/£5

Frauds, Heinemann, 1957 . . . . . £10/£5

A Tourist's Rome, Melissa Press (France), [1960 or 1961] (wraps) £75

Portrait of a Rebel, The Life and Works of Robert Louis Stevenson, Evans, 1957 . . . . . £15/£5

A Letter from Richard Aldington and a Summary Bibliography of Count Potocki's Published Works, Melissa Press (France), 1962 . . . . . £100

D.H. Lawrence in Selbstzeugnissen und Bilddokumenten, Rowohlt Taschenbuch (Hamburg), 1961 . . . . £10/£5

Selected Critical Writings 1928-60, Southern Illinois Univ. Press (U.S.), 1970. . . . . . £10/£5

A Passionate Prodigality: Letters to Alan Bird from Richard Aldington 1949-1962, New York Public Library & Readers Books (U.S.), 1975. . £10/£5

Literary Lifelines: The Richard Aldington - Lawrence Durrell Correspondence, Faber, 1981 . . £15/£5

ditto, Viking (U.S.), 1981. . . . . . £15/£5

BRIAN ALDISS
(b.1925)

First published during the 1950s, Aldiss is best known for science fiction novels. He is able to push the genre to the limits of convention, however. *Barefoot in the Head* owes much to Joyce, and *A Report on Probability* is in essence an 'anti-novel'.

Novels

The Brightfount Diaries, Faber, 1955 . . £100/£40

Non-Stop, Faber, 1958 (first printing red boards) . . . . £125/£30

ditto, Faber, 1958 (second printing, brown cloth) . . . . £75/£30

ditto, as *Starship,* Criterion (U.S.), 1959 . £60/£20

Vanguard from Alpha, Ace (U.S.), 1959 (paperback double with Kenneth Bulmer's *The Changeling Worlds*) £5

ditto, as *Equator,* Digit, 1961 (wraps) . . £5

Bow Down to Nul, Ace (U.S.), 1960 (paperback double with Manly Wade Wellman's *The Dark Destroyers*) £5

ditto, as *The Interpreter,* Digit, 1961 (wraps) . £5

The Male Response, Beacon Press (U.S.), 1961 (wraps) £10

ditto, Dobson, 1963 . . . . £20/£5

The Primal Urge, Ballantine (U.S.), 1961 (wraps) £5

ditto, Sphere, 1967 (wraps) £5

Hothouse, Faber, 1962 . . . . . . £50/£20

ditto, as *The Long Aftermath of Earth,* NAL (U.S.), 1962 (abridged, wraps) £5

The Dark Light Years, Faber, 1964 . . . £25/£10

ditto, NAL (U.S.), 1964 (wraps) £5

Greybeard, Harcourt Brace (U.S.), 1964 . £50/£10

ditto, Faber, 1964 . . . . £30/£10

Earthworks, Faber, 1965 . . . . . £30/£10

ditto, Doubleday (U.S.), 1966 . . . £15/£5

An Age, Faber, 1967 . . . . . £25/£10

ditto, as *Cryptozoic,* Doubleday, 1968 . . £15/£5

Report on Probability A, Faber, 1968 . . £15/£5

ditto, Doubleday (U.S.), 1968 . . . . £15/£5

Barefoot in the Head, Faber, 1969 . . £15/£5

ditto, Doubleday (U.S.), 1970 . . . . £15/£5

The Hand-Reared Boy, Weidenfeld, 1970 . £15/£5

ditto, McCann (U.S.), 1970 . . . . £15/£5

A Soldier Erect, Weidenfeld, 1971 . . . £15/£5

ditto, McCann (U.S.), 1971 . . . . £15/£5

Frankenstein Unbound, Cape, 1973 . £25/£10

ditto, Random House (U.S.), [1974] . . . £15/£5

The Eighty-Minute Hour, Doubleday (U.S.), 1974 . . . . £15/£5

ditto, Cape, 1974 . . . . £15/£5

The Malacia Tapestry, Cape, 1976 . . £10/£5

ditto, Harper & Row (U.S.), [1977] . . . £10/£5

Brothers of the Head, Pierrot (UK & US), 1977 . . . . £10/£5

ditto, as *Brothers of the Head,* and *Where the Lines Converge,* Panther, 1979 (wraps) £5

Enemies of the System, Cape, 1978 . . . £10/£5

ditto, Harper & Row (U.S.), 1978 . . . £10/£5

A Rude Awakening, Weidenfeld, 1978 . . £10/£5

ditto, Random House (U.S.), 1979 . . £10/£5

Life in the West, Weidenfeld, 1980 . . . £10/£5

ditto, Carroll & Graf (U.S.), 1990 . . . £10/£5

Moreau's Other Island, Cape, 1980 . . . £10/£5

ditto, as *An Island Called Moreau,* Simon & Schuster (U.S.), 1981 . . . . £10/£5

Helliconia Spring, Cape, 1982 . . . . £10/£5

ditto, Atheneum (U.S.), 1982. . . . . £10/£5

Helliconia Summer, Cape, 1983. . . . £10/£5

ditto, Atheneum (U.S.), 1983. . . . . £10/£5

Helliconia Winter, Cape, 1985 . . . . £10/£5

ditto, Atheneum (U.S.), 1985. . . . . £10/£5

The Year Before Yesterday, Watts (U.S.) 1987. . . . . £10/£5

ditto, as *Cracken at Critical,* Kerosina, 1987 £15/£5

ditto, Kerosina, 1987 (250 signed, numbered copies, with dustjacket and in slipcase with *The Magic of the Past*) . . . . £45 the set
ditto, Kerosina, 1987 (26 lettered, ¼ leather copies) .
. . . . £75
The Magic of the Past, Kerosina, 1987 (350 copies, wraps). £25
ditto, Kerosina, 1987 (250 cloth copies without jacket, in slipcase with *Cracken at Critical*) . £45 the set
Forgotten Life, Gollancz, 1988 . . . . £10/£5
ditto, Atheneum (U.S.), 1989. . . . £10/£5
Sex and the Black Machine, Avernus: Titan Books, 1988 (wraps) £20
Dracula Unbound, HarperCollins (U.S.), 1991 £10/£5
ditto, Gollancz, 1991 . . . . . . £10/£5
Remembrance Day, HarperCollins (U.S.), 1992 .
. . . . £10/£5
ditto, St Martin's Press (U.S.), 1993 . . £10/£5

Short Stories
Space, Time and Nathaniel, Faber, 1957 . £150/£45
ditto, as *No Time Like Tomorrow,* NAL (U.S.), 1959 (wraps) £5
The Canopy of Time, Faber, 1959 . . . £50/£15
ditto, as *Galaxies Like Grains of Sand,* NAL (U.S.), 1960 (wraps) £5
The Airs of Earth, Faber, 1963 . . . . £45/£20
ditto, as *Starswarm,* NAL (U.S.), 1964 (wraps) £5
Best SF Stories of Brian W. Aldiss, Faber, 1965 . .
. . . . £15/£5
ditto, as *Who Can Replace a Man?,* Harcourt Brace (U.S.), 1966 . . . . £10/£5
ditto, Faber, 1971 (revised edition) . . . £10/£5
The Saliva Tree and Other Strange Growths, Faber, 1966 . . . . £50/£20
Intangibles Inc. and Other Stories, Faber, 1969 . .
. . . . £20/£5
ditto, as *Neanderthal Planet,* Avon, Science Fiction Book Club (U.S.), 1970 . . . . . £10/£5
The Moment of Eclipse, Faber, 1970 . . . £10/£5
ditto, as *Moment of Eclipse,* Doubleday (U.S.), 1972 .
. . . . £10/£5
The Comic Inferno, Daw Books (U.S.), 1972 . £10/£5
ditto, as *The Book of Brian Aldiss,* N.E.L., 1973 . .
. . . . £10/£5
Last Orders, Cape, 1977 . . . . . £10/£5
ditto, Carroll & Graf (U.S.) 1989. . . . £10/£5
New Arrivals, Old Encounters, Cape, 1979 . £10/£5
ditto, Harper & Row (U.S.), 1979 . . . £10/£5
A Romance of the Equator, Birmingham Science Fiction Group, 1980 (wraps) £15
ditto, as *A Romance of the Equator: Best Fantasy Stories,* Gollancz, 1989 . . . . . £10/£5
ditto, Atheneum (U.S.), 1990. . . . . £10/£5
The Life of Samuel Johnson, as edited (ie. written) by Aldiss, Oxford Polytechnic Press, 1980 (60 signed, numbered copies) £35
Foreign Bodies, Chapman (Singapore), 1981 . £15/£5
Seasons in Flight, Cape, 1984 . . . . £10/£5

ditto, Atheneum (U.S.), 1986. . . . . . £10/£5
My Country 'Tis Not Only of Thee, Aldiss Appreciation Society, 1986 (100 signed copies) £25
Best SF Stories of Brian W. Aldiss, Gollancz, 1988 (new collection) . . . . £10/£5
ditto, as *Man in His Time,* Atheneum (U.S.), 1989 .
. . . . £10/£5
Bodily Functions, Avernus, 1991 (100 signed copies).
. . . . £60/£40
A Tupolev Too Far, HarperCollins, 1993. . £10/£5
The Secret of This Book, HarperCollins, 1995 £10/£5
ditto, as *Common Clay: 20 Odd Stories,* St Martin's (U.S.), 1996 . . . . £10/£5

Verse
Pile: A Poem, Cape, 1979 (illustrated by Mike Wilks).
. . . . £15
ditto, Holt Rineheart (U.S.), 1980 . . . . £10
Farewell to a Child, Priapus, 1982 (315 of 350 unsigned copies) £15
ditto, Priapus, 1982 (35 signed, numbered copies of 350) £25
At the Caligula Hotel, Sinclair Stevenson, 1995 (wraps) £10

Non Fiction
Cities and Stones: A Traveller's Yugoslavia, Faber, 1966 . . . . £10/£5
The Shape of Further Things, Faber, 1970 . £10/£5
ditto, Doubleday (U.S.), 1971 . . . . £10/£5
Billion Year Spree: The History of Science Fiction, Weidenfeld, 1973 . . . . . . £10/£5
ditto, Doubleday (U.S.), 1973 . . . . £10/£5
Science Fiction Art, N.E.L., 1977 (oversized soft cover). £35
Science Fiction as Science Fiction, Bran's Head Books, 1979 (wraps). £5
This World and Nearer Ones: Essays Exploring the Familiar, Weidenfeld, 1979 . . . . £10/£5
ditto, Kent State (U.S.), 1981 (wraps) . . . £5
The Pale Shadow of Science, Serconia Press (U.S.), 1985 . . . . £10/£5
Trillion Year Spree: The History of Science Fiction, Gollancz, 1986 (with David Wingrove) . £25/£10
ditto, Gollancz, 1986 (100 signed copies of 126, slipcase) £75
ditto, Gollancz, 1986 (26 signed, lettered copies of 126) £150
ditto, Atheneum (U.S.), 1986. . . . . £10/£5
...And the Lurid Glare of the Comet, Serconia Press (U.S.), 1986 . . . . £10/£5
Ruins, Century Hutchinson, 1987 . . . £10/£5
Detached Retina, Liverpool Science Fiction Texts and Studies, No.4, 1994 . . . . . . £15
ditto, Liverpool Science Fiction Texts and Studies, No.4, 1994 (wraps) £10

Omnibus Editions
A Brian Aldiss Omnibus, Sidgwick & Jackson, 1969 .
. . . . £15/£5
Brian Aldiss Omnibus 2, Sidgwick & Jackson, 1971 .
. . . . £15/£5

Miscellaneous
Science Fiction Blues, co-written with Ken Campbell,
Avernus, 1988 (wraps, stage sketches) . . . £5
Bury my Heart at W.H. Smith's, Hodder & Stoughton,
1990 . . . . £10/£5
ditto, Avernus, 1990 (250 signed, numbered copies,
with six extra chapters) . . . . £40/£20

MARGERY ALLINGHAM
(b.1904 d.1966)

An author of detective fiction from its 'Golden Age',
whose hero is an aristocratic adventurer known as
Albert Campion.

Albert Campion Titles
The Crime at Black Dudley, Jarrolds, 1929 £300/£125
ditto as the *Black Dudley Murder*, Doubleday (U.S.),
1930 . . . . £175/£75
Mystery Mile, Jarrolds, 1930 . . . . . £200/£75
ditto, Doubleday (U.S.), 1930 . . . £100/£25
Look to the Lady, Jarrolds, 1931 . . . £200/£75
ditto as *The Gyrth Chalice Mystery*, Doubleday (U.S.),
1931 . . . . £75/£20
Police at the Funeral, Heinemann, 1931 . £150/£50
ditto, Doubleday (U.S.), 1932 . . . £75/£20
Sweet Danger, Heinemann, 1933 . . . £150/£50
ditto, as *Kingdom of Death*, Doubleday (U.S.), 1933 .
. . . . £75/£20
Death of a Ghost, Heinemann, 1934. . . £125/£50
ditto, Doubleday (U.S.), 1934 . . . . £50/£15
Flowers for the Judge, Heinemann, 1936 . £100/£35
ditto, Doubleday (U.S.), 1936 . . . £25/£10
Dancers in Mourning, Heinemann, 1937 . £100/£35
ditto, Doubleday (U.S.), 1937 . . . £25/£10
The Case of the Late Pig, Hodder & Stoughton, 1937
(wraps) £100
Mr. Campion Criminologist, Doubleday (U.S.), 1937
. . . . £75/£25
The Fashion in Shrouds, Heinemann, 1938 £100/£35
ditto, Doubleday (U.S.), 1938 . . . . £35/£10
Mr Campion and Others, Heinemann, 1939 £250/£150
Traitor's Purse, Heinemann, 1941 . . £75/£20
ditto, Doubleday (U.S.), 1941 . . . £35/£10
Coroner's Pidgin, Heinemann, 1945 . . £75/£20
ditto, as *Pearls Before Swine*, Doubleday (U.S.), 1945
. . . . £45/£10
The Case Book of Mr Campion, Spivak (U.S.), 1947 .
. . . . £25
More Work for the Undertaker, Heinemann, 1948 .
. . . . £35/£10

ditto, Doubleday (U.S.), 1949 . . . . £25/£5
The Tiger in the Smoke, Chatto & Windus, 1952 . .
. . . . £35/£10
ditto, Doubleday (U.S.), 1952 . . . . £25/£5
The Beckoning Lady, Chatto & Windus, 1955 . . .
. . . . £25/£5
ditto, as *The Estate of the Beckoning Lady*, Doubleday
(U.S.), 1955 . . . . £25/£5
Hide My Eyes, Chatto & Windus, 1958 . . £25/£5
ditto, as *Tether's End*, Doubleday (U.S.), 1958 . .
. . . . £25/£5
The China Governess, Doubleday (U.S.), 1962 .
. . . . £25/£5
ditto, Chatto & Windus, 1963 . . . . £25/£5
*The Mysterious Mr Campion, An Allingham
Omnibus*, Chatto & Windus, 1963 . . . £20/£5
The Mind Readers, Morrow (U.S.), 1965 . £25/£5
ditto, Chatto & Windus, 1965 . . . . £25/£5
Mr Campion's Lady, An Allingham Omnibus, Chatto
& Windus, 1965 . . . . £20/£5
Mr Campion's Clowns, An Allingham Omnibus,
Chatto & Windus, 1967 . . . . . . £10/£5
Cargo of Eagles, Chatto & Windus, 1968 . £20/£5
ditto, Morrow (U.S.), 1968 . . . . . £20/£5
The Allingham Casebook, Chatto & Windus, 1969
. . . . £10/£5
ditto, Morrow (U.S.), 1969 . . . . £10/£5
The Allingham Minibus, Chatto & Windus, 1973 .
. . . . £10/£5
ditto, Morrow (U.S.), 1973 . . . . . £10/£5
ditto, as *Mr. Campion's Lucky Day and other Stories*,
Penguin, 1992 . . . . £5
ditto, Carroll & Graf (U.S.), 1992 . . . £5
The Return of Mr Campion, Hodder & Stoughton,
1989 . . . . £10/£5
ditto, St Martin's Press (U.S.), 1990 . . £10/£5

Books written as 'Maxwell March'
Other Man's Danger, Collins, 1933 . . . £75/£25
ditto, as *The Man of Dangerous Secrets*, Doubleday
(U.S.), 1933 . . . . £60/£25
The Rogues' Holiday, Collins, 1935. . . £75/£15
ditto, Doubleday (U.S.), 1935 . . . . £60/£15
The Shadow in the House, Collins (Crime Club) 1936
. . . . £50/£10
ditto, Doubleday (U.S.), 1936 . . . . £50/£10

Other Crime Titles
The White Cottage Mystery, Jarrolds, 1928 £250/£45
ditto, Carroll & Graf (U.S.), 1990 . . . £20
Black Plumes, Doubleday (U.S.), 1940 . . £250/£45
ditto, Heinemann, 1940 . . . . . £250/£45
Wanted: Someone Innocent, Stamford House (U.S.),
1946 (wraps) £50
Deadly Duo, Doubleday (U.S.), 1949. . . £30/£10
ditto, as *Take Two at Bedtime*, World's Work, 1950 .
. . . . £30/£10
No Love Lost, World's Work, 1954 . . . £20/£10
ditto, Doubleday (U.S.), 1954 . . . . £20/£10

The Darings of the Red Rose, Crippen & Landru
(U.S.), 1995 . . . . £5

Other Titles
Blackkerchief Dick, Hodder & Stoughton, 1923 . .
. . . . £600/£100
ditto, as *Black'erchief Dick*, Doubleday (U.S.), 1923 .
. . . . £500/£75
Dance of the Years, Michael Joseph, 1943 . £30/£10

Play
Water in a Sieve, French, 1925 (wraps) . . . £25

Non Fiction
The Oaken Heart, Michael Joseph, 1941 . £50/£20
ditto, Doubleday (U.S.), 1941 . . . . £45/£15

ERIC AMBLER
(b.1909 d.1998)

A popular and influential thriller writer who deftly
directs his heroes through fast-moving plots.

The Dark Frontier, Hodder & Stoughton, 1936 . .
. . . . £2,500/£250
Uncommon Danger, Hodder & Stoughton, 1937 . .
. . . . £2,500/£250
Epitaph for a Spy, Hodder & Stoughton, 1938 . . .
. . . . £2,000/£200
ditto, Knopf (U.S.), 1952 . . . . . . £350/£40
Cause for Alarm, Hodder & Stoughton, 1938 . .
. . . . £1,750/£200
ditto, Knopf (U.S.), 1939 . . . . . £350/£40
The Mask of Dimitrios, Hodder & Stoughton, 1939
. . . . £2,500/£300
Journey into Fear, Hodder & Stoughton, 1940 . .
. . . . £750/£100
ditto, Knopf (U.S.), 1940 . . . . . £125/£25
Skytip, Doubleday (U.S.), 1950 (pseud. 'Eliot Reed',
written with Charles Rhoda) . . . £75/£15
ditto, Hodder & Stoughton, 1951 . . . £75/£15
Judgement on Deltchev, Hodder & Stoughton, 1951 .
. . . . £50/£25
ditto, Knopf (U.S.), 1951 . . . . . £25/£10
Tender to Danger, Doubleday (U.S.), 1951 (pseud.
'Eliot Reed', written with Charles Rhoda) . £75/£15
ditto, as *Tender to Moonlight*, Hodder & Stoughton,
1951 . . . . £75/£15
The Malas Affair, Collins, 1953 (pseud. 'Eliot Reed',
written with Charles Rhoda) . . . . £75/£15
The Schirmer Inheritance, Heinemann, 1953 £75/£20
ditto, Knopf (U.S.), 1953 . . . . . £45/£15
Charter to Danger, Collins, 1954 (pseud. 'Eliot Reed',
written with Charles Rhoda) . . . . £75/£15
The Night Comers, Heinemann, 1956 . . £25/£10
ditto as *State of Siege*, Knopf (U.S.), 1956 . £25/£10
Passage of Arms, Heinemann, 1959 . . . £25/£10

ditto, Knopf (U.S.), 1959 . . . . . £15/£5
The Light of Day, Heinemann, 1962 . . £25/£10
ditto, Knopf (U.S.), 1963 . . . . . . £15/£5
A Kind of Anger, Bodley Head, 1964 . . £25/£10
ditto, Atheneum (U.S.), 1964 . . . . . £15/£5
The Jealous God Stellar Press, 1964 (200 copies,
wraps) £50
Dirty Story, Bodley Head, 1967 . . . . £25/£10
ditto, Atheneum (U.S.), 1967 . . . . . £15/£5
The Intercom Conspiracy, Atheneum (U.S.), 1969 .
. . . . £25/£10
ditto, Weidenfeld & Nicolson, 1970 . . . £25/£10
The Levanter, Weidenfeld & Nicolson, 1972 £25/£10
ditto, Atheneum (U.S.), 1972 . . . . . £15/£5
Doctor Frigo, Weidenfeld & Nicolson, 1974 £25/£10
ditto, Atheneum (U.S.), 1974 . . . . . £15/£5
Send No More Roses, Weidenfeld & Nicolson, 1977 .
. . . . £15/£5
ditto as *The Siege of the Villa Lipp*, Random House
(U.S.) 1977 . . . . £20/£5
The Care of Time, Farrar Straus Giroux (U.S.), 1981 .
. . . . £15/£5
ditto, Farrar Straus Giroux (U.S.), 1981 (300 signed
copies, slipcase) . . . . £50/£35
ditto, Weidenfeld & Nicolson, 1981 . . . £15/£5

Short Stories
The Army of the Shadows and Other Stories,
Eurographica (Helsinki), 1986 (350 signed copies)
. . . . £75/£45
Waiting for Orders, Mysterious Press (U.S.), 1991 .
. . . . £15/£5
ditto, Mysterious Press (U.S.), 1991 (26 signed copies,
slipcase) . . . . £200/£150
The Story So Far, Weidenfeld & Nicholson, 1993 .
. . . . £15/£5

Essays
The Ability to Kill and Other Pieces, Bodley Head,
1962 (first issue with essay) . . . . £125/£75
ditto, Bodley Head, 1963 (2nd issue) . £35/£10
ditto, The Mysterious Press (U.S.), [1987] (250 signed
copies in slipcase) . . . . £45/£35
ditto, The Mysterious Press (U.S.), [1987] (unlimited
edition in dustjacket) . . . . . . £10/£5

Autobiography
Here Lies Eric Ambler, Weidenfeld & Nicolson, 1985
. . . . £10/£5
ditto, Farrar Straus Giroux (U.S.) 1986 . . £10/£5
ditto, Farrar Straus Giroux (U.S.) 1986 (100 signed
copies, slipcase) . . . . £50/£35

Edited by Ambler
To Catch a Spy, Bodley Head, 1964 . . . £15/£5
ditto, Atheneum (U.S.), 1965 . . . . . £10/£5

KINGSLEY AMIS
(b.1922 d.1995)

A poet and novelist who has the ability to be satirical and inventive whilst being thoroughly readable.

Novels

Lucky Jim, Gollancz, 1953 [1954] . . £2,000/£200
ditto, Doubleday (U.S.), 1954 . . . . £250/£35
That Uncertain Feeling, Gollancz, 1955 . £100/£20
ditto, Harcourt Brace (U.S.), 1956 . . . £50/£15
I Like it Here, Gollancz, 1958 . . . . £65/£20
ditto, Harcourt Brace (U.S.), 1958 . . . £45/£15
Take a Girl Like You, Gollancz, 1960 . . £65/£20
ditto, Harcourt Brace (U.S.), 1961 . . . £25/£10
One Fat Englishman, Gollancz, 1963 . . £25/£10
ditto, Harcourt Brace (U.S.), 1964 . . . £15/£5
The Egyptologists (with Robert Conquest), Jonathan Cape, 1965 . . . . £45/£15
ditto, Random House (U.S.), 1966 . . . £25/£10
The Anti-Death League, Gollancz, 1966 . £25/£10
ditto, Harcourt Brace (U.S.), 1966 . . . £15/£5
Colonel Sun, Jonathan Cape, 1968 (pseud. 'Robert Markham') . . . . £60/£15
ditto, Harper (U.S.), 1968. . . . . . £45/£15
I Want it Now, Jonathan Cape, 1968. . . £20/£5
ditto, Harcourt Brace (U.S.), 1969 . . . £15/£5
The Green Man, Jonathan Cape, 1969 . . £50/£15
ditto, Harcourt Brace (U.S.), 1970 . . . £35/£10
Girl, 20, Jonathan Cape, 1971 . . . . £20/£5
ditto, Harcourt Brace (U.S.), 1972 . . . £20/£5
The Riverside Villas Murder, Jonathan Cape, 1973 . . . . £20/£5
ditto, Harcourt Brace (U.S.), 1973 . . . £15/£5
Ending Up, Jonathan Cape, 1974 . . . £15/£5
ditto, Harcourt Brace (U.S.), 1974 . . . £15/£5
The Alteration, Jonathan Cape, 1976 . . £20/£5
ditto, Viking Press (U.S.), 1977 . . . . £15/£5
Jake's Thing, Hutchinson, 1978 . . . . £15/£5
ditto, Viking Press (U.S.), 1979 . . . . £15/£5
Russian Hide-and-Seek, Hutchinson, 1980. £15/£5
Stanley and the Women, Hutchinson, 1984. £15/£5
ditto, Summit (U.S.), 1985 . . . . . £15/£5
The Old Devils, Hutchinson, 1986 . . . £20/£5
ditto, Hutchinson/London Limited Editions, 1986 (250 signed copies, tissue jacket). . . . £50/£45
ditto, Summit (U.S.), 1986 . . . . . .£10/£5
Difficulties With Girls, Hutchinson, 1988 . .£10/£5
ditto, Hutchinson, 1988 (500 numbered proof copies, wraps) £15
ditto, Summit (U.S.), 1989 . . . . £10/£5
The Folks That Live on the Hill, Hutchinson, 1990 . . . . £10/£5
ditto, Hutchinson, 1990 (500 numbered proof copies) £40
ditto, Summit (U.S.), 1990 . . . . £10/£5
The Russian Girl, Hutchinson, 1992 . . £10/£5
ditto, Viking (U.S.), 1992. . . . . . £10/£5

We Are All Guilty, Reinhardt Books/Viking, 1991 . . . . £10/£5
You Can't Do Both, London Limited Editions, 1994 (150 copies in glassine d/w). . . . . £45/£35
ditto, Hutchinson, 1994 . . . . . £10/£5
The Biographer's Moustache, Flamingo/Harper Collins, 1995. . . . . £10/£5

Omnibus Editions
The Kingsley Amis Omnibus, Hutchinson, 1992 . . . . £10/£5

Short Stories
My Enemy's Enemy, Gollancz, 1962 . . £75/£15
ditto, Harcourt Brace (U.S.), 1963 . . . £45/£10
Dear Illusion, Covent Garden Press, 1972 (500 copies, wraps). £20
ditto, Covent Garden Press, 1972 (100 signed copies, wraps) £50
The Darkwater Hall Mystery, Tragara Press (Edinburgh), 1978 (165 copies, wraps) . . £75
Collected Short Stories, Hutchinson, 1980 . £15/£5
The Crime of the Century, Hutchinson, 1989 £10/£5
ditto, Mysterious Press (U.S.), 1989 . . . £10/£5
ditto, Mysterious Press (U.S.), 1989 (100 signed copies in slipcase) . . . . £60/£40
Mrs Barrett's Secret and Other Stories, Hutchinson, 1993 . . . . £10/£5

Verse
Bright November, Fortune Press, [1947] £1,000/£250
A Frame of Mind, Reading School of Art, 1953 (250 numbered copies, wraps) £250
Fantasy Poets No.22, Fantasy Press, 1954 (wraps) £150
A Case of Samples: Poems, 1946-1956, Gollancz, 1956. . . . . £75/£30
ditto, Harcourt Brace (U.S.), 1957 . . £60/£20
Penguin Modern Poets No.2, Penguin, 1962, (with Dom Moraes and Peter Porter, wraps) . . . £5
The Evans Country, Fantasy Press, 1962 (wraps) £70
A Look Round the Estate: Poems, 1957-1967, Jonathan Cape, 1967 . . . . . £45/£15
ditto, Harcourt Brace (U.S.), 1968 . . £20/£5
Wasted and *Kipling at Batemans*, Poem of the Month Club, 1973 (broadsheet). £15
Collected Poems 1944-1979, Hutchinson, 1979 . . . . £15/£5
ditto, Viking (U.S.), 1980. . . . . . £15/£5

Non Fiction
Socialism and the Intellectuals, Fabian Press, 1957 (wraps) £50
New Maps of Hell: A Survey of Science Fiction, Harcourt Brace (U.S.), 1960 . . . . £45/£15
ditto, Gollancz, 1961 . . . . . . £45/£15
The James Bond Dossier, Jonathan Cape, 1965 . . . . £50/£15
ditto, NAL (U.S.), 1965 . . . . . . £35/£10

Lucky Jim's Politics, Conservative Policy Centre, 1968 (wraps) £25
What Became of Jane Austen? and Other Questions, Jonathan Cape, 1970 . . . . . £35/£10
ditto, Harcourt Brace (U.S.), 1971 . . . £25/£10
On Drink, Jonathan Cape, 1972 . . . . £35/£10
ditto, Harcourt Brace (U.S.), 1973 . . . £25/£10
Rudyard Kipling and his World, Thames & Hudson, 1975 . . . . £15/£5
ditto, Scribner (U.S.), 1975 . . . . . £15/£5
An Arts Policy?, Centre for Policy Studies, 1979 (wraps) £10
Every Day Drinking, Hutchinson, 1983 . . . £15/£5
How's Your Glass? A Quizzical Look at Drinks and Drinking, Weidenfeld & Nicolson, 1984 . £15/£5
Selected Non-Fiction, Hutchinson, 1990 . £15/£5
Memoirs, Hutchinson, 1991 . . . . . £10/£5
ditto, Summit (U.S.), 1991 . . . . . £10/£5
The King's English, HarperCollins, 1997 . £10/£5
ditto, St Martin's Press (U.S.), 1998 . . . £10/£5

MARTIN AMIS
(b.1949)

The son of Kingsley Amis, Martin wrote his first novel at the age of 21.

Novels
The Rachel Papers, Cape, 1973 . . . . . £450/£100
ditto, Knopf (U.S.), 1974 . . . . . . £75/£15
Dead Babies, Cape, 1975 . . . . . . £300/£30
ditto, Knopf (U.S.), 1976 . . . . . . £45/£10
ditto, as *Dark Secrets*, Triad, 1977 (wraps) . £10
Success, Cape, 1978 . . . . £200/£25
ditto, Harmony (U.S.), 1987 . . . . . £20/£5
Other People: A Mystery Story, Cape, 1981 £100/£15
ditto, Viking Press (U.S.), 1981 . . . . £30/£5
Money: A Suicide Note, Cape, 1984 . . . £75/£15
ditto, Viking Press (U.S.), 1985 . . . £25/£5
London Fields, Cape, 1989 . . . . . £20/£5
ditto, London Limited Editions, 1989 (150 signed copies, glassine d/w) . . . . . . £125/£100
ditto, Harmony (U.S.), 1990 . . . . . £15/£5
Time's Arrow, or the Nature of the Offence, Cape, 1991 . . . . £20/£5
ditto, London Limited Editions, 1991 (200 signed copies, glassine d/w) . . . . . . £75/£50
ditto, Harmony (U.S.), 1991 . . . . . £15/£5
The Information, Flamingo, 1995 . . . £15/£5
ditto, Flamingo, 1995 (350 signed, numbered copies of 376, slipcase) . . . . £75/£55
ditto, Harmony (U.S.), 1995 . . . . . £15/£5
Night Train, Cape, 1997 . . . . . . £15/£5
ditto, Cape, 1997 (26 signed deluxe copies) . . £175
ditto, Cape, 1997 (74 signed copies) . . . £100
ditto, Harmony (U.S.), 1997 . . . . . £15/£5

Short Stories
Einstein's Monsters, Cape, 1987 . . . . £25/£10
ditto, Harmony (U.S.), 1987 . . . . . £20/£5
Two Stories, Moorhouse & Sorensen, 1994 (26 signed copies, bound in aluminium, of 326) . . . £250
ditto, Moorhouse & Sorensen, 1994 (100 signed copies bound in cloth of 326) £100
ditto, Moorhouse & Sorensen, 1994 (200 signed copies in card covers of 326) £50
Heavy Weather and Other Stories, Jonathan Cape, 1998 . . . . £15/£5
ditto, Harmony (U.S.), 1999 . . . . . £15/£5

Non Fiction
Invasion of the Space Invaders, Hutchinson, 1982 (wraps) £75
The Moronic Inferno and Other Visits to America, Cape, 1986 . . . . £35/£10
ditto, Viking Press (U.S.), 1987 . . . . £25/£10
Visiting Mrs Nabokov and Other Excursions, Cape, 1993 . . . . £15/£5
ditto, Harmony (U.S.), 1993 . . . . . £15/£5
Experience, Cape, 2000 . . . . . . £10/£5
ditto, Cape, 2000 (150 signed copies, slipcase) . . . . £125/£100
ditto, Hyperion (U.S.), 2000 . . . . . £10/£5

MAYA ANGELOU
(b. 1928)

Maya Angelou is a poet, historian, author, actress, playwright, civil-rights activist, producer and director. Her books of autobiography have become international bestsellers.

Autobiography
I Know Why the Caged Bird Sings, Random House (U.S.), 1969 . . . . £125/£45
ditto, Virago, 1984 (wraps) £5
Gather Together in My Name, Random House (U.S.), 1974 . . . . £45/£20
ditto, Virago, 1974 (wraps) £5
Singin' and Swingin' and Gettin' Merry Like Christmas, Random House (U.S.), 1976 . £25/£10
ditto, Virago, 1985 (wraps) £5
The Heart of a Woman, Random House (U.S.), 1981 . . . . £25/£10
ditto, Virago, 1986 (wraps) £5
All God's Children Need Travelling Shoes, Random House (U.S.), 1986 . . . . £30/£10
ditto, Franklin Library (U.S.), 1986 (signed copies) £50

Essays
Wouldn't Take Nothing for my Journey Now, Random House (U.S.), 1993 . . . . £15/£5
Even the Stars Look Lonesome, Random House (U.S.), 1997 . . . . £15/£5

Poetry
Just Give Me a Cool Drink of Water 'fore I Diiie,
Random House (U.S.), 1971 . . . £50/£20
Oh Pray My Wings are Gonna Fit Me Well, Random
House (U.S.), 1975 . . . . . £30/£10
And Still I Rise, Random House (U.S.), 1978 £40/£15
Shaker, Why Don't You Sing?, Random House (U.S.),
1983 . . . . £30/£10
Now Sheba Sings the Song, Dutton/Dial (U.S.), 1987 .
. . . . £25/£10
I Shall Not Be Moved, Random House (U.S.), 1990 .
. . . . £20/£5
On the Pulse of the Morning, Random House (U.S.),
1993 (wraps) £15
The Complete Collected Poems of Maya Angelou,
Random House (U.S.), 1994 . . . £10/£5

EDWARD ARDIZZONE
(b.1900 d.1979)

Ardizzone studied at the Westminster School of Art
and in 1927 became a full-time artist. He is best
known for his illustrations of children's books, some
of which he wrote himself.

**Children's Books written and illustrated by
Ardizzone**
Little Tim and the Brave Sea Captain, O.U.P., [1936]
. . . . £600/£300
ditto, O.U.P., 1955 (revised edition) . . £45/£20
Lucy Brown and Mr Grimes, O.U.P., [1937] . .
. . . . £500/£250
ditto, O.U.P., 1970 (revised edition) . . £60/£20
Tim and Lucy go to Sea, O.U.P., [1938] £500/£250
ditto, O.U.P., 1958 (revised edition) . . £50/£20
Nicholas the Fast-Moving Diesel, Eyre & Spottis-
woode [1947]. . . . . . . £450/£200
Paul, The Hero of the Fire, Puffin, 1948 (wraps) £45
ditto, Constable, 1962 (revised edition) . . £40/£15
Tim to the Rescue, O.U.P., 1949. . . £350/£150
Tim and Charlotte, O.U.P., 1951 . . £300/£150
Tim in Danger, O.U.P., 1953 . . . £250/£100
Tim all Alone, O.U.P., 1956 . . . £100/£45
Johnny the Clockmaker, O.U.P., 1960 . £100/£45
Tim's Friend Towser, O.U.P., 1962 . . . £100/£45
Peter the Wanderer, O.U.P., 1963 . . £75/£35
Diana and her Rhinoceros, The Bodley Head, 1964
. . . . £75/£35
Sarah and Simon and No Red Paint, Constable [1965]
. . . . £75/£30
Tim and Ginger, O.U.P., 1965 . . . £65/£30
The Little Girl and the Tiny Doll, Constable, 1966
(with Aingelda Ardizzone) . . . . £60/£30
Tim to the Lighthouse, O.U.P., 1968 . . £50/£20
Johnny's Bad Day, The Bodley Head, 1970 £45/£20
Tim's Last Voyage, The Bodley Head, 1972 £45/£20

Ship's Cook Ginger: Another Time Story, The Bodley
Head, 1977 . . . . £35/£15
The Adventures of Tim, The Bodley Head, 1977 . .
. . . . £35/£15

Children's Books illustrated by Ardizzone
Tom, Dick and Harriet, by Albert N. Lyons, Cresset
Press, 1937 . . . . £450/£175
Great Expectations, by Charles Dickens, Heritage
Press, 1939 . . . . £100/£45
ditto, Limited Editions Club (U.S.) [1939] £600/£350
MIMFF, by H.J. Kaeser, O.U.P., 1939 . . £100/£45
Peacock Pie, by Walter de la Mare, Faber, 1946 .
. . . . £75/£40
The Pilgrim's Progress, by John Bunyan, Faber, 1947
. . . . £100/£45
Three Brothers and a Lady, by Margaret Black, Acorn
Press, 1947 . . . . £80/£35
*A True and Pathetic History of Desbarollda, The
Waltzing Mouse*, by Noel Langley, Lindsay
Drummond, 1947 . . . . . . £80/£35
*Hey Nonny Yes: Passions and Conceits from
Shakespeare*, edited by Hallam Fordham, John
Lehmann, 1947 . . . . £65/£25
The Life and Adventures of Nicholas Nickleby, Ealing
Studios, 1947 (promotional booklet) . . £100
Charles Dickens' Birthday Book, edited by Enid
Dickens Hawksley, Faber, 1948 . . . £75/£25
The Otterbury Incident, by Cecil Day Lewis, Putnam,
1948 . . . . £80/£35
The Rose and the Ring, by William Makepeace
Thackeray, Guilford Press/Wilfrid David, 1948 . .
. . . . £50/£20
MIMFF in Charge, by H.J. Kaeser, (translated by
David Ascoli), O.U.P., 1949 . . . £60/£25
The Tale of Ali Baba, (translated by J.C. Mardrus and
E. Powys Mathers), Limited Editions Club (U.S.),
1949 (2,500 signed copies) £150
Somebody's Rocking My Dreamboat, by Noel Langley
and Hazel Pynegar, Barker, 1949 . . £50/£20
The Humour of Dickens, News Chronicle, 1952 £40
The Blackbird in the Lilac, by James Reeves, O.U.P.,
1952 . . . . £60/£25
MIMFF Takes Over, by H.J. Kaeser, O.U.P., 1954 . .
. . . . £50/£20
*The Fantastic Tale of the Plucky Sailor and the
Postage Stamp*, by Stephen Corrin, Faber, 1954 . .
. . . . £45/£20
The Little Bookroom, by Eleanor Farjeon, O.U.P.,
1955 . . . . £50/£20
The Suburban Child, by James Kenward, O.U.P., 1955
. . . . £75/£25
Minnow on the Say, by Phillippa Pearce, O.U.P., 1955
. . . . £75/£25
David Copperfield, by Charles Dickens, (abridged by
S. Wood), O.U.P., 1955 . . . . . £45/£20
Bleak House, Charles Dickens, (abridged by S. Wood),
O.U.P., 1955 . . . . £45/£20

Sun Slower, Sun Faster, by Meriol Trevor, Collins, 1955 . . . . £45/£20

Pigeons and Princesses, by James Reeves, Heinemann, 1956 . . . . £40/£20

Marshmallow, by Claire Newberry, Studio, 1956 £30

St Luke's Life of Christ (translated by J.B. Phillips), Collins, 1956 . . . . £45/£20

Wandering Moon, by James Reeves, Heinemann, 1957 . . . . £60/£25

A Stickful of Nonpareil, by George Scurfield, (500 copies) CUP, 1956 . . . . £100

Hunting with Mr Jorrocks, by Robert Surtees (edited by Lionel Gough) O.U.P., 1956. . . . £100/£45

Prefabulous Animiles, by James Reeves, Heinemann, 1957 . . . . £50/£20

The School in Our Village, by Joan M. Goldman, Batsford, 1957 . . . . . . £50/£20

The Boy Down Kitchiner Street, by Leslie Paul, Faber, 1957 . . . . £50/£20

Lottie, by John Symonds, The Bodley Head, 1957 . . . . £50/£20

MIMFF-Robinson, by H.J. Kaeser, (translated by Ruth Michaelis and Jena & Arthur Ratcliff), O.U.P., 1958 . . . . £50/£20

The Story of Joseph, by Walter de la Mare, Faber, 1958 . . . . £45/£20

Jim at the Corner, by Eleanor Farjeon, O.U.P., 1958 . . . . £75/£30

Pinky Pye, by Eleanor Estes, Constable, 1959 £50/£20

The Nine Lives of Island Mackenzie, by Ursula Moray Williams, Chatto & Windus, 1959 . . £45/£15

Titus in Trouble, by James Reeves, The Bodley Head, 1959 . . . . £50/£20

Exploits of Don Quixote, by Cervantes, (abridged by James Reeves), Blackie [1959] . . . £50/£20

Story of Moses, by Walter de la Mare, Faber, 1959 . . . . £50/£20

Elfrida and the Pig, by John Symonds, Harrap, 1959 . . . . £60/£25

Holiday Trench, by Joan Ballantyne, Nelson, 1959 . . . . £35/£15

The Godstone and the Blackymor, by T.H. White, Cape, 1959 . . . . £65/£25

The Story of Samuel and Saul, by Walter de la Mare, Faber, 1960 . . . . £50/£20

Kidnappers at Coombe, by Joan Ballantyne, Nelson, 1960 . . . . £45/£15

The Rib of the Green Umbrella, by Naomi Mitchison, Collins, 1960 . . . . £50/£20

Eleanor Farjeon's Book, edited by Eleanor Graham, Puffin, 1960 (wraps) £20

Merry England, by Cyril Ray, Vista Books, 1960 . . . . £60/£25

Italian Peepshow, by Eleanor Farjeon, O.U.P., 1960 . . . . £60/£25

The Penny Fiddle: Poems for Children, by Robert Graves, Cassell, 1960 . . . . . £125/£50

ditto, Doubleday (U.S.), 1960 . . . . £75/£20

Boyhoods of the Great Composers, O.U.P., 1960 &, 1963 (2 vols). . . . . £75/£30

Hurdy Gurdy, by James Reeves, Heinemann, 1961 . . . . £75/£30

No Mystery for the Maitlands, by Joan Ballantyne, Nelson, 1961 . . . . £60/£25

Down in the Cellar, by Nicholas Gray, Dobson, 1961 . . . . £50/£20

The Adventures of Huckleberry Finn, by Mark Twain, Heinemann, 1961 . . . . . £60/£25

The Adventures of Tom Sawyer, by Mark Twain, Heinemann, 1961 . . . . . £60/£25

Stories from the Bible, by Walter de la Mare, Faber, 1961 . . . . £50/£20

The Witch Family, by Eleanor Estes, Constable, 1962 . . . . £60/£25

Naughty Children, by Christianna Brand, Gollancz, 1962 . . . . £75/£30

Sailor Rumbelow and Britannia, by James Reeves, Heinemann, 1962 . . . . . £75/£25

Peter Pan, by J.M. Barrie, Brockhampton Press, 1962 . . . . £75/£30

A Ring of Bells, by John Betjeman, John Murray, 1962 . . . . £60/£25

The Story of Let's Make an Opera, by Eric Crosier, O.U.P., 1962 . . . . £50/£25

The Singing Cupboard, by Dan Farralla, Blackie, 1962 . . . . £60/£20

Mrs Malone, by Eleanor Farjeon, O.U.P., 1962 . . . . £60/£25

Stig of the Dump, by Clive King, Puffin Original, 1963 (wraps) £25

Kaleidoscope, by Eleanor Farjeon, O.U.P., 1963 . . . . £75/£30

Swanhilda-of-the-Swans, by Dana Farralla, Blackie [1964] . . . . £50/£20

Ann at Highwood Hall, by Robert Graves, Cassell, 1964 . . . . £50/£20

ditto, Doubleday (U.S.), 1964 . . . . £30/£10

Three Tall Tales, by James Reeves, Abelard-Schumann, 1964 . . . . . . £50/£20

The Alley, by Eleanor Estes, Harcourt Brace (U.S.), 1964 . . . . £35/£15

Nurse Matilda, by Christianna Brand, Brockhampton Press, 1965 . . . . £60/£20

Island of Fish in the Trees, by Eva-Lis Wuorio, Dobson, 1964. . . . . . . £60/£20

The Land of Right Up and Down, by Eva-Lis Wuorio, Dobson, 1965 . . . . . . £60/£25

Open the Door, edited by Margery Fisher, Brockhampton Press, 1965 . . . . £50/£20

The Story of Jackie Thimble, by James Reeves, Chatto & Windus, 1965 . . . . . £50/£20

Old Perisher, by Diana Ross, Faber, 1965 . £50/£20

The Old Nurse's Stocking Basket, by Eleanor Farjeon, O.U.P., 1965 . . . . £50/£20

The Truants and Other Poems for Children, by John Walsh, Heinemann, 1965 . . . . £50/£20

The Growing Summer, by Noel Streatfield, Collins, 1966 . . . . £70/£25
Long Ago When I Was Young, by E. Nesbit, Whiting & Wheaton, 1966 . . . . £50/£20
Daddy Longlegs, by Jean Webster, Brockhampton Press, 1966 . . . . £50/£20
The Land of Green Ginger, by Noel Langley, Puffin, 1966, (wraps). £20
The Dragon, by Archibald Marshall, Warne, 1966. .
. . . . £40/£15
The Secret Shoemaker and Other Stories, by James Reeves, Abelard-Schumann, 1966 . . . £75/£20
Timothy's Song, by W.J. Lederer, Lutterworth Press, 1966 . . . . £40/£15
The Year Round, by Leonard Clark, Hart-Davis, 1966
. . . . £40/£15
Rhyming Will, by James Reeves, Hamish Hamilton, 1967 . . . . £70/£25
Travels with a Donkey, by Robert Louis Stevenson, Folio Society, 1967 . . . . . . £35/£15
Miranda The Great, by Eleanor Estes, Harcourt Brace (U.S.), 1967 . . . . £35/£15
A Likely Place, by Paula Fox, Macmillan [1967] . .
. . . . £35/£15
Kali and the Golden Mirror, by Eva-Lis Wuorio, World Publishing, 1967. . . . . . £45/£20
The Stuffed Dog, by John Symonds, Barker, 1967. .
. . . . £40/£15
Nurse Matilda Goes to Town, by Christianna Brand, Brockhampton Press, 1967 . . . . £40/£15
Robinson Crusoe, by Daniel Defoe, Nonesuch Press, 1968 . . . . £40/£15
Upside-Down Willie, by Dorothy Clewes, Hamish Hamilton, 1968 . . . . £35/£15
Special Branch Willie, by Dorothy Clewes, Hamish Hamilton, 1969 . . . . £35/£15
The Angel and the Donkey, by James Reeves, Hamish Hamilton, 1969 . . . . . . £35/£10
Dick Wittington, retold by Kathleen Lines, The Bodley Head, 1970 . . . . £25/£10
Fire Brigade Willie, by Dorothy Clewes, Hamish Hamilton, 1970 . . . . £45/£15
Home From the Sea, by Robert Louis Stevenson, (verse, selected and introduced by Ivor Brown), The Bodley Head, 1970 . . . . . . £25/£10
How the Moon Began, by James Reeves, Abelard-Schumann, 1971 . . . . £40/£15
The Old Ballad of the Babes in the Wood, The Bodley Head, 1972 . . . . £25/£10
The Second Best Children in the World, by Mary Lavin, Longmans, 1972 . . . . . £25/£10
The Tunnel of Hugsy Goode, by Eleanor Estes, Harcourt Brace (U.S.), 1972 . . . . £25/£10
The Little Fire Engine, by Graham Greene, The Bodley Head, 1973 . . . . . . £45/£20
The Little Train, by Graham Greene, The Bodley Head, 1973 . . . . £45/£20
Complete Poems for Children, by James Reeves, Heinemann, 1973 . . . . . . £30/£10

The Night Ride, by Aingelda Ardizzone, The Bodley Head, 1973 . . . . £25/£10
The Little Horse Bus, by Graham Greene, The Bodley Head, 1974 . . . . £50/£20
The Little Steam Roller, by Graham Greene, The Bodley Head, 1974 . . . . . . £50/£20
The Lion That Flew, by James Reeves, Chatto & Windus, 1974 (issued without d/w). . . £35/£15
Nurse Matilda goes to Hospital, by Christianna Brand, Brockhampton Press, 1974 . . . . £45/£15
More Prefabulous Animiles, by James Reeves, Heinemann, 1975 . . . . £30/£15
Ardizzone's Kilvert, Cape, 1976 . . . . £25/£10
Arcadian Ballads, by James Reeves, Heinemann, 1978
. . . . £25/£10
Ardizzone's Hans Andersen, Deutsch, 1978 £35/£15
A Child's Christmas in Wales, by Dylan Thomas, Dent, 1978 . . . . £45/£20
The James Reeves Story Book, Heinemann, 1978 . .
. . . . £25/£10
Ardizzone's English Fairy Tales, Deutsch, 1980 . .
. . . . £25/£10

Adult Books written and illustrated by Ardizzone
Baggage to the Enemy, John Murray, 1941 £50/£20
The Young Ardizzone: An Autobiographical Fragment, Studió Vista, 1970 . . . . £30/£10
Diary of a War Artist, The Bodley Head, 1974 £30/£10
From Edward Ardizzone's Indian Diary, Stellar Press/The Bodley Head, 1983 (225 copies, wraps) .
. . . . £75
Indian Diary, The Bodley Head, 1984 . . £25/£10

Adult Books illustrated by Ardizzone
In a Glass Darkly, by Sheridan Le Fanu, Peter Davis, 1929 . . . . £250/£125
ditto, Peter Davis, 1929 (second impression) £100/£45
The Library, by George Crabbe, De la More Press, 1930 . . . . £75/£30
The Mediterranean, edited by Paul Bloomfield, Cassell, 1935 . . . . £100/£35
The Local, by Maurice Gorham, Cassell, 1939 £75/£25
My Uncle Silas, by H.E. Bates, Cape, 1939 £175/£75
The Road to Bordeaux, by C.D. Freeman and D. Cooper, Cresset Press, 1940. . . . £45/£20
The Battle of France, by A. Maurois, The Bodley Head, 1940 . . . . £45/£20
Women, O.U.P., 1943 (wraps) £25
The Poems of Francois Villon, Cresset Press, 1946 .
. . . . £70/£20
Back to the Local, by Maurice Gorham, Percival Marshall, 1949 . . . . £75/£25
The Londoners, by Maurice Gorham, Percival Marshall, 1951 . . . . £45/£20
Showmen and Suckers, by Maurice Gorham, Percival Marshall, 1951 . . . . £45/£20
The Modern Prometheus, by Zara Nuber, Forge Press, 1952 . . . . £25/£10

The Warden, by Anthony Trollope, O.U.P., 1952 . .
. . . . £60/£25
Barchester Towers, by Anthony Trollope, O.U.P.,
1953 . . . . £60/£25
Christmas Eve, by Cecil Day Lewis, Faber, 1954 £15
The Newcomes, by William Makepeace Thackeray,
Limited Edition Club, 1954, (1,500 signed copies,
slipcase, 2 vols) . . . . £65/£45
The Tale of an Old Tweed Jacket, by Eric Keown,
Moss Bros, [1955] . . . . . . £75/£25
The History of Henry Esmond, by William Makepeace
Thackeray, The Limited Editions Club (U.S.), 1956
(1,500 signed, numbered copies, slipcase). £125/£75
Sugar for the Horse, by H.E. Bates, Joseph, 1957 . .
. . . . £35/£15
Not Such An Ass, by Henry Cecil, Hutchinson, 1961 .
. . . . £30/£10
Folk Songs of England, Ireland, Scotland and Wales,
by W. Cole, Doubleday (U.S.), 1961 . . £40/£15
London Since, 1912, by John T. Hayes, Museum of
London, 1962 . . . . £35/£10
The Thirty-Nine Steps, by John Buchan, Dent, 1964 .
. . . . £35/£10
The Milldale Riot, by Freda P. Nichols, Ginn, 1965 .
. . . . £35/£10
Know About English Law, by Henry Cecil, Blackie,
1965 . . . . £35/£10
The Short Stories, by Charles Dickens, Limited
Edition Club (U.S.), 1971, (1,500 signed copies,
slipcase) . . . . £125/£75
Learn More About English Law, by Henry Cecil,
William Luscombe, 1974 . . . . £20/£10
Fragment, Macmillan, 1984 . . . . . £20/£10

MICHAEL ARLEN
(b.1895 d.1956)

Born Dikran Kouyoumdjian in Bulgaria of Armenian
ancestry, Arlen became a naturalised British subject in
1922 and was a popular writer during the 20s and 30s.

Short Stories
The Romantic Lady and Other Stories, Collins, [1921]
. . . . £50/£20
ditto, Doran (U.S.), 1921 . . . . . £45/£15
These Charming People, Collins, [1923] . £35/£10
ditto, Doran (U.S.), 1924 . . . . . £30/£10
*May Fair, In Which Are Told the Last Adventures of
These Charming People*, Collins, [1925] . £40/£10
ditto, Doran (U.S.), [1925] . . . £25/£5
ditto, Doran (U.S.), [1925] (550 signed copies in
slipcase) . . . . £50/£40
Ghost Stories, Collins, [1927] . . £45/£20
Babes in the Wood, Hutchinson, [1929]. . £25/£10
ditto, Doran (U.S.), 1929 . . . . . £20/£5
The Ancient Sin and Other Stories, Collins, 1930 . .
. . . . £20/£5

The Short Stories of Michael Arlen, Collins, 1933 .
. . . . £15/£5
*The Crooked Coronet and Other Misrepresentations
of the Real Facts of Life*, Heinemann, 1937 . £20/£5
ditto, Doran (U.S.), 1937 . . . . . £15/£5

Novels
The London Venture, Heinemann, 1920 . £75/£20
ditto, Doran (U.S.), 1920 . . . . . £60/£20
'Piracy': A Romantic Chronicle of These Days,
Collins, [1922] . . . . £50/£10
ditto, Doran, 1923 . . . . £40/£10
The Green Hat: A Romance for a Few People,
Collins, 1924 . . . . £75/£20
ditto, Doran, 1924 . . . . £25/£10
Young Men in Love, Hutchinson, [1927] . £25/£10
ditto, Doran, 1927 . . . . £20/£5
Lily Christine, Hutchinson, [1928] . . £25/£15
ditto, Doran, 1928 . . . . £15/£5
Men Dislike Women, Heinemann, 1931. . £15/£5
ditto, Doran, 1931 . . . . £15/£5
A Young man Comes to London, Keliher & Co., 1931
(brochure to promote Dorchester Hotel) . . £30
Man's Mortality, Heinemann, 1933 . . £15/£5
ditto, Doran, 1933 . . . . £15/£5
Hell! Said the Duchess: A Bed-Time Story,
Heinemann, [1934] . . . . . . £25/£10
ditto, Doran, 1934 . . . . £15/£5
The Flying Dutchman, Heinemann, 1939 . £15/£5
ditto, Doran, 1939 . . . . £15/£5

Plays
The Zoo, French, 1927 (wraps, with Winchell Smith) .
. . . . £15
Good Losers, French, 1933 (wraps, with Walter
Hackett) £15
The Green Hat: A Romance, Doran, 1925 (175 signed
copies, glassine d/w and slipcase) . . . £45/£20

DAISY ASHFORD
(b.1881 d.1972)

Written when the author was a child, Ashford's books
are classics of unconscious humour.

The Young Visitors or, Mr Salteenas Plan, Chatto &
Windus, 1919 (Preface by J. M. Barrie) . £125/£25
ditto, Doran (U.S.), 1919 . . . . . £125/£25
Daisy Ashford: Her Book, Chatto & Windus, 1920 .
. . . . £65/£15
ditto, Doran (U.S.), 1920 . . . . . £65/£15
Love and Marriage, Hart Davis, 1965 (illustrated by
Ralph Steadman) . . . . £20/£5
Where Love Lies Deepest, Hart Davis, 1966 (illustrated
by Ralph Steadman) . . . . . . £20/£5
The Hangman's Daughter, O.U.P., 1983 . £10/£5

ISAAC ASIMOV
(b.1920 d.1992)

Born in Russia, Asimov was taken to the U.S. in infancy. A hugely successful science fiction writer, his many non-fiction writings have also served to make scientific ideas popular and easily understandable.

Novels

Pebble in the Sky, Doubleday (U.S.), 1950 . £400/£75
ditto, Sidgwick & Jackson, 1968. . . . £125/£30
The Stars, Like Dust, Doubleday (U.S.), 1951 . .
. . . . £250/£35
Foundation, Gnome Press (U.S.), 1951 . . £500/£100
ditto, Weidenfeld, 1953 . . . . . . £300/£50
Foundation and Empire, Gnome Press (U.S.), 1952 .
. . . . £300/£50
The Currents of Space, Doubleday (U.S.), 1952 . .
. . . . £250/£45
ditto, Boardman, 1955. . . . . . £125/£20
Second Foundation, Gnome Press (U.S.), 1953 . .
. . . . £500/£100
The Caves of Steel, Doubleday (U.S.), 1954 . .
. . . . £250/£40
ditto, Boardman, 1954. . . . . . £135/£20
The End of Eternity, Doubleday (U.S.), 1955 . .
. . . . £200/£15
The Naked Sun, Doubleday (U.S.), 1957 . £250/£35
ditto, Joseph, 1958. . . . . . . £100/£20
The Death Dealers, Avon (U.S.), 1958 (wraps) £15
ditto, as *A Whiff of Death*, Walker (U.S.), 1968 .
. . . . £100/£20
ditto, Gollancz, 1968 . . . . . . £100/£20
Fantastic Voyage, Houghton Miffin (U.S.), 1966 . .
. . . . £100/£20
ditto, Dobson, 1966 . . . . . . £100/£20
The Gods Themselves, Doubleday (U.S.), 1972 . .
. . . . £100/£20
ditto, Gollancz, 1972 . . . . . . £75/£15
Authorised Murder, Doubleday (U.S.), 1976 £45/£10
ditto, Gollancz, 1976 . . . . . . £45/£10
Murder at the Aba, Doubleday (U.S.), 1976 £25/£5
Foundation's Edge, Doubleday (U.S.), 1982 £45/£10
ditto, Whispers Press (U.S.), 1982 (1,000 signed, numbered copies, no d/w) £100
ditto, Whispers Press (U.S.), 1982 (26 signed, lettered copies, all edges gilt, slipcase, no d/w). . . £350
ditto, Granada, 1982 . . . . . . £30/£5
Robots of Dawn, Doubleday (U.S.), 1983 . £35/£10
ditto, Phantasia Press (U.S.), 1983 (750 signed, numbered copies, slipcase and d/w) . . £125/£75
ditto, Granada, 1984 . . . . . . £25/£5
Foundation and Earth, Doubleday (U.S.), 1986 . .
. . . . £25/£5
ditto, Grafton, 1986 . . . . . . £20/£5

Fantastic Voyage II: Destination Britain, Doubleday (U.S.), 1987 . . . . £20/£5
ditto, Grafton, 1987 . . . . £20/£5
Prelude to Foundation, Doubleday (U.S.), 1988 . .
. . . . £20/£5
ditto, Grafton, 1988 . . . . £20/£5
Azazel, Doubleday (U.S.), 1988 . . . . £20/£5
ditto, Doubleday (U.K.), 1989 . . . . £20/£5
Nemesis, Doubleday (U.S.), 1989 . . . . £20/£5
ditto, Doubleday (U.K.), 1989 . . . . £15/£5
Nightfall, Doubleday (U.S.), 1990 (with Robert Silverberg) . . . . £15/£5
ditto, Gollancz, 1990 . . . . £15/£5
Child of Time, Gollancz, 1991 . . . . £15/£5
The Positronic Man, Doubleday (U.S.), 1992 (with Robert Silverberg) . . . . . . £15/£5
ditto, Gollancz, 1992 . . . . £15/£5
Forward the Foundation, Doubleday (U.S.), 1993 .
. . . . £10/£5
Magic: The Final Fantasy Collection, Harper (U.S.) 1996 . . . . £10/£5
ditto, Voyager, 1996 . . . . . . £10/£5

Short Stories

I, Robot, Gnome Press (U.S.), 1950 . . . £500/£100
ditto, Grayson, 1952 . . . . . . £125/£40
The Martian Way and Other Stories, Doubleday (U.S.), 1955 . . . . £250/£35
ditto, Dobson, 1964 . . . . . . £50/£20
Earth Is Room Enough, Doubleday (U.S.), 1957 . .
. . . . £100/£20
Nine Tomorrows: Tales of the Near Future, Doubleday (U.S.), 1959 . . . . . . £50/£10
ditto, Dobson, 1963 . . . . . . £40/£10
The Rest of the Robots, Doubleday (U.S.), 1964 . .
. . . . £35/£10
ditto, Dobson, 1967 . . . . . . £25/£5
Through a Glass, Clearly, New English Library, 1967 . . . . £25/£5
Asimov's Mysteries, Doubleday (U.S.), 1968 . £25/£5
ditto, Rapp & Whiting, 1968 . . . . £25/£5
Nightfall and Other Stories, Doubleday (U.S.), 1969 . .
. . . . £25/£5
ditto, Rapp & Whiting, 1969 . . . . £20/£5
The Early Asimov, Doubleday (U.S.), 1972 . £20/£5
The Best of Isaac Asimov, Sidgwick & Jackson, 1973 . . . . £20/£5
ditto, Doubleday (U.S.), 1974 . . . . £20/£5
Tales of the Black Widowers, Doubleday (U.S.), 1974 . . . . £20/£5
ditto, Gollancz, 1975 . . . . . . £20/£5
Buy Jupiter and Other Stories, Doubleday (U.S.), 1975 . . . . £20/£5
ditto, Gollancz, 1976 . . . . . . £20/£5
The Bicentennial Man and Other Stories, Doubleday (U.S.), 1976 . . . . £20/£5
ditto, Gollancz, 1977 . . . . . . £20/£5
More Tales of the Black Widowers, Doubleday (U.S.), 1976 . . . . £20/£5

ditto, Gollancz, 1977 . . . . £20/£5
The Key Word and Other Mysteries, Walker (U.S.),
1977 . . . . £20/£5
The Casebook of the Black Widowers, Doubleday
(U.S.), 1980 . . . . £20/£5
ditto, Gollancz, 1980 . . . . £20/£5
Three Science Fiction Tales, Targ Editions (U.S.),
1981 (250 signed copies in plain d/w) . £75/£60
Banquets of the Black Widowers, Doubleday (U.S.),
1985 . . . . £15/£5
ditto, Granada, 1985 . . . . £15/£5
Alternative Asimovs, Doubleday (U.S.), 1986 . £15/£5
Robot Dreams, Berkley (U.S.), 1986 . . . £15/£5
ditto, Gollancz, 1987 . . . . £15/£5
The Best Science Fiction of Isaac Asimov, Doubleday
(U.S.), 1986 . . . . £15/£5
ditto, Grafton, 1987 . . . . £15/£5
The Best Mysteries of Isaac Asimov, Doubleday
(U.S.), 1986 . . . . £15/£5
ditto, Grafton, 1987 . . . . £15/£5
The Asimov Chronicles: Fifty Years of Isaac Asimov,
Dark Harvest (U.S.), 1989 . . . . . £15/£5
ditto, Century, 1991 . . . . £15/£5
Robot Visions, NAL, 1990 . . . . . . £15/£5
ditto, Gollancz, 1990 . . . . £15/£5
Puzzles of the Black Widowers, Doubleday (U.S.),
1990 . . . . £10/£5
ditto, Doubleday (U.K.), 1990 . . . . . £10/£5
The Complete Stories I, Doubleday (U.S.), 1990 .
. . . . £10/£5
The Complete Stories, Harper/Collins, 1992 . £10/£5
Gold: The Final Science Fiction Collection, Harper
Collins, 1995 . . . . £10/£5

Children's Titles written as 'Paul French'
David Starr: Space Ranger, Doubleday (U.S.), 1953 .
. . . . £125/£45
Lucky Starr and the Pirates of the Asteroids,
Doubleday (U.S.), 1954 . . . . . £100/£20
Lucky Starr and the Oceans of Venus, Doubleday
(U.S.), 1954 . . . . £75/£15
Lucky Starr and the Big Sun of Mercury, Doubleday
(U.S.), 1956 . . . . £75/£15
Lucky Starr and the Moons of Jupiter, Doubleday
(U.S.), 1957 . . . . £50/£10
Lucky Starr and the Rings of Saturn, Doubleday
(U.S.), 1958 . . . . £50/£10

MABEL LUCIE ATTWELL
(b.1879 d.1964)

Attwell illustrated not only classic children's books
such as *Alice in Wonderland*, but drew comic strips
and produced her own books, postcards and annuals.

'Bunty and the Boo Boos' Titles
Bunty and the Boo Boos, Valentine, [1921] . £175

The Boo Boos and Bunty's Baby, Valentine, [1921] .
. . . . £175
The Boo Boos at School, Valentine, [1921]. . £175
The Boo Boos at the Seaside, Valentine, [1921] £175
The Boo Boos at Honeysweet Farm, Valentine, [1921]
. . . . £175
The Boo Boos and Santa Claus, Valentine, [1921] .
. . . . £175

Annuals
The Lucie Attwell Annual No. 1, Partridge, 1922 £225
The Lucie Attwell Annual No. 2, Partridge, 1923 £200
The Lucie Attwell Annual No. 3, Partridge, 1924 £200
Lucie Attwell's Children's Book, Partridge, 1925-32 .
. . . . £200 each
Lucie Attwell's Annual, Dean, 1934-35, 1937-41 . .
. . . . £125 each
Lucie Attwell's Annual, Dean, 1942. . . . £100
Lucie Attwell's Annual, Dean, 1945-68 . . . £75
Lucie Attwell's Annual, Dean, 1969-74 . . . £50

Others written and illustrated by Attwell
Peggy: The Lucie Attwell Cut-Out Dressing Doll,
Valentine, [1921] £125
Stitch Stitch, Valentine, [1922] £125
Comforting Thoughts, Valentine, [1922] . . £60
Baby's Book, Raphael Tuck, [1922] £100
All About Bad Babies, John Swain, [c1925] . £75
All About the Seaside, John Swain, [c1925] . £60
All About Fairies, John Swain, [c1925] . . . £65
All About the Country, John Swain, [c1925] . £65
All About School, John Swain, [c1925] . . . £65
All About Fido, John Swain, [c1925] . . . £65
Lucie Attwell's Rainy-Day Tales, Partridge [1931]
(with other authors) £125
Lucie Attwell's Rock-Away Tales, London, 1931 (with
other authors) £100
Lucie Attwell's Fairy Book, Partridge, 1932 . £200
Lucie Attwell's Happy-Day Tales, Partridge, [1932] .
. . . . £100
Lucie Attwell's Quiet Time Tales, Partridge, [1932] .
. . . . £100
Lucie Attwell's Painting Book, Dean, [1934] . £65
Lucie Attwell's Great Big Midget Book, Dean, [1934].
. . . . £100
Lucie Attwell's Great Big Midget Book, Dean, [1935]
(different from above) £100
Lucie Attwell's Playtime Pictures, Carlton Publishing
Co, 1935 . . . . £75
Lucie Attwell's Story Book, Dean, [1943] . . £65
Lucie Attwell's Story Book, Dean, [1945] (different
from above) £65
Lucie Attwell's Jolly Book, Dean, [1953] . . £50
Lucie Attwell's Nursery Rhymes Pop-Up Book, Dean,
1958 . . . . £45
Lucie Attwell's Storytime Tales, Dean, [1959] . £30
Lucie Attwell's Book of Verse, Dean, 1960 . . £30
Lucie Attwell's Book of Rhymes, Dean, 1962 . £30
Stories for Everyday, Dean, 1964 . . . . £20

A Little Bird Told Me, Dean, 1964 . . . . £20
A Little Bird Told Me Another Story, Dean, 1966 £20
Tinie's Book of Prayers, Dean, 1967 . . . £20
Lucie Attwell's Tiny Rhymes Pop-Up Book, Dean, 1967 . . . . £35
Lucie Attwell's Tell Me A Story Pop-Up Book, Dean, 1968 . . . . £35
Lucie Attwell's Book of Rhymes, Dean, 1969 . £20

Books illustrated by Attwell
That Little Limb, by May Baldwin, Chambers, 1905 . . . . £75
The Amateur Cook, by K. Burrill, Chambers, 1905 £50
Troublesome Ursula, by Mabel Quiller-Couch, Chambers, 1905. . . . . £65
Dora: A High School Girl, by May Baldwin, Chambers, 1906. . . . . £65
A Boy and a Secret, by Raymond Jacberns, Chambers, 1908 . . . . £40
The Little Tin Soldier, by Graham Mar, Chambers, 1909 . . . . £50
The February Boys, by Mrs Molesworth, Chambers, 1909 . . . . £60
Old Rhymes, Raphael Tuck, 1909 . . . . £45
The Old Pincushion, by Mrs Molesworth, Chambers, 1910 . . . . £60
Mother Goose, Raphael Tuck, 1910 . . . . £150
Alice in Wonderland, by Lewis Carroll, Raphael Tuck [1910] (12 colour plates by Attwell) . . . £200
My Dolly's House ABC, Raphael Tuck, [c.1910] £150
Grimm's Fairy Tales, Cassell [1910] (4 full-page illustrations by Attwell) £125
Tabitha Smallways, by Raymond Jacberns, Chambers, 1911 . . . . £65
Grimm's Fairy Stories, Raphael Tuck, 1912 (12 colour plates by Attwell) £150
Troublesome Topsy and Her Friends, by May Baldwin, Chambers, 1913 . . . . . . £50
Hans Andersen's Fairy Tales, Raphael Tuck [1914] (12 colour plates by Attwell) £150
A Band of Mirth, by L.T. Meade, Chambers, 1914 £50
The Water Babies, by Charles Kingsley, Raphael Tuck [1915] (12 colour plates by Attwell) . . . £200
Children's Stories from French Fairy Tales, by Doris Ashley, Raphael Tuck, 1917 . . . . . £165
Peeping Pansy, by Marie, Queen of Roumania, Hodder & Stoughton [1919] (issued with d/w) . . £375
Wooden, by Archibald Marshall, Collins, [1920] £75
Peter Pan and Wendy, by J.M. Barrie, Hodder & Stoughton [1921] £250
The Lost Princess: A Fairy Tale, by Marie, Queen of Roumania, Partridge, 1924 . . . . £125
Children's Stories, Whitman Publishing Co. [c.1930] £250

MARGARET ATWOOD
(b.1939)

Atwood is a Canadian writer, most popularly known for her prose following the success of *Cat's Eye*. A versatile writer, she works successfully in various genres.

Verse
Double Persephone, Hawkshead Press (Canada), 1961 (wraps) £1,000
The Circle Game, Cranbrook Academy, 1964 (15 copies) £2,500
ditto, Contact Press (Canada), 1966 (50 copies) £1,000
ditto, Contact Press (Canada), 1966 (200 copies, wraps) £450
ditto, House of Anansi (Canada), 1967 (100 signed copies) £200
ditto, House of Anansi (Canada), 1967 (wraps) £25
Talismans for Children, Cranbrook Academy, 1965 . (10 copies). £2,000
Kaleidoscopes: Baroque, Cranbrook Academy, 1965 (20 copies) £2,000
Speeches for Doctor Frankenstein, Cranbrook Academy, 1966 (10 copies). . . . £2,000
Expeditions, Cranbrook Academy, 1966 (15 copies) £2,000
The Animals in that Country, O.U.P. (Canada), 1968 . . . . £200/£45
ditto, O.U.P. (Canada), 1968 (wraps). . . £35
ditto, Little, Brown (U.S.), [1969] . . £45/£10
What Was in the Garden?, Unicorn (U.S.), 1969 £30
The Journals of Susanna Moodie, O.U.P. (Canada), 1970 . . . . £25
ditto, Manuel and Abel Bello-Sanchez (Canada), 1980 (20 deluxe signed copies, numbered I-XX) . £500
ditto, Manuel and Abel Bello-Sanchez (Canada), 1980 (100 signed copies) £75
Oratorio for Sasquatch, Man and Two Androids: Poems for Voices, C.B.C. (Canada), 1970 . £20
Procedures for Underground, O.U.P. (Canada), 1970 . . . . £15
ditto, Little, Brown (U.S.), 1970 . . . . £10
Power Politics, Anansi (Canada), 1971 . £100/£25
ditto, Anansi (Canada), 1971 (wraps) . . £25
ditto, Harper (U.S.), 1973. . . . . . £20/£5
You Are Happy, O.U.P. (Canada), 1974 . . £25
ditto, Harper (U.S.), 1974. . . . . . £15/£5
Selected Poems, O.U.P. (Canada), 1976. . £25
ditto, Simon & Schuster (U.S.), 1978 . . £15/£5
Marsh, Hawk, Dreadnought, 1977 . . . £25
Two-headed Poems, O.U.P. (Canada), 1978 . £25
ditto, Simon & Schuster (U.S.), 1980 . . £15/£5
A Poem for Grandmothers, Square Zero Editions (U.S.), 1978 . . . . £40
True Stories, O.U.P. (Canada), 1981 . . . £20
ditto, Simon & Schuster (U.S.), 1982 . . £20/£10
ditto, Cape, 1982 . . . . £20/£10

Notes Towards a Poem that can Never be Written, Salamander Press (Canada), 1981 (200 numbered, signed copies) £100
Snake Poems, Salamander Press (Canada), 1983 (100 numbered, signed copies) £175
Interlunar, O.U.P. (Canada), 1984 . . . . £15
ditto, Cape, 1988 . . . . £15/£5
Selected Poems 2, O.U.P. (Canada), 1986 . . £15
ditto, Houghton Mifflin (U.S.), 1987 . . £10/£5
ditto, as *Poems, 1976-1986*, Virago, 1992 . . £10
Selected Poems, 1966-1984, O.U.P. (Canada), 1990 . . . . £15
Poems, 1965-1975, Virago, 1991 . . . . £10
ditto, Houghton Mifflin (U.S.), 1987 . . £10/£5
Good Bones, Harbour Front Reading Series (Canada), 1992 (150 signed copies) £15
Murder in the Dark, Virago, 1995 (wraps) . . £5
Morning in the Burned House, McClelland & Stewart (Canada), [1995] . . . . . . £10/£5
ditto, Virago, 1995 (wraps) £5
ditto, Houghton Mifflin (U.S.), 1995 . . £10/£5
Bones and Murder, Virago, 1995 (wraps) . . £5

Novels

The Edible Woman, McClelland & Stewart (Canada), 1969 . . . . £200/£35
ditto, Deutsch, 1969 . . . . . £150/£30
ditto, Little, Brown (U.S.), 1970 . . . . £75/£15
Surfacing, McClelland & Stewart (Canada), 1972 . . . . £40/£15
ditto, Deutsch, 1973 . . . . . £40/£15
ditto, Simon & Schuster (U.S.), 1973 . . £15/£5
Lady Oracle, McClelland & Stewart (Canada), 1976 . . . . £20/£5
ditto, Simon & Schuster (U.S.), 1976 . . £15/£5
ditto, Deutsch, 1977 . . . . . £15/£5
Life Before Man, McClelland & Stewart (Canada), 1979 . . . . £20/£5
ditto, Simon & Schuster (U.S.), 1979 . . £15/£5
ditto, Cape, 1980 . . . . . . £15/£5
Bodily Harm, McClelland & Stewart (Canada), 1981 . . . . £20/£5
ditto, Simon & Schuster (U.S.), 1982 . . £10/£5
ditto, Cape, 1982 . . . . . . £10/£5
The Handmaid's Tale, McClelland & Stewart (Canada), 1985 . . . . £35/£10
ditto, Houghton Mifflin (U.S.), 1986 . . £25/£5
ditto, Cape, 1986 . . . . . £25/£5
Cat's Eye, McClelland & Stewart (Canada), 1988 . . . . £30/£10
ditto, Doubleday (U.S.), 1989 . . . . £15/£5
ditto, Bloomsbury, 1989 . . . . £15/£5
Robber Bride, McClelland & Stewart (Canada), 1993 . . . . £30/£10
ditto, Doubleday (U.S.), 1993 . . . . £15/£5
ditto, Bloomsbury, 1993 . . . . . £10/£5
Alias Grace, McClelland & Stewart (Canada), 1996 . . . . £30/£10
ditto, Doubleday (U.S.), 1996 . . . . £15/£5

ditto, Bloomsbury, 1996 . . . . . £10/£5
The Margaret Atwood Omnibus, Deutsch, 1987 . . . . £10/£5

Short Stories

Dancing Girls and Other Stories, McClelland & Stewart (Canada), 1977 . . . . . £75/£20
ditto, Simon & Schuster (U.S.), 1982 . . £25/£5
ditto, Cape, 1982 . . . . . £25/£5
Encounters with the Element Man, Ewert (U.S.), 1982 . . . . £60
ditto, Ewert (U.S.), 1982 (100 copies, wraps) . £25
Murder in the Dark: Short Fictions and Prose Poems, Coach House Press (Canada), 1983 . . . £20
ditto, Cape, 1984 . . . . £10/£5
Bluebeard's Egg and Other Stories, McClelland & Stewart (Canada), 1983 . . . . £25/£10
ditto, Houghton Mifflin (U.S.), 1986 . . £10/£5
ditto, Cape, 1987 . . . . . £10/£5
Unearthing Suite, Grand Union Press, 1983 (175 copies) £75
Hurricane Hazel and Other Stories, Eurographica, (Helsinki), 1987 (350 signed copies) . . £75/£50
Wilderness Tips, McClelland & Stewart (Canada), 1991 . . . . £15/£5
ditto, Doubleday (U.S.), 1991 . . . . £10/£5
ditto, Bloomsbury, 1991 . . . . . £10/£5
Good Bones, Coach House (Canada), 1992 . £20/£5
ditto, Bloomsbury, 1992 . . . . . £10/£5
Good Bones and Simple Murders, Doubleday (U.S.), 1994 . . . . £10/£5

Children's

Up in the Tree, McClelland & Stewart (Canada), 1978 . . . . £75
Anna's Pet, Lorimer (Canada), 1980 (with Joyce Barkhouse) £60
For the Birds, Douglas & McIntyre (Canada), 1990 . . . . £10
Princess Prunella and the Purple Peanut, Key Porter Kids, 1995 . . . . £5

Criticism

Survival: A Thematic Guide to Canadian Literature, Anansi (Canada), 1972 . . . . . £35/£10
Second Words: Selected Critical Prose, Anansi, (Canada), 1982 . . . . . . £30/£10
ditto, Beacon Press (U.S.), 1984 . . . £10
New Critical Essays, Macmillan, 1994 . . £10/£5
Strange Things: The Malevolent North in Canadian Literature, O.U.P., 1995 . . . . £10/£5

Other

Margaret Atwood: Conversations, Ontario Review Press (Canada), 1990 . . . . . £15/£5
ditto, Virago, 1991 . . . . . . £10
Winner of the Welsh Arts Council International Writer's Prize, Welsh Arts Council, 1982 (wraps) £5

W.H. AUDEN
(b.1907 d.1973)

Auden's early poetry was markedly left-wing, but Christianity was the dominant influence in his later life and art. He is considered to be one of the most influential poets of the twentieth century.

Verse

Poems, privately printed by Stephen Spender, 1928 (30 copies, orange wraps) £15,000
Poems, Faber, 1930 (wraps) £500
ditto, Random House (U.S.), 1934 . . . £150/£50
The Orators: an English Study, Faber, [1932] . .
. . . . £200/£75
ditto, Random House (U.S.), 1967 . . . £20/£5
The Dance of Death, Faber, 1933 . . . £150/£35
The Witnesses, privately printed, 1933 (broadside, 20 copies, illustrated by Gwen Raverat) . . . £3,000
Poem, privately printed, 1933 (22 copies, wraps) . .
. . . . £5,000
Two Poems, privately printed, 1934 (22 copies, wraps)
. . . . £5,000
Our Hunting Fathers, privately printed, 1935 (22 copies, wraps) £5,000
Sonnet, privately printed, 1935 (22 copies, wraps) .
. . . . £5,000
Look Stranger!, Faber, 1936 . . . . . £100/£35
ditto, as *On This Island*, Random House (U.S.), [1937]. . . . . £75/£20
Spain, Faber, [1937] (wraps). £100
Deux Poemes, Hours Press (Paris), 1937 (100 copies).
. . . . £350
Night Mail, G.P.O., 1938 (broadside). . . . £40
Selected Poems, Faber, 1938 . . . . £75/£25
Journey to a War, Faber, 1939 (with Christopher Isherwood) . . . . £100/£35
ditto, Random House (U.S.), 1939 . . . £75/£25
Another Time, Faber, 1940 . . . . £75/£25
ditto, Random House (U.S.), 1940 . . . £65/£20
Some Poems, Faber, 1940 . . . . £75/£25
New Year Letter, Faber, 1941 . . . . £75/£25
ditto, as *The Double Man*, Random House (U.S.), 1941 . . . . £75/£25
Three Songs for St Cecilia's Day, privately printed, 1941 (250 copies, wraps) £400
For the Time Being, Random House (U.S.), 1944 . .
. . . . £125/£35
ditto, Faber, 1945 . . . . £125/£35
The Collected Poetry, Random House, 1945 £75/£15
Litany and Anthem for St Matthew's Day, privately printed, 1946 (single sheet) £50
The Age of Anxiety, Random House (U.S.), [1947] .
. . . . £100/£25
ditto, Faber, 1948 . . . . £95/£25
Collected Shorter Poems 1930-1944, Faber, 1950 .
. . . . £65/£20

Nones, Random House (U.S.), 1951 . . . £75/£20
ditto, Faber, 1952 . . . . £75/£20
Mountains, Faber Ariel Poem, 1954 (wraps) . £25
The Shield of Achilles, Random House (U.S.), 1955 .
. . . . £50/£15
ditto, Faber, 1955 . . . . £50/£15
The Old Man's Road, Voyages Press (U.S.), 1956 (50 signed copies, wraps) £500
ditto, Voyages Press (U.S.), 1956 (750 copies, wraps) .
. . . . £65
W.H. Auden: A Selection by the Author, Penguin, 1958 (wraps) £5
ditto, as *Selected Poetry of W.H. Auden*, Modern Library (U.S.), 1959 . . . . . . £15/£5
Goodbye to the Mezzogiorno, All'Insegna del Pesce d'Oro (Spain), 1958 (1,000 numbered copies, wraps)
. . . . £50
Homage to Clio, Random House (U.S.), 1960 £45/£15
ditto, Faber, 1960 . . . . £45/£15
About the House, Random House (U.S.), 1965 . . .
. . . . £45/£15
ditto, Faber, 1966 . . . . £40/£15
Collected Shorter Poems, 1927-1957, Faber, 1966 .
. . . . £75/£20
ditto, Random House (U.S.), 1967 . . . £65/£20
Marginalia, Ibex Press (U.S.), 1966 (150 signed copies, wraps) £350
Selected Poems, Faber, 1968 (wraps) . . . £5
Collected Longer Poems, Faber, 1968 . . £35/£10
ditto, Random House (U.S.), 1969 . . . £35/£10
City Without Walls, Faber, 1969. . . . £30/£10
ditto, Random House (U.S.), 1970 . . . £30/£10
Natural Linguistics, Poem-of-the-month-Club, 1970 (1,000 signed copies, broadsheet) £75
Academic Graffiti, Faber, 1971 . . . . £25/£5
ditto, Random House (U.S.), 1972 . . . . £25/£5
Epistle to a Godson, Faber, 1972 . . . £35/£10
ditto, Random House (U.S.), 1972 . . . £35/£10
The Ballad of Barnaby, no place, 1973 (broadside) .
. . . . £35
Thank You Fog: Last Poems, Faber, 1974 £35/£10
ditto, Random House (U.S.), 1974 . . . £30/£10
Collected Poems, Faber, 1976 . . . . £35/£10
ditto, Random House (U.S.), 1976 . . . £35/£10
ditto, Franklin Centre (U.S.), 1976 (full leather edition)
. . . . £50
The English Auden, Faber, 1977 . . . . £25/£5
ditto, Random House (U.S.), 1978 . . . £25/£5
Norse Poems, Athlone Press, 1981 . . . £25/£5

Plays

The Dog Beneath the Skin (with Christopher Isherwood), Faber, 1935. . . . . £125/£35
ditto, Random House (U.S.), 1935 . . . £75/£25
The Ascent of F6, Faber, 1936 (with Christopher Isherwood) . . . . £75/£20
ditto, Random House (U.S.), 1937 . . . £50/£20
On the Frontier, Faber, [1938] (with Christopher Isherwood) . . . . £100/£25

ditto, Random House (U.S.), 1939 . . . £75/£20

Prose
Letters from Iceland, Faber, 1937 (with Louis MacNeice) . . . . £75/£25
ditto, Harcourt Brace (U.S.), 1937 . . . £50/£15
Education Today and Tomorrow, Hogarth Press, 1939 (with T. S. Worsley, wraps). £30
The Enchaféd Flood or The Romantic Iconography of the Sea, Random House (U.S.), 1950 . £30/£10
ditto, Faber, 1951 . . . . £25/£5
Making, Knowing and Judging, O.U.P., 1956 (wraps) £20
The Dyer's Hand, Random House (U.S.), 1962 . .
. . . . £25/£10
ditto, Faber, 1963 . . . . £20/£10
Louis MacNeice - A Memorial Address, privately printed Faber, 1963 (1,500 copies, wraps). . £25
Selected Essays, Faber, 1964 (wraps) . . . £15
Secondary Worlds, Random House (U.S.), 1968 . .
. . . . £20/£5
ditto, Faber, 1969 . . . . £20/£5
Forewords and Afterwords, Faber, 1973 . £15/£5
ditto, Viking (U.S.), 1973. . . . . . £15/£5

Others
The Rake's Progress, Boosey & Hawkes Ltd, 1951 (libretto, with Chester Kallman, wraps) . . £75
The Magic Flute, Random House, 1956 (libretto, with Chester Kallman) . . . . . . £25/£10
ditto, Faber, 1957 . . . . . . £25/£10
Elegy for Young Lovers, Schott, 1961 (libretto, with Chester Kallman, wraps) £35
The Bassarids, Schott, 1966 (libretto with Chester Kallman, wraps) £35
A Certain World, Viking (U.S.), [1970]. . £30/£10
ditto, Faber, 1971 . . . . £30/£5

JANE AUSTEN
(b.1775 d.1817)

Generally regarded as the greatest of English women novelists, Austen's novels are particularly noted for their sparkling social comedy and accurate portrayal of human relationships.

Novels
Sense and Sensibility, T. Egerton, 1811, (3 vols in original boards) £20,000
ditto, T. Egerton, 1811, (other bindings). . £7,500
Pride and Prejudice, T. Egerton, 1813, (3 vols in original boards) £20,000
ditto, T. Egerton, 1813, (other bindings). . £7,500
Mansfield Park, T. Egerton, 1814, (3 vols in original boards) £17,500
ditto, T. Egerton, 1814, (other bindings). . £7,500

Emma, J. Murray, 1816, (3 vols in original boards) .
. . . . £10,000
ditto, J. Murray, 1816, (other bindings) . . £7,500
Northanger Abbey and Persuasion, J. Murray, 1818, (4 vols in original boards) £10,000
ditto J. Murray, 1818, (other bindings) . . £3,500

Miscellaneous
The Watsons, Mathews and Marrot, 1871 . . £1,000
Letters, R. Bentley, 1884, (2 vols) £600
Charades, Spottiswoode & Co., 1895 . . . £400
Love and Freindship (sic) *and Other Early Works (Volume the second)*, Chatto & Windus, 1922 . .
. . . . £150/£50
ditto, Chatto & Windus, 1922 (260 copies, special edition) £400
ditto, Stokes (U.S.), 1922 . . . . . £140/£40
ditto, (*Volume the First*), Clarendon Press, 1933 . .
. . . . £75/£25
ditto, (*Volume the Second*), Clarendon Press, 1951 .
. . . . £50/£20
Five Letters from Jane Austen to her Niece, Fanny Knight, Clarendon Press, 1924 (250 copies) . £100
Fragment of a Novel, O.U.P., 1925 ('Sanditon') £35
ditto, O.U.P., 1925 (250 copies on handmade paper) .
. . . . £100
Lady Susan, O.U.P., 1925 . . . . . £35
ditto, O.U.P., 1925 (250 copies on handmade paper) .
. . . . £100
Two Chapters from Persuasion, O.U.P., 1926 . £35
Plan of a Novel, Clarendon Press, 1926 (350 copies) .
. . . . £75
Letters, O.U.P., 1932, (2 vols) £75
Three Evening Prayers, Colt Press (U.S.), 1940 £40
Sanditon: A Facsimile of the Manuscript, O.U.P., 1975 . . . . £25
ditto, Houghton Mifflin (U.S.), 1975 . . £10/£5
Jane Austen's Sir Charles Grandison, O.U.P., 1980 .
. . . . £20

REV. W. AWDRY
CHRISTOPHER AWDRY
(b. 1911 d.1998, b.1940)

Thomas the Tank Engine is the most famous of all of the Rev. Awdry's railway characters, in a series of books which have been continued by his son, Christopher.

'Railway Series' Titles by Rev. W. Awdry
The Three Railway Engines, Edmund Ward, 1945 (illustrated by Middleton) . . . . . £75/£20
Thomas the Tank Engine, Edmund Ward, 1946 (illustrated by Payne) . . . . . . £100/£25
James the Red Engine, Edmund Ward, 1948 (illustrated by Dalby) . . . . . . £70/£20

Tank Engine Thomas Again, Edmund Ward, 1949
(illustrated by Dalby) . . . . . £70/£15
Troublesome Engines, Edmund Ward, 1950
(illustrated by Dalby) . . . . . £65/£10
Henry the Green Engine, Edmund Ward, 1951
(illustrated by Dalby) . . . . . £25/£10
Toby the Tram Engine, Edmund Ward, 1952
(illustrated by Dalby) . . . . . £65/£10
Gordon the Big Engine, Edmund Ward, 1953
(illustrated by Dalby) . . . . . £65/£10
Edward the Blue Engine, Edmund Ward, 1954
(illustrated by Dalby) . . . . . £65/£10
Four Little Engines, Edmund Ward, 1955 (illustrated
by Dalby) . . . . £65/£10
Percy the Small Engine, Edmund Awdry, 1956
(illustrated by Dalby) . . . . . £55/£10
The Eight Famous Engines, Edmund Ward, 1957
(illustrated by Kenney) . . . . . £55/£10
Duck and the Diesel Engine, Edmund Ward, 1958
(illustrated by Kenney) . . . . . £50/£10
The Little Old Engine, Edmund Ward, 1959
(illustrated by Kenney) . . . . . £50/£10
The Twin Engines, Edmund Ward, 1960 (illustrated by
Kenney) . . . . £50/£10
Branch Line Engines, Edmund Ward, 1961 (illustrated
by Kenney) . . . . £50/£10
Gallant Old Engine, Edmund Ward, 1962 (illustrated
by Kenney) . . . . £50/£10
Stepney the 'Bluebell' Engine, Edmund Ward, 1963
(illustrated by G. & P. Edwards) . . . £50/£10
Mountain Engines, Edmund Ward, 1964 (illustrated
by G. & P. Edwards). . . . . . £50/£10
Very Old Engines, Edmund Ward, 1965 (illustrated by
G. & P. Edwards) . . . . . . £50/£10
Main Line Engines, Edmund Ward, 1966 (illustrated
by G. & P. Edwards). . . . . . £50/£10
Small Railway Engines, Kaye & Ward, 1967
(illustrated by G. & P. Edwards) . . . £50/£10
Enterprising Engines, Kaye & Ward, 1968 (illustrated
by G. & P. Edwards). . . . . . £50/£10
Oliver the Western Engine, Kaye & P. Edwards, 1969
(illustrated by G. & P. Edwards) . . . £50/£10
Duke the Lost Engine, Kaye & Ward, 1970 (illustrated
by G. & P. Edwards). . . . . . £50/£10
Tramway Engines, Kaye & Ward, 1972 (illustrated by
G. & P. Edwards) . . . . . . £45/£10

'Railway Series' Titles by Christopher Awdry
Really Useful Engines, Kaye & Ward, 1983
(illustrated by Spong) . . . . . £15/£5
James and the Diesel Engines, Kaye & Ward, 1984
(illustrated by Spong) . . . . . £15/£5
Great Little Engines, Kaye & Ward, 1985 (illustrated
by Spong). . . . . £15/£5
More about Thomas the Tank Engine, Kaye & Ward,
1986 (illustrated by Spong) . . . . £15/£5
Gordon the High-Speed Engine, Kaye & Ward, 1987
(illustrated by Spong) . . . . . £15/£5

Toby, Trucks and Trouble, Kaye & Ward, 1988
(illustrated by Spong) . . . . . £10/£5
Thomas and the Twins, Kaye & Ward, 1989
(illustrated by Spong) . . . . . £10/£5
Jock the New Engine, Kaye & Ward, 1990 (illustrated
by Spong). . . . . £10/£5
Thomas and the Great Railway Show, Kaye & Ward,
1991 (illustrated by Spong) . . . . £10/£5
Thomas Comes Home, Kaye & Ward, 1992 (illustrated
by Spong). . . . . £10/£5
Henry and the Express, Kaye & Ward, 1993
(illustrated by Spong) . . . . . £10/£5
Wilbert the Forest Engine, Kaye & Ward, 1994
(illustrated by Spong) . . . . . £10/£5
Thomas and the Fat Controller's Engines, Kaye &
Ward, 1995 (illustrated by Spong) . . . £10/£5

ALAN AYCKBOURN
(b.1939)

A popular playwright, Ayckbourn excels at high-
lighting the neuroses and anxieties of the English
middle-class.

Relatively Speaking, Evans, 1968 (wraps) . . £45
ditto, French (U.S.), 1968 (wraps) £15
Playbill One, edited by Alan Durband, Hutchinson
Educational, 1969 (contains 'Ernie's Incredible
Illucinations' wraps) £10
We Who Are About To ..., Methuen, 1970 (contains
'Countdown') (wraps) £10
How the Other Half Loves, French (U.S.), 1972
(wraps) £15
ditto, Evans, 1972 (wraps) £15
Time and Time Again, French, 1973 (wraps) . £15
ditto, French (U.S.), 1973 (wraps) £15
Absurd Person Singular, French, 1974 (wraps) £15
ditto, French (U.S.), 1974 (wraps) £15
The Norman Conquests, French, 1975 (wraps). £30
ditto, French (U.S.), 1975 (wraps) £25
ditto, Chatto & Windus, 1975 . . . . £30/£10
Absent Friends, French, 1975 (wraps) . . . £15
ditto, French (U.S.), 1975 (wraps) £15
Bedroom Farce, French, 1977 (wraps) . . . £15
ditto, French (U.S.), 1977 (wraps) £15
Three Plays, Chatto & Windus, 1977 . . £25/£10
ditto, Grove Press, 1979 . . . . . £25/£10
Just Between Ourselves, French, 1978 (wraps). £10
ditto, French (U.S.), 1978 (wraps) £10
Ten Times Table, French, 1978 (wraps). . . £10
ditto, French (U.S.), 1978 (wraps) £10
Joking Apart, French, 1979 (wraps) £15
ditto, French (U.S.), 1979 (wraps) £15
ditto, Chatto & Windus, 1979 . . . . £15/£5
Confusions, French, 1979 (wraps) £10
ditto, French (U.S.), 1979 (wraps) £10
Sisterly Feelings, French, 1981 (wraps). . . £10

ditto, French (U.S.), 1981 (wraps) £10
Taking Steps, French, 1981 (wraps) . . . £10
ditto, French (U.S.), 1981 (wraps) £10
Suburban Strains, French, 1982 (wraps) . . £5
ditto, French (U.S.), 1982 (wraps) £5
Season's Greetings, French, 1982 (wraps) . . £5
ditto, French (U.S.), 1982 (wraps) £5
Way Upstream, French, 1983 (wraps) . . . £5
ditto, French (U.S.), 1983 (wraps) £5
Intimate Exchanges, French, 1985 (2 vols, wraps) £15
ditto, French (U.S.), 1985 (2 vols, wraps) . . £15
Chorus of Disapproval, French, 1985 (wraps) . £5
ditto, French (U.S.), 1985 (wraps) £5
Woman in Mind, Faber, 1986 . . . . £10/£5
ditto, Fireside (U.S.), 1986 . . . . . £10/£5
A Small Family Business, Faber, 1987 . . £10/£5
ditto, Faber (U.S.), 1987 . . . . . . £10/£5
Henceforward, Faber, 1988 . . . . . £5
Mr A's Amazing Maze Plays, Faber, 1989 . . £5
A Man of the Moment, Faber, 1990 . . . . £5
Invisible Friends, Faber, 1991 . . . . £5
Callisto 5, Faber, 1992 . . . . . . £5
My Very Own Story, Faber, 1992 . . . . £5

'BB'

(b.1905 d.1990)

'BB' was the pseudonym used by Denys James Watkins-Pitchford, an author and illustrator of countryside books for both adults and children.

Adult Books written and illustrated by 'BB'

The Sportsman's Bedside Book, Eyre & Spottiswoode, 1937 . . . . £60/£20
The Countryman's Bedside Book, Eyre & Spottiswoode, 1941 . . . . . . £50/£20
The Idle Countryman, Eyre & Spottiswoode, 1943 . . . . £50/£20
The Fisherman's Bedside Book, Eyre & Spottiswoode, 1945 . . . . £75/£25
The Wayfaring Tree, Hollis & Carter, 1945 £50/£15
The Shooting Man's Bedside Book, Eyre & Spottiswoode, 1948 . . . . . . £40/£15
A Stream in Your Garden, Eyre & Spottiswoode, 1948 . . . . £35/£15
Be Quiet and Go A-Angling, Lutterworth, 1949 (pseud. Michael Traherne) . . . . £200/£75
Confessions of a Carp Fisher, Eyre & Spottiswoode, 1950 . . . . £150/£60
Letters from Compton Deverell, Eyre & Spottiswoode, 1950 . . . . £25/£10
Tides Ending, Hollis & Carter, 1950 . £125/£50
Dark Estuary, Hollis & Carter, 1953 . £125/£50
A Carp Water (Wood Pool), Putnam, 1958 . £200/£75
Autumn Road to the Isles, Kaye, 1959 . £50/£15
The White Road Westward, Kaye, 1961 £35/£15

The September Road to Caithness, Kaye, 1962 . . . . £35/£15
Pegasus Book of the Countryside, Hamish Hamilton, 1964 . . . . £35/£15
The Summer Road to Wales, Kaye, 1964 . £35/£15
A Summer of the Nene, Kaye, 1967 . . . £60/£25
Recollections of a Longshore Gunner, Boydell, 1976 . . . . £30/£10
A Child Alone: The Memoirs of 'BB', Michael Joseph, 1978 . . . . £50/£25
Ramblings of a Sportsman-Naturalist, Michael Joseph, 1979 . . . . £35/£15
The Naturalist's Bedside Book, Michael Joseph, 1980 . . . . £25/£10
The Quiet Fields, Michael Joseph. 1981 . £30/£15
Indian Summer, Michael Joseph, 1984 . . £25/£10
The Best of 'BB', Michael Joseph, 1985 . £25/£10
Fisherman's Folly, Boydell, 1987 (wraps) . . £5

Children's Books written and illustrated by 'BB'

Wild Lone: The Story of a Pytchley Fox, Eyre & Spottiswoode, 1938 . . . . . £150/£50
Manka, The Sky Gipsy, Eyre & Spottiswoode, 1939 . . . . £125/£50
The Little Grey Men: A Story for the Young in Heart, Eyre & Spottiswoode, 1942 . . . . . £100/£40
ditto, Eyre & Spottiswoode, 1946 (8 colour plates). . . . . £150/£75
Brendon Chase, Hollis & Carter, 1944 . . £75/£25
Down the Bright Stream, Eyre & Spottiswoode, [1948] . . . . £75/£25
Meeting Hill: BB's Fairy Book, Hollis & Carter, 1948 . . . . £125/£50
The Wind in the Wood, Hollis & Carter, 1952 . . . . £125/£50
Fairy Tales of Long Ago, Dent, 1952 . . £25/£10
The Forest of Boland Light Railway, Eyre & Spottiswoode, 1955 . . . . . . £45/£20
Monty Woodpig's Caravan, Ward, 1957 . £100/£30
Ben the Bullfinch, Hamish Hamilton, 1957. £35/£15
Wandering Wind, Hamish Hamilton, 1957 . £75/£25
Alexander, Blackwell, 1957 [1958] . . . £65/£25
Monty Woodpig and his Bubblebuzz Car, Ward, 1958 . . . . £100/£35
Mr Bumstead, Eyre & Spottiswoode, 1958 . £60/£25
The Wizard of Boland, Ward, 1959 . . . £50/£20
Bill Badger's Winter Cruise, Hamish Hamilton, 1959 . . . . £50/£20
Bill Badger and the Pirates, Hamish Hamilton, 1960 . . . . £50/£20
Bill Badger's Finest Hour, Hamish Hamilton, 1961 . . . . £50/£20
Bill Badger's Whispering Reeds Adventure, Hamish Hamilton, 1962 . . . . . . £50/£20
Lepus the Brown Hare, Benn, 1962 . . . £40/£15
Bill Badger's Big Mistake, Hamish Hamilton, 1963 . . . . £45/£20
Granny's Wonderful Chair, by Frances Browne, Dent, 1963 . . . . £30/£10

Bill Badger and the Big Store Robbery, Hamish
Hamilton, 1967 . . . . £40/£15
The Whopper, Benn, 1967 . . . . £200/£75
At the Back O'Ben Dee, Benn, 1968 . . £50/£20
Bill Badger's Voyage to the World's End, Kaye &
Ward, 1969 . . . . £50/£20
The Tyger Tray, Methuen, 1971 . . . . £45/£20
The Pool of the Black Witch, Methuen, 1974 £30/£10
Lord of the Forest, Methuen, 1975 . . . £25/£10
Stories of the Wild, Benn, 1975 (with A.L.E. Fenton
and A. Windsor Richards) . . . . £25/£10
More Stories of the Wild, Benn, 1977 (with A.
Windsor Richards) . . . . . . £25/£10
A Child Alone, Joseph, 1978 . . . . £25/£10

Other Books illustrated by 'BB'
Sport in Wildest Britain, by H.V. Prichard, Philip
Allan, 1936 . . . . £30/£10
Winged Company, by R.G. Walmsley, Eyre &
Spottiswoode, 1940 . . . . . . £25/£10
England is a Village, by C.H. Warren, Eyre &
Spottiswoode, 1940 . . . . . . £15/£5
Southern English, by E. Benfield, Eyre &
Spottiswoode, 1942 . . . . . . £15/£5
Narrow Boat, by L.T.C. Rolt, Eyre & Spottiswoode,
1944 . . . . £25/£10
It's My Delight, by B. Vesey-Fitzgerald, Eyre &
Spottiswoode, 1947 . . . . . . £15/£5
Philandering Angler, by A. Applin, Hurst & Blackett,
[1948] . . . . £25/£10
A Sportsman Looks at Eire, by J.B. Drought,
Hutchinson, 1949 . . . . . . £30/£10
Landmarks, by A.G. Street, Eyre & Spottiswoode,
1949 . . . . £25/£10
Red Vagabond, by G.D. Adams, Batchworth Press,
1951 . . . . £10/£5
The White Foxes of Gorfenletch, by H. Tegner, Hollis
& Carter, 1954 . . . . £25/£10
The Secret of Orra, by E. Vipont, Blackwell, 1957 .
. . . . £30/£10
The Long Night, by William Mayne, Blackwell, 1957
[1958] . . . . £40/£15
The Long-Bow, by Ronald Welch, Blackwell, 1958 .
. . . . £20/£10
Sailors All by Peter Dawlish, Blackwell, 1958 £15/£5
A Snowdon Stream, by W.H. Canaway, Putnam:
Fisherman's Choice Series, 1958 . . . £25/£10
Trout Fisherman's Saga, by I.D. Owen, Putnam:
Fisherman's Choice Series, 1959 . . . £25/£10
Thirteen O'Clock by William Mayne, Blackwell, 1960.
. . . . £25/£10
Vix: The Story of a Fox Cub, by A. Windsor-Richards,
E. Benn, 1960 . . . . £25/£5
Beasts of the North Country, by H. Tegner, Galley
Press, 1961 . . . . £10/£5
Birds of the Lonely Lake, by A. Windsor-Richards,
Benn, 1961 . . . . £20/£5
Prince Prigio and Prince Ricardo, by Andrew Lang,
Dent, 1961 . . . . £20/£5

The Rogue Elephant, by Arthur Catherall, Dobson,
1962 . . . . £40/£15
Guns This Way, by H.W. Pearson-Rogers, Witherby,
1962 . . . . £25/£10
King Todd, by N. Burke, Putnam, 1963 . . £20/£5
A Cabin in the Woods, by A. Windsor-Richards,
Friday Press, 1963 . . . . . . £25/£10
Red Ivory, by A.R. Channel, Dobson, 1964 (pseud.
Arthur Catherall) . . . . . . £20/£5
The Lost Princess, by George Macdonald, Dent, 1965
. . . . £25/£10
To Do With Birds, by H. Tegner, H. Jenkins, 1965
. . . . £15/£5
The Wild White Swan, by A. Windsor-Richards,
Friday Press, 1965 . . . . . . £30/£10
Jungle Rescue, by A.R. Channel, Dobson, 1967 . .
. . . . £25/£10
Great Nature Stories, by A. Windsor-Richards, E.
Benn, 1967 . . . . £15/£5
The Shadow on the Moor, by I. Alan, 8th Duke of
Northumberland, privately printed, 1967 (200 copies).
. . . . £450
Where Vultures Fly, by G. Summers, Collins, 1974 .
. . . . £15/£5
Stories of the Wild, by A.L.E. Fenton and A.W.
Richards, Benn, 1975 . . . . . £25/£10
More Stories of the Wild, by A. Windsor-Richards,
Benn, 1977 . . . . £25/£10

H.C. BAILEY
(b.1878 d.1961)

Bailey's reputation is based on his dandy detective,
Reggie Fortune.

Reggie Fortune Short Story Collections
Call Mr Fortune, Methuen, 1921 . . . £500/£75
ditto, Dutton (U.S.), 1923 . . . . . £250/£45
Mr Fortune's Practice, Methuen, 1923 . . £400/£75
ditto, Dutton (U.S.), 1924 . . . . . £250/£45
Mr Fortune's Trials, Methuen, 1925 . . £350/£75
ditto, Dutton (U.S.), 1926 . . . . . £200/£35
Mr Fortune, Please, Methuen, 1927 . . . £350/£75
ditto, Dutton (U.S.), 1928 . . . . . £200/£35
Mr Fortune Speaking, Ward Lock, 1929 . £350/£75
ditto, Dutton (U.S.), 1931 . . . . . £200/£35
Mr Fortune Explains, Ward Lock, 1930 . £300/£50
ditto, Dutton (U.S.), 1931 . . . . . £200/£35
Case for Mr Fortune, Ward Lock, 1932 . £300/£50
ditto, Dutton (U.S.), 1932 . . . . . £200/£35
Mr Fortune Wonders, Ward Lock, 1933 . £300/£50
ditto, Dutton (U.S.), 1933 . . . . . £200/£35
Mr Fortune Objects, Gollancz, 1935 . . £350/£75
ditto, Doubleday (U.S.), 1935 . . . . £150/£35
Clue for Mr Fortune, Gollancz, 1936 . . £350/£75
ditto, as *A Clue for Mr Fortune*, Doubleday (U.S.),
1936 . . . . £150/£35

This is Mr Fortune, Gollancz, 1938 . . . £250/£45
ditto, Doubleday (U.S.), 1938 . . . . £100/£25
Mr Fortune Here, Gollancz, 1940 . . . £250/£45
ditto, Doubleday (U.S.), 1940 . . . . £75/£20

Reggie Fortune Novels
Shadow on the Wall, Gollancz, 1934 . £350/£75
ditto, Doubleday (U.S.), 1934 . . . £100/£25
Black Land, White Land, Gollancz, 1937 . £300/£65
ditto, Doubleday (U.S.), 1937 . . . . £100/£25
The Great Game, Gollancz, 1939 . . . £350/£65
ditto, Doubleday (U.S.), 1939 . . . . £100/£25
The Bishop's Crime, Gollancz 1940 . . £200/£45
ditto, Doubleday (U.S.), 1940 . . . . £100/£25
No Murder, Gollancz 1942 . . . . . £125/£30
ditto, as *The Apprehensive Dog*, Doubleday (U.S.),
1942 . . . . £75/£20
Mr Fortune Finds a Pig, Gollancz 1943 . £100/£25
ditto, Doubleday (U.S.), 1943 . . . £75/£20
The Cat's Whisker, Doubleday (U.S.) 1944 £50/£15
ditto, as *Dead Man's Effects*, Macdonald, n.d. [1945] .
. . . . £45/£10
The Life Sentence, Macdonald 1946 . . £40/£15
ditto, Doubleday (U.S.), 1946 . . . . £35/£10
Saving a Rope, Macdonald 1948 . . . £40/£15
ditto, as *Save a Rope*, Doubleday (U.S.) 1948 £35/£10

Joshua Clunk Novels
Garstons, Methuen, 1930 . . . . . . £350/£60
ditto, as *The Garston Muder Case*, Doubleday (U.S.),
1930 . . . . £125/£25
The Red Castle, Ward Lock, 1932 . . . £350/£60
ditto, as *The Red Castle Mystery*, Doubleday (U.S.),
1932 . . . . £100/£25
The Sullen Sky Mystery, Gollancz, 1935 . £350/£60
ditto, Doubleday (U.S.), 1935 . . . . £75/£20
Clunk's Claimant, Gollancz, 1937 . . . £350/£60
ditto, as *The Twittering Bird Mystery*, Doubleday
(U.S.), 1937 . . . . £75/£20
The Veron Mystery, Gollancz, 1939 . . . £350/£60
ditto, as *Mr Clunk's Text*, Doubleday (U.S.) 1939 .
. . . . £65/£15
The Little Captain, Gollancz 1941 . . . £300/£50
ditto, as *Orphan Ann*, Doubleday (U.S.) 1941 £65/£15
Dead Man's Shoes, Gollancz 1942 . . £250/£45
ditto, as *Nobody's Vineyard*, Doubleday (U.S.), 1942 .
. . . . £65/£15
Slippery Ann, Gollancz 1944 . . . £75/£20
ditto, as *The Queen of Spades*, Doubleday (U.S.) 1944
. . . . £45/£10
The Wrong Man, Doubleday (U.S.), 1945 . £45/£10
ditto, Macdonald, n.d. [1946]. . . . . £45/£10
Honour Among Thieves, Macdonald, 1947 . £35/£10
ditto, Doubleday (U.S.) 1947 . . . . £35/£10
Shrouded Death, Macdonald, 1950 . . . £35/£10

Others Novels
The Man in the Cape, Benn, 1933 . . . £200/£45

BERYL BAINBRIDGE
(b.1934)

Bainbridge's books, usually controversial, often involve several deaths.

Novels
A Weekend with Claud, New Authors Limited,
Hutchinson, 1967 . . . . £75/£25
ditto, as *A Weekend with Claude*, Duckworth, 1981 .
. . . . £25/£5
ditto, Braziller (U.S.), 1981 . . . . £25/£5
Another Part of the Wood, Hutchinson, 1968 £65/£20
ditto, Duckworth, 1979 . . . . . £25/£5
ditto, Braziller (U.S.), 1980 . . . . £25/£5
Harriet Said ..., Duckworth, 1972 . . . £25/£5
ditto, Braziller (U.S.), 1972 . . . . £25/£5
The Dressmaker, Duckworth, 1973 . . £25/£5
ditto, as *The Secret Glass*, Braziller (U.S.), 1973 . .
. . . . £25/£5
The Bottle Factory Outing, Duckworth, 1974 £25/£5
ditto, Braziller (U.S.), 1974 . . . . £25/£5
Sweet William, Duckworth, 1975 . . . £20/£5
ditto, Braziller (U.S.), 1975 . . . . £20/£5
A Quiet Life, Duckworth, 1976 . . . . £20/£5
ditto, Braziller (U.S.), 1977 . . . . £20/£5
Injury Time, Duckworth, 1977 . . . . £20/£5
ditto, Braziller (U.S.), 1977 . . . . £20/£5
Young Adolf, Duckworth, 1978 . . . . £25/£5
ditto, Braziller (U.S.), 1979 . . . . £20/£5
Winter Garden, Duckworth, 1980 . . . £20/£5
ditto, Braziller (U.S.), 1981 . . . . £20/£5
Watson's Apology, Duckworth, 1984 . . £20/£5
ditto, McGraw Hill (U.S.), 1985 . . . £20/£5
Filthy Lucre, Duckworth, 1986 . . . £20/£5
An Awfully Big Adventure, Duckworth, 1989 £20/£5
ditto, HarperCollins (U.S.), 1991. . . . £20/£5
The Birthday Boys, Duckworth, 1991 . . £20/£5
ditto, Carroll & Graf, 1991 . . . . . £20/£5
Every Man for Himself, Duckworth, 1996 . £20/£5
ditto, Carroll & Graf, 1996 . . . . . £20/£5
Master Georgie, Duckworth, 1998 . . . £20/£5

Omnibus Editions
A Bainbridge Omnibus, Duckworth, 1989 . £15/£5

Short Stories
Mum and Mr Armitage: Selected Stories, Duckworth,
1985 . . . . £15/£5
ditto, McGraw Hill (U.S.), 1987 . . . . £15/£5
Collected Stories, Penguin, 1994 (wraps) . . £5

Travel
English Journey: or, The Road to Milton Keynes,
Duckworth, 1984 . . . . £15/£5
ditto, Braziller (U.S.), 1984 . . . . . £15/£5

Forever England: North and South, Duckworth, 1987
. . . . £15/£5

Essays
Something Happened Yesterday, Duckworth, 1993
(wraps) £5

R.M. BALLANTYNE
(b.1825 d.1894)

A Scottish author, Ballantyne's first published work
was an account of his time as a fur trader in Canada,
followed by a series of popular adventure stories. By
the time of his death he had written over 80 books in
40 years.

Snowflakes and Sunbeams, or The Young Fur-Traders, Nelson, 1856 . . . . £150
Three Little Kittens, Nelson, [1856] (pseud. 'Comus').
. . . . £125
My Mother, Nelson, 1857 (pseud. 'Comus') . £75
The Butterfly's Ball, Nelson, 1857 (pseud. 'Comus') .
. . . . £100
Mister Fox, Nelson, 1857 (pseud. 'Comus') . £75
Ungava, A Tale of Esquimaux Land, Nelson, 1858
[1857]. £75
The Coral Island, A Tale of the Pacific Ocean,
Nelson, 1858 [1857]. £400
The Robber Kitten, Nelson, 1858 (pseud. 'Comus')
. . . . £100
*Martin Rattler, or A Boy's Adventures in the Forests
of Brazil*, Nelson, 1858 . . . . . . £100
Mee-a-ow! or Good Advice to Cats and Kittens,
Nelson, 1859 . . . . £100
The World of Ice, or Adventures in the Polar Regions,
Nelson, 1860 [1859]. £100
The Dog Crusoe, A Tale of the Western Prairies,
Nelson, 1861 [1860]. £100
The Golden Dream, or Adventures in the Far West,
Shaw, 1861 [1860] £100
The Gorilla Hunters, A Tale of the Wilds Of Africa,
Nelson, 1861 . . . . £100
The Red Eric, or The Whaler's Last Cruise: A Tale,
Routledge, 1861 . . . . £100
Man on the Ocean, A Book for Boys, Nelson, 1863
[1862]. £100
*The Wild Man of the West, A Tale of the Rocky
Mountains*, Routledge, 1863 [1862] . . . £125
Ballantyne's Miscellany, Nisbet, 1863-1886 (15 vols).
. . . . £500
*Gascoyne, The Sandal-Wood Trader, A Tale of the
Pacific*, Nisbet. 1864 [1863] £100
The Lifeboat, A Tale of Our Coast Heroes, Nisbet,
1864 . . . . £75
*Freaks on the Fells, or Three Months' Rustication:
And Why I did not Become a Sailor*, Routledge, 1865
[1864]. £100

*The Lighthouse, Being the Story of a Great Fight
Between Man and the Sea*, Nisbet, 1865 . . £75
Shifting Winds, A Tough Yarn, Nisbet, 1866 . £75
Silver Lake, or Lost in the Snow, Jackson, 1867 £75
*Fighting the Flames, A Tale of the London Fire
Brigade*, Nisbet, 1868 . . . . . . £100
*Away in the Wilderness, or Life Among the Red-
Indians and Fur-Traders of North America*, Porter
S. Coates (U.S.), 1869 . . . . . . £125
Deep Down, A Tale of the Cornish Mines, Nisbet,
1869 . . . . £75
Erling the Bold, A Tale of the Norse Sea-Kings,
Nisbet, 1869 . . . . £75
The Floating Lights of the Godwin Sands, A Tale,
Nisbet, 1870 . . . . £75
*The Iron Horse, or Life on the Line: A Tale of the
Grand National Trunk Railway*, Nisbet, 1871 £125
*The Norsemen in the West, or America Before
Columbus*, Nisbet, 1872. . . . . . £100
The Pioneers, A Tale of the Western Wilderness,
Nisbet, 1872 . . . . £100
*Black Ivory, A Tale of Adventure among the Slavers
of East Africa*, Nisbet, 1873 . . . . £100
Life in the Red Brigade, A Story for Boys, Routledge
[1873]. £75
The Ocean and Its Wonders, Nelson, 1874. . £45
The Pirate City, An Algerine Tale, Nisbet, 1875 £100
*Rivers of Ice, A Tale Illustrative of Alpine Adventure
and Glacier Action*, Nisbet, 1875 . . . £75
Under the Waves, or Diving In Deep Waters, A Tale,
Nisbet, 1876 . . . . £75
*The Settler and the Savage, A Tale of Peace and War
in South Africa*, Nisbet, 1877 . . . . £100
In the Track of the Troops, A Tale of Modern War,
Nisbet, 1878 . . . . £75
Jarwin and Cuffy, A Tale, Warne, [1878] . . £100
*Six Months at the Cape, or Letters to Periwinkle from
South Africa*, Nisbet, 1879 [1878] . . . £100
Post Haste, A Tale of Her Majesty's Mails, Nisbet,
1880 [1879] £100
Philosopher Jack, A Tale of the Southern Seas,
Nisbet, 1880 . . . . £75
The Lonely Island, or the refuge of the Mutineers,
Nisbet, 1880 . . . . £75
*The Redman's Revenge, A Tale of the Red River
Flood*, Nisbet, 1880 . . . . £100
*The Collected Works of Ensign Sopht, Late of the
Volunteers*, Nisbet, 1881 . . . . . £175
My Doggy and I, Nisbet, [1881] £75
The Giant of the North, or Pokings Round the Pole,
Nisbet, 1882 [1881] £100
*The Kitten Pilgrims, or Great Battles and Grand
Victories*, Nisbet, [1882] £100
*The Battery and the Boiler, or Adventures in the Lay-
ing of Submarine Cable*, Nisbet, 1883 [1882] £100
The Madman and the Pirate, Nisbet, 1883 . . £75
*Battles with the Sea, or Heroes of the Lifeboat and
Rocket*, Nisbet, 1883. . . . . . . £100

The Young Trawlers, A Story of Life and *Death and Rescue on the North Sea*, Nisbet, 1884 . . £75
Dusty Diamonds Cut and Polished, A Tale of City-Arab Life and Adventure, Nisbet, 1884 [1883] £75
Twice Bought, A Tale of the Oregon Gold Fields, Nisbet, 1885 [1884] £75
The Rover of the Andes, A Tale of Adventure in South America, Nisbet, 1885 . . . . . . £75
The Island Queen, A Tale of the Southern Hemisphere, Nisbet, 1885 . . . . . . £75
Red Rooney, or Last of the Crew, Nisbet, 1886 £75
The Big Otter, A Tale of the Great Nor'West, Routledge, 1887 [1886] £75
Blue Lights, or Hot Work in the Soudan: A Tale of Soldier Life, Nisbet, 1888 . . . . . £75
The Middy and the Moors, An Algerine Story, Nisbet, 1888 . . . . £75
The Crew of the Water Wagtail, A Story of Newfoundland, Nisbet, [1889] £75
The Garrett and the Garden, or Low Life High Up, and *Jeff Benson, or The Young Coastguardsman*, Nisbet, [1890] £75
Charlie to the Rescue, A Tale of the Sea and the Rockies, Nisbet, 1890 . . . . . . £75
The Coxswain's Bride, or The Rising Tide and Other Tales, Nisbet, 1891 . . . . £75
The Hot Swamp, A Romance of Old Albion, Nisbet, 1892 . . . . £75
Hunted and Harried, A Tale of the Scottish Covenanters, Nisbet, [1892] £75
The Walrus Hunters, A Romance of the Realms of Ice, Nisbet, 1893 . . . . £75
Fighting the Whales, Blackie, [1915] . . . £75
The Jolly Kitten Book, Blackie, [1925] . . £50/£20
Ballantyne Omnibus for Boys, Collins, [1932] £30/£10

J. G. BALLARD
(b.1930)

Despite shifting from avant-garde science fiction to surreal contemporary writing, Ballard is best known as the author of the *Empire of the Sun*, based on his own experiences of internment by the Japanese in World War Two.

Novels
The Wind from Nowhere, Berkley (U.S.), 1962 (wraps) £20
ditto, Doubleday (U.S.), 1965 (with *The Drowned World*) . . . . £125/£35
ditto, Penguin, 1967 (wraps) £10
The Drowned World, Berkley (U.S.), 1962 (wraps) £15
ditto, Gollancz, 1963 . . . . £450/£75
The Burning World, Berkley (U.S.), 1964 (wraps) £25
ditto, as *The Drought*, Cape, 1965 . . . £225/£50
The Crystal World, Cape, 1966 . . . . £175/£45
ditto, Farrar Straus (U.S.), 1966 . . . . £125/£10

Crash!, Cape, 1973 . . . . £150/£45
ditto, Farrar Straus (U.S.), 1973 . . . . £125/£35
Concrete Island, Cape, 1974 . . . . . £125/£30
ditto, Farrar Straus (U.S.), 1974 . . . . £65/£15
High Rise, Cape, 1975 . . . . £75/£15
ditto, Holt Rinehart (U.S.), 1977 . . . . £35/£5
The Unlimited Dream Company, Cape, 1979 £65/£5
ditto, Holt Rinehart (U.S.), 1979 . . . . £25/£5
Hello America, Cape, 1981 . . . . . £45/£10
ditto, Carroll & Graf (U.S.), 1988 . . . £15/£5
Empire of the Sun, Gollancz, 1984 . . . £40/£10
ditto, Gollancz, 1984 (100 signed copies, slipcase) .
. . . . £250/£200
ditto, Simon & Schuster (U.S.), 1985 . . £25/£5
The Day of Creation, Gollancz, 1987 . £25/£5
ditto, Gollancz, 1987 (100 signed copies, slipcase) . .
. . . . £125£100
ditto, Farrar Straus (U.S.), 1988 . . . . £20/£5
Running Wild, Hutchinson, 1988 (novella) . £20/£5
ditto, Farrar Straus (U.S.), 1989 . . . . £20/£5
The Kindness of Women, Harper Collins, 1991 £10/£5
ditto, Farrar Straus (U.S.), 1991 . . . . . £15/£5
Rushing to Paradise, Harper Collins, 1994 . £15/£5
ditto, Picador (U.S.), 1995 . . . . . £15/£5
Cocaine Nights, Harper Collins, 1996 . . £10/£5
ditto, Counterpoint (U.S.), 1998 . . . . £10/£5

Short Stories
Billenium and Other Stories, Berkley (U.S.), 1962 (wraps) £35
The Voices of Time and Other Stories, Berkley (U.S.), 1962 (wraps) £25
ditto, Gollancz, 1985 . . . . . . £30/£10
The Four-Dimensional Nightmare, Gollancz, 1963 .
. . . . £300/£125
Passport to Eternity and Other Stories, Berkley (U.S.), 1963 (wraps) £15
The Terminal Beach, Berkley (U.S.), 1964 (wraps) .
. . . . £15
ditto, Gollancz, 1964 . . . . £250/£45
The Impossible Man and Other Stories, Berkley (U.S.), 1966 (wraps) £30
The Day of Forever, Panther, 1967 (wraps) . £10
ditto, Gollancz, 1986 (hardback) . . . . . £20/£5
The Disaster Area, Cape, 1967 . . . . £250/£45
The Overloaded Man, Panther, 1967 (wraps) . £10
The Atrocity Exhibition, Cape, 1970 . . £175/£45
ditto, as *Love and Napalm: Export USA*, Grove Press (U.S.), 1972 . . . . £45/£15
ditto, as *The Atrocity Exhibition*, Doubleday (U.S.), 1970 . . . . £2,500/£2,250
Chronopolis 1972, Putnam (U.S.), 1971 . £75/£20
Vermilion Sands, Berkley (U.S.), 1971 (wraps) £20
ditto, Cape, 1973 . . . . £125/£35
Low Flying Aircraft, Cape, 1976 . . . £25/£10
The Best of J.G. Ballard, Sidgwick & Jackson, 1977 .
. . . . £25/£10
The Best Sort Stories of J.G. Ballard, Holt, Rinehart and Winston, 1978 . . . . . . £25/£10

The Venus Hunters, Granada, 1980 (wraps) . £10
ditto, Gollancz, 1986 . . . . . . £20/£10
Myths of the Near Future, Cape, 1982 . . £25/£10
Memories of the Space Age, Arkham House (Sauk
City, U.S.), 1988 . . . . £25/£10
War Fever, Collins, 1990 . . . . . £10/£5
ditto, Farrar Straus (U.S.), 1991 . . . . £10/£5

Others
Why I Want to Fuck Ronald Reagan, Unicorn
Bookshop, 1968 (50 signed copies of 250) . £600
ditto, Unicorn Bookshop, 1968 (200 unsigned copies of
250) £250
Users Guide to the Millennium, HarperCollins, 1996 .
. . . . £10/£5
ditto, Picador (U.S.), 1996 . . . . . £10/£5

IAIN BANKS
(b.1954)

The Wasp Factory was a controversial success, and
Banks has become more than a cult writer. His
subsequent works of fiction and science fiction often
stray into the realm of the bizarre and the sinister.

Novels
The Wasp Factory, Macmillan, 1984 . . £125/£35
ditto, Houghton Mifflin (U.S.), 1984 . . . £30/£5
Walking on Glass, Macmillan, 1985 . . £45/£10
ditto, Houghton Mifflin (U.S.), 1986 . . £20/£5
The Bridge, Macmillan, 1986 . . . £95/£20
ditto, St Martin's Press (U.S.), 1989 . . . £15/£5
Consider Phlebas, Macmillan, 1987 . . £40/£10
ditto, Macmillan, 1987 (176 signed copies, slipcase) .
. . . . £85/£70
ditto, St Martin's Press (U.S.), 1988 . . . £15/£5
Espedair Street, Macmillan, 1987 . . . £25/£10
The Player of Games, Macmillan, 1988 . . £35/£10
ditto, Macmillan, 1988 (201 signed copies, slipcase) .
. . . . £75/£60
ditto, St Martin's Press (U.S.), 1989 . . . £10/£5
Canal Dreams, Macmillan, 1989 . . . £15/£5
ditto, Doubleday (U.S.), 1991 . . . . £10/£5
Use of Weapons, Orbit, 1990 . . . . £20/£5
ditto, Bantam (U.S.), 1992 . . . . £10/£5
The Crow Road, Scribners, 1992 . . . £10/£5
Complicity, Little, Brown, 1993 . . . £10/£5
ditto, Doubleday (U.S.), 1992 . . . . £10/£5
Against a Dark Background, Orbit, 1993 . £20/£5
Feersum Endjinn, Orbit, 1994 . . . . £20/£5
ditto, Bantam (U.S.), 1995 (wraps) . . . £5
Whit, Little, Brown, 1995 . . . . . £10/£5
Excession, Orbit, 1996 . . . . . £10/£5
ditto, Bantam (U.S.), 1997 (wraps) . . . £5
A Song of Stone, Abacus, 1997 . . . £10/£5
ditto, Simon & Schuster (U.S.), 1998 . £10/£5
Inversions, Orbit, 1998 . . . . . £10/£5

ditto, Pocket Books (U.S.), 2000 . . . . £10/£5
The Business, Little, Brown, 1999 . . . . £10/£5
ditto, Simon & Schuster (U.S.), 2000 . . . £10/£5

Others
Cleaning Up, Birmingham Science Fiction Group,
1987 (500 signed, numbered copies, wraps) . £45
The State of the Art, Ziesing (U.S.), 1989 . . £10/£5
ditto, Ziesing (U.S.), 1989 (400 signed copies) £50/£20
ditto, Orbit, 1991 (further uncollected stories) £10/£5

HELEN BANNERMAN
(b.1863 d.1946)

Born in Scotland, Helen Bannerman married an army
doctor and settled in India where she wrote *Little
Black Sambo* for her own children. She returned in
later life to her native land.

The Story of Little Black Sambo, Grant Richards'
'Dumpy Books for Children', No. 4, 1899
(anonymous) £6,000
The Story of Little Black Mingo, Nisbet, 1901
(anonymous) £250
The Story of Little Black Quibba, Nisbet, 1902
(anonymous) £250
*Little Degchie-Head: An Awful Warning to Bad
Babas*, Nisbet, 1903 (anonymous) £200
Pat and the Spider: The Biter Bit, Nisbet, 1904
(anonymous) £150
The Story of the Teasing Monkey, Nisbet, 1906
(anonymous) £150
The Story of Little Black Quasha, Stokes, 1908
(anonymous) £100
The Story of Little Black Bobtail, Nisbet, 1909
(anonymous) £75
The Story of Sambo and the Twins, Nisbet [1937]. .
. . . . £150/£50
The Story of Little White Squibba, Chatto & Windus,
1966 . . . . £25/£10

JOHN BANVILLE
(b.1945)

Banville is a well respected Irish author, whose novel
The Book of Evidence was shortlisted for the Booker
prize.

Novels
Nightspawn, Secker & Warburg, 1970 . . £250/£50
ditto, Norton (U.S.), 1971 . . . . . £50/£35
Birchwood, Secker & Warburg, 1971 . . £50/£20
ditto, Norton (U.S.), 1973 . . . . . £25/£10
Doctor Copernicus, Secker & Warburg, 1976 £45/£15

ditto, Norton (U.S.), 1976. . . . . . £25/£10
Kepler, Secker & Warburg, 1981 . . . £35/£10
ditto, Godline (U.S.), 1983 . . . . . £10/£5
The Newton Letter: an Interlude, Secker & Warburg, 1982 . . . . £20/£5
ditto, Godline (U.S.), 1987 . . . . . £10/£5
Mefisto, Secker & Warburg, 1986 . . . £20/£5
ditto, Godline (U.S.), 1989 . . . . . £10/£5
The Book of Evidence, Secker & Warburg, 1989 . .
. . . . £25/£10
ditto, Scribner (U.S.), 1990 . . . . £10/£5
Ghosts, Secker & Warburg, 1993 . . . £15/£5
ditto, Knopf (U.S.), 1993 . . . . . £10/£5
Athena, Secker & Warburg, 1995 . . . £10/£5
ditto, Knopf (U.S.), 1995 . . . . . £10/£5
The Untouchable, Picador, 1997. . . . £10/£5
ditto, Knopf (U.S.), 1997 . . . . . £10/£5
Eclipse, Bridgewater Press, 2000 (26 signed, lettered copies) £225
ditto, Bridgewater Press, 2000 (100 signed, numbered copies) £75
ditto, Picador, 2000 . . . . £10/£5

Short Stories
Long Lankin, Secker & Warburg, 1970 . £450/£75
ditto, Galley Press (Dublin), 1984 (revised edition) .
. . . . £25/£5

CLIVE BARKER
(b.1952)

A novelist and short story writer in the horror genre, Barker was born in Liverpool but now lives in Los Angeles. He also illustrates his own work, and writes, directs and produces for the stage and screen.

'Books of Blood' Titles
Books of Blood, Vols. 1-6, Sphere, 1984-85 (first issue with original covers, wraps). £65
Books of Blood, Vols. 1-6, Sphere, 1984-85 (second issue with Barker designed covers, wraps). . £30
ditto, Vols. 1 and 2, Sphere, 1984 . . . £50/£20
ditto, Vol. 1, Weidenfeld & Nicolson, 1985 . £45/£15
ditto, Vol. 2, Weidenfeld & Nicolson, 1985 . £45/£15
ditto, Vol. 3, Weidenfeld & Nicolson, 1985 . £45/£15
ditto, Vols. 1-3, Weidenfeld & Nicholson, 1985 (200 signed, numbered sets, slipcase) . . . £175/£100
ditto, Vols. 4 & 5, Leisure circle, 1985 . £75/£15
ditto, Vol. 4, Weidenfeld and Nicholson, 1986 £45/£15
ditto, Vol. 5, Weidenfeld and Nicholson, 1986 £45/£15
ditto, Vol. 6, Weidenfeld and Nicholson, 1986 £45/£15
ditto, Vols. 4-6, Weidenfeld and Nicholson, 1986 (200 signed, numbered sets, slipcase) . . . £175/£100

Other Titles
The Damnation Game, Weidenfeld & Nicolson, 1985
. . . . £75/£15

ditto, Weidenfeld & Nicolson, 1985 (250 signed, numbered copies, slipcase) . . . . . £125/£75
ditto, Putnam (U.S.), 1987 . . . . £25/£10
The Inhuman Condition, Poseidon Press (U.S.), 1986
. . . . £10/£5
Weaveworld, Poseidon (U.S.), 1987 . . . £10/£5
ditto, Poseidon (U.S.), 1987 (500 signed, numbered copies) . . . . £125/£75
ditto, Poseidon (U.S.), 1987 (52 signed copies lettered a-zz) £200
ditto, Collins, 1987 . . . . £10/£5
ditto, Collins, 1987 (500 signed, numbered copies, slipcase) £125/75
Cabal, Poseidon (U.S.), 1988. . . . . £10/£5
ditto, Poseidon (U.S.), 1988 (750 signed, numbered copies) . . . . £80/£50
ditto, Fontana, 1988 (wraps) £5
The Great and Secret Show, Collins, 1989 . £10/£5
ditto, Collins, 1989 (500 signed copies, slipcase) . .
. . . . £125/£75
ditto, Harper & Row (U.S.), 1990 . . . £10/£5
Imajica, HarperCollins (U.S.), 1991 . . . £10/£5
ditto, HarperCollins (U.S.), 1991 (500 signed copies, slipcase) . . . . £125/£75
ditto, HarperCollins, 1991 . . . . . £10/£5
Pandemonium, Eclipse (U.S.), 1991 . . £40/£10
ditto, Eclipse (U.S.), 1991 (300 signed copies) . . .
. . . . £1250/£75
The Thief of Always, HarperCollins (U.S.), 1992 . . .
. . . . £10/£5
ditto, HarperCollins, 1992 . . . . . £10/£5
The Yattering and Jack, Eclipse (U.S.), 1992 (with Steve Niles, wraps) £10
ditto, Eclipse, 1992 (wraps) £10
Clive Barker's Revelations, Eclipse (U.S.), 1992 (with Steve Niles, wraps) £10
ditto, Eclipse, 1992 (wraps) £10
The Age of Desire, Eclipse (U.S.), 1992 (wraps) £10
ditto, Eclipse, 1993 (wraps) £10
The Life of Death, Eclipse (U.S.), 1993 (wraps) £10
ditto, Eclipse, 1993 (wraps) £10
Everville, HarperCollins, 1994 . . . £10/£5
ditto, HarperCollins (U.S.), 1994. . . . £10/£5
Sacrament, HarperCollins, 1994. . . . £10/£5
ditto, HarperCollins (U.S.), 1996. . . . £10/£5
Imajica, Volume 2, Reconciliations, HarperCollins, 1996 . . . . £10

PAT BARKER
(b.1943)

Pat Barker is a novelist and short story writer whose *The Ghost Road*, the last of her 'Regeneration trilogy', won the Booker Prize in 1995.

Union Street, Virago, 1982 . . . . . £150/£35
ditto, Virago, 1982 (wraps) £10

ditto, Putnam (U.S.), 1983	£50/£15
Blow Your House Down, Virago, 1984 . .	£100/£25
ditto, Virago, 1984 (wraps)	£10
ditto, Putnam (U.S.), 1984	£20/£5
The Century's Daughter, Virago, 1986 . .	£25/£10
ditto, Virago, 1986 (wraps)	£5
ditto, Putnam (U.S.), 1986	£15/£5
The Man Who Wasn't There, Virago, 1989	£25/£5
ditto, Ballantine (U.S.), 1990 (wraps) . .	£5
Regeneration, Viking, 1991	£175/£35
ditto, Dutton (U.S.), 1992	£35/£15
The Eye in the Door, Viking, 1993 . . .	£100/£15
ditto, Dutton (U.S.), 1994	£20/£5
The Ghost Road, Viking, 1995	£100/£15
ditto, Dutton (U.S.), 1995	£20/£5
The Regeneration Trilogy, Viking, 1996 .	£10/£5
Another World, Viking, 1998	£15/£5
ditto, Farrar, Straus & Giroux (U.S.), 1999 .	£10/£5

ROBERT BARNARD

(b.1936)

Barnard is the author of many light and entertaining detective novels.

Trethowan Novels

Sheer Torture, Collins Crime Club, 1981 .	£40/£10
ditto, as *Death by Sheer Torture*, Scribners (U.S.), 1982	£20/£5
Death and the Princess, Collins Crime Club, 1982 .	
. . . .	£30/£10
ditto, Scribners (U.S.), 1982	£15/£5
The Missing Bronte, Collins Crime Club, 1983 .	
. . . .	£25/£10
ditto, as *The Case of the Missing Bronte*, Scribners (U.S.), 1983	£15/£5
Bodies, Collins Crime Club, 1986, . . .	£25/£10
ditto, Scribners (U.S.), 1986	£10/£5
Death in Purple Prose, Collins Crime Club, 1987 . .	
. . . .	£25/£10
ditto, as *The Cherry Blossom Corpse*, Scribners (U.S.), 1987	£10/£5

Meredith Novels

Unruly Son, Collins Crime Club, 1978 .	£40/£10
ditto, as *Death of a Mystery Writer*, Scribners (U.S.), 1979	£20/£5
At Death's Door, Collins Crime Club, 1988	£30/£10
ditto, Scribners (U.S.), 1988	£15/£5

Oddie Novels

A City of Strangers, Bantam, 1990 . . .	£20/£5
ditto, Scribners (U.S.), 1990	£15/£5
A Fatal Attachment, Bantam, 1992 . . .	£15/£5
ditto, Scribners (U.S.), 1992	£10/£5
A Hovering of Vultures, Bantam, 1993 . .	£15/£5
ditto, Scribners (U.S.), 1993	£10/£5

Bad Samaritan, Collins Crime Club, 1995 .	£15/£5
ditto, Scribners (U.S.), 1995	£10/£5

Other Novels

Death of an Old Goat, Collins Crime Club, 1974 . .	
. . . .	£200/£25
ditto, Walker (U.S.), 1977	£60/£15
A Little Local Murder, Collins Crime Club, 1976 . .	
. . . .	£100/£15
ditto, Scribners (U.S.), 1983	£25/£5
Death on the High C's, Collins Crime Club, 1977 . .	
. . . .	£100/£15
ditto, Walker (U.S.), 1978	£25/£5
Blood Brotherhood, Collins Crime Club, 1977	
. . . .	£200/£45
ditto, Walker (U.S.), 1978	£25/£5
Posthumous Papers, Collins Crime Club, 1979 . .	
. . . .	£75/£15
ditto, as *Death of a Literary Widow*, Scribners (U.S.), 1980	£25/£5
Death in a Cold Climate, Collins Crime Club, 1980 .	
. . . .	£75/£15
ditto, Scribners (U.S.), 1981	£15/£5
Mother's Boys, Collins Crime Club, 1981 .	£45/£10
ditto, as *Death of a Perfect Mother*, Scribners (U.S.), 1981	£15/£5
Little Victims, Collins Crime Club 1983 . .	£40/£10
ditto, as *School for Murder*, Scribners (U.S.), 1984 . .	
. . . .	£15/£5
A Corpse in a Gilded Cage, Collins Crime Club, 1984	
. . . .	£30/£10
ditto, Scribners (U.S.), 1984	£15/£5
Out of the Blackout, Collins Crime Club, 1985	£25/£5
ditto, Scribners (U.S.), 1985	£15/£5
The Disposal of the Living, Collins Crime Club, 1985	
. . . .	£20/£5
ditto, as *Fete Fatale*, Scribners (U.S.), 1985	£15/£5
Political Suicide, Collins Crime Club, 1986	£20/£5
ditto, Scribners (U.S.), 1986	£10/£5
The Skeleton in the Grass, Collins Crime Club, 1987 .	
. . . .	£15/£5
ditto, Scribners (U.S.), 1988	£10/£5
Death and the Chaste Apprentice, Collins Crime Club, 1989	£15/£5
ditto, Scribners (U.S.), 1989	£10/£5
A Scandal in Belgravia, Bantam, 1991 . .	£15/£5
ditto, Scribners (U.S.), 1991	£10/£5
Masters of the House, Collins Crime Club 1994 . .	
. . . .	£15/£5
ditto, Scribners (U.S.), 1994	£10/£5
No Place of Safety, Collins Crime Club, 1997	£15/£5
ditto, Scribners (U.S.), 1997	£10/£5
The Corpse at the Haworth Tandoori, Collins Crime Club, 1998	£25/£5
ditto, Scribners (U.S.), 1999	£10/£5
Touched by the Dead, Collins Crime Club, 1999 . .	
. . . .	£15/£5
ditto, as *Murder in Mayfair*, Scribners (U.S.), 2000 .	
. . . .	£10/£5

Short Stories
Death of a Salesperson, Collins Crime Club, 1989 .
.   .   .   .   .   .   £20/£5
ditto, Scribners (U.S.), 1990 .   .   .   .   £15/£5
The Habit of Widowhood, Collins Crime Club, 1996 .
.   .   .   .   .   .   £20/£5
ditto, Scribners (U.S.), 1996 .   .   .   .   £15/£5

Novels as 'Bernard Bastable'
To Die like a Gentleman, Macmillan 1993 .   £20/£5
ditto, St Martin's Press (U.S.), 1993 .   .   .   £15/£5
Too Many Notes, Mr. Mozart, Little, Brown, 1995
.   .   .   .   .   .   £15/£5
ditto, Carroll & Graf (U.S.), 1995 .   .   .   £10/£5
A Mansion and It's Murder, Carroll & Graf (U.S.),
1998 .   .   .   .   £10/£5

DJUNA BARNES
(b.1892 d.1982)

Considered an important writer in the 1930s, her books have become collector's items rather than popular successes.

Fiction
The Book of Repulsive Women, Guido Bruno (U.S.),
1915 (wraps) £450
ditto, Alicat Bookshop (U.S.), 1948 (1,000 copies,
wraps). £50
A Book, Boni & Liveright (U.S.), [1923]   . £300/£75
ditto, as *A Night Among the Horses*, Liveright (U.S.),
1929 .   .   .   .   £250/£50
ditto, as *Spillway*, Faber, 1962 .   .   .   £25/£10
Ryder, Liveright (U.S.), 1928   .   .   . £150/£25
Nightwood, Faber, 1936 .   .   .   .   £200/£75
ditto, Harcourt, Brace (U.S.), 1937 .   .   £125/£30
Vagaries Malicieux, Hallman (U.S.), 1974 (500
copies, no d/w) £50
Smoke and Other Early Stories, Sun & Moon Press
(U.S.), 1982 .   .   .   .   £25/£10
Collected Stories, Sun & Moon Press (U.S.), 1996 .
.   .   .   .   .   .   £25/£10

Plays
The Antiphon, Faber, 1958 .   .   .   . £100/£20
ditto, Farrar, Straus (U.S.), 1958 .   .   .   £75/£20
To The Dogs, The Press of the Good Mountain (U.S.),
1982 (110 copies) £100

Others
Ladies Almanack, Titus (Paris), 1928 (1,050 copies,
wraps). £200
ditto, Titus (Paris), 1928 (40 copies on Rives paper) .
.   .   .   .   .   .   £500
Selected Works, Farrar, Straus (U.S.), 1958. £25/£10
ditto, Faber, 1980 .   .   .   .   .   .   £20/£10

Creatures in an Alphabet, Dial Press (U.S.), 1982 . .
.   .   .   .   .   .   £40/£10
New York, Sun and Moon Press (U.S.), 1989   £25/£10
Interviews, Sun and Moon Press (U.S.), 1986 £25/£10
Poe's Mother, Sun and Moon Press (U.S.), 1995   . .
.   .   .   .   .   .   £25/£10

JULIAN BARNES
(b.1946)

A clever and inventive post-modernist writer, Barnes moves between genres, probing the boundaries of convention.

Novels
Metroland, Cape, 1980 .   .   .   .   . £300/£45
ditto, St Martin's Press (U.S.), 1980 .   .   £75/£25
Before She Met Me, Cape, 1982 .   .   .   £75/£20
ditto, McGraw-Hill (U.S.), 1986 (wraps)   .   . £10
Flaubert's Parrot, Cape, 1984 .   .   .   £225/£35
ditto, Knopf (U.S.), 1985 .   .   .   .   £65/£10
Staring at the Sun, Cape, 1986 .   .   .   £45/£10
ditto, London Limited Editions, 1986 (150 signed
copies, glassine d/w).   .   .   .   .   £60/£50
ditto, Knopf (U.S.), 1987 .   .   .   .   £20/£5
A History of the World in 10½ Chapters, Cape, 1989
.   .   .   .   .   .   £45/£10
ditto, Knopf (U.S.), 1989 .   .   .   .   £15/£5
Talking it Over, Cape, 1991 .   .   .   .   £20/£5
ditto, London Limited Editions, 1991 (200 signed
copies, glassine d/w).   .   .   .   .   £50/£40
ditto, Knopf (U.S.), 1991 .   .   .   .   £15/£5
Bodlivo Svinche, Obsidian (Bulgaria), 1992 (wraps) .
.   .   .   .   .   .   £10
ditto, as *The Porcupine*, Cape, 1992 (novella) £15/£5
ditto, Knopf (U.S.), 1992 .   .   .   .   £10/£5
England, England, Cape, 1998 .   .   .   £10/£5

Novels as 'Dan Kavanagh'
Duffy, Cape, 1980 .   .   .   .   .   .   £50/£10
ditto, Pantheon (U.S.), 1986 (wraps)   .   .   £5
Fiddle City, Cape, 1981 .   .   .   .   £65/£10
ditto, Pantheon (U.S.), 1986 (wraps).   .   .   £5
Putting the Boot In, Cape, 1985 .   .   .   £25/£10
Going to the Dogs, Viking UK, 1987   .   £25/£10
ditto, Viking (U.S.), 1987.   .   .   .   £10/£5
The Duffy Omnibus, Penguin, 1991 .   .   .   £5

Short Stories
Cross Channel, Cape, 1996 .   .   .   .   £25/£5
ditto, Cape, 1996 (50 special copies, signed and
numbered) £250
ditto, Knopf (U.S.), 1996 .   .   .   .   £15/£5

Other
Letters from London, 1990-1995, Picador, 1995   . .
.   .   .   .   .   .   £15/£5
ditto, Vintage (U.S.) 1995 .   .   .   .   £15/£5

H.E. BATES
(b.1906 d.1974)

A British author of popular novels, novellas and short stories, many of which have been adapted for television. He is perhaps best known for the Larkin family novels, including *The Darling Buds of May*.

Novels

The Two Sisters, Cape, 1926	£200/£65
Catherine Foster, Cape, 1929 . . .	£95/£35
ditto, Viking (U.S.), 1929	£50/£15
Charlotte's Row, Cape, 1931	£75/£25
ditto, Cape, 1931 (107 signed, numbered copies) £200
The Fallow Land, Cape, 1932 . . .	£75/£25
The Poacher, Cape, 1935.	£65/£25
ditto, Macmillan (U.S.), 1935 . . .	£35/£15
A House of Women, Cape, 1936. . .	£65/£25
'Spella Ho', Cape, 1938	£65/£20
ditto, Little, Brown (U.S.), 1938 . . .	£35/£15
Fair Stood the Wind for France, Joseph, 1944 . .	
. . . .	£45/£15
ditto, Little, Brown (U.S.), 1944 . . .	£35/£10
The Cruise of the 'Breadwinner', Joseph, 1946 . .	
. . . .	£45/£15
The Purple Plain, Joseph, 1947 . . .	£20/£5
ditto, Little, Brown (U.S.), 1947 . . .	£15/£5
The Jacaranda Tree, Joseph [1949]. . .	£20/£5
ditto, Little, Brown (U.S.), 1949 . . .	£15/£5
Dear Life, Joseph, 1949	£15/£5
The Scarlet Sword, Joseph, 1950 . . .	£15/£5
ditto, Little, Brown (U.S.), 1951 . . .	£15/£5
Love for Lydia, Joseph, 1952. . . .	£15/£5
ditto, Little, Brown (U.S.), 1952 . . .	£15/£5
The Feast of July, Joseph, 1954 . . .	£15/£5
ditto, Little, Brown (U.S.), 1954 . . .	£10/£5
The Sleepless Moon, Joseph, 1956 . .	£15/£5
ditto, Little, Brown (U.S.), 1956 . . .	£15/£5
Death of a Huntsman, Joseph, 1957 . .	£65/£15
ditto, as *Summer in Salandar*, Little, Brown (U.S.), 1957	£25/£5
The Darling Buds of May, Joseph, 1958 .	£45/£15
ditto, Little, Brown (U.S.), 1958	£40/£10
A Breath of French Air, Joseph, 1959 .	£40/£10
ditto, Little, Brown (U.S.), 1959	£35/£10
When the Green Woods Laugh, Joseph, 1960	£25/£5
The Day of the Tortoise, Joseph, 1961 . .	£30/£5
The Crown of Wild Myrtle, Joseph, 1962 .	£15/£5
ditto, Farrar, Straus (U.S.), 1963	£15/£5
Oh! to be in England, Joseph, 1963 . . .	£25/£10
ditto, Farrar, Straus (U.S.), 1964 . . .	£20/£5
A Moment in Time, Joseph, 1964 . . .	£15/£5
ditto, Farrar, Straus (U.S.), 1964	£15/£5
The Distant Horns of Summer, Joseph, 1967	£15/£5
A Little of What You Fancy, Joseph, 1970 .	£25/£10
The Triple Echo, Joseph, 1970	£15/£5

Short Stories

The Spring Song, and In View of the Fact That ... Two Stories, Archer, 1927 (100 numbered, signed copies, wraps)	£200
ditto, Lantern Press (U.S.), 1927 (50 signed copies) .	
. . . .	£200
Day's End, Cape, 1928	£150/£45
ditto, Viking, 1928	£125/£35
Seven Tales and Alexander, Scholartis Press, 1929 (50 signed copies of an edition of 1,000) . .	£100
ditto, Scholartis Press, 1929 (950 unsigned copies of an edition of 1,000)	£50/£20
The Tree, A Story, Blue Moon Booklets, 1930 (wraps)	
. . . .	£45
The Hessian Prisoner, Furnival Books, 1930 (550 signed copies)	£100
Mrs. Esmond's Life, privately printed, 1931 (300 signed copies)	£75
ditto, privately printed, 1931 (50 signed copies, leaf of manuscript bound in)	£275
A Threshing Day, Foyle, 1931 (300 signed copies) .	
. . . .	£100
A German Idyll, Golden Cockerel Press, 1932 (307 signed copies)	£250
The Black Boxer, Pharos Editions (Cape), 1932, (100 signed copies)	£200/£150
ditto, Pharos Editions (Cape), 1932 . .	£75/£25
The Story Without an End and The Country Doctor, White Owl Press, 1932	£65/£25
ditto, White Owl Press, 1932 (125 signed copies) . .	
. . . .	£150/£75
Sally Go Round the Moon, White Owl Press, 1932 .	
. . . .	£65/£25
ditto, White Owl Press, 1932 (129 signed copies) . .	
. . . .	£150/£75
ditto, White Owl Press, 1932 (21 signed copies with leaf of manuscript bound in) . . .	£300
The House with the Apricot and Two Other Tales, Golden Cockerel Press, 1933 (300 signed copies). .	
. . . .	£250
The Woman Who Had Imagination, Cape, 1934 . .	
. . . .	£65/£25
ditto, Macmillan (U.S.), 1934	£50/£20
Thirty Tales, Cape, Traveller's Library, 1934	£15/£5
Cut and Come Again: Fourteen Stories, Cape, 1935 .	
. . . .	£100/£25
The Duet, A Story, Grayson Books, 1935 (285 signed copies)	£125/£65
Something Short and Sweet, Cape, 1937 .	£30/£5
Country Tales, Readers Union, 1938 (tissue jacket) .	
. . . .	£35/£25
ditto, Cape, 1940	£10/£5
My Uncle Silas, Cape, 1939	£175/£75
The Flying Goat, Cape, 1939 . . .	£75/£25
The Beauty of the Dead and Other Stories, Cape, 1940.	£75/£25
The Greatest People in the World. 1942 Cape (pseud. Flying Officer 'X')	£45/£15

ditto, as *There's Something in the Air*, Knopf, 1943 .
    . . . . £45/£15
How Sleep the Brave and other Stories, Cape, 1943
  (pseud. Flying Officer 'X') . . . . . £40/£15
The Daffodil Sky, Cape, 1943 . . . . £40/£10
The Bride Comes to Evensford, Cape, 1943 £60/£15
Thirty-One Selected Tales, Cape, 1947 . £15/£5
Dear Life, Joseph, 1950 . . . . . . £20/£5
Colonel Julian and Other Stories, Joseph, 1951 . .
    . . . . £45/£15
ditto, Little, Brown (U.S.), 1952 . . . . £30/£10
Twenty Tales, Cape, 1951 . . . . . £15/£5
The Nature of Love, Joseph, 1953 . . . £30/£10
Sugar for the Horse, Joseph, 1957 . . £35/£15
The Watercress Girl and other Stories, Joseph, 1959 .
    . . . . £25/£10
ditto, Little, Brown, 1959 . . . . . £20/£5
An Aspidistra in Babylon: Four Novellas, Joseph,
  1960 . . . . £25/£10
Now Sleeps the Crimson Petal and Other Stories,
  Joseph, 1961 . . . . £25/£5
The Golden Oriole: Five Novellas, Joseph, 1962 . .
    . . . . £25/£5
ditto, Little, Brown (U.S.), 1962 . . . . £20/£5
Seven by Five: Stories 1926-1961, Joseph, 1963 . .
    . . . . £20/£10
ditto, as *The Best of H. E. Bates*, Little, Brown (U.S.),
  1963 . . . . £15/£5
The Fabulous Mrs V., Joseph, 1964 . . . £20/£5
The Wedding Party, Joseph, 1965 . . £20/£5
The Wild Cherry Tree, Joseph, 1968 . . £20/£5
The Four Beauties, Joseph, 1968 . . £20/£5
The Song of the Wren, Joseph, 1972 . . £15/£5
The Yellow Meads of Asphodel, Joseph, 1976 £15/£5
A Month by the Lake & Other Stories, New Directions
  (U.S.), 1987 . . . . £35/£5
Elephants Nest in a Rhubarb Tree & Other Stories,
  New Directions (U.S.), 1989 . . . . £35/£5

Plays

The Last Bread, Labour Publishing Co., 1926 (wraps)
    . . . . £125
The Day of Glory, Joseph, 1945 . . . . £25/£5

Children's

The Seekers, Bumpus, 1926 (tissue jacket) . £60/£50
The Seasons and the Gardener, C.U.P., 1940 £25/£10
Achilles the Donkey, Dobson Books, 1962 . £75/£25
ditto, Franklin-Watts (U.S.), 1963 . . £45/£15
Achilles and Diana, Dobson Books, 1964 . £75/£25
Achilles and the Twins, Dobson Books, 1964 £75/£25
The White Admiral, Dobson Books, 1968 . £45/£20

Verse

Song for December, privately printed, 1928 (wraps) .
    . . . . £250
Christmas 1930, privately printed, 1930 (wraps) £250
Holly and Sallow, Blue Moon, 1931 (100 signed
  copies, broadside) £65

Autobiography
The Vanished World, Joseph, 1969 . . . £25/£5
ditto, Univ. of Missouri Press (U.S.), 1969 . £25/£5
The Blossoming World, Joseph 1971 . . £20/£5
ditto, Univ. of Missouri Press (U.S.), 1971 . £15/£5
The World in Ripeness, Joseph,1972 . . £20/£5
ditto, Univ. of Missouri Press (U.S.), [1972] £15/£5

Others
Flowers and Faces, Golden Cockerel Press, 1935 (325
  signed copies) £300
Through the Woods: The English Woodland - April to
  April, Gollancz, 1936 . . . . . . £100/£45
ditto, Macmillan (U.S.), 1936 . . . . £50/£25
Down the River, Gollancz, 1937 . . . . £75/£25
ditto, Henry Holt & Co. (U.S.), 1937 . . £65/£25
In the Heart of the Country, Country Life, 1942
  (illustrated by Tunnicliffe) . . . . . £75/£25
O More Than Happy Countryman, Country Life, 1943
  (illustrated by Tunnicliffe) . . . . . £45/£15
Country Life, Penguin Books, 1943 (wraps) . £5
There's Freedom in the Air: The Official Story of the
  Allied Air Forces from the Occupied Countries,
  H.M.S.O., 1944 (anonymous, wraps) . . . £35
The Tinkers of Elstow, [no place] 1946 . . . £35
Edward Garnett, Parrish, 1950 . . . £25/£10
The Country of White Clover, Joseph, 1952 £35/£5
ditto, Joseph, 1952 (100 signed copies) . . . £75
The Face of England, Batsford Ltd, 1952 . £35/£5
A Love of Flowers, Joseph, 1971 . . . £15/£5

L. FRANK BAUM
(b.1856 d.1919)

An American author who had a varied career until he
started to write for children with *Mother Goose in
Prose*. Three years later he brought out the classic *The
Wonderful Wizard of Oz*. In this and its 13 sequels,
Baum was attempting to write fantasies with distinctly
American origins.

Mother Goose in Prose, Way & Williams (U.S.),
  [1897]. £2,500
ditto, Duckworth, 1899 . . . . . . £600
Father Goose, His Book, Way & Williams (U.S.),
  1899 . . . . £2,500
A New Wonderland, Russell (U.S.), 1900 . £2,000
ditto, as *The Surprising Adventures of the Magical*
  Monarch of Mo and His People, Bobbs-Merrill
  (U.S.). [1903]. £750
The Wonderful Wizard of Oz, Hill (U.S.), 1900 . . .
    . . . . £12,000
ditto, as *The New Wizard of Oz*, Bobbs-Merrill (U.S.)
  [1903]. £750
ditto, Hodder & Stoughton, 1906. . . . £600
The Army Alphabet, Hill (U.S.), 1900 . . £1,000
The Navy Alphabet, Hill (U.S.), 1900 . . £1,000

American Fairy Tales, Hill (U.S.), 1901 . . £1,000
Dot and Tot of Merryland, Hill (U.S.), 1901 £1,000
The Master Key: An Electrical Fairy Tale, Bobbs-
Merrill (U.S.), 1901 . . . . £600
ditto, Stevens & Brown, [1902] £500
The Life and Adventures of Santa Claus, Bobbs-
Merrill (U.S.), 1902 . . . . £2,500
ditto, Stevens & Brown, 1902 . . . . £2,000
*The Surprising Adventures of the Magical Monarch
of Mo and His People*, Bobbs-Merrill (U.S.), [1903].
. . . . £500
The Enchanted Island of Yew, Bobbs-Merrill (U.S.),
[1903]. £500
The Marvellous Land of Oz, Reilly & Britton (U.S.),
1904 . . . . £2,000
ditto, Revell, 1906 (copyright edition) . . . £600
ditto, Hodder & Stoughton, 1906. . . . . £300
Queen Zixi of Ix, Century (U.S.), 1905 . . . £250
ditto, Hodder & Stoughton, 1905. . . . . £200
The Woggle-Bug Book, Reilly & Britton (U.S.), 1905
. . . . £1,000
John Dough and The Cherub, Reilly & Britton (U.S.),
1906 . . . . £250
ditto, Constable, 1906 . . . . £200
Ozma of Oz, Reilly & Britton (U.S.), 1907 . . £2,000
The Last Egyptian: A Romance of the Nile, Reilly &
Britton (U.S.), 1908 . . . . £225
Dorothy and the Wizard in Oz, Reilly & Britton (U.S.),
1908 . . . . £1,000
The Road to Oz, Reilly & Britton (U.S.), 1909 £2,000
The Emerald City of Oz, Reilly & Britton (U.S.), 1910
. . . . £2,000
The Sea Fairies, Reilly & Britton (U.S.), 1911. £250
Sky Island, Reilly & Britton (U.S.), 1912 . . £200
The Patchwork Girls of Oz, Reilly & Britton (U.S.),
1913 . . . . £2,000
Tik-Tok of Oz, Reilly & Britton (U.S.), 1914 £1,000
The Scarecrow of Oz, Reilly & Britton (U.S.), 1915 .
. . . . £600
Rinkitink in Oz, Reilly & Britton (U.S.), 1916 . £600
The Lost Princess of Oz, Reilly & Britton (U.S.), 1917
. . . . £750
The Tin Woodman of Oz, Reilly & Britton (U.S.),
1918 . . . . £750
The Magic of Oz, Reilly & Lee (U.S.), 1919 . £500
Glinda of Oz, Reilly & Lee (U.S.), 1920 . . £450

THE BEANO

The Beano is arguably the most famous of all British
children's comics, first appearing on 30th July 1938.
The first Beano Annual was issued in 1940

Comics

No.1, D.C. Thomson, 30th July 1938 (with Whoopee
Mask) £6,000

ditto, D.C. Thomson, 30th July 1938 (without
Whoopee Mask) £3,000
No.2, D.C. Thomson, 1938 . . . . . . £500
No.3, D.C. Thomson, 1938 . . . . . . £400
No.4, D.C. Thomson, 1938 . . . . . . £400
No.5, D.C. Thomson, 1938 . . . . . . £500
1938-39 . . . . £500 each
1940s . . . . £75 each
1941-45 . . . . £45 each

Annuals

The Beano Book 1940, D.C. Thomson . . £3,000
The Beano Book 1941, D.C. Thomson . . . £1,000
The Beano Book 1942, D.C. Thomson . . . £1,000
The Magic Beano Book 1943, D.C. Thomson . £700
The Magic Beano Book 1944, D.C. Thomson . £450
The Magic Beano Book 1945, D.C. Thomson . £400
The Magic Beano Book 1946, D.C. Thomson . £350
The Magic Beano Book 1947, D.C. Thomson . £250
The Magic Beano Book 1948, D.C. Thomson . £250
The Magic Beano Book 1949, D.C. Thomson . £250
The Magic Beano Book 1950, D.C. Thomson . £125
The Beano Book 1951, D.C. Thomson . . . £100
The Beano Book 1952, D.C. Thomson . . . £75
The Beano Book 1953, D.C. Thomson . . . £75
The Beano Book 1954, D.C. Thomson . . . £70
The Beano Book 1955, D.C. Thomson . . . £70
The Beano Book 1956, D.C. Thomson . . . £70
The Beano Book 1957, D.C. Thomson . . . £70
The Beano Book 1958, D.C. Thomson . . . £65
The Beano Book 1959, D.C. Thomson . . . £60
The Beano Book 1960, D.C. Thomson . . . £55
The Beano Book 1961, D.C. Thomson . . . £50
The Beano Book 1962, D.C. Thomson . . . £50
The Beano Book 1963, D.C. Thomson . . . £50
The Beano Book 1964, D.C. Thomson . . . £45
The Beano Book 1965, D.C. Thomson . . . £45
The Beano Book 1966, D.C. Thomson . . . £40
The Beano Book 1967, D.C. Thomson . . . £40
The Beano Book 1968, D.C. Thomson . . . £40
The Beano Book 1969, D.C. Thomson . . . £15
The Beano Book 1970-75, D.C. Thomson . £10 each
The Beano Book 1976-80, D.C. Thomson . £5 each

AUBREY BEARDSLEY
(b.1872 d.1898)

British illustrator and writer who came to prominence
in the 1890s. His sinuous black and white illustrations
became as synonymous with the 'decadence' of the
period as did the name of Oscar Wilde. See also under
'Keynotes', 'Yellow Book' and 'The Savoy' for
further publications containing his illustrations.

Major Works

Le Morte d'Arthur, by Thomas Malory, Dent, 1893-4,
(12 parts, green wraps) . . . . the set £15,000

ditto, Dent, 1893-4, (12 parts, handmade paper, grey wraps). . . . . the set £20,000
ditto, Dent, 1893, (2 vols). £2,000
ditto, Dent, 1893, (3 vols, 300 copies, handmade paper) £25,000
ditto, Dent, 1909, (2nd edition, 1 vol., 1,500 copies) £250
ditto, Dent, 1927, (3rd edition, 1,600 copies) . . . . £2,000/£1,500
ditto, Dent, 1927, (portfolio of eleven unpublished designs, 300 copies). £750
Bon-Mots of Sydney Smith and R. Brinsley Sheridan, Dent, 1893 . . . . £75
ditto, Dent, 1893 (100 numbered copies, large paper issue) £350
Bon-Mots of Charles Lamb and Douglas Jerrold, Dent, 1893 . . . . £75
ditto, Dent, 1893 (100 numbered copies, large paper issue) £350
Bon-Mots of Samuel Foot and Theodore Hook, Dent, 1894 . . . . £75
ditto, Dent, 1894, (100 numbered copies, large paper issue) £350
Salomé, by Oscar Wilde, Lane & Mathews, 1894 (755 copies) £2,000
ditto, Lane & Mathews, 1894 (125 copies, on Japan vellum, large paper issue) £10,000
ditto, Melmoth & Co., 1904 (250 numbered copies) £350
ditto, Melmoth & Co., 1904 (50 numbered copies). £500
The Rape of the Lock, by Alexander Pope, [Smithers], privately printed, 1896 (1,000 copies) . . . £350
ditto, [Smithers], privately printed, 1896 (25 copies on Japan vellum) £5,000
Lysistrata of Aristophanes, [Smithers], privately printed, 1896 (100 copies) £6,500
A Book of Fifty Drawings, Smithers, 1897 (500 copies) £200
ditto, Smithers, 1897 (50 copies on Japan vellum) £3,000
The Pierrot of the Minute, by Ernest Dowson, Smithers, 1897 (300 copies printed on handmade paper). £500
ditto, Smithers, 1897 (30 copies printed on Japanese vellum) £2,000
ditto, Grolier Club (U.S.), 1923 (300 copies printed on Dutch antique paper) £200
A Second Book of Fifty Drawings, Smithers, 1898 . . . . £200
Mademoiselle de Maupin, by Theophile Gautier, Smithers, 1898 (portfolio, 50 numbered copies) £2,500
Volpone, by Ben Jonson, Smithers, 1898 (1,000 copies) £250
ditto, Smithers, 1898 (100 numbered copies on Japanese vellum). £1,750
The Early Work of Aubrey Beardsley, Bodley Head, 1899 . . . . £250

ditto, Bodley Head, 1899 (100 copies) . . . £500
ditto, Bodley Head, 1912 . . . . £75
The Later Work of Aubrey Beardsley, Bodley Head, 1901 . . . . £250
ditto, Bodley Head, 1901 (100 copies) . . . £500
ditto, Bodley Head, 1912 . . . . £75
Under the Hill, Lane, 1904 . . . . . £250
ditto, Lane, 1904 (50 copies on Japan vellum) £2,500
ditto, Olympia Press (Paris), 1959 . . . £100
The Uncollected Works of Aubrey Beardsley, Bodley Head, 1925 . . . . £150
ditto, Bodley Head, 1925 (100 copies) . . . £450

Other Titles with illustrations, cover designs etc by Beardsley

Evelina, by Frances Burney, Dent, 1893 . . £100
Pastor Sang, by Bjornstjerne Bjornson, Longmans 1893 . . . . £100
The Wonderful History of Virgilus the Sorceror of Rome, Nutt, 1893 . . . . £100
The Pagan Papers, by Kenneth Grahame, Mathews & Lane, 1894 (615 copies) £150
Plays, by John Davidson, Mathews & Lane, 1894 £200
The Land of Heart's Desire, by W.B. Yeats, Unwin, 1894 (500 copies) £175
Baron Verdigris, by Jocelyn Quilp, Henry, 1894 £150
Lucian's True History, by Lucian, [Lawrence & Bullen], 1894 (251 numbered copies) . . . £150
ditto, by Lucian, [Lawrence & Bullen], 1894 (54 numbered copies with extra plate) £400
A London Garland, Macmillan, 1895 . . . £150
Tales of Mystery and Wonder, by Edgar Allan Poe, Stone & Kimball (U.S.), 1895 . . . . . £250
Earl Lavender, by John Davidson, Ward & Downey, 1895 . . . . £150
Young Ofeg's Ditties, by Ola Hansson, Lane, 1895 . . . . £75
Sappho, by H.T. Wharton, Lane, 1895 . . . £125
An Evil Motherhood, by Walt Ruding, Mathews, 1896 ('Black Coffee' frontispiece) £750
ditto, Mathews, 1896 ('Portrait of the Author' frontispiece) £200
ditto, Mathews, 1896 (remainder issue with 'Portrait of the Author' frontispiece glued in and 'Black Coffee' inserted or tipped in). £200
The Barbarous Britishers, by H.D.Traill, Lane, 1896 . . . . £100
The Life and Times of Madame du Barry, by Douglas, Smithers, 1897 . . . . £150
Verses, by Ernest Dowson, Smithers, 1896 (300 copies) £400
ditto, Smithers, 1896 (30 copies on Japanese Vellum) £3,000
A Book of Bargains, by V. O'Sullivan, Smithers, 1896 . . . . £175
Pierrot!, by Henry de Vere Stacpoole, Lane, 1896. . . . . £125
My Little Lady Anne, by Mrs Egerton Castle, Lane, 1896 . . . . £100

Simplicity, by A.T.G. Price, Lane, 1896. . . £100
My Brother, by Vincent Brown, Lane, 1896 . £100
The Pierrot of the Minute, by Ernest Dowson,
Smithers, 1897 (300 copies) £400
ditto, Smithers, 1897 (30 copies on Japanese Vellum) .
. . . . £3,000
Le Comédie Humaine, Scenes of Parisian Life, by
Honoré de Balzac, Smithers, 1897 (11 vols, 250 sets)
. . . . £350
ditto, Smithers, 1897 (50 sets on Japanese Vellum) .
. . . . £750
Le Comédie Humaine, Scenes of Private Life, by
Honoré de Balzac, Smithers, 1897-98 (11 vols) . .
. . . . £300
The Souvenirs of Leonard, by Jean Leonard, Smithers,
1897 (2 vols, 250 numbered sets) £100
A History of Dancing, Gaston Vuillier, Heinemann,
1898 (2 vols, Beardsley plate in 35 numbered copies
on Japanese vellum only) £500
The House of Sin, by V. O'Sullivan, Smithers, 1897 .
. . . . £350
Decorations, in Verse & Prose, Smithers, 1899 £250
The Poems of Ernest Dowson, Lane, 1905 (edited and
with a memoir by Arthur Symons) £75

Other Titles containing illustrations by Beardsley
Aubrey Beardsley, by Arthur Symons, Unicorn Press,
1898 . . . . £60
ditto, Dent, 1905 . . . . £25
The Last Letters of Aubrey Beardsley, ed. by John
Gray, Longmans, 1904 . . . . . . £100
Aubrey Beardsley, by Robert Ross, Lane, 1909 £45
The Beardsley Period, by O. Burdett, Bodley Head,
1925 . . . . £75/£25
ditto, Boni & Liveright (U.S.), 1925 . . . £75/£25
The Best of Beardsley, by R.A. Walker, Bodley Head,
1948 . . . . £50/£15
A Beardsley Miscellany, ed. by R.A. Walker, London,
1949 . . . . £50/£15
Beardsley: A Catalogue of an Exhibition, V&A
Museum, 1966 . . . . £10

Others
*The Story of Venus and Tanhauser, A Romantic
Novel*, Smithers, 1907 ('Under the Hill', 250
numbered copies on handmade paper, no illustrations)
. . . . £250
ditto, Smithers, 1907 ('Under the Hill', 50 numbered
copies on Japanese vellum, no illustrations) . £750
Letters to Leonard Smithers, First Editions Club, 1937
. . . . £75

SAMUEL BECKETT
(b.1906 d.1989)

An individual and experimental Irish playwright,
novelist and poet who received the Nobel Prize for
Literature in 1969.

*Our Exagmination Round His Factification for
Incamination of 'Work in Progress'*, Shakespeare &
Co (Paris), 1929 (300 copies, wraps) . . . £300
ditto, Shakespeare & Co (Paris), 1929 (96 large paper
copies) £750
ditto, Faber, 1936 . . . . £200/£75
ditto, New Directions (U.S.), 1939 . . . £125/£50
Whoroscope, Hours Press, 1930 (200 numbered copies
of 300, wraps) £1,500
ditto, Hours Press, 1930 (100 signed, numbered copies
of 300, wraps) £4,000
ditto, Grove Press (U.S.), 1957 . . . £45/£15
Proust, Chatto & Windus, 1931 . . . £200/£100
ditto, Grove Press (U.S.), 1957 (250 signed copies) .
. . . . £350
ditto, Grove Press (U.S.), 1957 (wraps) . . £40
More Pricks than Kicks, Chatto & Windus, 1934 . .
. . . . £3,500/£1,500
ditto, Caldar & Boyars, 1966 (wraps) . . . £50
ditto, Grove Press (U.S.), 1970 . . . £30/£10
Echo's Bones, Europa Press (Paris), 1935 (25 signed
copies) £2,000
ditto, Europa Press (Paris), 1935 (250 numbered
copies, wraps) £250
ditto, Europa Press (Paris), 1935 (50 'H.C.' copies) .
. . . . £1,000
Murphy, Routledge, 1938 . . . £3,000/£1,500
ditto, Grove Press (U.S.), [c. 1957] . . . £100/£35
ditto, Grove Press (U.S.), [c. 1957] (100 signed copies,
acetate d/w) . . . . . . £1,000/£750
Molloy, Éditions de Minuit (Paris), 1951 (550
numbered copies, wraps) £100
ditto, Grove Press (U.S.), 1955 . . . £100/£35
ditto, Olympia Press (Paris), 1955 (wraps) . . £100
ditto, Calder, 1959 . . . . £100/£45
Malone Meurt, Éditions de Minuit (Paris), [1951]
(wraps) £200
ditto, as *Malone Dies*, Grove Press (U.S.), 1956 .
. . . . £65/£35
ditto, Grove Press (U.S.), 1956 (500 numbered copies,
acetate d/w) . . . . £100/£65
ditto, Calder, 1958 . . . . £100/£45
En Attendant Godot, Éditions de Minuit (Paris), 1952
(wraps) £1,000
ditto, as *Waiting for Godot*, Grove Press (U.S.), 1954
. . . . £800/£250
ditto, Faber, 1956 . . . . £300/£100
L'Innommable, Éditions de Minuit (Paris), 1953
(wraps) £150
ditto, Éditions de Minuit (Paris), 1953 (50 signed
copies, wraps) £2,000
The Unnamable, Calder, 1959 . . . . £125/£50

ditto, Grove Press (U.S.), 1959 (100 numbered copies, acetate d/w) . . . . £225/£175
ditto, Grove Press (U.S.), 1959 (26 signed, lettered copies, acetate d/w) . . . . . £1,000/£900
ditto, Grove Press (U.S.), 1959 (acetate d/w) . . . . £125/£100
ditto, Grove Press (U.S.), 1959 (wraps) . . . £25
ditto, Olympia Press (Paris), 1959 (wraps) . . £65
Watt, Olympia Press (Paris), 1953 (1,100 numbered copies, wraps) £125
ditto, Olympia Press (Paris), 1953 (25 signed, lettered copies) £1,000
ditto, Grove Press (U.S.), 1953 (100 numbered copies) £200
ditto, Grove Press (U.S.), 1953 (26 signed, lettered copies) £1,000
ditto, Olympia Press (Paris), 1958 . . £95/£25
ditto, Calder, 1963 . . . . £75/£35
Nouvelles et Textes pour Rien, Éditions de Minuit (Paris), 1955 (1,100 numbered copies, wraps). £65
ditto, Éditions de Minuit (Paris), 1958 (2,000 numbered copies, illustrated, wraps) . . . £65
Fin de Partie, Éditions de Minuit (Paris), 1957 (wraps) £100
ditto, Éditions de Minuit (Paris), 1957 (65 deluxe issues). £2,000
Tous Ceux Qui Tombent, Éditions de Minuit (Paris), 1957 (wraps) £65
ditto, as *All That Fall*, Grove Press (U.S.), 1958 . . . . £45/£30
ditto, Grove Press (U.S.), 1958 (100 numbered copies, acetate jacket) . . . . . . £225/£200
ditto, Grove Press (U.S.), 1958 (25 signed, numbered copies) £750
ditto, Faber, 1958 (wraps). £30
Endgame, Faber, 1958 . . . . . . £125/£45
ditto, Grove Press (U.S.), 1958 . . . £125/£45
ditto, Grove Press (U.S.), 1958 (100 signed copies) £300
From an Abandoned Work, Faber, 1958 (wraps) £65
Krapp's Last Tape and Embers, Faber, 1959 (wraps) £40
ditto, Grove Press (U.S.), 1960 . . £20/£10
Three Novels, Grove Press (U.S.), 1958. . £45/£15
ditto, Calder, 1959 . . . . £40/£15
La dernière bande, Éditions de Minuit (Paris), 1959 [1960] (wraps) £20
ditto, Éditions de Minuit (Paris), 1959 [1960] (40 numbered copies, wraps) £250
Molloy, Malone Dies, The Unnamable: A Trilogy, Olympia Press (Paris), 1959 (wraps) . . £65
ditto, as *The Trilogy*, Calder, 1960 . . £40/£15
Poems in English, Calder, 1961 . . . £75/£35
ditto, Calder, 1961 (100 signed copies, slipcase) . . . . £250/£200
ditto, Grove Press (U.S.), 1963 . . . £60/£30
Comment c'est, Éditions de Minuit (Paris), 1961 (wraps) £100

ditto, Éditions de Minuit (Paris), 1961 (197 copies, wraps). £250
ditto, as *How It Is*, Calder, 1964 . . . . £60/£20
ditto, as *How It Is*, Calder, 1964 (100 signed copies, slipcase) £600
Happy Days, Grove Press (U.S.), 1961 (wraps) £40
ditto, Faber, 1962 . . . . £50/£15
ditto, as *Oh Les Beaux Jours*, Éditions de Minuit (Paris), 1963 (412 copies, wraps) . . . £200
ditto, as *Oh Les Beaux Jours*, Éditions de Minuit (Paris), 1963 (wraps) £65
Play and Two Short Pieces for Radio, Faber, 1964 . . . . £45/£15
ditto, Faber, 1964 (signed, limited edition) . . £200
Proust and Three Dialogues with Georges Duthuit, Calder, 1965 . . . . £65/£15
Imagination Morte Immaginez, Éditions de Minuit (Paris), 1965 (612 signed copies) . . . £125
ditto, as *Imagination Dead Imagine*, Calder, 1965 (wraps) £35
ditto, as *Imagination Dead Imagine*, Calder, 1965 (100 signed, numbered copies) . . £500/£450
Comedie et actes diversz, Éditions de Minuit (Paris), 1966 (112 copies, wraps) £500
ditto, Éditions de Minuit (Paris), 1966 (wraps) . £45
Come and Go, Calder, 1967 . . . . . £65/£20
ditto, Calder, 1967 (100 signed copies, slipcase) . . . . £600/£550
Eh Joe and Other Writings, Faber, 1967 . £35/£10
Stories & Texts for Nothing, Grove Press (U.S.), 1967 . . . . £35/£10
Têtes Mortes, Éditions de Minuit (Paris), 1967 (wraps) £45
No's Knife, Calder, 1967 . . . . . £40/£10
ditto, Calder, 1967 (100 signed copies, slipcase) £250
Poèms, Éditions de Minuit (Paris), 1968 (550 copies, wraps) £125
ditto, Éditions de Minuit (Paris), 1978 . . £45
Sans, Éditions de Minuit (Paris), 1969 (742 copies, wraps) £125
ditto as *Lessness*, Calder, 1970 . . £65/£20
ditto, Calder, 1970 (100 signed copies, slipcase) . . . . £600/£550
Film, Grove Press (U.S.), 1969 (wraps) . . . £20
ditto, Grove Press (U.S.), 1969 (200 numbered copies) £125
ditto, Faber, 1972 (wraps) £35
Le Depeupleur, Éditions de Minuit (Paris), 1970 (92 of 399 copies) £150
ditto, Éditions de Minuit (Paris), 1970 (201 of 399 copies) £75
ditto, *as The Lost Ones*, Calder, 1972 . . £40/£15
ditto, Calder, 1972 (100 signed copies, slipcase) . . . . £300/£250
ditto, Grove Press (U.S.), 1972 . . . £40/£15
Premier Amour, Éditions de Minuit (Paris), 1970 (92 of 399 copies) £150
ditto, Éditions de Minuit (Paris), 1970 (201 of 399 copies) £75

ditto, as *First Love*, Calder, 1973 . . . £40/£15
ditto, Grove Press (U.S.), 1974 . . . . £40/£15
Mercier et Camier, Éditions de Minuit (Paris), 1970
(399 copies) £145
ditto, Éditions de Minuit (Paris), 1970 (wraps) . £45
ditto, as *Mercier and Camier*, Calder, 1974. £45/£10
ditto, as *Mercier and Camier*, Grove Press (U.S.), 1974
. . . . £45/£10
Six Residua, Calder, 1972 (wraps) . . . £15
Breath and Other Short Plays, Faber, 1972 £60/£25
ditto, Faber, 1972 (wraps). £10
ditto, Faber, 1972 (signed, limited edition) . . £125
Not I, Faber, 1973 . . . . £10
The North, Enitharmon Press, 1973 (137 signed,
numbered copies, wraps) £500
ditto Enitharmon Press, 1973 (15 signed copies with
three extra etchings, heavyweight paper, wraps) . .
. . . . £2,000
Still, M'Arte Edizioni (Milan), 1974 (30 signed copies
with extra portfolio of plates, slipcase). . £2,000
ditto, M'Arte Edizioni (Milan), 1974 (signed copies,
slipcase) £1,000
All Strange Away, Gotham Book Mart (U.S.), 1976 .
. . . . £50/£15
ditto, Gotham Book Mart (U.S.), 1976 (200 signed,
numbered copies, slipcase) . . . . £1,000/£900
ditto, Calder, 1979. . . . . . . £20/£5
Footfalls, Faber, 1976. . . . . . . £10
Pour finir encore et autres foirades, Éditions de
Minuit (Paris), 1976 (wraps) £15
That Time, Faber, 1976 (wraps) £10
For to End Yet Again and Other Fizzles, Calder, 1976
. . . . £30/£10
ditto as *Fizzles*, Grove Press (U.S.), 1977 . £30/£10
Ends and Odds, Faber, 1977 . . . . . £25/£10
ditto, Grove Press (U.S.), 1977 . . . . £20/£5
Collected Poems in French and English, Calder, 1977
. . . . £25/£10
Four Novellas, Calder, 1978 . . . . . £25/£10
Three Occasional Pieces, Faber, 1982 (wraps) £10
Worstward Ho, Calder, 1983 . . . . . £25/£10
ditto, Grove Press (U.S.), 1983 . . . . £25/£10
ditto, as *Cap au pire*, Éditions de Minuit (Paris), 1991
(wraps) £15
Company, Éditions de Minuit (Paris), 1979 (wraps) .
. . . . £15
ditto, Calder, 1980. . . . . £25/£10
ditto, Calder, 1980 (100 signed copies, slipcase) . .
. . . . £450/£400
ditto, Grove Press (U.S.), 1980 . . . . £25/£10
Mirlitonnades, Éditions de Minuit (Paris), 1979
(wraps) £10
Rockaby and Other Short Pieces, Grove Press (U.S.),
1981 . . . . £25/£10
Ill Seen Ill Said, Grove Press (U.S.), 1981 . £25/£10
ditto, Calder, 1982. . . . . £25/£10
ditto, Lord John Press (U.S.), 1982 (299 signed copies
of 325) £300

ditto, Lord John Press (U.S.), 1982 (26 signed, lettered
copies of 325) £750
ditto, as *Mal vu mal dit*, Éditions de Minuit (Paris),
1987 (wraps) £40
ditto, Éditions de Minuit (Paris), 1987 (99 numbered
copies, wraps) £150
Disjecta, Calder, 1983. . . . . . . £30/£10
ditto, Grove Press (U.S.), 1983 . . . . £15/£5
Quoi Ou, Éditions de Minuit (Paris), 1983 (99 copies,
wraps) £75
Catastrophe, Lord John Press (U.S.), 1983 (100
numbered signed copies, broadside) . . . £300
ditto, Lord John Press (U.S.), 1983 (26 lettered signed
copies, broadside) £1,000
Collected Shorter Plays, Faber, 1984 . . £20/£5
ditto, Grove Press, 1984 . . . . . . £20/£5
Collected Poems, 1930-1978, Calder, 1984 £20/£5
Collected Shorter Prose, 1945-1980, Calder, 1984 .
. . . . £20/£5
The Collected Works, Grove Press (U.S.), (16 vols 200
signed, numbered sets) . . . .£,1000
As the Story Was Told, Rampant Lions Press, 1987
(325 numbered copies) £100
ditto, Calder, 1990. . . . . £25/£10
Stirrings Still, Calder/Blue Moon Books, [1988] (200
of 226 signed, numbered copies, slipcase) . £1,500
ditto, Calder/Blue Moon Books, [1988] (26 lettered,
signed copies of 226, slipcase) . . . £2,000
ditto, Calder/Blue Moon Books, [1988] (15 roman-
numeraled 'hors de commerce' copies, slipcase) . .
. . . . £2,000
Le Monde et le Pantalon, Éditions de Minuit (Paris),
1989 (99 copies, wraps) £45
Nohow On, Calder, 1989 . . . . . £25/£10
ditto, Limited Editions Club (U.S.), [1989] (550 signed
copies in box) £2,000
Comment dire, Éditions de Minuit (Paris), 1989 (single
sheet folded) £15
Dream of Fair to Middling Women, Black Cat Press
(Dublin), 1992 . . . . £25/£10
Eleutheria, Éditions de Minuit (Paris), 1995 (wraps) .
. . . . £10
ditto, Foxrock (U.S.), 1995 . . . . £15/£5

MAX BEERBOHM

(b.1872 d.1956)

Humorist, caricaturist, essayist and novelist, and
survivor of the 1890s decadent scene.

Fiction
The Happy Hypocrite, Wayside Press (U.S.), 1896
(wraps) £125
ditto, John Lane, 1897. . . . . . . £50
Zuleika Dobson, Heinemann, 1911 . . . . £100
ditto, John Lane (U.S.), 1912. . . . . £50
A Christmas Garland, Heinemann, 1912 . . £50

ditto, Dutton & Co. (U.S.), 1912 . . . . . £25
Seven Men, Heinemann, 1919 . . . . . £25
ditto, Knopf (U.S.) 1920 (2,000 numbered copies) . .
. . . . £50/£25
ditto, as **Seven Men and Two Others**, Heinemann, 1946 . . . . £15/£5
The Dreadful Dragon of Hay Hill, Heinemann, 1928
. . . . £35/£10

Non Fiction
The Works of Max Beerbohm, Scribners (U.S.), 1896
(1,000 copies, of which 401 were pulped) . . £200
ditto, John Lane, 1896. . . . . £100
More, John Lane, 1899 . . . . £50
Yet Again, Chapman and Hall, 1909. . . . £50
ditto, Knopf (U.S.) 1923 . . . . . . £55/£20
And Even Now, Heinemann, 1920 . . . £50/£10
ditto, Dutton (U.S.) 1921 . . . . . £45/£10
Around Theatres, Heinemann, 1924 (2 vols) . .
. . . . £200/£50
ditto, Knopf (U.S.) 1930 (2 vols). . . . £150/£45
A Variety of Things, Heinemann, 1928 . . £40/£10
ditto, Knopf (U.S.) 1928 (2,000 numbered copies) . .
. . . . £40/£10
Lytton Strachey, C.U.P., 1943 (wraps). . . £10
ditto, Knopf (U.S.) 1943 . . . . . £25/£10
Mainly on the Air, Heinemann, 1946 . . £20/£5
ditto, Knopf (U.S.) 1947 . . . . . £15/£5
Sherlockiana: A Reminiscence of Sherlock Holmes, Hill (U.S.), 1948 (36 copies) £250
Letters Of Max Beerbohm, 1892-1956, John Murray, 1988 . . . . £10/£5
ditto, Norton (U.S.), 1989. . . . . £10/£5
More Theatres, Hart-Davis, 1969 . . . £10/£5
ditto, Taplinger (U.S.) 1969 . . . . £10/£5
Last Theatres, Hart-Davis, 1970. . . . £10/£5
ditto, Knopf (U.S.) 1970 . . . . . £10/£5

Drawings and Caricatures
Caricatures of Twenty-Five Gentleman, Leonard Smithers, 1896 (500 copies) £500
Poets' Corner, Heinemann, 1904 . . . £250
A Book of Caricatures, Methuen, 1907 . . £150
Cartoons: The Second Childhood of John Bull, Stephen Swift, [1911] £175
Fifty Caricatures, Heinemann, 1913. . . £75
ditto, Dutton (U.S.), 1913. . . . . . £50
A Survey, Heinemann, 1921 . . . . £125/£50
ditto, Heinemann, 1921 (275 signed, numbered copies)
. . . . £250/£175
ditto, Doubleday, 1921 . . . . . £100/£50
Rossetti and His Circle, Heinemann, 1922 . £125/£50
ditto, Heinemann, 1922 (380 signed, numbered copies)
. . . . £250/£175
Things New and Old, Heinemann, 1923 . £100/£45
ditto, Heinemann, 1923 (350 signed, numbered copies, with additional signed coloured plate) . £250/£175
Observations, Heinemann, 1925 . . . £75/£45

The Heroes and Heroines of Bitter Sweet, [Leadley, 1931] (900 numbered copies, portfolio) . . £200

Edited by Beerbohm
Herbert Beerbohm Tree, Hutchinson, 1920. £125/£40
ditto, Dutton (U.S.), [1920] . . . . . £120/£40

BRENDAN BEHAN
(b.1923 d.1964)

An Irish playwright, Behan spent many years in prison as a result of his IRA activities. Although released in 1947, it was in prison that he started to write, and his first success came with the publication of *The Quare Fellow* in 1956.

Plays
The Quare Fellow, Methuen, 1956 . . . £175/£45
ditto, Grove Press (U.S.), 1956 . . . . £40/£20
The Hostage, Methuen, 1958. . . . . £50/£15
ditto, Grove Press (U.S.), 1958 . . . . £40/£20
Borstal Boy, Random House (U.S.), 1971 . £15/£5
Richard's Cork Leg, Methuen, 1973 . . £20/£5
ditto, Grove Press (U.S.), 1974 . . . . £20/£5
An Giall and The Hostage, C. Smythe, 1988 . £5

Novels
Borstal Boy, Knopf (U.S.), 1957. . . . £75/£20
ditto, Hutchinson, 1958 . . . . . . £75/£20
Hold Your Hour and Have Another, Hutchinson, 1963
. . . . £40/£10
ditto, Little, Brown (U.S.), 1964 . . . . £25/£10
The Scarperer, Hutchinson, 1964 . . . £20/£5
ditto, Doubleday (U.S.), 1964 . . . . £20/£5
Confessions of an Irish Rebel, Hutchinson, 1965 . .
. . . . £20/£5
ditto, Geis (U.S.), 1966 . . . . . . £15/£5

Verse
Poems and A Play in Irish, Gallery Press (Dublin), 1981 . . . . £25/£10

Non Fiction
Brendan Behan's Island, Hutchinson, 1962 £20/£5
ditto, Geis (U.S.), 1962 . . . . . . £15/£5
Brendan Behan's New York, Hutchinson, 1964 £15/£5
ditto, Geis (U.S.), 1964 . . . . . . £15/£5

Miscellaneous
After the Wake: Uncollected Prose, O'Brien Press (Ireland), 1983 . . . . £10

HILLAIRE BELLOC
(b.1870 d.1953)

Belloc was a poet, novelist, essayist, and travel writer, but is best known and most often collected for his humorous verse for children.

Verse

Verses and Sonnets, Ward & Downey, 1896 . £300	
The Bad Child's Book of Beasts, Alden Press, 1896 (pseud 'H.B.') £200	
More Beasts (For Worse Children), Arnold, 1897 . . . . £100	
The Modern Traveller, Arnold, 1898 . . . £75	
A Moral Alphabet, Arnold, 1899 . . . . £75	
Cautionary Tales for Children, Eveleigh Nash, 1907 . . . . £75	
Verses, Duckworth, 1910 . . . . . . £50	
More Peers, Stephen Swift, 1911 . . . . £45	
Sonnets and Verse, Duckworth, 1923 . . £45/£10	
ditto, Duckworth, 1923 (525 signed copies). . £75	
The Chanty of the Nona, Faber, Arial Poem, 1928 £15	
ditto, Faber, Arial Poem, 1928 (500 signed, large paper copies) £50	
New Cautionary Tales, Duckworth, 1930 . £100/£30	
ditto, Duckworth, 1930 (110 signed copies). . £150	
In Praise of Wine: A Heroic Poem, Peter Davies, 1931 . . . . £25/£10	
Ladies and Gentlemen, Duckworth, 1932 . £25/£10	
The Verse of Hilaire Belloc, The Nonesuch Press, 1954 (1,250 numbered copies) £35	

Novels

Emmanuel Burden, Methuen, 1904 . . . . £45	
Mr Clutterbuck's Election, Eveleigh Nash, 1908 £25	
A Change in the Cabinet, Methuen, 1909 . . £25	
Pongo and the Bull, Constable, 1910 . . . £50	
Mr Girondin, Nelson, 1911 . . . . . £20	
The Green Overcoat, Arrowsmith, 1912 . . £35	
The Mercy of Allah, Chatto & Windus, 1922 £75/£20	
Mr Petre, Arrowsmith, 1925 . . . . . £45/£15	
ditto, McBride (U.S.), 1925 . . . . . £45/£15	
The Emerald, Arrowsmith, 1926. . . . . £45/£15	
ditto, Harpers (U.S.), 1926 . . . . . £45/£15	
The Haunted House, Arrowsmith, 1927 . £200/£95	
ditto, Harper (U.S.), 1928. . . . . . £90/£25	
But Soft, We Are Observed, Arrowsmith, 1928. . . . . £35/£10	
Belinda, Constable, 1928 . . . . . . £45/£15	
The Missing Masterpiece, Arrowsmith, 1929 £75/£20	
The Man Who Made Gold, Arrowsmith, 1930 £45/£15	
ditto, Harper (U.S.), 1931. . . . . . £25/£10	
The Post-Master General, Arrowsmith, 1932 £100/£25	
ditto, Lippincott (U.S.), 1932. . . . . £25/£10	
The Hedge and the Horse, Cassell, 1936 . £25/£10	

History

Danton, John Nisbet & Co., 1899 . . . . £50	
ditto, Putnams (U.S.), 1928 . . . . . £20/£10	

Robespierre, John Nisbet & Co., 1901 . . . £40	
The Eye Witness, Eveleigh Nash, 1908 . . . £40	
Marie Antoinette, Methuen, 1909 . . . . £40	
The French Revolution, Williams and Norgate, 1911 . . . . £30	
The Battle of Blenheim, Stephen Swift, 1911 . £20	
Malplaquet, Stephen Swift, 1911 . . . . £20	
Crecy, Stephen Swift, 1911 . . . . . . £20	
Poitiers, Stephen Swift, 1911. . . . . . £20	
Waterloo, Stephen Swift, 1912 . . . . . £20	
Turcoing, Stephen Swift, 1912 . . . . . £20	
Warfare in England, Williams & Norgate, 1912 £20	
The Book of the Bayeaux Tapestry, Chatto & Windus, 1914 . . . . £30	
History of England, (Vol. 11), Catholic Publications Society of America, 1915 . . . . . . £15	
Land and Water Map of the War, Land and Water, 1915 . . . . £25	
A General Sketch of the European War: The First Phase, Nelson, 1915 . . . . £40	
The Two Maps of Europe, Arthur Pearson, 1915 £30	
The Last Days of the French Monarchy, Chapman and Hall, 1916 . . . . £10	
A General Sketch of the European War: The Second Phase, Nelson, 1916. . . . . £40	
The Second Year of the War, Land & Water, 1916 . . . . £30	
The Principles of War, by Foch, Chapman & Hall, 1919 (translation) £25	
Precepts and Judgements, by Foch, Chapman & Hall, 1919 (translation) £25	
The Jews, Constable, 1922 . . . . . . £20/£5	
The Campaign of 1812, Nelson, 1924 . . £30/£10	
History of England Vol. 1, Methuen, 1925 . £25/£10	
Miniatures of French History, Nelson, 1925 £25/£10	
Mrs Markham's New History of England, Cayme Press, 1926 . . . . £25/£10	
History of England Vol. 2, Methuen, 1927 . £25/£10	
Oliver Cromwell, Benn, 1927 . . . . . £20/£5	
History of England Vol. 3, Methuen, 1928 . £25/£10	
James II, Faber & Gwyer, 1928 . . . . £25/£10	
ditto, as *James the Second*, Lippincott (U.S.), 1928 . . . . £25/£10	
How the Reformation Happened, Cape, 1928 £15/£5	
ditto, McBride & Co (U.S.), 1928 . . . £15/£5	
Joan of Arc, Cassell, 1929 . . . . . £25/£10	
Richelieu, Benn, 1930 . . . . £15/£5	
Wolsey, Cassell, 1930 . . . . £15/£5	
ditto, Lippincott (U.S.), 1930. . . . . £15/£5	
History of England Vol. 4, Methuen, 1931 . £25/£5	
Cranmer, Cassell, 1931 . . . . . . £15/£5	
ditto, Lippincott (U.S.), 1931. . . . . £15/£5	
The Tactics and Strategy of the Great Duke of Marlborough, Arrowsmith, 1931 . . . £40/£10	
Six British Battles, Arrowsmith, 1931 . . £20/£5	
Napoleon, Cassell, 1932 . . . . . . £15/£5	
ditto, Lippincott (U.S.), 1932. . . . . £15/£5	
William the Conqueror, Peter Davies, 1933 £15/£10	
Beckett, Catholic Truth Society, 1933 . . £15/£5	

Charles I, Cassell, 1933 . . . . . . £15/£5
ditto, Lippincott (U.S.), 1933 . . . . . £15/£5
Cromwell, Cassell, 1934 . . . . . . £15/£5
A Shorter History of England, Harrap, 1934 £25/£10
Milton, Cassell, 1935 . . . . £25/£5
The Battleground, Cassell, 1936 . . . . £15/£5
ditto, Lippincott (U.S.), 1936 . . . . . £15/£5
Characters of the Reformation, Sheed & Ward (U.S.),
1936 . . . . £15/£5
The Crusade, Cassell, 1937 . . . . . £25/£5
The Crisis of Our Civilization, Cassell, 1937 (wraps) .
. . . . £10
ditto, Fordham Univ. Press (U.S.), 1937 . . £10
The Great Heresies, Sheed & Ward (U.S.), 1938 . .
. . . . £15/£5
Monarchy: A Study of Louis XIV, Cassell, 1938 . .
. . . . £15/£5
ditto, as *Louis XIV*, Harper (U.S.), 1938 . £15/£15
The Last Rally, Cassell, 1940 . . . . £15/£5
Elizabethan Commentary, Cassell, 1942 . £15/£5

Travel
Paris, Arnold, 1900 . . . . £25
The Path to Rome, Allen, 1902 . . . . £25
The Old Road, Constable, 1904 . . . . £75
Esto Perpetua, Duckworth, 1906 . . . . £45
Sussex, A.C. Black, 1906 . . . . . . £25
The Historic Thames, Dent, 1907 . . . £50
The Pyrenees, Methuen, 1909 . . . . £25
The River of London, Foulis, 1912 . . . £25
The Four Men, Foulis, 1912 . . . . . £20
The Stane Street, Constable, 1913 . . . £20/£5
The Road, Charles Hobson, 1923 . . . £25/£10
The Contrast, Arrowsmith, 1923 . . . . £15/£5
ditto, McBride (U.S.), 1924 . . . . . £10/£5
The Cruise of the Nona, Constable, 1925 . £40/£15
ditto, Houghton Mifflin, 1925 . . . . £25/£10
The Highway and its Vehicles, The Studio, 1926 .
. . . . £45/£15
Many Cities, Constable, 1928 . . . . £20/£5
Return to the Baltic, Constable, 1938 . . £20/£5
On Sailing the Sea, Methuen, 1939 . . . £10/£5
Places, Sheed and Ward (U.S.), 1941 . . £10/£5
ditto, Cassell, 1942 . . . . £10/£5

Politics
Socialism and the Servile State, I.L.P., 1910 . £10
The Party System and Cecil Chesterton, Stephen
Swift, 1911 . . . . £15
The Servile State, Foulis, 1912 . . . . £20
ditto, Henry Holt (U.S.), 1946 . . . . £10/£5
The Free Press, Allen & Unwin, 1918 . £25/£10
The House of Commons and the Monarchy, Allen &
Unwin, 1920 . . . . £25/£5
Economics for Helen, Arrowsmith, 1924 . £20/£10
The Political Effort, True Temperance Association,
1924 . . . . £15

Literature
Caliban's Guide to Letters, Duckworth, 1903 . £35
The Romance of Tristan and Iseult, Allen, 1903
(translation) £20
*Avril, Being Essays on the Poetry of the French
Renaissance*, Duckworth, 1904 . . . . . £20
On the Place of Gilbert Chesterton in English Letters,
Sheed & Ward, 1940 . . . . £15/£5

Religion
An Open Letter on the Decay of Faith, Burns & Oates,
1906 . . . . £20
The Catholic Church and Historical Truth, W.
Watson, 1908 . . . . £10
An Examination of Socialism, Catholic Truth Society,
1908 . . . . £10
The Church and Socialism, Catholic Truth Society,
1908 . . . . £10
The Ferrer Case, Catholic Truth Society, 1909 £10
Anti-Catholic History, Catholic Truth Society, 1914 .
. . . . £10
Religion and Liberty, Catholic Truth Society, 1918 .
. . . . £10
*The Catholic Church and the Purchase of Private
Property*, Catholic Truth Society, 1920 . £10
A Companion to Mr Wells' Outline of History, Sheed
& Ward, 1926 . . . . £25/£10
Mr Belloc Still Objects, Sheed and Ward, 1927 £15/£5
The Catholic Church and History, Burns, Oates &
Washbourne, 1927 . . . . £10/£5
Survivals and New Arrivals, Sheed & Ward, 1929 .
. . . . £10/£5
ditto, Macmillan (U.S.), 1929 . . . . £10/£5
The Case of Dr Coulton, Sheed & Ward, 1931 £10/£5
The Catholic and the War, Burns & Oates, 1940 . .
. . . . £10/£5

Essays
At the Sign of the Lion, Mosher (U.S.), 1896 (950
copies) £20
ditto, Mosher (U.S.), 1916 . . . . . £15
Hills and Seas, Methuen, 1906 . . . . £25
On Nothing, Methuen, 1908 . . . . . £15
On Everything, Methuen, 1909 . . . . £15
On Anything, Methuen, 1910 . . . . . £15
On Something, Methuen, 1910 . . . . £15
First and Last, Methuen, 1911 . . . . £10
This and That, Methuen, 1912 . . . . £10
On, Methuen, 1923 . . . . £15/£5
Hilaire Belloc: Essays, Harrap, 1926 . . £15/£5
Short Talks with the Dead, Cayme Press, 1926 £20/£5
A Conversation with an Angel, Jonathan Cape, 1928 .
. . . . £20/£5
Conversations with a Cat, Cassell, 1930 . £25/£10
ditto, Harper & Brothers (U.S.), 1931 . . £20/£5
Essays of a Catholic, Sheed & Ward, 1931 . £15/£5
Nine Nines, Blackwell, 1931 . . . . . £15/£5
An Essay on the Restoration of Property, Distributist
League, 1936 . . . . £10

An Essay on the Nature of Contemporary England,
Constable, 1937 . . . . £15/£5
The Silence of the Sea, Sheed & Ward (U.S.), 1940 .
. . . . £15/£5
ditto, Cassell, 1941 . . . . . . £15/£5

Others
Lambkin's Remains, by 'H.B.', J.C.R. 1900 . £75
The Great Inquiry, Duckworth, 1903 . . . £30
A Pamphlet, 1930, privately printed (for Belloc's 60th
birthday) £65
On Translation, Clarendon Press, 1931 . . £30/£15
The Issue, Sheed & Ward, 1937 . . . . £15/£5
The Question and the Answer, Longman's Green,
1938 . . . . £15/£5
The Test in Poland, Weekly Review, 1939 . . £10

SAUL BELLOW
(b.1915)

American novelist, and recipient of the Nobel Prize
for Literature in 1976, Bellow's writings frequently
address the problems of those living in urban areas,
and their place in the modern world.

Novels
Dangling Man, Vanguard Press (U.S.), 1944 . . .
. . . . £1,000/£200
ditto, Lehmann, 1946 . . . . . . £225/£35
The Victim, Vanguard Press (U.S.), 1945 . £750/£65
ditto, Lehmann, 1948 . . . . . . £125/£25
The Adventures of Augie March, Viking (U.S.), 1953
. . . . £350/£40
ditto, Weidenfeld, 1954 . . . . . £65/£15
*Seize the Day, with Three Short Stories and a One Act
Play,* Viking (U.S.), 1956 . . . . £100/£15
ditto, Weidenfeld, 1957 . . . . . £100/£15
Henderson the Rain King, Viking (U.S.), 1959 .
. . . . £60/£10
ditto, Weidenfeld, 1959 . . . . . £60/£10
Herzog, Viking (U.S.), 1964 . . . . . £90/£15
ditto, Weidenfeld, 1965 . . . . . . £40/£5
Mr Sammler's Planet, Viking (U.S.), 1970 . £40/£5
ditto, Weidenfeld, 1970 . . . . . £30/£5
Humboldt's Gift, Viking (U.S.), 1975 . . £40/£5
ditto, Alison Press/Secker & Warburg, 1975 £40/£5
The Dean's December, Harper (U.S.), 1982 £20/£5
ditto, Harper, 1982 (500 signed copies, glassine
wrapper, slipcase) . . . . . £125/£75
ditto, Secker & Warburg, 1982 . . . . £20/£5
More Die of Heartbreak, Morrow (U.S.), 1987 £10/£5
ditto, Alison Press, 1987 . . . . . £20/£5

Short Stories
Mosby's Memoirs and Other Stories, Viking (U.S.),
1968 . . . . £50/£15
ditto, Weidenfeld, 1969 . . . . . £20/£5

Him with His Foot in His Mouth and Other Stories,
Harper (U.S.), 1984 . . . . . . £20/£5
ditto, Secker & Warburg, 1984 . . . . £20/£5
A Theft, Penguin, 1989 (wraps) £10
The Bellarosa Connection, Penguin (U.S.), 1989
(wraps) £10
ditto, Penguin , 1989 (wraps) £10
Something to Remember Me By, Secker & Warburg,
1992 . . . . £20/£5
The Actual, Viking, 1997 . . . . . £10/£5

Plays
The Last Analysis, Viking (U.S.), 1965 . . £125/£25
ditto, Weidenfeld, 1966 . . . . . . £45/£15

Others
To Jerusalem and Back, Viking (U.S.), 1976 £25/£5
ditto, Secker & Warburg, 1976 . . . . £15/£5
The Nobel Lecture, U.S. Information Service
(Stockholm), 1977 . . . . £35
ditto, Targ editions (U.S.), 1979 (350 signed copies,
tissue wraps) . . . . £100/£65
It All Adds Up, Penguin (U.S.), 1994 . . £15/£5
ditto, Secker & Warburg, 1994 . . . £15/£5

LUDWIG BEMELMANS
(b.1898 d.1962)

An artist and writer who contributed to various
genres, Bemelmans is best known for his schoolgirl
character, Madeline.

Madeline Books
Madeline, Simon & Schuster (U.S.), 1939 . £450/£75
ditto, Derek Verschoyle, 1952 . . . £125/£25
Madeline's Rescue, Viking (U.S.), 1953 . £150/£45
ditto, Derek Verschoyle, 1953 . . . £75/£25
Madeline and the Bad Hat, Viking (U.S.), 1956 (985
signed copies) . . . . . . £350/£75
ditto, Viking (U.S.), 1956 . . . . . £75/£25
ditto, Andre Deutsch, 1958 . . . . £35/£10
Madeline and the Gypsies, Viking (U.S.), 1959 .
. . . . £75/£25
ditto, Andre Deutsch, 1961 . . . . £35/£10
Madeline in London, Viking (U.S.), 1961 . £75/£25
ditto, Andre Deutsch, 1962 . . . . £35/£10
Madeline's Christmas, Viking/Kestrel (U.S.), 1985
(completed by Madeline and Barbara Bemelmans) .
. . . . £10
ditto, Andre Deutsch, 1985 . . . . . £10

Other Children's Books
Hansi, Viking (U.S.), 1934 . . . . . £150/£25
ditto, Lovat Dickson, 1935 . . . . £75/£20
The Golden Basket, Viking (U.S.), 1936 . £50/£15
The Castle Number 9, Viking (U.S.), 1937 . £50/£15
Quito Express, Viking (U.S.), 1938 . . . £50/£15

Rosebud, Viking (U.S.), 1942 . . . . £40/£10
A Tale of Two Glimps, Columbia Broadcasting
Systems (U.S.), 1947 (wraps) £20
The Happy Place, Little, Brown (U.S.), 1952 £25/£10
The High World, Harper (U.S.), 1954 . . £25/£10
ditto, Hamish Hamilton, 1958 . . . . £20/£5
Parsley, Harper (U.S.), 1955 . . . . . £25/£10

Poetry
Fifi, Simon & Schuster (U.S.), 1940. . . . £25
Sunshine, Simon & Schuster (U.S.), 1950 . . £15
Welcome Home, Harper (U.S.), 1960 . . £25/£10
ditto, Hamish Hamilton, 1961 . . . . £20/£10
Marina, Harper (U.S.), 1962 . . . . . £25/£10

Novels for Adults
Now I Lay Me Down to Sleep, Viking (U.S.), 1943 .
. . . . £25/£10
ditto, Viking, 1943 (500 signed copies, illustrated). .
. . . . £100
ditto, Hamish Hamilton, 1944 . . . . £20/£10
The Blue Danube, Viking (U.S.), 1945 . . £20/£5
ditto, Hamish Hamilton, 1946 . . . . £15/£5
Dirty Eddie, Viking (U.S.), 1947. . . . £20/£5
ditto, Hamish Hamilton, 1948 . . . . £15/£5
The Eye of God, Viking (U.S.), 1949 . . £20/£5
ditto, as *The Snow Mountain*, Hamish Hamilton, 1950
. . . . £15/£5
The Woman of My Life, Viking (U.S.), 1957 £15/£5
ditto, Hamish Hamilton, 1957 . . . . £15/£5
Are You Hungry, Are You Cold, World (U.S.), 1960 .
. . . . £15/£5
ditto, Andre Deutsch, 1961 . . . . . £15/£5
The Street Where the Heart Lies, World (U.S.), 1963 .
. . . . £15/£5

Short Stories
Small Beer, Viking (U.S.), 1939 . . . . £25/£10
ditto, Viking (U.S.), 1939 (175 signed copies) . £100
ditto, John Lane, 1940. . . . . . £15/£5
I Love You, I Love You, I Love You, Viking (U.S.),
1942 . . . . £15/£5
ditto, Hamish Hamilton, 1943 . . . . £15/£5

Travel
The Donkey Inside, Viking (U.S.), 1941 . £25/£10
ditto, Viking (U.S.), 1941 (175 deluxe copies with
original watercolour) £150
ditto, Hamish Hamilton, 1947 . . . . £15/£5
The Best of Times, Simon & Schuster (U.S.), 1948 .
. . . . £25/£10
ditto, Cresset Press, 1949 . . . . . £25/£10
How To Travel Incognito, Little, Brown (U.S.), 1952 .
. . . . £25/£10
ditto, Hamish Hamilton, 1952 . . . . £15/£5
Father Dear Father, Viking (U.S.), 1953 . £15/£5
ditto, Viking (U.S.), 1953 (151 signed, deluxe copies
with original watercolour) £150
ditto, Hamish Hamilton, 1953 . . . . £10/£5

Holiday in France, Houghton Mifflin (U.S.), 1957 .
. . . . £15/£5
ditto, Andre Deutsch, 1958 . . . . . £15/£5
How To Have Europe All To Yourself, European
Travel Commission (U.S.), 1960 (wraps) . . £10
Italian Holiday, Houghton Mifflin (U.S.), 1961 . .
. . . . £25/£10
On Board Noah's Ark, Viking (U.S.), 1962 £25/£10
ditto, Collins, 1962 . . . . £15/£5

Others
My War with the United States, Viking (U.S.), 1937 .
. . . . £25/£10
ditto, Gollancz, 1938 . . . . £20/£5
Life Class, Viking (U.S.), 1938 . . . . £25/£10
ditto, John Lane, 1939. . . . . . . £15/£5
At Your Service, Peterson (U.S.), 1941 (wraps) £10
Hotel Splendide, Viking (U.S.), 1941 . . £15/£5
ditto, Viking (U.S.), 1941 (305 signed, deluxe copies).
. . . . £75
ditto, Hamish Hamilton, 1942 . . . . £10/£5
Hotel Bemelmans, Viking (U.S.), 1946 . . £15/£5
ditto, Hamish Hamilton, 1956 . . . . £10/£5
To The One I Love the Best, Viking (U.S.), 1955 . .
. . . . £15/£5
ditto, Hamish Hamilton, 1955 . . . . £10/£5
The World of Bemelmans, Viking (U.S.), 1955 £15/£5
My Life in Art, Harper (U.S.), 1958 . . . £15/£5
ditto, Andre Deutsch, 1958 . . . . . £10/£5
La Bonne Table, Simon & Schuster (U.S.), 1964 . .
. . . . £15/£5
ditto, Hamish Hamilton, 1964 . . . . £15/£5

ALAN BENNETT
(b.1934)

An actor and playwright, Alan Bennett's quiet, self-
effacing style has been as popular with television
audiences as it has with the readers of his books.

Plays
Beyond the Fringe, Souvenir Press, 1963 . £40/£10
ditto, French (U.S.), 1964 (wraps) . . . £10
Forty Years On, Faber, 1969 . . . . . £75/£20
ditto, Faber, 1969 (wraps). £5
Getting On, Faber, 1972 . . . . . . £20/£5
ditto, Faber, 1972 (wraps). £5
Habeas Corpus, Faber, 1973 . . . . . £20/£5
ditto, Faber, 1973 (wraps). £5
The Old Country, Faber, 1978 (wraps) . . £10
Enjoy, Faber, 1980 (wraps) £10
Office Suite: Two One-Act Plays, Faber, 1981 (wraps)
. . . . £15
Objects of Affection, BBC, 1983 (wraps) . . £10
The Writer in Disguise, Faber, 1985. . . £5/£10
Two Kafka Plays, Faber, 1987 (wraps) . . . £5
Talking Heads, BBC, 1987 (wraps) £5

ditto, as *Single Spies and Talking Heads*, Summit (U.S.), 1989 . . . . £15/£5

Screenplays

A Private Function, Faber, 1985 (wraps) . . £10
Prick Up Your Ears, Faber, 1987 (wraps) . . £10
The Madness of King George, Faber, 1992 (wraps) £5
ditto, Random House (U.S.), 1995 . . . . . £5

Others

Writing Home, Faber, 1994 . . . . . . £10/£5
ditto, Random House (U.S.), 1995 . . . £10/£5

ARNOLD BENNETT
(b.1867 d.1931)

Born in the Staffordshire Potteries, this novelist, short story writer, playwright and journalist's reputation today rests principally on his novels about the lives of ordinary people.

A Man from the North, John Lane, 1898 . . £250
Polite Farces for the Drawing Room, Lamley, 1900 .
. . . . £100
Anna of the Five Towns, Chatto & Windus, 1902 £150
The Grand Babylon Hotel, Chatto & Windus, 1902 .
. . . . £30
The Gates of Wrath, Chatto & Windus, 1903 . £45
Leonora, Chatto & Windus, 1903 . . . . £40
A Great Man, Chatto & Windus, 1904 . . . £30
Teresa of Watling Street, Chatto & Windus, 1904 £25
Sacred and Profane Love, Chatto & Windus, 1905 £30
Hugo, Chatto & Windus, 1906 . . . . . £30
The Sinews of War (with Eden Philpotts), T. Werner Laurie, 1906 . . . . £35
Whom God Hath Joined, David Nutt, 1906 . £15
The City of Pleasure, Chatto & Windus, 1907 . £15
The Ghost: A Fantasia on Modern Times, Chatto & Windus, 1907. . . . . £30
The Grim Smile of the Five Towns, Chatto & Windus, 1908 . . . . £30
Buried Alive, Chapman & Hall, 1908 . . . £25
The Old Wives' Tale, Chapman & Hall, 1908 . £60
ditto, Ernest Benn, 1927 (500 signed copies, 2 vols, slipcase) £145
The Statue (with Eden Philpotts), Cassell, 1908 £30
The Glimpse: An Adventure of the Soul, Chapman & Hall, 1909 . . . . £25
Cupid and Commonsense, New Age Press, 1909 £20
What the Public Wants, Duckworth, 1909 . . £20
Clayhanger, Methuen, 1910 . . . . . . £45
Helen with the High Hand, Chapman & Hall, 1910 .
. . . . £20
The Card, Methuen, 1911 . . . . . . £25
Hilda Lessways, Methuen, 1911 . . . . £40
The Honeymoon, Methuen, 1911 . . . . £15
The Matador of the Five Towns, Methuen, 1912 £20

Milestones (with Edward Knoblauch), Methuen, 1912.
. . . . £15
The Regent, Methuen, 1913 . . . . . £25
The Great Adventure, Methuen, 1913 . . . £15
The Price of Love, Methuen, 1914 . . . . £20
These Twain, Methuen, 1916 . . . . . £20
The Lion's Share, Cassell, 1916. . . . . £20
The Pretty Lady, Cassell, 1918 . . . . £20
The Roll Call, Hutchinson, 1918. . . . . £15
The Title, Chatto & Windus, 1918 . . . . £10
Judith, Chatto & Windus, 1919 . . . . £15
Lilian, Cassell, 1922 . . . . £75/£15
Mr Prohack, Methuen, 1922 . . . . . £65/£15
The Love Match, Chatto & Windus, 1922 . £45/£15
Body and Soul, Chatto & Windus, 1922 . £45/£15
Riceyman Steps, Cassell, 1923 . . . . £75/£20
ditto, Doran (U.S.), 1923 . . . . . . £45/£10
Don Juan de Marana, T. Werner Laurie, 1923 (1,000 signed copies) . . . . £50/£35
The Bright Island, Golden Cockerel Press, 1924 (200 signed copies) £200
London Life (with Edward Knoblauch), Chatto & Windus, 1924. . . . . £65/£20
The Clayhanger Family, Methuen, 1925 . £45/£15
ditto, Methuen, 1925 (200 signed copies) . . £75
Lord Riango, Cassell, 1926 . . . . . £30/£15
The Strange Vanguard, Cassell, 1929 . . £45/£15
Piccadilly, Readers Library Publishing Co., 1929 . .
. . . . £50/£15
Imperial Palace, Cassell, 1930 . . . . £50/£15
ditto, Cassell, 1930 (100 signed copies, 2 vols) . £175
Venus Rising from the Sea, Cassell, 1931 (350 numbered copies, in slipcase) £200
ditto, Cassell, 1932 . . . . £25/£10
Dream of Destiny, Cassell, 1932. . . . £40/£15
Flora, Rich & Cowan, 1933 . . . . . £40/£15
The Snake Charmer, Rich & Cowan, 1933 . £40/£15

E.F. BENSON
(b.1867 d.1940)

Benson's first book, *Dodo* was a huge success. Known for his light society novels, especially the 'Mapp and Lucia' series and also his supernatural fiction, of which *The Room in the Tower* is perhaps the most highly regarded.

Novels

Dodo: A Detail of Today, Methuen, 1893 (2 vols) £500
The Rubicon, Methuen, 1894 (2 vols) . . . £50
The Judgement Books, Osgood McIlvaine, 1895 £40
Limitations, Innes, 1896 . . . . £40
ditto, Harpers (U.S.), 1896 . . . . . £35
The Babe, B.A., Putnams (U.S.), 1896 . . . £40
ditto, Putnams, 1897 . . . . £30
The Vintage, Methuen, 1898 . . . . . £40
The Money Market, Arrowsmith, 1898 . . . £40

The Capsina, Methuen, 1899. . . . . . £40
Mammon and Co., Heinemann, 1899 . . . £40
The Princess Sophia, Heinemann, 1900 . . £35
The Luck of the Vails, Heinemann, 1901 . . £45
Scarlet and Hyssop, Heinemann, 1902 . . . £30
The Book of Months, Heinemann, 1903 . . £30
ditto, Harper & Bros (U.S.), 1903 . . . . £30
An Act in a Backwater, Heinemann, 1903 . . £25
The Valkyries, Dean, 1903 . . . . . £25
The Relentless City, Heinemann, 1903 . . . £25
ditto, Harper & Bros (U.S.), 1903 . . . . £25
The Challoners, Heinemann, 1904 . . . . £25
ditto, A.L. Burt Co (U.S.), 1904 . . . . £20
The Image in the Sand, Heinemann, 1905 . . £30
The Angel of Pain, Lippincott (U.S.), 1905. . £30
ditto, Heinemann, 1906 . . . . £25
Paul, Heinemann, 1906 . . . . . . £50
The House of Defense, Macleod & Allen, 1906 £25
ditto, Authors and Newspapers Association (U.S.),
1906 . . . . £20
Sheaves, Stanley Paul, 1907 . . . . . £25
The Blotting Book, Heinemann, 1908 . . . £25
ditto, Doubleday (U.S.), 1908 . . . . £25
The Climber, Heinemann, 1908 . . . . £25
A Reaping, Heinemann, 1909 . . . . . £25
Daisy's Aunt, Nelson, 1910 . . . . . £50
The Osbornes, Smith Elder, 1910 . . . . £25
Margery, Doubleday (U.S.), 1910 . . . . £25
ditto, as *Juggernaut*, Heinemann, 1911 . . £25
Account Rendered, Heinemann, 1911 . . . £25
Mrs Ames, Hodder & Stoughton, 1912 . . . £25
The Weaker Vessel, Heinemann, 1913 . . . £25
Thorley Weir, Heinemann, 1913 . . . . £25
Dodo's Daughter: A Sequel to Dodo, Century Co.
(U.S.), 1913 . . . . £75
ditto, as *Dodo the Second*, Hodder & Stoughton, 1914
. . . . £75
Arundel, Unwin, 1914 . . . . . . £25
The Oakleyites, Hodder & Stoughton, 1915 . £25
David Blaize, Hodder & Stoughton, 1916 . . £25
Mike, Cassell, 1916 . . . . £25
The Freaks of Mayfair, Foulis, 1916 . . £65
ditto, Doran (U.S.), [1918] £40
Mr Teddy, Unwin, 1917 . . . . . . £20
An Autumn Sowing, Collins, 1917 . . . . £20
David Blaize and the Blue Door, Hodder & Stoughton,
1918 . . . . £20
Up and Down, Hutchinson, 1918 . . . . £15
Across the Stream, John Murray, 1919 . . £65/£15
ditto, Doran (U.S.), 1919 . . . . . . £45/£15
Robin Linnet, Hutchinson, 1919 . . . . £45/£15
Queen Lucia, Hutchinson, 1920 . . . £300/£125
Dodo Wonders, Hutchinson, 1921 . . . £200/£45
Lovers and Friends, Unwin, 1921 . . . £65/£20
Miss Mapp, Hutchinson, 1922 . . . £275/£100
Peter, Cassell, 1922 . . . . £50/£15
Colin: A Novel, Hutchinson, [1923] . . . . £50/£15
David of King's, Hodder & Stoughton, 1924 £50/£15
Alan, Unwin, 1924 . . . . . . £50/£15

Colin II, Hutchinson, [1925] . . . . . £50/£15
Rex, Hodder & Stoughton, 1925 . . . . . £50/£15
Mezzanine, Cassell, 1926 . . . . . . £50/£15
Pharisees and Publicans, Hutchinson, 1926 £30/£10
Lucia in London, Hutchinson, 1927. . . £275/£100
Paying Guests, Hutchinson, 1929 . . . £50/£15
The Inheritor, Hutchinson, [1930] . . . £65/£25
ditto, Doran (U.S.), 1930 . . . . . . £65/£25
Mapp & Lucia, Hodder & Stoughton, 1931 £250/£75
Secret Lives, Hodder & Stoughton, 1932 . £45/£15
Travail of Gold, Hodder & Stoughton, 1933 £35/£15
Raven's Brood, Arthur Barker, 1934 . . £45/£15
ditto, Doran (U.S.), 1934 . . . . . . £35/£15
Lucia's Progress, Hodder & Stoughton, 1935 . . .
. . . . £250/£75
All About Lucia, Doubleday (U.S.), 1936 (the first four
Lucia novels in one vol.) . . . . . £65/£25
Old London, Appleton-Century, 1937, (4 vols in dust
wrappers, slipcase) . . . . £100/£65
Trouble for Lucia, Hodder & Stoughton, 1939 . .
. . . . £200/£45
ditto, Doran (U.S.), 1939 . . . . . . £100/£35

Short Stories
Six Common Things, Osgood McIlvaine, 1893 £35
A Double Overture, C.H. Sergel (U.S.), 1894 £30
The Countess of Lowndes Square and Other Stories,
Cassell, 1920 . . . . £300/£100
The Male Impersonator, Elkin Mathews & Marrot,
1929 (530 signed copies) . . . . . £65/£50
Desirable Residences, O.U.P., 1991 . . . £15/£5
Fine Feathers, O.U.P., 1994 . . . . £15/£5

Ghost Stories
The Room in the Tower, Mills & Boon, [1912] . .
. . . . £600/£200
Visible and Invisible, Hutchinson, 1923 £450/£100
ditto, Doran (U.S.), 1924 . . . . . £200/£75
'And the Dead Spake' & The Horror Horn, Doran
(U.S.), 1923 . . . . £150/£50
Expiation & Naboth's Vineyard, Doran (U.S.), 1924 .
. . . . £150/£50
The Face, Doran (U.S.), 1924 . . . . £175/£75
The Temple, Doran (U.S.), 1925 . . . £150/£50
A Tale of an Empty House & Bagnell Terrace, Doran
(U.S.), 1925 . . . . £150/£50
ditto, as *The Tale of an Empty House*, Black Swan/
Corgi, 1985 (wraps) £5
ditto, Black Swan/Corgi, 1986 (limited edition
hardback) . . . . £35/£15
Spook Stories, Hutchinson, [1928] . . . £600/£200
The Step, H.V. Marrot, 1930 . . . . £200/£75
More Spook Stories, Hutchinson, [1934] £500/£125
The Horror Horn, Panther, 1974 (wraps) . . £5
The Flint Knife, Equation, 1988 (wraps) . . £15
The Terror by Night, Ash Tree Press, 1998 (600
copies). . . . . £30/£10
The Passenger, Ash Tree Press, 1999 (600 copies) .
. . . . £30/£10

Collaborations with Eustace Miles
Daily Training, Hurst & Blackett, 1902 . . £45
Cricket of Abel, Hirst and Shrewsbury, Hurst &
Blackett, 1903 . . . . £75
The Mad Annual, Grant Richards, 1903 . . £45
A Book of Golf, Hurst Blackett, 1903 . . . £65
Diversions Day by Day, Hurst & Blackett, 1905 £45

Non Fiction
Sketches from Marlborough, 1888 (anonymous) £125
English Figure-Skating, Bell, 1908 . . . £35
Winter Sports in Switzerland, George Allen, 1913 £50
Skating Calls, Bell, 1909 . . . . . . £30
Deutschland Uber Allah, Hodder & Stoughton, 1917 .
. . . . £20
Crescent and Iron Cross, Hodder & Stoughton, 1918 .
. . . . £35
The White Eagle of Poland, Hodder & Stoughton,
1918 . . . . £30
ditto, Doran (U.S.), 1919 . . . . . . £25
Poland and Mittel-Europa, Hodder & Stoughton, 1918
. . . . £15
The Social Value of Temperance, True Temperance
Association, 1919 . . . . £15
Our Family Affairs, 1867-1896, Cassell, 1920 £35/£15
Mother, Hodder & Stoughton, 1925 . . . £35/£15
Sir Frances Drake, John Lane/Bodley Head, 1927. .
. . . . £35/£15
ditto, Harper (U.S.), 1927. . . . . £30/£10
The Life of Alcibiades, Ernest Benn, 1928 . £45/£15
Ferdinand Magellan, John Lane/Bodley Head, 1929 .
. . . . £35/£15
ditto, Harper (U.S.), 1930. . . . . £30/£15
*Henry James: Letters to A.C. Benson/Auguste
Monod*, Elkin Mathews & Marrot, 1930 (1,050
numbered copies) £30
As We Were: A Victorian Peepshow, Longmans, 1930
. . . . £35/£15
As We Are: A Modern Revue, Longmans, 1932 . .
. . . . £30/£15
Charlotte Brontë, Longmans, 1932 . . . £30/£15
King Edward VII, Longmans, 1933 . . . £35/£15
The Outbreak of War, Peter Davies, 1933 . £65/£20
Queen Victoria, Longmans (U.S.), 1935 . £30/£10
ditto, Longmans, 1935 . . . . . £30/£10
The Kaiser and English Relations, Longmans, 1934 .
. . . . £25/£10
Queen Victoria's Daughters, Appleton-Century (U.S.),
1938 . . . . £25/£10
ditto, as *Daughters of Queen Victoria*, Cassell, 1939 .
. . . . £25/£10
Final Edition: An Informal Autobiography, Longmans, 1940 . . . . £30/£15
ditto, Appleton-Century (U.S.), 1940 . . £30/£15

Others
Bensoniana: Maxims by E.F. Benson, Siegle Hill
Watteau, 1912 . . . . £45

ditto, A.L. Humphreys, 1912 . . . . . £45
Thoughts from E.F. Benson, Harrap, 1913 . £35
Thoughts from E.F. Benson, Holden & Hardingham,
1916 (leather bound). £75
ditto, Holden & Hardingham, 1916 (cloth bound) £30

E.C. BENTLEY
(b.1875 d.1956)

Bentley's oeuvre is very small but his first book,
Trent's Last Case, is an acknowledged classic of
detective fiction.

Novels
Trent's Last Case, Nelson, [1913] £125
ditto, as *The Woman in Black*, Century (U.S.), 1913 .
. . . . £125
Trent's Own Case, Constable, 1936 (with H. Warner
Allen) . . . . £400/£25
ditto, Knopf (U.S.), 1936 . . . . . £150/£25
Elephant's Work, Hodder & Stoughton, 1950 £20/£5
ditto, Knopf (U.S.), 1950 . . . . . £20/£5
ditto, as *The Chill*, Dell (U.S.), 1953 (wraps) . £10

Short Stories
Trent Intervenes, Nelson, 1938 . . . . £125/£20
ditto, Knopf (U.S.), 1938 . . . . . £125/£20

LORD BERNERS
(b.1883 d.1950)

Millionaire, composer, author and eccentric.

Fiction
The Camel, Constable, 1936 . . . . £75/£35
ditto, in *Collected Tales and Fantasies*, Turtle Point
Press (U.S.), 1999 (wraps) £10
The Girls of Radcliff Hall, privately published, 1937
(wraps) £80
Far from the Madding War, Constable, 1941 £65/£25
Count Omega, Constable 1941 . . . . £75/£35
Percy Wallingford and Mr Pidger, Blackwell, 1941
(wraps) £45
The Romance of a Nose, Constable, 1941 . £65/£25

Autobiography
First Childhood, Constable, 1934 . . . £75/£45
ditto, Farrar & Reinhart (U.S.), 1934 . . £45/£15
A Distant Prospect, Constable, 1945 . . £35/£10

Music
Intermezzo from "The Triumph of Neptune", J. &
W. Chester, Ltd, 1927 (quarto, wraps) . . . £75

Three Songs in the German Manner, J. & W. Chester, Ltd, [n.d.] (quarto, wraps) £95
Luna Park-Fantastic Ballet in One Act, J. & W. Chester, Ltd, [n.d., c.1930] (quarto, wraps) . £150
Trois Chansons, J. & W. Chester, Ltd, 1920 (quarto, wraps). £85
Suite from The Triumph of Neptune, J. & W. Chester, Ltd, [n.d.] (quarto, wraps) £50

JOHN BETJEMAN
(b.1906 d.1984)

As a broadcasting personality, commenting on the superficial and the middle class, Betjeman somehow missed serious recognition for his verse during his lifetime, despite becoming Poet Laureate in 1972.

Verse
Mount Zion or In Touch with the Infinite, James Press, [1931] (blue and gold patterened boards, no d/w) £700
ditto, James Press, [1931] (striped boards, no d/w) . .
. . . . £400
Continual Dew, John Murray, 1937 . . . £175/£65
Sir John Piers by 'Epsilon', Mullingar (Ireland), 1938, (50 copies, wraps) £1,000
Old Lights for New Chancels, John Murray, 1940 . .
. . . . £65/£25
ditto, John Murray, 1940 (signed, printed on blue laid paper) £450
New Bats in Old Belfries, John Murray, 1945 £60/£25
ditto, John Murray, 1945 (50 signed copies) . £400
Slick, But Not Streamlined, Doubleday (U.S.), 1947 (ed. W.H. Auden) . . . . . . £100/£40
Selected Poems, John Murray, 1948 . . . £45/£15
ditto, John Murray, 1948 (18 signed copies) . £500
Verses Turned in Aid of Public Subscription Toward the Restoration of the Church of St Katherine, Chislehampton, Oxon, St Katherine's Church, 1952 (wraps) £125
A Few Late Chrysanthemums, John Murray, 1954 .
. . . . £50/£20
ditto, John Murray, 1954 (50 signed copies) . £300
Poems in the Porch, SPCK, 1954 (wraps) . . £15
John Betjeman: A Selection, Edward Hulton Pocket Poets, 1958, (wraps) £10
Collected Poems, John Murray, 1958 . . £40/£15
ditto, John Murray, 1958 (100 signed copies, slipcase)
. . . . £250
ditto, Houghton Mifflin (U.S.), 1959 . . £35/£15
Lament for Moira McCavendish, Browne Lismore [n.d.] (20 copies, wraps). £300
Summoned by Bells, John Murray, 1960 . £30/£10
ditto, John Murray, 1960 (125 signed, numbered copies) £300
ditto, Houghton Mifflin (U.S.), 1960 . . £25/£10
A Ring of Bells, John Murray, 1962 . . £60/£25

ditto, Houghton Mifflin (U.S.), 1963 . . £45/£20
High and Low, John Murray, 1966 . . £30/£10
ditto, John Murray, 1966 (100 signed copies) £350
ditto, Houghton Mifflin (U.S.), 1967 . . £25/£10
Six Betjeman Songs, Duckworth, 1967 (wraps) £35
A Wembley Lad and The Crem, Poem of the Month Club, 1971 (signed broadsheet). £125
A Nip in the Air, John Murray, 1974 . . £25/£10
ditto, John Murray, 1974 (175 copies, signed by the author) £225
ditto, Norton (U.S.), [1974] . . . . . £20/£10
Betjeman in Miniature, Selected Poems, Gleniffer Press, 1976 (250 copies). £65
The Best of Betjeman, John Murray, 1978 £20/£5
Ode on the Marriage of H.R.H. Prince Charles to Lady Diana Spencer, Warren Editions, 1981 (125 signed copies, broadsheet) £125
Five Betjeman Songs, Weinberger, 1980 (wraps) £20
Church Poems, John Murray, 1981 (first issue, withdrawn) . . . . £100/£50
ditto, John Murray, 1981 (second issue) . £25/£10
ditto, John Murray, 1981 (100 copies, signed by the author and John Piper) . . . . . £350/£275
Uncollected Poems, John Murray, 1982. . £10/£5
St Mary-le-Strand, St Mary-le-Strand, 1981 (signed broadsheet) £75
Betjeman's Cornwall, John Murray, 1984 . £35/£10
Ah Middlesex, Warren, 1984 (250 copies) . . £75

Prose
Ghastly Good Taste, Chapman & Hall, 1933 . . .
. . . . £400/£175
ditto, Chapman & Hall, 1933 (200 signed copies in a slipcase) £400
Cornwall Illustrated in a series of views, Architectural Press, 1934 (spiral-bound) £75
Devon, Architectural Press, 1936 (spiral-bound) £65
An Oxford University Chest, John Miles, 1938 . .
. . . . £175/£65
A Handbook on Paint, with Hugh Casson, Silicate Paint Co., 1939 . . . . £450
Antiquarian Prejudice, Hogarth Sixpenny Pamphlets No. 3, 1939 (card wraps) £45
Vintage London, Collins, 1942 . . . £50/£20
English Cities and Small Towns, Britain in Pictures/ Collins, 1943 . . . . £20/£5
John Piper, Penguin Modern Painters, 1944, (wraps) .
. . . . £15
Murray's Buckinghamshire Architectural Guide, John Murray, 1949 (edited with John Piper). . £30/£10
Murray's Berkshire Architectural Guide, John Murray, 1949 (edited with John Piper). . £30/£10
Shropshire, Faber Shell Guide, 1951 . . £25/£10
The English Scene, CUP/NBL, 1951 (wraps) . £15
First and Last Loves, John Murray, 1952 . £100/£40
The English Town in the Last Hundred Years, CUP, 1956 (Rede Lecture, wraps). £25
Collins Guide to English Parish Churches, Collins, 1958 . . . . £35/£10

Ground Plan to Skyline (pseud. 'Richard M. Farran'), Newman Neame, 1960 (wraps) £25
English Churches, with Basil Clarke, Studio Vista, 1964 . . . . £25/£10
The City of London Churches, Pitkin Pictorial, 1965 (wraps) £5
Victorian and Edwardian London from Old Photographs, Batsford, 1969 . . . £15/£5
ditto, Viking (U.S.), 1969 . . . . £10
Ten Wren Churches, Editions Elector, 1970 (100 copies, folder) £150
Victorian and Edwardian Oxford from Old Photographs, with David Vaisey, Batsford, 1971. . . . . £15/£5
Victorian and Edwardian Brighton from Old Photographs, with J. S. Gray, Batsford, 1972 £15/£5
London's Historic Railway Stations, John Murray, 1972 . . . . £25/£5
A Pictorial History of English Architecture, John Murray, 1972 . . . . £20/£5
ditto, John Murray, 1972 (100 signed copies, slipcase) . . . . £225/£200
ditto, Macmillan (U.S.), 1972 . . . . £10/£5
West Country Churches, Society of Saints Peter & Paul, 1973 (wraps) £20
Victorian and Edwardian Cornwall from Old Photographs, with A. L. Rowse, Batsford, 1974 . . . . £15/£5
Plea for Holy Trinity Church, Sloane Street, Church Literature Association, 1974 . . . . . £10
Souvenir of Metroland, Warren Editions, 1977 (220 copies) £200
Archie and the Strict Baptists, John Murray, 1977. . . . . £35/£15
ditto, Lippincott (U.S.), 1978 . . . . £20/£10
Metroland, BBC Publications, 1977 . . . . £10

ALGERNON BLACKWOOD
(b.1869 d.1951)

An important British writer of supernatural fiction, Blackwood mined all aspects of the genre, and towards the end of his life became something of a radio and television personality.

Novels
Jimbo: A Fantasy, Macmillan, 1909 . . . £75
ditto, Macmillan (U.S.), 1909 . . . . £65
The Education of Uncle Paul, Macmillan, 1909 £65
ditto, Paget (U.S.), 1909 (abridged, wraps) . . £75
ditto, Holt (U.S.), 1914 . . . . . . £30
The Human Chord, Macmillan, 1910 . . . £45
The Centaur, Macmillan, 1911 . . . . £65
A Prisoner in Fairyland, Macmillan, 1913 . . £35
ditto, Macmillan (U.S.), 1913 . . . . £35
The Extra Day, Macmillan, 1915 . . . £35
ditto, Macmillan (U.S.), 1915 . . . . £35

Julius Levallon, Cassell, 1916 . . . . . £45
ditto, Dutton (U.S.), 1916 . . . . . . £40
The Wave: An Egyptian Aftermath, Macmillan, 1916. . . . . £45
ditto, Dutton (U.S.), 1916 . . . . . . £40
The Promise of Air, Macmillan, 1918 . . . £30
ditto, Dutton (U.S.), 1918 . . . . . . £25
The Garden of Survival, Macmillan, 1918 . . £30
ditto, Dutton (U.S.), 1918 . . . . . . £25
The Bright Messenger, Cassell, 1921 . £150/£45
ditto, Dutton (U.S.), 1922 . . . . . £150/£45

Short Story Collections
The Empty House and Other Ghost Stories, Nash, 1906 . . . . £250
ditto, Vaughan (U.S.), 1915 (limited to 500 copies) £100
The Listener and Other Stories, Nash, 1907 . £125
ditto, Vaughan & Gomme (U.S.), 1914 (limited to 500 copies) £100
John Silence, Physician Extraordinary, Nash, 1908 . . . . £250
ditto, John W. Luce (U.S.), 1909 . . . . £150
The Lost Valley and Other Stories, Nash, 1910 £150
ditto, Vaughan & Gomme (U.S.), 1914 (limited to 500 copies) £100
Pan's Garden, A Volume of Nature Stories, Macmillan, 1912 . . . . £75
Ten Minute Stories, Murray, 1914 . . . . £75
ditto, Dutton (U.S.), 1914 . . . . £75
Incredible Adventures, Macmillan, 1914 . . £75
ditto, Macmillan (U.S.), 1914 . . . . £65
Day and Night Stories, Cassell, 1917 . . . £125
ditto, Dutton (U.S.), 1917 . . . . . . £65
The Wolves of God, Cassell, 1921 (with Wilfrid Wilson) . . . . £300/£75
ditto, Dutton (U.S.), 1921 . . . . . £250/£65
Tongues of Fire and Other Sketches, Jenkins, 1924 . . . . £300/£75
ditto, Dutton (U.S.), 1925 . . . . . £250£65
Ancient Sorceries and Other Tales, Collins, [1927] . . . . £150/£50
The Dance of Death and Other Tales, Jenkins, 1927 . . . . £150/£65
ditto, Dial Press (U.S.), 1928 . . . . £75/£25
Strange Stories, Heinemann, 1929 . . . £45/£20
ditto, as The Best Supernatural Tales of Algernon Blackwood, Causeway Books (U.S.), 1973 (abridged facsimile of above edition) . . . . . £25/£10
Full Circle, Mathews & Marrot, 1929 (530 signed, numbered copies) . . . . £100/£50
Short Stories of Today and Yesterday, Harrap & Co, 1930 . . . . £35/£20
The Willows and Other Queer Tales, Collins, [1932] . . . . £150/£45
Shocks, Grayson, 1935 . . . . . £125/£25
ditto, Dutton (U.S.), 1936 . . . . . £125/£25
The Tales of Algernon Blackwood, Secker, 1938 . . . . £45/£15

ditto, Dutton (U.S.), 1939 . . . . . . £45/£15
Selected Tales of Algernon Blackwood, Penguin, 1942
(wraps) £15
Selected Short Stories of Algernon Blackwood, Armed
Services Editions (U.S.), [1942] (wraps) . . £20
The Doll and One Other, Arkham House (U.S.), 1946
. . . . £45/£20
Tales of the Uncanny and Supernatural, Nevill, 1949
. . . . £15/£5
ditto, Castle (U.S.), 1974 . . . . . . £15/£5
In the Realm of Terror, Pantheon Books (U.S.), 1957
. . . . £15/£5
Selected Tales of Algernon Blackwood, John Baker,
1964 . . . . £15/£5
ditto, Dutton (U.S.), 1965 . . . . . . £15/£5
Tales of the Mysterious and Macabre, Spring Books,
1967 . . . . £10/£5
ditto, Castle (U.S.), 1974 . . . . . . £10/£5
Ancient Sorceries and Other Stories, Penguin, 1968
(wraps) £10
Best Ghost Stories of Algernon Blackwood, Dover
(U.S.), 1973 (wraps) £10

Children's Books
Sambo and Snitch, Blackwell, 1927 . . . £75/£50
ditto, Appleton (U.S.), 1927 . . . . . £65/£40
Mr Cupboard, Blackwell, 1928 . . . . £75/£50
Dudley and Gilderoy: A Nonsense, Benn, 1929 . .
. . . . £75/£25
ditto, Dutton (U.S.), 1929 . . . . . . £45/£20
By Underground, Blackwell, 1930 . . . £75/£50
The Parrot and the Cat, Blackwell, 1931 . £75/£50
The Italian Conjuror, Blackwell, 1932 . . £75/£50
Maria (Of England) In the Rain, Blackwell, 1933 . .
. . . . £75/£50
Sergeant Poppett and Policeman James, Blackwell,
1934 . . . . £75/£50
The Fruit Stoners, Grayson, [1934] . . . £75/£25
ditto, Dutton (U.S.), 1935 . . . . . . £65/£20
ditto, Blackwell, 1935 (extract) . . . . £45/£30
How the Circus Came to Tea, Blackwell, 1936 . .
. . . . £70/£45
The Adventures of Dudley and Gilderoy, Dutton
(U.S.), 1941 (adapted by Marion B. Cottren) £35/£15
ditto, Faber, 1941 . . . . £35/£15

Plays
Karma: A Reincarnation Play, Macmillan, 1918 (with
Violet Pearn) £50
ditto, Dutton (U.S.), 1918 . . . . . . £45
Through the Crack, French, 1925 (with Violet Pearn,
wraps) £25

Other Works
Episodes Before Thirty, Cassell, 1923 . . £100/£25
ditto, Dutton (U.S.), 1924 . . . . . £100/£25
ditto, as **Adventures Before Thirty**, Cape, 1934 . .
. . . . £35/£15

NICHOLAS BLAKE
see C. Day Lewis

ROBERT BLOCH
(b.1917 d.1994)

Author of horror and crime stories, often underlain by
a black humour. *Psycho* became the best known of his
novels following Hitchcock's classic film.

Novels
The Scarf, Dial Press (U.S.), 1947 . . . £175/£45
ditto, New English Library, 1972 (wraps) . . £10
The Will to Kill, Ace (U.S.), 1954 (wraps) . . £25
The Kidnaper, Lion (U.S.), 1954 (wraps) . . £150
Spiderweb, Ace (U.S.), 1954 (wraps) . . £25
Shooting Star, Ace (U.S.), 1958 (wraps) . . £25
Psycho, Simon & Schuster (U.S.), 1959 . £800/£125
ditto, Robert Hale, 1960 . . . . . . £300/£75
The Dead Beat, Simon & Schuster (U.S.), 1960 . .
. . . . £60/£15
ditto, Robert Hale, 1971 . . . . . . £25/£10
Firebug, Regency (U.S.), 1961 (wraps) . . . £20
ditto, Corgi, 1977 (wraps) £10
The Couch, Fawcett (U.S.), 1962 (wraps) . . £25
ditto, Frederick Muller, 1962 . . . . . £10/£5
Terror, Belmont (U.S.), 1962 (wraps) . . . £15
ditto, Corgi, 1964 (wraps) £10
Ladies' Day/This Crowded Earth, Belmont (U.S.),
1968 (wraps) £15
The Star Stalker, Pyramid (U.S.), 1968 (wraps) £35
The Todd Dossier, Delacorte (U.S.), 1969 (pseud.
'Collier Young') . . . . £35/£10
ditto, Macmillan, 1969 (pseud. 'Collier Young') . .
. . . . £30/£10
It's All In Your Mind, Curtis (U.S.), 1971 (wraps) £10
Sneak Preview, Paperback Library (U.S.), 1971
(wraps) £10
Night World, Simon & Schuster (U.S.), 1972 £35/£15
ditto, Robert Hale, 1974 . . . . . . £30/£10
American Gothic, Simon & Schuster (U.S.), 1974 .
. . . . £30/£10
ditto, W. H. Allen, 1975 . . . . . . £20/£5
Strange Eons, Whispers Press (U.S.), 1978 [1979] .
. . . . £20/£5
ditto, Whispers Press (U.S.), 1978 [1979] (300 signed
copies, slipcase) . . . . £50/£35
There is a Serpent in Eden, Zebra Books, 1979
(wraps) £10
Psycho II, Warner Books (U.S.), 1982 (wraps) £5
ditto, Whispers Press (U.S.), 1982 . . . £20/£10
ditto, Whispers Press (U.S.), 1982 (750 signed,
numbered copies, slipcase) . . . . £75/£65
ditto, Whispers Press (U.S.), 1982 (26 signed, lettered
copies, slipcase) . . . . £250/£225
ditto, Corgi, 1983 (wraps) £5

Twilight Zone - The Movie, Warner Books (U.S.), 1983 (wraps) £5
ditto, Transworld, 1983 (wraps) £5
Night of the Ripper, Robert Hale, 1984 . . £15/£5
ditto, Doubleday (U.S.), 1984 . . . . £15/£5
Unholy Trinity, Scream Press, 1986 . . . £25/£10
ditto, Scream Press (U.S.), 1986 (250 signed, numbered copies, slipcase) . . . . £65/£50
Lori, Tor (U.S.), 1989. . . . . . . £10/£5
Screams, Underwood/Miller, 1989 . . . £25/£10
ditto, Underwood/Miller, 1989, (300 signed copies, slipcase) . . . . £75/£45
Psycho III: The Psycho House, Tor (U.S.), 1990 . .
. . . . £10/£5

Short Stories
Sea Kissed, Utopian Publications, [1945], (first issue printed in Great Britain, wraps) £500
ditto, Utopian Publications, [1945], (second issue printed in Eire, wraps) £350
The Opener of the Way, Arkham House (U.S.), 1945 .
. . . . £350/£75
ditto, Neville Spearman, 1974 . . . . £25/£10
Terror in the Night, Ace (U.S.), 1958 (wraps) £25
Pleasant Dreams, Arkham House (U.S.), 1960 . .
. . . . £100/£25
ditto, Whiting & Wheaton, 1967 . . . . £45/£15
Blood Runs Cold, Simon & Schuster (U.S.), 1961 . .
. . . . £25/£10
ditto, Robert Hale, 1963 . . . . . . £20/£10
Nightmares, Belmont Books (U.S.), 1961 (wraps) £10
Atoms and Evil, Fawcett (U.S.), 1962 (wraps) £10
ditto, Frederick Muller, 1963 (wraps) . . . £5
ditto, Hale, 1976 (hardback) . . . . £25/£10
More Nightmares, Belmont Books (U.S.), [1962] (wraps) £10
Yours Truly, Jack the Ripper, Belmont Books (U.S.), [1962] (wraps) £10
ditto, as *The House of the Hatchet*, Tandem, 1965 (wraps) £5
Horror-7, Belmont (U.S.), 1963 (wraps) . . £10
ditto, Four Square, 1965 (wraps). £5
Bogey Men: Ten Tales, Pyramid Books (U.S.), 1963 (wraps) £10
Tales in a Jugular Vein, Pyramid Books (U.S.), 1965 (wraps) £10
ditto, Sphere, 1970 (wraps) £5
The Skull of the Marquis de Sade, Pyramid Books (U.S.), 1965 (wraps). £25
ditto, Robert Hale, 1975 . . . . . £45/£15
Chamber of Horrors, Award (U.S.), 1966 (wraps) £5
ditto, Corgi, 1977 (wraps). £5
The Living Demons, Belmont Books, 1967 (wraps) £5
ditto, Sphere, 1970 (wraps) £5
Dragons and Nightmares, Mirage Press (U.S.), 1968 (1,000 numbered copies) . . . . £25/£10
Bloch and Bradbury, Tower (U.S.), 1969 (wraps) £5
ditto, Sphere, 1970 (wraps) £5

Fear Today, Gone Tomorrow, Award (U.S.), 1971 (wraps) £5
The King of Terrors, Mysterious Press (U.S.), 1977 (250 signed copies, slipcase) . . . . £50/£40
ditto, Mysterious Press (U.S.), 1977 . . . £25/£10
ditto, Robert Hale, 1978 . . . . . . £20/£5
Cold Chills, Doubleday (U.S.), 1977 . . £20/£10
ditto, Robert Hale, 1978 . . . . . . £15/£5
The Best of Robert Bloch, Ballantine (U.S.), 1977 (wraps) £5
Out of the Mouths of Graves, Mysterious Press (U.S.), 1978 . . . . £20/£5
ditto, Mysterious Press (U.S.), 1978 (26 signed, lettered copies, slipcase) . . . . £75/£50
ditto, Mysterious Press (U.S.), 1978 (250 signed, numbered copies, slipcase) . . . . . £50/£40
Such Stuff As Screams Are Made Of, Ballantine (U.S.), 1978 (wraps). £5
The Selected Stories of Robert Bloch, Underwood/ Muller (U.S.), 1987 (3 vols, 500 copies, slipcase, no dust jackets) . . . . . £20 each, £60 the set
ditto, Underwood/Muller (U.S.), 1987 (11 signed, numbered, leatherbound sets, 3 vols, slipcase, no dust jackets) £600
Midnight Pleasures, Doubleday (U.S.), 1987 £15/£5
Lost in Time and Space With Lefty Feep, Creatures at Large Press (U.S.), 1987 (wraps) £10
ditto, Creatures at Large Press (U.S.), 1987 (250 signed copies in d/w and slipcase) . . . . £45/£20
Fear and Trembling, Tor (U.S.), 1989 (wraps) £5

Others
The Eighth Stage of Fandom, Advent (U.S.), 1962 (125 numbered, signed copies) £150
ditto, Advent (U.S.), 1962 (200 copies) . . £100/£25
ditto, Advent (U.S.), 1962 (400 copies, wraps) £25

EDMUND BLUNDEN
(b.1896 d.1974)

Remembered primarily as a war poet, Blunden was later inspired by his adopted county of Kent.

Poetry
Poems, privately printed, 1914 (100 copies, wraps) .
. . . . £1,000
Poems Translated from the French, privately printed, 1914 (100 copies, wraps) £500
The Barn, privately printed, 1916 (50 copies, wraps) .
. . . . £500
Three Poems, privately printed, 1916 (50 copies, wraps). £500
The Harbingers, privately printed, 1916 (200 copies, 'The Barn' and 'Three Poems' bound together, wraps)
. . . . £250
Pastorals, Erskine Macdonald, 1916 (wraps) . £125
ditto, Erskine Macdonald, 1916 (50 cloth copies) £350

88

The Waggoner and Other Poems, Sidgwick & Jackson, 1920 . . . . £100/£35
The Shepherd and Other Poems of Peace and War, Cobden-Sanderson, 1922 . . . . . £75/£25
Dead Letters, Pelican Press, 1923 (50 numbered copies, wraps) £150
To Nature, The Beaumont Press, 1923 (310 numbered copies) £50
ditto, The Beaumont Press, 1923 (80 signed, numbered copies) £150
Masks of Time: A New Collection of Poems, The Beaumont Press, 1925 (310 numbered copies) £45
ditto, The Beaumont Press, 1925 (80 signed, numbered copies) £150
The Augustan Books of Modern Poetry, Benn, 1925 (wraps) £5
English Poems, Cobden-Sanderson, 1926 . £35/£10
ditto, Knopf (U.S.), 1926 . . . . . £30/£10
Retreat, Cobden-Sanderson, 1928 . . . £35/£10
ditto, Cobden-Sanderson, 1928 (112 signed, numbered copies) £150
ditto, Doubleday (U.S.), 1928 . . . . £30/£10
Japanese Garland, The Beaumont Press, 1928 (310 numbered copies) £45
ditto, The Beaumont Press, 1928 (80 signed, numbered copies) £150
Winter Nights: A Reminiscence, Faber, 1928 (wraps) £10
ditto, Faber, 1928 (500 signed, numbered, large paper copies) £45
Near and Far, Cobden-Sanderson, 1929 . £25/£10
ditto, Cobden-Sanderson, 1929 (160 signed, numbered copies) £100
ditto, Harper (U.S.), 1930 . . . . . £25/£10
Poems 1914-1930, Cobden-Sanderson, 1930 £35/£10
ditto, Cobden-Sanderson, 1930 (200 signed, numbered copies) £65
ditto, Harper (U.S.), 1930 . . . . . £30/£10
Halfway House: A Miscellany of New Poems, Cobden-Sanderson, 1932 . . . . £25/£10
ditto, Cobden-Sanderson, 1932 (70 signed, numbered copies) £75
Choice or Chance: New Poems, Cobden-Sanderson, 1934 . . . . £35/£10
ditto, Cobden-Sanderson, 1934 (45 signed, numbered copies) £65
An Elegy and Other Poems, Cobden-Sanderson, 1937 . . . . £35/£10
Poems 1930-1940, Macmillan, 1940 [1941] £20/£10
Shells by a Stream: New Poems, Macmillan, 1944 . . . . £20/£10
After the Bombing and Other Short Poems, Macmillan, 1949 . . . . £15/£5
Eastward: A Selection of Verses, privately printed, 1950 (250 copies) £45
Poems of Many Years, Collins, 1957 . . £20/£5
A Hong Kong House: Poems 1951-1981, Collins, 1962 . . . . £10/£5

Eleven Poems, The Golden Head Press, 1965 [1966] (wraps) £15
ditto, The Golden Head Press, 1965 [1966] (21 signed copies) £100
A Selection of the Shorter Poems, privately printed, 1966 (wraps) £5
The Midnight Skaters: Poems for Young Readers, The Bodley Head, 1968 . . . . £10/£5
A Selection from the Poems, privately printed, 1969 (wraps) £5
Selected Poems, Carcanet, 1982 . . . . £5
Overtones of War: Poems of the First World War, Duckworth, 1996. . . . . . . £10/£5

Prose
The Bonadventure: A Random Journal of an Atlantic Holiday, Cobden-Sanderson, 1922 . . . £50/£15
ditto, Putnam (U.S.), 1923 . . . . . £40/£10
Christ's Hospital: A Retrospect, Christophers, 1923 . . . . £50/£20
On the Poems of Henry Vaughan, Cobden-Sanderson, 1927 . . . . £20/£10
Undertones of War, Cobden-Sanderson, 1928 . . . . £200/£60
ditto, Doubleday (U.S.), 1929 . . . £40/£10
ditto, The Folio Society, 1989 (slipcase). . £10/£40
Nature in English Literature, The Hogarth Press, 1929 . . . . £50/£15
ditto, Harcourt (U.S.), 1929 . . . . £40/£15
Leigh Hunt, Cobden-Sanderson, 1930 . . £30/£10
ditto, Harper (U.S.), 1930 . . . . . £30/£10
De Bello Germanico: A Fragment of Trench History, G.A. Blunden, 1930 (250 copies) . . . £100
ditto, G.A. Blunden, 1930 (25 signed copies) . £200
Votive Tablets: Studies Chiefly Appreciative of English Authors and Books, Cobden-Sanderson, 1931 . . . . £40/£10
ditto, Cobden-Sanderson, 1931 (50 signed, numbered copies) £100
ditto, Harper (U.S.), 1931. . . . . £40/£10
The Face of England, Longmans Green, 1932 . . . . £25/£10
We'll Shift our Ground, or Two On a Tour, Cobden-Sanderson, 1933 (with Sylvia Norman) . £30/£15
Charles Lamb and His Contemporaries, CUP, 1933 . . . . £15/£5
ditto, Macmillan (U.S.), 1933 . . . . £15/£5
The Mind's Eye, Cape, 1934 . . . . . £15/£5
Keat's Publisher: A Memoir of John Taylor (1781-1864), Cape, 1938 . . . . . . £35/£10
English Villages, Collins, 1941 . . . . £15/£5
ditto, Hastings House (U.S.), [n.d.] . . . £10/£5
Thomas Hardy, Macmillan, 1941 [1942] . £25/£10
Cricket Country, Collins, 1944 . . . . £20/£5
Shelley: A Life Story, Collins, 1946 . . £35/£10
ditto, Viking Press (U.S.), 1947 . . . . £25/£10
John Keats, British Council, Longmans, 1950 (wraps) £10

Charles Lamb, British Council, Longmans, 1954 (wraps) £10
War Poets 1914-1918, British Council, Longmans, 1958 (wraps) £10
Guest of Thomas Hardy, Toucan Press, 1964 (wraps). £10

ENID BLYTON
(b.1897 d.1968)

A prolific children's author, best known for the 'Famous Five', 'Secret Seven' and 'Noddy' books. There are too many titles to list here, so only the most collectable have been included.

'Famous Five' Titles
Five on a Treasure Island: An Adventure Story, Hodder & Stoughton, 1942 . . . . . £750/£100
Five Go Adventuring Again, Hodder & Stoughton, 1943 . . . . £750/£75
Five Run Away Together, Hodder & Stoughton, 1944
. . . . £750/£75
Five Go To Smuggler's Top, Hodder & Stoughton, 1945 . . . . £600/£65
Five Go off in a Caravan, Hodder & Stoughton, 1946
. . . . £450/£45
Five on Kirrin Island Again, Hodder & Stoughton, 1947 . . . . £450/£35
Five Go Off to Camp, Hodder & Stoughton, 1948 . .
. . . . £450/£35
Five Get Into Trouble, Hodder & Stoughton, 1949 .
. . . . £225/£30
Five Fall into an Adventure, Hodder & Stoughton, 1950 . . . . £125/£25
Five on a Hike Together, Hodder & Stoughton, 1951 .
. . . . £125/£25
Five Have a Wonderful Time, Hodder & Stoughton [1952]. . . . . £125/£25
Five Go Down to the Sea, Hodder & Stoughton, 1953
. . . . £125/£20
Five Go to Mystery Moor, Hodder & Stoughton, 1954
. . . . £100/£15
Five Have Plenty of Fun, Hodder & Stoughton, 1955
. . . . £100/£15
Five on a Secret Trail, Hodder & Stoughton, 1956 .
. . . . £100/£15
Five Go To Billycock Hill, Hodder & Stoughton, 1957
. . . . £75/£15
Five get into a Fix, Hodder & Stoughton [1958] . .
. . . . £75/£15
The Famous Five Special, Hodder & Stoughton, 1959 (contains *Five Go Off to Camp*, *Five Go Off in a Caravan* and *Five Have a Wonderful Time*) £75/£15
Five on Finniston Farm, Hodder & Stoughton [1960]
. . . . £75/£15
Five Go To Demon's Rocks, Hodder & Stoughton, 1961 . . . . £75/£15

Five Have a Mystery to Solve, Hodder & Stoughton, 1962 . . . . £75/£15
Five are Together Again, Hodder & Stoughton, 1963
. . . . £75/£15
The Famous Five Big Book, Hodder & Stoughton, 1964 (contains *Five on a Treasure Island, Five Go Adventuring Again* and *Five Run Away Together*) .
. . . . £75/£10

'Adventure' Titles
The Island of Adventure, Macmillan, 1944 £450/£75
The Castle of Adventure, Macmillan, 1946 £250/£35
The Valley of Adventure, Macmillan, 1947 £200/£35
The Sea of Adventure, Macmillan, 1948 . £200/£35
The Mountain of Adventure, Macmillan, 1949. . .
. . . . £200/£25
The Ship of Adventure, Macmillan, 1950 . £125/£20
The Circus of Adventure, Macmillan, 1952 £125/£20
The River of Adventure, Macmillan, 1955 £125/£20

'Secret Seven' Titles
The Secret Seven, Brockhampton Press, 1949 £85/£15
Secret Seven Adventure, Brockhampton Press, 1950 .
. . . . £50/£15
Well Done, Secret Seven, Brockhampton Press, 1951 .
. . . . £50/£15
Secret Seven on the Trail, Brockhampton Press, 1952
. . . . £50/£15
Go Ahead Secret Seven, Brockhampton Press, 1953 .
. . . . £50/£15
Good Work, Secret Seven, Brockhampton Press, 1954
. . . . £50/£15
Secret Seven Win Through, Brockhampton Press, 1955 . . . . £50/£15
Three Cheers Secret Seven, Brockhampton Press, 1956
. . . . £50/£15
Secret Seven Mystery, Brockhampton Press, 1957 .
. . . . £45/£15
Puzzle for the Secret Seven, Brockhampton Press, 1958 . . . . £45/£15
Secret Seven Fireworks, Brockhampton Press, 1959 .
. . . . £45/£15
Good Old Secret Seven, Brockhampton Press, 1960 .
. . . . £45/£15
Shock for the Secret Seven, Brockhampton Press, 1961
. . . . £40/£15
Look out Secret Seven, Brockhampton Press, 1962 .
. . . . £40/£15
Fun for the Secret Seven, Brockhampton Press, 1963
. . . . £35/£15

'Mystery' Titles
The Mystery of the Burnt Cottage, Methuen, 1943 .
. . . . £95/£45
The Mystery of the Disappearing Cat, Methuen, 1944
. . . . £95/£45
The Mystery of the Secret Room, Methuen, 1945 . .
. . . . £95/£45

The Mystery of the Spiteful Letters, Methuen, 1946 .
. . . . £75/£20
The Mystery of the Missing Necklace, Methuen, 1947
. . . . £75/£20
The Mystery of the Hidden House, Methuen, 1948 .
. . . . £75/£15
The Mystery of the Pantomime Cat, Methuen, 1949 .
. . . . £75/£15
The Mystery of the Invisible Thief, Methuen, 1950 .
. . . . £65/£10
The Mystery of the Vanished Prince: Being the Ninth Adventure of the Five Find-Outers and Dog, Methuen, 1951 . . . . £65/£15
The Mystery of the Strange Bundle, Methuen, 1952 .
. . . . £50/£15
The Mystery of Holly Lane, Methuen, 1953 £50/£15
The Mystery of Tally-Ho Cottage, Methuen, 1954 .
. . . . £50/£15
The Mystery of the Missing Man, Methuen, 1956 . .
. . . . £50/£15
The Mystery of the Strange Messages, Methuen, 1957
. . . . £50/£15
The Mystery of Banshee Towers, Methuen, 1961 . .
. . . . £50/£15

'St Clare's School' Titles
The Twins at St Clare's, Methuen, 1941 . £50/£15
The O'Sullivan Twins, Methuen, 1942 . . £50/£15
Summer Term at St Clare's, Methuen, 1943 £50/£15
Claudine at St Clare's, Methuen, 1944 . . £50/£15
The Second Form at St Clare's, Methuen, 1944 . .
. . . . £50/£15
Fifth Formers at St Clare's, Methuen, 1945 £50/£15

'Malory Towers' Titles
First Terms at Malory Towers, Methuen, 1946. . .
. . . . £50/£15
The Second Form at Malory Towers, Methuen, 1947 .
. . . . £50/£15
Third Year at Malory Towers, Methuen, 1948 . . .
. . . . £45/£15
The Upper Fourth at Malory Towers, Methuen, 1949.
. . . . £45/£15
In the Fifth at Malory Towers, Methuen, 1950. . .
. . . . £45/£15
Last Term at Malory Towers, Methuen, 1951 . . .
. . . . £45/£15

'Noddy' Titles
Sampson Low, 1949-64, numbered Noddy books, 1-24,
. . . . £45/£10 each
Noddy's House of Books, Sampson Low [1951] ('The Tiny Noddy Book Nos. 1-6, in card case, no d/w) .
. . . . £175 the set
The Big Noddy Book, Sampson Low, 1952 (no d/w)
. . . . £75
Enid Blyton's Noddy's Ark of Books, Sampson Low, [1952] (5 books, cardboard case, no d/w) £165 the set

Noddy Cut-Out Model Book, Sampson Low, 1953 .
. . . . £150
Noddy's Garage of Books, Sampson Low [1953] (5 books, in cardboard case, no d/w) . . £165 the set
Noddy's Castle of Books, Sampson Low [1954] (5 books, in cardboard case, no d/w) . . £165 the set
The Noddy Toy Station Book Nos. 1-5, Sampson Low [1956]. . . . . £150 the set
Noddy's Shop of Books Nos. 1-5, Sampson Low [1958]. . . . . £150 the set
Noddy's Tall Blue (Green-Orange-Pink-Red-Yellow) Book, Sampson Low [1960] . . . £150 the set

Others
Sports and Games, [Birn, 1920] £125
Responsive Singing Games, J. Saville, 1923 . £125
Songs of Gladness, J. Saville, 1924 . . . . £125
The Enid Blyton Book of Fairies, Newnes [1924] .
. . . . £125/£45
The Enid Blyton Book of Bunnies, Newnes [1925]
. . . . £125/£45
The Enid Blyton Book of Brownies, Newnes [1926] .
. . . . £125/£45
Tales Half Told, Nelson, 1926 . . . . £125/£45
The Play's the Thing: Musical Plays for Children, Home Library Book Co. [1927] . . . £250/£75
Let's Pretend, Nelson [1928]. . . . . £75/£15
The Red Pixie Book, Newnes [1934] . . £125/£45
The Green Goblin Book, Newnes [1935] . £75/£15
The Yellow Fairy Book, Newnes [1936] . £75/£15
The Secret Island, Blackwell, 1938 . . . £125/£20
The Enchanted Wood, Newnes, 1939 . . £125/£20
The Secret of Spiggy Holes, Blackwood [1940] . .
. . . . £125/£20
The Babar Story Book, Methuen, 1941 . . £75/£15
The Three Golliwogs, Newnes, 1944 . . £75/£25
Rubbalong Tale Showbook, Werner Laurie, 1950 (complete with cut-outs). £300
Mary Mouse Showbook, Werner Laurie, 1950 (complete with cut-outs). £300

Verse
Child Whispers, J. Saville, [1922] (booklet) . £150
ditto, J. Saville, 1923 . . . . £225/£100
Real Fairies, J. Saville, 1923 . . . . . £250/£100
Silver and Gold, Nelson [1925] . . . . £225/£75

LUCY M. BOSTON
(b.1892 d.1990)

A British author who was inspired to write *The Children of Green Knowe* after buying the 800 year-old Grey Manor in Cambridgeshire in 1935

Green Knowe Novels
The Children of Green Knowe, Faber, 1954 £200/£30
ditto, Harcourt Brace (U.S.), 1955 . . . £150/£20

The Chimneys of Green Knowe, Faber, 1958 £150/£20
ditto, as *Treasure of Green Knowe*, Harcourt Brace
(U.S.), 1958 . . . . £75/£15
The River at Green Knowe, Faber, 1959 . £150/£20
ditto, Harcourt Brace (U.S.), 1959 . . . £75/£15
A Stranger at Green Knowe, Faber, 1961 . £150/£20
ditto, Harcourt Brace (U.S.), 1961 . . . £75/£15
An Enemy at Green Knowe, Faber, 1964 . £150/£20
ditto, Harcourt Brace (U.S.), 1964 . . . £75/£15
The Stones of Green Knowe, Faber, 1976 . £65/£10
ditto, Harcourt Brace (U.S.), 1976 . . . £35/£15

Other Novels
Yew Hall, Faber, 1954 . . . . . . £60/£15
The Castle of Yew, Bodley Head, 1965 . . £25/£5
ditto, Harcourt Brace (U.S.), 1964 . . . £15/£5
The Sea Egg, Faber, 1967 . . . . . £25/£5
ditto, Harcourt Brace (U.S.), 1967 . . . £15/£5
The House that Grew, Faber, 1969 . . . £25/£5
Persephone, Collins, 1969 . . . . . £25/£5
Nothing Said, Faber, 1971 . . . . . £20/£5
ditto, Harcourt Brace (U.S.), 1971 . . . £15/£5
The Guardians of the House, Bodley Head, 1974 . .
. . . . £15/£5
ditto, Atheneum (U.S.), 1975 . . . . . £10/£5
The Fossil Snake, Bodley Head, 1975 . . £15/£5
ditto, Atheneum (U.S.), 1976 . . . . £10/£5

Poetry
Time is Undone, privately printed, 1954 (750 copies,
wraps) £15

Play
The Horned Man, Faber, 1970 . . . . £15/£5

Autobiography
Memory in a House, Bodley Head, 1973 . £25/£5
ditto, Macmillan (U.S.), 1974 . . . . £20/£5
Perverse and Foolish, Bodley Head, 1979 . £25/£5
Memories, Colt Books, 1992 . . . . . £15/£5

KAY BOYLE
(b.1903 d.1992)

An American novelist and short story writer, Boyle
lived for many years in Europe and between 1946 and
1954 was a foreign correspondent for the *New Yorker*.

Novels
Plagued by the Nightingale, Cape & Smith (U.S.),
1931 . . . . £200/£30
ditto, Lehmann, 1951 . . . . £65/£20
Year Before Last, Smith (U.S.), 1932 . . £60/£20
ditto, Faber, 1932 . . . . £75/£25
Gentlemen, I Address You Privately, Smith & Haas
(U.S.), 1933 . . . . £200/£25
ditto, Faber, 1934 . . . . £75/£25

My Next Bride, Harcourt, Brace (U.S.), 1934 £50/£20
ditto, Faber, 1935 . . . . £50/£20
Death of a Man, Harcourt, Brace (U.S.), [1936] .
. . . . £45/£15
ditto, Faber, 1936 . . . . £50/£20
Monday Night, Harcourt, Brace (U.S.), 1938 £125/£25
ditto, Faber, 1932 . . . . £50/£20
The Crazy Hunter: Three Short Novels, Harcourt,
Brace (U.S.), 1940 . . . . £125/£10
ditto, Faber, 1940 . . . . £25/£10
Primer for Combat, Simon & Schuster (U.S.), 1942 .
. . . . £25/£10
ditto, Faber, 1943 . . . . £25/£10
Avalanche, Simon & Schuster (U.S.), 1944 £25/£10
ditto, Faber, 1945 . . . . £25/£10
A Frenchman Must Die, Simon & Schuster (U.S.),
1946 . . . . £25/£10
ditto, Faber, 1946 . . . . £25/£10
1939, Simon & Schuster (U.S.), 1948 . . £25/£10
ditto, Faber, 1948 . . . . £25/£10
His Human Majesty, Whittlesey House (U.S.), 1949 .
. . . . £25/£10
ditto, Faber, 1950 . . . . £25/£10
The Seagull on the Step, Knopf (U.S.), 1955 £25/£10
ditto, Faber, 1955 . . . . £25/£10
Generation Without Farewell, Knopf (U.S.), 1960 .
. . . . £25/£10
ditto, Faber, 1960 . . . . £25/£10
The Underground Woman, Doubleday (U.S.), 1975 .
. . . . £25/£10

Short Stories
Short Stories, Black Sun Press (France), 1929 (15
signed copies on Japan paper, wraps in tied protected
boards) £1,000
ditto, Black Sun Press, 1929 (20 copies on Arches
paper, wraps in tied protected boards) . . . £750
ditto, Black Sun Press, 1929 (150 copies on Van
Gelder paper, wraps in tied protected boards) £600
Wedding Day and Other Stories, Cape & Smith (U.S.),
1930 . . . . £250/£25
ditto, Pharos Edition, 1932 . . . . . £200/£20
The First Lover and Other Stories, Smith & Haas
(U.S.), 1933 . . . . £150/£25
ditto, Faber, 1937 . . . . £75/£25
The White Horses of Vienna and Other Stories,
Harcourt, Brace (U.S.), [1936] . . . . £150/£25
ditto, Faber, 1937 . . . . £45/£10
Thirty Stories, Simon & Schuster (U.S.), 1946 . . .
. . . . £100/£200
ditto, Faber, 1948 . . . . £40/£10
*The Smoking Mountain: Stories of Post-War
Germany*, McGraw-Hill (U.S.), 1951 . . £35/£10
ditto, Faber, 1952 . . . . £35/£10
Three Short Novels, Beacon Press (U.S.), 1958 (wraps)
. . . . £20
Nothing Ever Breaks Except the Heart, Doubleday
(U.S.), 1966 . . . . £25/£10

Verse

A Statement, Modern Edition Press (U.S.), 1932 (175 signed, numbered copies) £300

A Glad Day, New Directions (U.S.), 1938 . . £75

American Citizen: Naturalized in Leadville, Colorado, Simon & Schuster (U.S.), 1944 (wraps) . . £30

Collected Poems, Knopf (U.S.), 1962 . . £25/£10

Testament for My Students, Doubleday (U.S.), 1970 .
. . . . £25/£10

Others

The Youngest Camel, Little, Brown (U.S.), 1939 . .
. . . . £60/£15

ditto, Faber, 1939 . . . . £40/£15

Breaking the Silence: Why a Mother Tells Her Son about the Nazi Era, Institute of Human Relations Press (U.S.), 1962 (wraps) £20

Pinky: The Cat Who Liked to Sleep, Crowell-Collier (U.S.), 1966 . . . . £45/£15

Pinky in Persia, Crowell-Collier (U.S.), 1968 £40/£15

Being Geniuses Together, Doubleday (U.S.), 1968 (with Robert McAlmon). . . . . . £20/£5

ditto, Joseph, 1970. . . . . . . £20/£5

The Long Walk at San Francisco State and Other Essays, Grove (U.S.) 1970 . . . . . £20/£5

Four Visions of America, Capra Press (U.S.), 1977 .
. . . . £20/£5

ditto, Capra Press (U.S.), 1977 (wraps) . . . £5

ELIZABETH BOWEN

(b.1899 d.1973)

Anglo-Irish novelist and short story writer noted for her attention to detail and subtlety of style.

Short Stories

Encounters: Stories, Sidgwick & Jackson, 1923 .
. . . . £750/£175

ditto, Boni & Liveright, 1926. . . . . £100/£25

Ann Lee's and Other Stories, Sidgwick & Jackson, 1926 . . . . £500/£75

ditto, Boni & Liveright, 1926. . . . . £100/£25

Joining Charles and Other Stories, Constable, 1929 .
. . . . £175/£30

ditto, Dial Press, 1929. . . . . . £100/£25

The Cat Jumps and Other Stories, Gollancz, 1934 .
. . . . £175/£30

Look at All Those Roses, Gollancz, 1941 £75/£15

ditto, Knopf (U.S.), 1941 . . . . . £25/£10

The Demon Lover and Other Stories, Cape, [1945] .
. . . . £100£25

ditto, as Ivy Gripped the Steps and Other Stories, Knopf (U.S.), 1946 . . . . . . £40/£15

Selected Stories, Fridberg (Dublin), 1946 (wraps with d/w) . . . . £20/£5

Early Stories, Knopf (U.S.), 1951 . . . £20/£5

Stories, Knopf (U.S.), 1959 . . . . . £15/£5

A Day in the Dark and Other Stories, Cape, 1965 .
. . . . £15/£5

ditto, Random House (U.S.), 1982 . . . £20/£5

The Collected Stories, Cape, 1981 . . . £20/£5

ditto, Random House (U.S.), 1982 . . . £20/£5

Novels

The Hotel, Constable, 1927 . . . . . £250/£25

ditto, Dial Press, 1928. . . . . . . £65/£15

The Last September, Constable, 1929 . . £225/£25

ditto, Dial Press, 1929. . . . . . . £175/£20

Friends and Relations, Constable, 1931 . £200/£25

ditto, Dial Press, 1931. . . . . . . £175/£20

To the North, Gollancz, 1931 . . . . £175/£20

ditto, Knopf (U.S.), 1933 . . . . . . £75/£15

The House in Paris, Gollancz, 1935. . . £150/£20

ditto, Knopf (U.S.), 1936 . . . . . . £75/£15

The Death of the Heart, Gollancz, 1938 . £125£20

ditto, Knopf (U.S.), 1939 . . . . . . £75/£15

The Heat of the Day, Cape, 1949 . . . £15/£5

ditto, Knopf (U.S.), 1949 . . . . . . £15/£5

A World of Love, Cape, 1955 . . . . £15/£5

ditto, Knopf (U.S.), 1955 . . . . . . £15/£5

The Little Girls, Cape, 1964 . . . . £15/£5

ditto, Knopf (U.S.), 1964 . . . . . . £15/£5

Eva Trout, Knopf (U.S.), 1968 . . . . £20/£5

ditto, Cape, 1969 . . . . £15/£5

Non Fiction

Bowen's Court, Longman, 1942 . . . . £35/£10

ditto, Knopf (U.S.), 1942 . . . . . . £30/£10

English Novelists, Collins, 1942 . . . . £10/£5

ditto, Hastings House (U.S.), 1942 . . . £10/£5

Seven Winters, Cuala Press (Dublin), 1942 (450 numbered copies) . . . . . . £150/£100

ditto, Longman, 1943 . . . . . . £15/£5

ditto, Knopf (U.S.), 1943 . . . . . . £15/£5

Anthony Trollope: A New Judgement, O.U.P., 1946 .
. . . . £15/£5

Why Do I Write?: An Exchange of Views Between Elizabeth Bowen, Graham Greene, and V.S. Pritchett, Marshall, 1948 . . . . . £100/£25

Collected Impressions, Longman, 1950 . . £20/£5

ditto, Knopf (U.S.), 1950 . . . . . . £20/£5

The Shelbourne, Harrap, 1951 . . . £25/£10

ditto, as The Shelbourne Hotel, Knopf (U.S.), 1951 .
. . . . £20/£5

A Time in Rome, Longman, 1960 . . . £15/£5

ditto, Knopf (U.S.), 1960 . . . . . . £15/£5

Afterthought: Pieces About Writing, Longman, 1962 .
. . . . £15/£5

ditto, Knopf (U.S.), 1962 . . . . . . £15/£5

Pictures and Conversations, Knopf (U.S.), 1975 .
. . . . £20/£5

ditto, Knopf (U.S.), 1975 . . . . . . £20/£5

The Mulberry Tree, Virago, 1986 . . . £15/£5

Children's
The Good Tiger, Knopf (U.S.), 1965 . . £25/£5
ditto, Cape, 1970 . . . . £20/£5

WILLIAM BOYD
(b.1952)

Born in Ghana, Boyd's first two books remain highly collectable, although he is currently slightly out of vogue.

A Good Man in Africa, Hamish Hamilton, 1981 .
. . . . £450/£45
ditto, Morrow (U.S.), 1982 . . . . £65/£20
On the Yankee Station and Other Stories, Hamish Hamilton, 1982 . . . . £30/£35
ditto, Morrow (U.S.), 1984 . . . . £40/£10
An Ice Cream War, Hamish Hamilton, 1982 £75/£15
ditto, Morrow (U.S.), 1983 . . . . £35/£10
Stars and Bars, Hamish Hamilton, 1984 . £45/£10
ditto, Morrow (U.S.), 1985 . . . . £30/£5
School Ties, Hamish Hamilton, 1985 . . £35/£10
ditto, Penguin, 1985 (wraps) £5
ditto, Morrow (U.S.), 1986 . . . . £30/£5
The New Confessions, Hamish Hamilton, 1987 £25/£5
ditto, Morrow (U.S.), 1988 . . . . £15/£5
Brazzaville Beach, Sinclair Stevenson, 1990 £20/£5
ditto, London Limited Editions, 1990 (150 signed copies, cellophane d/w) . . . . . £65/£60
ditto, Morrow (U.S.), 1991 . . . . £10/£5
The Blue Afternoon, Sinclair Stevenson, 1993 £10/£5
ditto, London Limited Editions, 1993 (150 signed copies, cellophane d/w) . . . . . £50/£45
ditto, Knopf (U.S.), 1995 . . . . . £10/£5
Cork, Ulysses, 1994 (26 copies) £125
ditto, Ulysses, 1994 (60 copies) £75
ditto, Ulysses, 1994 (150 copies). . . . £35
The Destiny of Nathalie 'X' and Other Short Stories, Sinclair Stevenson, 1995 . . . . £10/£5
ditto, Knopf (U.S.), 1997 . . . . . £10/£5
Transfigured Night, One Horse press, 1995 (wraps) (2,000 signed, numbered copies) . . . £30
Armadillo, Hamish Hamilton, 1998 . . . £10/£5
ditto, Knopf (U.S.), 1998 . . . . . £10/£5
Protobiography, Bridgewater Press, 1998 (26 signed, lettered copies of 138 copies) £100
ditto, Bridgewater Press, 1998 (100 signed, lettered copies of 138 copies) £45
A Haunting, Bridgewater Press, 2000 (26 signed, lettered copies of 138 copies) £100
ditto, Bridgewater Press, 2000 (100 signed, lettered copies of 138 copies) £45

MALCOLM BRADBURY
(b.1932 d.2000)

A novelist and critic, The History Man is his best regarded novel, satirising the university culture of the 1960s and 70s.

Novels
Eating People is Wrong, Secker & Warburg, 1959 .
. . . . £125/£45
ditto, Knopf (U.S.), 1960 . . . . . £45/£15
Stepping Westward, Secker & Warburg, 1965 £75/£25
ditto, Houghton & Mifflin (U.S.), 1966 . . £15/£5
The History Man, Secker & Warburg, 1975 £50/£15
ditto, Houghton & Mifflin (U.S.), 1976 . . £15/£5
Rates of Exchange, Secker & Warburg, 1983 £15/£5
ditto, Knopf (U.S.), 1983 . . . . . . £10/£5
Doctor Criminale, Secker & Warburg, 1992 £10/£5
ditto, Viking (U.S.), 1992. . . . . . £10/£5
To the Hermitage, Picador, 2000 . . . £10/£5

Novella
Cuts, Hutchinson, 1987 . . . . . . £15/£5
ditto, Harper (U.S.), 1987. . . . . . £15/£5

Short Stories
Who Do You Think You Are?, Secker & Warburg, 1976 . . . . £15/£5

Criticism etc.
Phogey! How to Have Class in a Classless Society, Parrish, 1960 . . . . £25/£10
All Dressed Up and Nowhere to Go, Parrish, 1962 .
. . . . £25/£10
Evelyn Waugh, Oliver & Boyd, 1964 (wraps) . £25
What is a Novel?, Arnold, 1969 . . . . . £15
The Social Context of Modern English Literature, Blackwell, 1971 . . . . £20/£5
Possibilities: Essays on the State of the Novel, O.U.P., 1973 . . . . £10
Saul Bellow, Methuen, 1982 (wraps) . . . £10
The Modern American Novel, O.U.P., 1983 £10/£5
ditto, Viking (U.S.), 1993. . . . . . £10/£5
Why Come to Slaka?, Secker & Warburg, 1986 £10
ditto, Penguin (U.S.), 1988 . . . . . £10
My Strange Quest for Mensonge: Structuralism's Hidden Hero, Deutsch, 1987 . . . . £10/£5
ditto, Penguin (U.S.), 1988 . . . . . . £10
No, Not Bloomsbury, Deutsch, 1987 . . £10/£5
ditto, Columbia Univ. Press (U.S.), 1988 . £10/£5
The Modern World: Ten Great Writers, Secker & Warburg, 1988 . . . . £10/£5
ditto, Viking (U.S.), 1989. . . . . . £10/£5
Unsent Letters, Deutsch, 1988 . . . . £10/£5
ditto, Viking (U.S.), 1988. . . . . . £10/£5
From Puritanism to Post-modernism: The Story of American Literature, Routledge, 1991 (with Richard Ruland) . . . . £10/£5
ditto, Viking (U.S.), 1991. . . . . . £10/£5

The Modern British Novel, Secker & Warburg, 1993 .
. . . . £10/£5
Dangerous Pilgrimages, Secker & Warburg, 1995 .
. . . . £10/£5
ditto, Viking (U.S.), 1996 . . . . . £10/£5

RAY BRADBURY
(b.1920)

American author of fiction in various genres, Bradbury originally emerged from the science fiction pulp magazines and is considered a leading writer in the field.

Novels
Fahrenheit 451, Ballantine (U.S.), 1953 (wraps) £65
ditto, Ballantine (U.S.), 1953 (author's copies in cloth)
. . . . £2,000
ditto, Ballantine (U.S.), 1953 (200 signed, numbered copies) £3,000
ditto, Hart-Davis, 1954 . . . . . . £500/£65
ditto, Limited Editions Club (U.S.), 1982 (2,000 signed, numbered copies, slipcase) . . £150/£100
ditto, Simon & Schuster (U.S.), 1994 (500 signed, numbered copies, slipcase) . . . . £150/£100
Dandelion Wine, Doubleday (U.S.), 1957 . £600/£35
ditto, Hart-Davis, 1957 . . . . . . £200/£25
Something Wicked This Way Comes, Simon & Schuster (U.S.), 1962 . . . . . £300/£50
ditto, Hart-Davis, 1963 . . . . . £200/£20
ditto, Gauntlet Press (U.S.), 1999 (500 signed, numbered copies) . . . . . £65/£35
ditto, Gauntlet Press (U.S.), 1999 (52 signed, numbered deluxe copies) . . . . . £250/£200
Death is a Lonely Business, Knopf (U.S.), 1985 .
. . . . £20/£5
ditto, Knopf (U.S.), 1985 (60 signed presentation copies) £250
ditto, Franklin Press (U.S.), 1985 (signed, limited edition, full leather) £50
ditto, Grafton, 1986 . . . . . . £15/£5
A Graveyard for Lunatics, Knopf (U.S.), 1990 .
. . . . £15/£5
ditto, Grafton, 1990 . . . . . . £10/£5
Green Shadows, White Whale, Knopf (U.S.), 1992 .
. . . . £10/£5
ditto, Ultramarine Press (U.S.), 1992 (38 signed copies, no d/w) £100

Omnibus Editions
The Novels of Ray Bradbury, Granada, 1984 £15/£5

Short Stories
Dark Carnival, Arkham House (Sauk City, U.S.), 1947
. . . . £500/£75
ditto, Hamish Hamilton, 1948 . . . . £400/£35

The Martian Chronicles, Doubleday (U.S.), 1950 (green binding) . . . . £750/£125
ditto, as *The Silver Locusts*, Hart-Davis, 1951 . .
. . . . £200/£45
The Illustrated Man, Doubleday (U.S.), 1951 . . .
. . . . £250/£30
ditto, Hart-Davis, 1952 . . . . . . £125/£20
The Golden Apples of the Sun, Doubleday (U.S.), 1953 . . . . £250/£35
ditto, Hart-Davis, 1953 . . . . . £50/£15
The October Country, Ballantine (U.S.), 1955 . . .
. . . . £100/£30
ditto, Hart-Davis, 1956 . . . . . £60/£25
A Medicine for Melancholy, Doubleday (U.S.), 1959 .
. . . . £40/£15
ditto, as *The Day it Rained Forever*, Hart-Davis, 1959
. . . . £35/£10
The Machineries of Joy, Simon & Schuster (U.S.), 1964 . . . . £50/£15
ditto, Hart-Davis, 1964 . . . . . £30/£5
The Pedestrian, Roy Squires (U.S.), [1964] (280 copies, card wraps) £100
The Vintage Bradbury, Random House (U.S.), 1965 .
. . . . £15/£5
The Autumn People, Ballantine (U.S.), 1965 (cartoons, wraps) £10
Tomorrow Midnight, Ballantine (U.S.), 1966 (cartoons, wraps) £15
Twice Twenty Two, Doubleday (U.S.), 1966 £22/£10
I Sing the Body Electric!, Knopf (U.S.), 1969 £50/£10
ditto, Hart-Davis, 1970 . . . . . £25/£10
Bloch and Bradbury (with Robert Bloch), Tower (U.S.), 1969 (wraps) £5
Fever Dreams and Other Stories (with Robert Bloch), Sphere, 1970 (wraps) £5
The Small Assassin, New English Library, 1962 . .
. . . . £15/£5
Selected Stories, Harrap, 1975 (ed Anthony Adams) .
. . . . £15/£5
Long After Midnight, Knopf (U.S.), 1976 . £10/£5
ditto, Hart-Davis MacGibbon, 1977 . . . £15/£5
The Best of Bradbury, Bantam (U.S.), 1976 (wraps) .
. . . . £10
To Sing Strange Songs, Wheaton, 1979 . . £10
The Stories of Ray Bradbury, Knopf (U.S.), 1980 . .
. . . . £20/£10
ditto, Granada, 1980, (two vols, wraps) . . . £5
The Last Circus, and The Electrocution, Lord John Press (U.S.), 1980 (300 signed copies, slipcase) . .
. . . . £50/£40
Dinosaur Tales, Bantam (U.S.), 1983 (wraps) £5
A Memory for Murder, Dell (U.S.), 1984, (wraps) £5
The Toynbee Convector, Knopf (U.S.), 1988 £20/£10
ditto, Knopf (U.S.), 1988 (350 signed copies) £100/£85
ditto, Grafton, 1989 . . . . £5
The Dragon, Footsteps Press (U.S.), 1988 (26 signed, lettered copies of 300, wraps) £65
ditto, Footsteps Press (U.S.), 1988 (numbered copies, wraps) £25

Quicker Than The Eye, Avon (U.S.), 1996. £10/£5
ditto, Franklin Library (U.S.), 1996 (signed copies) .
. . . . £100/£85
Driving Blind, Avon (U.S.), 1997 . . . £10/£5

Verse

Old Ahab's Friend, Squires (U.S.), 1971 (445 unsigned copies of 485, wraps) £20
ditto, Squires (U.S.), 1971 (40 signed copies of 485) .
. . . . £75
That Son of Richard III, Squires (U.S.), 1974 (400 unsigned copies of 485, wraps) £20
ditto, Squires (U.S.), 1974 (85 signed copies of 485) .
. . . . £50
Twin Hieroglyphs that Swim the River Dust, Lord John Press (U.S.), 1978 (300 signed copies of edition of 326) £35
ditto, Lord John Press (U.S.), 1980 (26 signed, lettered deluxe copies) £100
The Bike Repairman, Lord John Press (U.S.), 1978 (limited edition) £35
The Poet Considers His Resources, Lord John Press (U.S.), 1979 (200 signed copies, broadside) . £25
The Aquaduct, Squires (U.S.), 1979 (230 copies, wraps) £25
The Attic Where The Meadow Greens, Lord John Press (U.S.), 1980 (300 copies, signed) . . £50
ditto, Lord John Press (U.S.), 1980 (75 deluxe copies, signed) £125
The Love Affair, Lord John Press (U.S.), 1983 (300 signed copies) . . . . . £45/£30
ditto, Lord John Press (U.S.), 1983 (100 signed deluxe copies) £65
Forever and the Earth, Croissant (U.S.), 1984 (300 signed copies, tissue d/w) £125
The Complete Poems of Ray Bradbury, Ballantine (U.S.), 1982 . . . . £5
Beyond 1984: Remembrance of Things Future, Targ (U.S.) 1979 (350 signed copies) . . . £65/£45
Then Is All Love? It Is, It Is!, Orange County Book Society (U.S.), 1981 (230 signed copies, broadside) .
. . . . £25
Death Has Lost Its Charm For Me, Lord John Press (U.S.), 1987 (150 signed copies, no d/w) . . £65
With Cat for Comforter, Gibbs-Smith (U.S.), 1997 .
. . . . £20/£5

Plays

The Meadow, (in *Best One-Act Plays of, 1947-48*) Dodd, Mead (U.S.), 1948 . . . . . £100/£25
The Anthem Sprinters and Other Antics, Dial Press (U.S.), 1963 . . . . £75/£15
A Device Out Of Time, privately printed (U.S.), 1965 (35 to 40 copies) £500
ditto, Dramatic Publishing Company, 1976 . . £15
The Day it Rained Forever, French (U.S.), 1966 £5
The Pedestrian, French (U.S.), 1966 . . . £5
The Wonderful Ice Cream Suit and Other Plays, Bantam (U.S.), 1972 . . . . £15

ditto, Hart-Davis, 1973 . . . . . . £25/£10
Pillar of Fire and Other Plays of Today, Tomorrow and beyond Tomorrow, Bantam (U.S.), 1975 £15
That Ghost, that Bride of Time: Excerpts from a Play-in-Progress, Squires (U.S.), 1976 (150 signed copies of 400, wraps) £75
ditto, Squires (U.S.), 1976 (250 unsigned copies of 400, wraps) £25

Children's Books

Switch on the Night, Pantheon (U.S.), 1955 . £45
ditto, Hart-Davis, 1955 . . . . . £35/£10
R is for Rocket, Doubleday (U.S.), 1962 . £45/£15
ditto, Hart-Davis, 1968 . . . . . £35/£5
S is for Space, Doubleday (U.S.), 1966 . £40/£15
ditto, Hart-Davis, 1968 . . . . . £35/£5
The Hallowe'en Tree, Knopf (U.S.), 1972 . £45/£15
ditto, Hart-Davis MacGibbon, 1973 . . . £45/£15
When Elephants Last in the Dooryard Boomed: Celebrations for Almost any Day of the Year, Knopf (U.S.), 1973 . . . . £25/£5
ditto, Hart-Davis, 1975 . . . . . £20/£5
Where Robot Mice and Robot Men Run Round in Robot Towns: New Poems both Light and Dark, Knopf (U.S.), 1977 . . . . . . £25/£5
ditto, Granada, 1979 . . . . . . £15/£5
The Haunted Computer and the Android Pope, Knopf (U.S.), 1981 . . . . £15/£5
ditto, Granada, 1981 . . . . . . £15/£5
Dogs Think That Every Day Is Christmas, Gibbs-Smith (U.S.) 1997 . . . . . . £15/£5

Miscellaneous

No Man is an Island, Brandeis University (U.S.), 1952 (wraps) £50
The Circus of Dr Lao and Other Improbable Stories (ed by Ray Bradbury), Bantam, 1956 (wraps) £5
Teacher's Guide: Science Fiction with Lewy Olfson, Bantam (U.S.), 1969 . . . . £10
Mars and the Mind of Man, Harper (U.S.), 1973 .
. . . . £15/£5
Zen and the Art of Writing, and The Joy of Writing, Capra Press (U.S.), 1973 (250 signed copies) £125
The Mummies of Guanajuato. Photographs by Archie Lieberman, Abrams (U.S.), 1978 . . . £50/£20
Beyond, 1984: Remembrance of Things Future, Targ (U.S.), 1979 (350 signed copies, acetate dust wrapper)
. . . . £50
Flatland: A Romance of Many Dimensions, by Edwin Abbott, (with an introduction by Bradbury, limited edition), Arion Press, 1980 . . . . . £100
Fantasmas Para Siempre, Ediciones Libreria (Buenos Aires), 1980 . . . . £75/£45
ditto, as *The Ghosts of Forever*, Rizzoli (U.S.), 1981 .
. . . . £50/£30
Los Angeles. Photographs by West Light, Skyline Press (U.S.), 1984 . . . . £5
Orange County. Photographs by Bill Ross and others, Skyline Press (U.S.), 1985 . . . . . £5

The Art of 'Playboy', Playboy Press, 1985 . £25/£15
Yestermorrow: Obvious Answers to Impossible Futures, Capra Press (U.S.), 1991 . . . £15/£5

JOHN BRAINE
(b.1922 d.1986)

A novelist best known for *Room at the Top*, a classic novel of the 'Angry Young Men' School.

Room at the Top, Eyre & Spottiswoode, 1957 . . .
. . . . £200/£25
ditto, Houghton Mifflin (U.S.), 1957 . . £25/£10
The Void, Eyre & Spottiswoode, 1959 . . £20/£5
Life at the Top, Eyre & Spottiswoode, 1962 £45/£10
ditto, Houghton Mifflin (U.S.), 1962 . . £25/£5
The Jealous God, Eyre & Spottiswoode, 1964 £10/£5
ditto, Houghton Mifflin (U.S.), 1965 . . £10/£5
The Crying Game, Eyre & Spottiswoode, 1968 . .
. . . . £15/£5
ditto, Houghton Mifflin (U.S.), 1968 . . £10/£5
Stay with Me till Morning, Eyre & Spottiswoode, 1970
. . . . £10/£5
The Queen of a Distant Country, Methuen, 1972 . .
. . . . £10/£5
ditto, Coward, McCann & Geoghegan (U.S.), 1973 .
. . . . £10/£5
Writing a Novel, Eyre Methuen, 1974 . . £10/£5
The Pious Agent, Eyre Methuen, 1975 . . £10/£5
ditto, Atheneum (U.S.), 1976 . . . . £10/£5
Waiting for Sheila, Eyre Methuen, 1976 . £10/£5
Finger of Fire, Eyre Methuen, 1977 . . £10/£5
J.B. Priestley, Weidenfeld & Nicolson, 1979 £10/£5
One and Last Love, Eyre Methuen, 1981 . £10/£5
The Two of Us, Methuen, 1984 . . . £10/£5
These Golden Days, Methuen, 1985 . . £10/£5

ERNEST BRAMAH
(b. 1868 d.1942)

Ernest Bramah Smith is read for his Kai Lung and Max Carrados stories, the former featuring a Chinese philosopher, the latter a blind detective.

Kai Lung Titles
The Wallet of Kai Lung, Grant Richards, 1900 £300
ditto, L.C. Page and Company (U.S.), 1900 . £150
ditto, Grant Richards's Colonial Library, 1900 . £200
ditto, Grant Richards, 1923 (200 signed copies) .
. . . . £175/£125
ditto, Doran (U.S.), [1923] . . . £150/£60
The Transmutation of Ling, Grant Richards (U.K.)/ Brentano's (U.S.), 1911 (500 copies) . . . £125
Kai Lung's Golden Hours, Grant Richards, 1922 .
. . . . £150/£50

ditto, Doran (U.S.), 1923 . . . . . £95/£60
ditto, Grant Richards, 1924 (200 signed copies) . .
. . . . £350/£200
The Story of Wan and the Remarkable Shrub ..., Doubleday Doran (U.S.), 1927 (wraps) . . £150
ditto, as *Kai Lung Unrolls His Mat*, Richards Press, 1928 (the above title comprises two chapters from this book) . . . . £75/£45
ditto, Doran (U.S.), 1928 . . . . . £75/£50
The Moon of Much Gladness, Cassell, 1932 £100/£50
ditto, as *The Return of Kai Lung*, Sheridan House (U.S.), 1937 . . . . £75/£45
The Kai Lung Omnibus, Philip Allan, 1936 £75/£25
Kai Lung Beneath the Mulberry-Tree, Richards Press, 1940 . . . . £150/£45
ditto, Arno Press (U.S.), 1978 . . . . £15
Kin Weng and the Miraculous Tusk, City of Birmingham School of Printing, 1941 . . . . £50
The Celestial Omnibus, Richards Press, 1963 £35/£10
Kai Lung: Six, Non-Profit Press (U.S.), 1974 (250 copies) . . . . £50/£15

Max Carrados Titles
Max Carrados, Methuen, 1914 . . . . £400/£150
ditto, Hyperion Press (U.S.), 1975 . . . £20
The Eyes of Max Carrados, Grant Richards, 1923 .
. . . . £250/£125
ditto, Doran (U.S.), 1924 . . . . . £75/£40
Max Carrados Mysteries, Hodder & Stoughton, 1927 .
. . . . £175/£100
ditto, Penguin (U.S.), 1964 . . . . . £10
The Bravo of London, Cassell, 1934 . . £600/£175

Kai Lung & Max Carrados Titles
The Specimen Case, Hodder & Stoughton, 1924 . . .
. . . . £200/£50
ditto, Doran (U.S.), 1925 . . . . . £100/£45
Short Stories of Today and Yesterday, Harrap, 1929 .
. . . . £65/£20

Other Fiction
The Mirror of Kong Ho, Chapman & Hall, 1905 . .
. . . . £100/£45
ditto, Doubleday (U.S.), 1930 . . . £45/£20
What Might Have Been, John Murray, 1907 (anonymous) £200
ditto, as *The Secret of the League: The Story of a Social War*, Nelson, [1909] £75
ditto, as *The Secret of the League: The Story of a Social War*, Specular Press (U.S.), 1995 (wraps) £10
A Little Flutter, Cassell, 1930 . . . . . £100

Non Fiction
English Farming and Why I Turned It Up, Leadenhall Press, 1894 . . . . £150
A Handbook for Writers and Artists, Deacon, 1898 .
. . . . £100
A Guide to the Varieties and Rarity of English Regal Copper Coins, Methuen, 1929 . . . . £50

ANGELA BRAZIL
(b.1868 d.1947)

A British born author who found success with school stories for girls.

A Terrible Tomboy, Gay & Bird, 1904 . . . £100
The Fortunes of Philippa, Blackie, 1907 [1906] £75
The Third Class at Miss Kaye's, Blackie, 1909 [1908]
. . . . £75
The Nicest Girl in the School, Blackie, 1910 . £65
Bosom Friends: A Seaside Story, Nelson, [1910] £50
The Manor House School, Blackie, 1911 . . £45
A Fourth Form Friendship, Blackie, 1912 . . £45
The New Girl at St. Chad's, Blackie, 1912 . . £45
A Pair of Schoolgirls, Blackie, [1912] . . . £45
The Leader of the Lower School, Blackie, [1914] £45
The Youngest Girl in the Fifth, Blackie, [1914] £45
The Girls of St. Cyprian's, Blackie, [1914]. . £45
The School by the Sea, Blackie, [1914]. . . £45
The Jolliest Term on Record, Blackie, [1915] . £40
For the Sake of the School, Blackie, [1915] . £40
The Luckiest Girl in the School, Blackie. [1916] £35
The Slap-Bang Boys, T. C. & E. G, Jack, [1917] £35
The Madcap of the School, Blackie, [1918] . £35
A Patriotic Schoolgirl, Blackie, [1918] . . . £30
For the School Colours, Blackie, [1918] . . £25
A Harum-Scarum Schoolgirl, Blackie, [1919]. £25
The Head Girl at The Gables, Blackie, [1919]. £20
Two Little Scamps and a Puppy, Nelson, [1919] £25
A Gift from the Sea, Nelson, [1920]. . . £100/£20
A Popular Schoolgirl, Blackie, [1920] . . £100/£20
The Princess of the School, Blackie, [1920] £100/£20
A Fortunate Term, Blackie, [1921] . . . £100/£20
Loyal to the School, Blackie, [1921] . . £100/£20
Moniteress Merle, Blackie, [1922] . . . £100/£20
The School in the South, Blackie. [1922] . £100/£20
The Khaki Boys and Other Stories, Nelson, [1923] .
. . . . £100/£20
Schoolgirl Kitty, Blackie, [1923]. . . . £100/£20
Captain Peggie, Blackie, [1924] . . . . £75/£15
Joan's Best Chum, Blackie, [1926] . . . £75/£15
Queen of the Dormitory and Other Stories, Cassell,
[1926]. . . . . £50/£15
Ruth of St. Ronans, Blackie, [1927]. . . £50/£15
At School with Rachel, Blackie, [1928]. . £50/£15
St. Catherine's College, Blackie, [1929] . £50/£10
The Little Green School, Blackie, [1931] . £50/£10
Nesta's New School, Blackie, [1932] . . £50/£10
Jean's Golden Term, Blackie, [1934] . . £50/£10
The School at the Turrets, Blackie, [1935] . £50/£10
An Exciting Term, Blackie, [1936] . . . £45/£10
Jill's Jolliest School, Blackie, 1937 . . . £45/£10
The School on the Cliff, Blackie, [1938] . £45/£10
The School on the Moor, Blackie, [1939] . £45/£10
The New School at Scawdale, Blackie, [1940] £45/£10
Five Jolly Schoolgirls, Blackie, [1941] . . £45/£10

The Mystery of the Moated Grange, Blackie [1942] .
. . . . £35/£10
The Secret of the Border Castle, Blackie, [1943] . .
. . . . £35/£10
The School in the Forest, Blackie, [1944] . £35/£10
Three Terms at Uplands, Blackie, [1945] . £35/£10
The School on the Loch, Blackie, [1946] . £35/£10

Plays
The Mischievous Brownie, Paterson, 'Children's
Plays' series No. 1, [1913] £40
The Fairy Gifts, Paterson, 'Children's Plays' series No.
2, [1913] £40
The Enchanted Fiddle, Paterson, 'Children's Plays'
series No. 3, [1913] £40
The Wishing Princess, Paterson, 'Children's Plays'
series No. 4, [1913] £40

Autobiography
My Own Schooldays, Blackie, [1925] . . £65/£15

ELINOR BRENT-DYER
(b.1894 d.1969)

Born Gladys Eleanor May Dyer, this British author of stories for girls worked for many years as a teacher.

'Chalet School' Titles
The School at the Chalet, Chambers, 1925 . £300/£75
Jo of the Chalet School, Chambers, 1926 . £250/£50
The Princess of the Chalet School, Chambers, 1927 .
. . . . £250/£50
The Head Girl of the Chalet School, Chambers, 1928.
. . . . £250/£50
The Rivals of the Chalet School, Chambers, 1929 . .
. . . . £250/£50
Eustacia Goes to the Chalet School, Chambers, 1930
. . . . £250/£50
The Chalet School and Jo, Chambers, 1931 £250/£50
The Chalet School in Camp, Chambers, 1932 . . .
The Exploits of the Chalet School Girls, Chambers,
1933 . . . . £250/£50
The Chalet School and the Lintons, Chambers, 1934 .
. . . . £250/£50
The New House at the Chalet School, Chambers, 1935
. . . . £250/£50
Jo Returns to the Chalet School, Chambers, 1936. .
. . . . £250/£50
The New Chalet School, Chambers, 1938 . £180/£40
The Chalet School in Exile, Chambers, 1940 (Nazi
d/w) . . . . £350/£30
The Chalet School Goes To It, Chambers, 1941 . .
. . . . £65/£30
The Highland Twins at the Chalet School, Chambers,
1942 . . . . £65/£30

Lavender Laughs in the Chalet School, Chambers, 1943 . . . . £65/£30
Gay from China at the Chalet School, Chambers, 1944 . . . . £65/£30
Jo to the Rescue, Chambers, 1945 . . . £65/£30
The Chalet School Book for Girls, Chambers, 1947 . . . . £45
The Second Chalet School Book for Girls, Chambers, 1948 . . . . £45
The Third Chalet School Book for Girls, Chambers, 1949 . . . . £75/£40
Three Go to the Chalet School, Chambers, 1949 . . . . £50/£25
The Chalet School and the Island, Chambers, 1950 . . . . £50/£25
Peggy of the Chalet School, Chambers, 1950 £40/£25
Carola Storms the Chalet School, Chambers, 1951 . . . . £50/£25
The Chalet School and Rosalie, Chambers, 1951 (wraps) £75
The Wrong Chalet School, Chambers, 1952 £40/£25
Shocks for the Chalet School, Chambers, 1952 . . . . £50/£25
The Chalet School in the Oberland, Chambers, 1952 . . . . £60/£30
Bride Leads the Chalet School, Chambers, 1953 . . . . £75/£35
Changes for the Chalet School, Chambers, 1953 . . . . £60/£30
The Chalet Girls' Cook Book, Chambers, 1953 . . . . £100/£75
Joey Goes to the Oberland, Chambers, 1954 £60/£35
The Chalet School and Barbara, Chambers, 1954 . . . . £60/£25
Tom Tackles the Chalet School, Chambers, 1955 . . . . £60/£35
The Chalet School Does it Again, Chambers, 1955 . . . . £75/£40
A Chalet Girl from Kenya, Chambers, 1955 £50/£30
Mary-Lou of the Chalet School, Chambers, 1956 . . . . £50/£25
A Genius at the Chalet School, Chambers, 1956 . . . . £50/£25
A Problem for the Chalet School, Chambers, 1956 . . . . £50/£25
The New Mistress at the Chalet School, Chambers, 1957 . . . . £50/£25
Excitements at the Chalet School, Chambers, 1957 . . . . £45/£25
The Coming of Age at the Chalet School, Chambers, 1958 . . . . £45/£25
The Chalet School and Richenda, Chambers, 1958 . . . . £45/£25
Trials for the Chalet School, Chambers, 1959 £45/£25
Theodora and the Chalet School, Chambers, 1959 . . . . £45/£25
Joey and Co. in Tirol, Chambers, 1960 . . £50/£25
Ruey Richardson, Chaletian, Chambers, 1960 £65/£30

A Leader in the Chalet School, Chambers, 1961 . . . . £50/£25
The Chalet School Wins the Trick, Chambers, 1961 . . . . £50/£25
A Future Chalet School Girl, Chambers, 1962 £55/£30
The Feud in the Chalet School, Chambers, 1962 . . . . £55/£25
The Chalet School Triplets, Chambers, 1963 £45/£25
The Chalet School Reunion, Chambers, 1963 (with d/w, chart and yellow band). . . . . £100/£30
Jane and the Chalet School, Chambers, 1964 £45/£25
Redheads at the Chalet School, Chambers, 1964 . . . . £45/£25
Adrienne and the Chalet School, Chambers, 1965 . . . . £45/£25
Summer Term at the Chalet School, Chambers, 1965. . . . . £45/£25
Challenge for the Chalet School, Chambers, 1966 . . . . £45/£25
Two Sams at the Chalet School, Chambers, 1967 . . . . £45/£25
Althea Joins the Chalet School, Chambers, 1969 . . . . £45/£25
Prefects of the Chalet School, Chambers, 1970 . . . . £60/£25

'La Rochelle' Titles
Gerry Goes to School, Chambers, 1922 . . £200/£50
ditto, Lippincott (Philadelphia), 1923 . . £175/£50
A Head Girl's Difficulties, Chambers, 1923 £175/£50
The Maids of La Rochelle, Chambers, 1924 £175/£50
Seven Scamps, Chambers, 1927 . . . . £175/£50
Heather Leaves School, Chambers, 1929 . £175/£50
Janie of La Rochelle, Chambers, 1932 . . £175/£45
Janie Steps in, Chambers, 1953 . . . . £45/£10

'Chudleigh Hold' Titles
Fardingales, Latimer House, 1950 . . . £125/£25
The 'Susannah' Adventure, Chambers, 1953 £50/£20
Chudleigh Hold, Chambers 1954 . . . £45/£10
The Condor Crags Adventure, Chambers 1954 . . . . £45/£10
Top Secret, Chambers 1955 . . . . . £45/£10

Other Titles
A Thrilling Term at Janeways, Nelson, 1927 . . . . £150/£50
The New Housemistress, Nelson, 1928 . . £45/£10
Judy the Guide, Nelson, 1928 . . . . £100/£45
The School by the River, Burns, Oates & Washbourne, 1930 . . . . £300/£75
The Feud in the Fifth Remove, Girl's Own Paper, 1931 . . . . £75/£25
The Little Marie-Jose, Burns, Oates & Washbourne, 1932 . . . . £300/£75
Carnation of the Upper Fourth, Girl's Own Paper, 1934 . . . . £75/£25
Elizabeth the Gallant, Butterworth, 1935 . £250/£100

Monica Turns Up Trumps, Girl's Own Paper, 1936 .
. . . . £65/£25
Caroline the Second, Girl's Own Paper, 1937 £75/£25
They Both Liked Dogs, Girl's Own Paper, 1938 . .
. . . . £75/£25
The Little Missus, Chambers, 1942 . . . £75/£25
The Lost Staircase, Chambers, 1946 . . £75/£25
Lorna at Wynyards, Lutterworth, 1947 . . £75/£25
Stepsisters for Lorna, Temple, 1948. . . £75/£25
Verena Visits New Zealand, Chambers, 1951 £150/£50
Bess on Her Own in Canada, Chambers, 1951. . .
. . . . £150/£50
Quintette in Queensland, Chambers, 1951 £150/£50
Sharlie's Kenya Diary, Chambers, 1951 £150/£50
Nesta Steps Out, Oliphants, 1954 . . . £50/£20
Kennelmaid Nan, Lutterworth, 1954 . . £50/£20
Beechy of the Harbour School, Oliphants, 1955 . .
. . . . £50/£20
Leader in Spite of Herself, Oliphants, 1956 £50/£20
The School at Skelton Hall, Max Parrish, 1962 . .
. . . . £50/£20
Trouble at Skelton Hall, Max Parrish, 1963 £50/£20

Short Stories
Sunday and Everyday Reading for the Young
(contains 'Jack's Revenge'), Wells, Gardner, Darton,
1914 . . . . £15
The Big Book for Girls (contains 'The Lady in the
Yellow Gown'), Humphrey Milford/O.U.P., 1925 £10
The Golden Story Book for Girls (contains 'The Lady
in the Yellow Gown'), Humphrey Milford/O.U.P.,
1931 . . . . £10
Stories of the Circus, Book 4 (magazine, contains
'Carlotta to the Rescue'), c.1931 . . . . £10
The Children's Circus Book (contains 'Carlotta to the
Rescue'), Associated Newspapers c.1934 . . £10
Come to the Circus (contains 'Carlotta to the Rescue'),
P.R. Gawthorn c.1938 . . . . . . £10
The Second Coronet Book for Girls (contains
'Cavalier Maid'), Sampson Low [n.d.]. . . £10
My Favourite Story (contains 'Rescue in the Snows'),
Thames [n.d.] £10
Sceptre Girls' Story Annual (contains 'House of
Secrets'), Purnell [n.d.] £10
Girl's Own Annual, Vol 57 (contains 'The Robins
Make Good'), Girl's Own [n.d.] £15
My Treasure Hour Bumper Annual (contains 'The
Chalet School Mystery'), Murrays Sales and Service
Co., 1970 . . . . £10

ANNE BRONTË
(b.1820 d.1849)

Not held in as much esteem as her sisters. *Agnes Grey*
was originally published alongside *Wuthering
Heights*.

Poems by Currer, Ellis and Acton Bell, Aylott &
Jones, 1846, first issue (with Charlotte and Emily
Brontë) £20,000
ditto, second issue £2,500
ditto, Smith, Elder & Co, 1846 [1848], second edition .
. . . . £1,500
ditto, Lea and Blanchard (U.S.), 1848 . . . £500
Wuthering Heights with *Agnes Grey*, Newby, 1847,
(pseud. Ellis and Acton Bell, 3 vols) . . £25,000
The Tenant of Wildfell Hall, Newby, 1848, (pseud.
Acton Bell, 3 vols) £20,000
ditto, Harper (U.S.), 1848. . . . . . £1,500

CHARLOTTE BRONTË
(b.1816 d.1855)

Sister to Emily and Anne, Charlotte was the only
Brontë to achieve literary fame in her own lifetime.
Charlotte was a champion of the female spirit, her
Jane Eyre an enduring classic.

Poems by Currer, Ellis and Acton Bell, Aylott &
Jones, 1846, first issue (with Anne and Emily Brontë)
. . . . £20,000
ditto, second issue £2,500
ditto, Smith, Elder & Co, 1846 [1848], second edition .
. . . . £1,500
ditto, Lea and Blanchard (U.S.), 1848 . . £500
Jane Eyre, Smith, Elder & Co., 1847, (3 vols, first
issue, with advertisements dated June, 1847) £20,000
ditto, (second issue, ads dated October, 1847) . £5,000
ditto, Harper (U.S.), 1848 (wraps) . . . £1,250
Shirley, Smith, Elder & Co., 1849, (3 vols) . £2,500
ditto, Harper (U.S.), 1850 (1 vol.) £400
Villette, Smith, Elder & Co., 1853, (3 vols) . £2,500
ditto, Harper (U.S.), 1853 (1 vol.) £400
The Professor, Smith, Elder & Co., 1857, (2 vols). .
. . . . £750
ditto, Smith, Elder & Co., 1857, second state, (2 vols
rebound together) £250
ditto, Harper (U.S.), 1857 (1 vol.) £150

Minor Works
The Last Sketch - Emma: A Fragment, The Cornhill
Magazine Vol I, 1860 . . . . . . £100
The Twelve Adventurers and Other Stories, Hodder &
Stoughton, 1925 . . . . £75/£25
The Spell, O.U.P., 1931 . . . . . £75/£25
Legends of Angria, edited by Fannie E. Ratchford,
Yale Univ. Press (U.S.), 1933 . . . . £45/£15

The Poems of Charlotte Brontë and Patrick Branwell Brontë, edited by T.J. Wise and J.A. Symington, O.U.P., 1934 . . . . £75/£25
The Miscellaneous and Unpublished Writings of Charlotte and Patrick Branwell Brontë, edited by T.J. Wise and J.A. Symington, O.U.P., 1934 (2 vols).
. . . . £75/£25
Tales from Angria, edited by Phyllis Bentley, Collins, 1954 . . . . £20/£5
The Search After Happiness, Harvill Press, 1969 . .
. . . . £20/£5
ditto, Smon & Schuster (U.S.), 1969. . . £20/£5
Five Novelettes, edited by Winifred Gerin, The Folio Society, 1971 (slipcase) . . . . . . £20/£10
A Leaf from an Unopened Volume, The Brontë Society, 1986 (wraps) £15

EMILY BRONTË
(b.1818 d.1848)

Wuthering Heights, now regarded as a classic novel, was published shortly after Charlotte's *Jane Eyre*, and the pseudonyms used by the sisters were originally thought to conceal the identity of a single male author. Emily's poems are often seen as some of the finest lyric verse in the English language.

Poems by Currer, Ellis and Acton Bell, Aylott & Jones, 1846, first issue (with Anne and Charlotte Brontë) £20,000
ditto, second issue £2,500
ditto, Smith, Elder & Co, 1846 [1848], second edition .
. . . . £1,500
Wuthering Heights with Agnes Grey, Newby, 1847, (pseud. Ellis and Acton Bell, 3 vols) . . £25,000

JOCELYN BROOKE
(b.1908 d.1966)

A novelist and poet, Brooke is considered a fine stylist.

The Orchid Series
The Military Orchid, Bodley Head, 1948 . £75/£15
A Mine of Serpents, Bodley Head, 1949 . £60/£15
The Goose Cathederal, Bodley Head, 1950. £40/£15

Other Fiction
The Scapegoat, Bodley Head, 1948 . . . £45/£15
ditto, Harper (U.S.), 1949. . . . . . £25/£10
The Image of a Drawn Sword, Bodley Head, 1950 .
. . . . £60/£20
ditto, Knopf (U.S.), 1951 . . . . . £15/£5
The Passing of a Hero, Bodley Head, 1953 £40/£15
Private View: Four Portraits, Barrie, 1954 . £30/£15

The Dog at Clambercrown, Bodley Head, 1955 . .
. . . . £45/£15
ditto, Vanguard Press (U.S.), 1955 . . . £20/£10
The Crisis in Bulgaria, or Ibsen to the Rescue!, Chatto & Windus, 1956 . . . . . . £80/£15
Conventional Weapons, Faber, 1961 . . £25/£10
ditto, as *The Name of Greene*, Vanguard Press (U.S.), 1961 . . . . £20/£10

Poetry
Six Poems, privately printed, 1928 (50 signed, numbered copies, wraps) £200
December Spring, Bodley Head, 1946 . . £30/£15
The Elements of Death and other poems, Hand & Flower Press, 1952 (wraps) £20

Children's
The Wonderful Summer, Lehmann, 1949 . £50/£20

Non Fiction
The Wild Orchids of Britain, Bodley Head, 1950 (40 specially bound, signed copies of 1,140) . . £750
ditto, Bodley Head, 1950 (1,100 copies of 1,140) . .
. . . . £175/£145
The Flower in Season, Bodley Head, 1952 . £35/£15
Ronald Firbank: A Critical Study, Barker, 1951 . .
. . . . £25/£15
ditto, Roy (U.S.), 1951 . . . . £15/£5
Elizabeth Bowen, British Council/Longmans Green, 1952 (wraps) £5
Aldous Huxley, British Council/Longmans Green, 1953 (wraps) £5
ditto, revised edition, British Council/Longmans Green, 1958 (wraps) £5
Ronald Firbank and John Betjeman, British Council/Longmans Green, 1962 (wraps) . . £5
The Birth of a Legend, Bertram Rota, 1964 (65 signed, numbered copies, wraps) £90

RUPERT BROOKE
(b.1887 d.1915)

Born and educated at Rugby, the future war poet subsequently went up to Cambridge University. Although already a published poet, Brooke achieved his greatest fame posthumously. He died of blood-poisoning aboard ship on his way to the great engagement of the Dardanelles at the age of 28.

Poetry
The Pyramids, privately printed, 1904 (wraps) £4,500
The Bastille, privately printed by A.J. Lawrence, 1905 (wraps) £2,500
ditto, privately printed by George E. Over, [1920] (wraps) £200
Prize Compositions, privately printed, 1905 (wraps) .
. . . . £2,500
Poems, Sidgwick & Jackson, 1911 (no d/w) . £450

1914 and Other Poems, Sidgwick & Jackson, 1915 .
. . . . £150
ditto, Doubleday, Page (U.S.), 1915 (87 copyright
copies, wraps) £1,250
1914, Five Sonnets, Sidgwick & Jackson, 1915
(wraps) £45
War Poems, privately printed, 1915 . . . . £45
The Collected Poems of Rupert Brooke, Lane (U.S.),
1915 (with a Memoir by Edward Marsh) . . £50
ditto, Lane (U.S.), 1915 (100 copies bound for
members of the Woodberry Society) . . . £200
ditto, Sidgwick & Jackson, 1918 . . . . £50
ditto, Riccardi Press, 1919 (1,000 numbered copies) .
. . . . £150
ditto, Riccardi Press, 1919 (13 copies bound in full
vellum) £1,250
The Old Vicarage, Grantchester, Sidgwick & Jackson,
1916 (wraps) £100
Selected Poems, Sidgwick & Jackson, 1917 . £20
Fragments Now First Collected, Hartford (U.S.), 1925
(94 copies) £200
ditto, Hartford (U.S.), 1925 (5 numbered copies on
vellum) £200
Twenty Poems, Sidgwick & Jackson, 1935 (wraps) .
. . . . £20
The Poetical Works of Rupert Brooke, Faber & Faber,
1946 . . . . £35/£10
Poems, Folio Society, 1948 (slipcase) . . £25/£15
Four Poems, Scolar Press, 1974 (100 copies signed by
editor of 500) £45
ditto, Scolar Press, 1974 (400 unsigned copies of 500).
. . . . £35

Prose
The Authorship of the Later 'Appius and Virginia',
privately printed, [1913] (20 copies) . . . £250
Lithuania, A Drama in One Act, Chicago Little
Theatre (U.S.), 1915 (wraps, 200 copies) . . £350
ditto, Sidgwick & Jackson, 1935 . . . . £75/£25
ditto, Sidgwick & Jackson, 1935 (wraps) . . £25
Letters from America, Scribner (U.S.), 1916 . £25
ditto, Sidgwick & Jackson, 1916. . . . . £25
John Webster and the Elizabethan Drama, John Lane
(U.S.), 1916 . . . . £50
ditto, Sidgwick & Jackson, 1916. . . . . £40
A Letter to the Editor of the Poetry Review, Watch Hill
Press, 1929 (50 copies) £150
Democracy and the Arts, Hart-Davis, 1946 (preface by
Geoffrey Keynes) . . . . £25/£10
ditto, Hart-Davis, 1946 (240 numbered copies) £100
The Prose of Rupert Brooke, Sidgwick & Jackson,
1956 (edited and with an introduction by Christopher
Hassall) . . . . £25/£10
The Letters of Rupert Brooke, Faber & Faber, 1968 .
. . . . £30/£10
ditto, Harcourt Brace (U.S.), 1968 . . . £30/£10
*Song of Love: The Letters of Rupert Brooke and Noel
Olivier*, Bloomsbury, 1991 . . . . . £25/£10
ditto, Crown (U.S.), 1992 . . . . . . £25/£10

ANITA BROOKNER
(b.1928)

Brookner's very literary novels are haunted by
solitary, sad women and the failures of their
relationships.

A Start in Life, Cape, 1981 . . . . . £60/£15
ditto, as *The Debut*, Linden Press (U.S.), 1981 £15/£5
Providence, Cape, 1982 . . . . . . £60/£15
ditto, Pantheon (U.S.), 1984 . . . . . £20/£5
Look at Me, Cape, 1983 . . . . . . £30/£5
ditto, Pantheon (U.S.), 1983 . . . . . £20/£5
Hotel Du Lac, Cape, 1984 . . . . . £65/£10
ditto, Pantheon (U.S.), 1985 . . . . . £20/£5
Family and Friends, Cape, 1985. . . . £20/£5
ditto, London Limited Editions, 1985 (250 signed
copies) . . . . £50/£45
ditto, Pantheon (U.S.), 1985 . . . . . £20/£5
A Misalliance, Cape, 1986 . . . . . £20/£5
ditto, as *The Misalliance*, Pantheon (U.S.), 1987 . .
. . . . £20/£5
A Friend From England, Cape, 1987 . . £20/£5
ditto, Pantheon (U.S.), 1988 . . . . . £20/£5
Latecomers, Cape, 1988 . . . . . . £15/£5
ditto, Pantheon (U.S.), 1989 . . . . . £15/£5
Lewis Percy, Cape, 1989 . . . . . . £15/£5
ditto, Pantheon (U.S.), 1990 . . . . . £15/£5
Brief Lives, Cape, 1990 . . . . . . £15/£5
ditto, Random House (U.S.), 1991 . . . £15/£5
A Closed Eye, Cape, 1991 . . . . . £15/£5
ditto, Random House (U.S.), 1992 . . . £15/£5
Fraud, Cape, 1992 . . . . £15/£5
ditto, Random House (U.S.), 1992 . . . £15/£5
A Family Romance, Cape, 1993 . . . . £15/£5
A Private View, Cape, 1994 . . . . . £10/£5
ditto, Random House (U.S.), 1994 . . . £10/£5
Incidents in the Rue Laugier, Cape, 1995 . £10/£5
ditto, Random House (U.S.), 1994 . . . £10/£5
Altered States, Cape, 1996 . . . . . £10/£5
ditto, Random House (U.S.), 1996 . . . £10/£5
Visitors, Cape, 1997 . . . . £10/£5
ditto, Random House (U.S.), 1998 . . . £10/£5
Falling Slowly, Viking, 1998. . . . . £10/£5
ditto, Random House (U.S.), 1999 . . . £10/£5
Undue Influence, Viking, 1999 . . . . £10/£5
ditto, Random House (U.S.), 1999 . . . £10/£5

FREDRIC BROWN
(b.1906 d.1972)

One of the most collectable authors of the pulp era, Brown's work is usually very original, well-plotted and fast-moving.

Novels

The Fabulous Clipjoint, Dutton (U.S.), 1947 £400/£50
ditto, Boardman, 1949 (wraps) £35
The Dead Ringer, Dutton (U.S.), 1948 . . £250/£35
ditto, Boardman, 1949 (wraps) £30
Murder Can be Fun, Dutton (U.S.), 1948 . £200/£35
ditto, Boardman, 1951. . . . . . . £75/£20
The Bloody Moonlight, Dutton (U.S.), 1949 £200/£35
ditto, as *Murder in Moonlight*, Boardman, 1949 . .
. . . . £50/£15
The Screaming Mimi, Dutton (U.S.), 1949 £275/£50
ditto, Boardman, 1950. . . . . . . £75/£20
What Mad Universe, Dutton (U.S.), 1949 . £200/£35
ditto, Boardman, 1951. . . . . . . £75/£20
Compliments of a Fiend, Dutton (U.S.), 1950 . . .
. . . . £200/£35
ditto, Boardman, 1951. . . . . . . £75/£20
Here Comes a Candle, Dutton (U.S.), 1950 £200/£35
ditto, Boardman, 1951. . . . . . . £75/£20
Night of the Jabberwock, Dutton (U.S.), 1950 . . .
. . . . £200/£35
ditto, Boardman, 1951. . . . . . . £75/£20
The Case of the Dancing Sandwiches, Dell (U.S.), 1951 (wraps) £200
Death Has Many Doors, Dutton (U.S.), 1951 £175/£25
ditto, Boardman, 1952. . . . . . . £75/£20
The Far Cry, Dutton (U.S.), 1951 . . £175/£25
ditto, Boardman, 1952. . . . . . . £75/£20
We All Killed Grandma, Dutton (U.S.), 1951 £150/£25
ditto, Boardman, 1952. . . . . . . £50/£15
The Deep End, Dutton (U.S.), 1952 . . . £150/£25
ditto, Boardman, 1953. . . . . . . £50/£15
Madball, Dell (U.S.), 1953 (wraps) . . . £50
ditto, Muller Gold Medal, 1962 (wraps) . . £10
The Lights in the Sky are Stars, Dutton (U.S.), 1953 .
. . . . £125/£25
ditto, as *Project Jupiter*, Boardman, 1954 . £50/£15
His Name Was Death, Dutton (U.S.), 1954 £125/£25
ditto, Boardman, 1955. . . . . . . £50/£15
The Wench is Dead, Dutton (U.S.), 1955 . £125/£25
Martians Go Home, Dutton (U.S.), 1955 . £150/£35
ditto, Grafton, 1987 (wraps) £10
The Lenient Beast, Dutton (U.S.), 1956 . . £125/£25
ditto, Boardman, 1957. . . . . . . £50/£15
Rogue in Space, Dutton (U.S.), 1957 . . £125/£25
One For the Road, Dutton (U.S.), 1958 . . £125/£25
ditto, Boardman, 1959. . . . . . . £50/£15
The Office, Dutton (U.S.), 1958 . . . . £200/£35
ditto, Dennis McMillan (U.S.), 1987 (425 copies) . .
. . . . £40/£10
The Late Lamented, Dutton (U.S.), 1959 . £100/£20
ditto, Boardman, 1959. . . . . . . £50/£15

Knock Three-One-Two, Dutton (U.S.), 1959 £150/£35
ditto, Boardman, 1960. . . . . . . £50/£15
The Murderers, Dutton (U.S.), 1961 . . £100/£20
ditto, Boardman, 1962. . . . . . . £45/£15
The Mind Thing, Bantam (U.S.), 1961 (wraps) £15
ditto, Hamlyn, 1979 (wraps) £10
The Five-Day Nightmare, Dutton (U.S.), 1963 . . .
. . . . £100/£20
ditto, as *Five Day Nightmare*, Boardman, 1963 . . .
. . . . £45/£15
Mrs Murphy's Underpants, Dutton (U.S.), 1963 . . .
. . . . £100/£20
ditto, Boardman, 1965. . . . . . . £45/£15
4 Novels by Fredric Brown, Zomba, 1983 (*Night of the Jabberwock*, *The Screaming Mimi*, *Knock Three-One-Two* and *The Fabulous Clipjoint*) . . . £30/£10

Short Stories

Space on My Hands, Shasta (U.S.), 1951 . £250/£35
ditto, Corgi, 1953 (wraps). £15
Mostly Murder: Eighteen Short Stories, Dutton (U.S.), 1953 . . . . £150/£35
ditto, Boardman, 1954. . . . . . . £100/£25
Angels and Spaceships, Dutton (U.S.), 1954 £125/£25
ditto, Gollancz, 1955 . . . . £50/£15
Honeymoon in Hell, Bantam (U.S.), 1958 (wraps) £15
The Shaggy Dog and Other Murders, Dutton (U.S.), 1963 . . . . £125/£25
ditto, Boardman, 1954. . . . . . . £45/£15
Carnival of Crime, Southern Illinois Univ. Press (U.S.), 1985 . . . . £35/£10
Nightmares and Geezenstacks, Bantam (U.S.), 1961 (wraps) £20
ditto, Corgi, 1962 (wraps). £10
Daymares, Lancer (U.S.), 1968 (wraps). . . £10
Paradox Lost, Random House (U.S.), 1973 £25/£5
ditto, Hale, 1975 . . . . £20/£5
The Best of Fredric Brown, Doubleday (U.S.), 1976 .
. . . . £35/£10
The Best Short Stories of Fredric Brown, NEL, 1982 (wraps) £5
And the Gods Laughed, Phantasia Press (U.S.), 1987 (1,525 copies) . . . . £25/£10
ditto, Phantasia Press (U.S.), 1987 (475 numbered copies) . . . . £50/£15

Fredric Brown in the Pulp Detectives

Homicide Sanatarium, Dennis McMillan (U.S.), 1984 (300 numbered copies) . . . . . £100/£25
Before She Kills, Dennis McMillan (U.S.), 1984 (350 numbered copies) . . . . . . £75/£20
Madman's Holiday, Dennis McMillan (U.S.), 1985 (350 numbered copies) . . . . . . £75/£20
The Case of the Dancing Sandwiches, Dennis McMillan (U.S.), 1985 (400 numbered copies) . .
. . . . £75/£20
The Freak Show Murders, Dennis McMillan (U.S.), 1985 (350 numbered copies) . . . . £50/£15

30 Corpses Every Thursday, Dennis McMillan (U.S.), 1985 (375 numbered copies) . . . . £50/£15
Pardon My Ghoulish Laughter, Dennis McMillan (U.S.), 1986 (400 numbered copies) . . £50/£15
Red is the Hue of Hell, Dennis McMillan (U.S.), 1986 (400 numbered copies) . . . . . . £50/£15
Sex Life on the Planet Mars, Dennis McMillan (U.S.), 1986 (400 numbered copies) . . . . £100/£25
Brother Monster, Dennis McMillan (U.S.), 1987 (400 numbered copies) . . . . £50/£15
Nightmare in the Darkness, Dennis McMillan (U.S.), 1987 (425 numbered copies) . . . . £50/£15
Who Was That Blonde I Saw You Kill Last Night?, Dennis McMillan (U.S.), 1988 (450 numbered copies) . . . . £40/£10
Three Corpse Parlay, Dennis McMillan (U.S.), 1988 (450 numbered copies) . . . . . £40/£10
Selling Death Short, Dennis McMillan (U.S.), 1988 (450 numbered copies) . . . . . £30/£10
Whispering Death, Dennis McMillan (U.S.), 1989 (450 numbered copies) . . . . . . £30/£10
Happy Ending, Dennis McMillan (U.S.), 1990 (450 numbered copies) . . . . . . £30/£10
The Water Walker, Dennis McMillan (U.S.), 1990 (425 numbered copies) . . . . . £30/£10
The Gibbering Night, Dennis McMillan (U.S.), 1991 (425 numbered copies) . . . . . £25/£10
The Pickled Punks, Dennis McMillan (U.S.), 1991 (450 numbered copies) . . . . . £25/£10

Poetry
Fermented Ink, privately published (U.S.), 1932 (wraps) £750
Shadow Suite, privately published (U.S.), 1932 (wraps) £750

Children's
Mitkey Astromouse, Quist (U.S. & U.K.), 1971 . . . . £75/£25

JEAN de BRUNHOFF
(b.1899 d.1937)

The creator of Babar the Elephant, after his death de Brunhoff's series of books were continued by his son, Laurent.

The Story of Babar, the Little Elephant, Methuen, 1934 . . . . £200
Babar's Travels, Methuen, 1937 . . . . £175
Babar the King, Methuen, 1936 . . . . . £165
Babar's ABC, Methuen, 1937 . . . . . £175
Babar's Friend Zephir, Methuen, 1937 . . . £100
Babar at Home, Methuen, 1938 . . . . . £150
Babar and Father Christmas, Methuen, 1940 . £125

'Babar' Books by Laurent de Brunhoff
Babar and that Rascal Arthur, Methuen, 1948 . £75
Picnic at Babar's, Methuen, 1950 . . . . £75
Babar's Visit to Bird Island, Methuen, 1952 . £50
Babar's Castle, Methuen, 1962 . . . . . £35
Babar's French Lessons, Cape, 1965 . . . £30
Babar Goes Visiting, Methuen, 1969 . . . £25
Babar Goes to America, Collins, 1969 . . . £25
Babar's Fair, Methuen, 1969 . . . . . £25
Babar Learns to Drive, Methuen, 1969 . . £25
Babar Keeps Fit!, Methuen, 1970 . . . . £25
Babar at the Seaside, Methuen, 1971 . . £15
Babar in the Snow, Methuen, 1971 . . . . £10
Babar the Gardener, Methuen, 1971 . . . £10
Babar's Birthday Surprise, Methuen, 1971 . £20
Babar's Day Out, Methuen, 1971 . . . . £10
Babar and the Christmas Tree, Methuen, 1972 £10
Babar and the Doctor, Methuen, 1972 . . £10
Babar and the Professor, Methuen, 1972 . . £10
Babar Goes Camping, Methuen, 1972 . . . £10
Babar and the Artist, Methuen, 1972 . . . £10
Babar on the Secret Planet, Methuen, 1973 . £20
Babar the Cook, Methuen, 1973 . . . . £10
Babar the Musician, Methuen, 1973 . . . £10
Babar the Pilot, Methuen, 1973 . . . . £10
Babar the Sportsman, Methuen, 1973 . . £10
Babar and the Wully-Wully, Methuen, 1977 . £10
Babar's Mystery, Methuen, 1979 . . . . £10
Babar and the Ghost, Methuen, 1981 . . . £10
Babar's ABC, Methuen, 1984 . . . . . £10
Babar's Book of Colour, Methuen, 1985 . . £10
Babar's Counting Book, Methuen, 1986 . . £10
Babar's Little Girl, Methuen, 1988 . . . . £10
Babar's Busy Week, Methuen, 1990 . . . £10
Babar's Battle, Methuen, 1992 . . . . £10
The Rescue of Babar, Methuen, 1993 . . . £10

'Serafina' books by Laurent de Brunhoff
Serafina the Giraffe, Methuen, 1964 [1965] . £25
Serafina's Lucky Find, Methuen, 1967 . . . £25
Captain Serafina, Methuen, 1969 . . . . £25

JOHN BUCHAN
(b.1875 d.1940)

Prolific Scottish writer whose talents ranged across novels, biographies, essays and poetry. Buchan's Richard Hannay mystery novels are still popular, and his historical romances have attracted much praise.

Historical Romances
Sir Quixote of the Moors, Fisher Unwin, 1895 . £300
John Burnet of Barns, John Lane, 1898 . . . £100
Grey Weather, Moorland Tales, John Lane, 1899 £100
A Lost Lady of Old Years, John Lane, 1899 . £75
Salute to Adventurers, Nelson [1915] . . . £50
ditto, Doran (U.S.), 1915 . . . . £25

The Path of the King, Hodder & Stoughton [1921] .
. . . .   £75/£15
ditto, Doran (U.S.), 1921 . . . . . .   £65/£10
Midwinter, Hodder & Stoughton [1923]   . £75/£15
ditto, Doran (U.S.), 1923 . . . . . .   £65/£10
Witch Wood, Hodder & Stoughton, 1927   . £200/£35
ditto, Houghton Mifflin (U.S.), 1927   . . £50/£10
The Blanket of the Dark, Hodder & Stoughton, 1931 .
. . . .   £100/£20
ditto, Houghton Mifflin (U.S.), 1931   . . £45/£10
The Free Fishers, Hodder & Stoughton, 1934 £75/£20
ditto, Houghton Mifflin (U.S.), 1934   . . £45/£10

The Richard Hannay Books
The Thirty-Nine Steps, Blackwood, 1915   . . £500
Greenmantle, Hodder & Stoughton, 1916   . . £75
ditto, Doran (U.S.), 1916 . . . .   £25
Mr Standfast, Hodder & Stoughton, 1918   . . £45
ditto, Doran (U.S.), 1919 . . . .   £25
The Three Hostages, Hodder & Stoughton [1924] . .
. . . .   £75/£15
ditto, Houghton Mifflin (U.S.), 1924   . . £45/£10
The Courts of the Morning, Hodder & Stoughton,
1929 . . . .   £75/£10
ditto, Houghton Mifflin (U.S.), 1929   . . £45/£10
The Island of Sheep, Hodder & Stoughton, 1936 . .
. . . .   £75/£10

The Edward Leithen Books
The Power House, Blackwood, 1916   . . . £50
John MacNab, Hodder & Stoughton [1925] £200/£50
ditto, Houghton Mifflin (U.S.), 1925   . . £45/£10
The Dancing Floor, Hodder & Stoughton [1926] . .
. . . .   £150/£45
ditto, Houghton Mifflin (U.S.), 1926   . . £45/£20
The Runagates Club and Other Stories, Hodder &
Stoughton, 1928 . . . .   £200/£45
ditto, Houghton Mifflin (U.S.), 1928   . . £45/£20
The Gap in the Curtain, Hodder & Stoughton, 1932 .
. . . .   £150/£45
ditto, Houghton Mifflin (U.S.), 1932   . . £45/£20
Sick Heart River, Hodder & Stoughton, 1941 £75/£15
ditto, as Mountain Meadow, Houghton Mifflin
(U.S.),1941 . . . .   £45/£10

The Dickson McCunn Books
Huntingtower, Hodder & Stoughton, 1922 . £75/£15
ditto, Doran (U.S.), 1916 . . . . . .   £65/£15
Castle Gay, Hodder & Stoughton, 1930 . . £100/£15
ditto, Houghton Mifflin (U.S.), 1930   . . £45/£10
The House of the Four Winds, Hodder & Stoughton,
1935 . . . .   £75/£15
ditto, Houghton Mifflin (U.S.), 1935   . . £45/£10

Contemporary Adventures
The Half-Hearted, Isbister, 1900   . . . . £125
The Watcher by the Threshold and Other Tales,
Blackwood, 1902 . . . .   £100
Prester John, Nelson, 1910 . . . . . .   £50

ditto, Doran (U.S.), 1910 . . . .   £25
A Prince of the Captivity, Hodder & Stoughton, 1933 .
. . . .   £100/£15
ditto, Houghton Mifflin (U.S.), 1933   . . £45/£10

Miscellaneous
A Lodge in the Wilderness, Blackwood, 1906 . £150
The Moon Endureth, Tales and Fancies, Blackwood,
1912 . . . .   £100
ditto, Sturgis & Walton (U.S.), 1912. . . . £25
The Island of Sheep (by 'Cadmus & Harmonia'),
Hodder & Stoughton, 1919 . . . . . .   £45
ditto, Houghton Mifflin (U.S.), 1920   . . £150/£30

Omnibus Editions
The Four Adventures of Richard Hannay, Hodder &
Stoughton, 1930 . . . .   £30/£10
The Adventures of Sir Edward Leithen, Hodder &
Stoughton, 1933 . . . .   £30/£10
Four Tales, Hodder & Stoughton, 1936 .   £30/£10
The Adventures of Dickson McCunn, Hodder &
Stoughton, 1937 . . . .   £30/£10
A Five-Fold Salute to Adventure, Hodder &
Stoughton, 1939 . . . .   £30/£10
Adventures of Richard Hannay, Houghton Mifflin
(U.S.), 1939 . . . .   £20/£5
Adventurers All, Houghton Mifflin (U.S.), 1942 . .
. . . .   £40/£10

Verse
Sir Walter Raleigh, Blackwell, 1897 (wraps)   . £150
The Pilgrim Fathers, Blackwell, 1898 (wraps). £150
Poems, Scots and English, Jack, 1917   . . . £50

Children's
Sir Walter Raleigh, T. Nelson & Sons, [1911] .   £70
The Magic Walking Stick, Hodder & Stoughton, 1932
. . . .   £40/£10
The Long Traverse, Hodder & Stoughton, 1941 . .
. . . .   £40/£10

Non Fiction
Scholar Gipsies, John Lane, 1896 . . . .   £150
Brasenose College, F.E. Robinson, 1898   . £125
The African Colony, Blackwood, 1903 . . .   £125
The Law Relating to Taxation of Foreign Income ...,
Stevens and Sons, 1905 . . . .   £200
Some Eighteenth Century Byways and other essays,
Blackwood, 1908 . . . .   £75
The Marquis of Montrose, T. Nelson & Sons, 1913 .
. . . .   £35
Andrew Jameson, Lord Ardwall, Blackwood, 1913 .
. . . .   £45
Nelson's History of the War, T. Nelson & Sons,
[1915-1919] (24 vols) £250
ditto, as A History of the Great War, Nelson, 1921-22
(4 vols, condensed version of the above) .   £100
ditto, Nelson, 1921-22 (500 numbered, signed copies, 4
vols) £275

ditto, Houghton Mifflin (U.S.), 1923 (4 vols) . £75
These for Remembrance, privately printed, 1919 £450
The History of the South African Forces in France, T.
Nelson & Sons, [1920] . . . . . . £100/£25
Francis and Riversdale Grenfell: A Memoir, T.
Nelson & Sons, [1920] . . . . . £75/£15
A Book of Escapes and Hurried Journeys, T. Nelson
& Sons, [1922] . . . . £150/£45
The Last Secrets: the final mysteries of exploration, T.
Nelson & Sons, [1923]. . . . . . £150/£35
ditto, Houghton Mifflin (U.S.), 1924 . £45/£10
***Days to Remember: the British Empire in the Great
War***, T. Nelson & Sons, 1923 (with Henry Newbolt)
. . . . £75/£20
Lord Minto: A Memoir, T. Nelson & Sons, [1924] .
. . . . £75/£20
The History of the Royal Scots Fusiliers, 1678-1918,
T. Nelson & Sons, [1925] . . . . . £150/£65
Homilies and Recreations, T. Nelson & Sons, [1926]
. . . . £50/£10
ditto, T. Nelson & Sons, [1926] (large paper edition,
200 signed and numbered copies) £150
Montrose, T. Nelson & Sons, [1928] . . £35/£10
ditto, Houghton Mifflin (U.S.), 1928 . £45/£10
The Kirk in Scotland, 1560-1929, Hodder and
Stoughton, [1930] (with George Adam Smith) . .
. . . . £100/£25
Sir Walter Scott, Cassell, [1932] . . . £30/£5
Julius Caesar, P. Davies, 1932 . . . £30/£5
The Massacre of Glencoe, P. Davies, 1933 . £50/£20
ditto, Putnam (U.S.), 1933 . . . . £35/£10
Gordon at Khartoum, P. Davies, 1934 . . £50/£20
Oliver Cromwell, Hodder and Stoughton, [1934] . .
. . . . £50/£20
ditto, Houghton Mifflin (U.S.), 1934 . . £35/£10
The King's Grace:, 1910-35, Hodder and Stoughton,
[1935] . . . . £30/£10
ditto, Hodder and Stoughton, 1935 (large paper edition,
500 numbered, signed copies) £100
Augustus, Hodder and Stoughton, 1937 . . £50/£20
ditto, Houghton Mifflin (U.S.), 1937 . . £35/£10
Memory Hold-the-Door, Hodder and Stoughton, 1940
. . . . £15/£5
Comments and Characters, T. Nelson & Sons, [1940]
. . . . £75/£25
Canadian Occasions, Hodder and Stoughton, [1940] .
. . . . £25/£10
The Clearing House: a John Buchan Anthology,
Hodder and Stoughton, 1946 . . . . £10/£5
Life's Adventure: a John Buchan Anthology, Hodder
and Stoughton, 1947. . . . . . . £15/£5

ANTHONY BUCKERIDGE
(b.1912)

Buckeridge was a teacher whose first successes were
radio plays for adults. The immortal Jennings
appeared later on, first on the radio and then in a
series of children's novels.

Children's Novels
Jennings Goes to School, Collins, 1950. . £50/£10
Jennings Follows a Clue, Collins, 1951 . £40/£10
Jennings' Little Hut, Collins, 1951 . . £35/£10
Jennings and Darbishire, Collins, 1952 . £35/£10
Jennings' Diary, Collins, 1953 . . . . £35/£10
A Funny Thing Happened!, Lutterworth Press [1953]
. . . . £35/£10
Rex Milligan's Busy Term, Lutterworth Press, 1953 .
. . . . £35/£10
According to Jennings, Collins, 1954 . . £35/£10
Our Friend Jennings, Collins, 1955. . . £35/£10
Rex Milligan Raises the Roof, Lutterworth Press, 1955
. . . . £35/£10
Rex Milligan Holds Forth, Lutterworth Press, 1955 .
. . . . £35/£10
Thanks to Jennings, Collins, 1957 . . . £35/£10
Take Jennings, for Instance, Collins, 1958. £35/£10
Jennings, as Usual, Collins, 1959 . . . £35/£10
The Trouble with Jennings, Collins, 1960 . £35/£10
Just Like Jennings, Collins, 1961 . . . £35/£10
Rex Milligan Reporting, Lutterworth Press, 1961 . .
. . . . £35/£10
Leave It to Jennings, Collins, 1963 . . . £35/£10
Jennings, of Course!, Collins, 1964. . . £35/£10
Especially Jennings!, Collins, 1965 . . . £35/£10
A Bookful of Jennings!, Collins, 1966 (anthology)
. . . . £35/£10
ditto, as ***The Best of Jennings***, Collins, 1972 £20/£5
Jennings Abounding, Collins, 1967. . . £35/£5
Jennings in Particular, Collins, 1968 . . £35/£5
Trust Jennings!, Collins, 1969 . . . . £35/£5
The Jennings Report, Collins, 1970 . . . £50/£10
Typically Jennings!, Collins, 1971 . . . £25/£5
Speaking of Jennings, Collins, 1973 . . £25/£5
Jennings at Large, Armada, 1977 (wraps) . . £5
ditto, Severn House, 1980. . . . . . £20/£5
Jennings Again!, Macmillan, 1991 . . . £15/£5
Jennings Unlimited, Macmillan, 1993. . . £15/£5
That's Jennings, Macmillan, 1994 . . . £15/£5

Plays
Jennings Abounding, A Comedy with Music, French,
1980 (wraps) £5

JAMES LEE BURKE
(b.?)

One of the biggest selling crime writers in America, Burke is best known for his novels about Vietnam veteran Dave Robicheaux.

'Dave Robicheaux' Books
The Neon Rain, Henry Holt & Co. (U.S.), 1987 . .
. . . . £175/£45
ditto, Mysterious, 1989 . . . . . . £35/£10
Heaven's Prisoners, Henry Holt (U.S.), 1988 . . .
. . . . £75/£25
ditto, Mysterious, 1990 . . . . . . £35/£10
Black Cherry Blues, Little, Brown (U.S.), 1989 . .
. . . . £50/£15
ditto, Century, 1990 . . . . £30/£10
A Morning for Flamingos, Little, Brown (U.S.), 1990
. . . . £50/£15
ditto, Century, 1992 . . . . £25/£10
A Stained White Radiance, Hyperion (U.S.), 1992 .
. . •. . . . . £45/£15
ditto, Century, 1993 . . . . £25/£10
In the Electric Mist with the Confederate Dead, Hyperion (U.S.), 1993 . . . . . £40/£10
ditto, Hyperion, (U.S.), 1993 (150 signed, numbered copies, slipcase) . . . . . . £150/£100
ditto, Orion, 1993 . . . . £20/£5
Dixie City Jam, Hyperion, (U.S.), 1994 . . £30/£5
ditto, Hyperion, (U.S.), 1994 (1,525 signed, numbered copies, slipcase) . . . . £45/£30
Burning Angel, Hyperion, (U.S.), 1995 . . £25/£10
ditto, Trice, (U.S.), 1995 (150 signed, numbered copies, slipcase), 1995 . . . . . £100/£75
ditto, Orion, 1995 . . . . £15/£5
Cadillac Jukebox, Hyperion (U.S.) 1996 . £25/£10
ditto, Hyperion, (U.S.), 1996 (ABA collectors edition)
. . . . £60/£35
ditto, Trice, (U.S.), 1996 (175 signed, numbered copies, slipcase), 1996 . . . . £100/£65
ditto, Orion, 1996 . . . . £15/£5
Sunset Limited, Doubleday (U.S.), 1998 . £20/£5
ditto, Orion, 1998 . . . . £20/£5
Purple Cain Road, Doubleday (U.S.), 2000 £10/£5
ditto, Trice, (U.S), 2000 (150 signed, numbered copies, slipcase) . . . . £100/£75
ditto, Orion, 2000 . . . . £10/£5

'Billy Bob Holland' Books
Cimarron Rose, Orion, 1997 . . . . £25/£10
ditto, Hyperion (U.S.), 1997 . . . . . £15/£5
ditto, Trice (U.S), 1997 (150 signed, numbered copies, slipcase) . . . . £100/£75
Heartwood, Doubleday (U.S.), 1999 . . £20/£5
ditto, Trice, (U.S), 1999 (26 signed, lettered copies, slipcase) . . . . £150/£125
ditto, Trice, (U.S), 1999 (150 signed, numbered copies, slipcase) . . . . £100/£75
ditto, Orion, 1999 . . . . £20/£5

Other Books
Half of Paradise, Houghton Mifflin (U.S.), 1965 . . .
. . . . £1,250/£200
To the Bright and Shining Sun, Scribner (U.S.), 1970
. . . . £650/£150
ditto, James Cahill (U.S.), 1992 (400 signed copies) .
. . . . £75/£45
Lay Down My Sword and Shield, Crowell (U.S.), 1971
. . . . £500/£100
Two for Texas, Pocket Books (U.S.), 1982 (wraps) £50
The Lost Get-Back Boogie, Louisiana State Univ. Press (U.S.), 1986 . . . . . . £400/£100

Short Stories
The Convict, Louisiana State Univ. Press (U.S.), 1985
. . . . £2,000/£750
ditto, Louisiana State Univ. Press (U.S.), 1985 (wraps)
. . . . £10
Winter Light, James Cahill (U.S.), 1992 (26 signed, lettered copies) £150
ditto, James Cahill (U.S.), 1992 (300 signed, numbered copies) £100
Texas City 1947, Lord John Press (U.S.) 1992 (26 signed, lettered copies) £150
ditto, Lord John Press (U.S.) 1992 (275 signed, numbered copies, slipcase) . . . . . £75/£65

ANTHONY BURGESS
(b.1917 d.1993)

Born John Burgess Wilson, this inventive, satirical author often presents a bleak outlook on life. He has produced very distinctive, well received novels, his best known work being the classic *The Clockwork Orange*.

Novels
Time for a Tiger, Heinemann, 1956 . . . £700/£75
The Enemy in the Blanket, Heinemann, 1958 . . .
. . . . £300/£45
Beds in the East, Heinemann, 1959 . . . £200/£20
The Right to an Answer, Heinemann, 1960 . £150/£20
ditto, Norton (U.S.), 1961 . . . . . . £35/£10
The Doctor is Sick, Heinemann, 1960 . . £150/£25
ditto, Norton (U.S.), 1966 . . . . . . £35/£10
The Worm and the Ring, Heinemann, 1961 £450/£125
Devil of a State, Heinemann, 1961 . . . £100/£10
ditto, Norton (U.S.), 1962 . . . . . . £25/£5
One Hand Clapping, Peter Davies, 1961 (pseud. 'Joseph Kell') . . . . £125/£45
ditto, Knopf (U.S.), 1961 . . . . . . £25/£5
A Clockwork Orange, Heinemann, 1962 (black boards)
. . . . £1,500/£100
ditto, Norton (U.S.), 1963 . . . . . . £250/£75
The Wanting Seed, Heinemann, 1962 . . £75/£35
ditto, Norton (U.S.), 1963 . . . . . . £15/£5
Honey for the Bears, Heinemann, 1963 . . £75/£10

ditto, Norton (U.S.), 1964. . . . . . £15/£5
Inside Mr Enderby, Heinemann, 1963 (pseud. 'Joseph Kell') . . . . £100/£45
Nothing Like the Sun, Heinemann, 1964 . £45/£10
ditto, Norton (U.S.), 1964. . . . . £15/£5
The Eve of Saint Venus, Sidgwick & Jackson, 1964 .
. . . . £45/£10
A Vision of Battlements, Sidgwick & Jackson, 1964 .
. . . . £45/£10
ditto, Norton (U.S.), 1966. . . . . £15/£5
Tremor of Intent, Heinemann, 1966. . . £40/£10
ditto, Norton (U.S.), 1966. . . . . £15/£5
Enderby Outside, Heinemann, 1968. . . £40/£10
Enderby, Norton (U.S.), 1968 . . . . £15/£5
MF, Cape, 1971 . . . . £30/£5
ditto, Knopf (U.S.), 1971 . . . . . £15/£5
Napoleon Symphony, Cape, 1974 . . . £30/£5
ditto, Knopf (U.S.), 1974 . . . . . £15/£5
The Clockwork Testament; or Enderby's End, Hart-Davis MacGibbon, 1974. . . . . £30/£5
ditto, Knopf (U.S.), 1974 . . . . . £15/£5
Moses: A Narrative, Dempsey & Squires, 1976 . .
. . . . £30/£5
ditto, Stonehill (U.S.), 1976 . . . . . £15/£5
Beard's Roman Women, McGraw Hill (U.S.), 1976 .
. . . . £30/£5
ditto, Hutchinson, 1977 . . . . . £15/£5
Abba Abba, Faber, 1977 . . . . . £20/£5
ditto, Little, Brown, (U.S.), 1977. . . . £15/£5
1985, Hutchinson, 1978 . . . . . £20/£5
ditto, Little, Brown, (U.S.), 1978. . . . £15/£5
Man of Nazareth, McGraw Hill (U.S.), 1979 £20/£5
ditto, Magnum, 1980 . . . . £15/£5
Earthly Powers, Hutchinson, 1980 . . . £30/£5
ditto, Simon & Schuster (U.S.), 1980 . . £15/£5
The End of the World News, Hutchinson, 1982 £20/£5
ditto, McGraw Hill (U.S.), 1983 . . . . £15/£5
Enderby's Dark Lady, Hutchinson, 1984 . £20/£5
ditto, McGraw Hill (U.S.), 1984 . . . . £15/£5
The Kingdom of the Wicked, Hutchinson, 1985 £20/£5
ditto, Franklin Library (U.S.), 1985 (signed edition) .
. . . . £30
ditto, Arbor House (U.S.), 1985 . . . . £10/£5
The Pianoplayers, Hutchinson, 1986 . . £15/£5
ditto, Arbor House (U.S.), 1986 . . . £10/£5
The Old Iron, Hutchinson, 1989 . . . . £15/£5
ditto, Random House (U.S.), 1989 . . . £10/£5
Mozart and the Wolf Gang, Hutchinson, 1991 £15/£5
Byrne, Hutchinson, 1995 . . . . . . £10/£5

Short Stories
The Devil's Mode, Hutchinson (U.S.), 1989. £15/£5

Autobiography
Little Wilson and Big God, Weidenfeld & Nicholson (U.S.), 1986 . . . . £20/£5
ditto, Heinemann, 1987 . . . . . £15/£5
You've Had Your Time, Heinemann, 1990 . £20/£5
ditto, Grove Weidenfeld (U.S.), 1991 . . £15/£5

Literary Criticism & Biography
English Literature: A Survey for Students, Longmans, Green, 1958 (pseud. 'John Burgess Wilson') . . .
. . . . £100/£15
The Novel Today, Longmans, Green, 1963 (wraps) £15
Language Made Plain, English Univ. Press, 1964 . .
. . . . £35/£10
ditto, Crowell (U.S.), 1965 . . . . . £10/£5
Here Comes Everybody, Faber, 1965 . . £50/£10
The Novel Now, Faber, 1967 . . . . . £25/£10
ditto, Norton (U.S.), 1967. . . . . . £15/£5
Urgent Copy, Literary Studies, Cape, 1968 . £30/£10
ditto, Norton (U.S.), 1969. . . . . . £15/£5
Shakespeare, Cape, 1970 . . . . . . £25/£10
ditto, Knopf (U.S.), 1970 . . . . . . £15/£5
Joysprick, Deutsch, 1973 . . . . . £30/£10
Ernest Hemingway and His World, Thames & Hudson, 1978. . . . . £15/£5
ditto, Scribner (U.S.), 1978 . . . . . £10/£5
Ninety-Nine Novels, Allison & Busby, 1984 £10/£5
ditto, Simon & Schuster (U.S.), 1984 . . £10/£5
Flame into Being: The Life and Works of D.H. Lawrence, Heinemann, 1985 . . . . £10/£5
ditto, Arbor House (U.S.), 1985 . . . . £10/£5
Mouthful of Air, Hutchinson, 1992 . . . £10/£5
ditto, Morrow (U.S.), 1992 . . . . . £10/£5

Miscellaneous Works
A Long Trip to Teatime, Dempsey & Squires, 1976 .
. . . . £15/£5
ditto, Stonehill (U.S.), 1976 . . . . . £10/£5
Moses: A Narrative, Dempsey & Squires, 1976 £15/£5
New York, Time-Life Books, 1977 . . . £10/£5
The Land Where Ice-Cream Grows, Benn, 1979 . .
. . . . £10/£5
ditto, Doubleday (U.S.), 1979 . . . . £10/£5
On Going to Bed, Deutsch, 1982. . . . £10/£5
ditto, Abbeville (U.S.), 1982 . . . . . £10/£5
This Man and Music, Hutchinson, 1982 . £10/£5
ditto, McGraw Hill (U.S.), 1983 . . . . £10/£5
Homage to Qwert Yuiop, Hutchinson, 1985 £10/£5
ditto, McGraw Hill (U.S.), 1986 . . . . £10/£5
Oberon Old and New, Hutchinson, 1985 . £10/£5
Carmen, Hutchinson, 1986 . . . . . £10/£5
Blooms of Dublin, Hutchinson, 1986 . . £10/£5

W.J. BURLEY
(b.1914)

Burley worked as an engineer until he won a mature state scholarship to Oxford where he read Zoology. Later working as a teacher, he is famous for his 'Wycliffe' detective novels set in Cornwall.

'Wycliffe' Novels
Three Toed Pussy, Gollancz, 1968 . . . £300/£25
To Kill A Cat, Gollancz, 1970 . . . . £150/£25

ditto, Walker (U.S.), 1972 . . . . . £35/£15
Guilt Edged, Gollancz, 1971 . . . . . £125/£20
ditto, Walker (U.S.), c.1972 . . . . . £35/£15
ditto, as **Wycliffe and the Guilt Edged Alibi**, Corgi, 1994 (wraps) £10
Death in a Salubrious Place, Gollancz, 1973 £75/£15
ditto, Walker (U.S.), 1973 . . . . . £30/£5
ditto, as **Wycliffe and Death in a Salubrious Place**, Corgi, 1995 (wraps) £5
Death in Stanley Street, Gollancz, 1975 . £75/£15
ditto, as **Wycliffe and Death in Stanley Street**, Corgi, 1990 (wraps) £5
Wycliffe and the Pea-Green Boat, Gollancz, 1975 .
. . . . £75/£15
ditto,. Walker (U.S.), 1975 . . . . . £30/£5
Wycliffe and the Schoolgirls, Gollancz, 1976 £75/£15
ditto, Walker (U.S.), 1976 . . . . . £25/£5
Wycliffe and the Scapegoat, Gollancz, 1978 £65/£10
ditto, Doubleday (U.S.), 1979 . . . . £25/£5
Wycliffe in Paul's Court, Gollancz, 1980 . £50/£10
ditto, Doubleday (U.S.), 1980 . . . £25/£5
Wycliffe's Wild Goose Chase, Gollancz, 1982 £45/£10
ditto, Doubleday (U.S.), 1982 . . . . £25/£5
Wycliffe and the Beales, Gollancz, 1983 . £45/£10
ditto, Doubleday (U.S.), 1984 . . . . £20/£5
Wycliffe and the Four Jacks, Gollancz, 1985 £35/£10
ditto, Doubleday (U.S.), 1986 . . . . £20/£5
Wycliffe and the Quiet Virgin, Gollancz, 1986 £35/£10
ditto, Doubleday (U.S.), 1986 . . . . £15/£5
Wycliffe and the Winsor Blue, Gollancz, 1987 £25/£10
ditto, Doubleday (U.S.), 1987 . . . . £15/£5
Wycliffe and the Tangled Web, Gollancz, 1988 £15/£5
ditto, Doubleday (U.S.), 1989 . . . . £15/£5
Wycliffe and the Cycle of Death, Gollancz, 1990 . .
. . . . £15/£5
ditto, Doubleday (U.S.), 1991 . . . . £15/£5
Wycliffe and the Dead Flautist, Gollancz, 1991 £15/£5
ditto, St Martin's Press (U.S.), 1992 . . . £15/£5
Wycliffe and the Last Rites, Gollancz, 1992 £15/£5
ditto, St Martin's Press (U.S.), 1993 . . . £15/£5
Wycliffe and the Dunes Mystery, Gollancz, 1994 . .
. . . . £15/£5
ditto, St Martin's Press (U.S.), 1994 . . . £15/£5
Wycliffe and the House of Fear, Gollancz, 1995 . .
. . . . £15/£5
ditto, St Martin's Press (U.S.), 1996 . . . £15/£5
Wycliffe Omnibus, Gollancz, 1996 . . . £10/£5
Wycliffe and the The Redhead, Gollancz, 1997 £15/£5
ditto, St Martin's Press (U.S.) 1998 . . . £15/£5
Wycliffe and the Guild of Nine, Gollancz, 2000 £15/£5

Other Novels
A Taste of Power: A Novel, Gollancz, 1966 £200/£30
Death in Willow Pattern, Gollancz, 1969 . £150/£25
The Schoolmaster, Gollancz, 1977 . . . £45/£10
ditto, Walker (U.S.), 1977 . . . . . £20/£5
The Sixth Day: A Novel, Gollancz, 1978 . £45/£10
Charles and Elizabeth: A Gothic Novel, Gollancz, 1979 . . . . £40/£10

ditto, Walker (U.S.), 1981 . . . . . £10/£5
The House of Care: A Novel, Gollancz, 1981 £45/£10
ditto, Walker (U.S.), 1981 . . . . . £10/£5

Non Fiction
City of Truro, 1877-1977, O. Blackford, Truro, 1977 (wraps) £10

FRANCES HODGSON BURNETT
(b.1849 d.1924)

Novelist and children's writer, Burnett was born in Manchester but spent many years in America, where she died. Her sentimental children's stories have often been filmed, with varying degrees of success.

Children's Books
Little Lord Fauntleroy, Scribners (U.S.), 1886 (first issue with 'De Vinne' imprint at end) . . . £750
ditto, Warne, 1886. . . . . £600
Sara Crewe; or What Happened at Miss Minchin's, Unwin, 1887 . . . . £45
ditto, Scribners (U.S.), 1888 . . . . . £35
ditto, as **Sara Crewe, and Editha's Burglar**, Warne, 1888 . . . . £30
Editha's Burglar, Jordan, Marsh (U.S.), 1888 . £25
Little Saint Elizabeth and Other Child Stories, Warne, 1890 . . . . £25
ditto, Scribners (U.S.), 1890 . . . . . £25
Children I Have Known, Osgood McIlvaine, 1892 [1891]. £30
The One I Knew the Best of All, Warne, 1893 . £25
ditto, Scribners (U.S.), 1893 . . . . . £25
The Captain's Youngest and Other Stories, Warne, 1894 . . . . £15
Two Little Pilgrims' Progress, Warne, 1895 . £25
ditto, Scribners (U.S.), 1895 . . . . . £25
A Little Princess, Warne, 1905 . . . . . £125
ditto, Scribners (U.S.), 1905 . . . . . £100
Racketty Packetty House, Warne, 1907 . . . £30
The Troubles of Queen Silver-Bell, Warne, 1907 £30
The Spring Cleaning, Century (U.S.), 1909 . £30
ditto, Tom Stacey, 1973 . . . . . . £10/£5
The Land of the Blue Flower, Moffat, Yard (U.S.), 1909 . . . . £30
ditto, Putnam, 1912 . . . . £30
The Secret Garden, Stokes (U.S.), 1911 . . . £500
ditto, Heinemann, 1911 . . . . . . £500
My Robin, Stokes (U.S.), 1912 . . . . . £500
ditto, Putnam, 1913 . . . . £25
The Lost Prince, Century (U.S.), 1915 . . . £30
ditto, Hodder & Stoughton, 1915. . . . . £30
The Little Hunchback Zia, Heinemann, 1916 . £50
The Cozy Lion, Tom Stacey, 1972 . . . £10/£5

Novels and Novellas for Adults
That Lass O'Lowrie's: A Lancashire Story, Scribners (U.S.), 1887 . . . . £75

ditto, Warne [1877] £30
Dolly: A Love Story, Routledge [1877] . . . £20
ditto, Warne, 1893 (new edition). £10
Theo: A Love Story, Ward Lock [1877]. . . £20
ditto, Warne, 1877 (new edition). £20
Pretty Polly Pemberton: A Love Story, Routledge, 1878 . . . . £20
Kathleen: A Love Story, Routledge, 1878 . . £20
ditto, as *Kathleen Mavourneen*, Chatto & Windus, 1879. . . . . £20
Miss Crespigny: A Love Story, Routledge [1878] £20
Haworth's, Macmillan, 1879 (2 vols) . . . £50
Louisiana, and That Lass O'Lowrie's, Macmillan, 1880 . . . . £30
A Fair Barbarian, Warne [1881] £20
Through One Administration, Warne, 1883 (3 vols) .
. . . . £75
A Woman's Will; or, Miss Defarge, Warne, 1887 £20
The Fortunes of Philippa Fairfax, Warne, 1888 £30
The Pretty Sister of Jose, Spencer Blackett, 1889 (wraps) £20
A Lady of Quality, Warne, 1896 . . . . . £10
His Grace of Ormonde, Warne, 1897 . . . £10
In Connection with the De Willoughby Claim, Warne, 1899 . . . . £10
The Making of a Marchioness, Smith Elder, 1901 £15
The Methods of Lady Walderhurst, Smith Elder, 1902
. . . . £10
In the Closed Room, Hodder & Stoughton, 1904 £50
The Dawn of Tomorrow, Warne, 1907 . . . £10
The Shuttle, Heinemann, 1907 . . . . . £10
T. Tembarom, Hodder & Stoughton [1913]. . £10
The White People, Heinemann, 1920 . . . £15/£5
The Head of the House of Coombe, Heinemann, 1922
. . . . £15/£5
Robin, Heinemann, 1922 . . . . £15/£5

Short Stories for Adults
Surly Tim and Other Stories, Ward Lock [1877] £20
Our Neighbour Opposite, Routledge [1878] . £20
Natalie and Other Stories, Warne [1879] . . £20
Lindsay's Luck, Routledge, 1879 . . . . £20
The Tide on the Moaning Bar and A Quiet Life, Routledge [1879]. £20

EDGAR RICE BURROUGHS
(b.1875 d.1950)

The 'Tarzan' titles are Burroughs' best known, but his many 'Martian' and other science fiction stories are of seminal importance in the development of the genre.

'Tarzan' Titles
Tarzan of the Apes, McClurg (U.S.), 1914 . . . .
. . . . £25,000/£1,000
ditto, Methuen, 1917 . . . . . . £1,250/£350

The Return of Tarzan, McClurg (U.S.), 1915 . . .
. . . . £6,000/£500
ditto, Methuen, 1918 '. . . . . . £1,000/£250
The Beasts of Tarzan, McClurg (U.S.), 1916 . . .
. . . . £6,000/£500
ditto, Methuen, 1918 . . . . . . £1,000/£50
The Son of Tarzan, McClurg (U.S.), 1917 . . . .
. . . . £4,000/£250
ditto, Methuen, 1919 . . . . . . £1,000/£50
Tarzan and the Jewels of Opar, McClurg (U.S.), 1918
. . . . £2,000/£250
ditto, Methuen, 1919 . . . . £750/£60
Jungle Tales of Tarzan, McClurg (U.S.), 1919 . .
. . . . £1,250/£150
ditto, Methuen, 1919 . . . . £750/£60
Tarzan the Untamed, McClurg (U.S.), 1920 . . .
. . . . £2,000/£100
ditto, Methuen, 1920 . . . . £750/£60
Tarzan the Terrible, McClurg (U.S.), 1921. . . .
. . . . £2,000/£100
ditto, Methuen, 1921 . . . . £750/£60
Tarzan and the Golden Lion, McClurg (U.S.), 1923 .
. . . . £2,000/£100
ditto, Methuen, 1924 . . . . £750/£60
Tarzan and the Ant Men, McClurg (U.S.), 1924 . .
. . . . £2,000/£100
ditto, Methuen, 1925 . . . . £225/£60
The Tarzan Twins, Volland (U.S.), 1924 . £450/£75
ditto, Collins, 1930 . . . . . . £500/£100
The Eternal Lover, McClurg (U.S.), 1925 . . .
. . . . £2,000/£100
ditto, Methuen, 1927 . . . . £500/£60
Tarzan, Lord of the Jungle, McClurg (U.S.), 1928 .
. . . . £2,000/£100
ditto, Cassell, 1928 . . . . £750/£60
Tarzan and the Lost Empire, Metropolitan (U.S.), 1929 . . . . £1,000/£50
ditto, Cassell, 1931 . . . . £750/£60
Tarzan at the Earth's Core, Metropolitan (U.S.), 1930
. . . . £1,000/£50
ditto, Methuen, 1938 . . . . £750/£60
Tarzan the Invincible, ERB Inc. (U.S.), 1931 . . .
. . . . £500/£45
ditto, John Lane, 1933. . . . . . . £750/£60
Tarzan Triumphant, ERB Inc. (U.S.), 1932 £400/£45
ditto, John Lane, 1933. . . . . . . £400/£60
Tarzan and the City of Gold, ERB Inc. (U.S.), 1933 .
. . . . £400/£45
ditto, John Lane, 1936. . . . . . . £400/£60
Tarzan and the Leopard Men, ERB Inc. (U.S.), 1935
. . . . £400/£45
ditto, John Lane, 1936. . . . . . . £300/£60
Tarzan and the Lion Man, ERB Inc. (U.S.), 1934 . .
. . . . £400/£45
ditto, Goulden, 1950 (wraps) £10
Tarzan's Quest, ERB Inc. (U.S.), 1936 . . £350/£40
ditto, Methuen, 1938 . . . . £300/£60
Tarzan and the Forbidden City, ERB Inc. (U.S.), 1938
. . . . £300/£30

ditto, Goulden, 1950 (wraps) £10
**Tarzan and the Tarzan Twins with Jad-Bal-Ja the
Golden Lion**, Whitman (U.S.), 1936 . . . £200
Tarzan the Magnificent, ERB Inc. (U.S.), 1939 .
. . . . £200/£30
ditto, Methuen, 1940 . . . . £150/£50
Tarzan and the Foreign Legion, ERB Inc. (U.S.),
1947 . . . . £100/£25
ditto, W.H.Allen, 1949 . . . . . . £45/£10
Tarzan the Madman, Canaveral (U.S.), 1964 £75/£25
ditto, Four Square, 1966 (wraps). £5
Tarzan and the Castaways, Canaveral (U.S.), 1965 .
. . . . £75/£25
ditto, Four Square, 1966 (wraps). £5
Tarzan: The Lost Adventure, Dark Horse (U.S.), 1995
. . . . £10
ditto, Dark Horse (U.S.), 1995 (signed, deluxe copies).
. . . . £75/£45

'Mars' Titles
A Princess of Mars, McClurg (U.S.), 1917 . . .
. . . . £6,000/£500
ditto, Methuen, 1920 . . . . . £1,000/£65
The Gods of Mars, McClurg (U.S.), 1918 £3,000/£200
ditto, Methuen, 1920 . . . . . . £750/£65
The Warlord of Mars, McClurg (U.S.), 1919 . . .
. . . . £3,000/£200
ditto, Methuen, 1920 . . . . . . £750/£65
Thuvia, Maid of Mars, McClurg (U.S.), 1920 . . .
. . . . £2,000/£100
ditto, Methuen, 1921 . . . . . . £650/£50
Chessmen of Mars, McClurg (U.S.), 1922 £2,000/£100
ditto, Methuen, 1923 . . . . . . £600/£50
Master Mind of Mars, McClurg (U.S.), 1928 . . .
. . . . £2,000/£100
ditto, Methuen, 1939 . . . . . . £200/£50
Fighting Man of Mars, Metropolitan (U.S.), 1931. .
. . . . £750/£50
ditto, Bodley Head, 1932 . . . . . £250/£50
Swords of Mars, ERB Inc. (U.S.), 1936. £1,250/£75
ditto, Four Square, 1966 (wraps). £5
Synthetic Men of Mars, ERB Inc. (U.S.), 1940 . .
. . . . £400/£45
ditto, Methuen, 1941 . . . . . . £150/£40
Llana of Gathol, ERB Inc. (U.S.), 1948 . £200/£45
ditto, Four Square, 1967 (wraps). £5
John Carter of Mars, Canaveral (U.S.), 1964 £100/£20
ditto, Four Square, 1967 (wraps). £5

'Venus' Titles
Pirates of Venus, ERB Inc. (U.S.), 1934 . £400/£35
ditto, John Lane, 1935. . . . . . £200/£35
Lost on Venus, ERB Inc. (U.S.), 1935 . £400/£25
ditto, Methuen, 1937 . . . . . . £200/£35
Carson of Venus, ERB Inc. (U.S.), 1939 . £400/£25
ditto, Goulden, 1950 (wraps). £10
Escape on Venus, ERB Inc. (U.S.), 1946 . £250/£25
ditto, Four Square, 1966 (wraps). £5

Wizard of Venus, New English Library, 1973 (wraps).
. . . . £5

'Pellucidar' Titles
At the Earth's Core, McClurg (U.S.), 1922. . . .
. . . . £2,000/£100
ditto, Methuen, 1923 . . . . . . £600/£50
Pellucidar, McClurg (U.S.), 1923 . . £2,000/£100
ditto, Methuen, 1924 . . . . . . £600/£50
Tanar of Pellucidar, Metropolitan (U.S.), 1930 . .
. . . . £1,000/£50
ditto, Methuen, 1939 . . . . . . £400/£50
Back to the Stone Age, ERB Inc. (U.S.), 1937 . . .
. . . . £500/£35
ditto, Tandem, 1974 (wraps) £5
Land of Terror, ERB Inc. (U.S.), 1944 . . £500/£35
ditto, Tandem, 1974 (wraps) £5
Savage Pellucidar, Canaveral (U.S.), 1963 £250/£25
ditto, Tandem, 1974 (wraps) £5

'Old West' Titles
The Bandit of Hell's Bend, McClurg (U.S.), 1925 .
. . . . £2,000/£100
ditto, Methuen, 1926 . . . . . . £750/£50
The War Chief, McClurg (U.S.), 1927 . £1,500/£75
ditto, Methuen, 1926 . . . . . . £500/£45
Apache Devil, ERB Inc. (U.S.), 1933 . £600/£50
The Oakdale Affair/The Rider, ERB Inc. (U.S.), 1937
. . . . £750/£50
The Deputy Sheriff of Comanche Country, ERB Inc.
(U.S.), 1940 . . . . £400/£35

Others
The Mucker, McClurg (U.S.), 1921 . . £3,000/£150
ditto, as **The Mucker** and **The Man Without a Soul**,
Methuen, 1921 and 1922 . . . £500/£50
The Girl from Hollywood, McCauley (U.S.), 1923 .
. . . . £2,000/£50
ditto, Methuen, 1924 . . . . . . £350/£60
The Land That Time Forgot, McClurg (U.S.), 1924 .
. . . . £4,500/£50
ditto, Methuen, 1927 . . . . . . £350/£60
The Cave Girl, McClurg (U.S.), 1925 . £1,000/£50
ditto, Methuen, 1927 . . . . . . £600/£50
The Moon Maid, McClurg (U.S.), 1926 £1,000/£50
ditto, Tom Stacey, 1972 . . . . . £50/£10
The Mad King, McClurg (U.S.), 1926 . £1,000/£50
The Outlaw of Torn, McClurg (U.S.), 1929 £600/£35
ditto, Methuen, 1929 . . . . . . £200/£20
The Monster Men, McClurg (U.S.), 1929 £2,000/£50
ditto, Tandem, 1976 (wraps) £5
Jungle Girl, ERB Inc. (U.S.), 1932 . . £175/£50
ditto, Odhams, [1934] . . . . . . £175/£45
The Resurrection of Jimber Jaw, Argosy (U.S.), 1937
(wraps) £120
The Lad and the Lion, ERB Inc. (U.S.), 1938 . . .
. . . . £175/£50
The Scientists Revolt, Fantastic Adventures (U.S.),
July 1939 (wraps) £100

Beyond Thirty and The Man Eater, Science Fiction and Fantasy Publications (U.S.), 1957 . . £250/£75
ditto, as *The Lost Continent*, Tandem, 1977 (wraps) £5
The Girl from Farris's, Wilma Co. (U.S.), 1959 (150 numbered copies, no d/w) £250
ditto, Wilma Co. (U.S.), 1959 (wraps) . . . £150
Tales of Three Planets, Canaveral (U.S.), 1963 . .
. . . . £150/£25
The Efficiency Expert, House of Greystoke, 1966 . .
. . . . £200
I Am A Barbarian, ERB Inc. (U.S.), 1967 £100/£20
Pirate Blood, Ace (U.S.), 1970 (wraps) . . . £5

WILLIAM S. BURROUGHS
(b.1914 d.1997)

A controversial American 'beat' novelist who wrote of his experience as a heroin addict in *Junkie* and *The Naked Lunch*. The latter became a cult classic, banned on the grounds of obscenity.

Novels
Junkie: Confessions of an Unredeemed Drug Addict, Ace (U.S.), 1953 (pseud. 'William Lee', bound back-to-back with *Narcotic Agent*, wraps) . . . £200
ditto, Digit, 1957 . . . . £75
ditto, as *Junky*, Penguin, 1977 . . . . . £5
The Naked Lunch, Olympia Press (Paris), 1959 (wraps, with d/w) . . . . £750/£250
ditto, as *Naked Lunch*, Grove Press (U.S.), 1959 [1962]. . . . . £200/£35
ditto, Calder, 1964. . . . . . . £75/£20
ditto, Grove Press (U.S.), 1984 (500 signed copies in box) . . . . £150/£100
The Soft Machine, Olympia Press (Paris), 1961 (wraps, with d/w) . . . . . . £300/£75
ditto, Grove Press (U.S.), 1966 . . . . £100/£25
ditto, Calder & Boyars, 1968 . . . . . £50/£15
The Ticket That Exploded, Olympia Press (Paris), 1962 (wraps, with d/w) . . . . £150/£100
ditto, Grove Press (U.S.), 1967 . . . . £100/£25
ditto, Calder & Boyars 1968 . . . . . £45/£15
Dead Fingers Talk, Olympia Press (Paris), 1963 (wraps) £75
ditto, Calder 1963 . . . . £50/£25
Nova Express, Grove Press (U.S.), 1964 . £50/£15
ditto, Cape 1966 . . . . £45/£15
The Wild Boys: A Book of the Dead, Grove Press (U.S.), 1971 . . . . £65/£20
ditto, Calder & Boyars, 1972 . . . . . £65/£20
Port of Saints, Covent Garden Press, 1973 [1975] (100 signed copies of 200) . . . . . £250/£200
ditto, Covent Garden Press, 1973 [1975] (100 unsigned copies of 200) . . . . £125/£75
ditto, Blue Wind Press (U.S.), 1980 . . . £25/£5

ditto, Blue Wind Press (U.S.), 1980 (200 signed copies, slipcase) . . . . £150/£125
ditto, Calder 1983 . . . . £25/£5
Short Novels, Calder, 1978 . . . . . £35/£10
Blade Runner: A Movie, Blue Wind Press (U.S.), 1979
. . . . £125/£30
Cities of the Red Night: A Boy's Book, Calder, 1981 .
. . . . £25/£10
ditto, Holt Rinehart (U.S.), 1981 . . . . £20/£5
ditto, Holt Rinehart (U.S.), 1981 (500 signed, numbered copies, slipcase, no d/w). . £150/£100
The Place of Dead Roads, Holt Rinehart (U.S.), 1983 .
. . . . £25/£5
ditto, Holt Rinehart (U.S.), 1983 (300 signed, numbered copies, slipcase, no d/w). . £125/£100
ditto, Calder 1984 . . . . £25/£5
Queer, Viking (U.S.), 1985 . . . . . £20/£5
ditto, Picador, 1985 . . . . £20/£5
The Western Lands, Viking (U.S.), 1987 . £15/£5
ditto, Picador 1988 . . . . £15/£5

Stories
Exterminator!, Viking (U.S.), 1973 . . . £30/£10
ditto, Calder & Boyars, 1974 . . . . . £30/£10
Early Routines, Cadmus (U.S.), 1981 (26 signed copies of 500) £500
ditto, Cadmus (U.S.), 1981 (125 signed copies of 151, glassine d/w) . . . . £175/£15
ditto, Cadmus (U.S.), 1981 (349 copies in wraps) £20

Verse
The Exterminator, Auerhahn Press (U.S.), 1960 (with Brion Gysin, wraps) £60
Minutes to Go, Two Cities (Paris), 1960 (with Gysin, Corso and Beiles, wraps) £50

Others
Letter from a Master Addict to Dangerous Drugs, privately published, 1957 (stapled sheets) . . £200
Yage Letters, City Lights Books (U.S.), 1963 (with Allen Ginsburg, wraps) £65
Takis, Gall Schwarz, 1962 (wraps) £25
Roosevelt After Inauguration, Fuck You Press (U.S.), 1964 (pseud. 'Willy Lee', wraps) £200
Time, 'C' Press (U.S.), 1965 (with Brion Gysin, 886 copies of 986, wraps) £100
ditto, 'C' Press (U.S.), 1965 (100 signed copies of 986, wraps). £500
ditto, 'C' Press (U.S.), 1965 (14 copies with page of manuscript and an original drawing by Gysin) £1,500
ditto, Urgency Press Rip-Off, 1972 (495 copies) £100
Valentine's Day Reading, American Theatre for Poets (U.S.), 1965 (wraps). £30
Health Bulletin: Apo-33, Fuck You Press (U.S.), 1965
. . . . £45
White Subway, Aloes Books, (1965) (975 copies of 1,000, wraps). £60
ditto, Aloes Books, (1965) (25 signed copies of 1,000)
. . . . £500

Apo-33 Bulletin: A Metabolic Regulator, Beach Books
(U.S.), 1966 (wraps) £75
So Who Owns Death TV?, Beach Books (U.S.), 1967
(first issue, 50 cent price, with Claude Pelieu and Carl
Weissner, wraps) £100
The Dead Star, Nova Broadcast Press (U.S.), 1969
(wraps) £50
Fernseh-Tuberkulose, Nova Press (Frankfurt), 1969
(with Claude Pelieu and Carl Weissner) . . £50
The Job, Interviews with William S. Burroughs,
Grove Press (U.S.), 1970 . . . . . £60/£25
ditto, Cape, 1970 . . . . £45/£15
The Third Mind, Viking (U.S.), 1978 . . £30/£10
Ali's Smile, Unicorn Books, 1971 (99 signed copies,
with record) £1,250
Electronic Revolution, 1970-71, Blackmoor Head
Press, 1971 (100 signed copies of 500, wraps) £1,000
ditto, Blackmoor Head Press, 1971 (400 copies of 500,
wraps) £200
Academy Series, Urgency Press Rip Off, [1973] (650
copies, wraps) £50
A Book of Breething, Chopin, 1974 (wraps) . £25
ditto, Chopin, 1974 (350 numbered copies, wraps) £65
ditto, Chopin, 1974 (50 signed copies) . . . £250
ditto, Blue Wind Press (U.S.), 1975 (wraps) . £10
ditto, Blue Wind Press (U.S.), 1975 (175 signed copies)
. . . . £75
Ah Pook is Here and Other Texts, Calder, 1979 . .
. . . . £50/£20
A William Burroughs Reader, Picador, 1982 (wraps) .
. . . . £10
The Adding Machine, Selected Essays, Calder, 1985 .
. . . . £25/£5
ditto, Seaver Books (U.S.), 1986 . . . . £25/£5
Interzone, Picador, 1989 . . . . . . £25/£10
ditto, Viking, 1989 . . . . . . £25/£10
The Letters of William S. Burroughs, 1945-59,
Picador, 1993 . . . . £25/£5
ditto, Viking, 1993 . . . . . . £15/£5
My Education, A Book of Dreams, Picador, 1995 . .
. . . . £20/£5
ditto, Viking, 1995 . . . . . . £20/£5

A.S. BYATT
(b.1936)

A novelist and critic, and sister of Margaret Drabble,
Byatt won the Booker prize for *Possession*, her best
known work.

Novels
Shadow of a Sun, Chatto & Windus, 1964 . £175/£25
ditto, as *Shadow of the Sun*, Harcourt Brace (U.S.),
1964 . . . . £75/£20
The Game, Chatto & Windus, 1967 . . . £100/£25

ditto, Scribner (U.S.), 1968 . . . . . £75/£15
The Virgin in the Garden, Chatto & Windus, 1978 .
. . . . £75/£10
ditto, Knopf (U.S.), 1979 . . . . . . £30/£5
Still Life, Chatto & Windus and The Hogarth Press,
1985 . . . . £30/£5
ditto, Scribner (U.S.), 1985 . . . . . £15/£5
Possession, Chatto & Windus, 1990 . . . £40/£5
ditto, Random House (U.S.), 1990 . . . £20/£5
Babel Tower, Chatto & Windus, 1996 . . £15/£5
ditto, Random House (U.S.), 1996 . . . £15/£5
ditto, Franklin Library (U.S.), 1996 (signed) . £45
The Biographer's Tale, Chatto & Windus, 2000 . .
. . . . £15/£5
ditto, Knopf (U.S.), 2001 . . . . . . £15/£5

Short Stories and Novellas
Sugar and Other Stories, Chatto & Windus, 1987 .
. . . . £30/£10
ditto, Scribner (U.S.), 1987 . . . . . £30/£10
Angels and Insects, Chatto & Windus, 1992 £15/£5
ditto, London Limited Editions, 1992 (150 signed
copies, acetate d/w) . . . . . . £65/£50
ditto, Random House (U.S.), 1992 . . . £10/£5
ditto, Franklin Library(U.S.), 1993 (signed). . £45
Matisse Stories, Chatto & Windus, 1993 . £15/£5
ditto, Random House (U.S.), 1993 . . . £10/£5
Djinn in the Nightingale's Eye, Five Fairy Stories,
Chatto & Windus, 1994 . . . . . £10/£5
ditto, Random House (U.S.), 1994 . . . £10/£5
Elementals: Stories of Fire and Ice, Chatto & Windus,
1998 . . . . £10/£5
ditto, Random House (U.S.), 1999 . . . £10/£5

Non Fiction
Degrees of Freedom: The Novels of Iris Murdoch,
Chatto & Windus, 1965 . . . . . £50/£25
ditto, Barnes & Noble (U.S.), 1965 . . . £45/£20
Wordsworth and Coleridge in their Time, Nelson,
1970 . . . . £75/£20
ditto, Crane, Russak (U.S.), 1973 . . . £35/£10
ditto, as *Unruly Times: Wordsworth and Coleridge in
Their Times*, Hogarth Press, 1989 . . . £10/£5
Iris Murdoch, Longman, 1970 . . . . . £10
ditto, Crane-Russak (U.S.), 1973 . . . . £10
Ford Madox Ford and the Prose Tradition, Chatto &
Windus, 1982 . . . . £25/£10
ditto, Knopf (U.S.), 1982 . . . . . £20/£10
Passions of the Mind, Chatto & Windus, 1991 £15/£5
ditto, Turtle Bay (U.S.), 1992 . . . . £10/£5
*Imagining Characters, Six Conversations with
Women Writers*, Chatto & Windus, 1995 (with Ignes
Sodre) . . . . £25/£10
ditto, as *Imagining Characters: Conversations about
Women Writers*, Vintage Books (U.S.), 1997 £10/£5

ALBERT CAMUS
(b.1913 d.1960)

One of the very few international goalkeepers to have gone on to establish an international literary reputation, for which he was awarded the Nobel Prize for literature in 1957.

Novels

The Outsider, Hamish Hamilton, 1946 (translated by Stuart Gilbert) . . . . £200/£25
ditto, as *The Stranger*, Knopf (U.S.), 1946 . £200/£20
The Plague, Hamish Hamilton, 1948 (translated by Stuart Gilbert) . . . . £225/£25
ditto, Knopf (U.S.), 1948 . . . . . . £200/£20
The Rebel, Hamish Hamilton, 1953 (translated by Anthony Bower) . . . . £125/£20
ditto, Knopf (U.S.), 1954 . . . . . . £100/£15
The Fall, Hamish Hamilton, 1957 (translated by Justin O'Brien) . . . . £100/£15
ditto, Knopf (U.S.), 1957 . . . . . . £100/£15
A Happy Death, Hamish Hamilton, 1972 (translated by Richard Howard) . . . . £15/£5
ditto, Knopf (U.S.), 1972 . . . . . £15/£5

Short Stories

Exile and the Kingdom, Hamish Hamilton, 1958 (translated by Justin O'Brien) . . . . £65/£15
ditto, Knopf (U.S.), 1958 . . . . . £60£10

Plays

Caligula and *Cross Purpose*, Hamish Hamilton, 1947 (Translated by Justin Kaplan) . . . . £100/£15
ditto, New Directions (U.S.), 1947 . . . £60/£15
ditto, Knopf (U.S.), 1948 . . . . . £35/£10
The Possessed, Hamish Hamilton, 1960 (Translated by Justin O'Brien) . . . . £65/£15
ditto, Knopf (U.S.), 1960 . . . . . £50£10

Others

The Myth of Sisyphus, Hamish Hamilton, 1955 (translated by Justin O'Brien) . . . . £50/£15
ditto, Knopf (U.S.), 1955 . . . . . £45/£10
Nobel Prize Acceptance Speech, Knopf (U.S.), 1958 (translated by Justin O'Brien , wraps) . . £40
Reflections on the Guillotine, Fridtjof-Karla (U.S.), 1959 . . . . £75/£20
Resistance, Rebellion and Death, Hamish Hamilton, 1961 (Translated by Justin O'Brien) . . £25/£5
ditto, Knopf (U.S.), 1961 . . . . . £25/£5
Lyrical and Critical, Hamish Hamilton, 1967 (Translated by Ellen Conroy Kennedy) . £25/£5
ditto, Knopf (U.S.), 1968 . . . . . £25/£5
Youthful Writings, Knopf (U.S.), 1976 (Translated by Ellen Conroy Kennedy) . . . . . £25/£5
ditto, Hamilton, 1977 . . . . . . £25/£5
Carnets 1935-1942, Hamish Hamilton, 1963 (Translated by Justin O'Brien) . . . . . £40/£15

ditto, as *Notebooks 1935-1942*, Knopf (U.S.), 1963 .
. . . . £40/£15
Carnets 1942-1951, Hamish Hamilton, 1965 (Translated by Justin O'Brien) . . . £40/£15
ditto, as *Notebooks 1942-1951*, Knopf (U.S.), 1965 .
. . . . £40/£15

RANDOLPH CALDECOTT
(b.1846 d.1886)

A British illustrator, Caldecott produced a series of popular picture books which are said to have had an influence on Beatrix Potter.

'Picture Books'

The Diverting History of John Gilpin, Routledge, [1878]. £30
The House that Jack Built, Routledge, [1878] . £30
The Mad Dog, Routledge, [1879] £75
The Babes in the Wood, Routledge, [1879] . . £30
The Three Jovial Huntsmen, Routledge, [1880] £25
Sing a Song for Sixpence, Routledge, [1880] . £25
The Queen of Hearts, Routledge, [1881] . . £25
The Farmer's Boy, Routledge, [1881] . . . £25
The Milkmaid, Routledge, [1882] £30
Hey Diddle Diddle and Baby Bunting, Routledge, [1882]. £25
The Fox Jumps Over the Parson's Gate, Routledge, [1883]. £25
A Frog He Would A-Wooing Go, Routledge, [1883] .
. . . . £25
Come Lasses and Lads, Routledge, [1884] . . £25
Ride a Cock Horse to Banbury Cross and A Farmer Went Trotting upon his Grey Mare, Routledge, [1884]. £25
An Elegy on the Glory of Her Sex, Mrs Mary Blaize, by Dr Oliver Goldsmith, Routledge, [1885] . £25
The Great Panjandrum Himself, Routledge, [1885] .
. . . . £25
R. Caldecott's Picture Book, Vol. 1, Routledge, [1879] (containing the first 4 'Picture Books') . . £50
R. Caldecott's Picture Book, Vol. 2, Routledge, [1881] (containing the second 4 'Picture Books') . . £50
R. Caldecott's Collection of Pictures and Songs, Routledge, [1881] (reissue of Caldecott's 'Picture Book' Vols 1 and 2). £50
The Hey Diddle Diddle Picture Book, Routledge, [1883] (contains 4 'Picture Books') . . . £50
The Panjandrum Picture Book, Routledge, [1885] (contains 4 'Picture Books'). £50
The Complete Collection of Randolph Caldecott's Pictures and Songs, Routledge, [1887] (contains all 16 'Picture Books', 800 copies). £250
R. Caldicott's Picture Books, Routledge, [1889-1892] (contains the first 4 'Picture Books') . . . £50
Randolph Caldecott's Second Collection of Pictures and Songs, Warne, [1895] (reissue of *The Hey Diddle*

Diddle Picture Book and *The Panjandrum Picture Book*) £50

Other Titles illustrated by Randolph Caldecott
Frank Mildmay, or The Naval Officer, by Captain Marryat, Routledge [1873] £35
Baron Bruno, or The Unbelieving Philosopher and Other Fairy Stories, by Louisa Morgan, Macmillan, 1875 . . . . £45
Old Christmas, From the Sketchbook of Washington Irving, Macmillan, 1876 . . . . . £35
Bracebridge Hall, or The Humorists, by Washington Irving, Macmillan. 1877 [1876] £35
What the Blackbird Said, A Story in Four Chirps, by Mrs Frederick Locker, Routledge, 1881 . . £45
Jackanapes, by Juliana Horatia Ewing, S.P.C.K., 1884 [1883] £25
Some of Aesop's Fables with Modern Instances, Macmillan 1883 . . . . £30
Daddy Darwin's Dovecote, A Country Tale, by Juliana Horatia Ewing, S.P.C.K., [1884] £25
Lob Lie-By-The-Fire, by Juliana Horatia Ewing, S.P.C.K. [1885] £25
Fables de la Fontaine, Macmillan, 1885 . . £30
Jack and the Beanstalk, by Hallam Tennyson, Macmillan, 1886 . . . . £30
The Owls of Olynn Belfry, by A.Y.D., Field & Tuer, [1886] £30
Jackanapes, by Juliana Horatia Ewing, S.P.C.K., [1892] (contains *Daddy Darwin's Dovecote* and *Lob Lie-By-The-Fire*) £25
Randolph Caldecott's Painting Book, S.P.C.K. [1895] £45

TRUMAN CAPOTE
(b.1924 d.1984)

American short story writer and novelist whose career developed after he won the O. Henry prize in 1946.

Novels
Other Voices, Other Rooms, Random House (U.S.), 1948 . . . . £350/£45
ditto, Heinemann, 1948 . . . . . £125/£20
ditto, Franklin Library (U.S.), 1979 . . . . £100
The Grass Harp, Random House (U.S.), [1951] . . . . £175/£25
ditto, Heinemann, 1952 . . . . £100/£20
Answered Prayers: The Unfinished Novel, Hamish Hamilton, 1986 . . . . £20/£55
ditto, Random House (U.S.), 1987 . . . £15/£5

Short Stories
A Tree of Night and Other Stories, Random House (U.S.), 1949 . . . . £100/£25
ditto, Heinemann, 1950 . . . . . £65/£10

Breakfast at Tiffany's, Random House (U.S.), 1958 . . . . £300/£35
ditto, Heinemann, 1959 . . . . . £125/£20
A Christmas Memory, Random House (U.S.), 1966 (slipcase, no d/w) £75
ditto, Random House (U.S.), 1966 (600 signed copies, slipcase, no d/w) . . . . . £350/£300
One Christmas, Random House (U.S.), 1983 (no d/w, slipcase) . . . . £50/£30
ditto, Random House (U.S.), 1983 (500 numbered copies signed by the author) . . . £300/£250
ditto, Hamish Hamilton, 1983 . . . £20/£5
Three by Truman Capote, Random House (U.S.), 1985 . . . . £20/£5

Plays
The Grass Harp, Random House (U.S.), [1952] . . . . £400/£150
The Thanksgiving Visitor, Random House (U.S.), 1967 (300 signed, numbered copies, slipcase). . . . . £400/£300
ditto, Random House (U.S.), 1968 (slipcase) £65/£45
ditto, Hamish Hamilton, 1969 . . . £50/£10
House of Flowers, Random House (U.S.), 1968 . . . . £300/£100
Trilogy: An Experiment in Multimedia. with Elinor Perry, Macmillan (U.S.), 1969 . . . . £30/£10

Non Fiction
Local Color, Random House (U.S.), 1950 . £150/£60
ditto, Heinemann, 1950 . . . . . £35/£10
ditto, Heinemann, 1950 (200 numbered copies) £200
The Muses are Heard: An Account, Random House (U.S.), 1956 . . . . £50/£25
ditto, Heinemann, 1957 . . . . . £25/£10
Observations, Simon & Schuster (U.S.), 1959 (glassine d/w, slipcase). . . . . £175/£150
ditto, Weidenfeld and Nicolson, 1959 (glassine d/w, slipcase) . . . . £175/£150
In Cold Blood: A True Account of a Multiple Murder and its Consequences, Random House (U.S.), 1965 . . . . £25/£10
ditto, Random House (U.S.), 1965 (extra signed leaf inserted) . . . . £400/£175
ditto, Random House (U.S.), 1965 (500 signed, numbered copies, slipcase) . . . . £750/£300
ditto, Hamish Hamilton, 1966 . . . £50/£10
The Dogs Bark: Public People and Private Places, Random House (U.S.), 1973 . . . . £20/£5
ditto, Weidenfeld and Nicolson, 1974 . . £15/£5
Then it All Came Down: Criminal Justice Today Discussed by Police, Criminals and Correcting Officers with Comments by Truman Capote, Random House (U.S.), 1976 . . . . £35/£10
Music for Chameleons, Random House (U.S.), 1980 . . . . £25/£10
ditto, Random House (U.S.), 1980 (350 signed copies, slipcase) . . . . £200/£150
ditto, Hamish Hamilton, 1980 . . . £25/£10

Collections
Selected Writings of Truman Capote, Random House
(U.S.), 1963 . . . . £25/£5
ditto, Hamish Hamilton, 1963 . . . . £20/£5
A Capote Reader, Random House (U.S.), 1987 £10/£5
ditto, Hamish Hamilton, 1987 . . . . £10/£5

Others
Bliss: The Screenplay, Univ. of Queensland Press
(Australia), 1986 . . . . £10/£5
ditto, as *Bliss: The Film*, Faber, 1986 . . £10/£5
A Letter to Our Son, Univ. of Queensland Press
(Australia), 1994 . . . . £10/£5
Big Bazoohley, Faber, 1995 . . . . . £10/£5

PETER CAREY
(b.1943)

An Australian author of novels and stories which have
been described as post-modern fables.

Novels
Bliss, Univ. of Queensland Press (Australia), 1981. .
. . . . £45/£15
ditto, Faber, 1981 . . . . £25/£10
ditto, Harper (U.S.), 1981 . . . . . £25/£10
Illywhacker, Univ. of Queensland Press (Australia),
1985 . . . . £20/£10
ditto, Faber, 1985 . . . . £20/£5
ditto, Harper (U.S.), 1985 . . . . . £15/£5
Oscar and Lucinda, Univ. of Queensland Press
(Australia), 1988 . . . . £20/£10
ditto, Faber, 1988 . . . . £15/£5
ditto, Harper (U.S.), 1988 . . . . . £15/£5
The Tax Inspector, Univ. of Queensland Press
(Australia), 1991 . . . . £10/£5
ditto, Faber, 1991 . . . . £10/£5
ditto, Knopf (U.S.), 1991 . . . . . £10/£5
ditto, Franklin Library (U.S.), 1991 (signed edition) .
. . . . £30
The Unusual Life of Tristan Smith, Univ. of
Queensland Press (Australia), 1994 . . £10/£5
ditto, Faber, 1994 . . . . £10/£5
ditto, Knopf (U.S.), 1995 . . . . . £10/£5
Jack Maggs, Univ. of Queensland Press (Australia),
1997 . . . . £10/£5
ditto, Faber, 1997 . . . . £10/£5
ditto, Knopf (U.S.), 1998 . . . . . £10/£5
True History of the Kelly Gang, Univ. of Queensland
Press (Australia), 2000 . . . . . £15/£5
ditto, Faber, 2001 . . . . £10/£5
ditto, Knopf (U.S.), 2001 . . . . . £10/£5

Short Stories
The Fat Man in History, Univ. of Queensland Press
(Australia), 1974 . . . . £45/£20
ditto, Faber, 1980 . . . . £30/£10
ditto, Random House (U.S.), 1980 . . £25/£10
War Crimes, Univ. of Queensland Press (Australia),
1979 . . . . £45/£25
Collected Stories, Faber, 1995 . . . . £15/£5

JOHN DICKSON CARR
(b.1906 d.1977)

Carr was one of the classic authors of 'locked room'
mysteries.

Dr Gideon Fell Titles
Hag's Nook, Harper (U.S.), 1933 . . £1,000/£150
ditto, Hamilton, 1933 . . . . . . £1,000/£150
The Mad Hatter Mystery, Harper (U.S.), 1933 . . .
. . . . £1,000/£150
ditto, Hamilton, 1933 . . . . . . £1,000/£150
The Eight of Swords, Harper (U.S.), 1934 £1,000/£150
ditto, Hamilton, 1934 . . . . . . £1,000/£150
The Blind Barber, Harper (U.S.), 1934 . £750/£150
ditto, Hamilton, 1934 . . . . . . £750/£150
Death Watch, Hamilton, 1935 . . . £750/£150
ditto, Harper (U.S.), 1935 . . . . . £750/£150
The Three Coffins, Harper (U.S.), 1935 . £750/£150
ditto as *The Hollow Man*, Hamilton, 1935 £750/£150
The Arabian Night's Murder, Hamilton, 1936 . . .
. . . . £750/£150
ditto, Harper (U.S.), 1936 . . . . . £750/£150
The Third Bullet, Hodder, 1937 (wraps) . . £100
To Wake the Dead, Hamilton, 1937 . . £500/£75
ditto, Harper (U.S.), 1938 . . . . . £500/£75
The Crooked Hinge, Harper (U.S.), 1938 . £500/£75
ditto, Hamilton, 1938 . . . . . . £500/£75
The Problem of the Green Capsule, Harper (U.S.),
1939 . . . . £500/£75
ditto as *The Black Spectacles*, Hamilton, 1939 . . .
. . . . £500/£75
The Problem of the Wire Cage, Harper (U.S.), 1939 .
. . . . £300/£50
ditto, Hamilton, 1940 . . . . . . £300/£50
The Man Who Could Not Shudder, Harper (U.S.),
1940 . . . . £250/£40
ditto, Hamilton, 1940 . . . . . . £250/£40
The Case of the Constant Suicides, Harper (U.S.),
1941 . . . . £250/£40
ditto, Hamilton, 1941 . . . . . . £250/£40
Death Turns the Tables, Harper (U.S.), 1941 £250/£40
ditto, as *The Seat of the Scornful*, Hamilton, 1941. .
. . . . £250/£40
Till Death Do Us Part, Harper (U.S.), 1944 £175/£30
ditto, Hamilton, 1944 . . . . . . £175/£30
He Who Whispers, Hamilton, 1946 . . . £150/£25
ditto, Harper (U.S.), 1947 . . . . . £150/£25
The Sleeping Sphinx, Harper (U.S.), 1947 . £150/£25
ditto, Hamilton, 1947 . . . . . . £150/£25

Dr Fell, Detective and Other Stories, Harper (U.S.)
1947 (wraps) £50
Below Suspicion, Harper (U.S.), 1949 . . £65/£10
ditto, Hamilton, 1950 . . . . . . £65/£10
The Dead Man's Knock, Harper (U.S.), 1958 £35/£10
ditto, Hamilton, 1958 . . . . . . £35/£10
In Spite of Thunder, Harper (U.S.), 1960 . £35/£10
ditto, Hamilton, 1960 . . . . . . £35/£10
The House at Satan's Elbow, Harper (U.S.), 1965. .
. . . . £35/£10
ditto, Hamilton, 1965 . . . . . . £35/£10
Panic in Box C, Harper (U.S.), 1966 . . £35/£10
ditto, Hamilton, 1966 . . . . . . £35/£10
Dark of the Moon, Harper (U.S.), 1967 . . £35/£10
ditto, Hamilton, 1968 . . . . . . £35/£10

Henri Bencolin Titles
It Walks by Night, Harper (U.S.),1930 . £1,750/£200
ditto, Harper (U.S.),1930 (unbroken seal on last
section) . . . . £3,000/£2,000
ditto, Harper (U.K.), 1930 . . . . £1,500/£200
ditto, Harper (U.K.),1930 (unbroken seal on last
section) . . . . £3,000/£1,250
The Lost Gallows, Harper (U.S.), 1931 . £1,500/£150
ditto, Hamilton, 1931 . . . . . £1,500/£150
Castle Skull, Harper (U.S.), 1931 . . £1,400/£200
ditto, Tom Stacey, 1973 . . . . . £100/£90
ditto, Severn House, 1976. . . . . £10/£5
The Waxworks Murder, Hamilton, 1932 £1,500/£150
ditto, as *The Corpse in the Waxworks*, Harper (U.S.),
1932 . . . . £1,500/£150
The Four False Weapons, Harper (U.S.), 1937 . .
. . . . £750/£100
ditto, Hamilton, 1938 . . . . . £750/£100
The Door to Doom and Other Detections, Harper,
1980 . . . . £10/£5
ditto, Hamilton, 1981 . . . . . . £10/£5

Sir Henry Merrivale Titles by 'Carter Dixon'
The Plague Court Murders, Morrow (U.S.), 1934 . .
. . . . £1,000/£150
ditto, Heinemann, 1935 . . . . . £1,000/£150
The White Priory Murders, Morrow (U.S.), 1934 . .
. . . . £1,000/£150
ditto, Heinemann, 1935 . . . . . £1,000/£150
The Red Widow Murders, Morrow (U.S.), 1935 . .
. . . . £1,000/£150
ditto, Heinemann, 1935 . . . . . £1,000/£150
The Unicorn Murders, Morrow (U.S.), 1935 . . .
. . . . £1,000/£150
ditto, Heinemann, 1936 . . . . . £1,000/£150
The Magic Lantern Murders, Heinemann, 1936 . .
. . . . £1,000/£150
ditto, as *The Punch and Judy Murders*, Morrow
(U.S.), 1937 . . . . . . £1,000/£150
The Peacock Feather Murders, Morrow (U.S.), 1937 .
. . . . £750/£125
ditto, as *The Ten Teacups*, Morrow (U.S.), 1937 . .
. . . . £750/£125

The Judas Window, Morrow (U.S.), 1938 £500/£100
ditto, Heinemann, 1938 . . . . . £500/£100
Death in Five Boxes, Heinemann, 1938. . £400/£75
ditto, Morrow (U.S.), 1938 . . . . £400/£75
The Reader is Warned, Heinemann, 1939 £750/£125
ditto, Morrow (U.S.), 1939 . . . . £750/£125
And So To Murder, Morrow (U.S.), 1940 £750/£125
ditto, Heinemann, 1941 . . . . . £750/£125
Murder in the Submarine Zone, Heinemann, 1940 .
. . . . £750/£125
ditto, as *Nine–And Death Makes Ten*, Morrow (U.S.),
1940 . . . . £750/£125
The Department of Queer Complaints, Heinemann,
1940 . . . . £750/£125
ditto, Morrow (U.S.), 1940 . . . . £750/£125
Seeing is Believing, Morrow (U.S.), 1941 £750/£125
ditto, Heinemann, 1942 . . . . . £750/£125
The Gilded Man, Morrow (U.S.), 1942 . . £250/£40
ditto, Heinemann, 1942 . . . . . £250/£40
She Died a Lady, Morrow (U.S.), 1943 . . £250/£40
ditto, Heinemann, 1943 . . . . . £250/£40
He Wouldn't Kill Patience, Morrow (U.S.), 1944 . .
. . . . £150/£25
ditto, Heinemann, 1944. . . . . . £150/£25
The Curse of the Bronze Lamp, Morrow (U.S.), 1946.
. . . . £100/£20
ditto, as *Lord of the Sorcerers*, Heinemann, 1946 . .
. . . . £100/£20
My Late Wives, Morrow (U.S.), 1946 . . £75/£15
ditto, Heinemann, 1947 . . . . . £75/£15
The Skeleton in the Clock, Morrow (U.S.), 1948 . .
. . . . £75/£15
ditto, Heinemann, 1949 . . . . . £75/£15
A Graveyard to Let, Morrow (U.S.), 1949 . £75/£15
ditto, Heinemann, 1950 . . . . . £65/£10
Night at the Mocking Widow, Morrow (U.S.), 1950 .
. . . . £65/£10
ditto, Heinemann, 1951 . . . . . £65/£10
Behind the Crimson Blind, Morrow (U.S.), 1952 . .
. . . . £65/£10
ditto, Heinemann, 1952 . . . . . £65/£10
The Cavalier's Cup, Morrow (U.S.), 1953 . £65/£10
ditto, Heinemann, 1953 . . . . . £65/£10
Fear is the Same, Morrow (U.S.), 1956. . £65/£10
ditto, Heinemann, 1956 . . . . . £65/£10

Other Titles
Poison in Jest, Harper (U.S.), 1932 . . £1,050/£100
ditto, Hamilton, 1932 . . . . . £1,000/£100
The Bowstring Murders, Morrow (U.S.) 1933 (pseud.
'Carter Dixon') . . . . . . £1,000/£150
ditto, Heinemann, 1934 . . . . . £1,000/£150
Devil Kinsmere, Hamilton, 1934 (pseud. 'Roger
Fairbairn') . . . . . . £1,000/£150
ditto, Harper (U.S.), 1934. . . . . £1,000/£150
The Murder of Sir Edmund Godfrey, Hamilton, 1936.
. . . . £250/£45
ditto, Harper (U.S.), 1936. . . . . £250/£45
The Third Bullet, Hodder, 1937 (wraps) . . £250

The Burning Court, Harper (U.S.), 1937 . £250/£45
ditto, Hamilton, 1937 . . . . . . £250/£45
Drop to His Death, Heinemann, 1939 (pseud. 'Carter Dixon', with John Rhode) . . . . . £250/£45
ditto, as *Fatal Descent*, Dodds Mead (U.S.), 1939 (pseud. 'Carter Dixon', with John Rhode) £250/£45
The Emperor's Snuffbox, Harper (U.S.), 1942 . . .
. . . . £250/£45
ditto, Hamilton, 1943 . . . . £250/£45
The Life of Sir Arthur Conan Doyle, Harper (U.S.), 1948 . . . . £75/£10
ditto, Hamilton, 1949 . . . . £65/£10
The Bride of Newgate, Harper (U.S.), 1950. £60/£20
ditto, Hamilton, 1950 . . . . £60/£20
The Devil in Velvet, Harper (U.S.), 1951 . £60/£20
ditto, Hamilton, 1951 . . . . £60/£20
The Nine Wrong Answers, Harper (U.S.), 1952 . .
. . . . £60/£20
ditto, Hamilton, 1952 . . . . . . £60/£20
The Third Bullet and Other Stories, Harper (U.S.), 1954 . . . . £60/£20
ditto, Hamilton, 1954 . . . . . . £60/£20
The Exploits of Sherlock Holmes, Random House (U.S.), 1954 (with Adrian Conan Doyle) . £60/£20
ditto, Murray, 1954 . . . . . . £60/£20
Captain Cut Throat, Harper (U.S.), 1955 . £60/£15
ditto, Hamilton, 1955 . . . . . . £60/£15
Patrick Butler for the Defence, Harper (U.S.), 1956 .
. . . . £60/£15
ditto, Hamilton, 1956 . . . . . . £60/£15
Fire, Burn!, Harper (U.S.), 1957 . . . £60/£15
ditto, Hamilton, 1957 . . . . . . £60/£15
Scandal at High Chimneys, Harper (U.S.), 1959 . .
. . . . £60/£15
ditto, Hamilton, 1959 . . . . . . £60/£15
The Witch of the Low-Tide, Harper (U.S.), 1961 . .
. . . . £50/£10
ditto, Hamilton, 1961 . . . . . . £50/£10
The Demoniacs, Harper (U.S.), 1962 . . £50/£10
ditto, Hamilton, 1962 . . . . . . £50/£10
The Men Who Explained Miracles, Harper (U.S.), 1963 . . . . £50/£10
ditto, Hamilton, 1964 . . . . . . £50/£10
Most Secret, Harper (U.S.), 1964 . . . £50/£10
ditto, Hamilton, 1964 . . . . . . £50/£10
Papa La-Bas, Harper (U.S.), 1968 . . . £50/£10
ditto, Hamilton, 1969 . . . . . . £50/£10
The Ghost's High Noon, Harper (U.S.), 1969 £50/£10
ditto, Hamilton, 1970 . . . . . . £50/£10
Deadly Hall, Harper (U.S.), 1971 . . . £45/£10
ditto, Hamilton, 1971 . . . . . . £45/£10
The Hungry Goblin, Hamilton, 1972 . . £45/£10
ditto, Harper (U.S.), 1972 . . . . . £45/£10
The Dead Sleep Lightly, Doubleday (U.S.) 1983 . .
. . . . £30/£10

LEWIS CARROLL
(b.1832 d.1898)

Born Charles Lutwidge Dodgson, Carroll was a humorist and children's writer. *Alice's Adventures in Wonderland* was an immediate success.

Alice's Adventures in Wonderland, Macmillan, 1865 (withdrawn, illustrated by Sir John Tenniel) . . .
. . . . £100,000
ditto, Appleton (U.S.), 1866 (illustrated by Sir John Tenniel) £3,500
ditto, Macmillan, 1866 (illustrated by Sir John Tenniel) £3,000
ditto, as *Alice's Adventures Under Ground*, Macmillan, 1886 . . . . £150
ditto, Macmillan, 1889 (illustrated by Gertrude Thomson) £125
ditto, Harper (U.S.), 1901 (illustrated by Peter Newell) £100
ditto, Mansfield (U.S.), 1896 (illustrated by Blanche McManus) £75
ditto, Ward Lock, 1907 (illustrated by Blanche McManus) £75
ditto, Cassell, 1907 (illustrated by Charles Robinson) .
. . . . £100
ditto, Heinemann, [1907] (illustrated by Arthur Rackham) £150
ditto, Heinemann, [1907] (illustrated by Arthur Rackham, deluxe edition of 1,130 copies) . £1,500
ditto, Doubleday (U.S.), [1907] (illustrated by Arthur Rackham, 550 signed copies) . . . £1,500
ditto, Doubleday (U.S.), [1907] (illustrated by Arthur Rackham, trade edition) £150
ditto, Routledge, 1907 (illustrated by Thomas Maybank) £100
ditto, Chatto & Windus, 1907 (illustrated by Millicent Sowerby) £100
ditto, Nelson, 1908 (illustrated by Harry Rountree) £75
ditto, Raphael Tuck [1910] (12 colour plates by Mabel Lucie Attwell) £150
ditto, Dutton (U.S.), 1929 (illustrated by Willy Pogany) . . . . £35/£10
ditto, Dutton (U.S.), 1929 (signed, limited edition, illustrated by Willy Pogany) . . . £250
ditto, Black Sun Press, Paris, 1930 (illustrated by Marie Lurencin) £1,500
ditto, with extra plates £4,500
ditto, Random House (U.S.), 1969 (illustrated by Salvador Dali) £3,000
Phantasmagoria and Other Poems, Macmillan, 1869
. . . . £250
ditto, Macmillan, 1911 (miniature edition) . £25
The Songs from Alice's Adventures in Wonderland, Weekes, [1870] (wraps) £75
Through the Looking Glass, Macmillan, 1872 (illustrated by Sir John Tenniel) . . . £250
ditto, Mansfield (U.S.), 1899 (illustrated by Blanche McManus) £50

ditto, Harper (U.S.), 1902 (illustrated by Peter Newell)
. . . . £100
The Hunting of the Snark, An Agony in Eight Fits,
Macmillan, 1876 . . . . £450
ditto, Chatto & Windus, 1941 (illustrated by Mervyn
Peake yellow boards) . . . . . £75/£20
ditto, by Lewis Carroll, Chatto & Windus, 1941 (large
format, pink boards) . . . . . . £125/£35
Rhyme? and Reason?, Macmillan, 1883 . . £150
A Tangled Tale, Macmillan, 1885 . . . . £100
The Game of Logic, Macmillan, 1886 (with envelope,
card and 9 counters) £100
Symbolic Logic, Macmillan, 1896 . . . . £500
Sylvie and Bruno, Macmillan, 1889 . . . . £50
Sylvie and Bruno Concluded, Macmillan, 1893 £45
Three Sunsets and Other Poems, Macmillan, 1898 £30
The Lewis Carroll Picture Book, T. Fisher Unwin,
1899 . . . . £50
Feeding the Mind, Chatto & Windus, 1907 (boards) .
. . . . £25
ditto, Chatto & Windus, 1907 (wraps) . . . £20
ditto, Chatto & Windus, 1907 (leather binding). £45
Bruno's Revenge, Collins [1924] . . . £15
Further Nonsense, Verse and Prose, T. Fisher Unwin,
1926 . . . . £35/£15
The Collected Verse of Lewis Carroll, Macmillan,
1932 . . . . £50/£20
For the Train, Denis Archer, 1932 . . . £40/£15
The Rectory Umbrella and Mischmasch, Cassell &
Co., 1932 . . . . £40/£15
Useful and Instructive Poetry, Butler and Tanner,
1954 . . . . £25/£10
ditto, Macmillan (U.S.), 1954 . . . . £25/£10
The Diaries of Lewis Carroll, Cassell, 1953 [1954] (2
vols) . . . . £75/£45
The Rectory Magazine, Univ. of Texas (U.S.), 1975 .
. . . . £20/£10
The Letters of Lewis Carroll, Macmillan, 1979 (2 vols)
. . . . £25/£20
ditto, as **The Selected Letters of Lewis Carroll**,
Macmillan, 1982 (1 vol.) . . . . . £10/£5
Alice in Wonderland and Through the Looking Glass,
Zephyr Books (Sweden), 1946 (illustrated by Mervyn
Peake, wraps with d/w) . . . . . £200/£75
ditto, Allan Wingate, 1954 . . . . . £450/£150
ditto, Schocken (U.S.), 1979 . . . . £25/£10

ANGELA CARTER
(b.1940 d.1992)

Carter was a novelist and short story writer whose
work explores the territory of magic realism.

Novels
Shadow Dance, Heinemann, 1966 . . . £175/£35
ditto, as **Honeybuzzard**, Simon & Schuster (U.S.),
1966 . . . . £75/£25

The Magic Toyshop, Heinemann, 1967 . . . £200/£45
ditto, Simon & Schuster (U.S.), 1968 . . £40/£15
Several Perceptions, Heinemann, 1968 . . £175/£20
ditto, Simon & Schuster (U.S.), 1968 . . £35/£10
Heroes and Villains, Heinemann, 1969 . . £150/£15
ditto, Simon & Schuster (U.S.), 1969 . . £35/£15
Love, Hart-Davis, 1971 . . . . . £75/£15
ditto, Chatto & Windus, 1987 (revised edition) £20/£5
The Infernal Desire Machines of Doctor Hoffman,
Hart-Davis, 1972. . . . . £60/£15
ditto, as **The War of Dreams**, Harcourt Brace (U.S.),
1974 . . . . £25/£10
The Passion of New Eve, Gollancz, 1977 . £35/£10
ditto, Harcourt Brace (U.S.), 1977 . . . £25/£5
Nights at the Circus, Chatto & Windus, 1984 £20/£5
ditto, Viking (U.S.), 1986 . . . . . £20/£5
Wise Children, Chatto & Windus, 1991 . . £20/£5
ditto, Farrar Straus (U.S.), 1992 . . . . £10/£5

Short Stories
Fireworks: Nine Profane Pieces, Quartet, 1974 . . .
. . . . £45/£15
ditto as **Fireworks: Nine Stories in Various Disguises**,
Harper & Row (U.S.), 1981 . . . . £15/£5
The Bloody Chamber and Other Stories, Gollancz,
1979 . . . . £50/£15
ditto, Harper (U.S.), 1979 . . . . . £20/£5
Black Venus's Tale, Next Editions, 1980 (spiral
bound, wraps) £10
Black Venus, Chatto & Windus, 1985 . . £20/£5
ditto, as **Saints and Strangers**, Viking (U.S.), 1986 .
. . . . £20/£5
Wayward Girls and Wicked Women, Virago, 1986
(wraps) £5
American Ghosts and Old World Wonders, Chatto &
Windus, 1993. . . . . £20/£5
Burning Your Boats, The Complete Short Stories,
Chatto & Windus, 1995 . . . . . £20/£10
ditto, Holt (U.S.), 1996 . . . . . £15/£5

Children's Fiction
Miss Z, The Dark Young Lady, Heinemann, 1970 .
. . . . £65/£15
ditto, Simon & Schuster (U.S.), 1970 . . £65/£10
The Donkey Prince, Simon & Schuster (U.S.), 1970 .
. . . . £25/£10
The Fairy Tales of Charles Perrault, Gollancz, 1977 .
. . . . £40/£20
Martin Leman's Comic and Curious Cats, Gollancz,
1979 . . . . £20/£5
ditto, Harmony/Crown (U.S.), 1979 . . . £25/£5
The Music People, Hamish Hamilton, 1980 (with
Leslie Carter). . . . . £15/£5
Moonshadow, Gollancz, 1982 (with Justin Todd, no
d/w) £100
Sleeping Beauty and Other Favourite Fairy Tales,
Gollancz, 1983 . . . . £15/£5
ditto, Schocken, 1984 . . . . . . £15/£5

Verse
The Unicorn, Tlaloc, 1966 (150 copies, mimeographed
sheets, stapled) £400

Others
The Sadeian Woman, Virago, 1979 . . £75/£20
ditto, Pantheon (U.S.), 1979 . . . . . £25/£5
Nothing Sacred, Selected Writings, Virago, 1982
(wraps) £10
Come Unto These Yellow Sands, Bloodaxe Books,
1984 . . . . £65/£20
Expletives Deleted, Chatto & Windus, 1992 £15/£5
The Curious Room, Collected Dramatic Works,
Chatto & Windus, 1996 . . . . . . £15/£5
ditto, Secker & Warburg (U.S.), 1997 . . £15/£5

RAYMOND CARVER
(b.1938 d.1988)

American short story writer and poet, Carver's work
has been translated into more than twenty languages.

Fiction
Put Yourself in My Shoes, Capra (U.S.), 1974 (wraps)
. . . . £75
ditto, Capra (U.S.), 1974 (75 numbered copies in hard
covers)) £600
Will you Please Be Quiet, Please?, McGraw-Hill
(U.S.), 1976 . . . . £250/£75
Furious Seasons and Other Stories, Capra (U.S.),
1977 (100 signed copies) . . . . £1,000/£350
ditto, Capra (U.S.), 1977 (wraps). £75
What We Talk About When We Talk About Love,
Knopf (U.S.), 1981 . . . . £50/£15
ditto, Collins, 1982 . . . . £50/£15
The Pheasant, Metacom (U.S.), 1982 (150 signed
copies, wraps) £125
ditto, Metacom (U.S.), 1982 (26 lettered signed copies,
no d/w) £500
Cathedral, Knopf (U.S.), 1983 . . . . £25/£10
ditto, Collins, 1984 . . . . £25/£10
The Stories of Raymond Carver, Picador, 1985
(wraps) £10
My Father's Life, Babcock & Koontz (U.S.), 1986
(200 signed copies of 240, wraps) £75
ditto, Babcock & Koontz (U.S.), 1986 (40 signed
copies of 240, wraps) £125
Those Days: Early Writings by Raymond Carver,
Raven (U.S.), 1987 (100 signed, numbered copies,
wraps) £125
ditto, Raven (U.S.), 1987 (26 signed, lettered copies) .
. . . . £350
ditto, Raven (U.S.), 1987 (14 signed, presentation
copies, quarter leather) £500
Where I'm Calling From: New and Selected Stories,
Atlantic Monthly (U.S.), 1988 . . . . £15/£5

ditto, Atlantic Monthly (U.S.), 1988 (250 signed
copies, slipcase) . . . . £250/£225
ditto, Franklin Library (U.S.), 1988 (signed) . £75
ditto, Harvill, 1993 . . . . £15/£5
Elephant, Jungle Garden Press, 1988 (200 signed
copies, wraps) £175
Elephant and Other Stories, Collins Harvill, 1988 .
. . . . £35/£10
Three Stories, Engdahl Typography, 1990 (400
numbered copies) . . . . . . £75/£25

Poetry
Near Klamath, English Club of Sacramento State
College (U.S.), 1968 (wraps) £1,250
Winter Insomnia, Kayak (U.S.), 1970 (wraps) . £125
At Night the Salmon Move, Capra (U.S.), 1976 (100
signed hardback copies) £250
ditto, Capra (U.S.), 1976 (1000 copies, wraps) . £75
Distress Sale, Lord John Press, 1981 (150 signed
copies) £100
Two Poems, Scarab (U.S.), 1982 (100 signed copies,
wraps) £175
This Water, Ewart (U.S.), 1985 (100 signed copies,
wraps) £125
ditto, Ewart (U.S.), 1985 (36 signed, hard back copies)
. . . . £200
Where Water Comes Together with Other Water,
Random House, 1985 . . . . . . £25/£10
Ultramarine, Random House (U.S.), 1986 . £25/£10
Two Poems, Ewart (U.S.), 1986 (100 copies, wraps) .
. . . . £25
ditto, Ewart (U.S.), 1986 (25 signed copies, wraps) .
. . . . £65
In a Marine Light: Selected Poems, Collins Harvill,
1987 . . . . £40/£15
The Painter and the Fish, Ewart (U.S.), 1988 (26
signed copies, hardcover) £250
ditto, Ewart (U.S.), 1988 (74 signed, numbered copies,
wraps). £100
ditto, Ewart (U.S.), 1988 (15 signed publisher's copies,
hardcover) £250
A New Path to the Waterfall, Atlantic Monthly (U.S.),
1989 . . . . £25/£10
ditto, Atlantic Monthly (U.S.), 1989 (200 copies signed
by editor, slipcase). . . . . . . £75/£65
ditto, Collins Harvill, 1989 . . . . £25/£10
All of Us, Collins Harvill, 1996 . . . . £30/£10
ditto, Knopf (U.S.), 1998 . . . . . £20/£10

Essays, Poems, and Stories
Fires, Capra (U.S.), 1983 (250 signed, hardback
copies, acetate d/w) . . . . . £150/£135
ditto, Capra (U.S.), 1983 (wraps). . . . £15
ditto, Collins Harvill, 1985 . . . . £25/£10
Music, Ewart (U.S.), 1985 (26 signed, lettered copies,
wraps). £150
ditto, Ewart (U.S.), 1985 (100 signed, numbered
copies, wraps) £75

No Heroics, Please: Uncollected Writings, Collins Harvill, 1991 . . . . £25/£10
ditto, Vintage Contemporaries (U.S.), 1992 (wraps) .
. . . . £10

Screenplay
Dostoevsky: A Screenplay, Capra (U.S.), 1985 (with Tess Gallagher, bound in with *King Dog* by Le Guin, wraps). £15
ditto, Capra (U.S.), 1985 (200 copies signed by all authors, wraps) £150

JOYCE CARY
(b.1888 d.1957)

A novelist, perhaps best known for his *The Horse's Mouth*, made into a film with Alec Guinness.

Novels
Aissa Saved, Benn, 1932 . . . . . . £300/£30
ditto, Harper & Row (U.S.), 1962 . . . £30/£10
An American Visitor, Benn, 1933 . . . £175/£20
ditto, Harper & Row (U.S.), 1961 . . . £25/£10
The African Witch, Gollancz, 1936 . . . £75/£25
ditto, Morrow (U.S.), 1936 . . . . . £25/£5
Castle Corner, Gollancz, 1938, . . . £75/£20
ditto, Harper & Row (U.S.) 1963 . . . £25/£10
Mister Johnson, Gollancz, 1939 . . . £75/£20
ditto, Harper & Row (U.S.), 1948 . . . £20/£5
Charley Is My Darling, Joseph, 1940 . . £50/£10
ditto, Harper & Row (U.S.), 1959 . . . £20/£5
A House of Children, Joseph, 1941 . . . £35/£10
ditto, Harper & Row (U.S.), 1955 . . . £20/£5
Herself Surprised, Joseph, 1941 . . . . £35/£10
ditto, Harper & Row (U.S.), 1941 . . . £20/£5
To Be a Pilgrim, Joseph, 1942 . . . . £35/£10
ditto, Harper & Row (U.S.), 1942 . . . £20/£5
The Horse's Mouth, Joseph, 1944 . . . £65/£20
ditto, Harper & Row (U.S.), 1944. . . . £30/£10
The Moonlight, Joseph, 1946 . . . . £35/£10
ditto, Harper & Row (U.S.), 1946. . . . £20/£5
A Fearful Joy, Joseph, 1949 . . . . . £25/£10
ditto, Harper & Row (U.S.), 1949. . . . .£20/£5
Prisoner of Grace, Joseph, 1952 . . . . £25/£10
ditto, Harper & Row (U.S.), 1952. . . . £20/£5
Except the Lord, Joseph, 1953 . . . . £20/£5
ditto, Harper & Row (U.S.), 1953. . . . £20/£5
Not Honour More, Joseph, 1955. . . . £20/£5
ditto, Harper & Row (U.S.), 1955. . . . £20/£5
The Old Strife at Plant's, New Bodlean, 1956 (100 signed, numbered copies, wraps) £60
The Horse's Mouth and The Old Strife at Plant's, George Rainbird/Joseph, 1957 (1500 copies, slipcase, acetate d/w) . . . . £50/£35
The Captive and the Free, Joseph, 1959 . £20/£10
ditto, Harper & Row (U.S.), 1959. . . . £15/£5
Spring Song and Other Stories, Joseph, 1960 £15/£10

ditto, Harper & Row (U.S.), 1960. . . . £15/£5
Cock Jarvis, Joseph, 1974 . . . . . £10/£5
ditto, St Martin's Press (U.S.), 1975 . . . £10/£5

Verse
Marching Soldier, Joseph, 1945 . . . . £25/£10
The Drunken Sailor: A Ballad-Epic, Joseph, 1947 .
. . . . £25/£10

Others
Power in Men, Liberal Book Club/Nicholson & Watson, 1939. . . . . £20/£10
ditto, Univ. of Washington Press (U.S.), 1963 £15/£5
The Case for African Freedom, Secker & Warburg, 1941 . . . . £25/£10
ditto, Secker & Warburg, 1941 (revised edition) . .
. . . . £20/£10
ditto, as *The Case for African Freedom and Other Writings on Africa*, Univ. of Texas (U.S.), 1962 . . .
. . . . £10/£5
Process of Real Freedom, Joseph, 1943 (wraps) £25
Britain and West Africa, Longman's Green and Co., 1946 (wraps) £25
Art and Reality, Ways of the Creative Process, C.U.P., 1958 . . . . £20/£5
ditto, Harper & Row (U.S.), 1958. . . . £20/£5
Memoir of the Bobotes, Univ. of Texas (U.S.), 1960 .
. . . . £20/£5
ditto, Joseph, 1964. . . . . £20/£5
Selected Essays, Joseph, 1976 . . . . £20/£5
ditto, St Martin's Press (U.S.), 1976 . . . £20/£5

WILLA CATHER
(b.1873 d.1947)

O Pioneers was Cather's first popular success, and serious critical recognition was to come with the award of the Pulitzer Prize for *One of Ours*, and the Prix Femina Americaine in 1933.

Novels
Alexander's Bridge, Houghton Mifflin/Riverside Press (U.S.), 1912 (blue cloth). £50
ditto, Houghton Mifflin/Riverside Press (U.S.), 1912 (later issues, other cloth colours) £30
ditto, Heinemann, 1912 . . . . . . £35
O Pioneers!, Houghton Mifflin/Riverside Press (U.S.), 1913 (tan or cream cloth) £75
ditto, Houghton Mifflin/Riverside Press (U.S.), 1913 (later issue, brown cloth) £45
ditto, Heinemann, 1913 . . . . . . £35
The Song of the Lark, Houghton Mifflin/Riverside Press (U.S.), 1915 . . . . £45
ditto, Murray, 1916 . . . . £25
My Ántonia, Houghton Mifflin/Riverside Press (U.S.), 1918 . . . . £45
ditto, Heinemann, 1919 . . . . . . £25

One of Ours, Knopf (U.S.), 1922 (35 signed, on Japanese vellum of 345 copies, glassine d/w) . . .
. . . . £1,500/£1,250
ditto, Knopf (U.S.), 1922 (310 signed of 345 copies, slipcase) . . . . £500/£400
ditto, Knopf (U.S.), 1922 . . . . . . £100/£25
ditto, Knopf (U.S.), 1922 (250 special copies) £75/£25
ditto, Heinemann, 1923 . . . . . . £75/£25
A Lost Lady, Knopf (U.S.), 1923 . . . £150/£45
ditto, Knopf (U.S.), 1923 (220 signed copies, slipcase)
. . . . £650/£550
ditto, Heinemann, 1924 . . . . . . £75/£25
The Professor's House, Knopf (U.S.), 1925 (40 signed, on Japanese vellum of 225 copies, glassine d/w) . . . . £600/£500
ditto, Knopf (U.S.), 1925 (185 signed of 225 copies, slipcase) . . . . £350/£300
ditto, Knopf (U.S.), 1925 . . . . . . £65/£20
ditto, Heinemann, 1925 . . . . . . £35/£10
My Mortal Enemy, Knopf (U.S.), 1926 (220 signed copies, slipcase) . . . . £450/£350
ditto, Knopf (U.S.), 1926 . . . . . . £65/£20
ditto, Heinemann, 1928 . . . . . . £35/£10
Death Comes for the Archbishop, Knopf (U.S.), 1927 (50 signed copies on Japanese vellum) . . £2,000
ditto, Knopf (U.S.), 1927 (175 signed copies) . £750
ditto, Knopf (U.S.), 1927 . . . . . . £75/£20
ditto, Heinemann, 1927 . . . . . . £35/£10
ditto, Knopf (U.S.), 1929 (170 signed copies) . . .
. . . . £350/£250
Shadows on the Rock, Knopf (U.S.), 1931 £75/£15
ditto, Knopf (U.S.), 1931 (619 signed, numbered copies) . . . . £250/£200
ditto, Cassell, 1932 . . . . . . £30/£10
Lucy Gayheart, Knopf (U.S.), 1935 . . . £50/£10
ditto, Knopf (U.S.), 1935 (749 signed, numbered copies, d/w and slipcase) . . . . £250/£175
ditto, Cassell, 1935 . . . . . . £25/£10
Sapphira and the Slave Girl, Knopf (U.S.), 1940 . .
. . . . £45/£10
ditto, Knopf (U.S.), 1940 (525 signed, numbered copies) . . . . £200/£150
ditto, Cassell, 1941 . . . . . . £15/£5

Short Stories
The Troll Garden, McClure, Phillips & Co. (U.S.), 1905 . . . . £100
Youth and the Bright Medusa, Knopf (U.S.), 1920 .
. . . . £100/£35
ditto, Knopf (U.S.), 1920 (35 signed copies) £400/£500
ditto, Heinemann, 1921 . . . . . £75/£25
The Fear that Walks by Noonday, Phoenix Bookshop, 1931 (30 numbered copies) £500
Obscure Destinies, Knopf (U.S.), 1932 (260 signed, numbered copies, d/w and slipcase) . £200/£150
ditto, Knopf (U.S.), 1932 . . . . . £35/£10
ditto, Cassell, 1932 . . . . . . £25/£10
The Old Beauty and Others, Knopf (U.S.), 1948 . .
. . . . £30/£10

ditto, Cassell, 1956 . . . . . . £10/£5
Five Stories, Vintage Books (U.S.), 1956 (wraps) £100
Father Junipero's Holy Family, Robbins (U.S.), 1955 (200 copies) . . . . £250/£200
Early Stories of Willa Cather, Dodd, Mead & Co. (U.S.), 1957 . . . . £20/£10
Willa Cather's Collected Short Fiction, Univ. of Nebraska Press (U.S.), 1965 . . . £20/£5
Uncle Valentine and Other Stories, Univ. of Nebraska Press (U.S.), 1973 . . . . . . £15/£5

Verse
April Twilights, Gorham Press (U.S.), 1903. . £200
April Twilights and other poems, Knopf (U.S.), 1923 (450 signed, numbered copies, slipcase) £150/£125
ditto, Knopf (U.S.), 1923 . . . . . . £50/£20

Essays
Not Under Forty, Knopf (U.S.), 1936 . . £20/£10
ditto, Knopf (U.S.), 1936 (313 signed, numbered copies on Japanese vellum, d/w and slipcase) . .
. . . . £250/£200
ditto, Cassell, 1936 . . . . . . £20/£5

Others
My Autobiography, Stokes (U.S.), 1914 (pseud. S.S. McClure) £15
ditto, Murray, 1914 . . . . £10
December Night, Knopf (U.S.), 1933 . . £75/£35
Not Under Forty, Knopf (U.S.), 1936 . . £30/£10
ditto, Knopf (U.S.), 1936 (333 signed large paper copies) . . . . £300/£200
Willa Cather on Writing, Knopf (U.S.), 1949 £30/£10
Writing from Willa Cather's Campus Years, Univ. of Nebraska Press (U.S.), 1950 . . . £25/£10
Willa Cather in Europe, Knopf (U.S.), 1956 £20/£5
The Kingdom of Art, Univ. of Nebraska Press (U.S.), 1966 . . . . £25/£10
The World and the Parish, Univ. of Nebraska Press (U.S.), 1970 (2 vols). . . . . . £30/£10
Willa Cather In Person, Univ. of Nebraska Press (U.S.), 1987 . . . . £20/£10

RAYMOND CHANDLER
(b.1888 d.1959)

Born in America, Chandler became a naturalised British citizen in 1907, but returned to the U.S. in 1912. A novelist and short story writer, Chandler was 45 before he started writing, and in *The Big Sleep* introduced one of the most famous fictional detectives of all time, Philip Marlowe.

Novels
The Big Sleep, Knopf (U.S.), 1939 . . £7,000/£250
ditto, Hamish Hamilton, 1939 . . . £1,500/£150
Farewell My Lovely, Knopf (U.S.), 1940 £2,250/£250

ditto, Hamish Hamilton, 1940 . . . £1,000/£100
The High Window, Knopf (U.S.), 1942 . £2,500/£250
ditto, Hamish Hamilton, 1943 . . . £1,000/£100
The Lady in the Lake, Knopf (U.S.), 1943 . . . .
. . . . £3,000/£250
ditto, Hamish Hamilton, 1944 . . . £1,000/£100
The Little Sister, Hamish Hamilton, 1949 £1,000/£125
ditto, Houghton Mifflin (U.S.), 1949 . . £175/£65
The Long Goodbye, Hamish Hamilton, 1953 £400/£75
ditto, Houghton Mifflin (U.S.), 1954 . . £350/£75
Playback, Hamish Hamilton, 1958 . . . £75/£20
ditto, Houghton Mifflin (U.S.), 1958 . £45/£20
Poodle Springs, Putnam (U.S.), 1989 (completed by
Robert Parker) . . . . £15/£5
ditto, Macdonald, 1990 . . . . . £15/£5
ditto, Macdonald, 1990 (250 copies signed by Parker,
slipcase, no d/w) . . . . £50/£30

Short Stories
Five Murderers, Avon (U.S.), 1944 (wraps) . £100
Five Sinister Characters, Avon (U.S.), 1945 (wraps) .
. . . . £75
Finger Man and Other Stories, Avon (U.S.), [1946]
(wraps) £60
Red Wind, World (U.S.), 1946 . . . . £45/£10
Spanish Blood, World (U.S.), 1946 . . . £40/£10
Trouble is My Business, Penguin, 1950 (wraps) £10
ditto, Pocket Books (U.S.), 1951 . . . . . £15
The Simple Art of Murder, Houghton Mifflin (U.S.),
1950 . . . . £250/£30
ditto, Hamish Hamilton, 1950 . . . . £200/£30
Pick-Up on Noon Street, Pocket Books (U.S.), 1952 .
. . . . £15
Smart Aleck Kill, Hamish Hamilton, 1953 . £100/£25
Pearls are a Nuisance, Hamish Hamilton, 1953
(wraps) £40
ditto, Hamish Hamilton, 1953 . . . . £30/£10
ditto, as *Finger Man*, Ace Books (U.S.), 1960 . £40
Killer in the Rain, Hamish Hamilton, 1964 . £60/£15
ditto, Houghton Mifflin (U.S.), 1964 . . £50/£15
The Smell of Fear, Hamish Hamilton, 1965 £60/£15
Goldfish, Penguin, 1995 (wraps). £5

Omnibus Editions
Raymond Chandler's Mystery Omnibus, Tower
Books, 1944 . . . . £25/£10
The Raymond Chandler Omnibus, Hamish Hamilton,
1953 . . . . £65/£15
ditto, Knopf (U.S.), 1964 . . . . . £40/£10
The Second Raymond Chandler Omnibus, Hamish
Hamilton, 1962 . . . . £50/£15

Others
Raymond Chandler On Writing, Houghton Mifflin
(U.S.), 1962 (wraps). £200
Raymond Chandler Speaking, Hamish Hamilton, 1962
. . . . £75/£15
ditto, Houghton Mifflin (U.S.), 1962 . . £50/£15

Chandler On Proof Reading, Merrion Press, 1963
(wraps) £200
*Chandler Before Marlowe: Raymond Chandler's
Early Prose and Poetry, 1908-1912*, Univ. of South
Carolina Press (U.S.), 1973 (wraps) . . . £15
ditto, Univ. of South Carolina Press (U.S.), 1973 (499
numbered copies, slipcase, no d/w). . . . £75
The Blue Dahlia, Southern Illinois Univ. Press, 1976 .
. . . . £45/£10
ditto, Elm Tree Books, 1976 . . . . . £20/£5
*The Notebooks of Raymond Chandler and English
Summer - A Gothic Romance*, The Ecco Press (U.S.),
1976 . . . . £45/£20
ditto, Weidenfeld & Nicolson, 1977 . . . £25/£10
Letters, Raymond Chandler and James M. Fox,
Nevile & Yellin (U.S.), 1978 (350 numbered copies,
no d/w) £45
ditto, Nevile & Yellin (U.S.), 1978 (26 lettered copies
numbered copies, no d/w) £150
The Selected Letters of Raymond Chandler, Columbia
Univ. Press (U.S.), 1981. . . . . . £40/£15
ditto, Cape, 1981 . . . . £25/£10
Backfire: Story for the Screen, Santa Barbara Press
(U.S.), 1984 (200 copies, wraps) £30
ditto, Santa Barbara Press (U.S.), 1984 (26 lettered
copies, signed by Robert Parker, splcase, no d/w) .
. . . . £200
ditto, Santa Barbara Press (U.S.), 1984 (100 signed,
numbered copies, splcase, no d/w). . . . £75
*Raymond Chandler's Unknown Thriller: The
Screenplay of 'Playback'*, Mysterious Press (U.S.),
1985 . . . . £30/£15
ditto, Mysterious Press (U.S.), 1985 (250 copies,
signed by Robert Parker, slipcase) . . £100/£75
ditto, Mysterious Press (U.S.), 1985 (26 signed, lettered
copies, splcase) . . . . £200/£175
ditto, Harrap, 1985 . . . . £20/£10

LESLIE CHARTERIS
(b.1907 d.1993)

Leslie Charteris was born in Singapore to a Chinese
father and English mother. Educated and living in
England for several years he wrote a number of crime
novels before hitting upon the character of Simon
Templar, a gentleman burglar nicknamed 'The Saint'.
He later moved to America, and in 1941 became an
American citizen.

'Saint' Novels
Meet-the Tiger!, Ward Lock, 1928 . . £1,500/£125
ditto, Doubleday (U.S.), 1929 . . . £1,000/£65
ditto, as *The Saint Meets The Tiger*, Hodder &
Stoughton, 1963 . . . . £25/£10

The Last Hero, Hodder & Stoughton, [1930] . . .
. . . . £1,000/£100
ditto, Doubleday (U.S.), 1931 . . . . £750/£75
ditto, as *The Saint Closes The Case*, Hodder & Stoughton, 1951 . . . . £25/£10
Knight Templar, Hodder & Stoughton, [1930] . . .
. . . . £1,000/£100
ditto, as *The Avenging Saint*, Hodder & Stoughton, 1949 . . . . £25/£10
ditto, as *The Avenging Saint*, Doubleday (U.S.), 1931.
. . . . £200/£35
She was a Lady, Hodder & Stoughton, 1931 . . .
. . . . £1,000/£100
ditto, as *Angels of Doom*, Doubleday (U.S.), 1932 .
. . . . £750/£75
ditto, as *The Saint Meets His Match*, Hodder & Stoughton, 1950 . . . . £25/£10
Getaway, Hodder & Stoughton, 1932 . £1,000/£100
ditto, as *Getaway: The New Saint Mystery*, Doubleday (U.S.), 1933 . . . . £750/£75
ditto, as *The Saint's Getaway*, Hodder & Stoughton, 1950 . . . . £25/£10
The Saint in New York, Hodder & Stoughton, 1935 .
. . . . £1,000/£100
ditto, Doubleday (U.S.), 1935 . . . . £750/£75
The Saint Overboard, Hodder & Stoughton, 1936 . .
. . . . £1,000/£100
ditto, Doubleday (U.S.), 1936 . . . . £750/£75
Thieves' Picnic, Hodder & Stoughton, 1937 £400/£35
ditto, Doubleday (U.S.), 1937 . . . . £300/£30
ditto, as *The Saint Bids Diamonds*, Hodder & Stoughton, 1950 . . . . £25/£10
Prelude for War, Hodder & Stoughton, 1938 £300/£25
ditto, Doubleday (U.S.), 1938 . . . . £200/£25
ditto, as *The Saint Plays With Fire*, Hodder & Stoughton, 1951 . . . . £25/£10
The Saint in Miami, Doubleday (U.S.), 1940 £200/£20
ditto, Hodder & Stoughton, 1941. . . . £150/£15
The Saint Steps In, Doubleday (U.S.), 1943 £75/£15
ditto, Hodder & Stoughton, 1944. . . . £65/£10
The Saint Sees it Through, Doubleday (U.S.), 1946 .
. . . . £75/£15
ditto, Hodder & Stoughton, 1947. . . . £65/£10
The Saint and the Fiction Makers, Doubleday (U.S.), 1968 . . . . £65/£10
ditto, Hodder & Stoughton, 1969. . . £65/£10
The Saint in Pursuit, Doubleday (U.S.), 1970 . .
. . . . £100/£20
ditto, Hodder & Stoughton, 1971. . . £1250/£25
The Saint and the People Importers, Hodder & Stoughton, 1971 (wraps) £10
ditto, Doubleday (U.S.), 1972 . . . . £40/£10
ditto, Hodder & Stoughton, 1973. . . £125/£25
The Saint and the Hapsburg Necklace, Doubleday (U.S.), 1976 . . . . £40/£10
ditto, Hodder & Stoughton, 1976. . . £40/£10
Send for The Saint, Hodder & Stoughton, 1977 . .
. . . . £25/£10
ditto, Doubleday (U.S.), 1978 . . . . £25/£10

The Saint and the Templar Treasure, Doubleday (U.S.), 1979 . . . . £25/£10
ditto, Hodder & Stoughton, 1979. . . . £25/£10
Count on The Saint, Doubleday (U.S.), 1980 £15/£5
ditto, Hodder & Stoughton, 1980. . . £15/£5
Salvage for The Saint, Doubleday (U.S.), 1983 £15/£5
ditto, Hodder & Stoughton, 1983 . . . £15/£5

'Saint' Novellas and Short Stories
Enter The Saint, Hodder & Stoughton, [1930] . . .
. . . . £1,000/£100
ditto, Doubleday (U.S.), 1931 . . . . £750/£75
Featuring The Saint, Hodder & Stoughton, 1931 . .
. . . . £1,000/£100
Alias The Saint, Hodder & Stoughton, 1931 . . .
. . . . £1,000/£100
The Holy Terror, Hodder & Stoughton, 1932 . . .
. . . . £1,000/£100
ditto, as *The Saint Versus Scotland Yard*, Doubleday (U.S.), 1932 . . . . £750/£75
ditto, as *The Saint Versus Scotland Yard*, Hodder & Stoughton, 1949 . . . . £25/£10
Once More The Saint, Hodder & Stoughton, 1933. .
. . . . £1,000/£100
ditto, as *The Saint and Mr Teal*, Doubleday (U.S.), 1933 . . . . £750/£75
The Brighter Buccaneer, Hodder & Stoughton, 1933 .
. . . . £1,000/£100
ditto, Doubleday (U.S.), 1933 . . . . £750/£75
The Misfortunes of Mr Teal, Hodder & Stoughton, 1934 . . . . £1,000/£100
ditto, Doubleday (U.S.), 1934 . . . . £750/£75
ditto, as *The Saint In London*, Hodder & Stoughton, 1952 . . . . £25/£10
Boodle, Hodder & Stoughton, 1934 . £1,000/£100
ditto, *The Saint Intervenes*, Doubleday (U.S.), 1934 .
. . . . £750/£75
The Saint Goes On, Hodder & Stoughton, 1934 . .
. . . . £1,000/£100
ditto, Doubleday (U.S.), 1935 . . . . £750/£75
The Ace of Knaves, Hodder & Stoughton, 1937 . . .
. . . . £400/£35
ditto, Doubleday (U.S.), 1937 . . . . £300/£30
Follow The Saint, Doubleday (U.S.), 1938 . £300/£25
ditto, Hodder & Stoughton, 1939. . . . £200/£25
The Happy Highwayman, Doubleday (U.S.), 1939 .
. . . . £300/£25
ditto, Hodder & Stoughton, 1939. . . . £200/£25
The Saint Goes West, Doubleday (U.S.), 1942 £75/£15
ditto, Hodder & Stoughton, 1942 . . . £50/£15
The Saint on Guard, Doubleday (U.S.), 1944 £75/£15
ditto, Hodder & Stoughton, 1945. . . . £50/£15
Call For The Saint, Doubleday (U.S.), 1948 £45/£15
ditto, Hodder & Stoughton, 1948. . . . £30/£10
Saint Errant, Doubleday (U.S.), 1948 . . £35/£10
ditto, Hodder & Stoughton, 1949. . . . £25/£10
The Saint in Europe, Doubleday (U.S.), 1953 £35/£10
ditto, Hodder & Stoughton, 1954. . . . £25/£10

The Saint on the Spanish Main, Doubleday (U.S.),
1955 . . . . £30/£10
ditto, Hodder & Stoughton, 1956. . . . £25/£10
The Saint Around the World, Doubleday (U.S.), 1956
. . . . £25/£10
ditto, Hodder & Stoughton, 1957. . . . £25/£10
Thanks to The Saint, Doubleday (U.S.), 1957 £25/£10
ditto, Hodder & Stoughton, 1958. . . . £25/£10
Señor Saint, Doubleday (U.S.), 1958 . . . £25/£10
ditto, Hodder & Stoughton, 1959. . . . £25/£10
The Saint to the Rescue, Doubleday (U.S.), 1959 . .
. . . . £25/£10
ditto, Hodder & Stoughton, 1961 . . . £25/£10
Trust The Saint, Doubleday (U.S.), 1962 . £25/£10
ditto, Hodder & Stoughton, 1962. . . . £25/£10
The Saint in the Sun, Doubleday (U.S.), 1963 £25/£10
ditto, Hodder & Stoughton, 1964. . . . £25/£10
Vendetta for The Saint, Doubleday (U.S.), 1964 . .
. . . . £25/£10
ditto, Hodder & Stoughton, 1965 . . . £25/£10
The Saint on TV, Doubleday (U.S.), 1968 . £25/£10
ditto, Hodder & Stoughton, 1968. . . . £25/£10
The Saint Returns, Doubleday (U.S.), 1968 £25/£10
ditto, Hodder & Stoughton, 1969. . . . £25/£10
The Saint Abroad, Doubleday (U.S.), 1969. . £20/£5
ditto, Hodder & Stoughton, 1970. . . . £15/£5
Catch The Saint, Hodder & Stoughton, 1975 . £15/£5
ditto, Doubleday (U.S.), 1975 . . . . £15/£5
The Saint in Trouble, Doubleday (U.S.), 1978 . £15/£5
ditto, Hodder & Stoughton, 1979 . . £15/£5

Collected Editions

Wanted for Murder, Doubleday (U.S.), 1931 £75/£25
ditto, as *Paging the Saint*, Jacobs (U.S.), 1945 (wraps)
. . . . £25
The First Saint Omnibus, Hodder & Stoughton, 1939.
. . . . £35/£10
ditto, Doubleday (U.S.), 1939 . . . . £35/£10
ditto, as *Arrest the Saint*, PermaBooks (U.S.), 1951 .
. . . . £20/£10
The Saint Two in One, Sun Dial Press (U.S.), 1942 .
. . . . £15/£5
The Saint at Large, Sun Dial Press (U.S.), 1943 . .
. . . . £15/£5
The Second Saint Omnibus, Doubleday (U.S.), 1951 .
. . . . £25/£10
ditto, Hodder & Stoughton, 1952. . . . £25/£10
Concerning The Saint, Avon (U.S.), 1958 (wraps) £25
The Saint Cleans Up, Avon (U.S.), 1959 (wraps) £25
The Saint Magazine Reader, Doubleday (U.S.), 1966.
. . . . £15/£5
ditto, as *The Saint's Choice*, Hodder & Stoughton,
1976 . . . . £15/£5
Saints Alive, Hodder & Stoughton, 1974 . £15/£5
The Saint: Good as Gold, The Ellery Queen Mystery
Club (U.S.), 1979 . . . . £10
The Fantastic Saint, Doubleday (U.S.), 1982 . £10/£5
ditto, Hodder & Stoughton, 1982. . . . £10/£5

The Saint: Five Complete Novels, Avenel Books
(U.S.), 1983 . . . . £10/£5

Other Titles
X Esquire, Ward Lock, 1927. . . . £1,250/£125
The White Rider, Ward Lock, 1928 . . . £500/£75
ditto, Doubleday (U.S.), 1930 . . . . £350/£35
Daredevil, Ward Lock, 1929. . . . . £300/£75
ditto, Doubleday (U.S.), 1929 . . . . £200/£25
The Bandit, Ward Lock, 1929 . . . . £300/£75
ditto, Doubleday (U.S.), 1930 . . . . £200/£25
Killer of Bulls, Heinemann, 1937 (with Juan Belmonte)
. . . . £75/£25
ditto, Doubleday (U.S.), 1937 . . . . £50/£15
Lady on a Train, Shaw Press (U.S.), 1945 (wraps) £65
Spanish for Fun, Hodder & Stoughton, 1964 (wraps)
. . . . £15
Paleneo: A Universal Sign Language, Hodder &
Stoughton, 1972 (wraps) £15

BRUCE CHATWIN
(b.1940 d.1989)

A travel writer and novelist, Chatwin's first book, *In
Patagonia*, won both the Hawthornden Prize and the
E.M. Forster Award of the American Academy of
Arts and Letters.

Novels
The Viceroy of Ouidah, Jonathan Cape, 1980 £65/£10
ditto, Summit (U.S.), 1980 . . . . . £25/£10
On the Black Hill, Jonathan Cape, 1982 . £30/£10
ditto, Viking, 1982 . . . . . . £25/£10
The Songlines, Jonathan Cape, 1987 . . £60/£10
ditto, London Limited Editions, 1987 (150 signed
copies, glassine wrapper) . . . . £300/£250
ditto, Viking (U.S.), 1987. . . . . £25/£5
ditto, Franklin Library (U.S.), 1987 (200 signed copies)
. . . . £75
Utz, Jonathan Cape, 1988. . . . . £15/£5
ditto, Viking (U.S.), 1989. . . . . £10/£5

Travel
In Patagonia, Jonathan Cape, 1977 (map endpapers) .
. . . . £400/£100
ditto, Jonathan Cape, 1977 (white endpapers) . . .
. . . . £300/£75
ditto, Summit (U.S.) . . . . . . £75/£25
Patagonia Revisited, Russell, 1985 (with Paul
Theroux) . . . . £25/£10
ditto, Russell, 1985 (250 copies, cellophane d/w) . .
. . . . £200/£165
ditto, Houghton Mifflin (U.S.), 1986 . . £20/£10
ditto, as *Nowhere Is a Place*, Sierra Club (U.S.), 1991
. . . . £20/£10

Short Stories
The Attractions of France, Colophon Press, 1993 (26 lettered copies of 211 bound in cloth) . . . £400
ditto, Colophon Press, 1993 (175 numbered copies of 211, wraps) £75

Biography
What am I Doing Here?, Jonathan Cape, 1989 £25/£5
ditto, Viking (U.S.), 1989. . . . . . £20/£5
Photographs and Notebooks, Cape, 1993 . £35/£10
ditto, as *Far Journeys: Photographs and Notebooks*, Viking (U.S.), 1993 . . . . . . £25/£10

Others
Animal Style: Art From East to West, Asia Society (U.S.), 1970 (with Emma Bunker and Ann Farkas, wraps). £30
Lady Lisa Lyon, Viking (U.S.), 1983 (Robert Mapplethorpe, text by Chatwin, wraps) . . £20
ditto, St Martin's Press (U.S.), 1983 . . . £40/£15
ditto, Blond & Briggs, 1983 . . . . . £75/£25
The Morality of Things, Typographeum (U.S.), 1993 (175 copies, no d/w) £75
The Anatomy of Restlessness, Selected Writings, 1969-89, Cape, 1996. . . . . . . £30/£10
ditto, Viking (U.S.), 1996. . . . . £25/£5

JOHN CHEEVER
(b.1912 d.1982)

An American short story writer and novelist, his *Stories* won a Pulitzer Prize in 1978.

Fiction
The Way Some People Live: A Book of Stories, Random House (U.S.), 1943 . . . £750/£125
The Enormous Radio and Other Stories, Funk & Wagnalls (U.S.), 1953 . . . . . £150/£25
ditto, Gollancz, 1953 . . . . . . £75/£15
The Wapshot Chronicle, Harpers (U.S.), 1957 . . .
. . . . £125/£25
ditto, Gollancz, 1957 . . . . . . £75/£15
ditto, Franklin Library (U.S.), 1978 (signed) . £65
The Housebreaker of Shady Hill and Other Stories, Harpers (U.S.), [1958] . . . . . . £125/£25
ditto, Gollancz, 1958 . . . . . . £75/£15
Some People, Places, and Things That Will Not Appear in My Next Novel, Harpers (U.S.), 1961 . .
. . . . £100/£20
ditto, Gollancz, 1961 . . . . . . £75/£15
The Wapshot Scandal, Harpers (U.S.), 1964 £40/£10
ditto, Gollancz, 1964 . . . . . . £40/£10
The Brigadier and the Golf Widow, Harpers (U.S.), 1964 . . . . £40/£10
ditto, Gollancz, 1965 . . . . . . £40/£10
Bullet Park, Knopf (U.S.), 1969 . . . £100/£25

ditto, Cape, 1969 . . . . £40/£10
The World of Apples, Knopf (U.S.), 1973 . £30/£10
ditto, Cape, 1974 . . . . £25/£10
Falconer, Knopf (U.S.), 1977 . . . . £25/£10
ditto, Cape, 1977 . . . . £25/£10
The Stories of John Cheever, Knopf (U.S.), 1978 . . .
. . . . £25/£10
ditto, Cape, 1979 . . . . £20/£5
Oh, What a Paradise it Seems, Knopf (U.S.), 1982 .
. . . . £20/£5
ditto, Cape, 1982 . . . . £20/£5
The Letters of John Cheever, Simon & Schuster (U.S.) 1988 (ed. by Benjamin Cheever) . . . £25/£10
ditto, Cape, 1989 . . . . £20/£5
The Journals of John Cheever, Knopf (U.S.), 1991 .
. . . . £20/£5
ditto, Cape, 1991 . . . . £15/£5

G.K. CHESTERTON
(b.1874 d.1936)

Poet, novelist, journalist and essayist, Chesterton is best remembered for his detective stories featuring Father Brown, an unassuming Catholic priest.

'Father Brown' Stories
The Innocence of Father Brown, Cassell, 1911 £275
ditto, John Lane (U.S.), 1911 . . . . . £65
The Wisdom of Father Brown, Cassell, 1914 . £100
ditto, John Lane (U.S.), 1915. . . . . . £45
The Incredulity of Father Brown, Cassell, 1926 . .
. . . . £750/£50
ditto, Dodd, Mead (U.S.), 1927 . . £300/£35
The Secret of Father Brown, Cassell, 1927. £500/£25
ditto, Harper & Bros (U.S.), 1928 . . . £200/£25
The Scandal of Father Brown, Cassell, 1935 . . .
. . . . £400/£20
ditto, Dodd, Mead (U.S.), 1935 . . . £200/£20

Omnibus Editions of 'Father Brown' Stories
The Father Brown Stories, Cassell, 1929 . £250/£25
ditto, as *The Father Brown Omnibus*, Dodd, Mead (U.S.), 1933 . . . . £175£20

Novels
The Napoleon of Notting Hill, John Lane, 1904 £75
ditto, John Lane (U.S.), 1906. . . . . . £65
The Man who was Thursday, Arrowsmith, [1908]. .
. . . . £150
ditto, Dodd, Mead (U.S.), 1908 . . . . £150
The Ball and the Cross, John Lane (U.S.),1909 £45
ditto, Wells Gardner, 1910 . . . . . £40
Manalive, Nelson, 1912 . . . . . . £35
ditto, John Lane (U.S.), 1912. . . . . . £30
The Flying Inn, Methuen, 1914 . . . . . £45
ditto, John Lane (U.S.), 1914. . . . . . £35

The Return of Don Quixote, Chatto & Windus, 1927 .
. . . . £100/£20
ditto, Dodd, Mead (U.S.), 1927 . . . . £75/£15

Short Stories
The Club of Queer Trades, Harper & Bros, 1905 £250
ditto, Harper & Bros (U.S.), 1905 . . . . £200
The Man who Knew too Much, Cassell, 1922 . . .
. . . . £450/£25
ditto, Harper & Bros (U.S.), 1922 . . . £225/£20
Tales of the Long Bow, Cassell, 1925 . £500/£75
ditto, Dodd, Mead (U.S.), 1925 . . . . £350/£40
The Sword of Wood, Elkin Mathews & Marrott, 1928
(530 signed copies) . . . . £125/£75
The Poet and the Lunatics, Cassell, 1929 . £500/£65
ditto, Dodd, Mead (U.S.), 1929 . . . . £400/£45
Four Faultless Felons, Cassell, 1930 . £400/£45
ditto, Dodd, Mead (U.S.), 1930 . . . . £300/£40
The Paradoxes of Mr Pond, Cassell, 1937 . £200/£40
ditto, Dodd, Mead (U.S.), 1937 . . . . £125/£25

Plays
Magic, A Fantastic Comedy, Secker, 1913 (wraps) £65
ditto, Martin Secker, 1913 (150 signed copies, tissue
d/w) . . . . £350/£275
ditto, Putnam's (U.S.), 1913 . . . . . £65
The Judgement of Dr. Johnson, Sheed & Ward, 1927
. . . . £75/£20
ditto, Putnam's (U.S.), 1928 . . . . . £50/£10
The Surprise, Sheed & Ward, 1952 . . . £45/£15
ditto, Sheed & Ward (U.S.), 1953 . . . £45/£15

Verse
Greybeards at Play, Brimley Johnson, 1900 . £500
The Wild Knight and Other Poems, Grant Richards,
1900 . . . . £200
The Ballad of the White Horse, Methuen, 1911 £30
ditto, Methuen, 1911 (100 signed copies, handmade
paper) £175
The Nativity, Albany (U.S.), 1911 (wraps) . . £40
Poems, Burns & Oats Ltd, 1915 . . . . . £40
Wine, Water and Song, Methuen, 1915 . . £30
The Ballad of St. Barbara and Other Verses, Cecil
Palmer, 1922 . . . . £200/£35
ditto, Putnam's (U.S.), 1923 . . . . . £75/£20
The Queen of Seven Swords, Sheed & Ward, 1926 .
. . . . £50/£20
Collected Poems, Cecil Palmer, 1927 . £65/£25
ditto, Cecil Palmer, 1927 (350 signed copies, slipcase)
. . . . £150/£125

Others
The Defendant, Brimley Johnson, 1901 . . . £65
Twelve Types, Humphreys, 1902 . . . . £65
ditto, as Varied Types, Dodd, Mead (U.S.), 1908 £30
Robert Browning, Macmillan, 1903 . . . £25
G.F. Watts, Duckworth, 1904 . . . . . £25
ditto, Dutton (U.S.), 1904 . . . . . . £25
Charles Dickens, Methuen, 1906 . . . . £45

ditto, as Charles Dickens, a critical study, Dodd, Mead
(U.S.), 1906 . . . . £35
All Things Considered, Methuen, 1908 . . . £30
Orthodoxy, John Lane, 1909 . . . . . . £30
George Bernard Shaw, John Lane and the Bodley
Head, 1909 . . . . £40
ditto, John Lane (U.S.), 1909 . . . . . £40
Tremendous Trifles, Methuen, 1909 . . . £40
What's Wrong with the World, Cassell, 1910 . £35
Five Types, Humphries, 1910 (wraps) . . . £35
ditto, Hole (U.S.), 1911 . . . . £35
Alarms and Discursions, Methuen, 1910 . . £45
ditto, Dodd, Mead (U.S.), 1911 . . . . . £40
William Blake, Duckworth, 1910 . . . . £40
Appreciations and Criticisms of the Works of Dickens,
Dent & Sons, 1911 . . . . £40
ditto, Dutton (U.S.), 1911 . . . . . . £35
The Future of Religion. Mr. G.K. Chesterton's Reply
to Mr. Bernard Shaw, The Heritics Club (U.S.), 1911
(wraps) £50
A Miscellany of Men, Methuen, 1912 . . . £40
ditto, Dodd, Mead (U.S.), 1912 . . . . . £35
Victorian Age in Literature, Williams & Norgate,
1913 . . . . £30
The Barbarism of Berlin, Cassell, 1914 (wraps) £40
ditto, as The Appetite of Tyranny, Dodd, Mead (U.S.),
1915 . . . . £25
London, Privately Printed for Edmund D. Brooks and
Alvin Langdon Coburn etc (U.S.), 1914 . . £250
The Crimes of England, Cecil, Palmer & Hayward,
1915 (wraps) £65
ditto, Cecil, Palmer & Hayward, 1915 (wraps) . £25
Lord Kitchener, privately published, 1917 (wraps) £75
A Short History Of England, John Lane, 1917 . £35
ditto, John Lane (U.S.), 1917 . . . . . £35
Utopia of Usurers and Other Essays, Boni & Liveright
(U.S.), 1917 . . . . £35
Irish Impressions, John Lane (U.S.), 1920 . £75/£25
The Superstition of Divorce, Chatto & Windus, 1920 .
. . . . £65/£15
The New Jerusalem, Hodder & Stoughton, 1920 . .
. . . . £100/£15
ditto, Doran (U.S.) 1921 . . . . . . £100/£15
Eugenics and Other Evils, Cassell, 1922 . £100/£15
ditto, Dodd, Mead (U.S.) 1922 . . . . £100/£15
What I Saw In America, Hodder & Stoughton, 1922 .
. . . . £75/£25
Fancies Versus Fads, Methuen, 1923 . . £75/£25
ditto, Dodd, Mead (U.S.) 1923 . . . . £75/£25
St Francis of Assisi, Hodder & Stoughton, 1923 . .
. . . . £75/£25
The Superstitions of the Sceptic, Heffers, 1925 (wraps)
. . . . £45
The Everlasting Man, Dodd, Mead (U.S.) 1925 . .
. . . . £75/£25
William Cobbett, Hodder & Stoughton, 1925 £75/£15
The Outline of Sanity, Methuen, 1926 . £75/£25
ditto, Dodd, Mead (U.S.) 1927 . . . . £75/£25

The Catholic Church and Conversion, Burns, Oates &
Washbourne, 1926 . . . . £75/£15
The Gleaming Cohort, Methuen, 1926 . . £75/£25
Robert Louis Stevenson, Hodder & Stoughton, [1927]
. . . . £75/£30
ditto, Dodd, Mead (U.S.), 1928 . . . . £75/£30
Generally Speaking, Methuen, 1928 . . £65/£25
Do We Agree? A Debate Between G. K. Chesterton
and George Bernard Shaw. With Hilaire Belloc in
the Chair, Mitchell (U.S.), 1928 . . . £75/£25
The Thing, Sheed & Ward, 1929 . . . £85/£30
ditto Dodd, Mead (U.S.), 1930 . . . . £50/£20
The Resurrection of Rome, Hodder & Stoughton,
[1930]. . . . . £75/£30
ditto, Dodd, Mead (U.S.), 1927 . . . . £75/£30
Come to Think of It, Methuen, 1930 . . £75/£25
All Is Grist, Methuen, 1931 . . . . . £75/£25
ditto, Dodd, Mead (U.S.), 1932 . . . . £45/£20
Chaucer, Faber & Faber, 1932 . . . . £75/£25
ditto, Farrar & Rinehart (U.S.), 1932 . . £45/£15
Sidelights on New London and Newer York and Other
Essays, Sheed & Ward, 1933 . . . . £75/£30
ditto Dodd, Mead (U.S.), 1932 . . . . £75/£30
Christendom in Dublin, Sheed & Ward, 1933 £65/£20
ditto, Sheed & Ward (U.S.), 1933 . . . £65/£20
All I Survey, Methuen, 1933 . . . . . £45/£15
ditto, Dodd, Mead (U.S.), 1933 . . . . £45/£15
St. Thomas Aquinas, Hodder & Stoughton, 1933 . .
. . . . £35/£15
ditto, Sheed & Ward (U.S.), 1933 . . . £35/£15
Avowals and Denials, Methuen, 1934 . . £35/£15
The Well and the Shallows, Sheed & Ward, 1933 . .
. . . . £35/£15
ditto, Sheed & Ward (U.S.), 1935 . . . £35/£15
Autobiography, Hutchinson, 1936 . . . £35/£15
ditto, Hutchinson, 1936 (250 deluxe copies in slipcase)
. . . . £95/£75
ditto, Sheed & Ward (U.S.), 1936 . . . £35/£15
The Coloured Lands, Sheed & Ward, 1938. £35/£15
ditto, Sheed & Ward (U.S.), 1938 . . . £35/£15
The Common Man, Sheed & Ward, 1950 . £25/£10
ditto, Sheed & Ward (U.S.), 1950 . . . £25/£10
A Handful Of Authors, Sheed & Ward, 1953 . . .
. . . . £25/£10
ditto, Sheed & Ward (U.S.), 1953 . . . £25/£10
The Glass Walking-Stick and Other Essays from the
Illustrated London News, Metheun, 1955. £15/£5
Lunacy and Letters, Sheed & Ward, 1958 . £25/£10
ditto, Sheed & Ward (U.S.), 1958 . . . £25/£10

AGATHA CHRISTIE
(b.1890 d.1976)

The Queen of detective fiction, and creator of the
immortal Hercule Poirot and Miss Marple.

Novels
The Mysterious Affair at Styles, John Lane (U.S.),
1920 . . . . £15,000/£1,500
ditto, John Lane, 1921. . . . . . £12,000/£2,250
The Secret Adversary, John Lane, 1922. . . . .
. . . . £10,000/£1,000
ditto, Dodd, Mead (U.S.), 1922 . . . £7,500/£750
Murder on the Links, John Lane, 1923 . . . . .
. . . . £10,000/£1,000
ditto, Dodd, Mead (U.S.), 1923 . . . £7,500/£750
The Man in the Brown Suit, John Lane, 1924 . .
. . . . £7,500/£750
ditto, Dodd, Mead (U.S.), 1924 . . . £6,000/£500
The Secret of Chimneys, John Lane, 1925 £7,500/£750
ditto, Dodd, Mead (U.S.), 1925 . . . £5,000/£500
The Murder of Roger Ackroyd, Collins, 1926 . . .
. . . . £10,000/£750
ditto, Dodd, Mead (U.S.), 1926 . . . £3,000/£350
The Big Four, Collins, 1927 . . . . £5,000/£250
ditto, Dodd, Mead (U.S.), 1927 . . . £4,000/£100
The Mystery of the Blue Train, Collins, 1928 . . .
. . . . £5,000/£250
ditto, Dodd, Mead (U.S.), 1928 . . . £3,500/£75
The Seven Dials Mystery, Collins, 1929 £5,000/£250
ditto, Dodd, Mead (U.S.), 1929 . . . £3,500/£75
The Murder at the Vicarage, Collins, 1930 . . .
. . . . £4,000/£250
ditto, Dodd, Mead (U.S.), 1930 . . . £3,000/£75
Giant's Bread, Collins, 1930 (pseud. 'Mary
Westmacott') . . . . . . £1,000/£100
ditto, Doubleday (U.S.), 1930 . . . . £500/£75
The Sittaford Mystery, Collins, 1931 . £3,000/£200
ditto, as The Murder at Hazelmoor, Dodd, Mead
(U.S.), 1931 . . . . £2,000/£50
Peril at End House, Collins, 1931 . £3,000/£200
ditto, Dodd, Mead (U.S.), 1932 . . . £2,000/£50
Lord Edgware Dies, Collins, 1933 . . £3,000/£200
ditto, as Thirteen at Dinner, Dodd, Mead (U.S.), 1933
. . . . £2,000/£50
Murder on the Orient Express, Collins, 1934 . . .
. . . . £4,000/£250
ditto, as Murder on the Calais Coach, Dodd, Mead
(U.S.), 1942 . . . . £2,500/£200
Why Didn't They Ask Evans?, Collins, 1934 . . .
. . . . £3,000/£200
ditto, as Boomerang Clue, Dodd, Mead (U.S.), 1935 .
. . . . £2,000/£50
Murder in Three Acts, Dodd, Mead (U.S.), 1934 . .
. . . . £2,000/£75
ditto, as Three Act Tragedy, Collins, 1935 £2,000/£75
Unfinished Portrait, Collins, 1934, (pseud. 'Mary
Westmacott') . . . . £1,500/£65
ditto, Doubleday (U.S.), 1934 . . . £1,250/£35

Death in the Clouds, Collins, 1935 . . £1,500/£75
ditto, as *Death in the Air*, Dodd, Mead (U.S.), 1935 .
. . . . £1,250/£35
The A.B.C. Murders: A New Poirot Mystery, Collins,
1936 . . . . £2,500/£75
ditto, Dodd, Mead (U.S.), 1936 . . . £2,000/£65
Murder in Mesopotamia, Collins, 1936 . £2,500/£75
ditto, Dodd, Mead (U.S.), 1936 . . . £2,000/£65
Cards on the Table, Collins, 1936 . . £2,500/£75
ditto, Dodd, Mead (U.S.), 1936 . . . £2,000/£65
Dumb Witness, Collins, 1937 . . £4,0000/£200
ditto, as *Poirot Loses a Client*, Dodd, Mead (U.S.),
1937 . . . . £2,500/£100
Death on the Nile, Collins, 1937 . . . £2,000/£125
ditto, Dodd, Mead (U.S.), 1938 . . . £1,250/£75
Appointment With Death: A Poirot Mystery, Collins,
1938 . . . . £1,750/£65
ditto, Dodd, Mead (U.S.), 1938 . . . £1,000/£35
Hercule Poirot's Christmas, Collins, 1939 £1,500/£75
ditto, as *Murder for Christmas, A Poirot Story*, Dodd,
Mead, 1939 . . . . £1,250/£45
Murder Is Easy, Collins, 1939 . . . £1,000/£50
ditto, as *Easy to Kill*, Dodd, Mead, 1939 . £750/£25
Ten Little Niggers, Collins, 1939 . . £2,500/£200
ditto, as *And Then There Were None*, Dodd, Mead,
1940 . . . . £750/£25
One, Two, Buckle My Shoe, Collins, 1940 £500/£75
ditto, as *The Patriotic Murders*, Dodd, Mead, 1941 .
. . . . £300/£25
Sad Cypress, Collins, [1940] . . . . . £500/£75
ditto, Dodd, Mead (U.S.), 1940 . . . £300/£25
Evil Under the Sun, Collins, 1941 . . . £500/£75
ditto, Dodd, Mead (U.S.), 1941 . . . £250/£25
N or M?, Collins, 1941 . . . . . £500/£75
ditto, Dodd, Mead (U.S.), 1941 . . . £300/£25
The Body in the Library, Collins, 1942 . £500/£75
ditto, Dodd, Mead (U.S.), 1942 . . . £200/£25
The Moving Finger, Dodd, Mead (U.S.), 1942. . .
. . . . £350/£40
ditto, Collins, 1943 . . . . . . £350/£40
Five Little Pigs, Collins, 1942 . . . . £500/£75
ditto, as *Murder in Retrospect*, Dodd, Mead (U.S.),
1942 . . . . £200/£25
Death Comes as the End, Dodd, Mead (U.S.), 1942 .
. . . . £200/£25
ditto, Collins, 1945 . . . . . . £150/£25
Towards Zero, Collins, 1944 . . . . . £250/£40
ditto, Dodd, Mead (U.S.), 1944 . . . £200/£25
Absent in the Spring, Collins, 1944 (pseud. 'Mary
Westmacott') . . . . £125/£40
ditto, Farrar & Rinehart (U.S.), 1944 . £125/£25
Sparkling Cyanide, Collins, 1945 . . . £125/£40
ditto, as *Remembered Death*, Dodd, Mead (U.S.), 1945
. . . . £125/£35
The Hollow, Collins, 1946 . . . . . £125/£40
ditto, Dodd, Mead (U.S.), 1946 . . . . £125/£25
Taken at the Flood, Collins, 1948 . . . £125/£40
ditto, as *There is a Tide*, Dodd, Mead (U.S.), 1948 .
. . . . £125/£25

The Rose and the Yew Tree, Heinemann, 1948 (pseud.
'Mary Westmacott') . . . . . . £125/£40
ditto, Rinehart (U.S.), 1948 . . . . £125/£25
Crooked House, Collins, 1949 . . . . £125/£40
ditto, Dodd, Mead (U.S.), 1949 . . . . £100/£25
A Murder is Announced, Collins, 1950 . . £75/£15
ditto, Dodd, Mead (U.S.), 1950 . . . . £65/£15
They Came to Baghdad, Collins, 1951 . . £75/£15
ditto, Dodd, Mead (U.S.), 1951 . . . . £65/£15
They Do It with Mirrors, Collins, 1951 . . £75/£15
ditto, as *Murder with Mirrors*, Dodd, Mead (U.S.),
1951 . . . . £65/£15
Mrs McGinty's Dead, Collins, 1952 . . . £75/£15
ditto, Dodd, Mead (U.S.), 1952 . . . . £65/£15
A Daughter's a Daughter, Heinemann, 1952 (pseud.
'Mary Westmacott') . . . . . . £75/£15
After the Funeral, Collins, 1953 . . . . £65/£10
ditto, as *Funerals are Fatal*, Dodd, Mead (U.S.), 1953
. . . . £45/£10
A Pocket Full of Rye, Collins, 1953 . . . £60/£10
ditto, Dodd, Mead (U.S.), 1954 . . . . £40/£10
Destination Unknown, Collins, 1954 . . £50/£10
ditto, as *So Many Steps to Death*, Dodd, Mead (U.S.),
1955 . . . . £40/£10
Hickory, Dickory, Dock, Collins, 1955 . . £40/£10
ditto, as *Hickory, Dickory, Death*, Dodd, Mead (U.S.),
1955 . . . . £35/£10
Dead Man's Folly, Collins, 1956 . . . £40/£10
ditto, Dodd, Mead (U.S.), 1956 . . . . £40/£10
The Burden, Heinemann, 1956 (pseud. 'Mary
Westmacott') . . . . £40/£10
4.50 from Paddington, Collins, 1957 . . £40/£10
ditto, as *What Mrs McGillicuddy Saw!*, Dodd, Mead
(U.S.), 1957 . . . . £35/£10
Ordeal by Innocence, Collins, 1958 . . . £35/£10
ditto, Dodd, Mead (U.S.), 1958 . . . . £35/£10
Cat Among the Pigeons, Collins, 1959 . . £35/£10
ditto, Dodd, Mead (U.S.), 1959 . . . . £25/£10
The Pale Horse, Collins, 1961 . . . . £20/£10
ditto, Dodd, Mead (U.S.), 1962 . . . . £20/£10
The Mirror Crack'd from Side to Side, Collins, 1962 .
. . . . £20/£10
ditto, as *The Mirror Crack'd*, Dodd, Mead (U.S.),
1963 . . . . £20/£10
The Clocks, Collins, 1963 . . . . . £15/£5
ditto, Dodd, Mead (U.S.), 1964 . . . . £15/£5
A Caribbean Mystery, Collins, 1964. . . £15/£5
ditto, Dodd, Mead (U.S.), 1965 . . . . £15/£5
At Bertram's Hotel, Collins, 1965 . . . £15/£5
ditto, Dodd, Mead (U.S.), 1965 . . . . £15/£5
Third Girl, Collins, 1966 . . . . . £15/£5
ditto, Dodd, Mead (U.S.), 1967 . . . . £15/£5
Endless Night, Collins, 1967 . . . . . £15/£5
ditto, Dodd, Mead (U.S.), 1968 . . . . £15/£5
By the Pricking of My Thumbs, Collins, 1968 £15/£5
ditto, Dodd, Mead (U.S.), 1968 . . . . £15/£5
Passenger to Frankfurt, Collins, 1970 . . £15/£5
ditto, Dodd, Mead (U.S.), 1970 . . . . £15/£5
Nemesis, Collins, 1971 . . . . . . £15/£5

ditto, Dodd, Mead, (U.S.), 1971 . . . . £15/£5
Elephants Can Remember, Collins, 1972 . £15/£5
ditto, Dodd, Mead (U.S.), 1972 . . . . £15/£5
Postern of Fate, Collins, 1973 . . . £15/£5
ditto, Dodd, Mead (U.S.), 1973 . . . . £15/£5
Murder on Board; Three Complete Mystery Novels,
Dodd, Mead (U.S.), 1974 . . . . £15/£5
Curtain: Hercule Poirot's Last Case, Collins, 1975 .
. . . . £15/£5
ditto, Dodd, Mead (U.S.), 1975 . . . . £15/£5
Sleeping Murder, Collins, 1976 . . . . £15/£5
ditto, Dodd, Mead (U.S.), 1976 . . . . £10/£5

Short Stories
Poirot Investigates, John Lane, 1924 . £7,500/£750
ditto, Dodd, Mead (U.S.), 1924 . . . £6,000/£500
Partners in Crime, Collins, 1929 . £4,000/£250
ditto, Dodd, Mead (U.S.), 1929 . . . £3,000/£75
Two New Crime Stories, Reader's Library, 1929
(includes 'The Underdog' by Christie). . £400/£75
The Mysterious Mr Quinn, Collins, 1930 £4,000/£250
ditto, Dodd, Mead (U.S.), 1930 . . . £3,000/£75
The Thirteen Problems, Collins, 1932 . ˙£3,000/£200
ditto, as **The Tuesday Club Murders**, Dodd, Mead
(U.S.), 1933 . . . . £2,000/£50
The Hound of Death and Other Stories, Odhams,
1933 . . . . £350/£75
Parker Pyne Investigates, Collins, 1934 £2,500/£75
ditto, as **Mr Parker Pyne, Detective**, Dodd, Mead
(U.S.), 1934 . . . . £2,000/£65
The Listerdale Mystery and Other Stories, Collins,
1934 . . . . £2,000/£75
Murder in the Mews and Other Stories, Collins, 1937
. . . . £3,000/£250
ditto, as **Dead Man's Mirror and Other Stories**, Dodd,
Mead (U.S.), 1937 . . . . . . £2,500/£150
The Regatta Mystery and Other Stories, Dodd, Mead
(U.S.), 1939 . . . . £2,000/£150
The Labours of Hercules: Short Stories, Collins, 1947
. . . . £150/£25
ditto, as **Labours of Hercules**, Dodd, Mead (U.S.),
1947 . . . . £100/£25
Witness for the Prosecution, Dodd, Mead (U.S.), 1948
. . . . £150/£25
Three Blind Mice and Other Stories, Dodd, Mead
(U.S.), 1950 . . . . £150/£25
Under Dog and Other Stories, Dodd, Mead (U.S.),
1951 . . . . £125/£20
The Adventure of the Christmas Pudding, Collins,
1960 . . . . £75/£20
Double Sin and Other Stories, Dodd, Mead (U.S.),
1961 . . . . £40/£15
Thirteen for Luck, Dodd, Mead (U.S.), 1961 £20/£10
ditto, Collins, 1966 . . . . . . £20/£10
Star over Bethlehem and Other Stories, Collins, 1965
(pseud. 'A.C. Mallowan') . . . . . £15/£5
ditto, Dodd, Mead (U.S.), 1965 . . . . £10/£5
Surprise! Surprise!, Dodd, Mead (U.S.), 1965 £15/£5
13 Clues for Miss Marple, Dodd, Mead, 1965 £15/£5

The Golden Ball and Other Stories, Dodd, Mead
(U.S.), 1971 . . . . £10/£5
Hercule Poirot's Early Cases, Collins, 1974 £15/£5
ditto, Dodd, Mead (U.S.), 1974 . . . . £10/£5
Miss Marple's Final Cases and Others, Collins, 1979
. . . . £15/£5
ditto, Dodd, Mead (U.S.), 1979 . . . . £10/£5
Remembrance, Souvenir Press, 1988 . . £10/£5

Verse
The Road of Dreams, Bles, 1925 . . . £500/£100
ditto, as **Poems**, Collins, 1973 (glassine d/w) £45/£40
ditto, Dodd, Mead (U.S.), 1973 (glassine d/w) £25/£20

Plays
Black Coffee, Ashley, 1934 (wraps). . . . £125
ditto, French, 1952 (wraps) £35
Ten Little Niggers, French, 1944 (wraps) . . £50
ditto, as **Ten Little Indians**, French (U.S.), 1946
(wraps) £10
Appointment with Death, French, 1945 (wraps) £50
Murder on the Nile, French, 1946 (wraps) . . £40
ditto, French (U.S.), 1946 (wraps) . . . £20
The Hollow, French, 1952 (wraps) . . . £35
ditto, French (U.S.), 1952 (wraps) . . . £20
The Mousetrap, French, 1954 (wraps) . . . £100
ditto, French (U.S.), 1954 (wraps) . . . £75
Witness for the Prosecution, French (U.S.), 1954
(wraps) £40
ditto, French, 1956 (wraps) £40
The Spider's Web, French, 1957 (wraps) . . £30
ditto, French (U.S.), 1957 (wraps) . . . £10
Towards Zero, Dramatist's Play Service (U.S.), 1957
(wraps) £50
ditto, French, 1958 (wraps) £35
Verdict, French, 1958 (wraps) £35
The Unexpected Guest, French, 1958 (wraps) . £35
Go Back for Murder, French, 1960 (wraps) . £35
Rule of Three, French, 1963 (3 vols, wraps) . £50
Akhnaton, Collins, 1973 . . . . . £15/£5
ditto, Dodd, Mead (U.S.), 1973 . . . . £15/£5

Travel
Come Tell Me How You Live, Collins, 1946 £65/£10
ditto, Dodd, Mead (U.S.), 1946 . . . . £50/£10

Autobiography
Autobiography, Collins, 1977 . . . . £15/£5
ditto, Dodd, Mead (U.S.), 1977 . . . . £10/£5

TOM CLANCY
(b.1947)

Clancy is considered to be a master of the 'techno thriller'. The successful filming of his books has widened his audience.

Fiction

The Hunt for Red October, Naval Institute Press
(U.S.), 1984 . . . . £450/£75
ditto, Collins, 1985 . . . . . . £90/£15
Red Storm Rising, G.P. Putnam (U.S.), 1986 £25/£5
ditto, Collins, 1987 . . . . . £25/£5
Patriot Games, G.P. Putnam (U.S.), 1987 . £65/£15
ditto, Collins, 1987 . . . . . £50/£15
The Cardinal of the Kremlin, G.P. Putnam (U.S.),
1988 . . . . £20/£5
ditto, Collins, 1988 . . . . . £20/£5
Clear and Present Danger, G.P. Putnam (U.S.), 1988 .
. . . . £15/£5
ditto, Collins, 1989 . . . . . . £15/£5
The Sum of All Fears, G.P. Putnam (U.S., signed, limited edition of 600 numbered copies in slipcase),
1991 . . . . £125
ditto, G.P. Putnam (U.S.) 1991 . . . £10/£5
ditto, HarperCollins, 1991 . . . . £10/£5
Without Remorse G.P. Putnam (U.S., signed, limited edition of 600 numbered copies in slipcase), 1993 .
. . . . £100
ditto, G.P. Putnam (U.S.) 1993 . . . £10/£5
Debt of Honor, G.P. Putnam (U.S., signed, limited edition of 447 numbered copies in slipcase), 1994 .
. . . . £130
ditto, G.P. Putnam (U.S.) 1994 . . . £10/£5
ditto, Collins, 1994 . . . . . £10/£5
Executive Orders, G.P. Putnam, (U.S.), 1996 £10/£5
ditto, Collins, 1996 . . . . . £10/£5
Rainbow Six, G.P. Putnam (U.S., signed, limited edition of 600 numbered copies in slipcase), 1998 .
. . . . £75
ditto, G.P. Putnam (U.S.) 1998 . . . £10/£5
ditto, Joseph, 1998. . . . . . £10/£5
The Bear and the Dragon, G.P. Putnam, (U.S.), 2000 .
. . . . £10/£5
ditto, Joseph, 2000. . . . . . £10/£5

Non Fiction

Submarine, A Guided Tour inside a Nuclear Warship,
G.P. Putnam (U.S., signed, limited edition of 300 numbered copies in slipcase), 1993. . . . £125
ditto, Berkley (U.S.), 1993 . . . . . £10
Armoured Cav: A Guided Tour of an Armoured Cavalry Regiment, Putnam (U.S.) 1994 . £25/£10
ditto, Berkley (U.S.) 1994 (wraps) . . . £5
ditto, as *Armoured Warfare*, HarperCollins 1996
(wraps) £5
Fighter Wing: A Guided Tour of an Airforce Combat Wing, Berkley (U.S.) 1995 (wraps) . . . £5
ditto, HarperCollins 1995 (wraps) . . . £5

SSN: Strategies of Submarine Warfare, Berkley
(U.S.) 1996 . . . . £5
Marine: A Guided Tour of a Marine Expeditionary Team, Berkley (U.S.) 1996 (wraps) . . . £5
Airborne: A Guided Tour of an Airborne Task Force,
Berkley (U.S.) 1997 . . . . . . £25/£10
ditto, Berkley (U.S.) 1997 (wraps) . . . £5
Into the Storm: A Study in Command, Putnam (U.S.)
1997 (with Fred Franks Jr). . . . . £25/£10
Carrier: A Guided Tour of an Aircraft Carrier,
Berkley (U.S.) 1999 (wraps) £5
Every Man a Tiger, Putnam (U.S.) 1999 (with Chuck Horner) . . . . £25/£10
Special Forces: A Guided Tour of U.S. Special Forces, Berkley (U.S.) 2001 (with John Grisham) £5

JOHN CLARE
(b.1793 d.1864)

A poet who excels in his descriptions of rural life, and the thoughts and feelings of humble country people.

Verse

Poems Descriptive of Rural Life and Scenery, Taylor
& Hessey, 1820 . . . . £750
The Village Minstrel and Other Poems, Taylor & Hessey (and) Stamford: E. Drury, 1821 . . £350
The Shepherd's Calendar, Taylor, 1827 . . £350
The Rural Muse, Whittaker & Co., 1835 . £200
Poems by John Clare, G.E. Over, 1901 (selected by Norman Gale) £50
Poems by John Clare, Frowde, 1908 (selected by Arthur Symons) £20
Poems Chiefly From Manuscript, Cobden-Sanderson,
1920 . . . . £150/£45
Madrigals and Chronicles, Beaumont Press, 1924
(398 numbered copies, edited by Edmund Blunden) .
. . . . £100

Others

The Life and Remains of John Clare, by J. L. Cherry,
Warne, 1873 . . . . £100
Sketches in the Life of John Clare, Cobden-Sanderson, 1931 . . . . £100/£35
The Letters of John Clare, Routledge & Kegan Paul,
1951 . . . . £35/£10

ARTHUR C. CLARKE
(b.1917)

Clarke's much admired science fiction has successfully popularised and experimented with speculative science.

Novels

Prelude to Space, World Editions (U.S.), 1951 (wraps)
. . . . £45
ditto, Sidgwick & Jackson, 1953. . . . £125/£35
ditto, Gnome Press (U.S.), 1954 . . . . £75/£25
The Sands of Mars, Sidgwick & Jackson, 1951 . .
. . . . £125/£35
ditto, Gnome Press (U.S.), 1952 . . . . £75/£35
Islands in the Sky, Winston (U.S.), 1952 . £125/£35
ditto, Sidgwick & Jackson, 1952. . . . £100/£35
Against the Fall of Night, Gnome Press (U.S.), 1953 .
. . . . £125/£35
Childhood's End, Ballantine (U.S.), 1953 . £250/£75
ditto, Sidgwick & Jackson, 1954. . . . £95/£35
Earthlight, Ballantine (U.S.), 1955 . . . £200/£75
ditto, Muller, 1955. . . . . £125/£45
The City and the Stars, Harcourt Brace (U.S.), 1956 .
. . . . £100/£35
ditto, Muller, 1956. . . . . £75/£35
The Deep Range, Harcourt Brace (U.S.), 1957 . . .
. . . . £75/£25
ditto, Muller, 1957. . . . . £75/£25
A Fall of Moondust, Harcourt Brace (U.S.), 1961 . .
. . . . £75/£25
ditto, Gollancz, 1961 . . . . £75/£25
Dolphin Island, Holt Rinehart (U.S.), 1963. £50/£20
ditto, Gollancz, 1963 . . . . £50/£20
Glide Path, Harcourt Brace (U.S.), 1963 . £50/£20
ditto, Sidgwick & Jackson, 1969. . . . £50/£20
2001: A Space Odyssey, NAL (U.S.), 1968 £175/£45
ditto, Hutchinson, 1968 . . . . . . £125/£45
The Lion of Comarre, Harcourt Brace (U.S.), 1968 .
. . . . £45/£15
ditto, Gollancz, 1970 . . . . £45/£15
Rendezvous with Rama, Harcourt Brace (U.S.), 1973 .
. . . . £45/£15
ditto, Gollancz, 1973 . . . . £45/£15
Imperial Earth, Gollancz, 1975 . . . £25/£10
ditto, Harcourt Brace (U.S.), 1976 . . . £25/£10
The Fountains of Paradise, Gollancz, 1979 £25/£10
ditto, Harcourt Brace (U.S.), 1979 . . . £25/£10
2010: Odyssey Two, Granada, 1982 . . £20/£5
ditto, Granada, 1982 (author's name misspelt 'Clark' on title page) . . . . £75/£45
ditto, Phantasia (U.S.), 1982 (650 signed copies, slipcase) . . . . £75/£65
ditto, Phantasia (U.S.), 1982 (26 signed, lettered copies, leather box) . . . . . . £500/£45
ditto, Ballantine (U.S.), 1982. . . . . £15/£5
The Songs of Distant Earth, Grafton, 1986. £15/£5
ditto, Ballantine (U.S.), 1986. . . . . £15/£5
Odyssey Three, Ballantine (U.S.), 1988 . . £15/£5

ditto, Grafton, 1988 . . . . £15/£5
Cradle, Gollancz, 1988 (with Gentry Lee) . £15/£5
ditto, Warner (U.S.), 1988 . . . . . £15/£5
Rama II, Gollancz, 1989 (with Gentry Lee) £20/£10
ditto, Ballantine (U.S.), 1989 . . . . . £10/£5
Beyond the Fall of Night, Putnam (U.S.), 1990 (with Gregory Benford) . . . . £10/£5
ditto, as *Against the Fall of Night*, Gollancz, 1991 .
. . . . £10/£5
The Ghost from the Grand Banks, Bantam (U.S.), 1990 . . . . £10/£5
ditto, Gollancz, 1990 . . . . £10/£5
The Garden of Rama, Gollancz, 1991 (with Gentry Lee) . . . . £10/£5
ditto, Bantam (U.S.), 1991 . . . . . £10/£5
Rama Revealed, Gollancz, 1993 (with Gentry Lee) .
. . . . £10/£5
ditto, Bantam (U.S.), 1994 . . . . . £10/£5
The Hammer of God, Gollancz, 1993 . . £10/£5
ditto, Bantam (U.S.), 1993 . . . . . £10/£5

Stories

Expedition to Earth, Ballantine (U.S.), 1953 £175/£45
ditto, Sidgwick & Jackson, 1954. . . . £90/£25
Reach for Tomorrow, Ballantine (U.S.), 1956 . .
. . . . £125/£35
ditto, Gollancz, 1962 . . . . £75/£25
Tales from the White Hart, Ballantine (U.S.), 1957 .
. . . . £100/£25
ditto, Sidgwick & Jackson, 1972. . . . £30/£10
The Other Side of the Sky, Harcourt Brace (U.S.), 1958 . . . . £100/£35
ditto, Gollancz, 1961 . . . . £35/£10
Tales of Ten Worlds, Harcourt Brace (U.S.), 1962 .
. . . . £25/£10
ditto, Gollancz, 1963 . . . . £25/£10
The Nine Billion Names of God, Harcourt Brace (U.S.), 1967 . . . . £15/£5
A Meeting with Medusa, Harcourt Brace (U.S.), 1971 .
. . . . £15/£5
The Wind from the Sun, Harcourt Brace (U.S.), 1971 .
. . . . £15/£5
Of Time and Stars, Gollancz, 1972 . . . £15/£5
Report on Planet Three and Other Speculations, Gollancz, 1972 . . . . £15/£5
The Sentinel, Berkley (U.S.), 1983 . . . £10/£5
ditto, Panther, 1985 . . . . £10/£5
Tales from Planet Earth, Century, 1989 . £10/£5

Miscellaneous Collections

Across the Sea of Stars, Harcourt Brace (U.S.), 1959 .
. . . . £45/£10
From the Oceans, From the Stars, Harcourt Brace (U.S.), 1962 . . . . £50/£25
Prelude to Mars, Harcourt Brace (U.S.), 1965 £35/£10
An Arthur C. Clarke Omnibus, Sidgwick & Jackson, 1965 . . . . £25/£10
An Arthur C. Clarke Second Omnibus, Sidgwick & Jackson, 1968 . . . . £25/£10

The Lost Worlds of 2001, NAL (U.S.), 1972 £25/£10
ditto, Sidgwick & Jackson, 1972 . . . . £25/£10
Best of Arthur C. Clarke: 1937-1971, Sidgwick &
Jackson, 1973 . . . . £25/£10

HARRY CLARKE
(b.1889 d.1931)

An Irish artist in the tradition of Beardsley, but whose
detail and decoration are distinctively his own.

Illustrated by Clarke
Hans Andersen's Fairy Tales, Harrap, [1916] (125
signed copies) £1,000
ditto, Harrap, [1916] (full leather edition) . . £450
ditto, Harrap, [1916] (cloth edition) £200
ditto, Bretano's (U.S.), 1916 . . . . . . £175
Tales of Mystery and Imagination, by Edgar Allan
Poe, Harrap, 1919 (170 signed copies) . . . £2,000
ditto, Harrap, [1919] (morocco leather edition) . £400
ditto, Harrap, [1919] (cloth edition) £200
ditto, Bretano's (U.S.), 1919 . . . . . . £200
ditto, Harrap, [1923] (new edition with colour plates,
antique leather) £250
ditto, Harrap, [1923] (new edition with colour plates,
cloth edition) . . . . £250/£125
The Year's at the Spring, Harrap, 1920 (250 signed
copies) £600
ditto, Harrap, 1920 (cloth edition) . . . £250/£150
ditto, Bretano's (U.S.), 1920 . . . . £200/£125
The Fairy Tales of Perrault, Harrap, [1922] (Persian
levant leather edition) £350
ditto, Harrap, [1922] (Buckram edition) . . £250/£150
ditto, Harrap, [1922] (cloth edition) . . . £200/£125
ditto, Dodge (U.S.), [1922] . . . . £200/£125
Faust, by Goethe, Harrap, 1925 (1,000 signed copies).
. . . . £750/£450
ditto, Harrap/Dingwall-Rock (U.S.), 1925 (1,000
signed copies) . . . . £750/£450
*Elixir of Life Being a slight account of the romantic
rise to fame of a great house*, John Jameson & Son
Limited (Dublin), 1925 . . . . . £750/£450
Selected Poems of Algernon Charles Swinburne, John
Lane, 1928 . . . . £400/£125
ditto, Dodd, Mead (U.S.), 1928 . . . . £250/£125

LIZA CODY
(b.1944)

Best known for her 'Anna Lee' novels about an
everyday female detective.

Anna Lee Novels
Dupe, Collins, 1980 . . . . £175/£25
ditto, Scribners (U.S.), 1981 . . . . . £50/£15

Bad Company, Collins, 1982. . . . . . £75/£15
ditto, Scribners (U.S.), 1981 . . . . . £50/£15
Stalker, Collins, 1984. . . . . . . £45/£15
ditto, Scribners (U.S.), 1984 . . . . . £25/£15
Headcase, Collins, 1985 . . . . . . £35/£10
ditto, Scribners (U.S.), 1985 . . . . . £25/£15
Under Contract, Collins, 1986 . . . . £25/£10
ditto, Scribners (U.S.), 1986 . . . . . £25/£15
Backhand, Chatto & Windus, 1991 . . . £15/£5
ditto, Little, Brown (U.S.), 1991 . . . . £15/£5

Other Novels
Rift, Collins, 1988. . . . . £45/£10
ditto, Scribners (U.S.), 1988 . . . . . £25/£10
Bucket Nut, Chatto & Windus, 1992 . . £25/£5
ditto, Doubleday (U.S.), 1993 . . . . £20/£5
Monkey Wrench, Chatto & Windus, 1994 . £20/£5
ditto, Mysterious Press (U.S.), 1995 . . . £15/£5
Musclebound, Bloomsbury, 1997 . . . £15/£5
ditto, Mysterious Press (U.S.), 1997 . . . £15/£5
Gimme More, Bloomsbury, 2000 (wraps) . . £10

WILKIE COLLINS
(b.1824 d.1889)

A friend of Charles Dickens, Collins was a popular
and skilful author of sensation fiction.

Memoirs of the Life of William Collins, R.A.
Longmans, 1848 (2 vols) £1,000
Antonina, or the Fall of Rome, Bentley, 1850 (3 vols)
. . . . £750
*Rambles Beyond Railways: Notes in Cornwall Taken
A-Foot*, Bentley, 1851 . . . . . . £250
Mr Wray's Cash-Box, Bentley, 1852 . . . £500
Basil: A Story of Modern Life, Bentley, 1852 (3 vols).
. . . . £500
Hide and Seek, Bentley, 1854 (3 vols) . . . £750
After Dark, Smith & Elder, 1855 (3 vols) . £500
The Dead Secret, Bradbury and Evans, 1857 (2 vols) .
. . . . £750
The Queen of Hearts, Hurst & Blackett, 1859 (3 vols)
. . . . £1,750
The Woman in White, Sampson Low, 1860 (3 vols) .
. . . . £7,500
No Name, Sampson Low, 1862 (3 vols). . £1,250
My Miscellanies, Sampson Low, 1863 (3 vols) . £750
Armadale, Smith, Elder & Co., 1866 (2 vols) . £500
The Moonstone, William Tinsley, 1868 (3 vols) £8,000
Man and Wife, F. S. Ellis, 1870 (3 vols) . . £750
Poor Miss Finch, Bentley, 1872 (3 vols) . . £450
The New Magdalen, Bentley, 1873 (2 vols) . £500
Miss or Mrs? and Other Stories, Bentley, 1873 £450
The Frozen Deep and Other Tales, Bentley, 1874 (2
vols) £1,250
The Law and the Lady, Chatto & Windus, 1875 (3
vols) £650

The Two Destinies, Chatto & Windus, 1876 (2 vols) .
. . . . £500
The Haunted Hotel and My Lady's Money, Chatto &
Windus, 1879 (2 vols) £600
A Rogue's Life, Bentley, 1879 . . . . . £350
The Fallen Leaves, Chatto & Windus, 1879 (3 vols) .
. . . . £300
Jezebel's Daughter, Chatto & Windus, 1880 (3 vols) .
. . . . £300
The Black Robe, Chatto & Windus, 1881 (3 vols) . .
. . . . £300
Heart and Science, Chatto & Windus, 1883 (3 vols) .
. . . . £300
I Say No, Chatto & Windus, 1884 (3 vols) . . £300
The Evil Genius, Chatto & Windus, 1886 (3 vols) . .
. . . . £300
The Guilty River, Arrowsmith, 1886 . . . £500
Little Novels, Chatto & Windus, 1887 (3 vols) . £500
The Legacy of Cain, Chatto & Windus, 1889 (3 vols) .
. . . . £250
Blind Love, Chatto & Windus, 1890 (3 vols, completed
by Walter Besant) £150
The Lazy Tour of Two Idle Apprentices, Chapman &
Hall, 1890 (in collaboration with Charles Dickens)
. . . . £250

IVY COMPTON-BURNETT
(b.1892 d.1969)

The author of incisive, if claustrophobic domestic
novels, told principally through the dialogue of her
characters.

Dolores, Blackwood, 1911 . . . . . . £400
Pastors and Masters, A Study, Heath Cranton, 1925 .
. . . . £200/£75
Brothers and Sisters, Heath Cranton, 1929 £150/£75
ditto, Zero Press (U.S.), 1956 (includes introductory
pamphlet). . . . . £65/£10
Men and Wives, Heinemann, 1931 . . . £90/£40
ditto, Harcourt Brace (U.S.), [1939] . . . £30/£10
More Women than Men, Heinemann, 1933 £90/£40
ditto, Simon & Schuster (U.S.), 1965 (with *A Family
and Its Fortune*) . . . . £20/£5
A House and its Head, Heinemann, 1935 . £90/£40
Daughters and Sons, Gollancz, 1937 . . £65/£25
A Family and its Fortune, Gollancz, 1939 . £60/£25
Parents and Children, Gollancz, 1941 . £60/£25
Elders and Betters, Gollancz, 1944 . £50/£20
Manservant and Maidservant, Gollancz, 1947 . .
. . . . £40/£10
ditto, as *Bullivant and the Lamb*, Knopf (U.S.), 1948 .
. . . . £40/£10
Two Worlds and their Ways, Gollancz, 1949 £40/£10
ditto, Knopf (U.S.), 1949 . . . . . . £30/£10
Darkness and Day, Gollancz, 1951 . . £30/£10
ditto, Knopf (U.S.), 1951 . . . . . . £30/£10

The Present and the Past, Gollancz, 1953 . £25/£5
ditto, Messner (U.S.), 1953 . . . . . £25/£5
Mother and Son, Gollancz, 1955 . . . £25/£5
ditto, Messner (U.S.), 1955 . . . . . £25/£5
A Father and his Fate, Gollancz, 1957 . £25/£5
ditto, Messner (U.S.), 1958 . . . . . £25/£5
A Heritage and its History, Gollancz, 1959. £25/£5
ditto, Simon & Schuster (U.S.), 1960 . . £20/£5
The Mighty and their Fall, Gollancz, 1961 £20/£5
ditto, Simon & Schuster (U.S.), 1962 . . £20/£5
A God and His Gifts, Gollancz, 1963 . . £20/£5
ditto, Simon & Schuster (U.S.), 1964 . . £20/£5
The Last and the First, Gollancz, 1971 . £15/£5
ditto, Knopf (U.S.), 1971 . . . . . . £10/£5
Collected Works, Gollancz, 1972 (deluxe edition of
500 sets in 19 vols) £400

CYRIL CONNOLLY
(b.1903 d.1974)

Principally a critic and literary editor, Connolly
founded the influential literary magazine *Horizon*.

The Rock Pool, Obelisk Press (Paris), 1936 (wraps) .
. . . . £400
ditto, Scriber (U.S.), 1936. . . . . . £200/£75
ditto, Hamish Hamilton, 1947 . . . . £60/£20
Enemies of Promise, Routledge, 1938 . . £200/£50
ditto, Little, Brown (U.S.), 1939 . . . . £100/£35
The Unquiet Grave, Horizon, 1944 (500 numbered
hardback copies of 1,000, pseud. 'Palinurus') . .
. . . . £300/£75
ditto, Horizon, 1944 (500 numbered copies of 1,000,
wraps). £75
ditto, Hamish Hamilton, [1945] (new edition) £20/£5
ditto, Harper (U.S.), 1945 (new edition). . £20/£5
The Condemned Playground, Routledge, [1945] . .
. . . . £25/£10
ditto, Macmillan, 1946 . . . . . . £15/£5
The Missing Diplomats, Queen Anne Press, 1952
(wraps) £25
Ideas and Places, Weidenfeld, 1953 . £25/£10
ditto, Harper (U.S.), 1953. . . . . . £25/£10
The Golden Horizon, Weidenfeld, 1953 . £15/£5
ditto, University Books (U.S.), 1955. . . £10/£5
Les Pavillons, Macmillan (U.S.), 1962 (with Jerome
Zerbe). . . . . £25/£10
ditto, Hamish Hamilton, 1962 . . . . £25/£10
Previous Convictions, Hamish Hamilton, 1963. . .
. . . . £20/£10
ditto, Harper (U.S.), 1964. . . . . . £15/£5
*The Modern Movement: 100 Key Books from
England, France and America, 1880-1950*, Deutsch/
Hamilton, 1965 . . . . £45/£15
ditto, Atheneum (U.S.), 1966. . . . . £45/£15
ditto, H.R.C. (U.S.), 1971 (wraps) . . . £20
ditto, H.R.C. (U.S.), 1971 (520 copies, cloth) . £50

The Evening Colonnade, Bruce & Watson, 1973 . .
. . . . £10/£5
ditto, Harcourt Brace (U.S.), 1975 . . . £10/£5
*A Romantic Friendship: The Letters of Cyril Connolly
to Noel Blakiston*, Constable, 1975 . . £15/£5
Journal and Memoir, Collins, 1983 . . . £10/£5
ditto, Ticknor & Fields (U.S.), 1984 . . . £10/£5
Shade Those Laurels, Bellew, 1990 . . £10/£5
ditto, Panthen (U.S.), 1991 . . . . . £10/£5

JOSEPH CONRAD
(b.1857 d.1924)

Conrad served for twenty years at sea, becoming a
naturalised British subject in 1886. The sea provided
the background for a number of powerful, novels. His
classic 'Heart of Darkness' was first published in
Youth: A Narrative, and Other Stories in 1902.

Novels
Almayer's Folly, T. Fisher Unwin, 1895 (first issue,
with 'e' omitted in 'generosity' at bottom of page
110) £1,500
ditto, T. Fisher Unwin, 1895 (second issue, corrections
made) £100
ditto, Macmillan (U.S.), 1895 . . . . . £500
An Outcast of the Islands, T. Fisher Unwin, 1896
('this' for 'their' on line 31, p.26) £400
ditto, Appleton (U.S.), 1896 (wraps) . . . £250
ditto, Appleton (U.S.), 1896 (green cloth) . . £150
The Children of the Sea, Dodd, Mead (U.S.), 1897 .
. . . . £650
ditto, as *The Nigger of the Narcissus*, Heinemann,
August 1898 (copyright edition, 7 copies, wraps) . .
. . . . £4,000
ditto, as *The Nigger of the Narcissus*, Heinemann,
1898 (first issue: 'H' in 'Heinemann' on spine
5.5mm, 16 pages of advertisements) . . . £400
ditto, as *The Nigger of the Narcissus*, Heinemann,
1898 (second issue: 'Heinemann' on spine 3mm, 16
pages of advertisements) £300
ditto, as *The Nigger of the Narcissus*, Heinemann,
1898 (second issue: 32 pages of advertisements) £200
Lord Jim, William Blackwood, 1900 . . £1,750
ditto, Doubleday (U.S.), 1900 . . . . £350
Nostromo, Harper, 1904 . . . . . . £500
ditto, Harper (U.S.), 1904 . . . . . . £200
The Secret Agent, Methuen, 1907 (40 pages of adverts
dated September) £750
ditto, Harper (U.S.), 1907 . . . . . . £200
Under Western Eyes, Methuen, 1911 . . £350
ditto, Harper (U.S.), 1911 . . . . . . £100
Chance, Methuen, 1913 ('Methven' on spine, 32 page
catalogue) £2,000
ditto, Methuen, 1914 ('Methuen' on spine, no
catalogue) £1,500
ditto, Methuen, 1914 (authorised issue) . . . £500

ditto, Doubleday (U.S.), 1913 (150 copyright copies) .
. . . . £500
ditto, Doubleday (U.S.), 1914 . . . . . £100
Victory, An Island Tale, Doubleday (U.S.), 1915 £75
ditto, Methuen, 1915 . . . . £65
The Shadow Line, Dent, 1917 . . . . . £65
ditto, Doubleday (U.S.), 1917 . . . . . £50
The Arrow of Gold, Doubleday (U.S.), 1919
('credentials and apparently' in line 15, p.5) . £35
ditto, Doubleday (U.S.), 1919 ('credentials and who' in
line 15, p.5)) £25
ditto, T. Fisher Unwin, 1919 . . . . . £45
The Rescue, Doubleday (U.S.), 1920 ($1.90 d/w) . .
. . . . £200/£25
ditto, Doubleday (U.S.), 1920 ($2.00 d/w) . £150/£25
ditto, Dent, 1920 (40 copies for private distribution) .
. . . . £1,000
ditto, Dent, 1920 (trade edition, green cloth) £300/£35
The Rover, Doubleday (U.S.), 1923 (377 signed
copies, slipcase) . . . . £325£275
ditto, Doubleday (U.S.), 1923 . . . . £125£20
ditto, T. Fisher Unwin, 1923 . . . . . £125/£20
Suspense, Dent, 1925 . . . . £150/£25
ditto, Doubleday (U.S.), 1925 (limited edition of 377
copies, glassine d/w, slipcase) . . . £200/£250
ditto, Doubleday (U.S.), 1925 . . . £125/£25
The Sisters, Crosby Gaige (U.S.), 1928 (926 copies) .
. . . . £100

Titles written with Ford Maddox Hueffer/Ford
The Inheritors, McClure, Phillips & Co. (U.S.), 1901
(dedicated to Boys & Christina) . . . £3,000
ditto, McClure, Phillips & Co. (U.S.), 1901 (dedicated
to Borys & Christina) £300
ditto, Heinemann, 1901 (32 pages adverts, top edge
untrimmed, publisher's device on spine with initials) .
. . . . £500
ditto, Heinemann, 1901 (no catalogue, top edge
trimmed, publisher's device on spine with initials) .
. . . . £300
ditto, Heinemann, 1901 (without initials in publisher's
device) £250
ditto, Heinemann, 1901 (remainder issue, non-pictorial
cloth) £125
Romance, Smith Elder, 1903 . . . . . £150
ditto, McClure (U.S.), 1904 . . . . . £125
The Nature of a Crime, Duckworth, 1924 £125/£25
ditto, Doubleday (U.S.), 1924 . . . £125/£25

Short Stories
Tales of Unrest, Scribners (U.S.), 1898 . . £250
ditto, T. Fisher Unwin, 1898 (top edge gilt) . . £300
ditto, T. Fisher Unwin, 1898 . . . . . £225
Youth: A Narrative, and Other Stories, William
Blackwood, 1902 (adverts dated '10/02') . . £200
ditto, William Blackwood, 1902 (adverts dated '11/02')
. . . . £175
ditto, McClure, Phillips & Co. (U.S.), 1903 . . £200

Typhoon, Putnam/Knickerbocker Press, 1902 (green cloth) £400
ditto, Putnam/Knickerbocker Press, 1902 (maroon cloth) £350
ditto, as *Typhoon and Other Stories*, Heinemann, 1903 (grey cloth) £150
A Set of Six, Methuen, 1908 (first issue, adverts dated Feb. 1908, list of works including 'The Secret Agent (with Ford M. Hueffer)') £750
ditto, Methuen, 1908 (second issue, adverts dated Feb. 1908, list of works including 'The Secret Agent' with 'FORD M. HUEFFER' below) £400
ditto, Methuen. 1908 (third issue, adverts dated June. 1908) £350
'Twixt Land and Sea, Dent, 1912 (first issue with 'Secret' instead of 'Seven' on front cover) . £2,000
ditto, Dent, 1912 (second issue with 'Seven' stamped over erased 'Secret'). £200
ditto, Dent, 1912 (third issue with front cover corrected). £100
ditto, Hodder & Stoughton/Doran (U.S.), 1912 . £100
Within the Tides, Dent, 1915. . . . . . £150
Tales of Hearsay, T. Fisher Unwin, 1925 . £150/£20
ditto, Doubleday (U.S.), 1925 . . . . £150/£20

Plays
One Day More: A Play in One Act, privately printed, Clement Shorter. 1917 (25 copies, wraps) . £1,500
ditto, Beaumont Press. 1919 (250 copies) . . £200
ditto, Beaumont Press. 1919 (24 signed copies on Japanese vellum). £2,000
ditto, Doubleday (U.S.), 1920 (377 signed copies) .
. . . . £300
The Secret Agent: A Drama, Goulden, 1921 (wraps) .
. . . . £1,500
ditto, T. Werner Laurie, 1923 (printed for subscribers only, 1,000 signed copies) . . . . . £700/£300
Laughing Anne, Moorland Press, 1923 (200 signed, numbered copies) £500
Laughing Anne and One More Day, John Castle, 1924
. . . . £75/£20
Three Plays, Methuen, 1934 (contains 'One Day More', 'The Secret Agent' and 'Laughing Anne') .
. . . . £35/£10

Miscellaneous
The Nigger of the Narcissus: A Preface, privately printed, 1902 (100 copies, wraps) £1,500
The Mirror of the Sea, Methuen, [1906] . . £250
ditto, Harper (U.S.), 1906. . . . . . . £100
Some Reminiscences, Eveleigh Nash, 1912. . £100
ditto, as *A Personal Record*, Harper, 1912 . . £100
Notes on Life and Letters, Dent, 1921 (33 copies, privately printed). £1,500
ditto, Dent, 1921 ('S' and 'a' missing from 'Sea', line 8 of table of contents) . . . . £175/£45
ditto, Dent, 1921 (corrected page on cancel leaf) . .
. . . . £150/£20
ditto, Doubleday (U.S.), 1921 . . . . £150/£20

Notes On My Books, Heinemann, 1921 (250 signed copies) £400
The Dover Patrol: A Tribute, privately printed, Canterbury, 1922, (75 copies, first state without title page, wraps) £750
ditto, privately printed, Canterbury, 1922, (75 copies, second state with added title page, wraps) . . £300
Five Letters by Joseph Conrad, privately printed, 1925 (100 numbered copies, wraps) £225
Notes by Joseph Conrad, privately printed, 1925 (100 numbered copies) £250
Last Essays, Dent, 1926 . . . . . . £125/£20
ditto, Doubleday (U.S.), 1926 . . . . £120/£20
Joseph Conrad's Letters to His Wife, privately printed, 1927 (220 copies, signed by his widow) . . £200
Letters ... 1895 to 1924, Nonesuch Press, 1928 (925 numbered copies) £75
A Sketch of Joseph Conrad's Life Written by Himself, privately printed, 1939 (75 copies). . . . £150
Letters to William Blackwood, Duke Univ. Press (U.S.). 1958 . . . . £25/£10
Congo Diary and other Uncollected Pieces, Doubleday (U.S.), 1979 . . . . £20/£10

A.E. COPPARD
(b.1878 d.1957)

An acknowledged master of the short story form, Coppard is at his best in his evocation of the English countryside.

Short Stories
Adam and Eve and Pinch Me, Golden Cockerel Press, 1921 (white buckram issue of 550 signed copies). .
. . . . £150
ditto, Golden Cockerel Press, 1921 (orange baords issue of 550 signed copies) £125
ditto, Cape, 1921 . . . . £125
ditto, Knopf (U.S.), 1922 . . . . . . £75
Clorinda Walks in Heaven, Golden Cockerel Press, 1922 . . . . £45/£20
The Black Dog and Other Stories, Cape, 1923 . . .
. . . . £75/£25
ditto, Knopf (U.S.), 1924 . . . . . £65/£25
Fishmonger's Fiddle, Cape, 1925 . . . £75/£25
ditto, Knopf (U.S.), 1925 . . . . . £65/£25
The Field of Mustard, Cape, 1926 . . . £65/£20
ditto, Cape, 1926 (85 signed, numbered copies) £75
ditto, Knopf (U.S.), 1927 . . . . . £65/£15
Silver Circus, Cape, 1928. . . . . . £65/£15
ditto, Cape, 1928 (125 signed copies) . . . £125
ditto, Knopf (U.S.), 1929 . . . . . £65/£15
Count Stefan, Golden Cockerel Press, 1928 (600 signed copies) . . . . £95/£75
The Gollan, privately printed, 1929 (75 copies) £150
The Man from Kilsheelan, Furnival Books, 1930 (550 signed copies) £65

The Hundredth Story, Golden Cockerel Press, 1931
(1,000 copies) . . . . £95/£75
Pink Furniture: A Tale for Lovely Children with
Noble Natures, Cape, 1930 . . . . £30/£10
ditto, Cape, 1930 (260 signed copies) . . £100/£75
Nixey's Harlequin, Cape, 1931 . . . £30/£10
ditto, Cape, 1931 (304 signed copies) . . £75/£60
ditto, Knopf (U.S.), 1932 . . . . . £25/£10
Crotty Shinkwin, The Beauty Spot, Golden Cockerel
Press, 1932 (500 numbered copies). . . . £65
Cheefoo, privately printed (U.S.), 1932. . . £150
Dunky Fitlow, Cape, 1933 . . . . . £25/£10
ditto, Cape, 1933 (300 signed copies) . . . £65
Ring the Bells of Heaven, White Owl Press, 1933 . .
. . . . £25/£10
ditto, White Owl Press, 1933 (150 signed copies) £50
Emergency Exit, Random House, 1934 (350 signed
copies) £45
Good Samaritans, privately printed (U.S.), 1934 (100
copies) £150
Polly Oliver, Cape, 1935 . . . . . £30/£10
The Ninepenny Flute: Twenty-One Tales, Macmillan,
1937 . . . . £35/£10
Tapster's Tapestry, Golden Cockerel Press, 1938 £45
You Never Know, Do You? and Other Tales, Methuen,
1939 . . . . £25/£10
Ugly Anna and Other Tales, Methuen, 1944 £25/£10
Selected Tales, Cape, 1946 . . . . . £25/£10
Fearful Pleasures, Arkham House (U.S.), 1946 . .
. . . . £75/£20
Dark-Eyed Lady: Fourteen Tales, Methuen, 1947. .
. . . . £30/£10
Collected Tales, Knopf (U.S.), 1948. . . £25/£10
Lucy in Her Pink Jacket, Peter Nevill, 1954 £25/£10
Selected Stories, Cape, 1972 . . . . . £15/£5

Verse
Hips and Haws, Golden Cockerel Press, 1922 (500
signed copies) £75
Pelagea and Other Poems, Golden Cockerel Press,
1926 (425 numbered copies) . . . . £100/£45
Yokohama Garland and Other Poems, Centaur Press
(U.S.), 1926 (500 signed, numbered copies) . £65
Collected Poems, Cape, 1928 . . . . £30/£10
ditto, Knopf (U.S.), 1928 . . . . . £30/£10
Easter Day, [no place], [1931] (145 copies, last four
lines written and signed). £125
Cherry Ripe, Hawthorn House, 1935 (300 signed,
numbered copies, slipcase) . . . . . £50/£35
ditto, Tintern Press, 1935 . . . . . £30/£10

Others
Rummy, The Noble Game, Golden Cockerel Press,
1932 (1,000 copies, with Robert Gibbings) £45/£15
ditto, Golden Cockerel Press, 1932 (250 signed copies
on handmade paper, with Robert Gibbings) . £50
ditto, Houghton Mifflin (U.S.), 1933 . . £25/£10
It's Me, O Lord!, Methuen, 1957 . . . £25/£10

PATRICIA CORNWELL
(b.1956)

With her first book, Post Mortem, Cornwell won four
major awards.

Scarpetta Books
Postmortem, Scribner (U.S.), 1990 . . . £550/£50
ditto, Macdonald, 1990 . . . . . . £300/£35
Body of Evidence, Scribner (U.S.), 1991 . £65/£15
ditto, Macdonald, 1991 . . . . . . £65/£15
All That Remains, Little, Brown, 1992 . . £20/£10
ditto, Scribner (U.S.), 1992 . . . . £20/£10
Cruel and Unusual, Scribner (U.S.), 1993 . £20/£10
ditto, Little, Brown, 1993 . . . . . £20/£10
The Body Farm, Scribner (U.S.), 1994 . . £20/£10
ditto, Little, Brown, 1994 . . . . . £20/£10
From Potter's Field, Scribner (U.S.), 1995 . £20/£10
ditto, Little, Brown, 1995 . . . . . £20/£10
Cause of Death, Putnam (U.S.), 1996 . . £20/£10
ditto, Putnam (U.S.), 1996 (185 signed, numbered
copies, slipcase) . . . . £125/£100
ditto, Little, Brown, 1996 . . . . . £20/£10
Unnatural Exposure, Putnam (U.S.), 1997 . £20/£10
ditto, Putnam (U.S.), 1997 (175 signed, numbered
copies, slipcase) . . . . £125/£100
ditto, Little, Brown, 1997 . . . . . £20/£10
Point of Origin, Putnam (U.S.), 1998 . . £10/£5
ditto, Putnam (U.S.), 2000 (500 signed, numbered
copies, slipcase) . . . . £100/£75
ditto, Little, Brown, 1998 . . . . . £10/£5
Black Notice, Putnam (U.S.), 1999 . . . £10/£5
ditto, Putnam (U.S.), 1999 (200 signed, numbered
copies, slipcase) . . . . £125/£100
ditto, Little, Brown, 1999 . . . . . £10/£5
The Last Precinct, Putnam (U.S.), 2000. . £10/£5
ditto, Putnam (U.S.), 2000 (175 signed, numbered
copies, slipcase) . . . . £125/£100
ditto, Little, Brown, 2000 . . . . . £10/£5

Others
A Time for Remembering: The Ruth Bell Graham
Story, Harper & Row (U.S.), 1983 . . . £50/£10
ditto, as *Ruth: A Portrait*, Hodder & Stoughton, 1998 .
. . . . £10/£5
Hornet's Nest, Putnam (U.S.), 1996 . . . £20/£10
ditto, Little, Brown, 1996 . . . . . £20/£10
Scarpetta's Winter Table, Wyrick & Company (U.S.),
1998 . . . . £10/£5
Southern Cross, Putnam (U.S.), 1999 . . £10/£5
ditto, Little, Brown, 1999 . . . . . £10/£5
Life's Little Fable, Putnam (U.S.), 1999 . £10/£5

HUBERT CRACKANTHORPE
(b.1870 d.1896)

In 1892 Crackanthorpe founded *The Albermarle*, a short-lived magazine of high reputation. His own writings gained notoriety, dealing with taboo subjects such as adultery, prostitution and social degradation.

Wreckage: Seven Studies, Heinemann, 1893 . £75
Sentimental Studies & A Set of Village Tales, Heinemann, 1895 . . . . £100
Vignettes, A Miniature Journal of Whim and Sentiment, John Lane/The Bodley Head, 1896 £85
Last Studies, Heinemann, 1897 . . . . . £75
The Light Sovereign: A Farcical Comedy in Three Acts, privately printed, Lady Henry Harland, 1917 (with Henry Harland) £150
Collected Stories (1893-1897) of Hubert Crackanthorpe, Scholar's facsimiles and Reprints (U.S.), 1969 . . . . £25

WALTER CRANE
(b.1845 d.1915)

A successful British artist, Crane was a colleague of William Morris, sharing many of Morris's political and artistic beliefs.

'Aunt Mavor' and Walter Crane Sixpenny Toy Books
The House that Jack Built, Ward, Lock & Tyler, 1865
. . . . £100
The Comical Cat, Ward, Lock & Tyler, 1865 . £75
The Affecting Story of Jenny Wren, Ward, Lock & Tyler, 1865 . . . . £75
The Railroad Alphabet, Routledge, 1865 . . £75
The Farmyard Alphabet, Routledge, 1865 . . £75
Cock Robin, Frederick Warne, 1866. . . . £75
Sing A Song of Sixpence, Frederick Warne, 1866 £75
A Gaping-Wide-Mouth Waddling Frog, Frederick Warne, [1866] £75
The Old Courtier, Frederick Warne, 1867 . . £75
Multiplication Rule in Verse, Routledge, [1867] £75
Chattering Jack's Picture Book, Routledge, [1867] .
. . . . £75
How Jessie Was Lost, Routledge, [1868] . . £75
Grammar in Rhyme, Routledge, [1868]. . . £75
Annie and Jack in London, Routledge, [1869]. £75
One, Two, Buckle My Shoe, Routledge, [1869] £75
The Fairy Ship, Routledge, 1870 . . . £75
The Adventures of Puffy, Routledge, 1870 . . £75
This Little Pig Went To Market, Routledge, [1870] .
. . . . £75
King Luckieboy's Party, Routledge, 1870 . . £125
King Luckieboy's Picture Book, Routledge, 1871 £125
Routledge's Book of Alphabets, Routledge, 1871 £75
Noah's Ark Alphabet, Routledge, 1872 . . . £75

My Mother, Routledge, 1873 . . . . . £75
Ali Baba and the Forty Thieves, Routledge, 1873 £75
The Three Bears, Routledge, 1873 . . . . £75
Cinderella, Routledge, 1873 . . . . . £75
Walter Crane's New Toy Book, Routledge, 1873 £250
Walter Crane's Picture Book, Routledge, 1874 £250
Valentine and Orson, Routledge, 1874 . . . £75
Puss in Boots, Routledge, 1874 . . . . £75
Old Mother Hubbard, Routledge, 1874 . . . £75
The Marquis of Caraba's Picture Book, Routledge, [1874]. £75
The Absurd ABC, Routledge, 1874 . . . . £65
The Frog Prince, Routledge: 'Walter Crane Shilling Series', 1874 . . . . £75
Goody Two Shoes, Routledge: 'Walter Crane Shilling Series', 1874 . . . . £75
Beauty and the Beast, Routledge: 'Walter Crane Shilling Series', 1874 . . . . . . £75
The Alphabet of Old Friends, Routledge: 'Walter Crane Shilling Series', 1874 . . . . £75
Little Red Riding Hood, Routledge, 1875 . . £75
Jack and the Beanstalk, Routledge, 1875 . . £75
The Bluebeard Picture Book, Routledge, 1875. £75
Baby's Own Alphabet, Routledge, 1875 . . £75
The Yellow Dwarf, Routledge: 'Walter Crane Shilling Series', 1875 . . . . £75
The Hind in the Wood, Routledge: 'Walter Crane Shilling Series', 1875 . . . . . . £75
Princess Belle Etoile, Routledge: 'Walter Crane Shilling Series', 1875 . . . . . . £75
Aladdin's Picture Book, Routledge: 'Walter Crane Shilling Series', 1875 [1876] £75
Song of Sixpence Toy Book, Warner, [1876] . £75
The Three Bears Picture Book, Routledge, [1876] £75
The Sleeping Beauty in the Wood, Routledge, 1876 .
. . . . £45
Walter Crane's Picture Books Vol. 1: The Little Pig: His Picture Book, John Lane, 1895 . . £50
Walter Crane's Picture Books Vol. 2: Mother Hubbard: Her Picture Book, John Lane, 1897 £50
Walter Crane's Picture Books Vol. 3: Cinderella's Picture Book, John Lane, 1897. . . . £50
Walter Crane's Picture Books Vol. 4: Red Riding Hood's Picture Book, John Lane, 1898 . . £50
Beauty and the Beast Picture Book, John Lane: Large Series Vol. l, 1901 . . . . £40
Goody Two Shoes Picture Book, John Lane: Large Series Vol. 2, 1901 . . . . £40
The Song of Sixpence Picture Book, John Lane: Large Series Vol. 3, 1909 . . . . . . £40
The Buckle My Shoe Picture Book, John Lane: Large Series Vol. 4, 1910 . . . . . . £40
Puss in Boots and *The Forty Thieves*, John Lane, 1914
. . . . £40
The Sleeping Beauty and *Bluebeard*, John Lane, 1914
. . . . £40
The Three Bears and *Mother Hubbard*, John Lane, 1914 . . . . £40

Books written by Mary Molesworth, illustrated by Crane

Tell Me A Story, Macmillan, 1875	£60
Carrots, Macmillan, 1876.	£50
The Cuckoo Clock, Macmillan, 1877	£50
Grandmother Dear, Macmillan, 1878	£45
The Tapestry Room, Macmillan, 1879	£40
A Christmas Child, Macmillan, 1880	£40
The Adventures of Herr Baby, Macmillan, 1881	£35
Rosy, Macmillan, 1882	£35
Two Little Waifs, Macmillan, 1883	£35
Christmas-Tree Land, Macmillan, 1884	£35
Us, An Old Fashioned Story, Macmillan, 1885	£35
Four Winds Farm, Macmillan, 1886	£30
Little Miss Piggy, Macmillan, 1887	£30
A Christmas Posy, Macmillan, 1888.	£30
The Rectory Children, Macmillan, 1889	£30
The Children of the Castle, Macmillan, 1890	£25
Studies and Stories, A.D. Innes, 1893	£25

Other Titles illustrated by Crane

The New Forest: Its History and Scenery, by John de Capel Wise, Smith & Elder, 1863	£100
A Merrie Heart, by Cassell, 1871	£125
Mrs Mundi at Home, by Walter Crane, Marcus Ward, 1875	£100
The Quiver of Love: A Collection of Valentines, Marcus Ward, 1876	£100
The Baby's Opera: Old Rhymes with New Dresses, by Walter Crane, Routledge, 1877	£100
The Baby's Bouquet, by Walter Crane, Routledge, 1878	£100
The Necklace of Princess Fiorimonde, by Mary de Morgan, Macmillan, 1880	£65
The First of May: A Fairy Masque, by John R Wise, Henry Southeran, 1881, (300 copies, signed by Crane).	£450
ditto, Henry Southeran, 1881, (folio edition, 200 copies, signed by Crane)	£750
Household Stories, by the Brothers Grimm, Macmillan, 1882.	£100
Art and the Formation of Taste, by Lucy Crane, Macmillan, 1882.	£75
Pan Pipes: A Book of Old Songs, by Theodore Marzials, Routledge, 1883	£165
The Golden Primer, Parts 1 & 2, by Professor J.M.D. Meiklejohn, William Blackwood, 1884-5 (2 vols)	£65
Folk and Fairy Tales, by Mrs Burton Harrison, Ward & Downey, 1885.	£65
Slateandpencilvania: Being the Adventures of Dick on a Desert Island, by Walter Crane, Marcus Ward, 1885	£175
Little Queen Annie, by Walter Crane, Marcus Ward, 1886	£175
Pothooks and Perseverance, by Walter Crane, Marcus Ward, 1886	£200
A Romance of the Three Rs, by Walter Crane, Marcus Ward, 1886	£150

The Sirens Three: A Poem, by Walter Crane, Macmillan, 1886.	£150
Legends for Lionel in Pen and Pencil, by Walter Crane, Cassell, 1887.	£150
The Baby's Own Aesop, by Walter Crane, Routledge, 1887	£150
Echoes of Hellas, Parts 1 & 2, by Professor George C. Warr, Marcus Ward, 1887-88 (2 vols).	£150
The Happy Prince and Other Tales, by Oscar Wilde, David Nutt, 1888.	£1,000
ditto, David Nutt, 1888 (75 signed copies, large hand made paper edition).	£6,000
The Book of Wedding Days, Compiled by K.E.J. Reid, Longmans, 1889	£75
Flora's Feast: A Masque of Flowers, by Walter Crane, Cassell, 1889.	£125
The Story of the Glittering Plain, by William Morris, Kelmscott Press, 1894 (250 copies)	£2,000
ditto, by William Morris, Kelmscott Press, 1894 (7 copies on vellum)	£6,000
Society for the Encouragement of Arts, Manufacture and Commerce: Lectures by Walter Crane, W. Trounce, 1891	£65
Queen Summer: or the Tourney of the Lily and the Rose, by Walter Crane, Cassell, 1891	£125
ditto, by Walter Crane, Cassell, 1891 (250 large paper copies)	£500
Renascence: A Book of Verse, by Walter Crane, Elkin Mathews, 1891 (350 numbered copies)	£75
ditto, by Walter Crane, Elkin Mathews, 1891 (25 signed, numbered copies on Japanese vellum)	£1,000
The Claims of Decorative Art, by Walter Crane, Lawrence & Bullen, 1892	£100
A Wonder Book for Boys and Girls, by Nathaniel Hawthorne, Osgood, McIlvaine, 1892	£175
Columbia's Courtship, by Walter Crane, Prang & Co. (U.S.), 1893	£100
The Old Garden and Other Verses, by Margaret Delane, Osgood, McIlvaine, 1893	£65
The Tempest, by William Shakespeare, Dent, 1893	£65
The History of Reynard the Fox, by F.S. Ellis, David Nutt, 1894	£65
The Merry Wives of Windsor, by William Shakespeare, George Allen, 1894.	£65
Two Gentlemen of Verona, by William Shakespeare, Dent, 1894	£65
The Faerie Queen, by Edmund Spenser, George Allen, 1894-97 (issued in 19 parts).	£650 the set
ditto, George Allen, 1897 (6 vols, 1,000 sets)	£1,000 the set
A Book of Christmas Verse, Methuen, 1895	£75
Cartoons for the Cause, Twentieth Century Press, 1896	£600
Of the Decorative Illustration of Books Old and New, by Walter Crane, Bell, 1896.	£100
The Work of Walter Crane, Virtue & Co., 1898	£125
A Floral Fantasy in an Old English Garden, by Walter Crane, Harper, 1898.	£150

The Shepherd's Calendar, by Edmund Spenser, Harper, 1898 . . . . £100
The Bases of Design, by Walter Crane, Bell, 1898 . .
. . . . £100
Triplets, by Walter Crane, Routledge, 1899 (500 numbered copies) £300
Don Quixote, translated by Judge Parry, Blackie, 1900
. . . . £65
Line and Form, by Walter Crane, Bell, 1900 . £50
Walter Crane's Picture Book, Frederick Warne, 1900 (750 copies, bound in vellum) £400
A Masque of Days, Cassell, 1901 . . . . £150
The Art of Walter Crane, by Paul George Konody, Bell, 1902. . . . . £250
A Flower Wedding, by Walter Crane, Cassell, 1905 .
. . . . £100
Flowers from Shakespeare's Garden, by Walter Crane, Cassell, 1906. . . . . . . £150
India Impressions, by Walter Crane, Methuen, 1907 .
. . . . £100
An Artists Reminiscences, by Walter Crane, Methuen, 1907 . . . . £75
A Child's Socialist Reader, by A.A. Watts, Methuen, 1907 . . . . £65
The Rosebud and Other Tales, by Arthur Kelly, Fisher & Unwin, 1909 . . . . £65
King Arthur's Knights, by H. Gilbert, Jack, 1911 £65
William Morris to Whistler, by Walter Morris, Bell, 1911 (350 copies) £250
Rumbo Rhymes, by A. Calmour, Harper, 1911. £125
Robin Hood, by H. Gilbert, Jack, 1912 . . . £65
The Story of Greece, by M. MacGregor, Jack, 1913 .
. . . . £65
Michael Mouse Unfolds His Tale, by Walter Crane, Yale Univ. Press (U.S.), 1956 (300 copies) . £125
ditto, by Walter Crane, Merrimack/Yale Univ. Press (U.S.), 1956 (wraps). £35

JOHN CREASEY
(b.1908 d.1973)

An author whose output was prodigious, Creasey is best known for his detective fiction, especially his Inspector West and Gideon novels. He used many pseudonyms.

Inspector West Novels
Inspector West Takes Charge, Stanley Paul, 1942 . .
. . . . £250/£35
Inspector West at Home, Stanley Paul, 1944 £200£30
Inspector West Regrets, Stanley Paul, 1945 £175/£25
Holiday for Inspector West, Stanley Paul, 1946 . .
. . . . £150/£20
Battle for Inspector West, Stanley Paul, 1948 £100/£20
Triumph for Inspector West, Stanley Paul, 1948 . .
. . . . £75/£15
Inspector West Kicks Off, Stanley Paul, 1949 £75/£15

Inspector West Alone, Evans, 1950 . . . £75/£15
Inspector West Cries Wolf, Evans, 1950 . £75/£15
A Case for Inspector West, Evans, 1951 . £50/£15
Puzzle for Inspector West, Evans, 1951. . £45/£10
Inspector West at Bay, Evans, 1952 . . . £40/£10
A Gun for Inspector West, Hodder & Stoughton, 1953
. . . . £35/£5
Send for Inspector West, Hodder & Stoughton, 1953 .
. . . . £35/£5
A Beauty for Inspector West, Hodder & Stoughton, 1954 . . . . £35/£5
Inspector West Makes Haste, Hodder & Stoughton, 1955 . . . . £30/£5
Two for Inspector West, Hodder & Stoughton, 1955 .
. . . . £30/£5
Parcels for Inspector West, Hodder & Stoughton, 1956
. . . . £25/£5
A Prince for Inspector West, Hodder & Stoughton, 1956 . . . . £25/£5
Accident for Inspector West, Hodder & Stoughton, 1957 . . . . £25/£5
Find Inspector West, Hodder & Stoughton, 1957 . .
. . . . £20/£5
Murder, London-New York, Hodder & Stoughton, 1958 . . . . £20/£5
Strike for Death, Hodder & Stoughton, 1958 £20/£5
Death of a Racehorse, Hodder & Stoughton, 1959. .
. . . . £20/£5
The Case of the Innocent Victims, Hodder & Stoughton, 1959 . . . . £20/£5
Murder on the Line, Hodder & Stoughton, 1960 . .
. . . . £20/£5
Death in Cold Print, Hodder & Stoughton, 1961 . .
. . . . £20/£5
The Scene of the Crime, Hodder & Stoughton, 1961 .
. . . . £20/£5
Policeman's Dread, Hodder & Stoughton, 1962 . .
. . . . £20/£5
Hang the Little Man, Hodder & Stoughton, 1963 . .
. . . . £15/£5
Look Three Ways at Murder, Hodder & Stoughton, 1964 . . . . £15/£5
Murder, London-Australia, Hodder & Stoughton, 1965 . . . . £15/£5
Murder, London-South Africa, Hodder & Stoughton, 1966 . . . . £15/£5
The Executioners, Hodder & Stoughton, 1967 £15/£5
So Young to Burn, Hodder & Stoughton, 1968 £15/£5
Murder, London-Miami, Hodder & Stoughton, 1969 .
. . . . £15/£5
A Part for a Policeman, Hodder & Stoughton, 1970 .
. . . . £15/£5
Alibi, Hodder & Stoughton, 1971 . . £15/£5
A Splinter of Glass, Hodder & Stoughton, 1972 £15/£5
The Theft of Magna Carter, Hodder & Stoughton, 1973 . . . . £15/£5
The Extortioners, Hodder & Stoughton, 1974 £15/£5
A Sharp Rise in Crime, Hodder & Stoughton, 1978 .
. . . . £10/£5

The Toff Novels

Introducing The Toff, Long, 1938 . . .	£200/£35
The Toff Goes On, Long, 1939	£150/£25
The Toff Steps Out, Long, 1939 . . .	£125/£20
Here Comes The Toff, Long, 1940 . .	£125/£20
The Toff Breaks In, Long, 1940 . . .	£125/£20
Salute the Toff, Long, 1941	£125/£20
The Toff Proceeds, Long, 1941 . . .	£125/£20
The Toff Goes to Market, Long, 1942 .	£100/£20
The Toff is Back, Long, 1942 . . .	£100/£20
The Toff Among the Millions, Long, 1943 .	£75/£15
Accuse the Toff, Long, 1943	£75/£15
The Toff and the Curate, Long, 1944 .	£75/£15
The Toff and the Great Illusion, Long, 1944	£50/£10
Feathers for the Toff, Long, 1945 . .	£50/£10
The Toff and the Lady, Long, 1946 . .	£40/£5
The Toff on Ice, Long, 1946	£30/£5
Hammer the Toff, Long, 1947 . . .	£30/£5
The Toff in Town, Long, 1948 . . .	£30/£5
The Toff Takes Shares, Long, 1948 . .	£30/£5
The Toff and Old Harry, Long, 1949 . .	£30/£5
The Toff on Board, Long, 1949 . . .	£30/£5
Fool The Toff, Evans, 1950	£30/£5
Kill The Toff, Evans, 1950	£30/£5
A Knife for The Toff, Evans, 1951 . .	£30/£5
The Toff Goes Gay, Evans, 1951 . . .	£30/£5
Hunt The Toff, Evans, 1952	£25/£5
Call The Toff, Hodder & Stoughton, 1953 .	£25/£5
The Toff Down Under, Hodder & Stoughton, 1953 .	
. . . .	£25/£5
The Toff at Butlins, Hodder & Stoughton, 1954 .	
. . . .	£25/£5
The Toff at the Fair, Hodder & Stoughton, 1954 . .	
. . . .	£20/£5
A Six for The Toff, Hodder & Stoughton, 1955	£20/£5
The Toff and the Deep Blue Sea, Hodder &	
Stoughton, 1955	£20/£5
Make-Up for The Toff, Hodder & Stoughton, 1956 .	
. . . .	£20/£5
The Toff in New York, Hodder & Stoughton, 1956 .	
. . . .	£20/£5
Model for The Toff, Hodder & Stoughton, 1957 . .	
. . . .	£20/£5
The Toff on Fire, Hodder & Stoughton, 1957	£20/£5
The Toff and the Stolen Tresses, Hodder & Stoughton,	
1958	£20/£5
The Toff on the Farm, Hodder & Stoughton, 1958 .	
. . . .	£20/£5
Double for The Toff, Hodder & Stoughton, 1959 . .	
. . . .	£20/£5
The Toff and the Runaway Bride, Hodder &	
Stoughton, 1959	£20/£5
A Rocket for The Toff, Hodder & Stoughton, 1960 .	
. . . .	£15/£5
The Toff and the Kidnapped Child, Hodder &	
Stoughton, 1960	£15/£5
Follow The Toff, Hodder & Stoughton, 1961	£15/£5
The Toff and the Teds, Hodder & Stoughton, 1961 .	
. . . .	£15/£5

A Doll for The Toff, Hodder & Stoughton, 1963 . .	
. . . .	£15/£5
Leave it to The Toff, Hodder & Stoughton, 1963 . .	
. . . .	£15/£5
The Toff and the Spider, Hodder & Stoughton, 1965 .	
. . . .	£15/£5
The Toff in Wax, Hodder & Stoughton, 1966	£15/£5
A Bundle for The Toff, Hodder & Stoughton, 1967 .	
. . . .	£15/£5
Stars for The Toff, Hodder & Stoughton, 1968	£15/£5
The Toff and the Golden Boy, Hodder & Stoughton,	
1969	£15/£5
The Toff and the Fallen Angels, Hodder & Stoughton,	
1970	£15/£5
Vote for The Toff, Hodder & Stoughton, 1971	£15/£5
The Toff and the Trip-Trip-Triplets, Hodder &	
Stoughton, 1972	£15/£5
The Toff and the Terrified Taxman, Hodder &	
Stoughton, 1973	£15/£5
The Toff and the Sleepy Cowboy, Hodder &	
Stoughton, 1975	£15/£5

The Toff Short Stories

The Toff on the Trail, Everybody's Books, [n.d.] . .	
. . . .	£20/£5
Murder out of the Past, Barrington Gray, 1953	£20/£5

Department Z Novels

The Death Miser, Melrose, 1932 . . .	£400/£50
Redhead, Hurst & Blackett, 1934 . .	£350/£45
First Came a Murder, Melrose, 1934 .	£300/£40
Death Round the Corner, Melrose, 1935 .	£300/£40
The Mark of the Crescent, Melrose, 1935 .	£300/£40
Thunder in Europe, Melrose, 1936 . .	£250/£35
The Terror Trap, Melrose, 1936 . . .	£250/£35
Carriers of Death, Melrose, 1937 . .	£200/£35
Days of Danger, Melrose, 1937 . . .	£200/£35
Death Stands By, Long, 1938 . . .	£150/£25
Menace, Long, 1938	£150/£25
Murder Must Wait, Melrose, 1939 . .	£125/£20
Panic, Long, 1939	£125/£20
Death By Night, Long, 1940	£125/£20
The Island of Peril, Long, 1940 . . .	£125/£20
Sabotage, Long, 1941	£125/£20
Go Away Death, 1941	£125/£20
The Day of Disaster, Long, 1942 . .	£100/£20
Prepare for Action, Stanley Paul, 1942 .	£100/£20
No Darker Crime, Stanley Paul, 1943 .	£75/£15
Dark Peril, Stanley Paul, 1944 . . .	£50/£10
The Peril Ahead, Stanley Paul, 1946 . .	£40/£5
The League of Dark Men, Stanley Paul, 1947	£30/£5
Department of Death, Evans, 1949 . .	£30/£5
The Enemy Within, Evans, 1950. . .	£30/£5
Dead or Alive, Evans, 1951	£30/£5
A Kind of Prisoner, Hodder & Stoughton, 1954	£20/£5
The Black Spiders, Hodder & Stoughton, 1957	£20/£5

Dr Palfrey Novels

Traitor's Doom, Long, 1942	£100/£20
The Legions of the Lost, Long 1943. . .	£75/£15
The Valley of Fear, Long, 1943	£75/£15
Dangerous Quest, Long, 1944	£50/£10
Death in the Rising Sun, Long, 1945 . .	£50/£10
The Hounds of Vengeance, Long, 1945 .	£45/£10
Shadow of Doom, Long, 1946	£40/£5
The House of the Bears, Long, 1946 . .	£40/£5
Dark Harvest, Long, 1947	£30/£5
Sons of Satan, Long, 1947	£30/£5
The Wings of Peace, Long, 1948 . . .	£30/£5
The Dawn of Darkness, Long, 1949. . .	£30/£5
The League of Light, Evans, 1949 . . .	£30/£5
The Man Who Shook the World, Evans, 1950	£30/£5
The Prophet of Fire, Evans, 1951 . . .	£25/£5
The Children of Hate, Evans, 1952 . . .	£25/£5
The Touch of Death, Hodder & Stoughton, 1954 . .	
. . . .	£20/£5
The Mists of Fear, Hodder & Stoughton, 1955	£20/£5
The Flood, Hodder & Stoughton, 1956 . .	£20/£5
The Plague of Silence, Hodder & Stoughton, 1958 .	
. . . .	£20/£5
The Drought, Hodder & Stoughton, 1959 .	£20/£5
The Terror, Hodder & Stoughton, 1962. .	£15/£5
The Depths, Hodder & Stoughton, 1963 .	£15/£5
The Sleep, Hodder & Stoughton, 1964 . .	£15/£5
The Inferno, Hodder & Stoughton, 1965 .	£15/£5
The Flame, Hodder & Stoughton, 1967. .	£15/£5
The Blight, Hodder & Stoughton, 1968 . .	£15/£5
The Oasis, Hodder & Stoughton, 1970 . .	£15/£5
The Smog, Hodder & Stoughton, 1970 . .	£15/£5
The Unbegotten, Hodder & Stoughton, 1971	£15/£5
The Insulators, Hodder & Stoughton, 1972	£15/£5
The Voiceless One, Hodder & Stoughton, 1973	£15/£5
The Thunder-Maker, Hodder & Stoughton, 1976 . .	
. . . .	£10/£5
The Whirlwind, Hodder & Stoughton, 1979	£10/£5

Sexton Blake Paperbacks

The Case of the Murdered Financier, Amalgamated Press, 1937	£25
The Great Air Swindle, Amalgamated Press, 1939	£25
The Man from Fleet Street, Amalgamated Press, 1940	
. . . .	£25
The Case of the Mad Inventor, Amalgamated Press, 1942	£25
Private Carter's Crime, Amalgamated Press, 1943	£25

Other Novels

Seven Times Seven, Melrose, 1932 . . .	£300/£50
Men, Maids and Murder, Melrose, 1933 .	£250/£45
Four of the Best, Hodder & Stoughton, 1955	£20/£5
The Mountain of the Blind, Hodder & Stoughton, 1960	£15/£5
The Foothills of Fear, Hodder & Stoughton, 1961. .	
. . . .	£15/£5
The Masters of Bow Street, Hodder & Stoughton, 1972	
. . . .	£15/£5

Children's Titles

Ned Cartwright, Middleweight Champion, Mellifont, 1935 (pseud. James Marsden, wraps) . . .	£35
The Men Who Died Laughing, D.C. Thomson, 1935 (wraps)	£25
The Killer Squad, Newnes, 1936 (wraps) . .	£25
Our Glorious Term, Sampson Low, [n.d.] .	£175/£25
The Captain of the Fifth, Sampson Low, [n.d.] . .	
. . . .	£175/£25
Blazing the Air Trail, Sampson Low, 1936.	£175/£25
The Jungle Flight Mystery, Sampson Low, 1936 . .	
. . . .	£175/£25
The Mystery 'Plane, Sampson Low, 1936 .	£175/£25
Murder by Magic, Amalgamated Press, 1937 (wraps)	
. . . .	£25
The Mysterious Mr Rocco, Mellifont, 1937 (wraps) .	
. . . .	£25
The S.O.S. Flight, Sampson Low, 1937. .	£150/£25
The Secret Aeroplane, Sampson Low, 1937	£150/£25
The Treasure Flight, Sampson Low, 1937 .	£150/£25
The Air Marauders, Sampson Low, 1937 .	£150/£25
The Black Biplane, Sampson Low, 1937 .	£150/£25
The Mystery Flight, Sampson Low, 1937 .	£150/£25
The Double Motive, Mellifont, 1938 . .	£150/£25
The Double-Cross of Death, Mellifont, 1938 (wraps) .	
. . . .	£25
The Missing Hoard, Mellifont, 1938 (wraps) .	£25
Mystery at Manby House, North News Syndicate, 1938 (wraps)	£25
The Fighting Flyers, Sampson Low, 1938 .	£150/£25
The Flying Stowaways, Sampson Low, 1938	£150/£25
The Miracle 'Plane, Sampson Low, 1938 .	£150/£25
Dixon Hawke, Secret Agent, D.C. Thomson, 1939 (wraps)	£22
Documents of Death, Mellifont, 1939 (wraps) .	£20
The Hidden Hoard, Mellifont, 1939 (wraps) .	£20
Mottled Death, D.C. Thomson, 1939 (wraps) .	£15
The Blue Flyer, Mellifont, 1939 (wraps) . .	£15
The Jumper, Northern News Syndicate, 1939 (wraps).	
. . . .	£15
The Mystery of Blackmoor Prison, Mellifont, 1939 (wraps)	£15
The Sacred Eye, D.C. Thomson, 1939 . .	£150/£25
The Ship of Death, D.C. Thomson, 1939 (wraps)	£15
Peril By Air, Newnes, 1939 (wraps) . . .	£15
The Flying Turk, Sampson Low, 1939 . .	£150/£25
The Monarch of the Skies, Sampson Low, 1939 . .	
. . . .	£125/£20
The Fear of Felix Corder, Fleetway, [n.d.] (wraps)£10	
John Brand, Fugitive, Fleetway, [n.d.] (wraps)	£10
The Night of Dread, Fleetway, [n.d.] (wraps) .	£10
Dazzle - Air Ace No. 1, Newnes, 1940 (wraps).	£10
Dazzle and the Red Bomber, Newnes, n.d. (wraps) £10	
Five Missing Men, Newnes, 1940 (wraps) . .	£10
The Poison Gas Robberies, Mellifont, 1940 (wraps) .	
. . . .	£10
The Cinema Crimes, Pemberton, 1945 (wraps) .	£10
The Missing Monoplane, Sampson Low, 1947£35/£10	

Novels written as J.J. Marric

Gideon's Day, Hodder & Stoughton, 1955	£75/£15
Gideon's Week, Hodder & Stoughton, 1956	£50/£10
Gideon's Night, Hodder & Stoughton, 1957	£35/£5
Gideon's Month, Hodder & Stoughton, 1958	£35/£5
Gideon's Staff, Hodder & Stoughton, 1959	£25/£5
Gideon's Risk, Hodder & Stoughton, 1960	£25/£5
Gideon's Fire, Hodder & Stoughton, 1961	£25/£5
Gideon's March, Hodder & Stoughton, 1962	£20/£5
Gideon's Ride, Hodder & Stoughton, 1963	£20/£5
Gideon's Vote, Hodder & Stoughton, 1964	£20/£5
Gideon's Lot, Hodder & Stoughton, 1965	£20/£5
Gideon's Badge, Hodder & Stoughton, 1966	£20/£5
Gideon's Wrath, Hodder & Stoughton, 1967	£20/£5
Gideon's River, Hodder & Stoughton, 1968	£20/£5
Gideon's Power, Hodder & Stoughton, 1969	£20/£5
Gideon's Sport, Hodder & Stoughton, 1970	£15/£5
Gideon's Art, Hodder & Stoughton, 1971	£15/£5
Gideon's Men, Hodder & Stoughton, 1972	£15/£5
Gideon's Press, Hodder & Stoughton, 1973	£15/£5
Gideon's Fog, Hodder & Stoughton, 1975	£15/£5
Gideon's Drive, Hodder & Stoughton, 1976	£15/£5

Novels written as Anthony Morton

Meet the Baron, Harrap, 1937	£250/£35
The Baron Returns, Harrap, 1937	£225/£35
The Baron Again, Sampson Low, 1938	£200/£30
The Baron At Bay, Sampson Low, 1938	£200/£30
Alias the Baron, Sampson Low, 1939	£150/£25
The Baron at Large, Sampson Low, 1939	£150/£25
Versus the Baron, Sampson Low, 1940	£125/£20
Call for the Baron, Sampson Low, 1940	£125/£20
The Baron Comes Back, Sampson Low, 1943	£75/£15
Mr Quentin Investigates, Sampson Low, 1943	£45/£5
Introducing Mr Brandon, Sampson Low, 1944	£45/£5
A Case for the Baron, Sampson Low, 1945	£50/£10
Reward for the Baron, Sampson Low, 1945	£50/£10
Career for the Baron, Sampson Low, 1946	£40/£5
The Baron and the Beggar, Sampson Low, 1947	£30/£5
Blame the Baron, Sampson Low, 1948	£30/£5
A Rope for the Baron, Sampson Low, 1948	£30/£5
Books for the Baron, Sampson Low, 1949	£30/£5
Cry for the Baron, Sampson Low, 1950	£30/£5
Trap the Baron, Sampson Low, 1950	£30/£5
Attack the Baron, Sampson Low, 1951	£30/£5
Shadow the Baron, Sampson Low, 1951	£25/£5
Warn the Baron, Sampson Low, 1952	£25/£5
The Baron Goes East, Sampson Low, 1953	£25/£5
The Baron in France, Hodder & Stoughton, 1953	£25/£5
Danger for the Baron, Hodder & Stoughton, 1953	£25/£5
The Baron Goes Fast, Hodder & Stoughton, 1954	£25/£5
Nest-Egg for the Baron, Hodder & Stoughton, 1954	£25/£5

Help from the Baron, Hodder & Stoughton, 1955	£25/£5
Hide the Baron, Hodder & Stoughton, 1956	£25/£5
Frame the Baron, Hodder & Stoughton, 1957	£25/£5
Red Eye for the Baron, Hodder & Stoughton, 1958	£25/£5
Black for the Baron, Hodder & Stoughton, 1959	£25/£5
Salute for the Baron, Hodder & Stoughton, 1960	£25/£5
A Branch for the Baron, Hodder & Stoughton, 1961	£25/£5
Bad for the Baron, Hodder & Stoughton, 1962	£20/£5
A Sword for the Baron, Hodder & Stoughton, 1963	£20/£5
The Baron on Board, Hodder & Stoughton, 1964	£20/£5
The Baron and the Chinese Puzzle, Hodder & Stoughton, 1964	£20/£5
Sport for the Baron, Hodder & Stoughton, 1966	£20/£5
Affair for the Baron, Hodder & Stoughton, 1967	£20/£5
The Baron and the Missing Old Masters, Hodder & Stoughton, 1968	£20/£5
The Baron and the Unfinished Portrait, Hodder & Stoughton, 1969	£20/£5
Last Laugh for the Baron, Hodder & Stoughton, 1970	£15/£5
The Baron Goes A-Buying, Hodder & Stoughton, 1971	£15/£5
The Baron and the Arrogant Artist, Hodder & Stoughton, 1972	£15/£5
Burgle the Baron, Hodder & Stoughton, 1973	£15/£5
The Baron, King-Maker, Hodder & Stoughton, 1975	£15/£5
Love for the Baron, Hodder & Stoughton, 1976	£15/£5

Novels written as Gordon Ashe

Death on Demand, Long, 1939	£125/£25
The Speaker, Long, 1939	£125/£25
Terror by Day, Long, 1940	£125/£20
Secret Murder, Long, 1940	£125/£20
Who Was the Jester?, Newnes, 1940	£125/£20
'Ware Danger, Long, 1941	£125/£20
Murder Most Foul, Long, 1942	£100/£20
There Goes Death, Long, 1942	£100/£20
Death in High Places, Long, 1942	£100/£20
Death in Flames, Long, 1943	£75/£15
Two Men Missing, Long, 1943	£75/£15
Rogues Rampant, Long, 1944	£50/£10
Death on the Move, Long, 1945	£50/£10
Invitation to Adventure, Long, 1945	£45/£10
Here is Danger, Long, 1946	£40/£5
Give Me Murder, Long, 1947	£30/£5
Murder Too Late, Long, 1947	£30/£5
Dark Mystery, Long, 1948	£30/£5
Engagement With Death, Long, 1948	£30/£5

A Puzzle in Pearls, Long, 1949	£30/£5
Kill or Be Killed, Evans, 1949	£30/£5
The Dark Circle, Evans, 1950	£30/£5
Murder With Mushrooms, Evans, 1950 .	£25/£5
Death in Diamonds, Evans, 1951 . . .	£25/£5
Missing or Dead?, Evans, 1951	£25/£5
Death in a Hurry, Evans, 1952	£25/£5
The Long Search, Evans, 1953	£25/£5
Sleep Death, Evans, 1953	£25/£5
Double Death, Evans, 1954	£20/£5
Death in the Trees, Evans, 1954	£20/£5
The Kidnapped Child, Evans, 1955 . . .	£20/£5
The Man Who Stayed Alive, Long, 1955 .	£20/£5
Day of Fear, Long, 1956	£20/£5
No Need to Die, Long, 1956	£20/£5
Wait for Death, Long, 1957	£20/£5
Come Home to Death, Long, 1958 . . .	£20/£5
Elope to Death, Long, 1959	£20/£5
Don't Let Him Kill, Long, 1960	£15£5
The Crime Haters, Long, 1961	£15/£5
Rogues Ransome, Long, 1962	£15/£5
Death from Below, Long, 1963	£15/£5
The Big Call, Long, 1964	£15/£5
A Promise of Diamonds, Long, 1965 . .	£15/£5
A Taste of Treasure, Long, 1966 . . .	£15/£5
A Clutch of Coppers, Long, 1967 . . .	£15/£5
A Shadow of Death, Long, 1968	£15/£5
A Scream of Murder, Long, 1970 . . .	£15/£5
A Nest of Traitors, Long, 1970	£15/£5
A Rabble of Rebels, Long, 1971	£15/£5
A Herald of Doom, Long, 1973	£15/£5
A Blast of Trumpets, Long, 1975 . . .	£10/£5
A Plague of Demons, Long, 1976 . . .	£10/£5

Paperbacks written as M.E. Cooke

Fire of Death, Fiction House, 1934	£10
The Black Heart, Gramol, 1935	£10
The Casino Mystery, Mellifont, 1935 . . .	£10
The Crime Gang, Mellifont, 1935	£10
The Death Drive, Mellifont, 1935	£10
No 1's Last Crime, Fiction House, 1935 . .	£10
The Stolen Formula Mystery, Mellifont, 1935 .	£10
The Big Radium Mystery, Mellifont, 1936 . .	£10
The Day of Terror, Mellifont, 1936	£10
The Dummy Robberies, Mellifont, 1936 . .	£10
The Hypnotic Demon, Fiction House, 1936 .	£10
The Moat Farm Mystery, Fiction House, 1936 .	£10
The Secret Formula, Fiction House, 1936 . .	£10
The Successful Alibi, Mellifont, 1936 . . .	£10
The Hadfield Mystery, Mellifont, 1937 . . .	£10
The Moving Eye, Mellifont, 1937	£10
The Raven, Fiction House, 1937	£10
The Mountain Terror, Mellifont, 1939 . .	£10
For Her Sister's Sake, Fiction House, 1938 .	£10
The Verrall Street Affair, Newnes, 1940 . .	£10

Paperbacks written as Margaret Cooke

For Love's Sake, Northern News Syndicate, 1934	£5
Troubled Journey, Fiction House, 1937	£5

False Love or True, Northern News Syndicate, 1937 .	
. . . .	£5
Fate's Playthings, Fiction House, 1938	£5
Web of Destiny, Fiction House, 1938	£5
Whose Lover?, Fiction House, 1938	£5
A Mannequin's Romance, Fiction House, 1938 .	£5
Love Calls Twice, Fiction House, 1938	£5
The Road to Happiness, Fiction House, 1938 .	£5
The Turn of Fate, Fiction House, 1939	£5
Love Triumphant, Fiction House, 1939	£5
Love Comes Back, Fiction House, 1939	£5
Crossroads of Love, Mellifont, 1939	£5
Love's Journey, Fiction House, 1940	£5

Novels written as Henry St John Cooper

Chains of Love, Sampson Low, 1937 . .	£15/£5
Love's Pilgrim, Sampson Low, 1937 . .	£15/£5
The Tangled Legacy, Sampson Low, 1938 .	£15/£5
The Greater Desire, Sampson Low, 1938 .	£15/£5
Love's Ordeal, Sampson Low, 1939 . . .	£15/£5
The Lost Lover, Sampson Low, 1940 . .	£15/£5

Novels written as Norman Deane

Secret Errand, Hurst & Blackett, 1939 . .	£125£20
Dangerous Journey, Hurst & Blackett, 1939	£125/£20
Unknown Mystery, Hurst & Blackett, 1940 .	£125/£20
The Withered Man, Hurst & Blackett, 1940	£125/£20
I Am the Withered Man, Hurst & Blackett, 1941 . .	
. . . .	£100/£15
Where is the Withered Man?, Hurst & Blackett, 1942 .	
. . . .	£100/£15
Return to Adventure, Hurst & Blackett, 1943	£75/£10
Gateway to Escape, Hurst & Blackett, 1944	£50/£5
Come Home to Crime, Hurst & Blackett, 1945	£50/£5
Play for Murder, Hurst & Blackett, 1946 .	£40/£5
The Silent House, Hurst & Blackett, 1947 .	£30/£5
Why Murder?, Hurst & Blackett, 1948 . .	£30/£5
Intent to Murder, Hurst & Blackett, 1948 .	£30/£5
The Man I Didn't Kill, Hurst & Blackett, 1950	£30/£5
Double for Death, Hurst & Blackett, 1950 .	£30/£5
Golden Death, Hurst & Blackett, 1952 . .	£25/£5
Look at Murder, Hurst & Blackett, 1952 .	£25/£5
Murder Ahead, Hurst & Blackett, 1953 . .	£25/£5
Death in the Spanish Sun, Hurst & Blackett, 1954 .	
. . . .	£25/£5
Incense of Death, Hurst & Blackett, 1954 .	£25/£5

Paperbacks written as Elise Felcamps

Love or Hate?, Fiction House, 1936	£75/£10
True Love, Fiction House, 1937	£75/£10
Love's Triumph, Fiction House, 1937 . .	£75/£10

Novels written as Robert Caine Frazer

Kilby Takes a Risk, Pocket (U.S.), 1962 (wraps)	£10
R.I.S.C., Collins, 1962	£15/£5
The Secret Syndicate, Collins, 1963 . . .	£15/£5
The Hollywood Hoax, Collins, 1964 . .	£15/£5
The Miami Mob and *Mark Kilby Stands Alone*,	
Collins, 1965	£15/£5

Paperbacks written as Patrick Gill
The Fighting Footballers, Mellifont, 1937 . . £25
The Laughing Lightweight, Mellifont, 1937 . £25
The Battle for the Cup, Mellifont, 1939. . . £25
The Fighting Tramp, Mellifont, 1939 . . . £25
The Mystery of the Centre-Forward, Mellifont, 1939 .
. . . . £25
The £10,000 Trophy Race, Mellifont, 1939. . £25
The Secret Super-Charger, Mellifont, 1940 . £25

Novels written as Michael Halliday
Three For Adventure, Cassell, 1937. . . £100/£15
Four Find Danger, Cassell, 1937 . . . £100/£15
Two Meet Trouble, Cassell, 1938 . . . £75/£15
Murder Comes Home, Stanley Paul, 1940 . £50/£10
Heir to Murder, Stanley Paul, 1940 . . . £50/£10
Murder By the Way, Stanley Paul, 1940 . £50/£10
Who Saw Him Die?, Stanley Paul, 1941 . £40/£5
Foul Play Suspected, Stanley Paul, 1942 . £40/£5
Who Died at the Grange, Stanley Paul, 1942 £40/£5
Five to Kill, Stanley Paul, 1943 . . . . £40/£5
Murder at King's Kitchen, Stanley Paul, 1943 £40/£5
No Crime More Cruel, Stanley Paul, 1944 . £30/£5
Who Said Murder, Stanley Paul, 1944 . . £30/£5
Crime With Many Voices, Stanley Paul, 1945 £30/£5
Murder Makes Murder, Stanley Paul, 1946 £25/£5
Mystery Motive, Stanley Paul, 1947 . . . £25/£5
Lend a Hand to Murder, Stanley Paul, 1947 £25/£5
First Murder, Stanley Paul, 1948 . . . £25/£5
No End to Danger, Stanley Paul, 1948 . . £25/£5
Who Killed Rebecca?, Stanley Paul, 1949 . £25/£5
The Dying Witness, Evans, 1949. . . . £25/£5
Dine With Murder, Evans, 1950. . . . . £25/£5
Murder Weekend, Evans, 1950 . . . . £25/£5
Quarrel With Murder, Evans, 1951 . . . £25/£5
Take a Body, Evans, 1951 . . . . . £25/£5
Lame Dog Murder, Evans, 1952. . . . £25/£5
Murder in the Stars, Hodder & Stoughton, 1953 . .
. . . . £25/£5
Man on the Run, Hodder & Stoughton, 1953 £20/£5
Death out of Darkness, Hodder & Stoughton, 1954 .
. . . . £20/£5
Out of the Shadows, Hodder & Stoughton, 1954 . .
. . . . £20/£5
Cat and Mouse, Hodder & Stoughton, 1955 £20/£5
Murder at End House, Hodder & Stoughton, 1955 .
. . . . £20/£5
Death of a Stranger, Hodder & Stoughton, 1957 . .
. . . . £20/£5
Runaway, Hodder & Stoughton, 1957 . . £25/£10
Murder Assured, Hodder & Stoughton, 1958 £25/£10
Missing from Home, Hodder & Stoughton, 1959 . .
. . . . £20/£5
Thicker Than Water, Hodder & Stoughton, 1959 . .
. . . . £20/£5
Go Ahead with Murder, Hodder & Stoughton, 1960 .
. . . . £20/£5
How Many to Kill?, Hodder & Stoughton, 1960 £20/£5

The Edge of Terror, Hodder & Stoughton, 1961 . .
. . . . £20/£5
The Man I Killed, Hodder & Stoughton, 1961 £15/£5
Hate to Kill, Hodder & Stoughton, 1962 . £15/£5
The Quiet Fear, Hodder & Stoughton, 1963 £15/£5
The Guilt of Innocence, Hodder & Stoughton, 1964 .
. . . . £15/£5
Cunning as a Fox, Hodder & Stoughton, 1965 £15/£5
Wicked as the Devil, Hodder & Stoughton, 1966 . .
. . . . £15/£5
Sly as a Serpent, Hodder & Stoughton, 1967 £15/£5
Cruel as a Cat, Hodder & Stoughton, 1968 £15/£5
Too Good to be True, Hodder & Stoughton, 1969 . .
. . . . £15/£5
A Period of Evil, Hodder & Stoughton, 1970 £10/£5
As Lonely as the Damned, Hodder & Stoughton, 1971
. . . . £10/£5
As Empty as Hate, Hodder & Stoughton, 1972. . .
. . . . £10/£5
As Merry as Hell, Hodder & Stoughton, 1973 . . .
. . . . £10/£5
This Man Did I Kill?, Hodder & Stoughton, 1974 . .
. . . . £10/£5
The Man Who was Not Himself, Hodder & Stoughton,
1976 . . . . £10/£5

Novels written as Kyle Hunt
Kill Once, Kill Twice, Barker, 1957 . . . £25/£5
Kill a Wicked Man, Barker, 1958 . . . £25/£5
Kill My Love, T.V. Boardman, 1959. . . £20/£5
To Kill a Killer, T.V. Boardman, 1960 . . £20/£5

Novels written as Peter Manton
Murder Manor, Wright & Brown, 1937. . £100/£20
The Greyvale School Mystery, Wright & Brown, 1937
. . . . £100/£20
Stand By For Danger, Wright & Brown, 1937 . . .
. . . . £100/£20
The Circle of Justice, Wright & Brown, 1938 £75/£15
Three Days' Terror, Wright & Brown, 1938 £75/£15
The Crime Syndicate, Wright & Brown, 1939 £50/£10
Death Looks On, Wright & Brown, 1939 . £50/£10
Murder in the Highlands, Wright & Brown, 1939. . .
. . . . £50/£10
The Midget Marvel, Mellifont, 1940 (wraps) . £25
Policeman's Triumph, Wright & Brown, 1948 £25/£5
Thief in the Night, Wright & Brown, 1950 . £25/£5
No Escape from Murder, Wright & Brown, 1953 . .
. . . . £20/£5
The Crooked Killer, Wright & Brown, 1954 £20/£5
The Charity Killers, Wright & Brown, 1954 £20/£5

Novels written as Richard Martin
Keys to Crime, Earl, 1947. . . . . . £25/£5
Vote to Murder, Earl, 1948 . . . . . £25/£5
Adrian and Jonathan, Hodder & Stoughton, 1954. .
. . . . £20/£5

Novels written as Jeremy York

By Persons Unknown, Bles, 1941 . . .	£75/£15
Murder Unseen, Bles, 1943	£50/£10
No Alibi, Melrose, 1944	£40/£10
Murder in the Family, Melrose, 1944 . .	£40/£10
Yesterday's Murder, Melrose, 1945 . . .	£30/£5
Find the Body, Melrose, 1945	£30/£5
Murder Came Late, Melrose, 1946 . . .	£30/£5
Run Away With Murder, Melrose, 1947 . .	£25/£5
Let's Kill Uncle Lionel, Melrose, 1947 . .	£25/£5
Death to My Killer, Melrose, 1950 . . .	£25/£5
Sentence of Death, Melrose, 1950 . . .	£25/£5
Voyage of Death, Melrose, 1952. . . .	£25/£5
Safari With Murder, Melrose, 1953 . . .	£20/£5
So Soon to Die, Stanley Paul, 1955 . . .	£20/£5
Seeds of Murder, Stanley Paul, 1956 . .	£20/£5
Sight of Death, Stanley Paul, 1956 . . .	£20/£5
My Brother's Killer, Stanley Paul, 1958 .	£20/£5
Hide and Kill, Long, 1959	£20/£5
To Kill or to Die, Long, 1960. . . .	£15/£5

Novels written as Ken Ranger

One Shot Marriott, Sampson Low, 1938 .	£125/£20
Roaring Guns, Sampson Low, 1939. . .	£100/£15

Novels written as William K Reilly

Range War, Stanley Paul, 1939	£100/£15
Two-Gun Texan, Stanley Paul, 1939 . .	£100/£15
Gun Feud, Stanley Paul, 1940	£100/£15
Stolen Range, Stanley Paul, 1940 . . .	£100/£15
War on Lazy K, Stanley Paul, 1941 . .	£75/£10
Outlaw's Vengeance, Stanley Paul, 1941 .	£75/£10
Guns Over Blue Lake, Jenkins, 1942 . .	£50/£10
Riders of Dry Gulch, Jenkins, 1943 . . .	£50/£10
Long John Rides the Range, Jenkins, 1944.	£40/£5
Miracle Range, Jenkins, 1945	£30/£5
Secret of the Range, Jenkins, 1946 . . .	£30/£5
Outlaws Guns, Earl, 1949	£25/£5
Range Vengeance, Ward Lock, 1953 . .	£20/£5

Novels written as Tex Riley

Two-Gun Girl, Wright & Brown, 1938 . .	£125/£20
Gun-Smoke Range, Wright & Brown, 1938	£125/£20
Gunshot Mesa, Wright & Brown, 1939 . .	£100/£15
The Shootin' Sheriff, Wright & Brown, 1940 . . .	
. . . .	£100/£15
Masked Riders, Wright & Brown, 1940. .	£100/£15
Rustler's Range, Wright & Brown, 1940 .	£100/£15
Death Canyon, Wright & Brown, 1941 . .	£75/£10
Guns on the Range, Wright & Brown, 1942	£50/£10
Range Justice, Wright & Brown, 1943 . .	£40/£5
Outlaw Hollow, Wright & Brown, 1944. .	£40/£5
Hidden Range, Earl, 1946	£30/£5
Forgotten Range, Earl, 1947.	£25/£5
Trigger Justice, Earl, 1948	£25/£5
Lynch Hollow, Earl, 1949	£25/£5

Others Pseudonymous Fiction

The Dark Shadow, Fiction House, [n.d.], (pseud. Rodney Mattheson, wraps)	£25
The House of Ferrars, Fiction House, [n.d.], (pseud. Rodney Mattheson, wraps) . . .	£25
Four Motives for Murder, Newnes, 1938, (pseud. Brian Hope, wraps)	£25
Triple Murder, Newnes, 1940, (pseud. Colin Hughes, wraps)	£20
Murder on Largo Island, Selwyn & Blount, 1944, (pseud. Charles Hogarth, with Ian Bowen)	£35/£5
Danger Woman, Pocket Books (U.S.), 1966, (pseud. Abel Mann, wraps)	£10

Non Fiction

Fighting Was My Business, by Jimmy Wilde, Joseph, 1935 (ghosted by Creasey)	£75/£15
Log of a Merchant Airman, Stanley Paul, 1943 (with John H. Lock)	£45/£10
Heroes of the Air: A Tribute to the Courage, Sacrifice end Skill of the Men of the R.A.F., Dorset Wings for Victory Committee, 1943 (wraps)	£15
The Printer's Devil: An Account of the History and Objects of the Printers' Pension, Aimshouse and Orphan Asylum Corporation, Hutchinson, 1943 (with Walter Hutchinson)	£45/£10
Man in Danger, Stanley Paul, 1950 (pseud. 'Credo', wraps)	£10
Round the World in 465 Days, Hale, 1953 (with Jean Creasey)	£25/£10
Let's Look at America, Hale, 1956 (with Jean Creasey)	£25/£10
They Didn't Mean to Kill: The Real Story of Road Accidents, Hodder & Stoughton, 1960 . .	£15/£5
Optimists in Africa, Timmins, 1963 (with Jean, Martin and Richard Creasey)	£20/£5
African Holiday, Timmins, 1963 . . .	£20/£5
Good, God and Man: An Outline of the Philosophy of Selfism, Hodder & Stoughton, 1967 . .	£25/£5
Evolution to Democracy, Hodder & Stoughton, 1969	£15/£5

MICHAEL CRICHTON
(b.1942)

An author whose interest in science and its effects on society is at the fore in his most successful work, *Jurassic Park*.

Novels

The Andromeda Strain, Knopf (U.S.), 1969	£150/£30
ditto, Cape, 1969	£125/£20
The Terminal Man, Knopf (U.S.), 1972 .	£75/£20
ditto, Cape, 1972	£65/£20
The Great Train Robbery, Knopf (U.S.), 1975	£50/£10
ditto, Cape, 1975	£45/£10

Eaters of the Dead, Knopf (U.S.), 1976 . . £40/£10
ditto, Cape, 1976 . . . . £40/£10
Congo, Knopf (U.S.), 1980 . . . . . £35/£10
ditto, Allen Lane, 1981 . . . . . . £35/£10
Sphere, Knopf (U.S.), 1987 . . . . . £25/£10
ditto, Macmillan, 1987 . . . . . . £25/£10
Jurassic Park, Knopf (U.S.), 1990 . . . £60/£10
ditto, Franklin Library (U.S.), 1990 (signed) . £150
ditto, Century, 1991 . . . . £50/£10
Rising Sun, Knopf (U.S.), 1992 . . . . £15/£5
ditto, Century, 1992 . . . . £15/£5
The Lost World, Knopf (U.S.), 1995 . . £15/£5
ditto, Century, 1995 . . . . £15/£5
Airframe, Knopf (U.S.), 1996 . . . . £15/£5
ditto, Knopf (U.S.), 1996 (50 signed deluxe copies) .
. . . . £200
ditto, Franklin Library (U.S.), 1996 (signed) . £50
ditto, Century, 1996 . . . . £15/£5
Timeline, Knopf (U.S.), 1999 . . . . £15/£5
ditto, Franklin Library (U.S.), 1999 (signed) . £50
ditto, Century, 1999 . . . . £15/£5

Novels as 'John Lange'
Odds On, New American Library/Signet (U.S.), 1966
(wraps) £150
Scratch One, New American Library/Signet (U.S.),
1967 (wraps) £25
Easy Go, New American Library/Signet (U.S.), 1968
(wraps) £20
ditto, Sphere, 1972 (wraps) £5
ditto, as *The Last Tomb*, Bantam (U.S.), 1974 (by
Michael Crichton, wraps) £5
The Venom Business, World (U.S.), 1969 . £75/£25
Zero Cool, New American Library/Signet (U.S.), 1969
(wraps) £20
ditto, Sphere, 1972 (wraps) £5
Grave Descend, New American Library/Signet (U.S.),
1970 (wraps) £20
Drug of Choice, New American Library/Signet (U.S.),
1970 (wraps) £20
ditto, as *Overkill*, Sphere, 1972 (wraps) . . £5
Binary, Knopf (U.S.), 1972 . . . . . £40/£10
ditto, Heinemann, 1972 . . . . . . £40/£10

Novels written as Jeffery Hudson
A Case of Need, World (U.S.), 1968 . . . £75/£20
ditto, Heinemann, 1968 . . . . . . £75/£20

Novels written as Michael Douglas
Dealing, Knopf (U.S.), 1971 . . . . . £50/£10
ditto, Talmy Franklin, 1971 . . . . . £45/£5

Screenplays
Westworld, Bantam, 1974. . . . . . . £5

Non Fictin
Five Patients: The Hospital Explained, Knopf (U.S.),
1970 . . . . £60/£15
ditto, Cape, 1971 . . . . £50/£10

Jasper Johns, Abrams (U.S.), 1977 . . . £100/£40
ditto, Thames & Hudson, 1977 . . . . £75/£35
Electronic Life: How to Think About Computers,
Knopf (U.S.), 1983 . . . . £70/£15
ditto, Heinemann, 1983 . . . . . . £65/£15
Travels, Knopf (U.S.), 1988 . . . . . £20/£5
ditto, Macmillan, 1988 . . . . . . £20/£5

EDMUND CRISPIN
(b.1921 d.1978)

Successful author of detective fiction. He was also a prolific editor of detective and science fiction anthologies.

Novels
The Case of the Gilded Fly, Gollancz, 1944 £250/£75
ditto, as *Obsequies at Oxford*, Lippincott (U.S.), 1945.
. . . . £150/£45
Holy Disorders, Gollancz, 1946 . . . . £200/£50
ditto, Lippincott (U.S.), 1946 . . . . . £150/£45
The Moving Toyshop, Gollancz, 1946 . . £200/£50
ditto, Lippincott (U.S.), 1946 . . . . . £150/£45
Swan Song, Gollancz, 1947 . . . . . £100/£25
ditto, as *Dead and Dumb*, Lippincott (U.S.), 1947 .
. . . . £75/£20
Love Lies Bleeding, Gollancz, 1948 . . . £75/£20
ditto, Lippincott (U.S.), 1948 . . . . . £50/£15
Buried for Pleasure, Gollancz, 1948 . . . £75/£20
ditto, Lippincott (U.S.), 1948 . . . . . £50/£15
Frequent Hearses, Gollancz, 1950 . . . £75/£20
ditto, as *Sudden Vengeance*, Dodd, Mead (U.S.), 1950
. . . . £50/£10
The Long Divorce, Gollancz, 1951 . . . £75/£15
ditto, Dodd, Mead (U.S.), 1951 . . . . £40/£10
ditto, as *A Noose for Her*, Spivak, 1952 . . £40/£10
The Glimpses of the Moon, Gollancz, 1977 £25/£10
ditto, Walker (U.S.), 1978 . . . . . £10/£5

Short Stories
Beware of the Trains: 16 Stories, Gollancz, 1953 . .
. . . . £75/£15
ditto, Walker (U.S.), 1962 . . . . . £40/£10
Fen Country: 26 stories, Gollancz, 1979 . £30/£10
ditto, Walker (U.S.), 1979 . . . . . £25/£10

FREEMAN WILLS CROFTS
(b.1879 d.1957)

Crofts is acknowledged as one of the first authors of detective fiction to methodically use police procedure.

Inspector French Novels
Inspector French's Greatest Case, Collins 1924 . .
. . . . £1,250/£200
ditto, Seltzer (U.S.), 1925. . . . . . £600/£75
Inspector French and the Cheyne Mystery, Collins, 1926 . . . . £1,000/£150
ditto, as *The Cheyne Mystery*, Boni (U.S.), 1926 . .
. . . . £600/£75
Inspector French and the Starvel Tragedy, Collins, 1927 . . . . £1,000/£150
ditto, as *The Starvel Hollow Tragedy*, Harper (U.S.), 1927 . . . . £500/£75
The Sea Mystery, Collins, 1928 . . . £1,000/£150
ditto, Harper (U.S.), 1928. . . . . . £500/£75
The Box Office Murders, Collins, 1929. £1,000/£150
ditto, as *The Purple Sickle Murders*, Harper (U.S.), 1929 . . . . £300/£45
Sir John Magill's Last Journey, Collins Crime Club, 1930 . . . . £1,000/£150
ditto, Harper (U.S.), 1930. . . . . . £300/£45
Mystery in the Channel, Crime Club, 1931 . . . . .
. . . . £1,000/£150
ditto, as **Mystery in the English Channel**, Harper (U.S.),1931 . . . . £300/£45
Sudden Death, Crime Club 1932 . . £1,000/£150
ditto, Harper (U.S.), 1932. . . . . . £300/£45
Death on the Way, Crime Club 1932 . £1,000/£150
ditto, as *Double Death*, Harper (U.S.), 1932 £300/£45
The Hog's Back Mystery, Hodder & Stoughton, 1933 .
. . . . £1,000/£150
ditto, as *The Strange Case of Dr Earle*, Dodd, Mead (U.S.), 1933 . . . . £300/£45
The 12.30 from Croydon, Hodder & Stoughton, 1934 .
. . . . £1,000/£150
ditto, as *Wilful and Premeditated*, Dodd (U.S.), 1934 .
. . . . £300/£45
Mystery on Southampton Water, Hodder & Stoughton 1934 . . . . £1,000/£150
ditto, as *Crime on the Solent*, Dodd (U.S.), 1934 . .
. . . . £300/£45
Crime at Guildford, Crime Club, 1935 . £1,000/£150
ditto, as *The Crime at Nornes*, Dodd (U.S.), 1935 . .
. . . . £300/£45
The Loss of the 'Jane Vosper', Crime Club, 1936 . .
. . . . £1,000/£150
ditto, Dodd (U.S.), 1936 . . . . . . £300/£45
Man Overboard!, Crime Club 1936 . . £1,000/£150
ditto, Dodd (U.S.), 1936. . . . . . £300/£45
ditto, as *Cold-Blooded Murder*, Avon 1947 (abridged, wraps). £20
Found Floating, Hodder & Stoughton, 1937 £850/£85
ditto, Dodd (U.S.), 1937 . . . . . . £300/£45
The End of Andrew Harrison, Hodder & Stoughton,

1938 . . . . £850/£85
ditto, as *The Futile Alibi*, Dodd (U.S.), 1938 £300/£50
Antidote to Venom Hodder & Stoughton, 1938. . .
. . . . £850/£85
ditto, Dodd (U.S.), 1939 . . . . . . £300/£50
Fatal Venture, Hodder & Stoughton, 1939 . £850/£85
ditto, as *Tragedy in the Hollow*, Dodd (U.S.), 1939 .
. . . . £300/£50
Golden Ashes, Hodder & Stoughton, 1940 . £850/£85
ditto, Dodd (U.S.), 1940 . . . . . . £300/£50
James Tarrant, Adventurer, Hodder & Stoughton, 1941 . . . . £850/£85
ditto, as *Circumstantial Evidence*, Dodd (U.S.), 1941
. . . . £300/£50
The Losing Game, Hodder & Stoughton,1941 . . .
. . . . £600/£60
ditto, as *A Losing Game*, Dodd (U.S.), 1941 £350/£50
Fear Comes to Chalfont, Hodder & Stoughton, 1942 .
. . . . £400/£50
ditto, Dodd (U.S.), 1942 . . . . . . £250/£25
The Affair at Little Wokeham, Hodder & Stoughton, 1943 . . . . £350/£50
ditto, as *Double Tragedy*, Dodd (U.S.), 1943 £250/£25
Enemy Unseen, Hodder & Stoughton, 1945 £200/£25
ditto, Dodd (U.S.), 1945 . . . . . . £175/£25
Death of a Train, Hodder & Stoughton, 1946 . . .
. . . . £125/£20
ditto, Dodd (U.S.), 1947 . . . . . . £100/£20
Silence for the Murderer, Dodd (U.S.), 1948 £175/£25
ditto, Hodder & Stoughton, 1949. . . . £200/£25
Dark Journey, Dodd (U.S.), 1951 . . . £175/£25
ditto, as *French Strikes Oil*, Hodder & Stoughton, 1952 . . . . £200/£25
Anything to Declare?, Hodder & Stoughton, 1957. . .
. . . . £200/£25

Inspector French Novel for Children
Young Robin Brand, Detective, U.L.P., 1947 £75/£25
ditto, Dodd (U.S.), 1948 . . . . . . £50/£15

Other Novels
The Cask, Collins, 1920 . . . . . £3,000/£600
ditto, Seltzer (U.S.), 1924 . . . . . £750/£75
The Ponson Case, Collins, 1921 . . . £1,500/£200
ditto, Boni (U.S.), 1927 . . . . . . £750/£75
The Pit-Prop Syndicate, Collins, 1922 . £1,500/£200
ditto, Seltzer (U.S.), 1925. . . . . . £750/£75
The Groote Park Murder, Collins, 1923 £1,250/£125
ditto, Seltzer (U.S.), 1925. . . . . . £750/£75

Short Stories
The Hunt Ball Murder, Todd 1943 (wraps) . £300
Mr. Sefton, Murderer, Vallancey Press, 1944 (wraps).
. . . . £300
Murderers Make Mistakes, Hodder & Stoughton, 1947
. . . . £250/£25
Many a Slip, Hodder & Stoughton, 1955 . £300/£25
The Mystery of the Sleeping Car Express, Hodder & Stoughton, 1956 . . . . £300/£25

RICHMAL CROMPTON
(b.1890 d.1969)

Born Richmal Crompton Lamburn, she began writing short stories for magazines whilst working as a teacher. When these stories were first collected together the resultant *Just William* was an immediate success.

'William' Titles

Just William, Newnes [1922]	. . .	£1,750/£100
More William, Newnes, 1922	. . . .	£650/£75
William Again, Newnes, 1923	. . . .	£300/£30
William the Fourth, Newnes, 1924 .	.	£250/£25
Still William, Newnes, 1925 .	. . .	£250/£25
William the Conqueror, Newnes, 1926 .	.	£250/£25
William the Outlaw, Newnes, 1927 .	.	£250/£25
William in Trouble, Newnes, 1927 .	. .	£250/£25
William the Good, Newnes, 1928	. .	£250/£25
William, Newnes, 1929 .	. . . .	£400/£45
William the Bad, Newnes, 1930 .	. .	£400/£45
William's Happy Days, Newnes, 1930 .	.	£400/£45
William's Crowded Hours, Newnes, 1931 .		£400/£45
William the Pirate, Newnes, 1932 .	. .	£400/£45
William the Rebel, Newnes, 1933 .	. .	£400/£45
William the Gangster, Newnes, 1934 .	.	£400/£45
William the Detective, Newnes, 1935 .	.	£400/£45
Sweet William, Newnes, 1936 .	. . .	£400/£45
William the Showman, Newnes, 1937 .	.	£400/£45
William the Dictator, Newnes, 1938.	.	£400/£45
William and A.R.P., Newnes, 1939 (title later changed to *William's Bad Resolution*) .	. . .	£350/£45
William and the Evacuees, Newnes, 1940 (title later changed to *William the Film Star*).	. .	£650/£75
William Does His Bit, Newnes, 1941 .	. .	£350/£45
William Carries On, Newnes, 1941 .	. .	£250/£45
William and the Brains Trust, Newnes, 1945 .	. .	
	. . . .	£125/£35
Just William's Luck, Newnes, 1948.	. .	£75/£20
William the Bold, Newnes, 1950.	. . .	£75/£20
William and the Tramp, Newnes, 1952 .	.	£65/£15
William and the Moon Rocket, Newnes, 1954		£65/£15
William and the Space Animal, Newnes, 1956		
	. . . .	£65/£15
William's Television Show, Newnes, 1958 .		£75/£15
William the Explorer, Newnes, 1960	. .	£75/£20
William's Treasure Trove, Newnes, 1962 .		£65/£20
William and the Witch, Newnes, 1964 .		£100/£25
William and the Ancient Briton, Mayfair, 1965	. .	
	. . . .	£20/£5
William and the Monster, Mayfair, 1965 .		£20/£5
William the Globetrotter, Mayfair, 1965 .		£20/£5
William the Cannibal, Mayfair, 1965 .	.	£20/£5
William and the Pop Singers, Newnes, 1965		£75/£25
William and the Masked Ranger, Newnes, 1966 .	.	
	. . . .	£75/£25

William the Superman, Newnes, 1968 .	.	£100£25
William the Lawless, Newnes, 1970.	. .	£350/£75

Adult Novels

The Innermost Room, Melrose, 1923 .	.	£250/£50
The Hidden Light, Hodder & Stoughton, [1924]	. .	
	. . . .	£175/£35
Anne Morrison, Jarrolds, 1925 .	. . .	£175/£35
The Wildings, Hodder & Stoughton, [1925]		£150/£30
David Wilding, Hodder & Stoughton, [1926]		£150/£30
The House, Hodder & Stoughton, [1926] .		£200/£35
Millicent Dorrington, Hodder & Stoughton, [1927] .		
	. . . .	£125/£25
Leadon Hill, Hodder & Stoughton, [1927] .		£125/£25
The Thorn Bush, Hodder & Stoughton, [1928]	. .	
	. . . .	£125/£25
Roofs Off!, Hodder & Stoughton, [1928] .		£100/£20
The Four Graces, Hodder & Stoughton, [1929]	. .	
	. . . .	£175/£35
Abbot's End, Hodder & Stoughton, [1929]		£175/£35
Blue Flames, Hodder & Stoughton, [1930]		£100/£20
Naomi Godstone, Hodder & Stoughton, [1930]	. .	
	. . . .	£100/£20
Portrait of a Family, Macmillan, 1931 .	.	£100/£20
The Odyssey of Euphemia Tracy, Macmillan, 1932 .		
	. . . .	£100/£20
Marriage of Hermione, Macmillan, 1932 .		£65/£20
The Holiday, Macmillan, 1933 .	. . .	£65/£20
Chedsy Place, Macmillan, 1934 .	. . .	£65/£20
The Old Man's Birthday, Macmillan, 1934		£65/£20
Quartet, Macmillan, 1935 .	. . . .	£65/£20
Caroline, Macmillan, 1936 .	. . . .	£65/£20
There are Four Seasons, Macmillan, 1937		£50/£15
Journeying Wave, Macmillan, 1938.	. .	£65/£20
Merlin Bay, Macmillan, 1939 .	. . .	£65/£20
Steffan Green, Macmillan, 1940.	. . .	£65/£20
Narcissa, Macmillan, 1941 .	. . . .	£65/£20
Mrs Frensham Describes a Circle, Macmillan, 1942 .		
	. . . .	£45/£15
Weatherley Parade, Macmillan, 1943 .	.	£25/£5
Westover, Hutchinson, [1946] .	. . .	£25/£5
The Ridleys, Hutchinson, [1947].	. . .	£25/£5
Family Roundabout, Hutchinson, [1948] .		£25/£5
Frost at Morning, Hutchinson, 1950 .	.	£25/£5
Linden Rise, Hutchinson, 1952 .	. . .	£25/£5
The Gypsy's Baby, Hutchinson, 1954 .	.	£50/£15
Four in Exile, Hutchinson, 1955.	. . .	£30/£5
Matty and the Dearingroydes, Hutchinson, 1956 .		
	. . . .	£25/£5
Blind Man's Buff, Hutchlnson, 1957 .	.	£25/£5
Wiseman's Folly, Hutchinson, 1959.	. .	£25/£5
The Inheritor, Hutchinson, 1960.	. . .	£15/£5

Adult Short Stories

Kathleen and I, and, Of Course, Veronica, Hodder & Stoughton, [1926] .	. . . .	£125/£25
Enter—Patricia, Newnes, [1927] .	. .	£65/£15
A Monstrous Regiment, Hutchinson, [1927]		£150/£40
Mist, Hutchinson, [1928] .	. . . .	£200/£45

The Middle Things, Hutchinson, [1928]	£175/£45
Felicity Stands By, Newnes, [1928]	£100/£25
Sugar and Spice, Ward Lock, 1929	£100/£25
Ladies First, Hutchinson, [1929].	£175/£45
The Silver Birch, Hutchinson, [1931]	£175/£45
The First Morning, Hutchinson, [1936].	£175/£45

HARRY CROSBY
(b.1898 d.1929)

A short-lived American poet whose ambition exceeded his ability, but whose self-published volumes are things of great beauty.

Sonnets for Caresse, Herbert Clarke (Paris), 1925 (17 copies) £3,000
ditto, Herbert Clarke (Paris), 1926 (second edition, 27 copies) £2,000
ditto, Albert Messein (Paris), 1926 (third edition, 108 copies) £750
ditto, Editions Narcisse (Paris), 1927 (fourth edition, 44 copies) £750
Red Skeletons, Editions Narcisse (Paris), 1927 (370 copies, illustrated by Alastair) . . . £1,250
Chariot of the Sun, At the Sign of the Sundial (Paris), 1928 (48 copies) £1,500
Shadows of the Sun, The Black Sun Press (Paris), 1928 (44 copies) £1,500
ditto, Black Sparrow Pres (U.S.), 1977 (acetate d/w) . . . . £50/£45
ditto, Black Sparrow Pres (U.S.), 1977 (wraps). . £5
Transit of Venus, The Black Sun Press (Paris), 1928 (44 copies) £1,500
ditto, The Black Sun Press (Paris), 1929 (200 copies) £1,000
Mad Queen: Tirades, The Black Sun Press (Paris), 1928 (141 copies, printed wrappers and glassine in gold foil folder with ties) . . . £1,000/£750
Six Poems, Latterday Pamphlets (U.S.), 1928 (225 copies, wraps) £400
Shadows of the Sun, second series, The Black Sun Press (Paris), 1929 (44 copies) . . . £1,500
The Sun, The Black Sun Press (Paris), 1929 (100 copies) £1,000
Sleeping Together, The Black Sun Press (Paris), 1929 (77 copies) £1,250
Aphrodite in Flight, The Black Sun Press (Paris), 1930 (27 copies) £2,000
Shadows of the Sun, third series , The Black Sun Press (Paris), 1930 (44 copies) . . . £1,500
The Collected Poems, Black Sun Press (Paris), 1931 (500 copies, 4 vols in box: *Chariot of the Sun*, introduction by D.H. Lawrence, *Transit of Venus*, preface by T.S. Eliot, *Sleeping Together*, introduction by Stuart Gilbert, *Torchbearer*, notes by Ezra Pound) £1,000

War Letters, The Black Sun Press (Paris), 1932 (125 copies, preface by Henrietta Crosby) . . £600
Devour the Fire, Twowindows Press (U.S.), 1983 (200 numbered copies) £100

As Editor
Anthology, Maurice Darantiere (U.S.), 1924 (edited by 'Henry Grew Crosby') £500

ALEISTER CROWLEY
(b.1875 d.1947)

Notorious British occultist and author of interminable magical works. The special copies on Japanese vellum etc were usually for presentation and will vary in value depending upon whom they were inscribed to.

Verse
Aceldama, A Place to Bury Strangers In, privately printed by Leonard Smithers, 1898 (88 copies, pseud. 'a gentleman of the University of Cambridge', wraps) £650
ditto, privately printed by Leonard Smithers, 1898 (10 large paper copies, pseud. 'a gentleman of the University of Cambridge', wraps) . . . £2,000
The Tale of Archais: a Romance in Verse, Kegan Paul & Co, 1898 (250 copies, pseud. 'a gentleman of the University of Cambridge') £300
Jezebel, privately printed, 1898 (40 copies, wraps). £350
ditto, privately printed, 1898 (10 copies in Japanese vellum, wraps) £2,000
Songs of the Spirit, Kegan Paul & Co, 1898 (200 copies) £250
ditto, Kegan Paul & Co, 1898 (50 signed, numbered copies) £750
Jephthah, and other mysteries, lyrical and dramatic, Kegan Paul & Co, 1899 . . . . £250
An Appeal to the American Republic, Kegan Paul & Co, 1899 (500 copies, wraps) £125
The Mother's Tragedy, privately printed, 1901 (500 copies) £200
The Soul of Osiris, Kegan Paul & Co, 1901 (500 copies) £300
ditto, Kegan Paul & Co, 1901 (6 copies on india paper) £1,500
Carmen Saeculare, Kegan Paul & Co, 1901 (450 copies, pseud. 'St. E. A. of M. and S', wraps) . £175
Tannhäuser, Kegan Paul & Co, 1902 . . . £200
The God-Eater, A Tragedy of Satire, Watts & Co, 1903 (300 copies, wraps) £175
Summa Spes, privately printed, 1903 . . . £200
Ahab and Other Poems, privately printed at the Chiswick Press, 1903 (150 copies). . . . £250
ditto, privately printed at the Chiswick Press, 1903 (10 copies on Japanese vellum) £1,000

Alice: an Adultery, privately printed, 1903 (100 copies, wraps). £300
The Star and the Garter, Watts & Co, 1903 (50 copies, wraps). £300
The Sword of Song, Society for the Propagation of Religious Truth, 1904 (100 copies, wraps). . £250
The Argonauts, Society for the Propagation of Religious Truth, 1904 (200 copies, wraps). . £200
In Residence: The Don's Guide to Cambridge, Elijah Johnson, 1904 (wraps) £200
Why Jesus Wept, A study of society and of the grace of God, privately printed, 1904 (wraps) . . £200
Oracles, The Biography of an Art, Society for the Propagation of Religious Truth, 1905 (wraps) £300
Orpheus, A Lyrical Legend, Society for the Propagation of Religious Truth, 1905 (2 vols, various coloured boards) £350
Rosa Mundi, A poem, Renouard (Paris), 1905 (pseud. H.D. Carr) £200
Collected Works of Aleister Crowley, Society for the Propagation of Religious Truth, 1905, 1906 & 1907 (3 vols, wraps) £500
ditto, Society for the Propagation of Religious Truth, 1907 (1 vol.) £400
Gargoyles: being strangely wrought images of life and death, Society for the Propagation of Religious Truth, 1906 (300 copies) £175
ditto, Society for the Propagation of Religious Truth, 1906 (50 copies on handmade paper) . . . £300
Rosa Coeli, Chiswick Press, 1907 (pseud. H.D. Carr) £250
Rosa Inferni, Chiswick Press, 1907 (pseud. H.D. Carr) £250
Rodin in Rhyme, Seven Lithographs by Clot from the Water-Colours of Auguste Rodin, with a chaplet of verse by Aleister Crowley, privately printed at the Chiswick Press, 1907 (488 copies) . . . £350
Amphora, privately printed 1908 . . . . £500
ditto, Burns & Oates: London, 1908 . . . . £250
Hail Mary, Wieland & Co, [1911] £200
Clouds Without Water, 'Privately printed for circulation among ministers of religion', 1909 (pseud. the Rev. C. Verey, wraps) £250
The World's Tragedy, privately printed (Paris), 1910 (100 copies) £300
The Winged Beetle, privately printed, 1910 (50 signed copies) £500
ditto, privately printed, 1910 (250 unsigned copies) £300
Ambergris, Elkin Mathews, 1910 . . . . £100
The High History of Good Sir Palamedes..., Wieland & Co., 1912 . . . . £75
Household Gods, A Comedy, privately printed, 1912 . . . . £125
Chicago May, privately printed (New York), 1914. . . . . £750
Songs for Italy, privately printed, 1923 (single folded sheet) £60

England, Stand Fast!, privately issued by the O.T.O., 1939 (single sheet folded) £75
Temperance, A Tract for the Times, privately issued by the O.T.O., 1939 (100 copies, wraps) . . £200
Thumbs up! A Pentagram-a Pentacle to Win the War, O.T.O., 1941 (100 copies, wraps) £200
La Gauloise-Song of the Fighting French, privately printed, 1942 (single sheet folded) £65
Fun of the Fair, O.T.O., 1942 (containing errata slip and mimeographed poem 'Landed gentry') . £250
The City of God, A Rhapsody, O.T.O., 1943 (wraps, 200 copies) £250
Olla, An Anthology of Sixty Years of Song, etc., O.T.O., [1946] (500 copies). . . . £350/£150
ditto, O.T.O., [1946] (20 copies on handmade paper) £650

Novels, Plays etc

Mortadello, or the Angel of Venice, Wieland & Co, 1912 . . . . £65
The Diary of a Drug Fiend, Collins, 1922 £2,000/£200
ditto, Dutton (U.S.), 1923 . . . . . £1,000/£100
Moonchild: A Prologue, Mandrake Press, 1929 . . . . £300/£125
The Stratagem and Other Stories, Mandrake Press, [1929] £100/175

Erotica

White Stains, privately printed (Amsterdam), 1898 (100 copies on handmade paper, pseud. George Archibald Bishop) £3,000
Snowdrops From A Curate's Garden, privately printed (Paris), [c.1904] £2,000
Bagh-I-Muattar, The Scented Garden of Abdullah the Satirist of Shiraz, privately printed, 1910 (100 copies, pseud. 'the late Major Lutiy and another', wraps). £1,500

Magical Titles

Berashith – An Essay in Ontology with some remarks on Ceremonial Magic by Abhavananda, privately printed for the Sangha of the West (Paris), 1903 (200 copies, pseud. 'Abhavananda', wraps) . . . £250
The Book of the Goetia of Solomon the King, Society for the Propagation of Religious Truth, 1904 ('Translated into the English tongue by a dead hand etc', 200 copies) £350
ditto, Society for the Propagation of Religious Truth, 1904 (10 copies on Japanese vellum) . . . £750
Konx om Pax, Essays in Light, Walter Scott Publishing Co. for The Society for the Propagation of Religious Truth, 1907 (500 copies on handmade paper) £500
ditto, Walter Scott Publishing Co. for The Society for the Propagation of Religious Truth, 1907 (10 copies on Japanese vellum) £1,000
777, Walter Scott Publishing Co. for The Society for the Propagation of Religious Truth, 1909 (500 copies on handmade paper) £300

The Rites of Eleusis, [The Equinox:], [1910] (wraps) .
. . . . £75
The Holy Books, privately printed, [c.1909] (3 vols) .
. . . . £1,000
Book Four, Part One, Wieland & Co, 1911 (pseud.
'Frater Perdurabo', with 'Soror Virakam'). . £150
Book Four, Part Two, Wieland & Co, 1912 (pseud.
'Frater Perdurabo', with 'Soror Virakam'). . £175
Liber CCCXXXIII, The Book of Lies, Wieland & Co.,
1913 . . . . £350
Liber II, The Message of the Master Therion,
privately printed, 1916 . . . . £75
*The Law of Liberty, A tract of Therion, that is a
Magus*, O.T.O., 1917 (single folded sheet) . £60
*Book Four, Part Three, Magick, in Theory and
Practice*, Lecram Press (Paris), 1929 (four parts,
pseud. 'Master Therion', wraps) £500
ditto, Lecram Press for Subscribers (Paris), 1929
[1930] . . . . £400/£250
The Book of the Law, O.T.O., 1938 . . . . £250
ditto, O.T.O., 1938 (wraps) £150
The Heart of the Master, O.T.O., 1938 (pseud.
'Khaled Khan') £300
Little Essays Towards Truth, etc., privately issued by
the O.T.O., [1938] £300
Liber XXI, Khing Kang King, the Classic of Purity,
O.T.O., 1939 . . . . £850
Eight Lectures on Yoga, O.T.O., 1939 (pseud.
'Mahatma Guru Sri Parahamsa Shivaji') . £400
*The Book of Thoth, A short essay on the Tarot of the
Egyptians*, O.T.O., 1944 (200 signed copies, pseud.
'Master Therion') £3,000

Others
*The Banned Lecture—Gilles de Rais—to have been
delivered before the Oxford University Poetry
Society, etc.*, Stephenson, [1930.] £200
The Spirit of Solitude, Mandrake Press, 1929 (limited
edition, 2 vols) £150
The Confessions of Aleister Crowley, Mandrake Press,
1929 (800 copies, 2 vols) £300
ditto, Cape (U.S.), 1969 . . . . . £25/£10
ditto, Hill & Wang (U.S.), 1970 . . . £25/£10
*The Scientific Solution of the Problem of
Government*, O.T.O. [c.1937] (pseud. 'Comte de
Fénix') £80
The Last Ritual, privately printed, [1947] (wraps) . .
. . . . £100

Translation
Little Poems in Prose by Baudelaire, Titus (Paris),
1928 (800 copies, with 12 copper plate engravings
from the original drawings by Jean de Bosschere) .
. . . . £350
The Key of the Mysteries, by Eliphas Levi, Rider &
Co., 1959 . . . . £35/£20

E.E. CUMMINGS
(b.1894 d.1962)

An innovative American poet, much influenced by
slang and jazz, whose work is characterised by
unconventional punctuation and typography. He
usually signed his work 'e.e. cummings'.

Verse
Eight Harvard Poets, Gomme (U.S.), 1917 . . £60
Tulips and Chimneys, Seltzer (U.S.), 1923 £750/£250
XLI Poems, Dial Press (U.S.), 1925 . . . £600/£100
&, privately printed (U.S.), 1925 (111 of 333 signed
copies copies, green gold-flecked boards, slipcase) .
. . . . £650/£600
ditto, privately printed (U.S.), 1925 (222 of 333 signed
copies, slipcase) . . . . £400/£350
Is 5, Boni & Liveright (U.S.), 1926 (orange gold-
flecked boards) £300
ditto, Boni & Liveright (U.S.), 1926 (77 signed copies,
slipcase) £1,250
[Untitled], Covici-Friede (U.S.), 1930 (491 signed
copies) £250
W [ViVa], Liveright Inc. (U.S.), 1931 . . £175/£40
ditto, Liveright Inc. (U.S.), 1931 (95 signed, numbered
copies, glassine d/w) £600
CIOPW, Covici-Friede (U.S.), 1931 (391 signed,
numbered copies) £750
No Thanks, Golden Eagle Press (U.S.), 1935 (90
signed copies) . . . . £250/£200
ditto, Golden Eagle Press (U.S.), 1935 (9 signed copies
with manuscript page) £1,500
ditto, Golden Eagle Press (U.S.), 1935 (900 copies) .
. . . . £75/£45
Tom, Arrow Editions (U.S.), 1935 (1500 copies) . .
. . . . £200/£40
1/20, Roger Roughton, 1936 (tissue d/w) . £350/£225
Collected Poems, Harcourt Brace (U.S.), 1938 . .
. . . . £150/£35
50 Poems, Duell, Sloane and Pearce, 1940 (150 signed
copies, glassine d/w slipcase) . . . £400/£350
1 x 1, Holt (U.S.), 1944 . . . . . £100/£35
ditto, Horizon, 1947 . . . . . . £40/£15
XAIPE: Seventy-One Poems, O.U.P. (U.S.), 1950 . .
. . . . £75/£25
Poems, 1923-1954, Harcourt Brace (U.S.), 1954 . .
. . . . £125/£25
95 Poems, Harcourt Brace (U.S.), 1958 (300 signed
copies, slipcase) . . . . . . £400/£250
ditto, Harcourt Brace (U.S.), 1958 . . . £20/£10
100 Selected Poems, Grove Press (U.S.), 1959 £35/£10
Selected Poems, Faber, 1960 . . . . . £50/£15
73 Poems, Harcourt (U.S.), 1963 . . . £65/£20
ditto, Faber, 1963 . . . . £50/£15
Complete Poems, MacGibbon & Kee (U.S.), 1968 (2
vols) . . . . £75/£35
Complete Poems 1913—1962, Harcourt Brace (U.S.),
1972 . . . . £50/£25

Poems 1905-1962, Marchim Press, 1973 (225 numbered copies) £75
Complete Poems 1910—1962, Granada, 1981 (2 vols in slipcase) . . . . . . £50/£25
Etcetera: The Unpublished Poems, Liveright (U.S.), 1983 . . . . £45/£15
Hist Whist and Other Poems for Children, Norton (U.S.), 1984 . . . . £25/£10
Complete Poems 1904-1962, Liveright, 1991 £20/£10

Fiction
The Enormous Room, Boni & Liveright (U.S.), 1911 (word 'shit' in last line on page page 219). . . . . £1,000/£250
ditto, Boni & Liveright (U.S.), 1911 (word 'shit' in last line on page page 219 inked out) . . . £750 /£75
ditto, Cape, 1928 . . . . £250/£40
Eimi, Covivi, Friede (U.S.), 1933 (1,381 signed, numbered copies) . . . . . £400/£300

Others
Him, Boni & Liveright (U.S.), 1927. . . £125/£25
ditto, Boni & Liveright (U.S.), 1927 (160 signed, numbered copies, slipcase) . . . . £300/£250
Santa Claus, Holt (U.S.), 1946 (250 signed copies, glassine d/w) . . . . £250/£200
ditto, Holt (U.S.), 1946 . . . . . £125/£35
i: Six Nonlectures, Harvard Univ. Press (U.S.), 1953 . . . . £40/£10
ditto, Harvard Univ. Press (U.S.), 1953 (350 signed copies) £400
Fairy Tales, Harcourt Brace (U.S.), 1965 . £25/£10
Selected Letters, Harcourt Brace (U.S.), 1969 £25/£10
ditto, Deutsch, 1972 . . . . £20/£5

ROALD DAHL
(b.1916 d.1990)

Principally a children's writer, although his short stories for adults are also well known. In the past Dahl's books for children often met with disapproval due to the unpleasant ends met by some of his characters—but it is precisely this that children seem to enjoy.

Children's Titles
The Gremlins, Random House (U.S.), [1943] . . . . £2,500/£750
ditto, Collins, [1944] (boards, no d/w) . . . £600
James and the Giant Peach, Knopf (U.S.), 1961 . . . . £300/£30
ditto, Allen & Unwin, 1967 (boards, no d/w) . £250
Charlie and the Chocolate Factory, Knopf (U.S.), 1964 . . . . £250/£30
ditto, Allen & Unwin, 1967 (boards, no d/w) . £250
The Magic Finger, Harper (U.S.), 1966. . £125/£30
ditto, Allen & Unwin, 1968 (boards, no d/w) . £150

Fantastic Mr Fox, Knopf (U.S.), 1970 . . £200/£30
ditto, Allen & Unwin, 1970 (boards, no d/w) . £150
Charlie and the Great Glass Elevator, Knopf (U.S.), 1972 . . . . £150/£25
ditto, Allen & Unwin, 1973 (boards, no d/w) . £250
Danny, The Champion of the World, Cape, 1975 . . . . £100/£25
ditto, Knopf (U.S.), 1975 . . . . . . £50/£15
The Wonderful Story of Henry Sugar and Six More, Cape, 1977 . . . . £100/£25
ditto, Knopf (U.S.), 1977 . . . . . . £65/£15
The Enormous Crocodile, Cape, 1978 . . . £65
ditto, Knopf (U.S.), 1978 . . . . . £45/£10
The Twits, Cape, 1980 . . . . . £500/£10
ditto, Knopf (U.S.), 1981 . . . . . £45/£10
George's Marvellous Medicine, Cape, 1981 £50/£20
ditto, Knopf (U.S.), 1982 . . . . . £45/£5
Roald Dahl's Revolting Rhymes, Cape, 1983 (no d/w) £65
ditto, Knopf (U.S.), 1983 . . . . . £45/£10
The BFG, Cape, 1982. . . . . . £35/£10
ditto, Farrar Straus (U.S.), 1982 . . . £35/£5
Dirty Beasts, Cape 1983 (no d/w) . . . £65
ditto, Farrar Straus (U.S.), 1983 . . . £45/£10
The Witches, Cape, 1983 . . . . . £60/£10
ditto, Farrar Straus (U.S.), 1983 . . £60/£10
The Giraffe, the Pelly and Me, Cape, 1985 (no d/w) £30
ditto, Farrar Straus (U.S.), 1985 (no d/w) . . £30
Matilda, Cape, 1988 . . . . . £40/£5
ditto, Viking Kestrel (U.S.), 1988 . . . £40/£5
Rhyme Stew, Cape, 1989 . . . . . £35/£5
ditto, Viking Penguin (U.S.), 1990 . . £25/£5
Esio Trot, Cape, 1990. . . . . . £35/£5
ditto, Viking Penguin (U.S.), 1990 . . £25/£5
Roald Dahl's Guide to Railway Safety, British Rail, 1991 (wraps) £5
The Vicar of Nibbleswicke, Random Century, 1991 . . . . £30/£5
ditto, Viking Penguin (U.S.), 1991 . . . £20/£5

Adult Novels
Sometime Never, Scribner (U.S.), 1948 . . £200/£35
ditto, Collins, 1949 . . . . . . £125/£35
My Uncle Oswald, Michael Joseph, 1979 . £50/£10
ditto, Knopf (U.S.), 1980 . . . . . £45/£10

Short Stories
Over to You, Reynal & Hitchcock (U.S.), 1946. . . . . £300/£50
ditto, Hamish Hamilton, 1946 . . . £300/£50
Someone Like You, Knopf (U.S.), 1953. . £90/£20
ditto, Secker & Warburg, 1954 . . £100/£20
Kiss Kiss, Knopf (U.S.), 1960 . . . £75/£15
ditto, Michael Joseph, 1960 . . . £75/£15
Switch Bitch, Knopf (U.S.), 1974 . . £75/£15
ditto, Michael Joseph, 1974 . . . £75/£15
Two Fables, Viking, 1986 . . . . £25/£10
ditto, Viking, 1986 (300 signed copies) . . £200

ditto, Farrar Straus (U.S.), 1987 . . . . £25/£10

Autobiography
Boy: Tales of Childhood, Cape, 1984 . . £45/£10
ditto, Farrar Straus, 1984 (signed, limited edition) £200
ditto, Farrar Straus, 1984 . . . . . . £35/£5
Going Solo, Cape, 1986 . . . . . . £15/£5
ditto, Farrar Straus, 1986 . . . . . . £15/£5

C. DAY LEWIS
(b.1904 d.1972)

An Anglo-Irish poet and critic. Cecil Day Lewis was appointed Poet Laureate in 1968. He is also remembered as a detective story writer under the pseudonym Nicholas Blake.

Poetry
Beechen Virgil and Other Poems, Fortune Press, 1925 (wraps) £150
Country Comets, Martin Hopkinson, 1928 (slipcase) .
. . . . £100/£65
Transitional Poems, Hogarth Press, 1929 . £100/£40
From Feathers to Iron, Hogarth Press, 1931 £100/£40
The Magnetic Mountain, Hogarth Press, 1932 £40/£15
ditto, Hogarth Press, 1932 (100 signed, numbered copies) . . . . £200/£100
Collected Poems 1929-33, Hogarth Press, 1935 . .
. . . . £65/£20
ditto, Random House (U.S.), 1935 . . . £50/£20
A Time to Dance and Other Poems, Hogarth Press, 1935 . . . . £75/£20
Noah and the Waters, Hogarth Press, 1936 . £40/£10
ditto, Hogarth Press, 1936 (100 signed, numbered copies) . . . . £125/£75
A Time to Dance, Noah and the Waters, Random House (U.S.), 1936 . . . . . . £30/£10
Overtures to Death and Other Poems, Cape, 1938. .
. . . . £35/£10
ditto, as *Short is the Time*, Poems 1936-1943, O.U.P. (U.S.), 1945 (with *Word Over All*) . . . £25/£10
Child of Misfortune, Cape, 1939. . . . £35/£10
Poems in Wartime, Cape, 1940 (250 copies, wraps) .
. . . . £65
Selected Poems, Hogarth Press, 1940 . . £60/£20
Word Over All, Cape, 1943 . . . . £40/£10
The Augustan Poets, Eyre and Spottiswoode, 1943 (wraps) £10
Poems 1943-47, Cape, 1948 . . . . . £25/£10
ditto, O.U.P. (U.S.), 1948 . . . . . . £25/£10
Collected Poems 1929-1946, Hogarth Press, 1948 .
. . . . £20/£5
Selected Poems, Penguin, 1951 . . . . . £5
An Italian Visit, Cape, 1953 . . . . . £25/£10
ditto, Harper (U.S.), 1953 . . . . . . £25/£10
Collected Poems, Cape/Hogarth Press, 1954 £35/£10

Christmas Eve, Faber, 1954 (wraps). . . . £15
Pegasus and Other Poems, Cape, 1957 . . £10/£5
The Buried Day, Chatto & Windus, 1960 . £25/£10
ditto, Harper (U.S.), 1960. . . . . . £20/£10
The Gate and Other Poems, Chatto & Windus, 1962 .
. . . . £10/£5
Requiem for the Living, Harper (U.S.), 1964 £10/£5
The Room and Other Poems, Cape, 1965 . £10/£5
Selected Poems, Harper (U.S.), 1967 . . £10/£5
The Abbey That Refused To Die, Dolmen Press (Dublin), 1967 (wraps) £10
The Whispering Roots, Cape, 1970 . . . £10/£5
ditto, Harper (U.S.), 1970. . . . . . £10/£5
Going My Way, Poem of the Month Club, 1970 (broadside) £5
Posthumous Poems, Whittington Press, 1979 (250 copies, slipcase) . . . . £100/£75
Complete Poems of C. Day Lewis, Stanford Univ. Press (U.S.), 1992 . . . . . . £20/£10

Detective Fiction written as 'Nicholas Blake
A Question of Proof, Collins Crime Club 1935. . . .
. . . . £1,500/£75
ditto, Harper (U.S.), 1935. . . . . . £500/£35
Thou Shell of Death, Collins Crime Club, 1936 . .
. . . . £1,500/£75
ditto, as *Shell of Death*, Harper (U.S.), 1936 £250/£35
There's Trouble Brewing, Collins Crime Club 1937 .
. . . . £1,500/£50
ditto, Harper (U.S.), 1937. . . . . . £250/£35
The Beast Must Die, Collins Crime Club 1938. . . .
. . . . £1,500/£50
ditto, Harper (U.S.), 1938. . . . . . £200/£35
The Smiler with the Knife, Collins Crime Club 1939 .
. . . . £1,250/£45
ditto, Harper (U.S.), 1939. . . . . . £200/£35
Malice in Wonderland, Collins Crime Club 1940 . .
. . . . £500/£45
ditto, as **The Summer Camp Mystery**, Harper (U.S.), 1940 . . . . £200/£35
ditto, as **Malice with Murder**, Pyramid (U.S.) 1964 (wraps) £15
ditto, as **Murder with Malice**, Carroll & Graf (U.S.), 1987 . . . . £20/£5
The Case of the Abominable Snowman, Collins Crime Club 1941. . . . . £250/£45
ditto, as *The Corpse in the Snowman*, Harper (U.S.), 1941 . . . . £100/£25
Minute for Murder, Collins Crime Club 1947 . . . .
. . . . £100/£35
ditto, Harper (U.S.), 1948. . . . . . £45/£15
Head of a Traveller, Collins Crime Club 1949 £75/£20
ditto, Harper (U.S.), 1949. . . . . . £35/£10
The Dreadful Hollow, Collins Crime Club 1953 . .
. . . . £75/£20
ditto, Harper (U.S.), 1953. . . . . . £35/£10
The Whisper in the Gloom, Collins Crime Club, 1954.
. . . . £60/£20
ditto, Harper (U.S.), 1954. . . . . . £35/£10

ditto, as *Catch and Kill*, Bestseller (U.S.) 1955
(abridged). . . . . £25/£10
A Tangled Web, Collins Crime Club, 1956. £50/£15
ditto, Harper (U.S.), 1956. . . . . £35/£10
ditto, as *Death and Daisy Bland*, Dell (U.S.), 1960
(wraps) £10
End of Chapter, Collins Crime Club, 1957 . £50/£15
ditto, Harper (U.S.), 1957. . . . . £35/£10
A Penknife in My Heart, Collins Crime Club, 1958 .
. . . . £50/£15
ditto, Harper (U.S.), 1959. . . . . £35/£10
The Widow's Cruise, Collins Crime Club, 1959 . .
. . . . £40/£10
ditto, Harper (U.S.), 1959. . . . . £30/£10
The Worm of Death, Collins Crime Club, 1961 . .
. . . . £40/£10
ditto, Harper (U.S.), 1961. . . . . £30/£10
The Deadly Joker, Collins Crime Club, 1963 £40/£10
The Sad Variety, Collins Crime Club, 1964. £40/£10
ditto, Harper (U.S.), 1964. . . . . £30/£10
The Morning After Death, Collins Crime Club, 1966 .
. . . . £40/£10
ditto, Harper (U.S.), 1966. . . . . £25/£10
The Nicholas Blake Omnibus, Collins Crime Club,
1966 . . . . £25/£10
The Private Wound, Collins Crime Club, 1968. . .
. . . . £35/£10
ditto, Harper (U.S.), 1968. . . . . £30/£10

Other Novels
The Friendly Tree, Cape, 1936 . . . . £25/£10
ditto, Harper (U.S.), 1937. . . . . £35/£10
Starting Point, Cape, 1937 . . . . £25/£10
ditto, Harper (U.S.), 1938. . . . . £35/£10

Childrens
Dick Willoughby, Blackwell, 1933 . . . . £600
ditto, Random House (U.S.), 1938 . . . £100/£30
The Otterbury Incident, Putnam, 1948 . . £80/£35
ditto, Viking (U.S.), 1949. . . . . £30/£10

Others
A Hope for Poetry, Blackwell, 1934 . . £25/£10
Revolution in Writing, Hogarth Press, 1935 (wraps) .
. . . . £25
Imagination and Thinking, British Institute of Adult
Education, 1936 (wraps) £15
*We're Not Going to do Nothing: A Reply to Mr
Aldous Huxley's Pamphlet*, The Left Review, 1936
(wraps) £20
ditto, The Left Review, 1936 (50 signed, numbered
copies, wraps) £100
Poetry for You, Blackwell, 1945. . . . £40/£10
ditto, O.U.P. (U.S.), 1947. . . . . £40/£10
The Poetic Image, Cape, 1947 . . . £30/£10
ditto, O.U.P. (U.S.), 1947. . . . . £30/£10
The Colloquial Element In English Poetry, Literary
Soc. of Newcastle, 1947 (wraps) . . . £10
Enjoying Poetry, C.U.P., 1947 (wraps) . . £5

The Poet's Task, O.U.P., 1951 (wraps) . . . £5
Notable Images of Virtue, Ryerson Press (Canada).,
1954 . . . . £20/£5
The Poet's Way of Knowledge, C.U.P., 1957 £10/£5
The Lyric Impulse, Harvard.U.P. (U.S.), 1965 £15/£5
ditto, Chatto & Windus, 1965 . . . . £10/£5
A Need for Poetry, Univ. of Hull., 1968 (wraps) £10

LOUIS DE BERNIÈRES
(b.1954)

The reputation of the author's best-known book,
Captain Corelli's Mandolin, is said to have been
spread almost entirely by word of mouth.

Novels
The War of Don Emmanuel's Nether Parts, Secker &
Warburg, 1990 . . . . £200/£35
ditto, Morrow (U.S.), 1990 . . . . £30/£10
Señor Vivo and the Coca Lord, Secker & Warburg,
1991 . . . . £150/£35
ditto, Morrow (U.S.), 1991 . . . . £25/£10
The Troublesome Offspring of Cardinal Guzman,
Secker & Warburg, 1992 . . . . £125/£25
ditto, Morrow (U.S.), 1994 . . . . £20/£10
Captain Corelli's Mandolin, Secker & Warburg, 1994
(white boards) . . . . £700/£400
ditto, Secker & Warburg, 1994 (black boards) . . .
. . . . £450/£125
ditto, as *Corelli's Mandolin*, Pantheon (U.S.), 1994 .
. . . . £125/£45

Others
Labels, One Horse Press, 1993 (2,000 signed copies,
wraps). £65
A Day Out for Mehmet Erbil, Belmont Press, 1999 (26
signed, lettered copies of 276) £300
ditto, Belmont Press, 1999 (100 signed, numbered
copies of 276) £175
ditto, Belmont Press, 1999 (150 signed, numbered
copies of 276) £125

THE DANDY

A successful rival to *The Beano*, *The Dandy* sported
Korky the Cat on its front cover for almost fifty years.

Comics
No.1, D.C. Thomson, 1937 (with free gift) . £3,500
ditto, D.C. Thomson, 1937 (without free gift) £2,000
No.2, D.C. Thomson, 1937 . . . . . £600
Nos 3-10, D.C. Thomson, 1937 . . . £500 each
1938 issues . . . . £75 each

Dandy Monster Comic

1939, D.C. Thomson	£2,500
1940, D.C. Thomson	£1,000
1941, D.C. Thomson	£750
1942, D.C. Thomson	£650
1943, D.C. Thomson	£500
1944, D.C. Thomson	£450
1945, D.C. Thomson	£400
1946, D.C. Thomson	£350
1947, D.C. Thomson	£300
1948, D.C. Thomson	£250
1949, D.C. Thomson	£200
1950, D.C. Thomson	£150
1951, D.C. Thomson	£100
1952, D.C. Thomson	£75

Dandy Books

1953-1960, D.C. Thomson	£50
1961-65, D.C. Thomson	£65
1966-69, D.C. Thomson	£25

DANIEL DEFOE
(b.1660 d.1730)

Daniel Defoe can be regarded as the father of the English novel, of modern journalism and the art of political propaganda. A prolific writer, he was at one time employed by the government as a policy adviser and in undercover espionage work.

Robinson Crusoe

The Life and Strange Surprizing Adventures of Robinson Crusoe; W. Taylor, London 1719 (first edition, first issue, anonymous). . . . £15,000
ditto, later impressions, W. Taylor, London 1719 (anonymous). £1,500
ditto, Etchells & MacDonald, 1929 (illustrated by E. McKnight Kauffer, limited edition, 525 copies) £600
ditto, Basilisk Press, 1979 (illustrated by Edward Gordon Craig, limited edition, 500 copies, slipcase) .
. . . . £500
The Farther Adventures of Robinson Crusoe, W. Taylor, London, 1719 (anonymous) . . £10,000
Serious Reflections During the Life and Surprising Adventures of Robinson Crusoe, W. Taylor, London 1720 (anonymous) £5,000
ditto, W. Mears/T. Woodward, London 1726 (2 vols made up of the abridged seventh edition of *The Life and Strange Adventures of Robinson Crusoe* and the fifth edition of *The Farther Adventures of Robinson Crusoe*) £1,000
The Life and Strange Surprising Adventures of Robinson Crusoe, John Stockdale, London 1790 (together with 'The Life of Daniel De Foe' and a bibliography of his writings by George Chalmers. 2 vols) £1,000

The Life and Adventures of Robinson Crusoe, sold by J. Walter, London 1790 (first joint edition of Parts I, II and III, printed at the Logographic Press, includes 'The True-Born Englishman, A Satire' and 'The Original Power of the People of England examined and asserted', 3 vols) £1,000
ditto, Constable Press, 1925 (reissued with facsimiles of Stothard's plates, as *The Life and Strange Surprising Adventures of Robinson Crusoe*, with an introduction by Charles Whibley. 3 vols, limited edition, 775 copies) £500
The Life and Adventures of Robinson Crusoe, John Major, 1831 (illustrated by George Cruikshank and Thomas Stothard, with introductory verses by Bernard Barton. 2 vols) £500
ditto, Dent, 1903 (illustrated by J. Ayton Symington) .
. . . . £45

Other Fiction
The Life ... of Captain Singleton, J. Brotherton, London 1720 (anonymous) £750
Moll Flanders, W. Chetwood/T. Edling, London [1722] (anonymous). £15,000
A Journal of the Plague Year, E. Nutt, London 1722 (anonymous) £750
The History ... of Col. Jacque, Commonly Call'd Col. Jack, J. Brotherton, London 1722 (anonymous) . .
. . . . £750
The Fortunate Mistress, or ... Roxana, T. Werner, London 1724 (anonymous) £750
Memoirs of a Cavalier, A. Bell, London 1720 . £750

Non Fiction
The Shortest-Way With Dissenters published anon, MDCCII [1702] £3,000
The History of the Union of Great Britain, Heirs and Successors of Andrew Anderson, Edinburgh 1709 (in 6 parts) £500
The Family Instructor [Vol I], Emanuel Matthews, London/J. Button, Newcastle-upon-Tyne 1715 (anonymous) £300
The Family Instructor [Vol II], Emanuel Matthews, London 1718 (2 parts) (anonymous) . . . £300
ditto, Thos. Longman, London 1741 (first combined edition, 2 vols) £300
The Compleat English Tradesman [Vol I], Charles Rivington, London 1726 [1725] (anonymous) £300
The Compleat English Tradesman [Vol II], Charles Rivington, London 1732 (2 parts, anonymous) £300
ditto, C. Rivington, London 1732 (first combined edition, 2 vols) £300
A Tour Thro' the Whole Island of Great Britain, G. Strahan, London 1724-27 [1726] (3 vols, anonymous)
. . . . £2,500
ditto, Peter Davis, 1927 (abridged version, 2 vols, limited edition, 1,000 copies) £300
A System of Magick, Roberts, 1727 . . . £1,500

LEN DEIGHTON
(b.1929)

Len Deighton worked as an illustrator until his first novel was published in 1962. He is best known for his popular thrillers and spy novels.

Novels

The Ipcress File, Hodder & Stoughton, 1962 £400/£35
ditto, Simon & Schuster (U.S.), 1963 . . £150/£35
ditto, Franklin Library (U.S.), 1988 (signed edition) .
. . . . £65
Horse Under Water, Cape, 1963, (with loose cross-word competition) . . . . . . £150/£75
ditto, Cape, 1963, (without loose crossword comp-etition) . . . . £75/£15
ditto, Putnam (U.S.), 1968 . . . . £65/£15
Funeral in Berlin, Cape, 1964 . . . £100/£15
ditto, Putnam (U.S.), 1965 . . . . £75/£10
Billion Dollar Brain, Putnam (U.S.), 1966 . £100/£15
ditto, Cape, 1966 . . . . £100/£15
An Expensive Place to Die, Putnam (U.S.), 1967 (with wallet of documents). . . . . . £75/£30
ditto, Putnam (U.S.), 1967 (without wallet of documents) . . . . £45/£10
ditto, Cape, 1967 (with wallet of documents) £75/£30
ditto, Cape, 1967 (without wallet of documents) £45/£5
Only When I Larf, privately printed, (limited edition, 150 copies in plastic binding) £1,000
ditto, Joseph, 1968 (boards) . . . . £100/£20
ditto, Joseph, 1968 (wraps) £10
ditto, as *Only When I Laugh*, The Mysterious Press (U.S.), 1987 (250 signed copies, slipcase, no d/w) .
. . . . £75/£45
Bomber, Cape, 1970 . . . . . . £40/£10
ditto, Harper & Row, 1970 . . . . £35/£10
Close-Up, Cape, 1972. . . . . . £40/£10
ditto, Atheneum (U.S.), 1972. . . . £30/£5
Spy Story, Cape, 1974. . . . . . £30/£5
ditto, Harcourt Brace (U.S.), 1974 . . . £25/£5
Yesterday's Spy, Cape, 1975 . . . . £30/£5
ditto, Harcourt Brace (U.S.), 1975 . . . £25/£5
Twinkle, Twinkle, Little Spy, Cape, 1976 . £30/£5
ditto, as *Catch a Falling Spy*, Harcourt Brace (U.S.), 1976 . . . . £25/£5
SS-GB, Cape, 1978 . . . . . . £30/£5
ditto, Knopf (U.S.), 1979 . . . . . £25/£5
XPD, Hutchinson, 1981 . . . . . £30/£5
ditto, Knopf (U.S.), 1981 . . . . . £25/£5
Goodbye, Mickey Mouse, Hutchinson, 1982 £30/£5
ditto, Knopf (U.S.), 1982 . . . . . £25/£5
Berlin Game, Hutchinson, 1983 . . . £30/£5
ditto, Knopf (U.S.), 1984 . . . . . £25/£5
Mexico Set, Hutchinson, 1984 . . . £30/£5
ditto, Knopf (U.S.), 1985 . . . . . £25/£5
London Match, Hutchinson, 1985 . . . £30/£5
ditto, Knopf (U.S.), 1986 . . . . . £25/£5
Winter, Hutchinson, 1987 . . . . £30/£5
ditto, Knopf (U.S.), 1987 . . . . . £25/£5

Spy Hook, Hutchinson, 1988 . . . . . £25/£5
ditto, Knopf (U.S.), 1988 . . . . . . £25/£5
Spy Line, Hutchinson, 1989 . . . . . £20/£5
ditto, Knopf (U.S.), 1989 . . . . . £15/£5
Spy Sinker, Hutchinson, 1989 . . . . £20/£5
ditto, HarperCollins (U.S.), 1990. . . . £15/£5
MAMista, Hutchinson, 1991 . . . . . £20/£5
ditto, HarperCollins (U.S.), 1991. . . . £15/£5
City of Gold, Century, 1992 . . . . . £20/£5
ditto, HarperCollins (U.S.), 1992. . . . £15/£5
Violent Ward, Scorpion Press, 1993 (130 signed copies) £100
ditto, Scorpion Press, 1993 (20 deluxe signed copies) .
. . . . £175
ditto, Harper Collins, 1993 . . . . . £20/£5
ditto, Harper Collins (U.S.), 1993 . . . £15/£5
Faith, Harper Collins, 1994 . . . . . £30/£5
ditto, Harper Collins (U.S.), 1994 . . . £25/£5
Hope, Scorpion Press, 1995 (15 copies of edition of 114) £175
ditto, Scorpion Press, 1995 (99 copies of edition of 114, glassine d/w) £100
ditto, HarperCollins, 1995 . . . . . £30/£5
ditto, HarperCollins (U.S.), 1995. . . . £20/£5
Charity, HarperCollins, 1996. . . . . £30/£5
ditto, HarperCollins (U.S.), 1996. . . . £25/£5

Omnibus Editions

Game, Set and Match, Hutchinson, 1986 . £40/£10
ditto, Knopf (U.S.), 1989 . . . . . £35/£10
ditto, Hutchinson, 1986 (presentation set of 3 first editions with *The Len Deighton Companion*, in slipcase) £100
Hook, Line and Sinker, Hutchinson, 1991 . £10/£5
ditto, Hutchinson, 1991 (presentation set of 3 first editions, in slipcase) £100

Short Stories

Declarations of War, Cape, 1971 (short stories) . .
. . . . £40/£10
ditto, as *Eleven Declarations of War*, Harcourt Brace (U.S.),1975 . . . . £35/£10

Cookery Titles

Action Cookbook, Len Deighton's Guide to Eating, Cape, 1965 (printed boards, clear d/w). . £100/£50
Ou Est le Garlic, Penguin, 1965 (wraps) . . £30
ditto, Harper & Row (U.S.), 1977 . . £25/£10
ditto, as *Basic French Cooking*, Cape, 1979 £50/£15
ditto, as *Basic French Cookery Course*, Century Hutchinson, 1990 . . . . . . £10/£5
ditto, as *Cookstrip Cookbook*, Bernard Geiss (U.S.), 1966 . . . : . . . . . £10/£5

Others

The Assassination of President Kennedy, Cape/ Jackdaw, 1967 (Portfolio containing 12 reproductions, 1 cut-out model and 5 broadsides, with Rand and Loxton) £350

Len Deighton's London Dossier, Cape, 1967 £50/£20
Len Deighton's Continental Dossier, Joseph, 1968 (no
d/w) £40
Fighter: The True Story of the Battle of Britain, Cape,
1977 . . . . £45/£10
ditto, Knopf (U.S.), 1978 . . . . . £10/£5
Airshipwreck, Cape, 1978 (6 postcards laid in, with
record) . . . . £175/£75
ditto, Cape, 1978 (no postcards or record) . £75/£15
ditto, Hart Rinehart (U.S.), 1979 . . . . £50/£10
Blitzkrieg, Cape, 1979 . . . . . . £30/£5
ditto, Knopf (U.S.), 1980 . . . . . £30/£5
Battle of Britain, Cape, 1980 . . . . £30/£5
ditto, Coward McCann & Geoghegan (U.S.), 1980. .
. . . . £30/£5
Blood, Tears and Folly: An Objective Look at World
War II, Cape, 1993 . . . . £30/£5
ditto, Harper Collins (U.S.), 1993 . . . £30/£5
Pests, A Play in Three Acts, Martin, 1994 (50 signed,
numbered copies of 226, slipcase) . . £75/£50
ditto, Martin, 1994 (150 signed, numbered copies of
226) . . . . £50/£40
ditto, Martin, 1994 (26 signed, lettered copies of 226) .
. . . .£200/£150

WALTER DE LA MARE
(b.1873 d.1956)

British author, poet and critic, whose delicate and
lyrical poems of fantasy and childhood are still
admired today.

Verse

Songs of Childhood, Longmans, 1902 (pseud. 'Walter
Ramal') £350
ditto, Longmans, 1923 (enlarged and revised) £25/£10
ditto, Longmans, 1923 (310 signed copies) £175/£150
Poems, Murray, 1906 . . . . . . £50
The Listeners and Other Poems, Constable, 1912 £45
ditto, Holt (U.S.), 1916 . . . . . £45
A Child's Day, A Book of Rhymes, Constable, 1912 .
. . . . £30
Peacock Pie, A Book of Rhymes, Constable, 1913 £25
ditto, Constable, 1924 (250 signed copies) . . £125
ditto, Holt (U.S.), 1924 (500 signed copies). . £125
The Old Men, Flying Fame, 1913 . . . £25
The Sunken Garden and Other Poems, Beaumont
Press, 1917 (250 signed, numbered copies) . £75
Motley and Other Poems, Constable, 1918 . . £35
ditto, Holt (U.S.), 1918 . . . . . £35
Flora: A Book of Drawings, by Pamela Bianco,
Heinemann, 1919 (with 27 poems by de la Mare) £45
ditto, Lippincott (U.S.), 1919 . . . . . £45
Poems, 1901 to 1918, Constable, 1920, (2 vols) . .
. . . . £65/£35
ditto, Constable, 1920, (210 signed, numbered sets) .
. . . . £750

The Veil and Other Poems, Constable, 1921 £50/£15
ditto, Constable, 1921 (250 signed, numbered copies) .
. . . . £75
ditto, Holt (U.S.), 1922 . . . . . . £35
Down-Adown-Derry, A Book of Fairy Poems,
Constable, 1922 . . . . £100/£50
ditto, Holt (U.S.), 1922 . . . . . £75/£35
Thus Her Tale, A Poem, Porpoise Press, 1923 (50
numbered copies, wraps) £40
A Ballad of Christmas, Selwyn & Blount, 1924 (100
copies) £40
Before Dawn, Selwyn & Blount, 1924 (100 copies) .
. . . . £40
The Hostage, Selwyn & Blount, 1925 (100 copies) £40
St Andrews, A & C Black, 1926 (with Rudyard
Kipling) . . . . £45/£25
Alone, Faber, 1927 (Ariel Poem No.4, wraps) . £10
Selected Poems, Holt (U.S.), 1927 . . . £30/£10
Stuff and Nonsense and So On, Constable, 1927 . .
. . . . £45/£15
ditto, as Stuff and Nonsense, Faber, 1946 (enlarged
and revised edition of above) . . . . £15/£5
The Captive and Other Poems, Bowling Green Press
(U.S.), 1928 (600 signed copies, glassine wraps) . .
. . . . £45/£35
Self to Self, Faber, 1928 (Ariel Poem No. 11, wraps) .
. . . . £10
ditto, Faber, 1928 (500 signed large paper copies) £45
A Snowdrop, Faber, 1929 (Ariel Poem No. 20, wraps).
. . . . £15
ditto, Faber, 1929 (500 signed large paper copies) £45
News, Faber, 1930 (Ariel Poem No. 31, wraps) £15
To Lucy, Faber, 1931 (Ariel Poem No. 33, wraps) £15
Poems for Children, Constable, 1930 . . £35/£10
ditto, Constable, 1930 (133 signed, numbered copies) .
. . . . £225
ditto, Holt (U.S.), 1930 (300 signed copies, slipcase) .
. . . . £175/£150
The Sunken Garden and Other Verses, Birmingham
School of Printing, 1931 (different selection to 1917
edition) £25
Two Poems, privately printed, 1931 (100 copies,
wraps) £75
Old Rhymes and New, Constable, 1932 (2 vols) . .
. . . . £50/£20
The Fleeting and Other Poems, Constable, 1933 . .
. . . . £25/£15
ditto, Constable, 1933 (150 signed copies) . £65
Poems, 1919 to 1934, Constable, 1935 . . £30/£15
This Year, Next Year, Faber, 1937 . . . . £125
ditto, Faber, 1937 (100 signed, numbered copies) . .
. . . . £450/£300
ditto, Holt (U.S.), 1937 . . . . . £125/£65
Poems, Corvinus Press, 1937 (40 copies) . . £150
Memory and Other Poems, Constable, 1938 £25/£5
Two Poems by Walter de la Mare and - but! - Arthur
Rogers, privately printed, 1938 (200 copies) . £45
Haunted: A Poem, Linden Broadsheet No. 4, 1939 £20

Bells and Grass, *a book of rhymes*, Faber, 1941 . . .
. . . . £50/£25
ditto, Viking (U.S.), 1942 . . . . . £50/£25
Collected Poems, Faber, 1942 . . . £35/£10
Time Passes and Other Poems, Faber, 1942 £20/£5
Collected Rhymes and Verses, Faber, 1944 . £20/£5
The Burning-Glass and Other Poems, Faber, 1945 .
. . . . £20/£5
ditto, Viking (U.S.), 1945 . . . . . £20/£5
The Traveller, Faber, 1946 . . . . £40/£20
Two Poems, Dropmore Press, 1946 . . . £20
Rhymes and Verses, Collected Poems for Children,
Holt (U.S.), 1947 . . . . . . £25/£10
Inward Companion, Faber, 1950 . . £25/£10
Winged Chariot, Faber, 1951 . . . £30/£10
ditto, Viking (U.S.), 1951 . . . . . £25/£10
O Lovely England and Other Poems, Faber, 1953 . .
. . . . £30/£10
The Winnowing Dream, Faber, 1954 (Ariel Poem,
wraps) £10
Selected Poems, Faber, 1954 . . . . £20/£5
The Morrow, privately printed, 1955 (50 copies,
wraps) £25
Poems, Puffin, 1962 (wraps) £5

Children's Stories
The Three Mulla-Mulgars, Duckworth, 1910 (later re-
titled **The Three Royal Monkeys**) . . . £45
ditto, Duckworth, 1910 (250 signed copies). . £125
ditto, Knopf (U.S.), 1919 . . . . . . £25
Broomsticks and Other Tales, Constable, 1925 (278
signed copies, slipcase) . . . . . £200/£165
ditto, Constable, 1925 . . . . . . £125/£25
ditto, Knopf (U.S.), 1930 . . . . £100/£25
Miss Jemima, Blackwell, 1925 . . . . £30
Lucy, Blackwell, 1925 . . . . . . £30
Old Joe, Blackwell, 1925 . . . . . . £30
Readings: Traditional Tales, told by de la Mare,
Blackwell, 1925-28 (set of 6 vols) . . £125
Told Again: Traditional Tales, Blackwell, 1927 . .
. . . . £65/£15
ditto, Blackwell, 1927 (260 signed copies) . . £100
ditto, Knopf (U.S.), 1927 . . . . . £35.£10
Stories from the Bible, Faber, 1929 . . £50/£20
ditto, Faber, 1929 (300 signed copies) . . . £75
The Dutch Cheese and The Lovely Myfanwy, Knopf
(U.S.), 1931 . . . . £65/£35
The Lord Fish and Other Tales, Faber, 1933 £60/£25
ditto, Faber, 1933 (60 signed copies, d/w, slipcase) .
. . . . £250
Mr Bumps and His Monkey, J.C. Winston (U.S.),
1942 . . . . £50/£10
The Old Lion and Other Stories, Faber, 1942 £20/£5
The Magic Jacket and Other Stories, Faber, 1943 .
. . . . £20/£5
The Scarecrow and Other Stories, Faber, 1945 £20/£5
The Dutch Cheese and Other Stories, Faber, 1946 .
. . . . £20/£5
Collected Stories for Children, Faber, 1947 £20/£5

Selected Stories and Verses, Puffin, 1952 (wraps) £5
Jack and the Beanstalk, Hulton Press, 1951 (from
Told Again) . . . . £20/£5
Dick Whittington, Hulton Press, 1951 . . £20/£5
Snow White, Hulton Press, 1952 . . . . £20/£5
Cinderella, Hulton Press, 1952 . . . . £20/£5
A Penny a Day and Other Stories, Knopf (U.S.), 1960
. . . . £15/£5

Novels
Henry Brocken, Murray, 1904 . . . . . £150
ditto, Collins, 1924 (250 signed copies) . . . £50
ditto, Knopf (U.S.), 1924 . . . . . . £50/£15
The Return, Arnold, 1910 . . . . . . £150
ditto, Collins, 1922 (250 signed copies) . . £50
ditto, Knopf (U.S.), 1922 . . . . . . £75/£25
Memoirs of a Midget, Collins, 1921 . . £150/£20
ditto, Collins, 1921 (210 signed, numbered copies) £75
The Walter de la Mare Omnibus, Collins, 1933 . .
. . . . £25/£10

Short Stories
Story and Rhyme, Dent, 1921 . . . £30/£10
Lispet, Lispet and Vaine, Bookman's Journal, 1923
(Vine Books No.3, 200 signed copies) . . . £100
The Riddle and Other Stories, Selwyn & Blount, 1923
. . . . £125/£25
Ding Dong Bell, Selwyn & Blount, 1924 . £30/£10
ditto, Selwyn & Blount, 1924 (300 signed copies) £30
**Two Tales: 'The Green Room' and 'The
Connoisseur'**, Bookman's Journal, 1925 (200 signed
copies) £50
The Connoisseur and Other Stories, Collins, 1926 .
. . . . £125/£25
ditto, Collins, 1926 (250 signed copies) . . . £125
Seaton's Aunt, Faber, 1927 (wraps) . . . £45
At First Sight, Crosby Gaige (U.S.), 1928 (650 signed
copies) £45
On the Edge, Faber, 1930 . . . . . £75/£25
ditto, Faber, 1930 (211 signed copies) . . . £50
Seven Short Stories, Faber, 1931 . . . £100/£25
ditto, Faber, 1931 (100 signed copies) . . . £300
A Froward Child, Faber, 1934 . . . . £15/£5
The Wind Blows Over, Faber, 1936 . . . £75/£20
ditto, Macmillan (U.S.), 1936 . . . . £65/£20
The Nap and Other Stories, Nelson Classics, 1938 .
. . . . £20/£5
Stories, Essays and Poems, Dent, Everyman's Library,
1938 . . . . £20/£5
The Picnic and Other Stories, Faber, 1941 . £20/£5
Best Stories of Walter de la Mare, Faber, 1942 £20/£5
The Almond Tree, Todd, 1943 (from **The Riddle**) £20
The Orgy, Todd, 1943 (from **On the Edge**) . £20
The Collected Tales of Walter de la Mare, Knopf
(U.S.), 1950 . . . . £25/£15
A Beginning and Other Stories, Faber, 1955 £75/£20
Ghost Stories, Folio Society, 1956 (slipcase) £10/£5
Walter de la Mare: A Selection from his Writings,
Faber, 1956 . . . . £15/£5

Some Stories, Faber, 1962 . . . . . £15/£5
Eight Tales, Arkham House (U.S.), 1971 . £30/£5

Miscellaneous
M.E. Coleridge: An Appreciation, The Guardian, 1907
(limited edition) £50
Rupert Brooke and the Intellectual Imagination,
Sidgwick & Jackson, 1919 . . . . . . £25
Some Thoughts on Reading, Yellowsands Press, 1923
(340 copies) £25
The Printing of Poetry, C.U.P., 1931 (limited to 90
copies) £100
Lewis Carroll, Faber, 1932 . . . . . £50/£15
Poetry in Prose, Humphrey Milford, 1936 . . £15
Arthur Thompson: A Memoir, privately printed, 1938
. . . . £15
An Introduction to Everyman, Dent, 1938 (400 copies)
. . . . £45
Pleasures and Speculations, Faber, 1940 . £30/£10
Private View, Faber, 1953 . . . . . £20/£5

MAURICE AND EDWARD DETMOLD
(b.1883 d.1908, b.1883 d.1957)

Brothers who collaborated in illustrating until the
suicide of the former. Edward continued illustrating
books until the late 1920s.

Books illustrated by Maurice and Edward Detmold
Pictures from Birdland, Dent, 1899 . . . £300
*Sixteen Illustrations of Subjects from Kipling's
'Jungle Book'*, Macmillan, 1903 (portfolio) . £750
The Jungle Book, Macmillan, 1908 . . . . £150

Books illustrated by Edward Detmold
The Fables of Aesop, Hodder & Stoughton, 1909 £300
ditto, Hodder & Stoughton, 1909 (750 signed copies) .
. . . . £750
Birds and Beasts, by Camille Lemonnier, Allen, 1911.
. . . . £125
The Book of Baby Beasts, by Florence E. Dugdale,
Frowde/Hodder & Stoughton, [1911] . . . £125
The Life of the Bee, by Maurice Maeterlinck, Allen,
1911 . . . . £250
ditto, Dodd, Mead (U.S.), 1919 . . . . £150
Hours of Gladness, by Maurice Maeterlinck, Allen,
1912 . . . . £400
The Book of Baby Birds, by Florence E. Dugdale,
Frowde/Hodder & Stoughton, [1912] . . £150
ditto, Hodder & Stoughton (U.S.), [no date] . £150
The Book of Baby Pets, by Florence E. Dugdale,
Frowde/Hodder & Stoughton, [1915] . . . £125
The Book of Baby Dogs, by Charles J. Kaberry,
Frowde/Hodder & Stoughton, [1915] . . . £125
Twenty-Four Nature Pictures, Dent, [1919] (portfolio)
. . . . £450

Birds in Town and Village, by W.H. Hudson, Dent,
1919 . . . . £50
Our Little Neighbours, by Charles J. Kaberry,
Frowde/Hodder & Stoughton, [1921] . . £150/£50
Fabre's Book of Insects, by J.H.C. Fabre, Hodder &
Stoughton, [1921] . . . . . . £450/£150
ditto, Dodd, Mead (U.S.), 1921 . . . . £100
Rainbow House for Boys and Girls, by Arthur Vine
Hall, Cape, 1923 . . . . £125/£50
*The Arabian Nights - Tales from the Thousand and
One Nights*, Hodder & Stoughton, [1924] . . £300
ditto, Hodder & Stoughton, [1924] (100 signed copies)
. . . . £750
ditto, Dodd, Mead (U.S.), 1925 . . . . £250
The Fantastic Creatures of Edward Julius Detmold,
Pan, 1976 (wraps) £15
ditto, Peacock Press/Bantam Books (U.S.), 1976
(wraps) £10
ditto, Scribners (U.S.), 1976 . . . . . £25/£10

COLIN DEXTER
(b.1930)

A crime writer whose Inspector Morse is pre-eminent
among the contemporary television detectives.

Novels
Last Bus to Woodstock, Macmillan, 1975 £1,000/£75
ditto, St Martin's Press (U.S.), 1975 . . . £750/£65
Last Seen Wearing, Macmillan, 1976 £1,000/£75
ditto, St Martin's Press (U.S.), 1976 . . . £600/£45
The Silent World of Nicholas Quinn, Macmillan, 1977
. . . . £1,000/£75
ditto, St Martin's Press (U.S.), 1977 . . . £250/£35
Service of All the Dead, Macmillan, 1979 . £250/£25
ditto, St Martin's Press (U.S.), 1980 . . . £150/£15
The Dead of Jericho, Macmillan, 1980 . . £200/£20
ditto, St Martin's Press (U.S.), 1980 . . . £150/£15
Riddle of the Third Mile, Macmillan, 1983 . £150/£15
ditto, St Martin's Press (U.S.), 1983 . . . £100/£10
The Secret of Annexe 3, Macmillan, 1986 . £100/£10
ditto, St Martin's Press (U.S.), 1987 . . . £75/£10
The Wench is Dead, Macmillan, 1989 . . £25/£5
ditto, St Martin's Press (U.S.), 1990 . . £15/£5
The Jewel That Was Ours, Scorpion Press, 1991 (150
signed copies, quarter leather) £150
ditto, Scorpion Press, 1991 (20 signed deluxe copies) .
. . . . £300
ditto, Macmillan, 1991 . . . . . £25/£5
ditto, Crown (U.S.), 1992 . . . . . £10/£5
The Way Through the Woods, Macmillan, 1992 . .
. . . . £15/£5
ditto, Scorpion Press, 1992 (150 signed copies, quarter
leather) £100
ditto, Scorpion Press, 1992 (20 signed deluxe copies) .
. . . . £300
ditto, Crown (U.S.), 1993 . . . . . . £10/£5

Daughters of Cain, Macmillan, 1992 . . £10/£5
ditto, Crown (U.S.), 1994. . . . . . £10/£5
Death is Now My Neighbour, Macmillan, 1996 £10/£5
ditto, as *Death is Now My Neighbor*, Crown (U.S.),
1997 . . . . £10/£5
The Remorseful Day, Macmillan, 1999 . . £10/£5
ditto, Crown (U.S.), 1999. . . . . . £10/£5

Short Stories
Morse's Greatest Mystery and Other Stories,
Macmillan, 1993 . . . . £10/£5
ditto, Scorpion Press, 1993 (99 signed copies, quarter
leather) £125
ditto, Scorpion Press, 1993 (20 signed deluxe copies) .
. . . . £250
ditto, Crown (U.S.), 1993. . . . . . £10/£5
Inside Story, Macmillan, 1993 (for American Express,
wraps). £15
Neighbourhood Watch, Moorhouse/Sorenson, 1993
(150 numbered copies, wraps) £25
ditto, Moorhouse/Sorenson, 1993 (50 signed, numbered copies, wraps). £50
ditto, Moorhouse/Sorenson, 1993 (26 signed, numbered copies). £100
A Good as Gold, Kodak/Pan, 1994 (wraps) . £5

Omnibus Editions
An Inspector Morse Omnibus, Macmillan, 1991 . .
. . . . £20/£5
The Second Inspector Morse Omnibus, Macmillan,
1992 . . . . £15/£5
The Third Inspector Morse Omnibus, Macmillan,
1993 . . . . £15/£5
The Fourth Inspector Morse Omnibus, Macmillan,
1996 . . . . £15/£5

MICHAEL DIBDIN
(b.1947)

A popular crime writer, Dibdin is considered by some
to be the next P.D. James.

The Last Sherlock Holmes Story, Jonathan Cape, 1978
. . . . £350/£50
ditto, Pantheon (U.S.), 1978 . . . . . £25/£5
A Rich Full Death, Jonathan Cape, 1986 . £125/£20
Ratking, Faber, 1988 . . . . £100/£15
ditto, Bantam (U.S.), 1989 . . . . . £25/£5
The Tryst, Faber, 1989 . . . . . . £40/£5
ditto, Summit (U.S.), 1990 . . . . . £25/£5
Vendetta, Faber, 1990. . . . . . . £25/£5
ditto, Doubleday (U.S.), 1991 . . . . £15/£5
Dirty Tricks, Faber, 1991 . . . . . £20/£5
ditto, Summit (U.S.), 1991 . . . . . £15/£5
Cabal, Faber, 1992 . . . . £20/£5
ditto, Doubleday (U.S.), 1993 . . . . £15/£5
The Dying of the Light, Faber, 1993 . . £15/£5

ditto, Pantheon (U.S.), 1993 . . . . . £10/£5
Dead Lagoon, Faber, 1994 . . . . . £15/£5
ditto, Pantheon (U.S.), 1994 . . . . . £10/£5
Dark Spectre, Faber, 1995 . . . . . £15/£5
ditto, Pantheon (U.S.), 1995 . . . . . £10/£5
Cosi Fan Tuti, Faber, 1996 . . . . . £10/£5
ditto, Pantheon (U.S.), 1996 . . . . . £10/£5
A Long Finish, Faber, 1998 . . . . . £10/£5
ditto, Pantheon (U.S.), 1998. . . . . £10/£5
Blood Rain, Faber, 1999 . . . . . . £10/£5
ditto, Pantheon (U.S.), 1999. . . . . £10/£5
Thanksgiving, Faber, 2000 . . . . . £10/£5

PHILIP K. DICK
(b.1928 d.1982)

Dick was an American writer of science fiction, often
dealing in his work with the effects of mechanisation,
hallucinogenic drugs and schizophrenic delusions.

Short Stories
A Handful of Darkness, Rich & Cowan, 1955 (first
issue boards blue, lettered silver, with first issue d/w
not listing *World of Chance* on rear panel). . . .
. . . . £1,000/£200
ditto, Rich & Cowan, 1955 (second issue, orange
boards, lettered black) . . . . . £450/£150
ditto, Gregg Press (U.S.), 1978 (no d/w). . . £50
The Variable Man, Ace Books (U.S.), 1957 (wraps) .
. . . . £35
The Preserving Machine, Ace Books (U.S.), 1969
(wraps) £25
ditto, Gollancz, 1971 . . . . £65/£15
The Book of Philip K. Dick, Daw Books (U.S.), 1973
(wraps) £10
ditto, as *The Turning Wheel*, Coronet, 1977 (wraps) .
. . . . £10
The Best of Philip K. Dick, Ballantine (U.S.), 1977
(wraps) £10
The Golden Man, Berkeley (U.S.), 1980 (wraps) £10
I Hope I Shall Arrive Soon, Doubleday (U.S.), 1985 .
. . . . £25/£5
ditto, Gollancz, 1986 . . . . £20/£5

Novels
Solar Lottery, Ace Books (U.S.), 1955 (wraps) £35
ditto, as *World of Chance*, Rich & Cowan, 1956 . .
. . . . £2,000/£400
ditto, Gregg Press (U.S.), 1979 (no d/w). . . £50
The World Jones Made, Ace Books (U.S.), 1956
(wraps) £30
ditto, Sidgwick & Jackson, 1968 . . . £650/£150
The Man Who Japed, Ace Books (U.S.), 1956 (wraps)
. . . . £30
ditto, Eyre Methuen, 1978 . . . . . £175/£35
Eye in the Sky, Ace Books (U.S.), 1957 (wraps) £30
ditto, Gregg Press (U.S.), 1979 . . . . £65

The Cosmic Puppets, Ace Books (U.S.), 1957 (wraps)
. . . . £35
ditto, Severn House, 1986. . . . . . £30/£10
Time Out Of Joint, Lippincott (U.S.), 1959 £600/£125
ditto, Science Fiction Book Club, 1961 . . £25/£10
Dr Futurity, Ace Books (U.S.), 1960 (wraps) £35
Vulcan's Hammer, Ace Books (U.S.), 1960 (wraps) .
. . . . £25
The Man in the High Castle, Putnam (U.S.), 1962 .
. . . . £400/£65
ditto, Penguin, 1965 (wraps) £10
ditto, Gollancz, 1975 . . . . £35/£10
The Game Players of Titan, Ace Books (U.S.), 1963
(wraps) £20
ditto, White Lion, 1974 . . . . . . £125/£25
Martian Time-Slip, Ballantine Books (U.S.), 1964
(wraps) £20
ditto, New English Library, 1976 . . . £175/£35
The Simulacra, Ace Books (U.S.), 1964 (wraps) £40
ditto, Eyre Methuen, 1977 . . . . . £250/£35
The Penultimate Truth, Belmont (U.S.), 1964 (wraps)
. . . . £20
ditto, Jonathan Cape, 1967 . . . . . £600/£75
Clans of the Alphane Moon, Ace Books (U.S.), 1964
(wraps) £20
ditto, Gregg Press (U.S.), 1979 (no d/w). . . £50
The Three Stigmata of Palmer Eldritch, Doubleday
(U.S.), 1965 . . . . £1,000/£150
ditto, Jonathan Cape, 1966 . . . . . £250/£35
Dr Bloodmoney, Ace Books (U.S.), 1965 (wraps) £20
Now Wait for Last Year, Doubleday (U.S.), 1966 . .
. . . . £175/£45
The Crack in Space, Ace Books (U.S.), 1966 (wraps) .
. . . . £25
ditto, Severn House, 1989. . . . . . £30/£5
The Unteleported Man, Ace Books (U.S.), 1966
(wraps) £20
ditto, Berkley (U.S.), 1983 (wraps, revised version) .
. . . . £10
ditto, as *Lies Inc.*, Gollancz, 1984 (further revisions) .
. . . . £40/£10
The Zap Gun, Pyramid (U.S.), 1967 (wraps) . £25
ditto, Gregg Press (U.S.), 1979 . . . . . £100
Counter-Clock World, Berkley (U.S.), 1967 (wraps) .
. . . . £30
ditto, White Lion, 1977 . . . . . . £75/£20
The Ganymede Takeover, Ace Books (U.S.), 1967
(with Ray Nelson, wraps) £20
ditto, Severn House, 1988. . . . . . £40/£5
Do Androids Dream of Electric Sheep?, Doubleday
(U.S.), 1969 . . . . £5,000/£1,000
ditto, Rapp & Whiting, 1969 . . . £650/£100
Ubik, Doubleday (U.S.), 1969 . . . . £600/£65
ditto, Rapp & Whiting, 1970 . . . . £175/£25
Galactic Pot-Healer, Berkeley (U.S.), 1969 (wraps) .
. . . . £20
ditto, Gollancz, 1971 . . . . . . £50/£10
A Maze of Death, Doubleday (U.S.), 1970 £750/£100
ditto, Gollancz, 1972 . . . . . . £250/£35

Our Friends from Frolix 8, Ace Books (U.S.), 1970
(wraps) £15
ditto, Ace Books (U.S.), 1971 . . . . £35/£10
ditto, Kinnell, 1989 . . . . £40/£10
A Philip K. Dick Omnibus, Sidgwick & Jackson, 1970
. . . . £50/£15
We Can Build You, Daw Books (U.S.), 1972 (wraps) .
. . . . £10
ditto, Severn House, 1988. . . . . . £35/£5
Flow My Tears, The Policeman Said, Doubleday
(U.S.), 1974 . . . . £275/£35
ditto, Gollancz, 1974 . . . . . . £35/£10
Confessions of a Crap Artist, Entwhistle Books (U.S.),
1975 (90 signed copies of 1,000, no d/w) . . £500
ditto, Entwhistle Books (U.S.), 1975 (410 copies of
1,000) £200
ditto, Entwhistle Books (U.S.), 1975 (500 copies of
1,000, wraps). £30
ditto, Magnum, 1979 (wraps). £10
Deus Irae, Doubleday (U.S.), 1976 (with Roger
Zelazny) . . . . £50/£10
ditto, Gollancz, 1977 . . . . . . £45/£10
A Scanner Darkly, Doubleday (U.S.), 1977 £35/£10
ditto, Gollancz, 1977 . . . . . . £25/£10
Valis, Bantam (U.S.), 1981 (wraps) . . . £10
ditto, Kerosina, 1987 . . . . . . £25/£10
ditto, Kerosina, 1987 (limited edition of 250 copies
with d/w, in slipcase together with the 325 copy
hardcover edition of *Cosmogony and Cosmology*,
Kerosina, 1987) £75
The Divine Invasion, Simon Schuster/Timescape
(U.S.), 1981 . . . . £25/£5
The Transmigration of Timothy Archer, Simon &
Schuster, 1982 . . . . £25/£5
ditto, Gollancz, 1982 . . . . £25/£5
The Man Whose Teeth Were Exactly Alike, Ziesling
(U.S.), 1984 . . . . £125/£35
In Milton Lumky Territory, Dragon Press, 1985 . .
. . . . £40/£10
ditto, Dragon Press, 1985 (50 signed, numbered copies)
. . . . £200
ditto, Gollancz, 1986 . . . . . . £40/£10
Ubik: The Screenplay, Corroboree Press (U.S.), 1985 .
. . . . £100/£45
ditto, Corroboree Press (U.S.), 1985 (20 signed copies
in leather). £250
Puttering About in a Small Land, Chicago Academy
(U.S.), 1985 . . . . £25/£5
Radio Free Albemuth, Arbor House (U.S.), 1985 . .
. . . . £20/£5
ditto, Severn House, 1987. . . . . . £20/£5
Humpty Dumpty in Oakland, Gollancz, 1986 £65/£15
Mary and the Giant, Arbor House (U.S.), 1987 £25/£5
ditto, Arbor House (U.S.), 1987 (50 copies bound in
quarter leather) £200
ditto, Gollancz, 1988 . . . . £25/£5
Collected Stories, Underwood Miller, 1987 (5 vols) .
. . . . £200

ditto, Underwood Miller, 1987 (deluxe limited edition)
. . . . £350
ditto, Gollancz, 1988-90 (4 vols). . . £25/£10 each
Cosmogony and Cosmology, Kerosina, 1987 (no d/w).
. . . . £65
ditto, Kerosina, 1987 (wraps). £15
Nick and the Glimmung, Gollancz, 1988 . £25/£10
ditto, Trafalgar Square (U.S.), 1988 . . . £25/£10
The Broken Bubble, Morrow/Arbor House (U.S.),
1988 . . . . £15/£5
ditto, Gollancz, 1989 . . . . £15/£5
ditto, Ultramarine Press, 1989 (150 copies, quarter
leather) £125
ditto, Ultramarine Press, 1989 (26 copies, full leather).
. . . . £200

CHARLES DICKENS

(b.1812 d.1870)

An acclaimed and prolific author, Dickens' position
as one of the 'greats' of English literature is beyond
dispute.

Sketches by 'Boz', John Macrone MDCCCXXXVI-VII
1836-7 (illustrated by George Cruikshank, first series
of 2 vols in 1836 in dark green cloth, second series of
1 vol. In 1837 in pink cloth) £10,000
ditto, John Macrone MDCCCXXXVI-VII 1836-7 (the
above rebound) £2,000
ditto, Chapman & Hall, November 1837-June 1839 (20
monthly parts, 13 extra plates by George Cruikshank,
pink wrappers) £20,000
ditto, Chapman & Hall, 1839 (first 1 vol. edition dated
'1837', monthly parts bound with wrapper in glossy
brown or purple cloth, with 40 plates by George
Cruikshank) £2,000
Sunday Under Three Heads, Chapman & Hall, 1836
(pseud. 'Timothy Sparks', 3 illustrations plus wrapper
by H.K. Browne, first edition the title appears as a
heading to Chapter III on p.35 and 'hair' spelt
correctly on p.7, line 15, buff wraps) . . £2,250
ditto, Chapman & Hall, 1836 (the above rebound) £750
The Village Coquettes, Richard Bentley, 1836 (wraps)
. . . . £3,000
ditto, Richard Bentley, 1836 (the above rebound) . .
. . . . £1,000
*The Posthumous Papers of the Pickwick Club edited
by 'Boz',* Chapman & Hall, April 1836-Nov 1837 (20
monthly parts in 19. Parts I & II Illustrated by Robert
Seymour, part III by R. W. Buss and parts IV-
XIX/XX by Phiz. Green wrappers). . . £5,000
ditto, Chapman & Hall, 1837 (first book edition, 1 vol,
monthly parts bound with or without wrappers. 43
illustrations by R. Seymour and Phiz. Slate or
purple/black cloth, first issue with 'S Veller' on
p.342, line 5) £5,000

ditto, Chapman & Hall, 1837 (the above rebound) . . .
. . . . £400
Oliver Twist; or, The Parish Boy's Progress, Richard
Bentley 1838 (pseud. 'Boz', 3 vols, illustrated by
George Cruikshank, red-brown cloth, first issue with
'Rose Maylie and Oliver' plate in vol 3 showing them
at fireside) £10,000
ditto, Richard Bentley 1838 (the above rebound) . .
. . . . £1,750
ditto, Richard Bentley 1838 (second issue showing
them at church) £2,500
ditto, Richard Bentley 1838 (second edition, or third
issue, with 'Dickens' on title page, not 'Boz') £2,000
ditto, Bradbury & Evans, January-October 1846 (10
monthly parts with illustrations by George
Cruikshank, green wrappers) . . . £10,000
ditto, Bradbury & Evans, MDCCCXLVI 1846 (first 1
vol. edition, with slate-coloured cloth) . £1,750
ditto, Bradbury & Evans, MDCCCXLVI 1846 (the
above rebound) £300
Sketches of Young Gentlemen, Chapman & Hall, 1838
(anonymous, 6 illustrations and cover by Phiz, blue-
green paper boards) £1,500
The Memoirs of Joseph Grimaldi, Richard Bentley
1838 (edited by 'Boz', 2 vols, 12 plates and
frontispiece on vol I by Cruikshank, first issue pink
cloth, without border around final plate 'The Last
Song'). £4,500
ditto, Richard Bentley 1838 (as above, second issue
brown cloth with border around final plate 'The Last
Song'). £1,000
The Life and Adventures of Nicholas Nickleby,
Chapman & Hall, April 1838-October 1839 (20
monthly parts in 19, illustrated by Phiz, green
wrappers, first issue with 'vister' on p.123, line 17) .
. . . . £3,000
ditto, Chapman & Hall, 1839 (first book edition,
monthly parts in 1 vol., illustrated by Phiz, dark olive
green cloth) £2,500
ditto, Chapman & Hall, 1839 (the above rebound) . .
. . . . £300
Sketches of Young Couples, Chapman & Hall, 1840
('By the Author of Sketches of Young Gentlemen', 6
illustrations and cover by Phiz, grey-green paper
boards) £1,500
Master Humphrey's Clock, Chapman & Hall, April
1840-Nov 1841 (by 'Boz', 88 weekly parts, illustrated
by G. Cattermole, Phiz & Daniel Maclise, white
wrappers). £1,750
ditto, Chapman & Hall April 1840-Nov 1841 (20
monthly parts, illustrated as above, green wrappers) .
. . . .£1,500
ditto, Chapman & Hall, MDCCCXL/MDCCCXLI
1841 (first book edition, 3 vols, weekly or monthly
parts, illustrated as above, brown cloth with clock on
front pointing to volume numbers), . . . £750
ditto, Chapman & Hall, MDCCCXL/MDCCCXLI
1841 (as above but variant cloth, no hands on clock),
. . . . £300

The Old Curiosity Shop, Chapman & Hall, 1841 (original monthly parts from 'Master Humphrey's Clock', cloth binding) £1,250
Barnaby Rudge, Chapman & Hall, 1841 (original monthly parts from 'Master Humphrey's Clock', cloth binding) £1,750
American Notes for General Circulation, Chapman & Hall, 1842 (2 vols, first issue with prelims misnumbered with p.10 (x) as 'xvi', purple cloth) .
. . . . £1,000
ditto, Chapman & Hall, 1842 (as above but prelims corrected). £500
Martin Chuzzlewit, Chapman & Hall, Jan 1843-July 1844 (20 monthly parts in 19, illustrated by Phiz, green wrappers) £1,250
ditto, Chapman & Hall, MDCCCXXLIV 1844 (first book edition made up of unsold monthly parts, Prussian blue cloth binding). . . . £4,000
ditto, Chapman & Hall, MDCCCXXLIV 1844 (as above, brown cloth binding) £3,500
ditto, Chapman & Hall, MDCCCXXLIV 1844 (as above rebound) £300
A Christmas Carol, Chapman & Hall, 1843 (many variants but earliest may have have title page dated 1843, brown cloth, green endpapers, and 'Stave 1' on first text page) £15,000
The Chimes, Chapman & Hall, 1845 (first issue with publisher's name in title vignette) £500
ditto, Chapman & Hall, 1845 (second issue with publisher's name below title vignette) . . . £300
The Cricket on the Hearth, Bradbury & Evans, 1846 (first issue with ad. page [175] without heading 'New Editions of Oliver Twist', red cloth) . . . £500
ditto, Bradbury & Evans, 1846 (second issue) . £300
The Battle of Life: A Love Story, Bradbury & Evans, 1846 (first issue, on engraved title page 'A Love Story' in heavy type and publisher's name at bottom of page) £30,000
ditto, Bradbury & Evans, 1846 (second issue with 'A Love Story' in light type supported by cupids and publisher's name at bottom of page) . . £5,000
ditto, Bradbury & Evans, 1846 (third issue as above but publisher's name not at bottom of page) . £1,000
Pictures from Italy, Bradbury & Evans, 1846 (illustrations by Samuel Palmer, blue cloth) . £500
Dombey and Son, Bradbury & Evans, 1848 (20 monthly parts in 19, illustrated by Phiz, with 12 line errata slip in part V) £1,250
ditto, Bradbury & Evans, 1848 (first book edition, monthly parts bound in dark green cloth.) . £2,000
ditto, Bradbury & Evans, 1848 (as above rebound.) .
. . . . £300
The Haunted Man and The Ghost's Bargain, Bradbury & Evans, 1848 (date on title page '1848', red cloth with blind-stamped borders) . . . £200
ditto, Bradbury & Evans, 1848 (as above but date on title page 'MDCCCXLVIII') £1,000

The Personal History of David Copperfield, Bradbury & Evans, May 1849-Nov, 1850 (20 monthly parts in 19, illustrated by Phiz, green wrappers) . £6,000
ditto, Bradbury & Evans, 1850 (first book edition, monthly parts bound in dark green cloth) . £5,000
A Child's History of England, Bradbury & Evans, 1852, 53, 54 (3 vols, first issue of vol. I with ad. page [211] listing 4 books plus 5 Christmas books, and vol. III with ad. page [324] 'Collected and Revised', red cloth) £1,500
ditto, Bradbury & Evans, 1852, 53, 54 (3 vols, second issue of vol. I with ad. page [211] listing this book, plus 7 books plus 5 Christmas books, and vol. III with ad page [324] 'Corrected and Revised', red cloth) .
. . . . £750
Bleak House, Bradbury & Evans, March 1852-Sept 1853 (20 monthly parts in 19, illustrated by Phiz, blue wrappers). £1,750
ditto, Bradbury & Evans, 1853 (first book edition, monthly parts bound in cloth) £3,000
ditto, Bradbury & Evans, 1853 (the above rebound) .
. . . . £250
Hard Times, Bradbury & Evans, 1854 (1 vol., green cloth, with 'Price 5/' on spine) £1,000
ditto, Bradbury & Evans, 1854 (1 vol., green cloth, no price on spine) £500
Little Dorrit, Bradbury & Evans, Dec 1855-June 1857 (20 monthly parts in 19, illustrated by Phiz, blue wrappers, errata slip in part XVI) . . . £1,500
ditto, Bradbury & Evans, 1857 (first book edition, monthly parts bound in olive green cloth), £2,500
A Tale of Two Cities, Chapman & Hall June-Dec MDCCCLIX 1859 (8 parts in 7, illustrated by Phiz, first issue page 213 misnumbered '113', blue wrappers) £7,500
ditto, Chapman & Hall, 1859 (first book edition, monthly parts bound in red cloth, first issue) £7,500
ditto, Chapman & Hall, 1859 (as above in green cloth, first issue) £5,000
ditto, Chapman & Hall, 1859 (as above, rebound) £750
ditto, Chapman & Hall, 1859 (second issue with pages correctly numbered, red cloth) . . . £5,000
ditto, Chapman & Hall, 1859 (second issue with pages correctly numbered, green cloth) . . . £3,500
Great Expectations, Chapman & Hall, MDCCCLXI 1861 (3 vols, purple, plum or yellow-green cloth, 32 pages of ads dated May 1861) . . . £17,500
The Uncommercial Traveller, Chapman & Hall, 1861 (ads dated December 1860, red/purple cloth) £1,250
Our Mutual Friend, Chapman & Hall, May 1864-May 1865 (20 monthly parts in 19, illustrated by Marcus Stone, green wrappers) £1,250
ditto, Chapman & Hall, 1865 (first book edition, 2 vols of monthly parts bound in brown cloth) . £1,500
ditto, Chapman & Hall, 1865 (the above rebound) £250
The Mystery of Edwin Drood, Chapman & Hall, April-Sept 1870 (unfinished, six monthly parts, illustrated by Luke Fildes with cover design by Charles Alston Collins, green wrappers). £750

ditto, Chapman & Hall, 1870 first book edition (monthly parts bound in green cloth, sawtooth border around front cover) £500
ditto, Chapman & Hall, 1870 first book edition (monthly parts bound in green cloth, no border around front cover) £200

BENJAMIN DISRAELI
(b.1804 d.1881)

Perhaps better-known as a politician, Disraeli was also a successful and popular novelist of the nineteenth century.

Fiction
Vivian Grey, Colburn, 1826-27 (5 vols, anonymous) .
. . . . £1,000
The Voyage of Captain Popanilla, Colburn, 1828 £300
The Young Duke, Colburn, 1831 (3 vols) . . £750
Contarini Fleming: A Pyschological Auto-biography, John Murray, 1832 (4 vols) £500
ditto, as *The Young Venetian*, John Murray, 1834 .
. . . . £250
The Wondrous Tale of Alroy, and *The rise of Iskander*, Saunders & Otley, 1833 (3 vols) . £500
A Year at Hartlebury, or The Election, Saunders & Otley, 1834 (pseud. 'Cherry' and 'Fair Star', with Sarah Disraeli, 2 vols) £300
Henrietta Temple, Colburn, 1836 (3 vols) . . £500
Venetia, or The Poet's Daughter, Colburn, 1837 (3 vols) £500
Coningsby, or The New Generation, Colburn, 1844 (3 vols) £500
Sybil, or The Two Nations, Colburn, 1845 (3 vols)
. . . . £500
Tancred, or The New Crusade, Colburn, 1847 (3 vols)
. . . . £400
Lothair, Longman, 1870 (3 vols) . . . £250
Endymion, Longman, 1880 (3 vols) £250
Ixion in Heaven, Cape, 1925 . . . . £25/£10
ditto, Holt (U.S.), 1925 . . . . . £25/£10
The Infernal Marriage, William Jackson, 1929 (850 numbered copies) £45

Poetry
The Revolutionary Epick, Moxon, 1834 (2 vols) £250

LORD ALFRED DOUGLAS
(b.1870 d.1945)

Notorious for his tempestuous affair with Oscar Wilde, Douglas was also a serious poet of some merit.

Verse
Poemes, Mercur de France, (Paris), 1896 . . £275
ditto, Mercur de France, (Paris), 1896 (50 deluxe copies) £350

ditto, Mercur de France, (Paris), 1896 (25 grande deluxe copies) £750
Perkin Warbeck and Some Other Poems, Chiswick Press, 1897 (50 copies) £350
Tails With a Twist: Animal Nonsense Verse, Arnold, 1898 . . . . £100
ditto, Batsford, 1979 . . . . . . £10/£5
The City of the Soul, Grant Richards, 1899 . . £175
The Duke of Berwick, Smithers, [1899]. . . £100
The Placid Pug, Duckworth, 1906 . . . . £75
The Pongo Papers and the Duke of Berwick, Greening, 1907 . . . . £100
Sonnets, W.H. Smith & Son/Academy Publishing Company, 1909 . . . . £75
ditto, Arden Press, 1909 (large paper edition) . £150
Collected Poems, Martin Secker, 1919 . . . £35
ditto, Martin Secker, 1919 (200 copies, signed by the author) £200
In Excelsis, Martin Secker, 1924. . . . £200/£75
ditto, Martin Secker, 1924 (100 signed copies) . £200
Nine Poems, privately printed for A.J.A. Symons, 1926 (50 copies) £500
Selected Poems, Martin Secker, 1926 . . £25/£10
Lord Alfred Douglas ['Selected Poems'], Ernest Benn, 'Augustan Books of Modern Poetry', [1926] (wraps).
. . . . £5
The Duke of Berwick and Other Rhymes, Secker, 1925 . . . . £65/£15
ditto, Knopf (U.S.), 1925 . . . . . £65/£15
Collected Satires, The Fortune Press, 1926 (550 copies) £100
ditto, The Fortune Press, 1926 (250 numbered copies signed by the author) £300
Complete Poems and Light Verse, Martin Secker, 1928 . . . . £125/£35
Lyrics, Rich & Cowan, 1935 . . . . £75/£25
ditto, Rich & Cowan, 1935 (50 copies signed by the author, cloth slipcase) £250
ditto, Richards Press, 1943 . . . . £25/£10
Sonnets, Rich & Cowan, 1935 . . . . £75/£25
ditto, Rich & Cowan, 1935 (edition limited to 50 copies signed by the author, cloth slipcase) . £250
ditto, Richards Press, 1943 . . . . £25/£10
Sonnets, Richards Press, 1943 (pocket edition) £15/£5

Prose
Oscar Wilde and Myself, Long, 1914 . . . £100
ditto, Duffield (U.S.), 1914 . . . . . £75
The Autobiography of Lord Alfred Douglas, Martin Secker, 1929 . . . . £125/£25
ditto, as *My Friendship With Oscar Wilde*, Coventry House (U.S.), 1932 . . . . . £75/£25
The True History of Shakespeare's Sonnets, Secker, 1933 . . . . £75/£25
Without Apology, Secker, 1938 . . . . £50/£20
Oscar Wilde: A Summing Up, Duckworth, 1940 . .
. . . . £75/£20
Ireland and The War Against Hitler, Richards Press, 1940 . . . . £75/£20

The Principles of Poetry, Richards Press, 1943 (1,000 copies, wraps) £20

Others

New Preface to 'The Life and Confessions of Oscar Wilde', The Fortune Press, 1925 (with Frank Harris).
. . . . £75/£45
ditto, The Fortune Press, 1925 (225 signed, numbered copies) £200
Songs of Cell, by Horatio Bottomley, Southern, 1928 (Introduction by Douglas) . . . . . £45/£15
The Pantomime Man, by Richard Middleton, Rich & Cowan, 1933 (Introduction by Douglas) . £75/£25
Bernard Shaw, Frank Harris and Oscar Wilde, by Robert Harborough Sherard, Werner Laurie, 1937 (Preface by Douglas) . . . . . . £45/£15
Brighton Aquatints, by John Piper, Duckworth, 1939 (Introduction by Douglas, 200 copies with uncoloured plates) £600
ditto, by John Piper, Duckworth, 1939 (55 copies with hand-coloured prints) £2,000
Wartime Harvest, by Marie Carmichael Stopes, De la Mare Press, 1944 (Preface by Douglas) . £45/£10
Salome: A Tragedy in One Act, by Oscar Wilde, Heritage Press, 1945 (translated by Douglas, with Sandglass booklet) £25

NORMAN DOUGLAS
(b.1868 d.1952)

A travel writer and novelist, Douglas's *South Wind* is perhaps his best known novel.

Pamphlets

Zur Fauna Santorins, Leipzig, 1892 (c.50 copies, no wraps). £500
Contributions to an Avifauna of Baden, London, 1894 (no wraps, pseud. G. Norman Douglass) . . £500
On the Herpetology of the Grand Duchy of Baden, London, 1894 (50 copies, pseud. G. Norman Douglass). £500
Report on the Pumice Stone Industry of the Lipari Islands, H.M.S.O., 1895 . . . . . . £350
ditto, Hours Press, 1928 (80 copies) £250
On the Darwinian Hypothesis of Sexual Selection, London, 1895 (25 copies, pseud. G. Norman Douglass). £300

Capri Monographs

The Blue Grotto and its Literature, privately printed, 1904 (100 copies) £250
The Forestal Conditions of Capri, privately printed, 1904 (100 copies) £250
Fabio Giordano's Relation of Capri, privately printed, 1906 (250 copies) £200
Three Monographs, privately printed, 1906 (250 copies) £200

The Life of the Venerable Suor Serafina Di Dio, privately printed, 1907 (100 copies) . . . £250
Some Antiquarian Notes, privately printed, 1907 (250 copies) £200
Dislecta Membra, privately printed, 1915 (100 copies) £250
Index, privately printed, 1915 (100 copies) . . £250

Novels

South Wind, Martin Secker, 1917 . . . . £150
ditto, Martin Secker, 1922 (150 signed copies) . £250
ditto, Dodd, Mead (U.S.), 1918 . . . . . £150
ditto, Limited Editions Club (U.S.), 1932 . . £50
They Went, Chapman & Hall, 1920 . . . £125/£45
ditto, Dodd, Mead (U.S.), 1921 . . . . £125/£45
In the Beginning, privately printed (Florence), 1927 (700 signed, numbered copies) . . . . £150/£75
ditto, Chatto & Windus, 1928 . . . . £40/£15
ditto, John Day (U.S.), 1928 . . . . . £50/£20
Nerinda, G. Orioli (Florence), 1929 (475 signed, numbered copies) . . . . . . £150/£75

Short Stories

Unprofessional Tales, T. Fisher Unwin, 1901 (pseud. 'Normyx') £300

Travel/Belles Lettres

Siren Land, J.M. Dent, 1911 . . . . . . £300
ditto, Durton (U.S.), 1911. . . . . . . £250
Fountains in the Sand, Martin Secker, 1912 . £100
ditto, James Pott (U.S.), 1912. . . . . . £25
Old Calabria, Martin Secker, 1915 . . . . £100
Alone, Chapman & Hall, 1921 . . . . £75/£25
ditto, McBride (U.S.), 1922 . . . . . £65/£25
Together, Chapman & Hall, 1923 . . . £75/£25
ditto, Chapman & Hall, 1923 (275 signed copies) £125
ditto, McBride (U.S.), 1923 . . . . . £65/£25
One Day, Hours Press (Paris), 1929 (300 copies) £200
ditto, Hours Press (Paris) (200 signed copies) . £350
Summer Islands, Desmond Harmsworth, 1931. . .
. . . . £35/£15
ditto, Desmond Harmsworth, 1931 (500 numbered copies) . . . . £100/£35
ditto, Colophon (U.S.), 1931 . . . . . £25
ditto, Colophon (U.S.), 1931 (550 signed copies) £100
ditto, Corvinus Press, 1942 [1944] (45 copies, various papers and bindings) £350
Footnote on Capri, Sidgwick & Jackson, 1952 £20/£5
ditto, McBride (U.S.), 1952 . . . . . £20/£5

Others

London Street Games, St Catherine's Press, 1916 £150
ditto, Chatto & Windus, 1931 . . . . £45/£10
ditto, Chatto & Windus, 1931 (110 signed copies) £150
D.H. Lawrence and Maurice Magnus: A Plea for Better Manners, privately printed (Florence), 1924 (wraps) £65
Experiments, privately printed (Florence), 1925 (300 signed, numbered copies) . . . . . £200/£100

ditto, Chapman & Hall, 1925 . . . . . £25/£10
ditto, McBride (U.S.), 1925 . . . . . £25/£10
Birds and Beasts of the Greek Anthology, privately printed (Florence), 1927 (500 signed, numbered copies . . . . £200/£100
ditto, Chapman & Hall, 1928 . . . . . £40/£20
ditto, Cape & Smith (U.S.), 1929 . . . £25/£10
Some Limericks, privately printed (Florence), 1928 (110 signed numbered copies) £250
ditto, privately printed (Florence), 1928 (750 unnumbered copies) £100
ditto, privately printed by Guy d'Isere for David Moss, U.S.), 1928 (750 numbered copies) . . . £75
ditto, privately printed (Florence), 1929 (1,000 numbered copies for subscribers) £100
How About Europe?, privately printed (Florence), 1929 (550 signed, numbered copies) . . £150/£100
ditto, Chatto & Windus, 1930 . . . . £65/£20
The Angel of Manfredonia, The Windsor Press, 1929 (225 numbered copies, no d/w) £150
Three of Them, Chatto & Windus, 1930 . £25/£10
Capri: Materials for a Description of the Island, G. Orioli (Florence), 1930 (525 signed, numbered copies) £300
ditto, G. Orioli (Florence), 1930 (103 signed copies) £500
Paneros, G. Orioli (Florence), 1930 (250 signed copies, slipcase) £200
ditto, Chatto & Windus, 1931 (650 numbered copies) £75
ditto, McBride (U.S.), 1932 (750 copies, box) £65/£50
Looking Back, Chatto & Windus, 1933 (2 vols, 535 signed, numbered sets) £150
ditto, Harcourt, Brace (U.S.), 1933 (1 vol.) . £100/£25
ditto, Chatto & Windus, 1934 (1 vol.) . . £35/£10
An Almanac, privately printed (Lisbon), 1941 (25 [c.50] signed, numbered copies) £400
ditto, Secker & Warburg, 1945 . . . . £25/£10
Late Harvest, Lindsay Drummond, 1946 . £20/£5
Venus in the Kitchen, Heinemann, 1952 . £25/£5
ditto, Viking (U.S.), 1953 . . . . . . £25/£5

ERNEST DOWSON
(b.1867 d.1900)

Dowson was one of the best of the decadent poets of the 1890s. He also prepared translations and wrote short stories, before dying of tuberculosis at the age of thirty-two.

Verse
Verses, Leonard Smithers, 1896 (300 copies. Cover design by Aubrey Beardsley) £750
ditto, Leonard Smithers, 1896 (30 copies on Japanese Vellum) £3,000

The Pierrot of the Minute, Leonard Smithers, 1897 (illustrated by Aubrey Beardsley, 300 copies printed on handmade paper) £500
ditto, Leonard Smithers, 1897 (30 copies printed on Japanese vellum) £3,000
ditto, Grolier Club (U.S.), 1923 (300 copies printed on Dutch antique paper, slipcase) £250
Decorations, in Verse & Prose, Leonard Smithers, 1899 . . . . £400
The Poems of Ernest Dowson, John Lane, 1905 (edited and with a memoir by Arthur Symons. Illustrated by Aubrey Beardsley) £125
Cynara: A Little Book of Verse, Thomas Mosher (U.S.), 1907 (950 copies, slipcase) £45
Poetical Works of Ernest Dowson, Cassell/John Lane, 1934 (edited by Desmond Flower) . . . £25/£10
ditto, Cassell's Pocket Library, 1950 . . . £10/£5
The Poems of Ernest Dowson, The Unicorn Press, 1946 . . . . £15/£5
The Poems of Ernest Dowson, Univ. of Pennsylvania Press (U.S.), 1962 (edited by Mark Longaker) £20/£5

Prose
A Comedy of Masks, Heinemann, 1893 (with Arthur Moore. Novel in 3 vols) £200
Dilemmas, Elkin Matthews, 1895 (short stories) £150
Adrian Rome, Methuen, 1899 (with Arthur Moore) £75
The Stories of Ernest Dowson, Univ. of Pennsylvania (U.S.), 1947 . . . . £20/£10
ditto, W.H. Allen [1949] (edited by Mark Longaker) . . . . £15/£5
The Letters of Ernest Dowson, Fairleigh Dickinson (U.S.), 1967 (collected and edited by Desmond Flower & Henry Maas) . . . . . . £30/£20
ditto, Cassell, 1967 . . . . £30/£20
Bouquet, Whittington Press, 1991 . . . . £90
New Letters from Ernest Dowson, Whittington Press, 1984 (220 copies, signed by Desmond Flower) £50

Translations
La Terre, by Emile Zola, Lutetian Society, 1894 £100
Majesty, by Couperus, T. Fisher Unwin, 1894 (translated with A. Teixera de Mattos) £35
La Fille Aux Yeux D'Or, by Honore de Balzac, Leonard Smithers, 1896 (illustrated by Charles Conder) £75
Memoirs of Cardinal Dubois, Leonard Smithers, 1899 (2 vols) £75
La Pucelle D'Orleans, by Voltaire, Lutetian Society, 1899 (500 sets, 2 vols) £125
The Conficantes of a King, by Edmond & Jules de Goncourt, T.N. Foulis, 1907 . . . . . £25
The Story of the Beauty and the Beast, John Lane, 1908 [1907] (illustrated by Charles Conder) . £40
Dangerous Acquaintances, by Pierre Choderlos de Lacios, Nonesuch Press, 1940 (illustrated by Charles Laborde) £40

SIR ARTHUR CONAN DOYLE
(b.1859 d.1930)

Best known, of course, for his creation of the ever-popular detective, Sherlock Holmes. Conan Doyle also wrote historical fiction, the genre of which he was most fond.

Sherlock Holmes Titles

A Study in Scarlet, 28th Beeton's Christmas Annual, 1887 (story contained in first 95pps, wraps) £40,000
ditto, 28ᵗʰ Beeton's Christmas Annual, 1887 (rebound)
. . . . £15,000
ditto, Ward Lock, 1888 (first book edition, first issue with 'younger' spelt correctly in preface, wraps). .
. . . . £50,000
ditto, Ward Lock, 1888 (second issue with 'youunger', wraps). £15,000
The Sign of Four, Lippincott's Magazine, February 1890 (pp. 147-223, wraps) £1,500
ditto, Lippincott's/Ward Lock, 1890, in *Six Complete Novels by Famous Authors*. £750
ditto, Lippincott's/Ward Lock, 1891, in *Five Complete Novels by Famous Authors*. £500
ditto, Spencer Blackett, 1890 (first book edition, first issue) £5,000
ditto, Spencer Blackett, 1890 (second issue, remainder sheets issued by Griffin Farran, with 'Griffith Farran and Co' at foot of spine). £2,500
ditto, Spencer Blackett, 1892 (third issue, remainder sheets issued by Newnes, with 'Griffith Farran and Co' on cover). £1,500
The Adventures of Sherlock Holmes, George Newnes, 1892 . . . . £2,000
ditto, Harper (U.S.), 1892 (first issue with 'if had' on page 65, line 4) £1,000
ditto, Harper (U.S.), 1892 (second issue with 'if he had') £500
The Memoirs of Sherlock Holmes, George Newnes, 1894 [1893] £1,000
ditto, Harper (U.S.), 1894. . . . . . £600
The Hound of the Baskervilles, George Newnes, 1902
. . . . £2,000
ditto, McClure, Phillips (U.S.), 1902 (first issue without 'Published 1902' on copyright page) £750
ditto, McClure, Phillips (U.S.), 1902 (second issue with 'Published 1902') £200
ditto, McClure, Phillips (U.S.), 1902 (third issue with tipped in title page with 'Illustrated') . . . £150
ditto, McClure, Phillips (U.S.), 1902 (fourth issue, as third but integral title page) £75
The Return of Sherlock Holmes, McClure, Phillips (U.S.), 1905 (black cloth) £500
ditto, McClure, Phillips (U.S.), 1905 ('special edition', dark-blue cloth) £150
ditto, George Newnes, 1905 . . . . . .£1,500
The Valley of Fear, Doran (U.S.), 1914. . . £300
ditto, Smith Elder, 1915 . . . . . . £300
His Last Bow, John Murray, 1917 . . . . £300

ditto, Doran (U.S.), 1917 (orange cloth). . . £135
ditto, Doran (U.S.), 1917 (red cloth). . . . £100
The Case-Book of Sherlock Holmes, John Murray, 1927 . . . . £2,500/£300
ditto, Doran (U.S.), 1927 . . . . . .£750/£100

Novels
The Mystery of Cloomber, Ward and Downey 1889 [1888] (wraps) £500
ditto, Fenno (U.S.), 1895 . . . . £75
Micah Clarke, Longmans Green, 1889 . . . £300
The Firm of Girdlestone, Chatto & Windus, 1890 (ads dated January 1890) £350
ditto, Chatto & Windus, 1890 (ads dated later) £250
The White Company, Smith Elder, 1891 (3 vols) . .
. . . .£3,000
ditto, Smith Elder, 1892 (1 vol.) £75
ditto, John Lovell Co (U.S.), 1891 (tan wraps) . £500
ditto, Lovell, Coryell & Co. (U.S.), 1892 (white pictorial wraps) £300
The Doings of Raffles Haw, Lovell (U.S.), 1891 £200
ditto, Cassell, 1892 . . . . £350
The Great Shadow, Arrowsmith's Christmas Annual, 1892 (pictorial wraps) £400
ditto, Arrowsmith's Christmas Annual, 1892 (cloth, brown endpapers) £150
Beyond the City, Rand McNally (U.S.), [1892] £125
The Great Shadow, and Beyond the City, Arrowsmith [1893] £75
ditto, Harper (U.S.), 1893. . . . . . . £75
The Refugees, Longmans Green, 1893 (3 vols) £3,000
ditto, Longmans Green [August], 1893 (1 vol.). £100
ditto, Harper (U.S.), 1893. . . . . . . £100
The Parasite, Constable, 1894 . . . . . £150
ditto, Constable, 1894 (wraps) £150
Rodney Stone, Smith Elder, 1896 . . . . £100
ditto, Appleton (U.S.) 1896 . . . . . . £75
Uncle Bernac, Horace Cox, 1896 [Jan 1897] (wraps, copyright edition: Chapters 1-10 only). . .£1,500
ditto, Smith Elder, 1897 . . . . . . £150
ditto, Appleton (U.S.) 1897 . . . . . £150
A Desert Drama, being the tragedy of the Korosko, Lippincott (U.S.), 1898 . . . . . . £100
ditto, as *The Tragedy of Korosko*, Smith Elder, 1898 .
. . . . £100
Sir Nigel, Smith Elder, 1906 . . . . . £75
ditto, McClure, Phillips (U.S.), 1906. . . . £65
The Lost World, Hodder & Stoughton, [1912] . £650
ditto, Hodder & Stoughton, [1912] (large paper edition, 190 of 1,000 copies comprise the first issue) £1,500
ditto, Henry Frowde/Hodder & Stoughton, [1912] (large paper edition, 810 of 1,000 copies comprise the second issue) £400
ditto, Doran (U.S.), 1912 . . . . . . £400
The Land Of Mist, Hutchinson, [1926] . £2,000/£200
ditto, Doran (U.S.),1926 . . . . . .£500/£50
The Maracot Deep, John Murray, 1929 (novel and 3 short stories) . . . .£750/£75

Short Stories
Mysteries and Adventures, Walter Scott, [1890] £1,500
ditto, Walter Scott, [1890], (wraps) £1,000
The Captain of the Polestar, Longmans, 1890 . £50
Round the Red Lamp, Methuen, 1894 . . . £45
ditto, Appleton (U.S.), 1894 . . . . . £45
The Exploits of Brigadier Gerard, Newnes, 1896
(advertisements dated 10/2/96) £75
ditto, Newnes, 1896 (later advertisements) . . £60
ditto, Appleton (U.S.), 1896 . . . . . £45
The Green Flag, Smith Elder, 1900 . . . . £50
Adventures of Gerard, Newnes, 1903 . . . £50
ditto, McClure, Phillips (U.S.), 1903 . . . . £30
The Croxley Master, A Great Tale of the Prize Ring,
McClure, Phillips (U.S.), 1907 . . . . . £50
Round the Fire Stories, Smith Elder, 1908 . . £30
ditto, McClure, Phillips (U.S.), 1908. . . . £30
The Last Galley, Smith Elder, 1911 . . . . £50
ditto, Doubleday (U.S.), 1911 . . . . . £30
Danger, John Murray, 1918 . . . . . . £30

Plays
Waterloo, French, 1907 . . . . £150

Collected Edition
*The Crowborough Edition of the Works of Sir Arthur
Conan Doyle*, Doubleday, Doran (U.S.) 1930 (24
volumes, 760 signed copies) £5,000

RODDY DOYLE
(b.1958)

Doyle achieved recognition when *The Commitments*
was filmed in 1991, the same year that *The Van* was
shortlisted for the Booker Prize. *Paddy Clarke Ha Ha
Ha* won the Booker Prize 1993, establishing Doyle as
a leading comic writer, earning comparisons to Irish
humorists O'Casey and Behan.

The Commitments, King Farouk (Dublin), 1987
(wraps) £100
ditto, Heinemann, 1988 . . . . . . £75/£15
ditto, Vintage (U.S.), 1989 (wraps) £10
The Snapper, Secker, 1990 . . . . . £200/£35
ditto, Penguin (U.S.), 1992 (wraps) £10
The Van, Secker, 1991 . . . . . £125/£20
ditto, Viking (U.S.), 1992. . . . . . £15/£5
The Barrytown Trilogy, Secker, 1992 (contains *The
Commitments, The Snapper*, and *The Van*) £50/£10
Paddy Clarke, Ha Ha Ha, Secker, 1993 . £75/£10
ditto, Viking (U.S.), 1994. . . . . . £15/£5
The Woman Who Walked Into Doors, Cape, 1996 .
. . . . £20/£5
ditto, Viking (U.S.), 1996 . . . . . £15/£5
Star Called Henry, Cape, 1999 . . . . £20/£5
ditto, Viking (U.S.), 1999 . . . . . £15/£5

Drama
War, Passion Machine, 1989 (wraps) . . . £150
ditto, Penguin (U.S.), 1992 (wraps) £10
Brownbread and War, Secker, 1992 (wraps) . £20
ditto, Penguin (U.S.), 1994 (wraps) £10

Children's
The Giggler Treatment, Scholastic Press, 2000 £20/£5
ditto, Levine/Scholastic (U.S.), 2000 . . £20/£5

MARGARET DRABBLE
(b.1939)

Drabble's novels often explore the struggle of the
individual against convention or repression. She was
awarded a C.B.E. in 1980 for her services to English
literature.

Novels
A Summer Bird-Cage, Weidenfeld, 1963 . £250/£35
ditto, Morrow (U.S.), 1964 . . . . . £50/£15
The Garrick Year, Weidenfeld, 1964 . . £75/£20
ditto, Morrow (U.S.), 1965 . . . . . £30/£10
The Millstone, Weidenfeld, 1965 . . . £50/£15
ditto, Morrow (U.S.), 1966 . . . . . £25/£5
Jerusalem the Golden, Weidenfeld, 1967 . £35/£10
ditto, Morrow (U.S.), 1967 . . . . . £25/£5
The Waterfall, Weidenfeld, 1969 . . . £30/£5
ditto, Knopf (U.S.), 1969 . . . . . . £20/£5
The Needle's Eye, Weidenfeld, 1972 . . £30/£5
ditto, Knopf (U.S.), 1972 . . . . . . £20/£5
The Realms of Gold, Weidenfeld, 1975 . . £15/£5
ditto, Knopf (U.S.), 1975 . . . . . . £15/£5
The Ice Age, Weidenfeld, 1977 . . . . £15/£5
ditto, Knopf (U.S.), 1977 . . . . . . £15/£5
The Middle Ground, Weidenfeld, 1980 . . £10/£5
ditto, Knopf (U.S.), 1980 . . . . . . £10/£5
The Radiant Way, Weidenfeld & Nicolson, 1987 . .
. . . . £10/£5
ditto, Knopf (U.S.), 1987 . . . . . . £10/£5
A Natural Curiosity, Viking, 1989 . . . £10/£5
ditto, London Limited Editions, 1989 (150 signed
copies) . . . . £65/£45
ditto, Viking (U.S.), 1989. . . . . . £10/£5
The Gates of Ivory, Viking, 1991 . . . £10/£5
ditto, Viking (U.S.), 1992. . . . . . £10/£5
The Witch of Exmoor, Viking, 1996 . . £10/£5
ditto, Harcourt Brace (U.S.), 1996 . . . £10/£5

Non Fiction
Wordsworth, Evans, 1966 . . . . . £35/£5
ditto, Arco (U.S.), 1969 (no d/w). £20
Virginia Woolf: A Personal Debt, Aloe Editions
(U.S.), 1973 (110 signed copies, wraps) . . £125
Arnold Bennett: A Biography, Weidenfeld, 1974 . .
. . . . £25/£5
ditto, Knopf (U.S.), 1974 . . . . . . £25/£5

A Writer's Britain: Landscape in Literature, Thames
& Hudson, 1979 . . . . £25/£10
ditto, Knopf (U.S.), 1979 . . . . . £20/£10
*The Tradition of Women's Fiction: Lectures in
Japan*, O.U.P., (Tokyo), 1985 . . . . . £25/£5
Case for Equality, Fabian Society, 1988 . . £10
Stratford Revisited: A Legacy of the Sixties, Celandine
Press, 1989 (150 signed copies, wraps) . . £20
*Safe As Houses: An Examination of Home Owner-
ship and Mortgage Tax Relief*, Chatto & Windus,
1990 . . . . £5
Angus Wilson: A Biography, Secker & Warburg, 1995
. . . . £15/£5
ditto, St Martin's Press (U.S.), 1996 . . . £10/£5

Children's
For Queen and Country: Britain in the Victorian Age,
Deutsch, 1978 . . . . £15/£5
ditto, Seabury Press (U.S.), 1979. . . . £10/£5

THEODORE DREISER
(b.1871 d.1945)

Considered by many to be the first exponent of
Naturalism in American writing, his writing dealt
with social problems and characters struggling to
survive. His sympathetic treatment of a 'morally
loose' woman in *Sister Carrie* was branded immoral
and he suffered, principally, at the hands of his own
publishers.

Novels
Sister Carrie, Doubleday (U.S.), 1900 . . £3,000
ditto, Heinemann, 1901 . . . . . . £500
Jennie Gerhardt, Harpers (U.S.) 1911 (first issue, 'is'
for 'it' on page 22, line 30, 'Theodore Dreiser' on
spine, mottled light blue cloth) £300
ditto, Harpers (U.S.) 1911 (second issue, text corrected,
'Dreiser 'on spine) £125
The Financier, Harpers (U.S.) 1912 (first issue with
'Published October, 1912' and 'K-M' on title page) .
. . . . £125
The Titan, John Lane/The Bodley Head (U.S), 1914 .
. . . . £125
The Genius, John Lane (U.S.), 1915 (first issue, 1¼
inches thick, p.497 correctly numbered) . . £200
ditto, John Lane (U.S.), 1915 (second issue, 1½ inches
thick, p.497 unnumbered) £100
ditto, John Lane (U.K.), 1915 (first issue, 1¼ inches
thick, p.497 correctly numbered) . . . £200
ditto, John Lane (U.K.), 1915 (second issue, 1½ inches
thick, p.497 unnumbered) £100
Twelve Men, Boni & Liveright (U.S.), 1919 . £50
An American Tragedy, Boni & Liveright (U.S.), 1925
(2 vols, first issue, black cloth, white endpapers,
slipcase) . . . . £600/£100

ditto, Boni & Liveright (U.S.), 1925 (2 vols, second
issue, blue cloth, slipcase) . . . . £500/£100
ditto, Boni & Liveright (U.S.), 1925 (795 signed
copies, 2 vols, slipcase) . . . . . £600/£100
A Gallery of Women, Boni & Liveright (U.S.), 1929
(560 signed copies, 2 vols, slipcase) . . £300/£50
ditto, Boni & Liveright (U.S.), 1929 (2 vols) £200/£50
ditto, Constable, 1930 . . . . . . £65/£15
The Bulwark, Doubleday, 1946 . . . . £65/£20
ditto, Constable, 1947 . . . . . . £50/£15
The Stoic, Doubleday, 1947 . . . . . £65/£20

Short Stories
Free and Other Stories, Boni & Liveright (U.S.), 1918
. . . . £125
Chains, Boni & Liveright (U.S.), 1927 (440 signed,
numbered copies, slipcase) . . . . £300/£200
ditto, Boni & Liveright (U.S.), 1927 . . £125/£35

Verse
Moods, Boni & Liveright (U.S.), 1926 (550 signed,
numbered copies) . . . . . . £250/£150
ditto, Constable 1929 . . . . . . £65/£15
The Aspirant, Random House (U.S.), 1929 . £65/£15
Epitaph, Heron Press (U.S.), 1929 (200 signed full
leather copies, slipcase) . . . . . £300/£250
ditto, Heron Press (U.S.), 1929 (200 signed copies
bound in silk, slipcase, glassine d/w) . £200/£150
ditto, Heron Press (U.S.), 1929 (700 signed copies
bound in cloth, slipcase, glassine d/w) . £150/£150

Others
A Traveller at Forty, Century, 1913 . . . . £75
A Hoosier Holiday, John Lane (U.S.), 1916 . £125
ditto, John Lane (U.K.), 1916 . . . . £125
*Hey Rub-a-Dub-Dub: A Book of the Mystery and
Wonder and Terror of Life*, Boni & Liveright (U.S.),
1920 . . . . £250/£45
A Book About Myself, Boni & Liveright (U.S.), 1922 .
. . . . £125/£45
ditto, as *Newspaper Days*, Boni & Liveright (U.S.),
1931 . . . . £100/£35
ditto, as *Dawn*, Boni & Liveright (U.S.), 1931 (275
signed copies, slipcase) . . . . . £225/£175
ditto, as *Dawn*, Boni & Liveright (U.S.), 1931 £75/£25
ditto, as *Autobiography*, Boni & Liveright (U.S.), 1965
(2 vols) . . . . £100/£25
The Color of a Great City, Boni & Liveright (U.S.),
1923 . . . . £100/£35
ditto, Constable, 1930 . . . . . . £50/£15
Dreiser Looks at Russia, Boni & Liveright (U.S.),
1928 . . . . £75/£25
The Carnegie Works at Pittsburgh, (privately printed),
1929 (150 numbered copies) £200
Tragic America, Boni & Liveright (U.S.), 1931 . .
. . . . £65/£20
America is Worth Saving, Modern Age Books, 1941 .
. . . . £65/£10

DAPHNE DU MAURIER
(b.1907 d.1989)

Du Maurier is the author of tense romances set against the background of Cornwall, her home for most of her life.

Novels

The Loving Spirit, Heinemann, 1931		£250/£45
ditto, Doubleday (U.S.), 1931		£200/£25
I'll Never Be Young Again, Heinemann, 1932		
		£250/£45
ditto, Doubleday (U.S.), 1932		£200/£25
The Progress of Julius, Heinemann, 1933		£250/£45
Jamaica Inn, Gollancz, 1936		£350/£75
ditto, Doubleday (U.S.), 1936		£250/£65
Rebecca, Gollancz, 1938		£2,500/£300
ditto, Doubleday (U.S.), 1938		£1,000/£150
Frenchman's Creek, Gollancz, 1941		£75/£20
ditto, Doubleday (U.S.), 1942		£65/£15
Hungry Hill, Gollancz, 1943		£30/£5
ditto, Doubleday (U.S.), 1943		£25/£5
The King's General, Gollancz, 1946		£30/£5
ditto, Doubleday (U.S.), 1946		£35/£5
The Parasites, Gollancz, 1949		£25/£5
ditto, Doubleday (U.S.), 1950		£20/£5
My Cousin Rachel, Gollancz, 1951		£20/£5
ditto, Doubleday (U.S.), 1952		£20/£5
Mary Anne, Gollancz, 1954		£20/£5
ditto, Doubleday (U.S.), 1954		£20/£5

The Daphne du Maurier Omnibus, Gollancz, 1956 (contains *Rebecca, Jamaica Inn* and *Frenchman's Creek*) . . . . £15/£5
The Scapegoat, Gollancz, 1957 . . . £20/£5
ditto, Doubleday (U.S.), 1957 . . . . £20/£5
Castle Dor, Gollancz, 1962 (with Sir Arthur Quiller-Couch) . . . . £15/£5
ditto, Doubleday (U.S.), 1962 . . . . £15/£5
The Glassblowers, Gollancz, 1963 . . . £20/£5
ditto, Doubleday (U.S.), 1963 . . . . £15/£5
The Daphne du Maurier Tandem, Gollancz, 1964 (contains *Mary Anne* and *My Cousin Rachel*) £15/£5
The Flight of the Falcon, Gollancz, 1965 . £15/£5
ditto, Doubleday (U.S.), 1965 . . . . £15/£5
The House on the Strand, Gollancz, 1969 . £15/£5
ditto, Doubleday (U.S.), 1969 . . . . £15/£5
Rule Britannia, Gollancz, 1972 . . . £15/£5
ditto, Doubleday (U.S.), 1972 . . . £15/£5
Three Famous Daphne du Maurier Novels, Gollancz, 1982 (contains *The Flight of the Falcon, The House on the Strand* and *The King's General*) . . £10/£5
Four Great Cornish Novels, Gollancz, 1982 (contains *Jamaica Inn, Rebecca, Frenchman's Creek* and *My Cousin Rachel*) . . . . £10/£5

Short Stories

Happy Christmas, Doubleday (U.S.), 1940 . £40/£10
ditto, Todd Publishing Co., 1943 . . . . £35/£10
Come Wind, Come Weather, Heinemann, 1940 (wraps) £15
ditto, Doubleday (U.S.), 1941 (wraps) . . . £15
Consider the Lilies, Polybooks/Todd Publishing Co., 1943 (wraps) £20
Escort, Polybooks/Todd Publishing Co., 1943 (wraps) £25
Nothing Hurts for Long; and Escort, Polybooks/Todd Publishing Co., 1943 (wraps) £20
Spring Picture, Todd Publishing Co., 1944 (no d/w) £25
Leading Lady, Polybooks/Vallancey Press, 1945 (wraps) £20
London and Paris, Polybooks/Vallancey Press, 1945 (wraps) £20
The Apple Tree, Gollancz, 1952 (later published as *The Birds*) . . . . £100/£15
Early Stories, Bantam Books, 1954 . . . . £15
The Breaking Point, Gollancz, 1959 (later published as *The Blue Lenses*) . . . . . . £30/£5
ditto, Doubleday (U.S.), 1959 . . . . £25/£5
The Treasury of du Maurier Short Stories, Gollancz, 1960 (contains *The Apple Tree* and *The Breaking Point*). . . . . £10/£5
The Lover, Ace Wraps (U.S.), 1961 . . . . £5
Not After Midnight, Gollancz, 1971 (later published as *Don't Look Now*) . . . . . . £40/£10
Echoes from the Macabre, Gollancz, 1976 . £40/£10
ditto, Doubleday (U.S.), 1976 . . . . £35/£10
The Rendezvous, Gollancz, 1980 . . . £15/£5
Classics of the Macabre, Gollancz, 1987 . £25/£5
ditto, Gollancz, 1987 (250 signed copies in slipcase) . . . . £175/£150
ditto, Doubleday (U.S.), 1987 . . . . £25/£5

Plays

Rebecca, Gollancz, 1940 . . . . . . £65/£15
The Years Between, Gollancz, 1945 . . . £30/£10
ditto, Doubleday (U.S.), 1946 . . . . £30/£10
September Tide, Gollancz, 1946 . . . . £30/£10
ditto, Doubleday (U.S.), 1950 . . . . £25/£10
The Little Photographer, French, 1979 (wraps, adapted by Derek Hoddinott) £5
My Cousin Rachel, French, 1979, (wraps, adapted by Diana Morgan) £5

Biographies

Gerald: A Portrait, Gollancz, 1934 . . . £50/£10
The du Mauriers, Gollancz, 1937 . . . £65/£15
The Infernal World of Branwell Brontë, Gollancz, 1960 . . . . £20/£5
ditto, Doubleday (U.S.), 1961 . . . . £15/£5
The Golden Lads, Gollancz, 1975 . . . £20/£5
ditto, Doubleday (U.S.), 1975 . . . . £15/£5
The Winding Stair: Francis Bacon, His Rise And Fall, Gollancz, 1976. . . . . . . £20/£5

ditto, Doubleday (U.S.), 1977 . . . . £15/£5
Growing Pains: The Shaping of a Writer, Gollancz,
1977 . . . . £20/£5
The Rebecca Notebook & Other Memories,
Doubleday (U.S.), 1980 . . . . . . £15/£5
ditto, Gollancz, 1981 . . . . £15/£5

Miscellaneous
Vanishing Cornwall, Gollancz, 1967 . . £20/£5
ditto, Doubleday (U.S.), 1967 . . . . £15/£5
ditto, Gollancz, 1981 (colour edition) . . £15/£5
ditto, Doubleday (U.S.), 1981 . . . . £10/£5

GEORGE DU MAURIER
(b.1834 d.1896)

Principally a novelist and critic, du Maurier's *Trilby*
brought the author fame. He also wrote humorous
verse.

Novels
Peter Ibbetson, Harper (U.S.), 1892 . . . . £30
ditto, Osgood, McIlvaine, 1892 (2 vols) . . . £90
Trilby, Osgood, McIlvaine, 1894, (3 vols) . . £250
ditto, Osgood, McIlvaine, 1895, (250 signed copies, 1
vol.) £100
ditto, Harper (U.S.), 1894. . . . . . £20
The Martian, Harper (U.S.), 1897 . . . . £25
ditto, Harper (U.K.), 1898 . . . . . £25
Svengali, W.H. Allen, 1982 (first unexpurgated edition
of *Trilby*) . . . . £10/£5

Others
Gauwaine Hys Penance: A Legend of Camelot,
Bradbury & Evans, 1866 (wraps) £500
English Society at Home, Bradbury, Agnew & Co.,
1880 . . . . £75
Society Pictures, Bradbury, Agnew & Co., 1890-91 (2
vols) £100
English Society, Osgood, McIlvaine, 1897 . . £75
ditto, Harper (U.S.), 1897. . . . . . £75
Social Pictorial Satire, Harper & Bros., 1898 . £45
ditto, Harper (U.S.), 1898. . . . . . £35
A Legend of Camelot, Bradbury, Agnew & Co., 1898
. . . . £20
The Young du Maurier: A Selection of his Letters,
Peter Davies, 1951 . . . . £15/£5

EDMUND DULAC
(b.1882 d.1953)

A French illustrator, and rival to Arthur Rackham,
Dulac illustrated many 'gift book' editions of popular
fairy tales.

Written and Illustrated by Dulac
Lyrics Pathetic and Humorous From A to Z, Warne,
1908 . . . . £350
ditto, Warne, 1908 [1909], (portfolio of 24 plates,
cloth-covered box) £2,500
*A Fairy Garland: Being Fairy Tales from the Old
French*, Cassell, 1928 . . . . . £350/£75
ditto, Cassell, 1928 (deluxe edition, 1,000 signed
copies, slipcase and glassine d/w) . . £400/£300
ditto, Scribner's (U.S.), 1929. . . . . £200/£75

Illustrated by Dulac
The Novels of the Brontë Sisters, by The Brontës,
Dent, 1905 (10 vols). . . . . . . £25 each
Fairies I Have Met, by Mrs R. Stawell, John Lane
[1901]. £60
ditto, Hodder & Stoughton, [1910] . . . £50
ditto, as *My Days With the Fairies*, Hodder &
Stoughton, [1913] £125
Stories from The Arabian Nights, retold by Laurence
Housman, Hodder & Stoughton, 1907 . . . £150
ditto, Hodder & Stoughton, 1907 (deluxe edition, 350
signed copies) £1,000
ditto, Scribner's (U.S.), 1907. . . . . £150
The Tempest, by William Shakespeare, Hodder &
Stoughton, [1908] £150
ditto, Hodder & Stoughton, [1908] (deluxe edition, 500
signed copies) £750
The Rubaiyat of Omar Khyyam, by Edward Fitzgerald,
Hodder & Stoughton, [1909] £100
ditto, Hodder & Stoughton, [1909] (deluxe edition, 750
signed copies) £500
The Sleeping Beauty, retold by Sir Arthur Quiller-
Couch, Hodder & Stoughton, [1910] . . . £250
ditto, Hodder & Stoughton, [1910] (deluxe edition,
1,000 signed copies). £750
Stories from Hans Andersen, Hodder & Stoughton,
1911 . . . . £250
ditto, Hodder & Stoughton, 1911 (deluxe edition, 750
signed copies) £1,000
ditto, Hodder & Stoughton, 1911 (deluxe edition, 100
signed copies, morocco binding) £2,500
The Bells and Other Poems, by Edgar Allan Poe,
Hodder & Stoughton, [1912] £150
ditto, Hodder & Stoughton, [1912] (deluxe edition, 750
signed copies) £600
Princess Badoura: A Tale from The Arabian Nights,
retold by Laurence Housman, Hodder & Stoughton,
[1913]. £150
ditto, Hodder & Stoughton, [1913] (deluxe edition, 750
signed copies) £750

Sinbad the Sailor and Other Stories from the Arabian Nights, Hodder & Stoughton, [1914] . . . £350
ditto, Hodder & Stoughton, [1914] (deluxe edition, 500 signed copies) £1,750
Edmund Dulac's Picture-Book for the French Red Cross, Hodder & Stoughton, [1915] . . . £40
The Dreamer of Dreams, by Queen Marie of Roumania, Hodder & Stoughton, [1915] . . £45
The Stealers of Light, by Queen Marie of Roumania, Hodder & Stoughton, 1916 . . . . . . £35
Edmund Dulac's Fairy-Book, Hodder & Stoughton, [1916]. £125
ditto, Hodder & Stoughton, [1916] (deluxe edition, 350 signed copies) £600
ditto, Hodder & Stoughton, 1919 (extra plate) . £100
Tanglewood Tales, by Nathaniel Hawthorne, Hodder & Stoughton, [1918]. £100
ditto, Hodder & Stoughton, [1918] (deluxe edition, 500 signed copies) £500
The Kingdom of the Pearl, by Leonard Rosenthal, Nisbet, [1920], (675 copies). . . . . . £350/£200
ditto, Nisbet, [1920] (100 signed copies) . . £1,250
ditto, Brentano's (U.S.) 1920 (675 numbered copies) . . . . £350/£200
Four Plays for Dancers, by W.B. Yeats, Macmillan, 1921 . . . . £100
The Green Lacquer Pavilion, by Helen Beauclerk, Collins, 1926 . . . . £25/£10
ditto, Doran (U.S.) 1926 . . . . . . £60/£20
Treasure Island, by Robert Louis Stevenson, Benn, 1927 . . . . £300/£150
ditto, Benn, 1927 (deluxe edition, 50 signed copies) £3,000
ditto, Doran (U.S.) [1927] . . . . . £125/£65
Gods and Mortals in Love, by Hugh Ross Williamson, Country Life, [1936]. . . . . . . £250/£50
The Daughters of the Stars, by Mary C. Crary, Hatchard, 1939 . . . . £25/£15
ditto, Hatchard, 1939 (deluxe edition, 500 copies signed by author and artist) £125
The Golden Cockerel, by Alexander Pushkin, Limited Editions Club (U.S.), [1950], (1,500 signed, numbered copies, slipcase) . . . . . £100/£85
ditto, Heritage Press, (U.S.) 1950 (slipcase) £50/£45
The Marriage of Cupid and Psyche, by Walter Pater, Limited Editions Club (U.S.), [1951], (1,500 signed, numbered copies) . . . . . . £100/£85
ditto, Heritage Press, (U.S.), 1951 (slipcase) £35/£30
The Masque of Comus, by John Milton, Limited Editions Club (U.S.), 1954, (1,500 numbered copies, slipcase) . . . . £100/£85
ditto, Heritage Press, (U.S.), 1955 (slipcase) £35/£30

DOUGLAS DUNN
(b.1942)

A Scottish poet whose early work shows the influence of Philip Larkin.

Verse
Terry Street, Faber, 1969 . . . . . . £35/£10
ditto, Chilmark (U.S.), 1969 . . . . . £20/£5
Backwaters, The Review, 1971 (wraps). . . £20
Night, Poem of the Month Club, 1971 (broadside) £15
The Happier Life, Faber, 1972 . . . . £25/£10
ditto, Chilmark (U.S.), [no date] . . . £20/£5
Love or Nothing, Faber, 1974 (wraps) . . . £10
Corporal Punishment, Sycamore Press, 1975 (broadside) £10
Barbarians, Faber, 1979 (wraps). . . . £10
St Kilda's Parliament, Faber, 1981 (wraps). . £10
Douglas Dunn: Writers in brief, No 18, National Book League, 1981 (broadside) £10
Europa's Lover, Bloodaxe, 1982 (wraps) . . £10
Elegies, Faber, 1985 . . . . £15/£5
ditto, Faber, 1985 (wraps). £5
Selected Poems 1964-1983, Faber, 1986 . £15/£5
ditto, Faber, 1986 (wraps). £5
Northlight, Faber, 1988 . . . . . . £15/£5
ditto, Faber, 1988 (wraps). £5
New and Selected Poems 1966-1988, Ecco Press (U.S.), 1989 . . . . £10/£5
Dante's Drum-Kit, Faber, 1993 . . . . £10/£5
Garden Hints, Carninorous Arpeggio Press, 1993 (50 numbered copies, wraps) £15
The Donkey's Ears, Faber, 2000 (wraps) . . £5

Prose
Secret Villages, Faber, 1985 . . . . . £15/£5
ditto, Dodd, Mead, 1985 . . . . . . £15/£5
Boyfriends and Girlfriends, Faber, 1995 . £10/£5

Others
Under the Influence: Douglas Dunn on Philip Larkin, Edinburgh Univ. Press Library, 1987 £10
Poll Tax, the Fiscal Fake: Why We Should Fight the Community Charge, Chatto & Windus, 1990 . £10
The Topical Muse on Contemporary Poetry, Kenneth Allott Lecture No 6, [1990] (wraps) . . . £10

LORD DUNSANY
(b.1878 d.1957)

A versatile Irish writer, Dunsany is read and appreciated today for his contributions to the genre of heroic fantasy.

Short Stories
The Gods of Pegana, Elkin Mathews, 1905 (drummer blind-stamped on front cover) £400

ditto, Elkin Mathews, 1905 (no drummer on front cover) £200
ditto, Luce (U.S.), [1916] £100
Time and the Gods, W. Heinemann, 1906 . . £150
ditto, Luce (U.S.), 1913 . . . . £75
ditto, Putnam's, 1922 [1923] (250 copies signed by Dunsany and Sime) £275
The Sword of Welleran, George Allen, 1908 (the first issue has 'George Allen & Sons' at base of spine) £100
ditto, George Allen, 1908 (second issue with 'George Allen' at base of spine) £75
A Dreamer's Tales, George Allen, 1910 . . £100
ditto, Luce (U.S.), 1911 . . . . £75
The Fortress Unvanquishable, Save for Sacnoth, School of Arts Press, 1910 (30 copies) . . . £500
Selections from the Writings of Lord Dunsany, Cuala Press, 1912 (250 copies) £200
The Book of Wonder, W. Heinemann, 1912 . £35
ditto, Luce (U.S.), 1912 . . . . £25
Fifty-One Tales, Elkin Mathews, 1915 . . . £45
ditto, Kennerly (U.S.), 1915 . . . . . . £25
Tales of Wonder, Elkin Mathews, 1916 . . . £40
ditto, as *The Last Book of Wonder*, Luce (U.S.), 1916 . . . . £60
Tales of War, Talbot Press/T. Fisher Unwin, 1918 £75
ditto, Little, Brown (U.S.), 1918 . . . . . £20
Unhappy Far Off Things, Elkin Mathews, 1919 £25
ditto, Little, Brown (U.S.), 1919 . . . . . £20
Tales of Three Hemispheres, Luce (U.S.), 1919 £35
ditto, T. Fisher Unwin, 1920 . . . . . £300/£40
The Travel Tales of Mr. Joseph Jorkens, Putnam's, 1931 . . . . £150/£35
ditto, Putnam's (U.S.), 1931 . . . . . £150/£35
Mr Jorkens Remembers Africa, W. Heinemann, 1934 . . . . £125/£40
Jorkens Has A Large Whiskey, Putnam, 1940 . . . . £100/£35
The Fourth Book of Jorkens, Jarrolds [1947] . . . . £100/£20
ditto, Arkham House (U.S.), 1948 . . . £75/£20
The Man Who Ate the Phoenix, Jarrolds [1949] . . . . £75/£15
The Little Tales of Smethers, Jarrolds, 1952 £65/£20
Jorkens Borrows Another Whiskey, Michael Joseph, 1954 . . . . £50/£15
The Edge of the World, Ballantine Adult Fantasy, 1970 (wraps) £5
Beyond the Fields We Know, Ballantine Adult Fantasy, 1972 (wraps) £5
Gods, Men and Ghosts: The Best Supernatural Fiction of Lord Dunsany, Dover, 1972 (wraps) £5
Over the Hills and Far Away, Ballantine Adult Fantasy, 1974 (wraps) £5

Novels

The Chronicles of Rodriguez, Putnam's, 1922 (500 copies numbered and signed by Dunsany and Sime) . . . . £400/£300

ditto, Putnam's, 1924 . . . . £175/£45
ditto, as *Don Rodriguez, Chronicles of Shadow Valley*, Putnam's (U.S.), 1924 . . . . . £125/£25
The King of Elfland's Daughter, Putnam's, 1924 (250 copies numbered and signed by Dunsany and Sime) . . . . £500/£350
ditto, Putnam's, 1924 . . . . £125/£35
ditto, Putnam's (U.S.), 1924 . . . . . £100/£25
The Charwoman's Shadow, Putnam's, 1926 £100/£20
ditto, Putnam's (U.S.), 1926 . . . . £100/£20
The Blessing of Pan, Putnam's, 1927 . . £100/£20
ditto, Putnam's (U.S.), 1928 . . . . . £100/£20
The Curse of the Wise Woman, W. Heinemann, 1933 . . . . £75/£15
ditto, Longman's (U.S.), 1933 . . . . . £20
Up in the Hills, W. Heinemann, 1935 . . £45/£15
ditto, Putnam's (U.S.), 1935 . . . . . £65/£15
Rory and Bran, W. Heinemann, 1936 . . £65/£10
ditto, Putnam's (U.S.), 1937 . . . . . £45/£10
My Talks with Dean Spanley, W. Heinemann, 1936 . . . . £50/£10
ditto, Putnam's (U.S.), 1936 . . . . . £35/£10
The Story of Mona Sheehy, W. Heinemann, 1939 . . . . £100/£25
Guerrilla, W. Heinemann, 1944 . . . . £35/£10
ditto, Bobbs-Merrill (U.S.), 1944 . . . . £25/£5
The Strange Journeys of Colonel Polders, Jarrolds, 1950 . . . . £50/£20
ditto, Jarrolds (U.S.), 1950 . . . . . £50/£20
The Last Revolution, Jarrolds, 1951 . . . £50/£20
His Fellow Men, Jarrolds, 1952 . . . . £50/£20

Plays

Five Plays, Grant Richards, 1914 . . . . £30
ditto, Little, Brown (U.S.), 1914 . . . . . £20
Plays of Gods and Men, Talbot Press, 1917 . £30
ditto, Luce (U.S.), 1917 . . . . £20
If, Putnam's, 1921 . . . . £25/£10
ditto, Putnam's, 1921 (large paper issue) . £35
ditto, Putnam's (U.S.), 1921 . . . . . £25/£10
The Laughter of the Gods, Putnam's, 1922 (from *Plays of Gods and Men*, wraps) £15
The Tents of the Arabs, Putnam's, [1922] (from *Plays of Gods and Men*, wraps) £15
The Queen's Enemies, Putnam's, 1922 (from *Plays of Gods and Men*, wraps) £15
A Night at an Inn, Putnam's, 1922 (from *Plays of Gods and Men*, wraps) £15
Plays of Near and Far, Putnam's, 1922 (500 copies) £50
ditto, Putnam's, 1923 . . . . £25/£10
ditto, Putnam's (U.S.), 1923 . . . . . £25/£10
The Gods of the Mountain, Putnam's, 1923 (from *Five Plays*, wraps) £10
The Golden Dome, Putnam's, 1923 (from *Five Plays*, wraps) £10
King Argimenes and the Unknown Warrior, Putnam's, 1923 (from *Five Plays*, wraps) . . £10

The Glittering Gate, Putnam's, 1923 (from Five Plays, wraps). £10
The Lost Silk Hat, Putnam's, 1923 (from Five Plays, wraps). £10
The Compromise of the King of the Golden Isles, Putnam's [1923] (from Plays of Near and Far, wraps). £10
The Flight of the Queen, Putnam's [1923] (from Plays of Near and Far, wraps) £10
Cheezo, Putnam's [1923] (from Plays of Near and Far, wraps) £10
A Good Bargain, Putnam's [1923] (from Plays of Near and Far, wraps) £10
If Shakespeare Lived To-day, Putnam's [1923] (from Plays of Near and Far, wraps) . . . £10
Fame and the Poet, Putnam's [1923] (from Plays of Near and Far, wraps) £10
Alexander, and Three Small Plays, Putnam's, 1925 .
  . . . . £25/£10
ditto, Putnam's, 1925 (250 copies) £60
ditto, Putnam's (U.S.), 1923 . . . . . £25/£10
Alexander, Putnam's, 1925 (from Alexander, and Three Small Plays, wraps) . . . , . £10
The Old King's Tale, Putnam's, 1925 (from Alexander, and Three Small Plays, wraps) . £10
The Evil Kettle, Putnam's, 1925 (from Alexander, and Three Small Plays, wraps) . . . £10
The Amusements of Khan Kharuda, Putnam's, 1925 (from Alexander, and Three Small Plays, wraps) £10
Seven Modern Comedies, Putnam's, 1928 . £25/£10
ditto, Putnam's, 1928 (250 copies) £60
ditto, Putnam's (U.S.), 1929 . . . . . £25/£10
Atlanta in Wimbledon, Putnam's, 1928 (from Seven Modern Comedies, wraps) £10
The Raffle, Putnam's, 1928 (from Seven Modern Comedies, wraps) £10
The Journey of the Soul, Putnam's, 1928 (from Seven Modern Comedies, wraps) £10
In Holy Russia, Putnam's, 1928 (from Seven Modern Comedies, wraps) £10
His Sainted Grandmother, Putnam's, 1928 (from Seven Modern Comedies, wraps) . . . £10
The Hopeless Passion of Mr Bunyon, Putnam's, 1928 (from Seven Modern Comedies, wraps) . . £10
The Jest of Hahalaba, Putnam's, 1928 (from Seven Modern Comedies, wraps) £10
The Old Folk of the Centuries, Elkin Mathews & Marrot, 1930 (100 signed copies of 900) . £75/£65
ditto, Elkin Mathews & Marrot, 1930 (800 unsigned copies of 900) . . . . . . £45/£20
Lord Adrian, Golden Cockerel Press, 1933 (325 copies, glassine d/w). £125
Mr Faithful, French [1935] (wraps) . £15
Plays for Earth and Air, W. Heinemann, 1937 £25/£10

Verse
Fifty Poems, Putnam's, 1929 (250 copies) . £125/£20
ditto, Putnam's, 1929 . . . . . . £50/£20
Mirage Water, Putnam's, 1938 . . . £35/£15

War Poems, Hutchinson [1941] . . . . £35/£15
Wandering Songs, Hutchinson [1943] . . £35/£15
A Journey, Macdonald [1944] (250 copies, initialed 'D', leather bound in slipcase, no d/w). . . £125
ditto, Macdonald [1944] (trade edition) . . £20/£5
The Year, Jarrolds, 1946 . . . . . £20/£5
To Awaken Pegasus, George Ronald, 1949. £25/£10

Autobiography
Patches of Sunlight, W. Heinemann, 1938 . £35/£15
ditto, Reynal Hitchcock (U.S.), 1938 . . £20/£10
While the Sirens Slept, Jarrolds [1944] . . £30/£10
The Sirens Wake, Jarrolds, 1945. . . . £25/£10

Miscellaneous
If I Were Dictator, Methuen, 1934 . . . £35/£10
My Ireland, Jarrolds, 1937 . . . . . £30/£10
ditto, Jarrolds, 1950 (revised edition) . . £20/£5
The Donnellan Lectures, 1943, W. Heinemann, 1945.
  . . . . £10/£5
A Glimpse from the Watch Tower, Jarrolds, 1946 .
  . . . . £25/£10
The Ghosts of the Heaviside Layer and other Phantasms, Owlswick Press (U.S.), 1980 £20/£10

FRANCIS DURBRIDGE
(b.1912 d.1998)

Durbridge's sleuth, Paul Temple, started his career as a radio detective, but moved to both film and TV, and even comic strips. The rest of his books are likewise fast-paced thrillers with twisting plots.

'Paul Temple' Books
Send for Paul Temple, Long, 1938 (with John Thewes)
  . . . . £50/£10
Paul Temple and the Front Page Men, Long, 1939 (with Charles Hatton) . . . . . £40/£10
News of Paul Temple, Long, [1940] (with Charles Hatton) . . . . £45/£10
Paul Temple Intervenes, Long, [1944] (with Charles Hatton) . . . . £45/£10
Send for Paul Temple Again!, Long, [1948] (with Charles Hatton) . . . . £45/£10
Paul Temple and the Kelby Affair, Coronet, 1970 (wraps) £5
Paul Temple and the Harkdale Robbery, Coronet, 1970 (wraps) £5
The Geneva Mystery, Coronet, 1971 (wraps) . £5
The Curzon Case, Hodder & Stoughton, 1971 £15/£5
Paul Temple and the Margo Mystery, Hodder & Stoughton, 1986 . . . . £10/£5
Paul Temple and the Maddison Case, Hodder & Stoughton, 1988 . . . . £10/£5

Other Books
Back Room Girl, Long, [1950] . . . . £35/£10

Beware of Johnny Washington, Long, 1951 £30/£10
Design For Murder, Long, 1951 . . . £30/£10
The Tyler Message, Hodder & Stoughton, 1957
(pseud. 'Paul Temple', with James Douglas
Rutherford MacConnell) . . . . £25/£10
The Other Man, Hodder & Stoughton, [1958] £25/£10
East of Algiers, Hodder & Stoughton, [1959] (pseud.
'Paul Temple', with James Douglas Rutherford
MacConnell) . . . . £25/£10
A Time of Day, Hodder & Stoughton, [1959] £25/£10
The Scarf, Hodder & Stoughton, [1960] . £25/£10
ditto, as *The Case of the Twisted Scarf*, Dodd, Mead
(U.S.), 1961 . . . . £20/£5
The World of Tim Frazer, Hodder & Stoughton, 1962
. . . . £20/£5
ditto, Dodd, Mead (U.S.), 1962 . . . . £20/£5
Portrait of Alison, Hodder & Stoughton, 1962 £25/£10
ditto, Dodd, Mead (U.S.), 1962 . . . . £20/£5
My Friend Charles, Hodder & Stoughton, 1963 . .
. . . . £25/£10
Tim Frazer Again, Hodder & Stoughton, 1964 . .
. . . . £20/£5
Another Woman's Shoes, Hodder & Stoughton, 1965.
. . . . £25/£10
The Desperate People, Hodder & Stoughton, [1966] .
. . . . £25/£10
Dead to the World, Hodder & Stoughton, [1967] . .
. . . . £25/£10
My Wife Melissa, Hodder & Stoughton, 1967 £25/£10
The Pig-Tail Murder, Hodder & Stoughton, 1969 .
. . . . £25/£10
A Man Called Harry Brent, Hodder & Stoughton,
1970 . . . . £25/£10
Bat Out Of Hell, Hodder & Stoughton, 1972 £25/£10
A Game of Murder, Hodder & Stoughton, 1975 . .
. . . . £25/£10
The Passenger, Hodder & Stoughton, 1977 £25/£10
Tim Frazer Gets the Message, Hodder & Stoughton,
1978 . . . . £20/£5
Breakaway, Hodder & Stoughton, 1981 . £25/£10
The Doll, Hodder & Stoughton, 1982 . £25/£10

Plays
Suddenly at Home, French, 1973 (wraps) . . £5
The Gentle Hook, French, 1975 (wraps) . £5
Murder With Love, French, 1977 (wraps) . . £5
House Guest, French, 1982 (wraps) . . . £5
Deadly Nightcap, French, 1986 (wraps) . . £5
A Touch of Danger, French, 1989 (wraps) . . £5
Small Hours, French, 1991 (wraps) . . . £5
Sweet Revenge, French, 1993 (wraps) . . . £5

GERALD DURRELL
(b.1925 d.1995)

Brother of Lawrence, Gerald Durrell wrote popular
travel and natural history books, and was appointed
an OBE in 1983.

Non Fiction
The Overloaded Ark, Faber & Faber, 1953 £35/£5
ditto, Viking (U.S.), 1953 . . . . . £30/£5
Three Singles to Adventure, Hart-Davis, 1954 £35/£5
The Bafut Beagles, Hart-Davis, 1954 . . £35/£5
ditto, Viking (U.S.), 1954 . . . . . £30/£5
The Drunken Forest, Hart-Davis, 1956 . . £25/£5
ditto, Viking (U.S.), 1956 . . . . . £25/£5
My Family and Other Animals, Hart-Davis, 1956 . .
. . . . £25/£10
ditto, Viking (U.S.), 1957 . . . . . £25/£5
Encounters With Animals, Hart-Davis, 1958 £15/£5
A Zoo in My Luggage, Hart-Davis, 1960 . £15/£5
ditto, Viking (U.S.), 1956 . . . . . £15/£5
The Whispering Land, Hart-Davis, 1961 . £15/£5
ditto, Viking (U.S.), 1962 . . . . . £10/£5
Menagerie Manor, Hart-Davis, 1964 . . £15/£5
ditto, Viking (U.S.), 1964 . . . . . £10/£5
Two In The Bush, Collins, 1966 . . . . £15/£5
ditto, Viking (U.S.), 1966 . . . . . £10/£5
Birds, Beasts & Relatives, Collins, 1969 . £15/£5
ditto, Viking (U.S.), 1969 . . . . . £10/£5
Fillets of Plaice, Collins, 1971 . . . £15/£5
ditto, Viking (U.S.), 1971 . . . . . £10/£5
Catch Me a Colobus, Collins, 1972 . . . £15/£5
ditto, Viking (U.S.), 1972 . . . . . £10/£5
Beasts in My Belfry, Collins, 1973 . . . £15/£5
The Stationary Ark, Collins, 1976 . . . £15/£5
ditto, Simon & Schuster (U.S.), 1976 . . £10/£5
Golden Bats and Pink Pigeons, Collins, 1977 £15/£5
ditto, Simon & Schuster (U.S.), 1977 . . £10/£5
The Garden of the Gods, Collins, 1978 . . £15/£5
The Amateur Naturalist, Hamish Hamilton, 1982 . .
. . . . £10/£5
ditto, as *A Practical Guide for the Amateur Naturalist*,
Knopf (U.S.), 1983 . . . . £10/£5
How To Shoot An Amateur Naturalist, Collins, 1982
. . . . £10/£5
ditto, Little, Brown (U.S.), 1984 . . . . £10/£5
Durrell in Russia, McDonald, 1986 (with Lee Durrell)
. . . . £10/£5
ditto, Simon & Schuster (U.S.), 1986 . . £10/£5
Ark's Anniversary, Collins, 1990 . . . £10/£5
ditto, Arcade (U.S.), 1991 . . . . . £10/£5
Gerald Durrell's Army, J. Murray, 1992 . £10/£5
Best of Durrell, HarperCollins, 1996 . . £10/£5

Novels
Rosy is My Relative, Collins, 1968 . . . £35/£5
ditto, Viking (U.S.), 1968 . . . . . £15/£5
The Mockery Bird, Collins, 1981 . . . £15/£5
ditto, Simon & Schuster (U.S.), 1981 . . £10/£5

Short Stories
The Picnic & Suchlike Pandemonium, Collins, 1979 .
. . . . £15/£5
ditto, as *The Picnic & Other Inimitable Stories*, Simon
& Schuster (U.S.), 1980 . . . . . . £15/£5

Children's
The New Noah, Collins, 1955 . . . . £30/£10
ditto, Viking (U.S.), 1964 . . . . . £20/£5
Island Zoo, Collins, 1961 . . . . . £30/£10
ditto, MacRae Smith (U.S.), 1963 . . . £15/£5
Look at Zoos, Collins, 1961 . . . . . £25/£5
My Favourite Animal Stories, Collins, 1962 £15/£5
The Donkey Rustlers, Collins, 1968 . . £25/£5
ditto, Viking (U.S.), 1968 . . . . . £25/£5
The Talking Parcel, Collins, 1974 . . . £25/£5
ditto, Lippincott (U.S.), 1975 . . . . £25/£5
Fantastic Flying Journey, Conran Octopus, 1987 . .
. . . . £15/£5
ditto, Simon & Schuster (U.S.), 1987 . . £15/£5
Animal Family Adventures with Gerald Durrell, Price
Stern Sloan, 1988 . . . . £10/£5
Fantastic Dinosaur Adventure, Conran Octopus, 1989
. . . . £10/£5
ditto, Simon & Schuster (U.S.), 1989 . . £10/£5
Toby the Tortoise, M. O'Mara Books, 1991 £10/£5
ditto, Little, Brown (U.S.), 1991 . . . . £10/£5

•

LAWRENCE DURRELL
(b.1912 d.1990)

Novelist, poet and travel writer, much of Lawrence
Durrell's work owes a debt to the Mediterranean
where he spent most of his life.

Verse
Quaint Fragment, Cecil Press, 1931 (red boards) . .
. . . . £15,000
ditto, Cecil Press, 1931 (blue wraps) . . . £15,000
Ten Poems, Caduceus Press, 1932 (wraps) . £2,500
ditto, Caduceus Press, 1932 (12 signed copies in cloth)
. . . . £7,500
Ballade of Slow Decay, privately printed, 1932 (single
sheet, folded) £2,000
Transition, Caduceus Press, 1934 . . . £2,500
A Private Country, Faber, 1943 . . . £250/£75
Cities, Plains and People, Faber, 1946 . £100/£20
On Seeming to Presume, Faber, 1948 . . £45/£10
Deus Loci, Ischia, 1950 (200 signed copies, wraps) .
. . . . £200
The Tree of Idleness, Faber, 1955 . . . £30/£10
Selected Poems, Faber, 1956 . . . . £35/£10
ditto, Faber, 1956 (wraps). £10
ditto, Grove Press (U.S.), 1956 . . . . £35/£10
Collected Poems, Faber, 1960 . . . . £40/£10

ditto, Dutton (U.S.), 1960 . . . . . . £40/£10
Beccafico Le Becfigue, La Licorne (France), 1963
(150 signed copies, wraps) £200
La Descente du Styx, La Murène (France), 1964 (250
signed copies, wraps) £150
ditto, as *Down the Styx*, Capricorn Press (U.S.), 1971
(200 of 1,000 copies) £75
ditto, as *Down the Styx*, Capricorn Press (U.S.), 1971
(800 of 1,000 copies, wraps) £25
Selected Poems, 1935-1963, Faber, 1964 (wraps) £10
The Ikons, Faber, 1966 . . . . . . £35/£5
ditto, Dutton (U.S.), 1967 . . . . . . £25/£5
Nothing Is Lost, Sweet Self, Turret, 1967 (100 signed
copies, wraps with d/w) . . . . . £100/£65
In Arcadia, Turret, 1968 (100 signed copies, wraps
with d/w) . . . . £100/£65
The Red Limbo Lingo, Faber, 1971 (500 numbered
copies of 1,200, glassine d/w, slipcase) . £75/£45
ditto, Faber, 1971 (100 signed copies, glassine d/w,
slipcase) . . . . £125/£75
ditto, Dutton (U.S.), 1971 (500 numbered copies,
glassine d/w, slipcase) . . . . . £75/£45
ditto, Dutton (U.S.), 1971 (100 signed, numbered
copies, glassine d/w, slipcase) . . . . £125/£75
On the Suchness of the Old Boy, Turret, 1972 (226
signed copies, wraps) £75
Vega and Other Poems, Faber, 1973 . . £25/£5
ditto, Overlook Press (U.S.), 1973 . . . £25/£5
Lifelines - Four Poems, Tragara Press, 1974 (15
signed copies of 115, wraps) £250
ditto, Tragara Press, 1974 (100 copies of 115, wraps) .
. . . . £75
ditto, Tragara Press, 1974 (25 'extra' author's copies,
usually inscribed) £250
Collected Poems: 1931-1974, Faber, 1980 . £25/£10
ditto, Faber, 1980 (26 signed copies, with signed
etching by Henry Moore, slipcase) £750
ditto, Viking (U.S.), 1980 . . . . . . £20/£10

Parody
Bromo Bombasts, Caduceus Press, 1933 (pseud.
'Gaffer Peeslake',100 copies) £2,500

Novels
Pied Piper of Lovers, Cassell, 1935 . £2,000/£1,250
Panic Spring, Faber, 1937 (pseud. 'Charles Norden') .
. . . . £2,000/£750
ditto, Covici Friede (U.S.), 1937 . . . £750/£250
The Black Book, Obelisk Press (Paris), 1938 (wraps) .
. . . . £500
ditto, Obelisk Press (Paris), 1959 (wraps and d/w) . .
. . . . £65/£25
ditto, Dutton (U.S.), 1960 . . . . . . £40/£10
ditto, Faber, 1973 . . . . £20/£5
Cefalû, Editions Poetry, 1947 . . . . £75/£25
ditto, as *The Dark Labyrinth*, Ace (U.S.), 1958
(wrappers) £10
ditto, Faber, 1961 . . . . £35/£10
Justine, Faber, 1957 . . . . £250/£65

ditto, Dutton (U.S.), 1957. . . . . . £75/£25
White Eagles over Serbia, Faber, 1957 . . £50/£25
ditto, Criterion (U.S.), 1957 . . . . . £50/£25
Balthazar, Faber, 1958 . . . . . . £175/£25
ditto, Dutton (U.S.), 1958. . . . . . £45/£10
Mountolive, Faber, 1958 . . . . . . £175/£25
ditto, Dutton (U.S.), 1959. . . . . . £45/£10
Clea, Faber, 1960 . . . . £125/£20
ditto, Dutton (U.S.), 1960. . . . . . £35/£5
The Alexandria Quartet, Faber, 1962 . . £75/£25
ditto, Faber, 1962 (500 signed copies, slipcase) . .
. . . . £400/£250
ditto, Dutton (U.S.), 1962. . . . . . £65/£20
ditto, Dutton (U.S.), 1962 (199 signed, numbered
copies) . . . . £500/£250
Tunc, Faber, 1968. . . . . £25/£5
ditto, Dutton (U.S.), 1968. . . . . . £20/£5
Nunquam, Faber, 1970 . . . . . . £25/£5
ditto, Dutton (U.S.), 1970. . . . . £15/£5
The Revolt of Aphrodite, Faber, 1973 . . £25/£10
Monsieur, or, The Prince of Darkness, Faber, 1974 .
. . . . £20/£5
ditto, Viking (U.S.), 1974. . . . . . £15/£5
Livia or Buried Alive, Faber, 1978 . . . £15/£5
ditto, Viking (U.S.), 1979. . . . . . £10/£5
Constance or Solitary Practices, Faber, 1982 £10/£5
ditto, Viking (U.S.), 1982. . . . . . £15/£5
Sebastian or Ruling Passions, Faber, 1983 . £15/£5
ditto, Viking (U.S.), 1984. . . . . . £15/£5
Quinx or The Ripper's Tale, Faber, 1985 . £15/£5
ditto, Viking (U.S.), 1985. . . . . . £10/£5
The Avignon Quintet, Faber, 1992 . . . £15/£5

Plays
Sappho, Faber, 1950 . . . . £45/£15
ditto, Dutton (U.S.), 1958. . . . . . £20/£5
An Irish Faustus, Faber, 1963 . . . . £20/£5
ditto, Dutton (U.S.), 1964. . . . . . £15/£5
ditto, Delos, 1987 (75 signed, numbered copies, no
d/w) £65
Acte, Faber, 1965 . . . . £15/£5
ditto, Dutton (U.S.), 1965. . . . . . £15/£5

Short Stories
Zero and Asylum in the Snow, privately printed
(Rhodes), 1946 (50 copies, wraps) £500
ditto, as *Two Excursions into Reality*, Circle Editions
(U.S.), 1947 . . . . £65/£25
Esprit de Corps, Faber, 1957. . . . . £50/£15
ditto, Dutton (U.S.), 1958. . . . . . £30/£10
Stiff Upper Lip, Faber, 1958 . . . . £40/£10
ditto, Dutton (U.S.), 1959. . . . . . £30/£10
Sauve Qui Peut, Faber, 1966. . . . . £25/£5
ditto, Dutton (U.S.), 1967. . . . . . £20/£5
The Best of Antrobus, Faber, 1974 . . . £15/£5

Non Fiction
Prospero's Cell, Faber, 1945. . . . . £75/£15
ditto, Dutton (U.S.), 1960. . . . . . £35/£10

Key to Modern Poetry, Nevill, 1952. . . £35/£10
Reflections on a Marine Venus, Faber, 1953 £75/£15
ditto, Dutton (U.S.), 1960. . . . . . £35/£5
Bitter Lemons, Faber, 1957 . . . . . £125/£15
ditto, Dutton (U.S.), 1958. . . . . . £65/£10
Art and Outrage, Putnam, 1959 . . . . £45/£10
ditto, Dutton (U.S.), 1960. . . . . . £40/£10
*Lawrence Durrell and Henry Miller: A Private
Correspondence*, Dutton (U.S.), 1963 . . £25/£10
ditto, Faber, 1963 . . . . £25/£10
Spirit of Place, Faber, 1969 . . . . . £35/£10
ditto, Dutton (U.S.), 1969. . . . . . £35/£10
Le Grand Suppositoire, Editions Pierre Belfond
(Paris), 1972. . . . . £15/£5
ditto, as *The Big Supposer*, Abelard-Schuman, 1973
(English translation) . . . . £15/£5
ditto, as *The Big Supposer*, Grove Press (U.S.), 1974 .
. . . . £15/£5
Blue Thirst, Capra Press (U.S.), 1975 (250 signed
copies, glassine d/w). . . . . . . £75/£45
ditto, Capra Press (U.S.), 1975 (10 signed, lettered
copies, glassine d/w). . . . . . £500/£450
Sicilian Carousel, Faber, 1977 . . . . £15/£5
ditto, Viking (U.S.), 1977. . . . . . £15/£5
The Greek Islands, Faber, 1978 . . . . £15/£5
ditto, Viking (U.S.), 1978. . . . . . £15/£5
A Smile in the Mind's Eye, Wildwood House, 1980 .
. . . . £15/£5
*Literary Lifelines: The Richard Aldington - Lawrence
Durrell Correspondence*, Faber, 1981 . . £15/£5
ditto, Viking (U.S.), 1981. . . . . . £15/£5
The Durrell/Miller Letters, Faber, 1988. . £15/£5
Letters to Jean Fanchette, 1958-1963, Editions Two
Cities, 1988 (1,800 of 2,000 copies, wraps) . £15
ditto, Editions Two Cities, 1988 (200 signed copies of
2,000, wraps). £150
Caesar's Vast Ghost: Aspects of Provence, Faber,
1990 . . . . £10/£5
ditto, Arcade (U.S.), 1990. . . . . . £10/£5

UMBERTO ECO
(b.1932)

Eco is a semiotician with an interest in the
philosophical and aesthetic theories of the Middle
Ages. He is best known, however, for his two novels,
The Name of the Rose, and *Foucault's Pendulum*.

Novels
The Name of the Rose, Secker & Warburg, 1984 £125
ditto, Harcourt Brace (U.S.), 1984 . . . £125
Travels in Hyperreality, Harcourt Brace (U.S.), 1986 .
. . . . £25/£5
Foucault's Pendulum, Secker & Warburg, 1989 . .
. . . . £35/£10
ditto, Harcourt Brace (U.S.), 1989 . . . £35/£10

ditto, Franklin Centre (U.S.), 1989 (signed, limited edition) £50
The Island of the Day Before, Harcourt Brace (U.S.), 1994 . . . . £10/£5
ditto, Harcourt Brace (U.S.), 1994 (250 signed copies, slipcase) . . . . £125/£100
ditto, Secker & Warburg, 1983 . . . . £10/£5

Children's Titles (with Eugenio Carmi)
The Three Astronauts, Secker & Warburg, 1989 . .
. . . . £25/£10
ditto, Harcourt Brace (U.S.), 1989 . . . £25/£10
The Bomb and the General, Secker & Warburg, 1989
. . . . £25/£10
ditto, Harcourt Brace (U.S.), 1989 . . . £25/£10

Academic
A Theory of Semiotics, Indiana Univ. Press (U.S.), 1976 . . . . £45/£20
Art and Beauty in the Middle Ages, Yale Univ. Press (U.S.), 1986 . . . . £25/£10
Limits of Interpretation, Indiana Univ. Press (U.S.), 1990 . . . . £25/£10
Apocalypse Postponed, Indiana Univ. Press (U.S.), 1994 . . . . £25/£10
Six Walks in the Fictional Woods, Harvard Univ. Press (U.S.), 1994 . . . . . £25/£10
The Search for thePerfect Language, Blackwell, 1995 (wraps) £40
Serendipities: Language and Lunacy, Univ. of Columbia Press (U.S.), 1998 . . . . £15/£5

Others
The Picture History of Inventions, Macmillan (U.S.), 1963 (with G.B. Zorzoli) . . . . £40/£10
The Bond Affair, Macdonald (U.S.), 1966 (with Oreste del Buono) . . . . £75/£20
Reflections on The Name of the Rose, Secker & Warburg, 1983 . . . . . . £20/£5
ditto, as *Postscript to The Name of the Rose*, Harcourt Brace (U.S.), 1984 . . . . . . £20/£5
How to Travel With A Salmon, Harcourt Brace (U.S.), 1989 . . . . £15/£5
Misreadings, Harcourt Brace (U.S.), 1993 (wraps) £20

BERESFORD EGAN
(b.1905 d.1984)

As an artist Egan's wickedly satirical black and white line drawings were at their most effective in *The Sink of Solitude*, a lampoon of the reactions to Radclyffe Hall's *The Well of Loneliness*.

Written and Illustrated by Egan
Pollen, Denis Archer, 1933 (patterned boards, glassine d/w) . . . . £45/£35

ditto, Denis Archer, 1933 (orange boards, glassine d/w)
. . . . £35/£25
No Sense in Form: A Tragedy of Manners, Denis Archer, 1933 . . . . £40
But The Sinners Triumph, Fortune Press, 1934 . .
. . . . £125/£35
Epitaph, A Double Bedside Book for Singular People, Fortune Press, [1943] . . . . . . £75/£25
Epilogue, A Potpourri of Prose, Verse and Drawings, Fortune Press, [1946] . . . . . . £75/£25
Bun-Ho!, Floris Bakeries Ltd, 1959 (edited and decorated by Egan) £50
Storicards, Barrigan Press, 1960 (5 cards) the set £50

Illustrated by Egan
The Sink of Solitude: A Broadside, preface by P.R. Stevensen, lampoons by various hands, Hermes Press, 1928 (250 numbered, signed copies) . . . £150
ditto, Hermes Press, 1928 (wraps) £50
Policeman of The Lord: A Political Satire, Sophistocles Press, 1929 (500 numbered copies) . . . £125
ditto, Sophistocles Press 1929 (wraps) . . . £50
Les Fleurs du Mal, In Pattern and Prose, by Baudelaire, translated by C. Bower Adcock, Sophistocles Press and T. Werner Laurie, 1929 (500 signed copies)
. . . . £150
ditto, Godwin (U.S.), 1933 (pirated edition). . £20
ditto, as *Flowers of Evil*, Sylvan Press (U.S.), 1947 (1,499 numbered copies) £40
ditto, as *Flowers of Evil*, Sylvan Press (U.S.), 1947 (unlimited reprint) £20
Aphrodite, by Pierre Loüys, The Fortune Press, 1929 (1,075 copies) £50
Cyprian Masques, by Pierre Loüys, The Fortune Press, 1929 . . . . £50
De Sade, by Beresford Egan and Brian de Shane, The Fortune Press, 1929 (1,600 copies). . . . £65
The Adventures of King Pausole, by Pierre Loüys, Fortune Press, 1930 (1,200 copies). . . . £65
Income and Outcome: A Study in Personal Finance, by Nigel Balchin, Hamish Hamilton, 1936 . £35
Pobottle, by Heavy Duty Alloys Ltd 1935-39, (advertising, 7 vols, wraps) . . . . £125 the set

Others
Beresford Egan: An Introduction to His Work, by Paul Allen, Scorpion Press, 1966 (limited edition) .
. . . . £35/£20
ditto, Scorpion Press, 1966 (25 signed copies, with extra plate) . . . .£125/£100

GEORGE ELIOT
(b.1819 d.1880)

George Eliot was the pseudonym of Mary Anne Evans, novelist, critic and poet. Her great power is her detailed depiction of character and motivation chiefly among middle class provincial society.

Novels
Adam Bede, Blackwood, 1859 (3 vols) . . . £1,500
ditto, Harper (U.S.), 1859 . . . . . . £200
The Mill on the Floss, Blackwood, 1860 (3 vols) £750
ditto, Harper (U.S.), 1860 . . . . . . £125
Silas Marner, The Weaver of Raveloe, Blackwood, 1861 . . . . £1,000
ditto, Harper (U.S.), 1860 (boards) £100
ditto, Harper (U.S.), 1860 (wraps) £200
Romola, Smith, Elder & Co., 1863 (3 vols, first issue with 2 pages of ads at end of vol. 2) . . £1,000
ditto, Smith, Elder & Co., 1863 (3 vols, second issue) .
. . . . £750
ditto, Harper (U.S.), 1863. . . . . . £125
Felix Holt, The Radical, Blackwood, 1866 (3 vols) .
. . . . £500
ditto, Harper (U.S.), 1866. . . . . . £75
Middlemarch, A Study of Provincial Life, Blackwood, 1871-1872 (8 parts, pictorial wraps) . . £3,000
ditto, Blackwood, 1871-1872 (8 parts bound together as vols) £2,000
ditto, Harper (U.S.), 1872 (2 vols) . . . £50
ditto, Blackwood, 1874 (4 vols in book form) . £2,000
Daniel Deronda, Blackwood, 1874-1876 (8 parts, with erratum slip in part 3, blue/grey wraps) . £2,500
ditto, Blackwood, 1874-1876 (8 parts, without erratum slip in part 3, blue/grey wraps) . . . £2,000
ditto, Blackwood, 1874-1876 (8 parts bound together as 1 vol.) £1,250
ditto, Blackwood, 1876 (4 vols in book form) £1,250
ditto, Harper (U.S.), 1876 (2 vols) . . . £125

Short Stories
Scenes of Clerical Life, Blackwood, 1858 (2 vols). .
. . . . £7,500
ditto, Harper (U.S.), 1858. . . . . . £125

Essays
Impressions of Theophrastus Such, Blackwood, 1879
. . . . £175
ditto, Harper (U.S.), 1879. . . . . . £65
Essays and Leaves from a Note-Book, Blackwood, 1884 . . . . £175

Verse
The Spanish Gypsy, Blackwood, 1868 . . . £600
ditto, Ticknor & Fields (U.S.), 1868. . . . £75
The Legend of Jubal and Other Poems, Blackwood, 1874 . . . . £500
ditto, Osgood (U.S.), 1874 . . . . . £35

Translations
The Life of Jesus, Critically Examined by D.F. Strauss, Chapman, 1846 (3 vols) £2,000
Feuerbach's Essence of Christianity, Chapman, 1854 (3 vols) £1,000

T.S. ELIOT
(b.1888 d.1965)

The American-born poet, critic and dramatist lived most of his adult life in England. Eliot received both the Nobel Prize for Literature and the Order of Merit in 1948.

Verse
Prufrock and Other Observations, Egoist Ltd, 1917 (wraps) £5,000
Poems, Hogarth Press, 1919 (wraps). . . £5,000
Ara Vus Prec (sic), Ovid Press, 1920 (30 signed, numbered copies) £5,000
ditto, Ovid Press, 1920 (220 numbered copies) £2,000
ditto, Ovid Press, 1920 (10 unnumbered copies, although there were probably more) . . £1,000
ditto, as *Poems*, Knopf (U.S.), 1920 . . £1,000/£450
The Waste Land, Boni & Liveright, 1922 (approx 500 of 1,000 copies with flexible black cloth, with 'mountain' spelt correctly on p. 41, line 339) £4,500
ditto, Boni & Liveright, 1922 (later copies, approx 500 of 1,000, with stiff black cloth and 'a' dropped from 'mountain' on p. 41, line 339) . . . £3,500
ditto, Boni & Liveright, 1922 (1,000 copies, with 'a' dropped from 'mountain' on p. 41, line 339) £1,000
ditto, Hogarth Press, 1923 . . . . £1,750
ditto, Faber, [1962] (300 numbered, signed copies) .
. . . . £2,000
Homage to John Dryden, Hogarth Press, 1924 (wraps)
. . . . £125
Poems, 1909-1925, Faber & Gwyer, 1925 £1,250/£300
ditto, Faber & Gwyer, 1925 (85 numbered and signed copies) £2,500
ditto, Harcourt Brace (U.S.), 1932 . . . £200/£45
Journey of the Magi, Faber & Gwyer, 1927 (wraps) .
. . . . £75
ditto, Faber & Gwyer, 1927 (350 copies, wraps with glassine d/w) . . . . £150/£125
ditto, Rudge (U.S.), (27 copies, copyright edition) . .
. . . . £1,000
A Song for Simeon, Faber & Gwyer, 1928 . . £30
ditto, Faber & Gwyer, 1928 (500 numbered, signed large paper copies) £400
Animula, Faber, [1929] (wraps) £65
ditto, Faber, [1929] (400 numbered, signed copies, slipcase) £450
Ash-Wednesday, Faber, 1930 . . . £200/£65
ditto, Faber/Fountain Press, 1930 (600 signed copies, glassine d/w with white paper flaps, slipcase) £750
ditto, Putnam (U.S.), 1930 . . . . . £150/£40

Marina, Faber, [1930] (wraps) £50
ditto, Faber, [1930] (400 numbered, signed copies) .
. . . . £300
Triumphal March, Faber, 1931 (wraps). . . £65
ditto, Faber, 1931 (300 numbered, signed copies, no
d/w) £400
Collected Poems, 1909-1935, Faber, 1936 . £45/£15
ditto, Harcourt Brace (U.S.), 1936 . . £25/£10
Old Possum's Book of Practical Cats, Faber, 1939 .
. . . . £600/£75
ditto, Harcourt Brace (U.S.), 1939 . . . £400/£75
The Waste Land and Other Poems, Faber, 1940 . .
. . . . £35/£10
ditto, Harcourt Brace (U.S.), 1955 . . . £25/£10
East Coker, New English Weekly, 1940 (stapled,
unbound supplement) £750
ditto, New English Weekly, 1940 (reprint, identified as
such on cover, of 500 copies) £300
ditto, Faber, 1940 (yellow wraps) . . . £150
Burnt Norton, Faber, 1941 (wraps) . . . £65
The Dry Salvages, Faber, 1941 (wraps). . . £125
Little Gidding, Faber, 1942 (wraps) . . . £100
Four Quartets, Harcourt Brace (U.S.), 1943 (first issue
states 'First American edition') . . . £1,250/£150
ditto, Harcourt Brace (U.S.), 1943 (second issue does
not state 'First American edition') . . £350/£150
ditto, Faber, 1944 . . . . £200/£45
ditto, Faber, 1960 (290 signed copies) . . . £2,000
A Practical Possum, Harvard Univ. Printing Office
(U.S.), 1947 (80 numbered copies, wraps)£1250/£150
Selected Poems, Penguin, 1948 (wraps). . . £10
ditto, Harcourt Brace (U.S.), 1967 . . . £25/£10
The Undergraduate Poems, Harvard Advocate, 1949,
(unauthorised publication, 1,000 copies, wraps) £100
Poems Written in Early Youth, privately printed
(Stockholm), 1950 (12 copies only) . . . £2,000
ditto, Faber, 1967 . . . . . . £65/£20
ditto, Farrar Straus (U.S.), 1967 . . . £50/£15
The Complete Poems and Plays, 1909-1950, Harcourt
Brace (U.S.), 1952 . . . . . . £175/£45
The Cultivation of Christmas Trees, Faber, 1954
(wraps & envelope) . . . . . . £100/£65
ditto, Farrar Straus (U.S.), 1956 . . . £35/£10
Collected Poems, 1909-1962, Faber, 1963 . £35/£10
ditto, Farrar Straus (U.S.), 1963 . . . . £35/£10
The Complete Poems and Plays, Faber, 1968 £150/£25
The Waste Land: A Facsimile and Transcript, Faber,
1971 . . . . £45/£15
ditto, Faber, 1971 (500 copies, in slipcase) £200/£100
ditto, Harcourt Brace (U.S.), 1971 (250 copies). . .
. . . . £125/£75

Prose
Ezra Pound: His Metric and Poetry, Knopf (U.S.),
1917 . . . .£300/£150
The Sacred Wood, Methuen, 1920 (first issue with
3mm 'Methuen' at foot of spine and d/w without
subtitle on front) . . . .£650/£100

ditto, Methuen, 1920 (second issue with 3.5mm
'Methuen' at foot of spine and d/w with subtitle on
front and 'Books by A. Clutton-Brock' on back). .
. . . . £400/£75
ditto, Methuen, 1920 (third issue with 8pps of ads after
p. 156) . . . . £300/£45
ditto, Knopf (U.S.), 1921 . . . . . £600/£75
Shakespeare and the Stoicism of Seneca, O.U.P., 1927
(wraps) £200
For Lancelot Andrewes, Faber & Gwyer, 1928 . . .
. . . . £200/£25
ditto, Doubleday (U.S.), 1929 . . . £150/£15
Dante, Faber, 1929 (grey d/w) . . . . £150/£35
ditto, Faber, 1929 (125 numbered, signed copies,
glassine d/w) . . . . £750/£700
Thoughts After Lambeth, Faber, 1931 (wraps). £65
ditto, Faber, 1931 (boards) . . . . . £200/£15
Charles Whibley: A Memoir, O.U.P., 1931 (wraps) .
. . . . £40
Selected Essays, 1917-1931, Faber, 1932 . £250/£20
ditto, Faber, 1932 (115 numbered, signed copies,
cellophane d/w) . . . . . £1,500/£1,400
ditto, Harcourt Brace (U.S.), 1932 . . . £125/£20
John Dryden: The Poet, the Dramatist, the Critic,
Holliday, 1931 . . . . £125/£40
ditto, Holliday, 1931 (110 signed, numbered copies) .
. . . . £750
The Use of Poetry and the Use of Criticism, Faber,
1933 . . . . £225/£20
ditto, Harvard Univ. Press (U.S.), 1933 £175/£15
After Strange Gods: A Primer of Modern Heresey,
Faber, 1934 . . . . £200/£25
ditto, Harcourt Brace (U.S.), 1934 . . £125/£20
Elizabethan Essays, Faber, 1934 (first issue with
misprint 'No.21' for 'No.23' on half title) £200/£25
ditto, Faber, 1934 (second issue with error corrected,
spine blocked in gold) . . . . . £125/£25
ditto, Faber, 1934 (third issue 18cm high, error
corrected, spine blocked in silver) . . £75/£25
Essays Ancient and Modern, Faber, 1936 . £75/£25
ditto, Harcourt Brace (U.S.), 1936 . . . £65/£15
The Idea of a Christian Society, Faber, 1939 £35/£10
ditto, Harcourt Brace (U.S.), 1940 . . . £25/£5
Points of View, Faber, 1941 . . . . . £25/£5
The Classics and the Man of Letters, O.U.P., 1942
(wraps) £25
The Music of Poetry, Jackson and Co., 1942 (wraps) .
. . . . £45
Reunion by Destruction, Vacher & Sons, 1943 £45
What is a Classic?, Faber, 1945 (Virgil Society issue,
with statement of aims, wraps) £150
ditto, Faber, 1945 (Virgil Society issue, without
statement of aims, wraps) £75
ditto, Faber, 1945 . . . . £45/£20
On Poetry, Concord, 1947, (750 copies, not for sale,
wraps). £100
Milton, Cumberlege, 1947, (500 copies, wraps) £50
A Sermon, C.U.P., 1948 (300 copies, not for sale,
wraps) £175

Notes Towards the Definition of Culture, Faber, 1948
. . . . £45/£15
ditto, Harcourt Brace (U.S.), 1949 . . . £35/£10
From Poe to Valéry, Harcourt Brace (U.S.), 1948
(1,500 copies, not for sale, boards and envelope) . .
. . . . £75/£65
The Aims of Poetic Drama, Poets' Theatre Guild, 1949
(wraps) £45
Poetry and Drama, Harvard Univ. Press (U.S.), 1951 .
. . . . £50/£15
ditto, Faber, 1951 . . . . £45/£10
The Value and Use of Cathedrals in England Today,
Chichester Cathedral, 1952 (wraps) . . . £65
An Address to the Members of the London Library,
Queen Anne Press, 1952 (500 copies, wraps) . £60
Selected Prose, Penguin, 1953 . . . . £5
American Literature and the American Language,
Washington University, 1953 (500 copies, wraps) £75
The Three Voices of Poetry, National Book League,
1953 (wraps) £45
ditto, C.U.P. (U.S.), 1954 . . . . . . £30
Religious Drama: Mediaeval and Modern, House of
Books (U.S.), 1954 (300 numbered copies, glassine
d/w) . . . . £350/£300
ditto, House of Books (U.S.), 1954 (26 lettered and
signed copies) £1,500
The Literature of Politics, Conservative Political
Centre, 1955 (wraps) £50
The Frontiers of Criticism, Univ. of Minnesota, 1956
(10,050 copies, not for sale, wraps) . . . £35
On Poetry and Poets, Faber, 1957 . . . £45/£15
ditto, Farrar Straus (U.S.), 1957 . . . . £30/£15
Geoffrey Faber, 1889-1961, Faber, 1961 (100 copies,
not for sale) . . . . £200/£125
George Herbert, Longmans, 1962 (wraps) . . £25
*Knowledge and Experience in the Philosophy of F.H.
Bradley*, Faber, 1964 . . . . . £40/£10
ditto, Farrar Straus (U.S.), 1964 . . . . £30/£10
To Criticize the Critic and Other Writings, Faber,
1965 . . . . £35/£10
ditto, Farrar Straus (U.S.), 1965 . . . . £25/£5
The Letters of T.S. Eliot, Vol. 1, 1898-1922, Faber,
1988 . . . . £25/£10
ditto, Faber, 1988 (250 signed by editor, slipcase) . .
. . . . £75/£50
ditto, Harcourt Brace (U.S.), 1988 . . . £25/£10
ditto, Harcourt Brace (U.S.), 1988 (250 signed by
editor, slipcase) . . . . . . £75/£50

Drama
Sweeney Agonistes, Faber, 1932 . . . . £125/£30
The Rock, Faber, 1934 (wraps) £100
ditto, Faber, 1934 (hardback). . . . £125/£15
ditto, Harcourt Brace (U.S.), 1934 . . . £100/£15
Murder in the Cathedral, Goulden, 1935 (750 copies,
grey wraps) £250
ditto, Goulden, 1935 (750 copies, white wraps) £300
ditto, Faber, 1935 (first complete edition) . £150/£15
ditto, Harcourt Brace (U.S.), 1935 . . . £125/£15

The Family Reunion, Faber, 1939 . . . £125/£25
ditto, Harcourt Brace (U.S.), 1939 . . . £100/£20
The Cocktail Party, Faber, 1950 (misprint 'here' for
'her' on page 29, line 1). . . . . £75/£25
ditto, Faber, 1950 (misprint corrected) . . £50/£15
ditto, Harcourt Brace (U.S.), 1950 (copies with pp.35-
36 on uncancelled leaf) . . . . . £500/£450
ditto, Harcourt Brace (U.S.), 1950 (copies with pp.35-
36 on cancel leaf) . . . . . . £50/£10
The Confidential Clerk, Faber, 1954 (first issue with
'Ihad' on p.7). . . . . £60/£20
ditto, Faber, 1954 (second issue with 'I had' on p.7) .
. . . . £50/£10
ditto, Harcourt Brace (U.S.), 1954 . . . £35/£10
The Elder Statesman, Faber, 1959 . . £45/£10
ditto, Farrar Straus (U.S.), 1959 . . . . £35/£10
Collected Plays, Faber, 1962 . . . . . £25/£10

ALICE THOMAS ELLIS
(b.1932)

An author whose novels are fashionable as well as
respected, Ellis has also written a number of non
fiction books.

Novels
The Sin Eater, Duckworth, 1977 . . . £35/£15
ditto, Moyar, Bell, (U.S.),1998 . . . £15/£5
The Birds of the Air, Duckworth, 1980 . . £20/£5
ditto, Viking Press (U.S.),1981 . . . . £15/£5
The 27th Kingdom, Duckworth, 1982 . . £40/£5
ditto, Moyar, Bell, (U.S.),1999 . . . . £10/£5
The Other Side of the Fire, Duckworth, 1983 £15/£5
ditto, Elisabeth Sifton (U.S.),1984 . . . £15/£5
Unexplained Laughter, Duckworth, 1985 . £15/£5
ditto, Harper (U.S.), 1987. . . . . . £10/£5
The Clothes in the Wardrobe, Duckworth, 1987 . .
. . . . £15/£5
The Skeleton in the Cupboard, Duckworth, 1988 . .
. . . . £15/£5
The Fly in the Ointment, Duckworth, 1989. £15/£5
The Inn at the Edge of the World, Viking , 1990 . .
. . . . £10/£5
ditto, Viking (U.S.), 1990. . . . . . £10/£5
Pillars of Gold, Viking, 1992. . . . . £10/£5
Fairy Tale, Viking, 1996 . . . . . . £10/£5
ditto, Moyer, Bell (U.S.), 1998 . . . . £10/£5

Cookery
Natural Baby Food: A Cookery Book, Duckworth,
1977 (pseud. 'Brenda O'Casey') . . . £15/£5
*Darling, You Shouldn't Have Gone to So Much
Trouble*, Cape, 1980 (pseud. 'Anna Haycraft', with
Caroline Blackwood) . . . . . . £15/£5

Others
Home Life, Duckworth, 1986 . . . . £10/£5

ditto, Moyer, Bell (U.S.), 1997 . . . . £10/£5
Secrets of Strangers, Duckworth, 1986 (with Tom Pitt-
Aikens) . . . . £10/£5
More Home Life, Duckworth, 1987 . . . £10/£5
Home Life 3, Duckworth 1988 . . . . £10/£5
*Loss of the Good Authority: The Cause of Delin-
quency*, Viking (U.S.), 1989 (with Tom Pitt-Aikens).
. . . . £10/£5
Home Life 4, Duckworth, 1989 . . . . £10/£5
A Welsh Childhood, Joseph, 1990 . . . £10/£5
ditto, Moyer, Bell (U.S.), 1990 . . . . £10/£5

JOHN MEADE FALKNER
(b.1858 d.1932)

A British industrialist and antiquarian, Falkner turned
his hand to novel writing and local history. In *The
Lost Stradivarius* he created an enduring classic.

Novels
The Lost Stradivarius, Blackwood, 1895 . . £250
ditto, Appleton (U.S.) 1896 . . . . . . £150
Moonfleet, Arnold, 1898 . . . . £300
ditto, Little, Brown & Co. (U.S.) 1951 . . £35/£10
The Nebuly Coat, Arnold, 1903 . . . . £100
ditto, O.U.P., 1954. . . . . £35/£10

Verse
Poems, Westminster Press, [c. 1935] (wraps) . £30

Others
Handbook for Travellers in Oxfordshire, John
Murray, 1894 (anonymous). £50
A History of Oxfordshire, John Murray, 1899 . £50
Handbook for Berkshire, Edward Stanford, 1902 £30
Bath in History and Social Tradition, John Murray,
1918 (anonymous) £20
A History of Durham Cathedral Library, Durham
Country Advertiser, 1925 . . . . . . £75

G.E. FARROW
(b.1862 d.*not known*)

An author of children's stories, somewhat in the
tradition of Lewis Carroll, Farrow is perhaps collected
as much for the artists who illustrated his books as on
his own account.

The Wallypug of Why, Hutchinson, [1895] (illustrated
by Harry Furniss, vignettes by Dorothy Furniss) £100
ditto, Dodd, Mead (U.S.), 1896 . . . . . £25
The King's Gardens: An Allegory, Hutchinson, 1896
(illustrated by A.L. Bowley) £45
The Missing Prince, Hutchinson, 1896 (illustrated by
Harry Furniss, vignettes by Dorothy Furniss) £45

The Wallypug in London, Methuen, 1898 [1897]
(illustrated by Alan Wright). £65
Adventures in Wallypug-land, Methuen, 1898
(illustrated by Alan Wright). £65
The Little Panjandrum's Dodo, Skeffington, 1899
(illustrated by Alan Wright) £45
*The Mandarin's Kite, or Little Tsu-Foo and Another
Boy*, Skeffington, 1900 (illustrated by Alan Wright) .
. . . . £20
Baker Minor and the Dragon, Pearson, 1902 [1901]
(illustrated by Alan Wright) £45
The New Panjandrum, Pearson, 1902 [1901]
(illustrated by Alan Wright). £45
An A.B.C. of Every-day People, Dean, [1902]
(illustrated by John Hassall). £65
In Search of the Wallypug, Pearson, 1903 [1902]
(illustrated by Alan Wright). £65
Absurd Ditties, Routledge, 1903 (illustrated by John
Hassall). £45
Professor Philanderpan, Pearson, 1904 [1903] . £35
All About the Wallypug, Raphael Tuck, [1904] £45
The Cinematograph Train and Other Stories,
Johnson, 1904 (illustrated by Alan Wright) . £65
*Pixie Pickles: The Adventures of Pixene and Pixette
in their Woodland Haunts*, Skeffington, [1904]
(illustrated by H.B. Neilson) £65
Wallypug Tales, Raphael Tuck, [1904] . . . £45
Round the World A.B.C., Nister, [1904] (illustrated by
John Hassall). £55
The Wallypug Birthday Book, Routledge, 1904
(illustrated by Alan Wright) £45
The Wallypug in Fogland, Pearson, 1904 (illustrated
by Alan Wright) £65
*Ruff and Ready, The Fairy Guide by May Byron and
G.E. Farrow*, Cooke, [1905] (illustrated by John
Hassall) £40
The Mysterious 'Mr Punch', A School Story, Christian
Knowledge Society, [1905]. £30
The Wallypug Book, Traherne, [1905] . . . £50
The Wallypug in the Moon, or His Badjesty, Pearson,
1905 (illustrated by Alan Wright) £50
The Adventures of Ji, Partridge, [1906] (illustrated by
G.C. Tresidder) £40
Essays in Bacon, An Autograph Book, Treherne,
[1906]. £40
*The Escape of the Mullingong, A Zoological
Nightmare*, Blackie, 1907 [1906] (illustrated by
Gordon Browne). £35
The Adventures of a Dodo, Unwin, [1907] (illustrated
by Willy Pogany) £65
ditto, as *A Mysterious Voyage, or The Adventures of a
Dodo*, Partridge, [1910] (illustrated by K.M. Roberts)
. . . . £35
The Dwindleberry Zoo, Blackie, 1909 [1908]
(illustrated by Gordon Browne). £35
The Mysterious Shin Shira, Hodder & Stoughton,
[1915]. £25
Zoo Babies, Frowde/Hodder & Stoughton, 1913
(illustrated by Cecil Aldin) £125

Don't Tell, Cooke, [no date] (illustrated by John Hassall) £40
Ten Little Jappy Chaps, Treherne, [no date] (illustrated by John Hassall). £30

Parodies
Lovely Man, Being the Views ol Mistress A. Crosapatch, Skeffington, 1904 . . . . £40

WILLIAM FAULKNER
(b.1897 d.1962)

A Nobel Prize winning American novelist, Faulkner often pushed the boundaries of narrative convention.

Novels
Soldier's Pay, Boni & Liveright (U.S.), 1926 . . .
. . . . £15,000/£500
ditto, Chatto & Windus, 1930 . . . £1,000/£250
Mosquitoes, Boni & Liveright, 1927 (no publisher on spine, d/w printed in red on green with mosquito) .
. . . . £4,000/£400
ditto, Boni & Liveright, 1927 (publisher's name on spine, d/w with card players on yacht) . £2,000/£400
ditto, Garden City (U.S.), 1937 . . £125/£50
ditto, Chatto & Windus, 1964 . . . £45/£20
Sartoris, Harcourt Brace (U.S.), 1929 £2,500/£250
ditto, Chatto & Windus, 1933 (top edge stained blue) .
. . . . £1,250/£300
ditto, Chatto & Windus, 1933 (top edge unstained). .
. . . . £950/£75
The Sound and the Fury, Cape & Smith (U.S.), 1929 (unpriced d/w with 'Humanity Uprooted' priced $3.00 on rear panel) . . . £20,000/£2,000
ditto, Cape & Smith (U.S.), 1929 ('Humanity Uprooted' priced $3.50 on rear panel) . . . . .
. . . . £15,000/£2,000
ditto, Chatto & Windus, 1931 (black cloth, top edge stained red) . . . . £1,250/£250
ditto, Chatto & Windus, 1931 (mustard cloth stamped in red, top edge unstained) . . . £1,000/£150
As I Lay Dying, Cape & Smith (U.S.), 1930 (first issue with capital 'I' on p.11, line1 not correctly aligned, stamping to boards complete and unbroken) . . .
. . . . £6,000/£600
ditto, Cape & Smith (U.S.), 1930 (second issue with capital 'I' correctly aligned). . . £3,500/£250
ditto, Chatto & Windus, 1935 . . . £1,000/£250
Sanctuary, Cape & Smith (U.S.), 1931 £2,500/£250
ditto, Chatto & Windus, 1931 (cloth stamped in gold, four pages of ads) . . . . . £1,500/£350
ditto, Chatto & Windus, 1931 (cloth stamped in black, no ads). . . . . . . £1,150/£150
Idyll in the Desert, Random House (U.S.), 1931 (400 signed, numbered copies, glassine d/w) £1,250/£1,000

Miss Zilphia Gant, Book Club of Texas (U.S.), 1932 (300 copies) £1,000
Light in August, Smith & Haas (U.S.), 1932 (tan cloth stamped in blue and orange, glassine d/w over paper d/w) . . . . £1,250£150
ditto, Smith & Haas (U.S.), 1932 (stamped in blue only, glassine d/w over paper d/w) . £650/£150
ditto, Chatto & Windus, 1933 . . . £750/£75
Pylon, Smith & Haas (U.S.), 1935 . . £750/£75
ditto, Smith & Haas, 1935 (310 signed copies, slipcase, no d/w) . . . . £1,750/£750
ditto, Chatto & Windus, 1936 (top edge stained red, bottom edge untrimmed) . . . . £1,250/£65
ditto, Chatto & Windus, 1936 (top edge unstained, bottom edge trimmed) . . . . £1,000/£65
Absalom, Absalom!, Random House (U.S.), 1936 . . .
. . . . £1,000/£200
ditto, Random House, 1936 (300 signed copies, slipcase and d/w). . . . . £4,000/£3,000
ditto, Chatto & Windus, 1937 (glassine d/w with glued-on front flaps) . . . . . . £1,000/£175
The Unvanquished, Random House (U.S.), 1938 . .
. . . . £750/£150
ditto, Random House, 1938 (250 signed copies) £2,500
ditto, Chatto & Windus, 1938 (clear d/w with paper flaps) . . . . £600/£125
The Hamlet, Random House (U.S.), 1940 (d/w with ads for other books) . . . . . £1,500/£150
ditto, Random House (U.S.), 1940 (d/w with reviews of this book). . . . . £1,000/£150
ditto, Random House, 1940 (250 signed copies) £3,000
ditto, Chatto & Windus, 1940 . . . £650/£75
Intruder in the Dust, Random House (U.S.), 1948 .
. . . . £300/£45
ditto, Chatto & Windus, 1949 . . . £200/£30
Notes on a Horsethief, Levee Press (U.S.), 1950 [1951] (975 signed, numbered copies, tissue d/w) .
. . . . £1,250/£1,000
Requiem for a Nun, Random House (U.S.), 1951 .
. . . . £75/£30
ditto, Random House, 1951 (750 signed, numbered copies) £1,000
ditto, Chatto & Windus, 1953 . . . £45/£20
A Fable, Random House (U.S.), 1954 . £125/£20
ditto, Random House, 1954 (1,000 signed copies, glassine d/w, slipcase) . . £1,250/£1,000
ditto, Chatto & Windus, 1954 . . . £60/£25
The Town, Random House (U.S.), 1957 (first issue red cloth, top edge stained grey, threaded grey endpapers, d/w with '5/57' on front flap) . . . £750/£200
ditto, Random House (U.S.), 1957 (later issues with various cloths, endpapers etc) . . . £50/£20
ditto, Random House (U.S.), 1957 (450 signed copies, acetate d/w) . . . . . £1,250/£1,000
ditto, Chatto & Windus, 1958 . . . £45/£15
The Mansion, Random House (U.S.), 1959. £50/£20
ditto, Random House, 1959 (500 signed copies, acetate d/w, no slipcase). . . . £750/£500
ditto, Chatto & Windus, 1960 . . . £40/£15

The Reivers, Random House (U.S.), 1962 . £100/£20
ditto, Random House (U.S.), 1962 (500 signed copies,
acetate d/w) . . . . £600/£500
ditto, Chatto & Windus, 1962 . . . . £75/£15

Short Stories
These Thirteen, Cape & Smith (U.S.), 1931 £750/£200
ditto, Cape & Smith (U.S.), 1931 (299 signed copies,
plain tissue d/w). . . . . . . £2,250/£2,000
ditto, Chatto & Windus, 1933 . . . £1,000/£75
Doctor Martino and Other Stories, Smith & Haas
(U.S.), 1934 . . . . £600/£250
ditto, Smith & Haas (U.S.), 1934 (360 signed,
numbered copies) £1,000
ditto, Chatto & Windus, 1934 . . . . £500/£50
The Wild Palms, Random House (U.S.), 1939
(stamped in gold and green on spine) . . £750/£50
ditto, Random House (U.S.), 1939 (stamped in brown
and green on spine) . . . . . . £500/£50
ditto, Random House (U.S.), 1939 (250 signed copies,
glassine d/w) . . . . . . £2,000/£1,750
ditto, Chatto & Windus, 1939 . . . . £750/£40
Go Down, Moses and Other Stories, Random House
(U.S.), 1942 . . . . £750/£125
ditto, Random House (U.S.), 1942 (100 signed copies)
. . . . £10,000
ditto, Chatto & Windus, 1942 . . . £300/£60
Knight's Gambit, Random House (U.S.), 1948 . . .
. . . . £125/£25
ditto, Chatto & Windus, 1951 . . . . £100/£15
Collected Stories, Random House (U.S.), 1950 . . .
. . . . £200/£25
ditto, Chatto & Windus, 1951 . . . . £150/£25
Mirrors of Chartres Street, Faulkner Studies (U.S.),
1953 (1,000 numbered copies) . . £200/£100
Big Woods, Random House (U.S.), 1955 £200/£35
Jealousy and Episode, Faulkner Studies (U.S.), 1955
(500 copies, no d/w) £250
The Collected Stories, Chatto & Windus, 1958 (3 vols)
. . . . £200/£45
Selected Short Stories, Random House (U.S.), 1962 .
. . . . £35/£10
Uncollected Stories, Chatto & Windus, 1980 £25/£5

Verse
Vision in Spring, privately printed (U.S.), 1921 . .
. . . . £20,000
The Marble Faun, Four Seas (U.S.), 1924 . . . .
. . . . £15,000/£7,500
This Earth: A Poem, Equinox (U.S.), 1932 (wraps) .
. . . . £2,500
A Green Bough, Smith & Haas, 1933 . £400/£150
ditto, Smith & Haas, 1933 (360 signed copies, no d/w)
. . . . £750

Others
Sherwood Anderson and Other Famous Creoles,
Pelican Bookshop Press, 1926 (50 copies signed by
caricaturist Spratling) £3,000

ditto, Pelican Bookshop Press, 1926 (200/250
numbered copies) £1,000
ditto, Pelican Bookshop Press, 1926 (label pasted over
original limitation stating 'Second Issue 150 copies
January 1927') £1,000
Salmagundi, Casanova Press, 1932 (first 26 copies of
525 with top edge level with boards and bottom edge
untrimmed, slipcase). . . . . . £1,000/£950
ditto, Casanova Press, 1932 (499 of 525 copies in
slipcase) . . . . £250/£200
An Address by William Faulkner, Delta State Teachers
College (U.S.), 1952 (wraps) £1,500
Faulkner's Country, Chatto & Windus, 1955 £45/£15
New Orleans Sketches, Hokuseido Press (Tokyo),
1955 . . . . £200
ditto, Hokuseido Press (Tokyo), 1955 (wraps) . £75
ditto, Rutgers Univ. Press (U.S.), 1958 . £45/£15
ditto, Sidgwick and Jackson, 1959 . . . £35/£10
Early Prose and Poetry, Little, Brown (U.S.), 1962 .
. . . . £35/£10
ditto, Cape, 1962 . . . . £35/£10
Essays, Speeches, and Public Letters, Random House
(U.S.), 1966 . . . . £35/£10
ditto, Chatto & Windus, 1966 . . . . £35/£10
Selected Letters, Franklin Library (U.S.), 1976 . £45

HENRY FIELDING
(b.1707 d.1754)

Fielding's reputation rests on his novels, especially
his classic *Tom Jones*, although he wrote plays, poetry
and other works.

Novels
*The History and the Adventures of Joseph Andrews
and his friend Mr Abraham Adams*, Millar, 1742 (2
vols, anonymous) £750
Miscellanies, privately printed by subscription, 1743
(vol 3) £750
The History of Tom Jones, A Foundling, Miller, 1749
(6 vols, with errata leaf in vol. 1) . . . £2,500
Amelia, A. Millar, 1752 [1751] (4 vols). . . £750
The Works of Henry Fielding, Miller, 1762 (4 vols) .
. . . . £500

RONALD FIRBANK
(b.1886 d.1926)

An eccentric, Roman Catholic author of witty and
artificial novels.

Novels
Vainglory, Grant Richards, 1915. . . . . £150
ditto, Brentano's (U.S.), 1925 . . . . £100/£20
Inclinations, Grant Richards, 1916 . . . . £75

Caprice, Grant Richards, 1917 . . . . . £75
Valmouth, Grant Richards, 1919. . . . . £60
ditto, New Directions (U.S.), 1966 . . . £25/£10
The Flower Beneath the Foot, Grant Richards, 1923 .
. . . . £150/£60
ditto, Brentano (U.S.),1924 . . . . . £100/£25
Prancing Nigger, Brentano's (U.S.), 1924 . £200/£25
ditto, as *Sorrow in Sunlight*, Brentano's, 1924 (1,000
numbered copies) . . . . . £150/£30
Concerning the Eccentricities of Cardinal Pirelli,
Grant Richards, 1926, ... £200/£30
ditto, as *Extravaganzas*, Coward-McCann (U.S.), 1935
(with *The Artificial Princess*) . . . . £45/£15
The Artificial Princess, Duckworth, 1934 . £75/£25
ditto, Centaur Press 1934, (60 copies) . . . £200
Three Novels, Duckworth, 1950 (contains *Vainglory*,
Inclinations and *Caprice*) . . . . . £35/£15
ditto, New Directions (U.S.), [1951] . . . £35/£15

Short Stories
Odette d'Antrevernes and A Study in Temperament,
Elkin Mathews, 1905, (wraps) £500
ditto, Elkin Mathews, 1905, (10 copies on Japanese
vellum) £2,000
ditto, as *Odette: A Fairy Tale for Weary People*, Grant
Richards, 1916 (wraps) £75
Santal, Grant Richards, 1921 (wraps) . . £75
ditto, Bonacio & Saul with Grove Press (U.S.), 1955 .
. . . . £35/£15
Two Early Stories, Albondocani Press (U.S.), 1971
(226 copies) £40

Others
The Princess Zoubaroff - A Play, Grant Richards,
1920 . . . . £200/£45
*A Letter from Arthur Ronald Firbank to Madame
Albani*, Centaur Press, 1934 (50 facsimile copies of
letter, issued in envelope) . . . . . £100/£75
The New Rythum and Other Pieces, Duckworth, 1962
. . . . £20/£10
ditto, New Directions (U.S.),1963 . . . £20/£10
The Wind and the Roses, Alan Clodd, 1966 (poem
limited to 50 copies, wraps) £75
Far Away, Typographical Lab Univ. of Iowa, 1966
(100 copies) £75
An Early Flemish Painter, The Enitharmon Press/
Miriam L. Benkowitz, 1969 (300 copies, wraps) £35
When Widows Love and *A Tragedy in Green*, The
Enitharmon Press, 1980 (300 copies) . . £75/£35

Collected Editions
The Works of Ronald Firbank, Duckworth, 1929, (235
numbered sets, 5 vols) £1,000
Rainbow Edition, Duckworth, 1929-1930, (8 vols) .
. . . . £350
The Complete Ronald Firbank, Duckworth, 1961, (1
vol.) . . . . £35/£10

F. SCOTT FITZGERALD
(b.1896 d.1940)

An American novelist and short story writer
synonymous with the jazz age, *The Great Gatsby* is
his enduring classic.

Novels
This Side of Paradise, Scribners (U.S.), 1920 . . .
. . . . £6,000/£300
ditto, Collins, 1921 . . . . . . £2,000/£300
The Beautiful and Damned, Scribner (U.S.), 1922
(first issue d/w title in white outlined in black) . .
. . . . £5,000/£300
ditto, Scribner (U.S.), 1922 . . . . £4,000/£300
ditto, Collins, 1922 . . . . . . £1,500/£300
The Great Gatsby, Scribner (U.S.), 1925 (first issue
with 'chatter' not 'echolalia' on p.60, line 16,
'northern' not 'southern' on p.119, line 22 etc, and
d/w with 'jay Gatsby' on back blurb, line 14) . . .
. . . . £15,000/£1,750
ditto, Scribner (U.S.), 1925 (second issue with
'echolalia' on p.60, line 16, 'southern' on p.119, line
22 etc, and d/w with 'Jay Gatsby' on back blurb, line
14) . . . . £10,000/£500
ditto, Chatto & Windus, 1926 (original binding) . .
. . . . £3,000/£500
ditto, Chatto & Windus, 1926 [1927] (cheap edition) .
. . . . £1,000/£100
Tender is the Night, Scribner (U.S.), 1934 (first issue
jacket, no reviews) . . . . . . £6,000/£400
ditto, Scribner (U.S.), 1934 (second issue jacket with
reviews) . . . . £2,000/£400
ditto, Chatto & Windus, 1934 (original binding) . .
. . . . £1,000/£250
ditto, Chatto & Windus, 1934 [1936] (cheap edition) .
. . . . £350/£65
ditto, Scribner (U.S.), 1951 . . . . £100/£30
ditto, Grey Walls Press, 1953 . . . £100/£30
The Last Tycoon, Scribner (U.S.), 1941 (unfinished) .
. . . . £250/£50
ditto, Grey Walls Press, 1949. . . . £100/£20

Short Stories
Flappers and Philosophers, Scribner (U.S.), 1920 .
. . . . £4,500/£300
ditto, Collins, 1922 . . . . . £1,500/£150
Tales of the Jazz Age, Scribner (U.S.), 1922 . . .
. . . . £3,000/£200
ditto, Collins, 1923 . . . . . £1,500/£100
All the Sad Young Men, Scribner (U.S.), 1926 . . .
. . . . £1,500/£200
John Jackson's Arcady, Baker (U.S.), 1928 (wraps) .
. . . . £1,000
Taps at Reveille, Scribner (U.S.), 1935 (first state, no
printed price on d/w, 'Oh, catch it-Oh catch it...' on
p.351, lines 29-30) . . . . . . £2,000/£250

ditto, Scribner (U.S.), 1935 (second state, printed price on d/w, 'Oh, things like that happen...' on p.351, lines 29-30) . . . . £1,750/£125
The Stories, Scribners (U.S.), 1951 . . . £75/£20
Borrowed Time, Grey Walls Press, 1951 . £150/£35
Afternoon of an Author, privately printed Princeton Univ. Press (U.S.), 1957. . . . . . £100/£25
ditto, Scribners (U.S.), 1958 . . . . . £75/£10
ditto, Bodley Head, 1958 . . . . . . £75/£20
The Mystery of Raymond Mortgage, Random House (U.S.), [1960] (750 copies, wraps) £150
The Pat Hobby Stories, Scribners (U.S.), 1962. . . . . £75/£20
ditto, Penguin, 1967 . . . . £5
Dearly Beloved, Windhover Press/Univ. of Iowa (U.S.), 1969 (300 numbered copies, no d/w) . £75
The Basil and Josephine Stories, Scribners (U.S.), 1973 . . . . £40/£10
Bits of Paradise, Scribners (U.S.), 1974. . £35/£10
ditto, Bodley Head, 1973 . . . . . . £35/£10
The Price Was High, Harcourt Brace (U.S.), 1979 .
. . . . £30/£5
ditto, Quartet, 1979 . . . . . . £25/£5

Others
The Vegetable: From President to Postman, Scribners, 1923 . . . . £1,000/£100
The Crack-Up, New Directions (U.S.), 1945 £250/£45
ditto, New Directions ('British Empire' issue), 1945 .
. . . . £125/£35
ditto, Grey Walls Press, 1947. . . . . £45/£15
The Letters, Scribners (U.S.), 1963 . . . £50/£15
ditto, Bodley Head, 1964 . . . . . . £40/£15
The Apprentice Fiction, Rutgers Univ. Press, 1965 .
. . . . £35/£10
Thoughtbook of Francis Scott Key Fitzgerald, Princeton Univ. Library (U.S.), 1965 (glassine d/w) .
. . . . £35/£30
In His Own Time, Kent State Univ. Press, 1971 . .
. . . . £30/£10
Dear Scott / Dear Max, Scribners (U.S.), 1971 . .
. . . . £30/£10
ditto, Cassell, 1973 . . . . £25/£10
As Ever, Scott Fitz, Lippincott (U.S.), 1972 £25/£10
ditto, Woburn, 1973 . . . . . . £25/£10
Preface to This Side of Paradise, Windhover Press (U.S.), 1975 (150 copies) £125
The Notebooks, Harcourt Brace, 1978 . . £30/£10
The Correspondence, Random House (U.S.), 1980 .
. . . . £30/£10

PENELOPE FITZGERALD
(b.1916 d.2000)

A Booker Prize winning novelist, Fitzgerald's novels are humorous and understated while often painfully revealing.

Novels
The Golden Child, Duckworth, 1977 . . £150/£25
ditto, Scribner (U.S.), 1978 . . . . . £50/£10
The Bookshop, Duckworth, 1978 . . . £40/£15
ditto, as *The Book Shop*, Houghton Mifflin (U.S.), 1997 (wraps) £5
Offshore, Collins, 1979 . . . . . £35/£5
ditto, Henry Holt (U.S.), 1979 . . . . £20/£5
Human Voices, Collins, 1980 . . . . £25/£5
ditto, Houghton Mifflin (U.S.), 1999 (wraps) . . £5
At Freddies, Collins, 1985 . . . . . £15/£5
ditto, Godine (U.S.), 1983 . . . . . £15/£5
Innocence, Collins, 1986 . . . . . . £10/£5
ditto, Holt (U.S.), 1987 . . . . . . £10/£5
The Beginning of Spring, Collins, 1988 . £10/£5
ditto, Holt (U.S.), 1989 . . . . . . £10/£5
The Gate of Angels, Collins, 1990 . . . £10/£5
ditto, Doubleday (U.S.), 1992 . . . . £10/£5
The Blue Flower, Flamingo, 1995 . . . £10/£5
ditto, Houghton Mifflin (U.S.), 1997 . . £10/£5

Others
Edward Burne-Jones: A Biography, Joseph, 1975 .
. . . . £75/£20
The Knox Brothers, Macmillan, 1977 . . £30/£5
ditto, Coward McCann (U.S.), 1977 . . . £15/£5
Charlotte Mew and Her Friends: With a Selection of Her Poems, Collins, 1984 . . . . . £15/£5
ditto, Addison Wesley (U.S.), 1988 . . . £15/£5

IAN FLEMING
(b.1908 d.1964)

Famous for the legendary James Bond stories. The condition of the early books is of paramount importance in determining their value.

Bond Titles
Casino Royale, Cape, 1953 . . . . £7,000/£500
ditto, Macmillan (U.S.), 1954. . . . £1,000/£75
Live and Let Die, Cape, 1954 . . . £3,500/£300
ditto, Macmillan (U.S.), 1955. . . . . £400/£35
Moonraker, Cape, 1955 . . . . . £1,750/£250
ditto, Macmillan (U.S.), 1955. . . . . £400/£35
Diamonds are Forever, Cape, 1956 . . . £750/£75
ditto, Macmillan (U.S.), 1956. . . . . £300/£50
From Russia, with Love, Cape, 1957 . . £600/£45
ditto, Macmillan (U.S.), 1957. . . . . £200/£20
Dr No, Cape, 1958 . . . . £350/£40
ditto, Macmillan (U.S.), 1958. . . . . £150/£15

Goldfinger, Cape, 1959 . . . . . . £250/£35
ditto, Macmillan (U.S.), 1959. . . . . £75/£15
For Your Eyes Only, Cape, 1960 (short stories) . .
. . . . £175/£35
ditto, Viking (U.S.), 1960. .` . . . £75/£15
Thunderball, Cape, 1961 . . . . . . £125/£20
ditto, Viking (U.S.), 1961. . . . . £50/£15
The Spy Who Loved Me, Cape, 1962 . . £100/£20
ditto, Viking (U.S.), 1962. . . . . £45/£15
On Her Majesty's Secret Service, Cape, 1963 £75/£20
ditto, Cape, 1963 (250 signed copies, glassine d/w) .
. . . . £3,000/£2,500
ditto, NAL (U.S.), 1963 . . . . . £35/£15
You Only Live Twice, Cape, 1964 . . . £40/£10
ditto, NAL (U.S.), 1964 . . . . . £20/£10
The Man with the Golden Gun, Cape, 1965 (with gold
blocked revolver on front cover) . £2,500/£2,500
ditto, Cape, 1965 (without gold blocked revolver on
front cover) . . . . £35/£10
ditto, NAL (U.S.), 1965 . . . . . £20/£10
Octopussy and The Living Daylights, Cape, 1966
(short stories). . . . . £25/£10
ditto, NAL (U.S.), 1966 . . . . . £20/£10
see also *The Ivory Hammer: The Year at Sotherby's*,
Longman, 1963 (Contains Bond story 'The Property
of a Lady') . . . . £45/£20
ditto, Holt, Rinehart & Winston (U.S.), 1964 £40/£15

Non Fiction
The Diamond Smugglers, Cape, 1957 . . £125/£35
ditto, Macmillan (U.S.), 1958 . . . . £45/£20
Thrilling Cities, Cape, 1963 . . . . £30/£15
ditto, NAL (U.S.), 1964 . . . . . £15/£10
Ian Fleming Introduces Jamaica, Deutsch, 1965 .
. . . . £20/£10
ditto, Hawthorne (U.S.), 1965 . . . £15/£10

Children's
Chitty Chitty Bang Bang, Cape, 1964-64 (3 books) .
. . . . £35 each, £200 the set
ditto, Random House (U.S.), 1964. . . . £25/£5

FORD MADDOX FORD
(b.1873 d.1939)

A novelist and editor, he was actually born Ford
Hermann Hueffer, although, unless noted otherwise,
titles listed below were published as by either Ford
Maddox Ford, Ford Maddox Hueffer or F. Maddox
Hueffer.

Novels
The Shifting of the Fire, T. Fisher Unwin, 1892
(pseud. 'H. Ford Hueffer') £250
The Benefactor, Brown, Langham & Co., 1905 £100
The Fifth Queen, Alston Rivers, 1906 . . . £75
ditto, Vanguard Press (U.S.), [c.1963] . . £15/£5

Privy Seal, Alston Rivers, 1907 . . . . . £50
An English Girl, Methuen & Co., 1907 . . . £50
The Fifth Queen Crowned, Eveleigh Nash, 1908 £50
Mr Apollo, Methuen & Co., 1908 . . . . £50
The Half Moon, Eveleigh Nash, 1909 . . . £50
A Call, Chatto & Windus, 1910 . . . . . £50
The Portrait, Methuen & Co., 1910 . . . . £50
The Simple Life Limited, John Lane, 1911 (pseud.
'Daniel Chaucer') £50
Ladies Whose Bright Eyes, Constable & Co., 1911 .
. . . . £50
ditto, Lippincott (U.S.), 1935. . . . . £65/£20
The Panel, Constable & Co., 1912 . . . . £50
The New Humpty-Dumpty, John Lane, 1912 (pseud.
'Daniel Chaucer') £50
Mr Fleight, Howard Latimer, 1913 . . . . £50
The Young Lovell, Chatto & Windus, 1913. . £50
The Good Soldier, John Lane, 1915 . . . . £1,000
Zeppelin Nights: A London Entertainment, John
Lane/Bodley Head, 1915 (with Violet Hunt) £100
The Marsden Case, Duckworth, 1923 . . £75/£25
Some Do Not, Duckworth, 1924 . . . . £100/£25
ditto, Seltzer (U.S.), 1925. . . . . £65/£20
No More Parades, Duckworth, 1925 . £125/£25
A Man Could Stand Up, Duckworth, 1926 £100/£25
ditto, Boni (U.S.), 1926 . . . . . £75/£15
The Last Post, The Literary Guild of America (U.S.),
1928 . . . . £75/£15
ditto, as *Last Post*, Duckworth, 1928 . . £75/£15
A Little Less Than Gods, Duckworth, [1928] £75/£20
ditto, Viking (U.S.), 1928. . . . . . £75/£20
No Enemy, Macaulay (U.S.), 1929 . . . £150/£35
When the Wicked Man, Horace Liveright (U.S.), 1931
. . . . £75/£20
ditto, Jonathan Cape, 1932 . . . . . £50/£20
The Rash Act, Long & Smith (U.S.), 1933 . £50/£20
ditto, Jonathan Cape, 1933 . . . . . £50/£20
Henry for Hugh, Lippincott (U.S.), 1934 . £50/£20
Vive le Roy, Lippincott (U.S.), 1936. . . £50/£20
ditto, George Allen & Unwin, 1937 . . . £50/£20

For titles written with Joseph Conrad (*The
Inheritors*, *Romance* and *The Nature of a Crime*)
please see under Conrad.

Verse
New Poems, Rudge (U.S.), 1927 (325 signed copies,
glassine d/w) £150
Selected Poems, Pym Randall, 1971 (1,000 copies) .
. . . . £25/£15
ditto, Pym Randall, 1971 (50 copies) . . £175/£125

Others
The Brown Owl: A Fairy Story, Unwin, 1892 (as Ford
H. Hueffer) £300
ditto, Putnam, 1892 . . . . £250
*The Cinque Ports: A Historical and Descriptive
Record*, Blackwood, 1900 . . . . . £400

Rossetti: A Critical Essay on His Art, Duckworth, [1902]. £15
The Soul of London: A Survey of a Modern City, Rivers, 1905 . . . . £50
The Heart of the Country: A Survey of a Modern Land, Duckworth, 1906. . . . . . . £50
The Critical Attitude, Duckworth, 1911 (pseud. 'Ford Maddox Hueffer') £35
Henry James: A Critical Study, Secker, 1913 . £50
Between St. Dennis and St. George: A Sketch of Three Civilizations, Hodder & Stoughton, 1915 £45
Women and Men, Three Mountains Press (Paris), 1923 (300 numbered copies, wraps) £350
Mister Bosphorus and the Muses; or, A Short History of Poetry in Britain, Duckworth, 1923. . £125/£20
ditto, Duckworth, 1923 (70 copies signed by artist) .
. . . . £400/£200
New York is Not America, Duckworth, 1927 £125/£20
ditto, Boni (U.S.), 1927 . . . . . . £75/£20
New York Essays, Rudge (U.S.), 1927 (750 signed copies) £200
The English Novel, Lippincott (U.S.), 1929 £50/£15
ditto, Constable, 1930 . . . . £45/£15
Provence, from Minstrels to the Machine, Allen & Unwin, 1935 . . . . £40/£15
ditto, Lippincott (U.S.), 1935. . . . . £40/£15
Great Trade Route, O.U.P. (U.S.), 1937 . £25/£15
The March of Literature from Confucius to Modern Times, Dial Press (U.S.), 1938 . . . . £50/£20
Your Mirror to My Times, Holt Rinehart & Winston (U.S.), 1971 . . . . £10/£5

C.S. FORESTER
(b.1899 d.1966)

Best remembered for the Hornblower series, and for *The African Queen.*

'Hornblower' Novels
Beat to Quarters, Little, Brown (U.S.), 1937 £500/£50
ditto, as *The Happy Return*, Joseph, 1937 £500/£50
A Ship of the Line, Little, Brown (U.S.), 1938 . . .
. . . . £500/£50
ditto, as *Ship of the Line* Joseph, 1938 . £500/£50
Flying Colours (including *A Ship of the Line*), The Book Society/Joseph, 1938 . . . . . £500/£50
Flying Colours, Joseph, 1938 . . . . £400/£45
ditto, Little, Brown (U.S.), 1939 . . . £300/£40
Commodore Hornblower, Little, Brown (U.S.), 1945 .
. . . . £75/£20
ditto, as *The Commodore*, Joseph, 1945. . £75/£20
Lord Hornblower, Little, Brown (U.S.), 1946 £50/£15
ditto, Joseph, 1946. . . . . £50/£15
Mr Midshipman Hornblower, Little, Brown (U.S.), 1950 . . . . £30/£10
ditto, Joseph, 1950. . . . . £30/£10

Lieutenant Hornblower, Little, Brown (U.S.), 1952 .
. . . . £30/£10
ditto, Joseph, 1952. . . . . £30/£10
Hornblower and the Atropos, Little, Brown (U.S.), 1953 . . . . £30/£10
ditto, Joseph, 1953. . . . . £30/£10
Admiral Hornblower in the West Indies, Little, Brown (U.S.), 1958 . . . . £30/£10
ditto, as *Hornblower in the West Indies*, Joseph, 1958
. . . . £30/£10
Hornblower and the Hotspur, Little, Brown (U.S.), 1962 . . . . £20/£5
ditto, Joseph, 1962. . . . . £15/£5
Hornblower and the Crisis: An Unfinished Novel, Joseph, 1967 . . . . £20/£10
ditto, as *Hornblower During the Crisis*, Little, Brown (U.S.), 1967 . . . . £20/£10

'Hornblower' Omnibus Editions
Captain Horatio Hornblower, Little, Brown (U.S.), 1939 . . . . £100/£25
Hornblower Takes Command, Little, Brown (U.S.), 1953 . . . . £30/£10
Young Hornblower, Little, Brown (U.S.), 1960 . .
. . . . £30/£10
ditto, Joseph, 1964. . . . . £20/£5
The Indominatable Hornblower, Little, Brown (U.S.), 1963 . . . . £25/£10
Captain Hornblower R.N., Joseph, 1965 . £25/£5
Admiral Hornblower, Joseph, 1968 . . . £25/£5

Other Novels
A Pawn Among Kings, Methuen, 1924 . £1,500/£450
Payment Deferred, Bodley Head, 1926 . £1,500/£150
ditto, Little, Brown (U.S.), 1942 . . . . £50/£15
Love Lies Dreaming, Bodley Head, 1927 . £600/£75
ditto, Bobbs-Merrill (U.S.), 1927 (first issue with 'C.E. Forester' on cover') . . . . . . £400/£50
The Wonderful Week, Bodley Head, 1927 £400/£75
ditto, as *One Wonderful Week*, Bobbs-Merrill (U.S.), 1927 . . . . £300/£40
The Shadow of the Hawk, Bodley Head, 1928 . . .
. . . . £400/£75
ditto, as *The daughter of the Hawk*, Bobbs-Merrill (U.S.), 1928 . . . . £300/£40
Brown on Resolution, Bodley Head, 1929 £400/£75
ditto, as *Single-Handed*, Putnam (U.S.), 1929 . .
. . . . £300/£40
Plain Murder, Bodley Head, 1930 . . . £400/£75
ditto, Dell (U.S.), 1954 (wraps) £15
Death to the French, Bodley Head, 1932 £350/£100
ditto, as *Rifleman Dodd*, Little, Brown (U.S.), 1943 .
. . . . £45/£15
The Gun, John Lane, 1933 . . . . . £400/£50
ditto, as *Rifleman Dodd and the Gun*, Little, Brown (U.S.), 1933 . . . . £300/£40
The Peacemaker, Heinemann, 1934 . . £300/£40
ditto, Little, Brown (U.S.), 1934 . . . . £200/£35
The African Queen, Heinemann, 1935 . £2,500/£500

ditto, Little, Brown (U.S.), 1935 . . . £2,000/£500
The General, Little, Brown (U.S.), 1936 . £350/£35
ditto, Joseph, 1936. . . . . £350/£35
The Captain from Connecticut, Joseph, 1941 . . .
. . . . £250/£15
ditto, Little, Brown (U.S.), 1941 . . . . £150/£10
The Ship, Joseph, 1943 . . . . . . £200/£25
ditto, Little, Brown (U.S.), 1943 . . . . £125/£15
The Bedchamber Mystery, S.J. Reginald Saunders
(Canada), 1944 . . . . £175/£40
The Sky and the Forest, Joseph, 1948 . . £75/£15
ditto, Little, Brown (U.S.), 1948 . . . . £75/£15
Randall and the River of Time, Little, Brown (U.S.),
1950 . . . . £45/£10
ditto, Joseph, 1951. . . . . £45/£10
The Good Shepherd, Joseph, 1955 . . . £45/£10
ditto, Little, Brown (U.S.), 1955 . . . . £45/£10

Short Stories
The Paid Piper, Methuen, 1924 (first issue with ads
dated September 1923) . . . . . £2,000/£300
ditto, Methuen, 1924 (second issue with ads dated May
1925) . . . . £1,500/£250
Two-and-Twenty, Bodley Head, 1931 . £1,000/£150
ditto, Appleton-Century Co. (U.S.), 1931 £500/£75
The Nightmare, Little, Brown (U.S.), 1954. £60/£10
ditto, Joseph, 1954. . . . . £60/£15
The Man in the Yellow Raft, Joseph, 1969 £35/£10
ditto, Little, Brown (U.S.), 1969 . . . . £35/£10
Gold From Crete, Little, Brown, 1970 . . £25/£10
ditto, Joseph (U.S.), 1971. . . . . . £25/£10

Plays
U 97, John Lane, 1931 . . . . . . £400/£50
Nurse Cavell, John Lane, 1933 . . . £300/£40

Children's
Marionettes At Home, Joseph, 1936 (first issue, sienna
cloth) . . . . £400/£75
ditto, Joseph, 1936 (second issue orange cloth, jacket
with '3/6 net' on spine) . . . . . £250/£45
Poo-Poo and the Dragons, Little, Brown (U.S.), 1942
. . . . £300/£45
ditto, Little, Brown (U.S.), 1942 . . . . £250/£40
The Barbary Pirates, Random House (U.S.), 1953. .
. . . . £125/£20
ditto, Macdonald, 1953 . . . . . . £50/£10
Hornblower Goes to Sea, Joseph, 1954 . . £45/£20
Hornblower's Triumph, Joseph, 1955 . . £45/£20

Non Fiction
Napoleon and His Court, Methuen, 1924 £1,250/£250
ditto, Dodd, Mead (U.S.), 1924 . . . £450/£100
Josephine, Napoleon's Empress, Methuen, 1925 . .
. . . . £850/£200
ditto, Methuen, 1925 (but with ads dated 1928). . .
. . . . £750/£100
ditto, Dodd, Mead (U.S.), 1924 . . . . £400/£60

Victor Emmanuel II and the Union of Italy, Methuen,
1927 . . . . £500/£100
ditto, Dodd, Mead (U.S.), 1927 . . . . £450/£75
Louis XIV, King of France and Navarre, Dodd, Mead
(U.S.), 1928 . . . . £500/£100
ditto, Methuen, 1928 . . . . . . £500/£100
Nelson, John Lane, 1929 . . . . . . £450/£75
ditto, as *Lord Nelson*, Bobbs-Merrill (U.S.), 1929 . .
. . . . £450/£75
The Voyage of the Annie Marble, John Lane, 1929 .
. . . . £500/£125
The Annie Marble in Germany, John Lane, 1930 . .
. . . . £500/£125
The Earthly Paradise, Joseph, 1940 . . £75/£25
ditto, as *To the Indies*, Little, Brown (U.S.), 1940 . .
. . . . £65/£20
The Naval War of 1812, Joseph, 1957 . . £50/£20
ditto, as *The Age of Fighting Sail: The Story of the
Naval War of 1812*, Doubleday (U.S.), 1956 £45/£15
Hunting the Bismark, Joseph, 1959 . . £50/£15
ditto, as *The Last Nine Days of the Bismark*, Little,
Brown (U.S.), 1959 . . . . £45/£15
The Hornblower Companion, Joseph, 1964 .
. . . . £125/£25
ditto, Little, Brown (U.S.), 1964 . . . . £125/£25
Long Before Forty, Joseph, 1967 . . . £30/£10
ditto, Little, Brown (U.S.), 1967 . . . . £25/£10

Editor
The Adventures of John Wetherell, Joseph, 1954 . .
. . . . £45/£10
ditto, Doubleday (U.S.), 1954 . . . . £35/£10

E.M. FORSTER
(b.1879 d.1970)

A novelist and essayist, Forster's writings often
reflect his loathing of public schools, imperialism,
and the repression of civil liberties. His books have
been popularised recently by the successful film
makers Merchant and Ivory.

Novels
Where Angels Fear to Tread, Blackwood, 1905 (first
issue with this title not mentioned in ads at rear) . .
. . . . £1,500
ditto, Blackwood, 1905 (second issue with this title
mentioned in ads) £1,000
ditto, Knopf (U.S.), 1920 . . . . . £350 /£75
The Longest Journey, Blackwood, 1907 . . £500
ditto, Knopf (U.S.), 1922 . . . . . £400/£75
A Room with a View, Arnold, 1908 . . . £1,000
ditto, Putnam (U.S.), 1911 . . . . . £250
Howard's End, Arnold, 1910 (first issue with 4 pages
of integral ads) £1,000
ditto, Arnold, 1910 (second issue with 8 pages of
inserted ads) £750

ditto, Putnam (U.S.), 1910 . . . . . . £500
A Passage to India, Arnold, 1924 . . £1,500/£400
ditto, Arnold, 1924 (200 numbered signed copies, fawn paper boards, grey slipcase). £3,500
ditto, Harcourt Brace (U.S.), 1924 . . . £250/£50
ditto, as *The Manuscripts of A Passage to India*, Arnold, 1978 (1,500 copies) . . . £35/£15
Maurice, Arnold, 1971 . . . . . . £25/£10
ditto, Norton (U.S.), 1971. . . . . £20/£5

Short Stories
The Celestial Omnibus and Other Stories, Sidgwick & Jackson, 1911 . . . . £200
ditto, Knopf (U.S.), 1923 . . . . . . £200/£35
The Story of the Siren, Hogarth Press, 1920 (first state with 'The Story/of the Siren' on front label, wraps) .
. . . . £500
ditto, Hogarth Press, 1920 (other states, wraps) £300
The Eternal Moment, Sidgwick & Jackson, 1928 (First issue cloth stamped in gold). . . . £350/£75
ditto, Sidgwick & Jackson, 1928 (Second issue cloth stamped in black) . . . . . . £325/£50
ditto, Harcourt Brace (U.S.), 1928 . . . £200/£45
The Collected Tales, Knopf (U.S.), 1947 £45/£15
ditto, as *The Collected Short Stories*, Sidgwick & Jackson, 1948 . . . . £45/£15
The Life to Come, Arnold, 1972 . . . . £25/£10
ditto, Norton (U.S.), 1973. . . . . . £25/£10

Essays
Pharos and Pharillon, Hogarth Press, 1923 (900 copies, no d/w) £250
ditto, Knopf (U.S.), 1923 . . . . . £250/£50
Anonymity: An Enquiry, Hogarth Press, 1925 (boards)
. . . . £175
ditto, Hogarth Press, 1925 (wraps) £75
A Letter to Madam Blanchard, Hogarth Press, 1931 (wraps) £35
ditto, Harcourt Brace (U.S.), 1932 (wraps) . . £25
Sinclair Lewis Interprets America, privately printed, 1932 (100 copies, wraps) £100
Pageant of Abinger, privately printed, 1934 (wraps) .
. . . . £65
Abinger Harvest, Arnold, 1936 (first issue with 'A Flood in the Office', cream d/w decorated orange) .
. . . . £300/£75
ditto, Arnold, 1936 (second issue without 'A Flood in the Office') . . . . £150/£20
ditto, Harcourt Brace (U.S.), 1936 . . . £75/£25
What I Believe, Hogarth Press, 1939 (wraps) . £35
Nordic Twilight, Macmillan, 1940 (wraps) . . £25
The Challenge of Our Time, Marshall, 1948 £35/310
Two Cheers for Democracy, Arnold, 1951 . £45/£15
ditto, Harcourt Brace (U.S.), 1951 . . . £45/£15

Others
The Government of Egypt, Labour Research Dept., [1920] (wraps) £300

Alexandria, A History and a Guide, Whitehead Morris, 1922 (no d/w) £500
ditto, Whitehead Morris, 1922 (revised edition with maps and plans) £75
ditto, Whitehead Morris, 1922 (250 signed copies). .
. . . . £500
ditto, Doubleday (U.S.), 1961 . . . . £25/£10
Aspects of the Novel, Arnold, 1927 . . . £250/£40
ditto, Harcourt Brace (U.S.), 1927 . . . £75/£20
Goldsworthy Lowes Dickinson, Arnold, 1934 . . .
. . . . £200/£30
ditto, Harcourt Brace (U.S.), 1934 . . . £150/£25
Reading as Usual, Tottenham Public Libraries, 1939 (wraps) £200
England's Pleasant Land, Hogarth Press, 1940 . .
. . . . £40/£15
Virginia Woolf, C.U.P., 1942 (wraps) . . . £30
ditto, Harcourt Brace (U.S.), 1942 . . . £50/£20
The Development of English Prose Between 1918 and 1930, Jackson, 1945 (wraps) £45
Desmond McCarthy, Mill House Press, 1952 (64 copies) £250
ditto, Mill House Press, 1952 (8 copies). . . £1,000
The Hill of Devi, Arnold, 1953 . . . . £65/£15
ditto, Harcourt Brace (U.S.), 1953 . . . £45/£15
I Assert There is an Alternative to Humanism, The Ethical Union, 1955 . . . . £50
Battersea Rise, privately printed (Harcourt Brace U.S.), 1955 . . . . £45
Marianne Thornton, Arnold, 1956 . . . £30/£10
ditto, Arnold, 1956 (200 signed copies, slipcase) £250
ditto, Harcourt Brace (U.S.), 1956 . . . £30/£5
Tourism vs Thuggism, privately printed, 1957 (wraps)
. . . . £25
E.K. Bennett, privately printed, 1958 (wraps) . £75
A View Without a Room, Albondocani Press (U.S.), 1973 (200 numbered copies, wraps) . . . £75
Letters to Donald Windham, Campbell (Verona), 1975 (300 copies) £75
Commonplace Book, Scolar Press, 1978 (facsimile, 350 numbered copies, boxed) £100
Selected Letters, Vol. 1, Collins, 1983 . . £25/£10
ditto, Harvard Univ. Press (U.S.), 1983 . . £25/£10
Selected Letters, Vol. 2, Collins, 1984 . . £25/£10
ditto, Harvard Univ. Press (U.S.), 1984 . . £25/£10

FREDERICK FORSYTH
(b.1938)

The author of the phenomenally successful *The Day of the Jackal*, Forsyth's forte is the tense thriller.

Novels
The Day of the Jackal, Hutchinson, 1971 . £65/£10
ditto, Viking (U.S.), 1971. . . . . . £25/£10
The Odessa File, Hutchinson, 1972 . . . £25/£5
ditto, Viking (U.S.), 1972. . . . . . £25/£5

The Dogs of War, Hutchinson, 1974 . . £25/£5
ditto, Viking (U.S.), 1974. . . . . . £20/£5
The Shepherd, Hutchinson, 1975 . . . £10/£5
ditto, Viking (U.S.), 1976. . . . . . £10/£5
The Devil's Alternative, Hutchinson, 1979 . £15/£5
ditto, Viking (U.S.), 1980. . . . . . £15/£5
The Fourth Protocol, Hutchinson, 1984 . £15/£5
ditto, Viking (U.S.), 1984. . . . . . £15/£5
The Negotiator, Bantam, 1989 . . . . £10/£5
ditto, London Limited editions, 1989 (150 signed
copies, glasssine d/w) . . . . . . £65/£50
ditto, Bantam (U.S.), 1989 . . . . . £10/£5
The Deceiver, Bantam, 1991 . . . . . £10/£5
ditto, Bantam (U.S.), 1991 . . . . . £10/£5
Fist of God, Bantam, 1994 . . . . . £10/£5
ditto, Bantam (U.S.), 1994 . . . . . £10/£5
Icon, Bantam, 1996 . . . . £10/£5
ditto, Bantam (U.S.), 1996 . . . . . £10/£5
The Phantom of Manhattan, Bantam, 1999 £10/£5
ditto, Franklin Library (U.S.), 1999 (signed) . £40

Short Stories
No Comebacks, Hutchinson, 1982 . . . £15/£5
ditto, Viking (U.S.), 1982. . . . . . £15/£5
ditto, Eurographica (Helsinki), 1986 (350 signed
copies, wraps with d/w) . . . . . . £60/£30

Non Fiction
The Biafra Story, Penguin Special, 1969 (wraps) £60
ditto, Penguin, 1967 (wraps) £10
ditto, as *The Biafra Story, The Making of an African
Legend*, Severn House, 1983 . . . . £20/£5

DION FORTUNE
(b.1890 d.1946)

British occultist and writer of occult fiction, Fortune's
books were published under her own name as well as
the pseudonyms V.M. Steele and Violet M. Firth.

Dion Fortune Novels
The Demon Lover, Noel Douglas, [1927] . £65/£25
The Winged Bull, Williams & Norgate, 1935 . .
. . . . £100/£35
The Goat-Foot God, Williams & Norgate, 1936 . .
. . . . £65/£25
The Sea Priestess, Inner Light, 1938 . . £65/£25
Moon Magic, Aquarian Press, 1956 . . . £35/£20

Dion Fortune Short Stories
The Secrets of Dr Taverner, Noel Douglas, 1926 . .
. . . . £65/£25

Dion Fortune Non Fiction
The Esoteric Philosophy of Love and Marriage, Rider,
1923 . . . . £45/£20

Esoteric Orders and Their Work, Rider, 1928 £45/£20
Sane Occultism, Rider, 1929 . . . . . £35/£15
The Training and Work of an Initiate, Rider, 1930 .
. . . . £35/£15
Mystical Meditations Upon the Collects, Rider, 1930 .
. . . . £35/£15
Spiritualism in the Light of Occult Science, Rider,
1931 . . . . £35/£15
Psychic Self-Defence, Rider, 1931 . . . £45/£20
Through the Gates of Death, Inner Light, 1932 . .
. . . . £35/£15
The Mystical Qabalah, Williams & Norgate, 1935 .
. . . . £45/£20
Practical Occultism in Daily Life, Williams &
Norgate, 1935 . . . . £35/£15
The Cosmic Doctrine, Inner Light, 1949 . £20/£10
Applied Magic, Aquarian Press, 1962 . . £20/£10
Aspects of Occultism, Aquarian Press, 1962 £20/£10
The Magical Battle of Britain, Golden Gates Press,
1994 . . . . £15/£5

Novels written as V.M. Steele
The Scarred Wrists, Stanley Paul, [1935] . £25/£10
Hunters of Humans, Stanley Paul, [1936] . £25/£10
Beloved of Ishmael, Stanley Paul, [1937] . £25/£10

Non Fiction written as Violet M. Firth
Machinery of the Mind, Allen & Unwin, 1922 £50/£20
The Psychology of the Servant Problem, C.W. Daniel,
1925 . . . . £20/£10
The Soya Bean, C.W. Daniel, 1925 . . . £20/£10
The Problem of Purity, Rider, [1928] . . £20/£10
Avalon of the Heart, Muller, 1934 . . . £20/£10

Verse written as Violet M. Firth
Violets, Mendip Press, [1904] £25
More Violets, Jarrold, [1906] £25

JOHN FOWLES
(b.1926)

Fowles has become both popularly and critically
acclaimed as a modern literary figure due to his
experimental style and the broad humanist content of
his novels.

Novels
The Collector, Jonathan Cape, 1963 (trial binding of
charcoal-black papered boards, no top edge stain, first
issue d/w without reviews quoted) . £5,000/£4,725
ditto, Jonathan Cape, 1963 (rust-coloured papered
boards, matching top edge stain, first issue d/w) . .
. . . . £300/£25
ditto, Jonathan Cape, 1963 (later issue rare d/w with
reviews). . . . . £2,000/£50
ditto, Little, Brown (U.S.), 1963 . . . . £75/£25

The Magus, Little, Brown (U.S.), 1965 . . £125/£25
ditto, Jonathan Cape, 1966 . . . . . £125/£25
ditto, Jonathan Cape, 1977 (revised edition) £20/£10
ditto, Little, Brown (U.S.), 1978 (revised edition) . .
. . . . £20/£10
The French Lieutenant's Woman, Jonathan Cape,
1969 . . . . £150/£25
ditto, Little, Brown (U.S.), 1969 . . . . £100/£15
The Ebony Tower, Jonathan Cape, 1974 (novellas) .
. . . . £50/£10
ditto, Little, Brown (U.S.), 1974 . . . . £35/£5
ditto, Little, Brown (U.S.), 1974 (signed issue, with a
special tipped-in leaf signed by John Fowles) . . .
. . . . £175/£150
Daniel Martin, Little, Brown (U.S.), 1977 . £25/£5
ditto, Jonathan Cape, 1977 . . . . . . £25/£5
Mantissa, Jonathan Cape, 1982 . . . . £20/£5
ditto, Little, Brown (U.S.), 1982 . . . . £20/£5
ditto, Little, Brown (U.S.), 1982 (500 signed copies,
slipcase) . . . . £75/£50
A Maggot, Jonathan Cape, 1985 . . . . £25/£5
ditto, Cape/London Limited Editions, 1985 (500 signed
copies, glassine d/w) ·   . . . . £75/£65
ditto, Little, Brown (U.S.), 1985 . . . . £20/£5
ditto, Little, Brown (U.S.), 1985 (260 signed copies,
slipcase) £100

Other Titles
The Aristos, Little, Brown (U.S.), 1964 . . £75/£15
ditto, Jonathan Cape, 1965 . . . . . £375/£65
My Recollections of Kafka, Univ. of Manitoba Press,
1970 (25 copies, wraps) £250
Poems, Ecco Press (U.S.), 1973 . . . £65/£20
Cinderella, by Perrault, translated by John Fowles,
Jonathan Cape, 1974 . . . . . . £45/£10
Shipwreck, Jonathan Cape, 1974 (photographs with
text by John Fowles). . . . . . . £30/£10
ditto, Little, Brown (U.S.), 1975 . . . . £15/£5
Ourika, Tom Taylor (U.S.), 1977 (500 signed copies) .
. . . . £100
Islands, Jonathan Cape, 1978 (photographs with text
by John Fowles) . . . . £15/£5
ditto, Little, Brown (U.S.), 1979 . . . . £10/£5
ditto, Little, Brown (U.S.), 1979 (160 signed, numbered copies, slipcase) . . . . . £200/£175
Conditional, Lord John Press (U.S.), 1979 (broadside,
150 numbered, signed copies) £100
The Tree, Aurum Press, 1979 (photographs with text
by John Fowles) . . . . £30/£10
ditto, Little, Brown (U.S.), 1980 . . . . £25/£10
A Letter from Charles I Concerning Lyme, Lyme
Regis Museum, 1980 (100 signed sets of 2 printed
sheets). £125
The Enigma of Stonehenge, Jonathan Cape, 1980
(photographs with text by John Fowles) . £20/£5
ditto, Summit (U.S.), 1980 . . . . . £20/£5
A Brief History of Lyme, Friends of the Lyme Regis
Museum, 1981 (wraps). £15

The French Lieutenant's Woman, A Screenplay,
Cape, 1981 (with Harold Pinter) . . . £20/£5
ditto, Little, Brown (U.S.), 1981 . . . . £20/£5
ditto, Little, Brown (U.S.), 1981 (360 signed,
numbered copies, slipcase) . . . £125/£75
Photographs of Lyme Regis, Skelton Press, 1982 (25
signed copies) £1,000
A Short History of Lyme Regis, Dovecote Press, 1982
. . . . £25/£10
ditto, Little, Brown (U.S.), 1983 . . . . £10/£5
Of Memories and Magpies, Tom Taylor (U.S.), 1983
(200 copies, wraps) £300
Land, Heinemann, 1985 . . . . . . £45/£10
ditto, Little, Brown (U.S.), 1985 . . . . £45/£10
Poor Koko, Eurographica (Helsinki), 1987 (350 signed,
numbered copies, wraps) £75
The Enigma, Eurographica (Helsinki), 1987 (350
signed, numbered copies, wraps) £75
Behind the Magus, Colophon Press, 1994 (26 signed,
lettered copies bound in goatskin) . . . £1,000
ditto, Colophon Press, 1994 (signed copies, wraps)
. . . . £150
ditto, privately printed by the author, 1995 (wraps) .
. . . . £150
The Nature of Nature and The Tree, Yolla Bolly Press
(U.S.), 1995 (140 signed copies, boards, slipcase) .
. . . . £500/£450
ditto, Yolla Bolly Press (U.S.), 1995 (275 signed
copies, wraps) £175
Wormholes, Colophon Press, 1998 (signed copies,
slipcase) £175
ditto, Cape, 1998 . . . . £15/£5
ditto, Holt (U.S.), 1998 . . . . . . £15/£5
ditto, Holt (U.S.), 1998 (150 signed copies, slipcase) .
. . . . £175/£150

DICK FRANCIS
(b.1920)

A former steeplechase jockey, Francis has become a
highly popular and collectable thriller writer, setting
his novels in the world of horse racing.

Novels
Dead Cert, Michael Joseph, 1962   . £2,000/£200
ditto, Holt Rinehart (U.S.), 1962 . . . £1,000/£100
Nerve, Michael Joseph, 1964 . . . . £1,000/£50
ditto, Harper (U.S.), 1964. . . . . . . £300/£65
For Kicks, Michael Joseph, 1965 . . . £600/£25
ditto, Harper (U.S.), 1965. . . . . . . £50/£10
Odds Against, Michael Joseph, 1965 . . £300/£15
ditto, Harper (U.S.), 1966. . . . . . £100/£10
Flying Finish, Michael Joseph, 1966 . . £200/£25
ditto, Harper (U.S.), 1967. . . . . . . £65/£10
Blood Sport, Michael Joseph, 1967 . . . £125/£15
ditto, Harper (U.S.), 1968. . . . . . . £35/£5

Forfeit, Michael Joseph, 1968 . . . . £100/£15	*ditto*, Putnam (U.S.), 1991 . . . . . £10/£5
ditto, Harper (U.S.), 1969. . . . . . £30/£5	*Driving Force*, Michael Joseph, 1992 . . £10/£5
Enquiry, Michael Joseph, 1969 . . . . £75/£10	*ditto*, Putnam (U.S.), 1992 . . . . . £10/£5
ditto, Harper (U.S.), 1969. . . . . . £25/£5	*Decider*, Michael Joseph, 1993 . . . . £10/£5
Rat Race, Michael Joseph, 1970 . . . . £75/£10	*ditto*, Putnam (U.S.), 1993 . . . . . £10/£5
ditto, Harper (U.S.), 1971. . . . . . £25/£5	*Wild Horses*, Michael Joseph, 1994 . . . £10/£5
Bonecrack, Michael Joseph, 1971 . . . £50/£5	*ditto*, Scorpion Press, 1994, (99 signed, numbered
ditto, Harper (U.S.), 1972. . . . . . £15/£5	copies, bound in quarter leather) £75
Smokescreen, Michael Joseph, 1972 . . £45/£5	*ditto*, Scorpion Press, 1994, (20 signed, lettered copies,
ditto, Harper (U.S.), 1972. . . . . . £15/£5	deluxe binding) £150
Slay-Ride, Michael Joseph, 1973. . . . £40/£5	*ditto*, Putnam (U.S.), 1994 . . . . . £10/£5
ditto, Harper (U.S.), 1974. . . . . . £15/£5	*Come to Grief*, Michael Joseph, 1995 . . £10/£5
Knock Down, Michael Joseph, 1974. . . £35/£5	*ditto*, Putnam (U.S.), 1995 . . . . . £10/£5
ditto, Harper (U.S.), 1975. . . . . . £15/£5	*To the Hilt*, Michael Joseph, 1996 . . . £10/£5
Across the Board, Harper (U.S.), 1975 (contains *Flying*	*ditto*, Scorpion Press, 1996, (99 signed, numbered
Finish, Blood Sport and *Enquiry*) . . £35/£5	copies, bound in quarter leather) £75
High Stakes, Michael Joseph, 1975 . . . £35/£5	*ditto*, Scorpion Press, 1996, (15 signed, lettered copies,
ditto, Harper (U.S.), 1976. . . . . . £15/£5	deluxe binding) £125
In The Frame, Michael Joseph, 1976 . . £25/£5	*ditto*, Putnam (U.S.), 1996 . . . . . £10/£5
ditto, Harper (U.S.), 1977. . . . . . £15/£5	*10lb Penalty*, Michael Joseph, 1997 . . . £10/£5
Risk, Michael Joseph, 1977 . . . . . £25/£5	*ditto*, Putnam (U.S.), 1997 . . . . . £10/£5
ditto, Harper (U.S.), 1978. . . . . . £15/£5	*Second Wind*, Michael Joseph, 1999 . . £10/£5
Three Winners, Michael Joseph, 1977, (contains *Dead*	*ditto*, Putnam (U.S.), 1999 . . . . . £10/£5
Cert, Nerve and *For Kicks*) . . . . £15/£5	*Shattered*, Michael Joseph, 2000. . . . £10/£5
Trial Run, Michael Joseph, 1978 . . . £15/£5	*ditto*, Putnam (U.S.), 2000 . . . . . £10/£5
ditto, Harper (U.S.), 1979. . . . . . £15/£5	
Three Favourites, Michael Joseph, 1978, (contains	**Miscellaneous**
Odds Against, Flying Finish and *Blood Sport*) £10/£5	*The Sport of Queens*, Michael Joseph, 1957, (auto-
Whip Hand, Michael Joseph, 1979 . . . £15/£5	biography) . . . . £250/£50
ditto, Harper (U.S.), 1980. . . . . . £10/£5	*ditto*, second edition (revised), Michael Joseph, 1968 .
Three To Follow, Michael Joseph, 1979, (contains	. . . . £15/£5
Forfeit, Enquiry and *Rat Race*) . . . . £10/£5	*ditto*, Harper (U.S.), 1969. . . . . . £40/£10
Reflex, Michael Joseph, 1980 . . . . £10/£5	*Best Racing and Chasing Stories*, Faber, 1966, (edited,
ditto, Putnam (U.S.), 1981 . . . . . £10/£5	with an introduction by, Dick Francis and John
Twice Shy, Michael Joseph, 1981 . . . £10/£5	Welcome) . . . . £15/£5
ditto, Putnam (U.S.), 1982 . . . . . £10/£5	*The Racing Man's Bedside Book*, Faber, 1969, (edited
Banker, Michael Joseph, 1982 . . . . £10/£5	, by Dick Francis and John Welcome) . . £15/£5
ditto, Putnam (U.S.), 1983 . . . . . £10/£5	*Best Racing and Chasing Stories Two*, Faber, 1972,
The Danger, Michael Joseph, 1983 . . . £10/£5	edited, with an introduction by Dick Francis and John
ditto, Putnam (U.S.), 1984 . . . . . £10/£5	Welcome . . . . £15/£5
Proof, Michael Joseph, 1984 . . . . . £10/£5	*Lester: The Official Biography*, Michael Joseph, 1986
ditto, Putnam (U.S.), 1985 . . . . . £10/£5	. . . . £10/£5
Break In, Michael Joseph, 1985 . . . . £10/£5	*ditto*, Michael Joseph, 1986, (500 signed copies, in
ditto, Putnam (U.S.), 1986 . . . . . £10/£5	slipcase) . . . . £50/£45
Bolt, Michael Joseph, 1986 . . . . . £10/£5	*Great Racing Stories*, Bellew, 1989, edited by Dick
ditto, Putnam (U.S.), 1987 . . . . . £10/£5	Francis . . . . £10/£5
Hot Money, Michael Joseph, 1987 . . . £10/£5	*ditto*, Bellew, 1989, (deluxe 75 numbered copies,
ditto, Putnam (U.S.), 1988 (250 signed copies, slipcase)	signed by Dick Francis and John Welcome; bound in
. . . . £60/£50	full leather) £225
ditto, Putnam (U.S.), 1988 . . . . . £10/£5	*ditto*, Bellew, 1989, (standard limited 175 numbered
The Edge, Michael Joseph, 1988. . . . £10/£5	copies, signed by Dick Francis and John Wellcome;
ditto, Putnam (U.S.), 1989 . . . . . £10/£5	bound in quarter leather) £200
Straight, Michael Joseph, 1989 . . . . £10/£5	
ditto, Michael Joseph, 1989, (500 signed copies, bound	
in quarter leather, in slipcase) . . . . £75/£65	
ditto, Putnam (U.S.), 1989 . . . . . £10/£5	
Longshot, Michael Joseph, 1990. . . . £10/£5	
ditto, Putnam (U.S.), 1990 . . . . . £10/£5	
Comeback, Michael Joseph, 1991 . . . £10/£5	

GEORGE MACDONALD FRASER
(b.1925)

A novelist and historian, Fraser's successful Flashman books have made an unlikely hero out of the bully who originally appeared in *Tom Brown's Schooldays.*

Novels

Flashman, Barrie & Jenkins, 1969 . . . £150/£25
ditto, World Publishing Co./New American Library
(U.S.), 1969 . . . . £75/£20
Royal Flash, Barrie & Jenkins, 1970 . . £125/£20
ditto, Knopf (U.S.), 1970 . . . . . . £50/£20
Flash for Freedom, Barrie & Jenkins, 1971 £75/£20
ditto, Knopf (U.S.), 1972 . . . . . £45/£20
Flashman at the Charge, Barrie & Jenkins, 1973 . .
. . . . £75/£20
ditto, Knopf (U.S.), 1973 . . . . . £45/£20
Flashman in the Great Game, Barrie & Jenkins, 1975
. . . . £45/£15
ditto, Knopf (U.S.), 1975 . . . . . . £30/£10
Flashman's Lady, Barrie & Jenkins, 1977 . £50/£15
ditto, Knopf (U.S.), 1978 . . . . . £30/£10
Flashman and the Redskins, Collins, 1982 . £35/£10
ditto, Knopf (U.S.), 1982 . . . . . £25/£10
Flashman and the Dragon, Collins, 1985 . £25/£5
ditto, Knopf (U.S.), 1986 . . . . . £20/£5
Flashman and the Mountain of Light, Collins, 1990 .
. . . . £25/£5
ditto, Knopf (U.S.), 1991 . . . . . £20/£5
Flashman and the Angel of the Lord, Collins, 1994 .
. . . . £25/£5
ditto, Scorpion Press, 1994 (99 signed copies, glassine
d/w) . . . . £150/£125
ditto, Scorpion Press, 1994 (20 signed copies, glassine
d/w) . . . . £200/£175
ditto, Knopf (U.S.), 1995 . . . . . . £10/£5
Flashman and the Tiger, Collins, 1999 . £10/£5
ditto, Knopf (U.S.), 2000 . . . . . £10/£5

Short Stories

The General Danced at Dawn, Collins, 1970 £127/£20
ditto, Knopf (U.S.), 1973 . . . . . . £75/£10
McAuslan in the Rough, Barrie & Jenkins, 1974 . .
. . . . £45/£15
ditto, Knopf (U.S.), 1974 . . . . . £35/£10
The Sheik and the Dustbin, Collins, 1988 £25/£10

Others

The Steel Bonnets, Barrie & Jenkins, 1971 £250/£45
ditto, Knopf (U.S.), 1972 . . . . . £75/£20
Mr American, Collins, 1980 . . . . £45/£10
ditto, Simon & Schuster (U.S.), 1980 . . £25/£5
The Pyrates, Collins, 1983 . . . . £40/£10
ditto, Knopf (U.S.), 1984 . . . . . £35/£10
The Hollywood History of the World, Joseph, 1988 .
. . . . £40/£10
ditto, Beech Tree/Morrow (U.S.), 1988 . £25/£10
Quartered Safe Out Here, Collins, 1992 . £125/£20

The Candlemass Road, Collins, 1993 . . £15/£5
Black Ajax, Collins, 1997 . . . . . £15/£5
ditto, Carroll & Graf (U.S.), 1998 . . . £10/£5

R. AUSTIN FREEMAN
(b.1862 d.1943)

In his best known character, Dr Thorndyke, Freeman created a forensic detective who must surely rival Doyle's Sherlock Holmes

Thorndyke Novels

The Red Thumb Mark, Collingwood Bros (U.S.),
[1907]. £750
ditto, Collingwood Bros (U.S.), [1907] (wraps) £500
ditto, Hodder & Stoughton, 1911. . . . . £50
The Eye of Osiris, Hodder & Stoughton, [1911] £200
ditto, Hodder & Stoughton, [1911] (Egyptian binding,
150 copies) £500
ditto, as *The Vanishing Man*, Dodd, Mead (U.S.),
1912 . . . . £150
The Mystery of 31 New Inn, Hodder & Stoughton,
1912 . . . . £200
ditto, John C. Winston (U.S.), 1913 (4 plates not in
U.K. edition) £150
A Silent Witness, John C. Winston (U.S.), 1913 £250
ditto, Hodder & Stoughton, [1914] £300
Helen Vardon's Confession, Hodder & Stoughton,
[1922] . . . . £1,000/£100
The Cat's Eye, Hodder & Stoughton, [1923] . . .
. . . . £1,000/£75
ditto, Dodd, Mead (U.S.), 1927 . . . £500/£50
The Mystery of Angelina Frood, Hodder & Stoughton,
[1924]. . . . . £1,000/£75
ditto, Dodd, Mead (U.S.), 1925 . . . £500/£50
The Shadow of the Wolf, Hodder & Stoughton, [1925]
. . . . £1,000/£75
ditto, Dodd, Mead (U.S.), 1925 . . . £500/£50
The D'Arblay Mystery, Hodder & Stoughton, [1926] .
. . . . £750/£65
ditto, Dodd, Mead (U.S.), 1926 . . . £350/£35
A Certain Dr Thorndyke, Hodder & Stoughton, [1927]
. . . . £750/£65
ditto, Dodd, Mead (U.S.), 1928 . . . £250/£25
As A Thief in the Night, Hodder & Stoughton, [1928].
. . . . £750/£65
ditto, Dodd, Mead (U.S.), 1928 . . . £250/£25
Mr Pottermack's Oversight, Hodder & Stoughton,
[1930]. . . . . £500/£25
ditto, Dodd, Mead (U.S.), 1930 . . . £150/£25
Dr Thorndyke Investigates, Univ. of London Press,
1930 . . . . £250/£25
Pontifex, Son & Thorndyke, Hodder & Stoughton,
1931 . . . . £500/£25
ditto, Dodd, Mead (U.S.), 1931 . . . £150/£25
When Rogues Fall Out, Hodder & Stoughton, 1932 .
. . . . £350/£25

ditto, as *Dr Thorndyke's Discovery,* Dodd, Mead (U.S.), 1932 . . . . £150/£25
Dr Thorndyke Intervenes, Hodder & Stoughton, 1933 . . . . £350/£25
ditto, Dodd, Mead (U.S.), 1933 . . . . £150/£25
For the Defence: Dr Thorndyke, Hodder & Stoughton, 1934 . . . . £350/£25
ditto, Dodd, Mead (U.S.), 1934 . . . . £150/£25
The Penrose Mystery, Hodder & Stoughton, 1936 . . . . £250/£25
ditto, Dodd, Mead (U.S.), 1936 . . . . £150/£25
Felo de Se?, Hodder & Stoughton, 1937 . £250/£25
ditto, as *Death at the Inn,* Dodd, Mead (U.S.), 1937 . . . . £150/£25
The Stoneware Monkey, Hodder & Stoughton, 1938 . . . . £250/£25
ditto, Dodd, Mead (U.S.), 1939 . . . . £150/£25
Mr Polton Explains, Hodder & Stoughton, 1940 . . . . £250/£25
ditto, Dodd, Mead (U.S.), 1940 . . . . £150/£25
Dr Thorndyke's Crime File, Dodd, Mead (U.S.), 1941 . . . . £150/£25
The Jacob Street Mystery, Hodder & Stoughton, 1942 . . . . £200/£20
ditto, as *The Unconscious Witness,* Dodd, Mead (U.S.), 1942 . . . . £150/£20

Thorndike Story Collections
John Thorndyke's Cases, Chatto & Windus, 1909 . . . . £300
ditto, as *Dr Thorndyke's Cases,* Dodd, Mead, (U.S.) 1931 . . . . £75
The Singing Bone, Hodder & Stoughton, 1912 £200
ditto, Dodd, Mead (U.S.), 1923 . . . . £100
The Great Portrait Mystery, Hodder & Stoughton, [1918] £250
Dr Thorndyke's Case-Book, Hodder & Stoughton, [1923] . . . . £1,000/£75
ditto, as *The Blue Scarab,* Dodd, Mead (U.S.), 1923 . . . . £500/£45
The Puzzle Lock, Hodder & Stoughton, [1925]. . . . . £1,000/£25
ditto, Dodd, Mead (U.S.), 1926 . . . . £500/£45
The Magic Casket, Hodder & Stoughton, [1927] . . . . £1,000/£25
ditto, Dodd, Mead (U.S.), 1927 . . . . £400/£30
The Famous Cases of Dr Thorndyke, Hodder & Stoughton, [1929] . . . . . . £200/£20
ditto, as *The Dr Thorndyke Omnibus,* Dodd, Mead (U.S.), 1932 . . . . £100/£15
The Best Dr Thorndyke Short Stories, Dover (U.S.), 1973 (wraps) £10
Dead Hand, Highfield Press, [1994]. . . £5

Story collections written as 'Clifford Ashdown' (written with J.J. Pitcairn)
The Adventures of Romney Pringle, Ward Lock, 1902 . . . . £1,000
ditto, Oswald Train (U.S.), 1975. . . . £25/£10

The Further Adventures of Romney Pringle, Oswald Train (U.S.), 1975 . . . . . . £25/£10
From a Surgeon's Diary, Ferret Fantasy, 1975 (wraps) £10
ditto, Oswald Train (U.S.), 1977. . . . £25/£10
The Queen's Treasure, Oswald Train (U.S.), 1975 . . . . £25/£10

Other Titles
The Golden Pool, Cassell, 1905 . . . . . £250
The Unwilling Adventurer, Hodder & Stoughton, [1913] £200
The Uttermost Farthing, Winston (U.S.), 1914 £75
ditto, as *A Savant's Vendetta,* Pearson, [1920] . £75
The Exploits of Danby Croker, Duckworth, 1916 £100
The Surprising Experiences of Mr Shuttlebury Cobb, Hodder & Stoughton, [1927] . . . £1,000/£50
Flighty Phyllis, Hodder & Stoughton, [1928] £750/£45

Non Fiction
Travels and Life in Ashant and Jaman, Constable, 1898 . . . . £250
Social Decay and Regeneration, Constable, 1921 . . . . £100/£25

ROBERT FROST
(b.1874 d.1963)

An American poet with the distinctive voice of his own country, whose poetry often addresses the problems of a solitary character attempting to make sense of the world.

[Twilight] Five Poems, (1894) £10,000
A Boy's Will, David Nutt, 1913 ('A' binding, bronze cloth) £4,000
ditto, David Nutt, 1913 ('B' binding, cream-coloured vellum-paper boards stamped in red cloth) £1,750
ditto, David Nutt, 1913 ('C' binding, cream-coloured linen-paper wraps stamped in black, and 8-petalled flowers) £1,000
ditto, David Nutt, 1913 ('D' binding, cream-coloured linen-paper wraps stamped in black, and 4-petalled flowers) £750
ditto, David Nutt, 1913 (135 signed, numbered copies, cream wraps) £1,500
ditto, David Nutt, 1913 (second issue, cream wraps) £500
ditto, Holt (U.S.), 1915 ('Aind' for 'And' on last line, p.14) £400
ditto, Holt (U.S.), 1915 (with 'And'). . . £150
North of Boston, David Nutt, 1914 (first issue, binding 'A' with coarse green cloth). £3,000
ditto, David Nutt/Holt (U.S.), 1914 (first issue, binding 'B', UK sheets with Holt title page) . . £1,750

ditto, David Nutt, 1914 (first issue, binding 'C', with fine green cloth) £1,250
ditto, David Nutt, 1914 (first issue, binding 'D', with blue cloth) £1,000
ditto, David Nutt, 1914 (first issue, binding 'E', with coarse green cloth, measuring 200x145mm, tall edges trimmed, rubber stamp p.iv). £750
ditto, David Nutt, 1914 (first issue, binding 'F', with coarse green cloth, measuring 195x150mm, top edge trimmed and others rough cut, rubber stamp p.iv). £1,250
Mountain Interval, Holt (U.S.), 1916 (first state, p.88, lines 6 and 7 repeated, p.63 line 6 from bottom 'Come' for Gone') . . . . . £1,250/£300
diitto, Holt (U.S.), 1916 (errors corrected) . £650/£100
Selected Poems, Holt (U.S.), 1923 . . . £650/£100
diitto, Heinemann, 1923 . . . . . £400/£50
New Hampshire, Holt (U.S.), 1923 . . . £500/£125
ditto, Holt (U.S.), 1923 (350 signed copies, slipcase) . . . . £1,000/£800
ditto, Grant Richards, 1924 . . . . £500/£75
ditto, The New Dresden Press (Hanover), 1955 (750 signed, numbered copies, semi-transparent d/w) . . . . £400/£300
West-Running Brook, Holt (U.S.), 1928 (without 'First Edition' statement) . . . . . £250/£100
ditto, Holt (U.S.), 1928 (with 'First Edition' statement) . . . . £150/£50
ditto, Holt (U.S.), 1928 (1,000 signed copies, slipcase, glasine d/w) . . . . £400/£350
A Way Out, Harbor Press (U.S.), 1929 (485 signed copies, glassine d/w). . . . . . £250/£225
The Lovely Shall Be Choosers, Random House (U.S.), 1929 (475 copies, wraps) £125
The Cow's in the Corn, Slide Mountain Press (U.S.), 1929 (91 signed copies) . . . . . £1,000/£600
Collected Poems, Random House (U.S.), 1930 . . . . £225/£30
ditto, Random House (U.S.), 1930 (1,000 signed copies) £500
ditto, Longman, 1930 . . . . £175/£25
The Lone Striker, Holt (U.S.), 1933 (wraps in envelope) . . . . £60/£45
A Further Range, Holt (U.S.), 1936. . . £125/£15
ditto, Spiral Press (U.S.), 1936 (800 signed copies in slipcase, no d/w) £300
ditto, Cape, 1937 . . . . £75/£10
Selected Poems, Cape, 1936 . . . . £100/£15
From Snow to Snow, Holt (U.S.), 1936 (no d/w) £100
A Witness Tree, Holt (U.S.), 1942 . . . £150/£20
ditto, Spiral Press (U.S.), 1942 (735 signed copies, slipcase) . . . . £300/£250
ditto, Cape, 1943 . . . . . . £100/£15
A Masque of Reason, Holt (U.S.), 1945 . £50/£15
ditto, Holt (U.S.), 1945 (800 signed copies, slipcase, no d/w) . . . . £250/£200
ditto, Cape, 1948 . . . . . . £30/£10
Steeple Bush, Holt (U.S.), 1947 . . . £75/£15

ditto, Holt (U.S.), 1947 (750 signed copies, slipcase, no d/w) . . . . £250/£200
A Masque of Mercy, Holt (U.S.), 1947 . . £65/£15
ditto, Holt (U.S.), 1947 (751 signed copies, slipcase) . . . . £250/£200
Hard Not to be a King, House of Books (U.S.), 1951 (300 signed copies) £300
The Complete Poems, Holt (U.S.), 1949 (500 signed copies, slipcase, no d/w). £500
ditto, Limited Editions Club (U.S.), 1950 (signed, 2 vols in slipcase) . . . . . . £450/£350
ditto, Cape, 1951 . . . . £100/£20
A Cabin in the Clearing, Blumenthal (U.S.), 1951 (wraps) £45
My Objection to Being Stepped On, Blumenthal (U.S.), 1957 (wraps). £45
A Wishing Well, Blumenthal (U.S.), 1959 (wraps) £45
In the Clearing, Holt (U.S.), 1962 . . . £45/£10
ditto, Spiral Press (U.S.), 1962 (1,500 signed copies, slipcase) . . . . £200/£150
The Prophets Really Prophecy as Mystics, Blumenthal (U.S.), 1962 . . . . £25
The Poetry of Robert Frost, Holt (U.S.), 1969 £20/£5
ditto, Cape, 1971 . . . . £15/£5

ALAN GARNER
(b.1934)

A writer of children's literature, the majority of Garner's books are set in his native Cheshire. His books are an evocative mix of myth, fantasy and reality.

The Weirdstone of Brisingamen: A Tale of Alderley, Collins, 1960 . . . . £250/£25
ditto, Philomel (U.S.), 1960 . . . . . £125/£10
The Moon of Gomrath, Collins, 1963 . £125/£25
ditto, Philomel (U.S.), 1963 . . . . £30/£10
Elidor, Collins, 1965 (Illustrated by Charles Keeping). . . . . £125/£15
ditto, Walck (U.S.), [1965] . . . . £25/£10
Holly from the Bongs: A Nativity Play, Collins, 1966 . . . . £75/£15
The Old Man of Mow, Collins, 1967 (Photographs by Roger Hill) . . . . £45/£15
ditto, Doubleday (U.S.), 1967 . . . . £35/£10
The Owl Service, Collins, 1967 . . . . £125/£25
ditto, Philomel (U.S.), 1967 . . . . £100/£15
Red Shift, Collins, 1973 . . . . . . £50/£10
ditto, Macmillan (U.S.), 1973 . . . . £35/£10
The Guizer: A Book of Fools, Hamish Hamilton, 1975 . . . . £25/£5
ditto, Greenwillow (U.S.), 1976 . . . . £25/£5
The Stone Book, Collins, 1976 (illustrated by Michael Foreman) . . . . £15/£5
ditto, Collins (U.S.), 1976. . . . . . £15/£5

Tom Fobble's Day, Collins, 1977 (illustrated by Michael Foreman) . . . . £15/£5
ditto, Collins (U.S.), 1979. . . . . . £15/£5
Granny Reardun, Collins, 1977 (illustrated by Michael Foreman) . . . . £15/£5
ditto, Collins (U.S.), 1978. . . . . . £15/£5
The Aimer Gate, Collins, 1978 (illustrated by Michael Foreman) . . . . £15/£5
ditto, Collins (U.S.), 1979. . . . . . £15/£5
Fairy Tales of Gold, Collins, 1979 (4 vols). £35/£10
ditto, Philomel (U.S.), 1980 (1 vol.) . . . £20/£5
The Lad of the Gad, Collins, 1980 . . . £15/£5
ditto, Philomel (U.S.), 1981 . . . . . £15/£5
The Stone Book Quartet, Collins, 1983 . . £20/£5
A Bag of Moonshine, Collins, 1986 (illustrated by Patrick Lynch) . . . . £15/£5
ditto, Delacorte Press (U.S.), 1986 . . . £15/£5
Jack and the Beanstalk, HarperCollins, 1992 £10/£5
Strandloper, Harvill Press, 1996 . . . . £10/£5

Verse
The Breadhorse, Collins, 1975 (illustrated by Albin Trowski) . . . . £35/£15

Plays
Potter Thompson, O.U.P., 1975 . . . . £20/£5

DAVID GARNETT
(b.1892 d.1981)

Principally a novelist, whose early works have a light, fantastic touch, Garnett was associated with the Bloomsbury Group. His *Aspects of Love* was recently turned into a successful stage musical.

Novels
Dope-Darling: A Story of Cocaine, Werner Laurie, [1919] (pseud. 'Leda Burke') £125
Lady Into Fox, Chatto & Windus, 1922 . . £100/£15
ditto, Knopf (U.S.), 1923 . . . . . . £15/£5
A Man in the Zoo, Chatto & Windus, 1924 £75/£15
ditto, Chatto & Windus, 1924 (110 signed, numbered copies) £75
ditto, Knopf (U.S.), 1924 . . . . . . £45/£10
The Sailor's Return, Chatto & Windus, 1925 £50/£10
ditto, Chatto & Windus, 1925 (160 signed, numbered copies) £75
ditto, Knopf (U.S.), 1925 . . . . . . £45/£10
Go She Must!, Chatto & Windus, 1927 . . £50/£10
ditto, Chatto & Windus, 1927 (160 signed, numbered copies) £75
ditto, Knopf (U.S.), 1927 . . . . . . £45/£10
No Love, Chatto & Windus, 1929 . . . £35/£10
ditto, Chatto & Windus, 1929 (160 signed, numbered copies) £65
ditto, Knopf (U.S.), 1929 . . . . . . £25/£10

The Grasshoppers Come, Chatto & Windus, 1931 . . . . £20/£5
ditto, Chatto & Windus, 1931 (210 signed, numbered copies) £50
ditto, Brewer, Warren & Putnam (U.S.), 1931 £20/£5
A Rabbit in the Air, Chatto & Windus, 1932 £20/£5
ditto, Chatto & Windus, 1932 (110 signed, numbered copies) £50
ditto, Brewer, Warren & Putnam (U.S.), 1932 £15/£5
Pocahontas, or the Nonpareil of Virginia, Chatto & Windus, 1933 . . . . £20/£5
ditto, Chatto & Windus, 1933 (550 signed, numbered copies) £50
ditto, Harcourt, Brace (U.S.), 1933 . . . £15/£5
Beany-Eye, Chatto & Windus, 1935 . . . £15/£5
ditto, Chatto & Windus, 1935 (110 signed, numbered copies) £50
ditto, Harcourt, Brace (U.S.), 1935 . . . £15/£5
Aspects of Love, Chatto & Windus, 1955 . £25/£10
ditto, Harcourt, Brace (U.S.), 1955 . . . £15/£5
A Shot in the Dark, Longmans, 1958 . . £10/£5
ditto, Little, Brown (U.S.), 1958 . . . . £10/£5
A Net for Venus, Longmans, 1959 . . . £10/£5
Two By Two: A Story of Survival, Longmans, 1963 . . . . £10/£5
ditto, Atheneum (U.S.), 1964 . . . . . £10/£5
Ulterior Motives, Longmans, 1966 . . . £10/£5
ditto, Harcourt, Brace (U.S.), 1967 . . . £10/£5
A Clean Slate, Hamish Hamilton, 1971 . . £10/£5
The Sons of the Falcon, Macmillan, 1972 £10/£5
Plough Over the Bones, Macmillan, 1973 £10/£5
Up She Rises, Macmillan, 1977 . . . . £10/£5
ditto, St Martin's Press (U.S.), 1977 . . . £10/£5

Short Stories
The Old Dovecote and Other Stories, Elkin Mathews & Marrot: No.8 in the Woburn Books series, 1928 (530 signed copies) . . . . . . £50/£35
A Terrible Day, William Jackson: No.9 in the Furnival Books series, 1932 (550 signed copies) . . £45
First 'Hippy' Revolution, San Marcos Press, (New Mexico), 1970 . . . . £25
Purl and Plain, Macmillan, 1973 . . . £10/£5

Autobiography
The Golden Echo, Chatto & Windus, 1953 . £10/£5
ditto, Harcourt, Brace (U.S.), 1954 . . . £10/£5
The Flowers of the Forest, Chatto & Windus, 1955 . . . . £10/£5
ditto, Harcourt, Brace (U.S.), 1956 . . . £10/£5
Familiar Faces, Chatto & Windus, 1962 . £10/£5
ditto, Harcourt, Brace (U.S.), 1962 . . . £10/£5

Miscellaneous
Never Be a Bookseller, Knopf (U.S.), 1929 (2,000 copies, none for sale) £75
ditto, The Fleece Press, 1995 (400 copies) . . £20
War in the Air: September 1939 to May 1941, Chatto & Windus, 1941 . . . . £30/£10

ditto, Doubleday (U.S.), 1941 . . . . £25/£10
The Battle of Britain, Puffin Picture Book No.21, 1941
(wraps) £15
The Campaign in Greece and Crete, Chatto &
Windus, 1942 (wraps) £15
A Historical Pageant of Huntingdonshire in
Celebration of the Coronation of Her Majesty
Elizabeth II, privately printed, (Huntingdon), 1953
(souvenir programme) £20
The White/Garnett Letters, Cape, 1968 . . £15/£5
ditto, Viking (U.S.), 1968 . . . . . . £15/£5
The Master Cat: The True and Unexpurgated Story of
Puss in Boots, Macmillan, 1974 . . . £10/£5
Sir Geoffrey Keynes: A Tribute, privately printed,
1978 . . . . £10
Great Friends: Portraits of Seventeen Writers,
Macmillan, 1979 . . . . £25/£10
ditto, Atheneum (U.S.), 1980 . . . . £25/£10

JONATHAN GASH
(b.1933)

Gash is the pseudonym of John Grant. His Lovejoy
novels have been adapted for television with great
success, although some feel that his hero has lost his
edge with this transition.

Lovejoy Novels
The Judas Pair, Collins, 1977 . . . . £250/£25
ditto, Harper & Row (U.S.), 1977 . . . £75/£10
Gold from Gemini, Collins, 1978 . . . £225/£25
ditto, as **Gold By Gemini**, Harper & Row (U.S.), 1978.
. . . . £65/£10
The Grail Tree, Collins, 1979 . . . £150/£15
ditto, Harper & Row (U.S.), 1979 . . . £50/£10
Spend Game, Collins, 1979 . . . . £250/£35
ditto, Ticknor & Fields (U.S.), 1979 . . . £50/£10
The Vatican Rip, Collins, 1981 . . . £250/£35
ditto, Ticknor & Fields (U.S.), 1981 . . . £25/£10
Firefly Gadroon, Collins, 1982 . . . . £125/£15
ditto, St Martin's Press (U.S.), 1982 . . . £25/£10
The Sleepers of Erin , Collins, 1983 . . £100/£15
ditto, Dutton (U.S.), 1983 . . . . . £25/£10
The Gondola Scam, Collins, 1984 . . . £65/£10
ditto, St Martin's Press (U.S.), 1984 . . . £15/£5
Pearlhanger, Collins, 1985 . . . . £25/£5
ditto, St Martin's Press (U.S.), 1985 . . . £15/£5
The Tartan Ringers, Collins, 1986 . . . £20/£5
ditto, as **The Tartan Sell**, St Martin's Press (U.S.),
1986 . . . . £15/£5
Moonspender, Collins, 1986 . . . . £20/£5
ditto, St Martin's Press (U.S.), 1987 . . . £15/£5
Jade Woman, Collins, 1988 . . . . £20/£5
ditto, St Martin's Press (U.S.), 1989 . . . £15/£5
The Very Last Gambado, Collins, 1989 . . £15/£5
ditto, St Martin's Press (U.S.), 1990 . . . £15/£5
The Great California Game, Century, 1991 £15/£5

ditto, St Martin's Press (U.S.), 1991 . . . £15/£5
Lies of Fair Ladies, Scorpion Press, 1991 (20 signed,
lettered copies) £175
ditto, Scorpion Press, 1991 (99 signed, numbered
copies) £75
ditto, Century, 1992 . . . . . . £15/£5
ditto, St Martin's Press (U.S.), 1992 . . . £15/£5
Paid and Loving Eyes, Century, 1993 . . £15/£5
ditto, St Martin's Press (U.S.), 1993 . . . £15/£5
The Sin Within Her Smile, Century, 1993 . £15/£5
ditto, Viking (U.S.), 1994 . . . . . £10/£5
The Grace in Older Women, Century, 1995 £15/£5
ditto, Viking (U.S.), 1995 . . . . . £10/£5
The Possessions of a Lady, Century, 1996 . £15/£5
ditto, Viking (U.S.), 1996 . . . . . £15/£5
The Rich and The Profane, Macmillan, 1998 £15/£5
ditto, Viking (U.S.), 1999 . . . . . £15/£5
A Rag, a Bone and a Hank of Hair, Macmillan, 1999
. . . . £15/£5
ditto, Viking (U.S.), 2000 . . . . . £15/£5

Other Titles
Streetwalker, Bodley Head, 1959 (anonymous) . .
. . . . £225/£35
ditto, Viking (U.S.), 1960 . . . . . £75/£15
The Incomer, Collins, 1981 (pseud. 'Graham Gaunt') .
. . . . £250/£35
ditto, Doubleday (U.S.), 1981 . . . . £25/£10
Mehala, Lady of Sealandings, Century, 1993 (pseud.
'Jonathan Grant') . . . . . . £25/£10
Different Women Dancing, Macmillan, 1997 (pseud.
'Jonathan Grant') . . . . . . £15/£5
ditto, Viking (U.S.), 1997 . . . . . £15/£5
Prey Dancing, Macmillan, 1998 (pseud. 'Jonathan
Grant') . . . . £15/£5
ditto, Viking (U.S.), 1998 . . . . . £15/£5

ELIZABETH GASKELL
(b.1810 d.1865)

A novelist whose work earned the respect of Dickens,
Mrs Gaskell is principally remembered for her friend-
ship with Charlotte Brontë, and her famous biography
The Life of Charlotte Brontë.

Novels
Mary Barton, A Tale of Manchester Life, Chapman &
Hall, 1848 (anonymous, 2 vols). . . £3,000
The Moorland Cottage, Chapman & Hall, 1850 £500
Ruth, A Novel, Chapman & Hall, 1853 (3 vols) £750
Cranford, Chapman & Hall, 1853 (by the author of
'Mary Barton, 'Ruth' etc.) £1,000
North and South, Chapman & Hall, 1855 (2 vols) . .
. . . . £600
The Sexton's Hero and Christmas Storms and
Sunshine, Chapman & Hall, 1855 . . . . £100
A Dark Night's Work, Smith Elder, 1863 . . £350

Wives and Daughters, An Everyday Story, Smith Elder, 1866 (illustrated by George du Maurier, 2 vols) £400

Short Stories
Libbie Marsh's Three Eras, A Lancashire Tale, Hamilton, Adams & Co., 1850 . . . . . £500
Lizzie Leigh and Other Tales, Smith Elder, 1855 [1854]) £250
The Sexton's Hero, Johnson, Rawson & Co., Manchester, 1850 . . . . £500
Round the Sofa, Sampson Low, 1858 (2 vols) £400 ditto, as *My Lady Ludlow and Other Tales*, Sampson Low, 1861 (1 vol.) £250
Right at Last and Other Tales, Sampson Low, 1860 . . . . £250
Lois the Witch and Other Tales, Tauchnitz, 1861 £35
Cousin Phyllis and Other Tales, Smith Elder, 1865 (illustrated by George du Maurier) £250
The Grey Woman and Other Tales, Smith Elder, 1865 (illustrated by George du Maurier) £250
The Half-Brothers, Gulliver Book Co., [1943] £25
The Squire's Story, Todd Publishing Co., 1943 £10/£5
The Cage at Cranford and Other Stories, Nelson Classics, [1937] . . . . £10/£5
Mrs Gaskell's Tales of Mystery and Horror, Gollancz, 1978 . . . . £10/£5

Miscellaneous
The Life of Charlotte Brontë, Smith Elder, 1857 (2 vols) £500
Letters of Charlotte Brontë, privately printed, 1915 (25 copies) £125
My Diary, The Early Years of My Daughter Marianne, privately printed by Clement Shorter, 1923 (50 copies, wraps) £75
Letters of Mrs Gaskell and Charles Eliot Norton, 1855-1865, O.U.P., 1932 . . . . £20/£10
The Letters of Elizabeth Gaskell, Manchester Univ. Press, [1966] . . . . £20/£10

Collected Editions
The Novels and Tales of Elizabeth Gaskell, Smith Elder, 1878-82 (7 vols) £150
The Works of Elizabeth Gaskell, Smith Elder, 1906 (8 vols) £100

LEWIS GRASSIC GIBBON
(b.1901 d.1935)

Grassic Gibbon was the pseudonym used by the Scot James Leslie Mitchell for his best-known works, *Sunset Song*, *Cloud Howe* and *Grey Granite* which together make up the *Scot's Quair* Trilogy.

Novels by Lewis Grassic Gibbon
Sunset Song, Jarrolds, 1932 . . . . . £50/£20
Cloud Howe, Jarrolds, 1933 . . . . . £50/£20

Grey Granite, Jarrolds, 1934 . . . . . £50/£20
A Scot's Quair: A Trilogy of Novels, Jarrolds, 1946 . . . . £30/£10
The Speak O' The Mearns, Ramsey Head Press, 1982 (unfinished) . . . . £10/£5

Others by Lewis Grassic Gibbon
Niger: The Life of Mungo Park, Faber, 1934 £35/£10
Scottish Scene: Or, The Intelligent Man's Guide to Albyn, Jarrolds, 1934 (with Hugh McDiarmid) . . . . £35/£10
Nine Against the Unknown: A Record of Geographical Exploration, Jarrolds, 1934 (as 'Lewis Grassic Gibbon and J. Leslie Mitchell') . £25/£10
A Scots Hairst: Essays and Short Stories, Hutchinson, 1967 . . . . £15/£5

Novels by J. Leslie Mitchell
Stained Radiance: A Fictionist's Prelude, Jarrolds, 1930 . . . . £75/£30
The Thirteenth Disciple, Jarrolds, 1931. . £75/£30
Three go Back, Jarrolds, 1932 . . . . £75/£30
The Lost Trumpet, Jarrolds, 1932 . . . £50/£20
Image and Superscription, Jarrolds, 1933 . £50/£20
Spartacus, Jarrolds, 1933 . . . . . £25/£10
Gay Hunter, Jarrolds, 1934 . . . . . £50/£20

Short Stories by J. Leslie Mitchell
The Calends of Cairo, Jarrolds, 1931 . £60/£25
Persian Dawns, Egyptian Nights, Jarrolds, [1933]. . . . . £60/£25

Other Titles by J. Leslie Mitchell
Hanno: Or, The Future of Exploration, Kegan Paul, 1928 . . . . £25/£10
The Conquest of the Maya, Jarrolds, 1934 . £35/£15

STELLA GIBBONS
·(b.1902 d.1989)

Author of many novels, but collected mainly for her first, the classic *Cold Comfort Farm*.

Novels
Cold Comfort Farm, Longmans, 1932 . . £500/£75
Bassett, Longmans, 1934 . . . . . £25/£10
Enbury Heath, Longmans, 1935. . . . £25/£10
Miss Linsey and Pa, Longmans, 1936 . . £25/£10
Nightingale Wood, Longmans, 1938 . . £25/£10
My American: A Romance, Longmans, 1939 £25/£10
The Rich House, Longmans, 1941 . . . £20/£5
Ticky, Longmans, 1943 . . . . . £20/£5
The Bachelor, Longmans, 1944 . . . £20/£5
Westwood, or, The Gentle Powers, Longmans, 1946 . . . . £20/£5
Conference at Cold Comfort Farm, Longmans, 1949 . . . . £35/£10

The Matchmaker, Longmans, 1949 . . . £10/£5
The Swiss Summer, Longmans, 1951 . . . £10/£5
Fort of the Bear, Longmans, 1953 . . . £10/£5
The Shadow of a Sorcerer, Hodder & Stoughton, 1955
. . . . £10/£5
Here Be Dragons, Hodder & Stoughton, 1956 £10/£5
White Sand and Grey Sand, Hodder & Stoughton,
[1958]. . . . . £10/£5
A Pink Front Door, Hodder & Stoughton, [1959] . .
. . . . £10/£5
The Weather at Tregulla, Hodder & Stoughton, [1962]
. . . . £10/£5
The Wolves Were in the Sledge, Hodder & Stoughton,
1964 . . . . £10/£5
The Charmers, Hodder & Stoughton, 1965. £10/£5
Starlight, Hodder & Stoughton, 1967 . . £10/£5
The Snow-Woman, Hodder & Stoughton, 1969 £10/£5
The Woods in Winter, Hodder & Stoughton, 1970. .
. . . . £10/£5

Short Stories
Roaring Tower and Other Short Stories, Longmans,
1937 . . . . £25/£10
Christmas at Cold Comfort Farm and Other Stories,
Longmans, 1940 . . . . £35/£10
Beside the Pearly Water and Other Stories, Peter
Nevill, 1954 . . . . £20/£5

Verse
The Mountain Beast and Other Poems, Longmans,
1930 (wraps) £40
The Priestess and Other Poems, Longmans, 1934
(wraps) £25
The Lowland Venus and Other Poems, Longmans,
1938 (wraps) £25
Collected Poems, Longmans, 1950 . . . £10/£5
ditto, Theodore Brun, 1950 (150 copies) . £40/£20

Children's
The Untidy Gnome, Longmans, 1935 . . £35/£10

GILES' ANNUALS

The distinctive cartoons drawn by Carl Giles, published in the Daily Express, have been collected
together annually.

No. 1, 1946 . . . . £200
No. 2, 1947 . . . . £225
No. 3, 1949 . . . . £175
No. 4, 1950 . . . . £175
No. 5, 1951 . . . . £150
No. 6, 1952 . . . . £65
No. 7, 1953 . . . . £65
No. 8, 1954 . . . . £25
No. 9, 1955 . . . . £25

No. 10, 1956 . . . . £15
No. 11, 1957 . . . . £15
No. 12, 1958 . . . . £15
No. 13, 1959 . . . . £15
No. 14, 1960 . . . . £5
No. 15, 1961 . . . . £5
No. 16, 1962 . . . . £10
No. 17, 1963 . . . . £10
No. 18, 1964 . . . . £5
No. 19, 1965 . . . . £5
No. 20, 1966 . . . . £5
No. 21, 1967 . . . . £10
No. 22, 1968 . . . . £5
No. 23, 1969 . . . . £5
No. 24, 1970 . . . . £5
No. 25, 1971 . . . . £5
No. 26, 1972 . . . . £5

WARWICK GOBLE
(b.1862 d.1943)

A British illustrator, Goble's work owes a great debt
to Chinese and Japanese art.

Children's Books
The Grim House, by Mrs Molesworth, Nisbet, 1899 .
. . . . £25
The Water Babies, by Charles Kingsley, Macmillan,
1909 (32 colour plates) £300
ditto, Macmillan, 1909 (260 copies) . . . £1,250
ditto, Macmillan, 1910 (16 colour plates) . £50
Green Willow and Other Japanese Fairy Tales, by
Grace James, Macmillan, 1910 (40 colour plates). .
. . . . £350
ditto, Macmillan, 1910 (500 copies) . . . £1,500
ditto, Macmillan, 1912 (16 colour plates) . . £30
Folk Tales of Bengal, by Lal Behari Day, Macmillan,
1912 . . . . £200
ditto, Macmillan, 1912 (150 copies) . . . £2,000
Peeps at Many Lands-Turkey, by Julius Van
Millingen, A. & C. Black, 1911 (12 colour plates) £25
Stories from the Pentamerone, by Giovanni Battista
Basile, Macmillan, 1911. . . . . . £200
ditto, Macmillan, 1911 (150 copies) . . . £1,000
The Fairy Book, by D.M. Craik, Macmillan, 1913 (32
colour plates). £250
The Book of Fairy Poetry, Dora Owen, ed., Long-
mans, 1920 (16 colour plates) £250
Treasure Island, by Robert Louis Stevenson,
Macmillan (U.S.), 1923 . . . . £100/£45
Kidnapped, by Robert Louis Stevenson, Macmillan
(U.S.), 1925 (3 colour plates) . . . £100/£45

Others
The Oracle of Baal, by J. Provand Webster, Lippincott
(U.S.), 1896 . . . . £75

Lad's Love, by S.R. Crockett, Bliss Sands & Co., 1897
(100 copies) £125
ditto, Hodder & Stoughton, 1902. . . . . £20
Constantinople, A.&C. Black, 1906 (63 colour plates)
. . . . £150
The Greater Abbeys of England, Chatto & Windus,
1908 (60 watercolours) £40
Letters from an Ocean Tramp, by William Morley
Punshon McFee, Cassell, 1908 . . . . . £75
Irish Ways, by Jane Barlow, Allen & Sons, 1909 £40
Turkey, A.&C. Black, 1911 . . . . . . £150
The Complete Poetical Works of Geoffrey Chaucer,
Macmillan (U.S.), 1912 (32 colour plates). . £125
Indian Myth and Legend, by Donald A. Mackenzie,
Gresham , 1913 (8 colour plates) . . . £45
*Indian Tales of the Great Ones Among Men, Women
and Bird-People*, by Cornelia Sohrabji, Blackie &
Son (Bombay), 1916. . . . . . . £100
The Cistercians in Yorkshire, by Joseph Smith
Fletcher, S.P.C.K., 1919. . . . . . £45
The Alhambra, by Washinton Irving, Macmillan
(U.S.), 1926 . . . . £100/£20

SIR WILLIAM GOLDING
(b.1911 d.1993)

Golding's novels often place his characters in extreme
situations, facing moral dilemmas. *Lord of the Flies* is
his disturbing classic.

Novels
Lord of the Flies, Faber, 1954 . . . £2,500/£200
ditto, Coward McCann (U.S.), 1955 . . . £600/£100
The Inheritors, Faber, 1955 . . . . . £350/£100
ditto, Harcourt Brace (U.S.), 1962 . . . £35/£15
Pincher Martin, Faber, 1956. . . . . £125/£35
ditto as *The Two Deaths of Christopher Martin*, Harcourt Brace (U.S.), 1956. . . . . . £40/£10
Free Fall, Faber, 1959 . . . . . . £75/£20
ditto, Harcourt Brace (U.S.), 1960 . . . £25/£10
The Spire, Faber, 1964 . . . . . . £40/£10
ditto, Harcourt Brace (U.S.), 1964 . . . £15/£5
The Pyramid, Faber, 1967 . . . . . £40/£10
ditto, Harcourt Brace (U.S.), 1967 . . . £15/£5
Darkness Visible, Faber, 1979 . . . £25/£10
ditto, Farrar Straus (U.S.), 1979 . . . £15/£5
Rites of Passage, Faber, 1980 . . . £25/£10
ditto, Farrar Straus (U.S.), 1980 . . . £15/£5
The Paper Men, Faber, 1984. . . . . £15/£5
ditto, Farrar Straus (U.S.), 1984 . . . £15/£5
Close Quarters, Faber, 1987 . . . . . £15/£5
ditto, Farrar Straus (U.S.), 1987 . . . £10/£5
Fire Down Below, Faber, 1989 . . . . £10/£5
ditto, Farrar Straus (U.S.), 1989 . . . £10/£5
Double Tongue, Faber, 1995. . . . . £10/£5
ditto, Farrar Straus (U.S.), 1995 . . . £10/£5

Short Stories
Sometime, Never: Three Tales of Imagination, Eyre &
Spottiswoode, 1956 . . . . . . £125/£35
ditto, Ballantine (U.S.), 1956 (wraps) . . £20
The Ladder and the Tree, Marlborough College Press,
1961 (wraps) £1,500
The Scorpion God, Faber, 1971 . . . £45/£15
ditto, Harcourt Brace (U.S.), 1972 . . . £25/£10

Collected Editions
To the Ends of the Earth: A Sea Trilogy ('*Rites of
Passage*', '*Close Quarters*' & '*Fire Down Below*'),
Faber, 1991 . . . . £20/£5
ditto, Faber, 1991 (400 signed copies, glassine d/w) .
. . . . £150/£135

Others
Poems, Macmillan, 1934 (wraps) £3,000
ditto, Macmillan (U.S.), 1935 . . . . . £500
The Brass Butterfly, A Play in Three Acts, Faber,
1958 . . . . £150/£20
The Hot Gates and Other Occasional Pieces, Faber,
1965 . . . . £45/£10
ditto, Harcourt Brace (U.S.), 1965 . . £35/£5
A Moving Target, Faber, 1982 . . . . £15/£5
ditto, Farrar Straus (U.S.), 1982 . . . £15/£5
Nobel Lecture, Sixth Chamber Press, 1983 (500
copies, wraps) £30
ditto, Sixth Chamber Press, 1983 (50 signed deluxe
copies, slipcase) . . . . . . £250/£225
An Egyptian Journal, Faber, 1985 . . . £10/£5
ditto, Farrar Straus (U.S.), 1985 . . . £10/£5

SUE GRAFTON
(b.1940)

Grafton's 'alphabet' novels feature the credible
female private detective Kinsey Millhone.

Alphabet Novels
A is for Alibi, Holt (U.S.), 1982 . . . £1,000/£100
ditto, Macmillan, 1986 . . . . . £150/£20
B is for Burglar, Holt (U.S.), 1985 . . . £750/£75
ditto, Macmillan, 1986 . . . . . £125/£20
C is for Corpse, Holt (U.S.), 1986 . . . £500/£45
ditto, Macmillan, 1987 . . . . . £75/£10
D is for Deadbeat, Holt (U.S.), 1987 . . £200/£20
ditto, Macmillan, 1987 . . . . . £75/£10
E is for Evidence, Holt (U.S.), 1988. . . £125/£15
ditto, Macmillan, 1988 . . . . . £50/£10
F is for Fugitive, Holt (U.S.), 1989 . . . £75/£10
ditto, Macmillan, 1989 . . . . . £25/£5
G is for Gumshoe, Holt (U.S.), 1990 . . £25/£5
ditto, Macmillan, 1990 . . . . . £20/£5
H is for Homicide, Holt (U.S.), 1991 . . £20/£5
ditto, Macmillan, 1991 . . . . . £15/£5
I is for Innocent, Holt (U.S.), 1992 . . . £15/£5

ditto, Macmillan, 1992	£15/£5
J is for Judgment, Holt (U.S.), 1993 . .	£15/£5
ditto, Macmillan, 1993	£15/£5
K is for Killer, Holt (U.S.), 1994	£15/£5
ditto, Macmillan, 1994	£15/£5
L is for Lawless, Holt (U.S.), 1995 . . .	£15/£5
ditto, Macmillan, 1995	£15/£5
M is for Malice, Holt (U.S.), 1996 . . .	£15/£5
ditto, Macmillan, 1997	£15/£5
N is for Noose, Holt (U.S.), 1998 . . .	£15/£5
ditto, Macmillan, 1998	£15/£5
O is for Outlaw, Holt (U.S.), 1999 . . .	£15/£5
ditto, Macmillan, 1999 (wraps)	£5

Short Stories

Kinsey and Me, Bench Press (U.S.), 1991 (300 numbered copies, slipcase) £300
ditto, Bench Press (U.S.), 1991 (26 lettered copies, slipcase) £500

Other Novels

Keziah Dane, Macmillan (U.S.), 1967 . . £600/£35
ditto, Owen, 1968 . . . . £250/£25
The Lolly Madonna War, Owen, 1969 . . £350/£25

ROBERT GRAVES
(b.1895 d.1985)

Known particularly for his poetry, fiction and his early autobiography, *Goodbye to All That*, Graves lived on Majorca for most of his life.

Verse

Over the Brazier, The Poetry Bookshop, 1916 (wraps)
. . . . £1,000
ditto, The Poetry Bookshop, 1917 (wraps) . . £200
ditto, The Poetry Bookshop, 1920 . . . £250/£35
Goliath and David, Chiswick Press, 1916 (200 copies, wraps). £1,500
Fairies and Fusiliers, Heinemann, 1917 . £450/£75
ditto, Knopf (U.S.), 1918 . . . . . . £300/£35
Treasure Box, [Chiswick Press, 1919] (200 copies, wraps). £750
ditto, [Chiswick Press, 1919] (200 copies, boards and d/w) £1,250
Country Sentiment, Secker, 1920 . . . £250/£45
ditto, Knopf (U.S.), 1920 . . . . . . £250/£45
The Pier-Glass, Secker, 1921 . . . . £300/£75
ditto, Knopf (U.S.), 1921 (green cloth) . . £300/£45
ditto, Knopf (U.S.), 1921 (orange paper-covered boards) . . . . £250/£45
Whipperginny, Heinemann, 1923 . . . £250/£45
ditto, Knopf (U.S.), 1923 . . . . . . £250/£45
The Feather Bed, Hogarth Press, 1923 (250 copies, signed by the author) £500
Mock Beggar Hall, Hogarth Press, 1923 (no d/w) £350

Welchman's Hose, The Fleuron, 1925 (525 copies, glassine d/w) . . . .£250/£225
Poems, Benn, 1925 (wraps) £100
The Marmosite's Miscellany, Hogarth Press, 1925 (pseud. 'John Doyle') £400
ditto, Pharos Press (Canada), 1975 (80 signed copies, slipcase) . . . . £225/£200
ditto, Pharos Press (Canada), 1975 (750 signed copies, slipcase) . . . . £125/£100
Poems, 1914-1926, Heinemann, 1927 . . £300/£75
ditto, Doubleday, Doran (U.S.), 1929 . . £300/£75
Poems, 1914-1927, Heinemann, 1927 (115 signed, numbered copies, slipcase and d/w) £1,000/£750
Poems, 1929, Seizin Press, 1929 (225 signed, numbered copies). £300
Ten Poems More, Hours Press (Paris), 1930 (200 signed copies) £350
Poems, 1926-1930, Heinemann, 1931 (first issue with misbound title-page). . . . . . £75/£25
To Whom Else?, Seizen Press (Majorca), 1931 (200 signed copies) £250
Poems, 1930-1933, Barker, 1933 . . . . £75
Collected Poems, Cassell, 1938 . . . . £100/£20
ditto, Random House (U.S.), 1939 . . . £100/£10
No More Ghosts: Selected Poems, Faber, 1940 .
. . . . £50/£15
Poems, Eyre & Spottiswoode, 1943 (wraps) . £30
Poems, 1938-1945, Cassell, 1946 . . . £35/£10
ditto, Creative Age Press (U.S.), 1946 . . £35/£10
Collected Poems, 1914-1947, Cassell, 1948 £50/£15
Poems and Satires, Cassell, 1951 . . . £35/£10
Poems, 1953, Cassell, 1953 . . . . . £35/£10
ditto, Cassell, 1953 (250 signed, numbered copies, tissue d/w) . . . .£200/£175
Collected Poems, 1955, Doubleday (U.S.), 1955 . .
. . . . £35/£10
Poems Selected by Himself, Penguin, 1957 (wraps) £5
The Poems of Robert Graves, Doubleday (U.S.), 1958
. . . . £25/£5
Collected Poems, 1959, Cassell, 1959 . . £75/£35
More Poems, 1961, Cassell, 1961 . . . £20/£5
Collected Poems, Doubleday (U.S.), 1961 . £35/£10
New Poems, 1962, Cassell, 1962. . . . £25/£5
The More Deserving Cases: Eighteen Old Poems for Reconsideration, Marlborough College Press, 1962 (350 signed copies) £125
ditto, Marlborough College Press, 1962 (400 signed copies, bound in morocco) £125
Man Does, Woman Is, Cassell, 1964 . . £25/£10
ditto, Cassell, 1964 (175 copies, signed by the author). . . . .£150/£100
ditto, Doubleday (U.S.), 1964 . . . £25/£10
Love Respelt, Cassell, 1965 (250 signed copies) . .
. . . .£200/£150
ditto, Doubleday (U.S.), 1966 . . . . £25/£10
Collected Poems, 1965, Cassell, 1965 . . £20/£5
Seventeen Poems Missing From 'Love Respelt', privately printed, 1966 (330 copies, signed by the author) . . . .£150/£100

Colophon to 'Love Respelt', privately printed, 1967 (386 copies, signed by the author) . . . £100/£75
Poems, 1965-1968, Cassell, 1968 . . . £15/£5
Poems About Love, Cassell, 1969 . . . £25/£10
Love Respelt Again, Doubleday (U.S.), 1969 (1,000 numbered copies, signed by the author) . £75/£50
Beyond Giving, privately printed, 1969 (536 copies, signed by the author, card covers, d/w) . £75/£60
Poems, 1968-1970, Cassell, 1970 . . . £20/£10
Advice from a Mother, Poem of the Month Club, 1970 (broadsheet) £25
The Green-Sailed Vessel, privately printed, 1971 (536 copies) . . . . £65/£45
Poems: Abridged for Dolls and Princes, Cassell, 1971
. . . . £25/£10
Poems, 1970-1972, Cassell, 1972 . . . £25/£10
Deya: A Portfolio, Motif Editions, 1972 (75 signed copies) £225
Timeless Meeting: Poems, privately printed, 1973 (536 signed, numbered copies) . . . . . £75/£50
At the Gate, Stellar Press (U.S.), 1974 (536 copies) .
. . . . £75/£50
Collected Poems, 1975, Cassell, 1975 . . £25/£10
New Collected Poems, Doubleday (U.S.), 1977 . .
. . . . £25/£10
Across the Gulf, Late Poems, The New Seizin Press, 1992 (175 copies) £75

Fiction
My Head! My Head!, Secker, 1925 (500 copies) . .
. . . . £350/£200
ditto, Knopf (U.S.), 1925 . . . . . £125/£50
The Shout, Mathews & Marrot, 1929 (530 signed, numbered copies) . . . . . . £175/£125
No Decency Left, Cape, 1932 (pseud. Barbara Rich, with Laura Riding) . . . . . . £250/£100
The Real David Copperfield, Barker, 1933 (spine stamped in gold) . . . . . . £250/£75
ditto, Barker, 1933 (spine stamped in black) £125/£25
ditto, as *David Copperfield*, Harcourt Brace (U.S.), 1934 (abridged version condensed by Robert Graves)
. . . . £45/£15
I, Claudius, Barker, 1934 (black cloth) £650/£250
ditto, Barker, 1934 (remainder copies, orange cloth) .
. . . . £500/£200
ditto, Smith & Haas (U.S.), 1934. . . . £250/£25
Claudius the God and his Wife Messalina, Barker, 1934 . . . . £250/£75
ditto, Smith & Haas (U.S.), 1935 (first word on back jacket flap 'suddenly', blue cloth blind stamped on front) . . . . £200/£35
ditto, Smith & Haas (U.S.), 1935 (first word on back jacket flap 'At', dark blue cloth stamped in gold) . .
. . . . £150/£25
Antigua, Penny, Puce, Constable/Selzin Press, 1936 .
. . . . £250/£75
ditto, as *The Antigua Stamp*, Random House (U.S.), 1937 . . . . £60/£15
Count Belisarius, Cassell, 1938 . . . . £75/£15

ditto, Random House (U.S.), 1938 . . . £50/£10
Sergeant Lamb of the Ninth, Methuen, 1940 £75/£10
ditto, Random House (U.S.), 1941 . . . £25/£10
Proceed, Sergeant Lamb, Methuen, 1941 . £75/£25
ditto, Random House (U.S.), 1941 . . . £65/£20
Wife to Mr Milton: The Story of Mary Powell, Cassell, 1943 . . . . £40/£15
ditto, Creative Age Press (U.S.), 1944 . £25/£10
The Golden Fleece, Cassell, 1944 . . . £45/£15
ditto, as *Hercules, My Shipmate*, Creative Age Press (U.S.), 1945 . . . . £35/£15
King Jesus, Creative Age Press (U.S.), 1946 £25/£10
ditto, Cassell, 1946 . . . . £25/£10
Watch the North Wind Rise, Creative Age Press (U.S.), 1949 . . . . £40/£15
ditto, as *Seven Days in New Crete*, Cassell, 1949 . .
. . . . £35/£10
The Islands of Unwisdom, Doubleday (U.S.), 1949 .
. . . . £25/£10
ditto, as *The Isles of Unwisdom*, Cassell, 1950 £25/£10
Homer's Daughter, Cassell, 1955 . . . £35/£10
ditto, Doubleday (U.S.), 1955 . . . . £25/£10
Catacrok! Mostly Stories, Mostly Funny, Cassell, 1956 . . . . £30/£10
They Hanged My Saintly Billy, Cassell, 1957 £25/£10
ditto, Doubleday (U.S.), 1957 . . . . £25/£10
Collected Short Stories, Doubleday (U.S.), 1964 . .
. . . . £30/£10
ditto, Cassell, 1965 . . . . £25/£10

Plays
John Kemp's Wager: A Ballad Opera, Blackwell, 1925 (100 signed, numbered copies) . . . £650
ditto, Blackwell, 1925 (750 unsigned copies, wraps) .
. . . . £125
ditto, French (U.S.), 1925 (250 copies) . . £175

Children's Books
The Penny Fiddle: Poems for Children, Cassell, 1960 (illustrated by Edward Ardizzone) . . £125/£50
ditto, Doubleday (U.S.), 1960 . . . . £75/£20
The Big Green Book, Crowell-Collier (U.S.), 1962 (illustrated by Maurice Sendak). . . . £35/£10
ditto, Puffin, 1978 (wraps) £5
Ann at Highwood Hall: Poems for Children, Cassell, 1964 (illustrated by Edward Ardizzone) . £50/£20
ditto, Doubleday (U.S.), 1964 . . . . £30/£10
Two Wise Children, Quist (U.S.), 1967 . . £35/£10
The Poor Boy Who Followed His Star, Cassell, 1968 .
. . . . £35/£10
ditto, Doubleday (U.S.), 1969 . . . . £35/£10
An Ancient Castle, Peter Owen, 1980 . . £20/£5
ditto, Kesend (U.S.), 1981 . . . . . £15/£5

As Editor
Oxford Poetry, 1921, Blackwell, 1921 (with Alan Porter and Richard Hughes). £100
ditto, Appleton (U.S.), 1922 . . . . £125/£35
John Skelton (Laureate), Benn, 1927 . . . £35

The Less Familiar Nursery Rhymes, Benn, 1927
(wraps) £50
T.E. Lawrence To His Biographers, Faber, 1938 (2
vols, 500 signed copies, with d/ws, in slipcase) . .
. . . . £450/£400
ditto, Doubleday Doran, 1938 (2 vols, 500 signed
copies, with d/ws, in slipcase) . . . £450/£400
The Comedies of Terence, Doubleday (U.S.), 1962
. . . . £25
ditto, Cassell, 1963 . . . . £10

Translations
Almost Forgotten Germany, by George Schwarz, (with
Laura Riding), Constable/Seizin Press, 1936 . . .
. . . . £250/£60
*The Transformation of Lucius, Otherwise Known as
the Golden Ass*, by Lucius Apuleius, Penguin, 1950
(2,000 signed, numbered copies, slipcase) £50/£40
ditto, Penguin, 1950 (wraps) £5
ditto, Farrar, Straus, Giroux (U.S.), 1951 . £20/£5
The Cross and the Sword from 'Enriquillio', by
Manuel de Jesus Galvan, Univ. Press: Bloomington
(U.S.), 1954 . . . . £45/£15
ditto, Gollancz, 1956 . . . . . . £45/£10
The Infant with the Globe from 'El Nino do la Bola',
by Pedro de Alarcon, Trianon Press, 1955 £25/£10
ditto, Yoseleff (U.S.), 1959 . . . £20/£10
Winter in Majorca, by George Sand, Cassell, 1956 .
. . . . £15/£5
ditto, Valldemosa Edition (Mallorca), 1959 (wraps) .
. . . . £10
Pharsalia, by Lucan, Penguin, 1956 (wraps) . . £5
ditto, Penguin (U.S.), 1957 . . . . £10/£5
The Twelve Caesars, by Suetonius, Penguin, 1957
(wraps) £5
The Anger of Achilles: Homer's Iliad, Homer,
Doubleday (U.S.)., 1959. . . . . £35/£10
ditto, Cassell, 1960 . . . . . £20/£10
The Rubaiyat of Omar Khayyam, by Omar Khayyam,
(with Omar Ali-Shah), Cassell, 1967 . . £20/£5
ditto, Doubleday (U.S.), 1968 . . . £20/£5
The Song of Songs, Clarkson Potter (U.S.), 1973 . .
. . . . £15/£5
ditto, Collins, 1973 . . . . . . £15/£5

Others
On English Poetry, Knopf (U.S.), 1922 . . £200/£30
ditto, Heinemann, 1922 . . . . . £150/£25
The Meaning of Dreams, Cecil Palmer, 1924 . .
. . . . £100/£35
ditto, Greenberg (U.S.), 1925. . . . . £50/£20
Poetic Unreason and Other Studies, Cecil Palmer,
1925 . . . . £150/£60
*Contemporary Techniques of Poetry: A Political
Analogy*, Hogarth Press, 1925 (wraps). . . £45
Another Future of Poetry, Hogarth Press, 1926 £100
Impenetrability, or the Proper Habit of English,
Hogarth Press, 1927 . . . . £200

The English Ballad: A Short Critical Survey, Benn,
1927 . . . . £75/£25
ditto, as *English and Scottish Ballads*, Heinemann,
1957 (revised edition) . . . . . £25/£10
*Lars Porsena, or 'The Future of Swearing and
Improper Language'*, Kegan Paul, Trench, Trubner,
1927 . . . . £200/£30
ditto, Dutton (U.S.), 1927 . . . . £175/£25
ditto, as *The Future of Swearing and Improper
Language*, Kegan Paul, Trench, Trubner, 1936
(revised edition) . . . . £25/£10
ditto, as *The Future of Swearing and Improper
Language*, Martin Brian & O'Keefe, 1972 (100
signed copies) £125
A Survey of Modernist Poetry, Heinemann, 1927 (with
Laura Riding) . . . . . . £75/£20
ditto, Doubleday (U.S.), 1928 . . . £50/£15
Lawrence and the Arabs, Cape, 1927 . . £250/£30
ditto, as *Lawrence and the Arabian Adventure*,
Doubleday (U.S.), 1928 . . . . . £150/£20
A Pamphlet Against Anthologies, Cape, 1928 (with
Laura Riding) £75
ditto, Doubleday (U.S.), 1928 . . . £75/£25
Mrs Fisher, or The Future of Humour, Kegan Paul,
Trench, Trubner, 1928 . . . . . £75/£25
ditto, Dutton (U.S.), 1928. . . . . £75/£25
Goodbye to All That: An Autobiography, Cape, 1929
(first issue with Sassoon poem on pps. 341-343) . .
. . . . £1,250/£750
ditto, Cape, 1929 (second issue, poem replaced by
asterisks) . . . . £600/£45
ditto, Cape & Smith (U.S.), 1930. . . . £300/£35
But it Still Goes On: An Accumulation, Cape, 1930
(first impression with 'the child she bare' first para.
on p.157) . . . . £250/£100
ditto, Cape, 1930 (second impression with 'child she
bare' deleted). . . . . £150/£20
ditto, Cape & Smith (U.S.), 1931. . . £125/£20
The Long Weekend (with Alan Hodge), Faber, 1940 .
. . . . £40/£10
ditto, Macmillan (U.S.), 1941 . . . . £35/£10
The Reader Over Your Shoulder (with Alan Hodge),
Cape, 1943 . . . . £40/£10
ditto, Macmillan (U.S.), 1943 . . . . £35/£10
The White Goddess, Faber, 1948 . . . £75/£20
ditto, Creative Age Press (U.S.), 1948 . . £65/£15
*The Common Asphodel: Collected Essays on Poetry,
1922-1949*, Hamish Hamilton, 1949 . . £75/£20
Occupation: Writer, Creative Age Press (U.S.), 1950 .
. . . . £35/£10
ditto, Cassell, 1951 . . . . . . £25/£10
The Nazarene Gospel Restored (with Joshua Podro),
Cassell, 1953 . . . . £100/£25
ditto, Doubleday (U.S.), 1954 . . . £65/£15
The Greek Myths, Penguin, 1955 (2 vols, wraps) £10
ditto, Cassell , 1958 . . . . . . £20/£10
The Crowning Privilege: The Clark Lectures, 1954-5,
Cassell, 1955 . . . . £25/£10
ditto, Doubleday (U.S.), 1956 . . . . £20/£5

Adam's Rib, Trianon Press, 1955 (illustrated by James Metcalf) . . . . £50/£15
ditto, Trianon Press, 1955 (26 signed, numbered copies, slipcase) . . . . £350/£150
ditto, Trianon Press, 1955 (250 signed, numbered copies, slipcase) . . . . £200/£150
ditto, Yoseloff (U.S.), 1955 . . . . £45/£15
ditto, Yoseloff (U.S.), 1955 (100 signed copies) . . . . £150/£125
Jesus in Rome (with Joshua Podro), Cassell, 1957 . . . . £45/£20
Steps, Cassell, 1958 . . . . £25/£10
5 Pens in Hand, Doubleday (U.S.), 1958 . £30/£10
Food for Centaurs, Doubleday (U.S.), 1960 £45/£15
Greek Gods and Heroes, Doubleday (U.S.), 1960 . . . . £25/£10
ditto as *Myths of Ancient Greece*, Cassell, 1961 . . . . £25/£10
Selected Poetry and Prose, Hutchinson, 1961, (edited James Reeves) . . . . £10/£5
Oxford Addresses on Poetry, Cassell, 1962 . £20/£5
ditto, Doubleday (U.S.), 1962 . . . . £20/£5
The Siege and Fall of Troy, Cassell, 1962 (illustrated by Walter Hodges) . . . . . . £15/£5
ditto, Doubleday (U.S.), 1962 . . . . £15/£5
Hebrew Myths: The Book of Genesis, Doubleday (U.S.), 1964 (with Raphael Patai) . . . £35/£10
ditto, Cassell, 1964 . . . . . . £35/£10
Majorca Observed, Cassell, 1965 . . . £15/£5
ditto, Doubleday (U.S.), 1965 . . . . £15/£5
Mammon and the Black Goddess, Cassell, 1965 . . . . £20/£5
ditto, Doubleday (U.S.), 1965 . . . £20/£5
Poetic Craft and Principle, Cassell, 1967 . £15/£5
Greek Myths and Legends, Cassell, 1968 . £10/£5
The Crane Bag, Cassell, 1969 . . . . £10/£5
On Poetry: Collected Talks and Essays, Doubleday (U.S.), 1969 . . . . £20/£5
Difficult Questions, Easy Answers, Cassell, 1972 . . . . £15/£5
ditto, Doubleday (U.S.), 1973 . . . . £15/£5
Collected Letters, Moyer Bell, (U.K./U.S.), 1984 & 1988 (2 vols) . . . . £50/£25

ALASDAIR GRAY
(b.1934)

An inventive Scottish writer of bizarre tales, strangely written.

Novels
Lanark, Canongate, 1981 . . . . . £300/£20
ditto, Harper Colophon (U.S.), 1981 (wraps) . £10
ditto, Canongate, 1985 (1000 signed copies) £100/£65
ditto, Braziller (U.S.), 1985 . . . . £50/£20
1982 Janine, Cape, 1984 . . . . . £25/£5
ditto, Viking (U.S.), 1984 . . . . . £20/£5

The Fall of Kelvin Walker, Canongate, 1985 £20/£5
ditto, Braziller (U.S.), 1986 . . . . £15/£5
Something Leather, Cape, 1990 . . . . £20/£5
ditto, Random House (U.S.), 1990 . . . £15/£5
McGrotty and Ludmilla, Dog and Bone, 1990 (wraps) £10
Poor Things, Bloomsbury, 1991 . . . . £15/£5
ditto, Harcourt (U.S.), 1992 . . . . £15/£5
History Maker, Canongate, 1994 . . . £15/£5
ditto, Harcourt (U.S.), 1996 . . . . £10/£5

Short Stories
The Comedy of the White Dog, Print Studio Press, 1979 (600 numbered copies, wraps) . . . £75
Unlikely Stories, Mostly, Canongate, 1983 . £40/£5
ditto, Penguin (U.S.), 1984 . . . . £15/£5
Lean Tales, Cape, 1985 (with James Kelman and Agnes Owens) . . . . £20/£5
Ten Tales Tall and True, Bloomsbury, 1993 £10/£5
ditto, Harcourt (U.S.), 1993 . . . . £10/£5
Mavis Belfrage, Bloomsbury, 1996 . . . £10/£5

Verse
Old Negatives: Four Verse Sequences, Cape, 1989 (500 signed copies) . . . . . . £65/£35
ditto, Cape, 1989 (wraps) £5
The Artist In His World: Prints 1986-1997, by Ian McCulloch, Argyll Publishing, 1998 (eight poems by Gray) . . . . £35/£10
Sixteen Occasional Poems: 1990-2000, McAlpine, 2000 (wraps) £10

Others
Dialogue, Scottish Theatre Magazine, 1971 . . £25
Self-portrait, Saltaire Society, 1988 (wraps) . £20
The Anthology of Prefaces, Canongate, 1989 . £10
ditto, as *The Book of Prefaces*, Bloomsbury, 2000 . . . . £10/£5
Why Scots Should Rule Scotland, Connongate, 1992 (wraps) £10
ditto, Cannongate, 1997 (wraps) £5
5 Scottish Artists Retrospective Show, Famedram Publishers, 1986 (five colour catalogues and an introduction by Gray) £50
Pierre Lavalle: Paintings 1947-75, Lavalle Retrospective Group 1990 (contains an essay by Gray, wraps) £10

HENRY GREEN
(b.1905 d.1973)

Henry Green was the pseudonym of the novelist Henry Vincent Yorke.

Novels
Blindness, Dent, 1926 . . . . . £1,500/£150
ditto, Dutton (U.S.), 1926 . . . . £750/£100

Living, Dutton (U.S.), 1929 . . . . £1,750/£150
ditto, Dent, 1929 . . . . £500/£75
Party Going, Hogarth Press, 1939 . . . £600/£100
ditto, Longman (Toronto), 1939 . . . £250/£75
ditto, Viking (U.S.), 1951 . . . . . £35/£5
Caught, Hogarth Press, 1943 . . . . £250/£50
ditto, Macmillan (Toronto), 1943 . . £100/£45
ditto, Viking (U.S.), 1950 . . . . . £20/£5
Loving, Hogarth Press, 1945 . . . . £225/£50
ditto, Macmillan (Toronto), 1945 . . £100/£45
ditto, Viking (U.S.), 1949 . . . . . £25/£5
Back, Hogarth Press, 1946 . . . . . £150/£40
ditto, Oxford (Toronto), 1946 . . . £60/£20
ditto, Viking (U.S.), 1950 . . . . . £20/£5
Concluding, Hogarth Press, 1948 . . £50/£15
ditto, Viking (U.S.), 1950 . . . . . £20/£5
Nothing, Hogarth Press, 1950 . . . . £40/£15
ditto, Viking (U.S.), 1950 . . . . . £15/£5
Doting, Hogarth Press, 1951 . . . . £40/£15
ditto, Viking (U.S.), 1952 . . . . . £15/£5

Others

Pack My Bag, Hogarth Press, 1940 . . . £450/£75
ditto, Macmillan (Toronto), 1940 . . . £125/£40
ditto, New Directions (U.S.), 1993 . . . £10/£5
Surviving, The Uncollected Writings of Henry Green,
 Chatto & Windus [1992] . . . . £20/£5
ditto, Viking (U.S.), 1993 . . . . . £15/£5

KATE GREENAWAY
(b.1846 d.1901)

British author and illustrator whose first success, *Under the Window*, had a major influence on children's fashion of the time.

Infant Amusements, by William Henry Giles Kingston, Griffith and Farran, [1867] . . . £500
Aunt Louisa's Nursery Favourite, Warne, 1870 £450
Diamonds and Toads, Warne, [1871] . . £1,000
The Children of the Parsonage, by Henry Courtney Selous, Griffith and Farran, 1874 . . . £400
Puck and Blossom, by Rosa Mulholland, Marcus Ward, [1874?] £300
Fairy Gifts, by K. Knox, Griffith and Farran, [1875] .
 . . . . £200
The Fairy Spinner, by Miranda Hill, Marcus Ward, [1875] (illustrations unattributed) £200
ditto, Nelson (U.S.), 1875 . . . . . £150
A Cruise in the Acorn, by Alice Jerrold, Marcus Ward, [1875] £150
Turnaside Cottage, by Mary Senior Clark, Marcus Ward, 1875 . . . . £150
ditto, Nelson (U.S.), 1875 . . . . . £150
Children's Songs, Marcus Ward, [1875] . . £100
Melcombe Manor, by F. Scarlet Potter, [1875] £150

Seven Birthdays, by K. Knox, Griffith and Farran, 1876 . . . . £150
ditto, Dutton (U.S.), [1876?] £150
A Quiver of Love: A Collection of Valentines, Marcus Ward, 1876 . . . . £350
Two Little Cousins, by Alice Hepburn, Marcus Ward, 1876 . . . . £150
What Santa Claus Gave Me, Griffith and Farran, [c.1876] £125
Starlight Stories, by Fanny Lablache, Griffith and Farran, 1876 . . . . £100
ditto, Pott, Young & Co (U.S.), 1879 . . £75
Tom Seven Years Old, by H. Rutherford Russell, Marcus Ward, [1877] £150
Pretty Stories for Tiny Folks, Cassell, 1877 £125
Woodland Romances, Cassell, Petter & Galpin, [1877]
 . . . . £150
ditto, as *The 'Little Folks' Painting Book*, Cassell, Petter & Galpin, [1879] (wraps) £300
Poor Nelly, by Mrs Bonavia Hunt, Cassell, 1878 £125
Topo, by G.E. Brunefille, Marcus Ward, 1878 . £125
Esther, by Geraldine Butt, Marcus Ward, 1878 . £125
A Little Maid and Her Moods, by Elizabeth Stewart Phelps, Lothrop (U.S.), [1878] £125
Under the Window, by Kate Greenaway, Routledge, [1878] £250
ditto, Routledge (U.S.), [1880] £150
Topo, Marcus Ward, 1878 . . . . . £100
Heartsease, by Charlotte M. Yonge, Macmillan, 1879.
 . . . . £150
The Heir of Redclyffe, by Charlotte M. Yonge, Macmillan, 1879 . . . . £150
Amateur Theatricals, by Walter Herries Pollock and Lady Pollock, Macmillan, 1879 . . . . £150
Trot's Journey, Worthington (U.S.), 1879 . . £150
A Favourite Album of Fun and Fancy, Cassell, Petter & Galpin, [1879] £150
Christmas Snowflakes, Lothrop (U.S.), [1879] . £150
Three Brown Boys, Cassell, 1879 . . . £150
ditto, Mallory (U.S.), 1879 . . . . . £150
Art in the Nursery, Lothrop (U.S.), [1879] . . £150
A Book for Every Jack and Gill, Dodd, Mead (U.S.), [1879]. £150
Once Upon a Time, by Emma E. Brown, Lothrop (U.S.), [1879]. £150
The Two Gray Girls, Cassell, Petter & Galpin, [1880].
 . . . . £150
Kate Greenaway's Birthday Book for Children, Routledge, [1880] £150
Little Folks Out and About Book, by Chatty Cheerful [William Martin] , Cassell, [1880] . . . £150
Illustrated Children's Birthday Book, Mack, [1880] .
 . . . . £125
Freddie's Letter, Routledge, 1880 . . . . £125
The Youngster, by Cousin Daisy, Lippincott, [1880] .
 . . . . £125
Stevie's Visit, Dodd, Mead (U.S.), 1880 . . . £125
The Quiver of Love, Marcus Ward, 1880 . . £250
The Purse of Gold, Dodd, Mead (U.S.), [1880] £125

The Lost Knife, Dodd, Mead (U.S.), 1880 . . £125
Little Sunbeam Stories, Cassell, Petter & Galpin,
[1880]. £150
Pleasant Hours and Golden Days, Lupton (U.S.),
[1880]. £125
Baby Dido, Lothrop (U.S.), [1880] (wraps) . . £125
Dumpy, by Archie Fell, Lothrop (U.S.), [1880] £125
The Easy Book for Children, Pictorial Litertaure
Society, [1880] £150
ditto, Butler (U.S.), [n.d.] £100
Five Mice in a Mousetrap, by Laura E. Richards, Estes
Lauriat (U.S.), [1880] £125
Grandmamma's Surprise Party, Dodd, Mead (U.S.),
1880 . . . . £125
The Library, by Andrew Lang, Macmillan, 1881 £125
London Lyrics, by Frederick Locker, Chiswick Press,
1881 . . . . £125
ditto, Scribner (U.S.), 1882 . . . . . . £100
A Day in a Child's Life, Routledge, [1881] . . £150
Mother Goose, or The Old Nursery Rhymes,
Routledge, [1881] (wraps) £250
ditto, Routledge, [1881] (cloth) £125
Elise, Dodd, Mead (U.S.), [1881] £125
Hide & Seek Illustrated, Dodd, Mead (U.S.), [1881] .
. . . . £125
King Christmas, Dodd, Mead (U.S.), [1881] . £125
Whose Fault Was It?, Dodd, Mead (U.S.), 1881 £125
Some Little People, Dodd, Mead (U.S.), [1881] £125
Art Hours, McLoughlin Bros (U.S.), 1882 . . £150
Steps to Art, McLoughlin Bros (U.S.), 1882 . £150
Happy Little People, by Olive Patch, Cassell, Petter &
Galpin, [1882] £150
Little Ann, by Jane and Ann Taylor, Routledge, [1882]
. . . . £150
Flowers and Fancies, by B. Montgomerie Ranking and
Thomas K Tully, Marcus Ward, 1882 . . . £150
The Wonderful Fan, Aunt Ella, Dutton (U.S.), 1882 .
. . . . £150
Toyland, Trot's Journey, Worthington (U.S.), [1882?]
. . . . £150
Tales from the Edda, told by Helen Zimmerman, Swan
Sonneschein, [1882] £150
Papa's Little Daughters, by Mary D Brine, Cassell,
Petter & Galpin, 1882 . . . . £150
Little Loving-Hearts Poem-Book, by Margaret
Eleanora Tupper, Dutton (U.S.), 1882 . . . £150
Little Gatherers, Cassell, Petter & Galpin, [1882] . .
. . . . £150
Greenaway Pictures to Paint, Cassell, Petter & Galpin,
[1882] £250
Jingles and Joys, by Mary D. Brine, Cassell (U.S.),
1883 . . . . £150
Baby Chatterbox, Worthington (U.S.), 1883 . £150
Art of England, by John Ruskin, George Allen, 1883 .
. . . . £150
Fors Clavigera, by John Ruskin, George Allen, 1884 .
. . . . £150
A Painting Book, Routledge, [1884]. . . . £250

Brothers of Pity, by Juliana Horatia Ewing, SPCK,
1884 . . . . £150
Language of Flowers, Routledge, [1884] . . £150
A Summer at Aunt Helen's, Dodd, Mead (U.S.), 1880
[1884]. £150
Baby's Birthday Book, Marcus Ward, [1894] . £150
English Spelling Book, by William Mavor, Routledge,
1885 . . . . £200
Chatterbox Hall, Worthington (U.S.), [1884] . £150
Children's Birthday Book, Marcus Ward, [1894] . .
. . . . £150
Little Castles with Big Wings, Dodd, Mead (U.S.),
1880 [1884] £150
A Painting Book, Routledge, [1884] (wraps.) . £250
Songs for the Nursery, Mack, [1884] . . . £125
Poems of Frederick Locker, White, Stokes & Allen
(U.S.), [1884]. £150
Dame Wiggins of Lee and Her Seven Wonderful Cats,
George Allen, 1885 . . . . £65
ditto, George Allen, 1885 (400 large paper copies). .
. . . . £225
Marigold Garden, Routledge, [1885] . . . £125
Kate Greenaway's Album, Routledge, [1885?] (8
copies, wraps) £7,500
Kate Greenaway's Alphabet, Routledge, [1885]
(miniature book, card covers) £100
ditto, as New Alphabet, Routledge (U.S.), [1885] . .
. . . . £125
Tick, Tick, Tick and Other Rhymes, Mayer, Merkel &
Ottmann (U.S.), [1885] £150
Mother Truths melodies, by Mrs E.P. Miller, Bay State
Publishing (U.S.), 1885. . . . . £150
Little Patience Picture Book, Routledge, [1885] £125
A Apple Pie, Routledge, 1886 . . . . . £200
ditto, Routledge (U.S.), [1886] £200
The Queen of the Pirate Isle, by Bret Harte, Chatto &
Windus, [1885] £200
ditto, Houghton Mifflin (U.S.), 1887 . . . £200
Rhymes for the Young Folk, by William Allingham,
Cassell, [1886] £200
Bib and Tucker, Lothrop (U.S.), [1886]. . . £125
Christmas Dreams, by Mary D. Brine, Cassell (U.S.),
[1886]. £125
Queen Victoria's Jubilee Garland, Routledge, 1887 .
. . . . £350
Lucy's Troubles, by Laurie Loring, Lothrop (U.S.),
1887 . . . . £125
Baby's Birthday Book, Marcus Ward, [1887] . £150
Orient Line Guide, Sampson Low, 1888 . . £125
Around the House, Worthington (U.S.), 1888 . £150
Pied Piper of Hamelin, by Robert Browning,
Routledge, [1888] £150
The Old Farm Gate, Routledge, [1888]. . . £150
Miss Rosebud, Lothrop (U.S.), [1888] . . . £125
Kate Greenaway's Painting Book, Warne (U.S.),
[1888]. £250
Kate Greenaway's Book of Games, Routledge, [1889]
. . . . £200

The *Royal Progress of King Pepito*, by Beatrice
Cresswell, S.P.C.K., [1889] £125
Our Girls, Belford, Vlarke & Co. (U.S.), 1890 . £125
Songs of the Month, by Lucie E. Wliieplait,
Worthington (U.S.), 1891 . . . . . £125
Soap Bubble Stories, by Fanny Barry, Skeffington,
1892 . . . . £125
Littledom Castle and Other Tales, by Mabel H.
Spielmann, Routledge, 1903 . . . . £200
Doll's Tea Party, Lothrop (U.S.), [1895] . £125
Every Girl's Stories, by Grace Aguilar, Geraldine Butt
and Jane Butt, Routledge, 1896. . . . . £125
Stories Witty and pictures Pretty, Conky (U.S.), 1896 .
. . . . £100
To Pass the Time, McLoughlin (U.S.), [1897] . £100
Little Folks' Speaker, Lothrop (U.S.), 1898 . £100
The April Baby's Book of Tunes, by the author of
'Elizabeth and her German Garden', Macmillan, 1900
. . . . £200
ditto, by the author of 'Elizabeth and her German
Garden', Macmillan (U.S.), 1900 . . . . £200

Almanacks
(assuming original envelope no longer present)
1883, Routledge, [1882] £125
1884, Routledge, [1883] (wraps) £125
1885, Routledge, [1884] £125
1886, Routledge, [1885] £125
1887, Routledge, [1886] £125
1888, Routledge, [1887] £125
1889, Routledge, [1888] £150
1890, Routledge, [1889] £125
1891, Routledge, [1890] £125
1892, Routledge, [1891] £125
1893, Routledge, [1892] £125
1894, Routledge, [1893] £125
1895, Routledge, [1894] £125
1897, Routledge, [1896] (imitation leather binding) .
. . . . £500
1924, Warne, [1923] £75
1925, Warne, [1924] £75
1926, Warne, [1923] £75
1927, Warne, [1926] £75
1928, Warne, [1927] £75
1929, Warne, [1928] (imitation leather binding) £125

Calendars
Calendar of the Seasons, 1876/1877/1881/1882,
Marcus Ward . . . . . . £100 each
A Calendar of the Months, Marcus Ward, 1884 £125
Kate Greenaway's Calendar, 1884/1897/1899,
Routledge . . . . £125 each

GRAHAM GREENE
(b.1904 d.1991)

Popularly known for his novels, Greene is equally
acclaimed as a short story writer, playwright, critic
and essayist. From his first real success, *Stamboul
Train*, to *Brighton Rock* and a host of other well-
known books, he appears preoccupied with the
themes of guilt, pursuit and failure, much of which
can be seen to stem from his conversion to
Catholicism.

Novels
The Man Within, Heinemann, 1929 . . £2,500/£250
ditto, Doubleday (U.S.), 1929 . . . £1,250/£75
The Name of Action, Heinemann, 1930 (d/w price
7s6d and reviews of *The Man Within* on back) . .
. . . . £3,000/£400
ditto, Heinemann, 1930 (d/w price 3s6d and reviews of
current book on d/w flap) . . . £1,500/£400
ditto, Doubleday (U.S.), 1931 . . . £1,000/£175
Rumour at Nightfall, Heinemann, 1931. £15,000/£300
ditto, Doubleday (U.S.), 1932 . . . £350/£75
Stamboul Train, Heinemann, 1932 (reference to 'Q.C.
Savory' on pps 77, 78, 82, 98, 131) . £3,000/£250
ditto, Heinemann, 1932 (reference to 'Quin Savory') .
. . . . £2,000/£75
ditto, as *Orient Express*, Doubleday (U.S.), 1933 . .
. . . . £1,250/£100
It's A Battlefield, Heinemann, 1934 (d/w price 7s6d) .
. . . . £1,500/£100
ditto, Heinemann, 1934 (d/w price 3/6) . £1,250/£100
ditto, Doubleday (U.S.), 1934 . . . £600/£45
England Made Me, Heinemann, 1935 . £7,500/£250
ditto, Doubleday (U.S.), 1935 . . . £750/£50
This Gun For Hire, Doubleday (U.S.), 1936 £750/£50
ditto, as *A Gun for Sale*, Heinemann, 1936 . . . .
. . . . £7,500/£250
Brighton Rock, Viking (U.S.), 1938. . £750/£50
ditto, Heinemann, 1938 . . . . . £25,000/£150
The Confidential Agent, Heinemann, 1939 . . . .
. . . . £5,000/£200
ditto, Viking (U.S.), 1939. . . . . £750/£65
The Power and the Glory, Heinemann, 1940 . . .
. . . . £7,500/£450
ditto as *The Labyrinthine Ways*, Viking (U.S.), 1940
(first state) . . . . £750/£250
ditto as *The Labyrinthine Ways*, Viking (U.S.), 1940
(second state with pp.165 and 256 in correct order) .
. . . . £350/£35
The Ministry of Fear, Heinemann, 1943 £3,000/£75
ditto, Viking (U.S.), 1943. . . . . £450/£35
The Heart of the Matter, Heinemann, 1948 £200/£20
ditto, Viking (U.S.), 1948 (750 copies 'For Friends of
the Viking Press') . . . . . . £75/£25
ditto, Viking (U.S.), 1948. . . . . £50/£15
The Third Man, Viking (U.S.), 1950 . . £175/£15
The Third Man and The Fallen Idol, Heinemann,
1950 . . . . £200/£15

ditto, Eurographica (Helsinki), 1988 (500 signed copies) . . . . £200/£150
The End of the Affair, Heinemann, 1951 . £100/£15
ditto, Viking (U.S.), 1951. . . . . . £45/£10
Loser Takes All, Heinemann, 1955 . . . £100/£15
ditto, Viking (U.S.), 1957. . . . . . £45/£10
The Quiet American, Heinemann, 1955. . £100/£15
ditto, Viking (U.S.), 1956. . . . . . £45/£10
Our Man in Havana, Heinemann, 1958. . £75/£10
ditto, Viking (U.S.), 1958. . . . . . £35/£10
A Burnt Out Case, Heinemann, 1961 . . £75/£5
ditto, Viking (U.S.), 1961. . . . . . £25/£5
The Comedians, Viking (U.S.), 1966 (500 advance copies, acetate d/w) . . . . £75/£50
ditto, Bodley Head, 1966 . . . . . . £35/£10
ditto, Viking (U.S.), 1966. . . . . . £25/£5
Travels with My Aunt, Bodley Head, 1969 £35/£10
ditto, Viking (U.S.), 1970. . . . . . £25/£5
The Honorary Consul, Bodley Head, 1973 £35/£10
ditto, Viking (U.S.), 1973. . . . . . £25/£5
The Human Factor, Bodley Head, 1978 . £35/£10
ditto, Simon & Schuster (U.S.), 1978 . . £25/£5
Dr Fischer of Geneva or The Bomb Party, Bodley Head, 1980 . . . . £20/£5
ditto, Simon & Schuster (U.S.), 1980 . . £15/£5
ditto, Simon & Schuster (U.S.), 1980, (500 signed copies, slipcase) . . . . £150/£125
How Father Quixote Became a Monsignor, Sylvester & Orphanos (U.S.), 1980 (330 numbered copies, acetate d/w) . . . . £150/£125
Monsignor Quixote, Lester & Orpen Dennys (Canada), 1982 . . . . £20/£5
ditto, Bodley Head, 1982 . . . . . . £20/£5
ditto, Simon & Schuster (U.S.), 1982 . . £15/£5
ditto, Simon & Schuster (U.S.), 1982, (250 signed copies in slipcase) . . . . £150/£125
The Tenth Man, Bodley Head, 1985 . . £15/£5
ditto, Simon & Schuster (U.S.), 1985 . . £10/£5
The Captain and the Enemy, Reinhardt, 1988 £15/£5
ditto, Viking (U.S.), 1988. . . . . . £10/£5

Short Stories
The Bear Fell Free, Grayson, 1935 (285 signed copies) . . . . £850/£450
The Basement Room, Cresset Press, 1935 . £500/£75
Twenty Four Stories, Cresset Press, 1939 (with James Laver and Sylvia Townsend Warner) . . £125/£30
Nineteen Stories, Heinemann, 1947 . . . £250/£45
ditto, Viking (U.S.), 1949. . . . . . £150/£35
ditto, as ***Twenty-One Stories***, Heinemann, 1954 (extra stories added). . . . . £100/£15
A Visit to Morin, Heinemann, [1959] (250 copies). . . . . £250/£125
A Sense of Reality, Bodley Head, 1963 . . £50/£15
ditto, Viking (U.S.), 1963. . . . . . £35/£10
May We Borrow Your Husband?, Bodley Head, 1967 . . . . £30/£10
ditto, Bodley Head, 1967 (500 signed copies, glassine d/w) . . . . £150/£125

ditto, Viking (U.S.), 1967. . . . . . £25/£10
The Collected Stories, Bodley Head/Heinemann, 1972 . . . . £30/£10
ditto, Viking (U.S.), 1973. . . . . . £15/£5
Shades of Greene, Bodley Head/Heinemann, 1975 . . . . £15/£5
The Last Word and Other Stories, Reinhardt, 1990 . . . . £10/£5

Plays
The Living Room, Heinemann, 1953 . . £45/£10
ditto, Viking (U.S.), 1954. . . . . . £25/£5
The Potting Shed, Viking (U.S.), 1957 . . £50/£15
ditto, Heinemann, 1958 . . . . . . £25/£10
The Complaisant Lover, Heinemann, 1959 £50/£15
ditto, Viking (U.S.), 1961. . . . . . £15/£5
Carving a Statue, Bodley Head, 1964 . . £45/£15
The Return of A.J. Raffles, Bodley Head, 1975 (wraps) £10
ditto, Bodley Head, 1975 (250 signed copies) . . . . £250/£150
ditto, Simon & Schuster (U.S.), 1978 . . £25/£5
The Great Jowett, Bodley Head, 1981 (525 signed copies, glassine d/w). . . . . . . £150/£125
Yes & No and For Whom the Bell Chimes, Bodley Head, 1983 (775 signed copies, glassine d/w) . . . . £100/£80
Yes & No-A Play in One Act, Eurographica (Helsinki), 1984 (350 signed copies, wraps) £100

Travel
Journey Without Maps, Heinemann, 1936 . . . . £4,000/£150
ditto, Doubleday (U.S.), 1936 . . . . £300/£45
The Lawless Roads, Longman, 1939 (red gloth, lettering in gold) . . . . £1,500/£350
ditto, Longman, 1939 (red gloth, lettering in blue) . . . . £750/£75
ditto, as ***Another Mexico***, Viking (U.S.), 1939 . . . . £250/£50

Children's
The Little Train, Eyre & Spottiswoode, 1946 (anonymous) . . . . £450/£100
ditto, Lothrop (U.S.), 1958 . . . . . £250/£50
The Little Fire Engine, Parrish, 1950 . . £250/£45
ditto, as ***The Little Red Fire Engine***, Lothrop (U.S.), 1952. . . . . £100/£35
The Little Horse Bus, Parrish, 1952 . . . £200/£45
ditto, Lothrop (U.S.), 1954 . . . . . £75/£25
The Little Steam Roller, Parrish, 1953 . . £200/£45
ditto, Lothrop (U.S.), 1955 . . . . . £75/£25

Others
Babbling April, Blackwell, 1925. . . . £2,250/£750
To Beg I am Ashamed, Vanguard Press (U.S.), 1938 (pseud. 'Sheila Cousins', with Ronald Matthews). . . . . £125/£25
ditto, Routledge, 1938. . . . . . . £125/£25

Men At Work, Penguin New Writing, 1941 (wraps)   .
. . . .   £20
British Dramatists, Collins, 1942   . . .   £40/£10
Why Do I Write?: An Exchange of Views Between
Elizabeth Bowen, Graham Greene, and V.S.
Pritchett, Marshall, 1948   . . . . .   £100/£25
The Lost Childhood, Eyre & Spottiswoode, 1951   . .
. . . .   £40/£15
ditto, Viking (U.S.), 1952 . . . . .   £20/£5
In Search of a Character: Two African Journals,
Bodley Head, 1961   . . . . . .   £45/£10
ditto, Viking (U.S.), 1961(600 advance copies).   £65
ditto, Viking (U.S.), 1961 . . . . .   £45/£10
Introductions to Three Novels, Norstedt (Stockholm),
1962 (wraps) £100
The Revenge, An Autobiographical Fragment, The
Stellar Press, 1963 (300 copies, wraps)   . .   £150
Victorian Detective Fiction, A Catalogue of the
Collection made by Dorothy Glover and Graham
Greene, Bodley Head, 1966 (500 signed copies). .
. . . .   £250/£150
Collected Essays, Bodley Head, 1969   . .   £20/£5
ditto, Viking (U.S.), 1969 . . . . .   £15/£5
Mr Visconti, Bodley Head, 1969 (300 copies, wraps) .
. . . .   £200
A Sort of Life, Bodley Head, 1971   . . .   £15/£5
ditto, Simon & Schuster (U.S.), 1971   . .   £15/£5
The Pleasure Dome: The Collected Film Criticism,
1935-1940, Secker & Warburg, 1972   . .   £15/£5
ditto, Simon & Schuster (U.S.), 1972   . .   £15/£5
The Virtue of Disloyalty, Bodley Head, 1972 (300
copies, wraps) £200
Lord Rochester's Monkey, Bodley Head, 1974 £15/£5
ditto, Viking (U.S.), 1974 . . . . .   £15/£5
An Impossible Woman, The Memories of Dottoressa
Moor of Capri, Bodley Head, 1975   . .   £20/£5
Ways of Escape, Lester & Orpen Dennys (Canada),
1980 . . . .   £25/£5
ditto, Lester & Orpen Dennys (Canada), 1980 (150
signed copies, slipcase) . . . . .   £250/£225
ditto, Bodley Head, 1980 . . . . . .   £10/£5
ditto, Simon & Schuster (U.S.), 1980   . .   £10/£5
J'Accuse: The Darker Side of Nice, *ditto*, Lester &
Orpen Dennys (Toronto), 1982 (wraps and d/w) . .
. . . .   £25/£15
ditto, Bodley Head, 1982 (wraps and d/w) .   £25/£15
The Other Man: Conversations with Graham Greene,
Bodley Head, 1983   . . . . .   £20/£5
ditto, Simon & Schuster (U.S.), 1983   . .   £20/£5
A Quick Look Behind, Sylvester & Orphanos, 1983
(300 signed, numbered copies of 330, slipcase)   . .
. . . .   £175/£125
ditto, Sylvester & Orphanos, 1983 (26 signed, lettered
copies, plus 4 presentaton copies, of 330, slipcase)   .
. . . .   £250/£200
Getting to Know The General, Bodley Head, 1984   .
. . . .   £15/£5
ditto, Simon & Schuster (U.S.), 1984   . .   £15/£5

The Monster of Capri, Eurographica (Helsinki), 1985
(500 signed copies) . . . . . .   £175/£125
Why the Epigraph?, Nonesuch, 1989 (950 signed
copies, glassine d/w). . . . . .   £150/£125
Dear David, Dear Graham, A Bibliophilic Corres-
pondence, The Alembic Press, 1989 (50 of 250
copies, slipcase) . . . .   £175/£125
ditto, The Alembic Press, 1989 (200 of 250 copies)   .
. . . .   £100
Yours, etc: Letters to the Press, Reinhardt, 1989   . .
. . . .   £10/£5
ditto, Viking (U.S.), 1990. . . . . .   £10/£5
Reflections on Travels with My Aunt, Firsts & Co.
(U.S.), 1989 (250 signed copies, wraps)   . .   £150
Reflections 1923-1988, Reinhardt, 1990   .   £10/£5
ditto, Viking (U.S.), 1990. . . . .   £10/£5
A World of My Own, Reinhardt, 1992   . .   £10/£5
ditto, Viking (U.S.), 1994. . . . . .   £10/£5

JOHN GRISHAM
(b.1955)

Grisham's reputation was established by his second
novel, *The Firm*. In 1990, a year before the novel was
published, Paramount Pictures purchased the film
rights for $600,000.

A Time to Kill, Wynwood (U.S.), 1989 (no mention of
The Firm on d/w) . . . . .   £3,000/£450
ditto, Doubleday (U.S.), 1993 (350 signed, numbered
copies, slicase. 'First edition' statement incorrect)   .
. . . .   £500/£450
ditto, Doubleday (U.S.), 1993 ('First edition' statement
incorrect) . . . .   £65/£10
ditto, Arrow, 1992 (wraps) £5
ditto, Century, 1993   . . . . . .   £45/£10
The Firm, Doubleday (U.S.), 1991   . . .   £150/£15
ditto, Doubleday (U.S.), 1991 (350 signed, numbered
copies, slipcase) . . . .   £500/£450
ditto, Century, 1991   . . . . . .   £45/£10
The Pelican Brief, Doubleday (U.S.), 1992.   £30/£10
ditto, Doubleday (U.S.), 1993 (350 signed, numbered
copies, slipcase) . . . .   £500/£450
ditto, Century, 1992   . . . . . .   £25/£5
The Client, Doubleday (U.S.), 1993 (350 signed,
numbered copies, slipcase) . . . .   £450/£400
ditto, Doubleday (U.S.), 1993   . . . .   £10/£5
ditto, Century, 1993   . . . . . .   £10/£5
The Chamber, Doubleday (U.S.), 1994 (350 signed,
numbered copies, slipcase) . . . .   £250/£200
ditto, Doubleday (U.S.), 1994   . . . .   £10/£5
ditto, Century, 1994   . . . . . .   £10/£5
The Rainmaker, Doubleday (U.S.), 1995 (350 signed,
numbered copies, slipcase) . . . .   £250/£200
ditto, Doubleday (U.S.), 1995   . . . .   £10/£5
ditto, Century, 1995   . . . . . .   £10/£5

The Runaway Jury, Doubleday (U.S.), 1996 (350 signed, numbered copies, slipcase) . . £250/£200
ditto, Doubleday (U.S.), 1996 . . . . £10/£5
ditto, Century, 1996 . . . . . . £10/£5
The Partner, Doubleday (U.S.), 1997 (275 signed, numbered copies, slipcase) . . . . £250/£200
ditto, Doubleday (U.S.), 1997 . . . . £10/£5
ditto, Century, 1997 . . . . £10/£5
The Street Lawyer, Doubleday (U.S.), 1998 (250 signed, numbered copies, slipcase) . . £250/£200
ditto, Doubleday (U.S.), 1998 . . . . £10/£5
ditto, Century, 1998 . . . . £10/£5
The Testament, Doubleday (U.S.), 1999 . £10/£5
ditto, Century, 1999 . . . . . . £10/£5
The Brethren, Doubleday (U.S.), 2000 (500 signed, numbered copies, slipcase) . . . . £200/£150
ditto, Doubleday (U.S.), 2000 . . . . £10/£5
ditto, Century, 2000 . . . . . . £10/£5

THOM GUNN
(b.1929)

While not commanding the respect he once did, Gunn remains a well-regarded post-war poet.

Verse
Poetry from Cambridge, 1951-1952, Fortune Press, 1952 . . . . £300/£65
The Fantasy Poets No. 16, Fantasy Press, 1953 (approx 300 copies, wraps) £250
Fighting Terms, Fantasy Press, 1954 (first issue with final 't' in 'thought'missed on first line of p.38) £300
ditto, Fantasy Press, 1954 (second issue, error corrected) £250
ditto, Hawks Well Press (U.S.), 1958 (1,500 copies, wraps with d/w) . . . . £125/£35
ditto, Faber, 1966 . . . . £25/£5
Poetry from Cambridge, 1952-1954, Fantasy Press, 1955 (wraps) £125
The Sense of Movement, Faber, 1957 . . £75/£10
ditto, Univ. of Chicago Press (U.S.), 1959 . £45/£10
My Sad Captains, Faber, 1961 . . . . £40/£10
ditto, Univ. of Chicago Press (U.S.), 1961 . £25/£10
Selected Poems, Faber 1962 (with Ted Hughes, wraps) £35
A Geography, Stone Wall Press (U.S.), 1966 (220 copies, wraps) £200
Positives, Faber 1966 . . . . £30/£10
ditto, Univ. of Chicago Press (U.S.), 1967 . £30/£10
Touch, Faber, [1967] . . . . . . £25/£5
ditto, Univ. of Chicago Press (U.S.), 1968 . £25/£5
The Garden of the Gods, Pym-Randall Press (U.S.), [1968] (200 of 226, signed copies, wraps) . . £65
ditto, Pym-Randall Press (U.S.), [1968] (26 lettered copies of 226, wraps) £150
The Explorers, Gilbertson (U.S.), 1969 (6 copies) £300

ditto, Gilbertson (U.S.), 1969 (deluxe issue of 10 copies) £200
ditto, Gilbertson (U.S.), 1969 (special issue of 20 copies) £150
ditto, Gilbertson (U.S.), 1969 (ordinary issue of 64 copies) £75
The Fair in the Woods, Sycamore Press, 1969 (broadsheet, 500 copies) £10
Poems 1950-1966: A Selection, Faber 1969 (wraps) £10
Sunlight, Albondocani Press (U.S.), 1969 (150 signed, numbered copies) £75
Moly, Faber, 1971 . . . . £25/£10
ditto, Farrar Straus (U.S.), 1973 . . . . £20/£5
Last Days at Teddington, John Roberts Press, 1971 (broadsheet, 1,000 copies) £10
Poem After Chaucer, Albondocani Press (U.S.), 1971 (300 copies, wraps) £50
The Spell, Steane, 1973 (broadsheet, 500 copies) £10
Songbook, Albondocani Press (U.S.), 1973 (200 signed copies, wraps) £65
To the Air, Godine, 1974 (no d/w) . . . £25
Mandrakes, The Rainbow Press, [1974] (150 signed copies, slipcase) . . . . £250/£200
Jack Straw's Castle, Hallman, 1975 (300 copies, wraps). £15
ditto, Hallman, 1976 (100 signed hardback copies) . . . . £100/£45
ditto, as *Jack Straw's Castle and Other Poems*, Faber 1976 (750 hardback copies) . . . . £40/£10
ditto, Faber 1976 (100 numbered, signed hardback copies) . . . . £100/£45
ditto, Faber 1976 (4,000 wraps copies) . . . £5
ditto, Farrar Straus (U.S.), 1976 . . . £15/£5
The Missed Beat, Janus Press (U.S.), 1976 (50 copies, slipcase) . . . . £350/£300
ditto, Gruffyground Press, 1976 (approx 70 copies, wraps) £75
A Crab, The Pirates, 1978 . . . . £20
Games of Chance, Abattoir, 1979 (220 copies) £25
Selected Poems 1950-1975, Faber, 1979 . £10/£5
ditto, Farrar Straus (U.S.), 1979 . . . . £10/£5
Talbot Road, Helikon Press, 1981 (150 signed, numbered copies of 400, wraps) £35
ditto, Helikon Press, 1981 (250 numbered copies of 400, wraps) £10
The Passages of Joy, Faber, 1982 . . . £15/£5
ditto, Farrar Straus Giroux (U.S.), 1982 . . £15/£5
Sidewalks, Albondocani Press (U.S.), 1985 (200 signed copies, wraps) £45
Lament, Doe Press (U.S.), 1985 (150 signed copies, wraps) £75
ditto, Doe Press (U.S.), 1985 (26 signed copies) £150
The Hurtless Trees, privately printed, 1986 (159 signed copies, wraps and d/w) £125
Night Sweats, Barth (U.S.), 1987 (200 signed, numbered copies, wraps) £50
ditto, Barth (U.S.), 1987 (wraps). £20

ditto, as *The Man with Night Sweats*, Faber, 1992 .
. . . . £15/£5
ditto, Farrar Straus Giroux (U.S.), 1992 . . £15/£5
Undesirables, Pig Press, 1988 (50 signed copies of
550) £35
ditto, Pig Press, 1988 (500 unsigned copies of 550) £15
At the Barriers, NADJA, 1989 (26 signed copies of
100) £150
ditto, NADJA (U.S.), 1989 (74 signed copies of 100,
wraps). £65
Death's Door, Red Hydra Press, 1989 (20 signed,
quarter morocco copies). £200
ditto, Red Hydra Press, 1989 (60 signed copies) £100
My Mother's Pride, DIA Center for the Arts (U.S.),
1990 (broadside). £10
Unsought Intimacies, Koch (U.S.), 1991 (130 copies,
slipcase) . . . . £150/£125
The Life of the Otter, Tucson Desert Museum (U.S.),
1991 (50 signed copies, broadside). . . £35
Old Stories, Sea Cliff Press, 1992 (100 copies, wraps).
. . . . £100
Collected Poems, Faber, 1993 . . . . £15/£5
ditto, Faber, 1993 (150 signed copies, slipcase). . .
. . . . £125/£100
ditto, Farrar, Straus & Giroux (U.S.), 1994 . £15/£5
Shelf Life, Univ. of Michigan Press (U.S.), 1993 (no
d/w) £10
ditto, Faber, 1994 . . . . £15/£5
Arthur In the Twilight Slot, Enitharmon Press, 1995
(75 copies, slipcase) . . . . . £250/£225
Dancing David, Nadja (U.S.), 1995 (26 signed, lettered
copies) £200
June, Wood Works (U.S.), 1998 (250 signed copies,
broadside) £20
A Green Place, Occasional Works (U.S.), 1999 (with
Eileen Hogan, 26 signed lettered copies, slipcase) .
. . . . £250
ditto, Occasional Works (U.S.), 1999 (80 signed,
numbered copies) £100
ditto, Occasional Works (U.S.), 1999 (220 numbered
copies) £25

H. RIDER HAGGARD
(b.1856 d.1925)

A successful British writer of heroic adventure
novels, Haggard's strengths are his story-telling
abilities and the authentic background to his books.

Novels
Dawn, Hurst & Blackett, 1884 (3 vols) . . £4,000
ditto, Appleton (U.S.), 1887 (2 vols, wraps). £2,000
ditto, Harpers (U.S.), 1887 . . . . . . £150
The Witch's Head, Hurst & Blackett, 1885 [1884]
(3 vols) £6,000
ditto, Appleton (U.S.), 1885 . . . . . £150

King Solomon's Mines, Cassell, 1885 (first issue with
'Bamamgwato' for 'Bamangwato' on line 14, p.10:
'twins to live' for 'twins live' line 27, p.122 and
'wrod' for 'word' line 29, p.307. Ads dated
'5G.8.85'). £5,000
ditto, Cassell, 1885 (second issue, uncorrected, with
ads dated '5G.10.85') £2,500
ditto, Cassell (U.S.), 1885 (third issue with no ads). .
. . . . £2,000
She, Harper (U.S.), 1886 (wraps) £700
ditto, Longmans, 1887 (first issue with 'Godness me'
in line 38, p.269). £500
Jess, Smith, Elder, & Co., 1887 . . . . £300
ditto, George Munro (U.S.), 1887 (wraps) . . £200
ditto, Harper (U.S.), 1887. . . . . . . £150
Allan Quartermain, Longmans, 1887 (first issue with
no footnote on frontispiece). £450
ditto, Longmans, 1887 (112 large paper copies) £1,500
Maiwa's Revenge, Longmans, 1888 . . . . £125
ditto, Harper (U.S.), 1888. . . . . . . £100
Mr Meeson's Will, Spencer Blackett, 1888 (first issue
with 'Johnson' for 'Johnston' in line 1, p.284,
catalogue dated October 1888). £300
ditto, Harper (U.S.), 1888. . . . . . . £125
Colonel Quaritch V.C., Longmans, 1888 (3 vols) £600
ditto, Lovell (U.S.), 1888 . . . . £45
Cleopatra, Longmans, 1889 (catalogue dated January
1889 . . . . £200
ditto, Longmans, 1889 (50 large paper copies) £2,000
ditto, Harper (U.S.), 1889 (wraps) £175
Allan's Wife, Spencer Blackett, 1889 . . . £200
ditto, Longmans, 1889 (100 large paper copies) £2,000
Beatrice, Longman's, 1890 . . . . . . £65
ditto, George Munro (U.S.), 1890 . . . . £45
The World's Desire, Longmans, 1890 (with Andrew
Lang) £30
ditto, Harper (U.S.), 1890. . . . . . . £30
Eric Brighteyes, Longmans, 1891 . . . . £35
ditto, Harper (U.S.), 1891. . . . . . . £30
Nada the Lily, Longmans, 1892 . . . . . £35
ditto, Longmans(U.S.), 1892 . . . . . . £30
Montezuma's Daughter, Longmans (U.S.), 1893 £35
ditto, Longmans, 1893 . . . . £30
The People of the Mist, Longmans, 1894 . . £65
ditto, Longmans (U.S.), 1894. . . . . . £35
Joan Haste, Longmans, 1895 . . . . . £65
ditto, Longmans (U.S.), 1895. . . . . . £35
Heart of the World, Longmans (U.S.), 1895 . £65
ditto, Longmans, 1896 . . . . £65
The Wizard, Arrowsmith, 1896 (wraps). . . £55
ditto, Longmans (U.S.), 1896 . . . . . £45
Doctor Therne, Longmans, 1898 . . . . £45
ditto, Longmans (U.S.), 1898 . . . . . £75
Allan the Hunter, Lothrop (U.S.), 1898. . . £100
Swallow, Longmans, 1899 . . . . . . £45
ditto, Longmans (U.S.), 1899 . . . . . £75
Black Heart and White Heart, Longmans, 1900 £100
ditto, as *Elissa*, Longmans (U.S.), 1900. . . £75
Lysbeth, Longmans, 1901 . . . . . . £45

ditto, Longmans (U.S.), 1901 . . . . . £45
Pearl-Maiden, Longmans, 1903 . . . . . £35
ditto, Longmans (U.S.), 1903 . . . . . £35
Stella Fregelius, Longmans (U.S.), 1903 . . £35
ditto, Longmans, 1904 . . . . £35
The Brethren, Cassell, 1904 . . . . . . £35
ditto, McClure, Phillips (U.S.), 1904 . . . £35
Ayesha, Ward Lock, 1905 . . . . . . £55
ditto, Doubleday. (U.S.), 1905 . . . . . £35
The Way of the Spirit, Hutchinson, 1906 . . £35
Benita, Cassell, 1906 . . . . £35
ditto, as *The Spirit of Bambatse*, Longmans (U.S.), 1906 . . . . £35
Fair Margaret, Hutchinson, 1907 . . . . £35
ditto, as *Margaret*, Longmans (U.S.), 1907 . . £35
The Ghost Kings, Cassell, 1908 . . . . . £35
ditto, as *The Lady of the Heavens*, Lovell (U.S.), 1908 . . . . £35
The Yellow God, Cupples & Leon (U.S.), 1908 £35
ditto, Cassell, 1909 . . . . £35
The Lady of Blossholme, Hodder & Stoughton, 1909 . . . . £45
Morning Star, Cassell, 1910 . . . . . . £35
ditto, Longmans (U.S.), 1910. . . . . . £25
Queen Sheba's Ring, Eveleigh Nash, 1910 . . £300
ditto, Doubleday Page & Co (U.S.), 1910 . . £25
Red Eve, Hodder & Stoughton, 1911 . . . £200
ditto, Doubleday (U.S.), 1911 . . . . . £25
The Mahatma and The Hare, Longmans, 1911 £55
ditto, Henry Holt & Co (U.S.), 1911 . . . £25
Marie, Cassell, 1912 . . . . £25
ditto, Longmans (U.S.), 1912. . . . . . £25
Child of Storm, Cassell, 1913 . . . . . £25
ditto, Longmans (U.S.), 1913. . . . . . £25
The Wanderer's Necklace, Cassell, 1914 . . £45
ditto, Longmans (U.S.), 1914. . . . . . £25
The Holy Flower, Ward Lock, 1915. . . . £25
ditto, as Allan and *The Holy Flower*, Longmans (U.S.), 1915 . . . . £25
The Ivory Child, Cassell, 1916 . . . . . £35
ditto, Longmans (U.S.), 1916. . . . . . £25
Finished, Ward Lock, 1917 . . . . . . £35
ditto, Longmans (U.S.), 1917. . . . . . £25
Love Eternal, Cassell, 1918 . . . . . . £25
ditto, Longmans (U.S.), 1918. . . . . . £25
Moon of Israel, Murray, 1918 . . . . . £45
ditto, Longmans (U.S.), 1918. . . . . . £25
When the World Shook, Cassell, 1919 . . . £35
ditto, Longmans (U.S.), 1919. . . . . . £25
The Ancient Allan, Cassell, 1920 . . . £250/£35
ditto, Longmans (U.S.), 1920. . . . . £250/£35
Smith and the Pharaohs, Arrowsmith, 1920 £300/£75
ditto, Longmans (U.S.), 1920. . . . . £250/£35
She and Allan, Longmans (U.S.), 1921 . . £125/£45
ditto, Hutchinson, 1921 . . . . . . £275/£65
The Virgin of the Sun, Cassell, 1922 . . £100/£35
ditto, Doubleday (U.S.), 1922 . . . . £100/£25
Wisdom's Daughter, Hutchinson, 1923 . . £200/£35
ditto, Doubleday (U.S.), 1923 . . . . £200/£35

Heu-Heu, Hutchinson, 1924 . . . . . £150/£45
ditto, Doubleday (U.S.), 1924 . . . . £150/£35
Queen of the Dawn, Doubleday Page (U.S.) 1925 . . . . £150/£25
ditto, Hutchinson, 1925 . . . . . . £150/£35
The Treasure of the Lake, Hutchinson, 1926 £150/£45
ditto, Doubleday (U.S.), 1926 . . . . £125/£25
Allan and the Ice Gods, Doubleday Page (U.S.) 1927 . . . . £255/£25
ditto, Hutchinson, 1927 . . . . . . £350/£45
Mary of Marion Isle, Hutchinson, 1929. . £150/£45
ditto, as *Marion Isle*, Doubleday (U.S.), 1929 . . . . £100/£25
Belshazzar, Stanley Paul, 1930 . . . . £400/£55
ditto, Doubleday (U.S.), 1930 . . . . . £250/£25

Non Fiction
Cetywayo and His White Neighbours, Trubner, 1882 . . . . £1,250
An Heroic Effort, 1893 (wraps) £35
Church and State, 1895 (wraps) £30
East Norfolk Representation, 1895 (wraps) . £30
Lord Kimberly in Norfolk, 1895 (wraps) . . £30
Speeches of the Earl of Iddesleigh, NSPCC, 1895 (wraps) £30
A Visit to Victoria Hospital, 1897 (wraps) . . £30
A Farmer's Year, Longmans, 1899 . . . . £100
ditto, Longmans, 1899 (100 numbered large paper copies) £300
The Last Boer War, Kegan Paul, 1899 . . . £125
ditto, as *A History of The Transvaal*, Kegan Paul (U.S.), 1899 . . . . £125
A Winter Pilgrimage, Longmans, 1901 . . . £200
Rural England, Longmans, 1902 (2 vols) . . £175
Rural Denmark, Longmans, 1902 . . . . £200
Rural England, Royal Institution of Great Britain, 1903 (wraps) £30
A Gardener's Year, Longmans, 1905 . . . £100
The Poor and the Land, Longmans, 1905 . . £125
The Real Wealth of England, Dr Barnados, 1908 (wraps) £25
The Royal Commission on Coast Erosion, HMSO, 1907-1911 (3 vols, wraps) £45
Regeneration, Longmans, 1910 . . . . . £30
Letters to the Right Honorable Lewis Harcourt, HMSO, 1913-1914 (2 vols, wraps). . . . £50
A Call to Arms, 1914 (wraps) £25
The After-War Settlement and Employment of Ex-Servicemen, Saint Catherine Press, 1916 (wraps) £30
The Salvation Army, 1920 (wraps) £30
The Days of My Life, Longmans, 1926 (2 vols) . . . . £350/£150
ditto, Longmans (U.S.), 1926. . . . . £250/£125
A Note on Religion, Longmans, 1927 (wraps) . £25
The Private Diaries of Sir H. Rider Haggard 1914-1925, Cassell, 1980 . . . . £10/£5
ditto, Stein & Day (U.S.), 1980 . . . . . £10/£5

KATHLEEN HALE
(b.1898 d.2000)

An artist whose reputation rests with books about a ginger tom cat, Orlando.

Books written and Illustrated by Hale
Orlando the Marmalade Cat: A Camping Holiday, Country Life, [1938]. . . . . . £200/£75
ditto, Scribners (U.S.), [1938] . . . . £175/£65
Orlando the Marmalade Cat: A Trip Abroad, Country Life, 1939. . . . . £150/£75
Orlando's Evening Out, Puffin, [1941] . . . £50
ditto, Puffin, [1941] (wraps) £20
Orlando's Home Life, Puffin, [1942] . . . £50
ditto, Puffin, [1942] (wraps) £20
ditto, Coward McCann (U.S.), [1953] . . . £50
Orlando the Marmalade Cat Buys A Farm, Country Life, 1942. . . . . £150
Orlando the Marmalade Cat: His Silver Wedding, Country Life, 1944 . . . . £150
Orlando the Marmalade Cat Becomes A Doctor, Country Life, 1944 . . . . £150
Orlando's Invisible Pyjamas, Transatlantic Arts, [1947] (wraps) £25
Henrietta the Faithful Hen, Transatlantic Arts, [1947] £75
ditto, Coward McCann (U.S.), [1953] . . £75
Orlando the Marmalade Cat Keeps A Dog, Country Life, [1949] . . . . £300/£125
Orlando The Judge, Murray, [1950] (wraps) . £25
Orlando the Marmalade Cat: A Seaside Holiday, Country Life, 1952 . . . . . £300/£125
Orlando's Zoo, Murray, [1950] (wraps). . £25
Orlando's Country Life: A Peep Show Book, Chatto & Windus, 1950. . . . . £150
Puss in Boots: A Peep Show Book, Chatto & Windus, 1951 . . . . £150
ditto, Houghton Mifflin (U.S.), [c.1951} . . £150
Matilda the Jersey Calf, Murray, 1952 . . . £30
ditto, as *Manda*, Coward McCann (U.S.), [1953] £30
Orlando the Marmalade Cat: The Frisky Housewife, Country Life, 1956 . . . . £75
Orlando's Magic Carpet, Murray, [1958] . £75/£35
Orlando the Marmalade Cat Buys A Cottage, Country Life, 1963. . . . . £50
Orlando and the Three Graces, Murray, 1965 £50/£25
Orlando the Marmalade Cat Goes to the Moon, Murray, 1968. . . . . £40/£20
Orlando the Marmalade Cat and the Water Cats, Cape, 1972 . . . . £40
Henrietta's Magic Egg, Allen & Unwin, 1973 . £25

Other Books Illustrated by Hale
I Don't Mix Much With Fairies, by Molly Harrower, Eyre & Spottiswoode, 1928 . . . . £75/£35
Plain Jane, by Molly Harrower, Eyre & Spottiswoode, 1929 . . . . £75/£35
ditto, Coward McCann (U.S.), 1929 . . . £75/£35

Basil Seal Rides Again, by Evelyn Waugh, Chapman & Hall, 1963 (750 copies signed by author) . . . . £250/£100

RADCLYFFE HALL
(b.1880 d.1943)

Hall's notoriety stems from the publication in 1928, and subsequent suppression in Britain for obscenity, of *The Well of Loneliness*. The book, a sympathetic study of lesbian love, was not republished in Britain until 1949.

Novels
The Forge, Arrowsmith, 1924 . . . . £175/£50
The Unlit Lamp, Cassell, 1924 . . . . £175/£50
ditto, Cape & Smith (U.S.), [1929] . . . £100/£25
A Saturday Life, Arrowsmith, 1925 . . . £100/£30
ditto, Cape & Smith (U.S.), [1930] . . . £75/£20
Adam's Breed, Cassell, 1926. . . . . £100/£30
ditto, Cape & Smith (U.S.), [1929] . . . £45/£10
The Well of Loneliness, Cape, 1928 . . . £125/£25
ditto, Pegasus Press (Paris), 1928 . . . £125/£40
ditto, Covici-Friede (U.S.), 1928 (glassine d/w, slipcase) . . . . £125/£100
ditto, Covici-Friede (U.S.), 1929 (225 signed copies, 2 vols, slipcase) £250
The Master of the House, Cape, 1932 . . £50/£15
ditto, Cape, 1932 (172 signed, numbered copies, slipcase) . . . . £200/£145
ditto, Cape & Ballou (U.S.), 1932 . . . £45/£10
The Sixth Beatitude, Heinemann, 1936 . . £45/£10
ditto, Heinemann, 1936 (125 signed, numbered copies, slipcase) . . . . £175/£135
ditto, Harcourt Brace (U.S.), [c.1936] . . £45/£10

Short Stories
Mrs Ogilvy Finds Herself, Heinemann, 1934 £75/£20
ditto, Harcourt Brace (U.S.), 1934 . . . £45/£10

Verse
Twixt Earth and Stars, Bumpus, 1906 . . . £150
A Sheaf of Verses, Bumpus, 1908 . . . . £125
Poems of Past and Present, Chapman & Hall, 1910 . . . . £75
Songs of Three Counties, Chapman & Hall, 1913 £60
The Forgotten Island, Chapman & Hall, 1915 £60

Others
Your John: Letters of Radclyffe Hall, New York Univ. (U.S.), 1997 . . . . £10/£5

PATRICK HAMILTON
(b.1904 d.1962)

Born in Sussex. Hamilton was a typically English writer, relishing the art of understatement.

Novels

Monday Morning, Constable, 1925 .	.	£250/£45
ditto, Houghton Mifflin (U.S.), 1925	.	£250/£40
Craven House, Constable, 1926 .	.	£200/£35
ditto, Houghton Mifflin (U.S.), 1927	.	£200/£25
ditto, Constable, 1943 (revised edition) .	.	£75/£20
Twopence Coloured, Constable, 1928	.	£200/£35
ditto, Houghton Mifflin (U.S.), 1928	.	£200/£30
The Midnight Bell: A Love Story, Constable, 1929		
. . . .		£200/£25
ditto, Little, Brown (U.S.), 1930 .	.	£200/£25
The Siege of Pleasure, Constable, 1932	.	£100/£25
ditto, Little, Brown (U.S.), 1932 .	.	£100/£20
The Plains of Cement, Constable, 1934 .	.	£100/£25
ditto, Little, Brown (U.S.), 1935 .	.	£100/£20
Twenty Thousand Streets Under The Sky: A London Trilogy, Constable, 1935 .	.	£75/£20
Impromptu in Moribundia, Constable, 1939		£200/£65
Hangover Square, or The Man with Two Minds: A Story of Darkest Earls Court, Constable, 1941 .		
. . . .		£1,000/£75
ditto, Random House (U.S.), 1942	.	£100/£15
The Slaves of Solitude, Constable, 1947	.	£50/£15
ditto, as *Riverside*, Random House (U.S.), 1947	.	
. . . .	.	£45/£15
The West Pier, Constable, 1951 .	.	£45/£15
ditto, Doubleday (U.S.), 1952	.	£45/£15
Mr Stimpson and Mr Gorse, Constable, 1953	.	
. . . .	.	£150/£15
Unknown Assailant, Constable, 1955	.	£100/£15

Plays

Rope: A Play, with a Preface on Thrillers, Constable, 1929		£150/£25
Gaslight: A Victorian Thriller, Constable, 1939 (wraps)	.	£25
Money With Menaces and To The Public Danger: Two Radio Plays, Constable, 1939 .	.	£45/£10
This Is Impossible, French, 1942 (wraps)	.	£15
The Duke in Darkness, Constable, 1943	.	£30/£10
The Man Upstairs, Constable, 1954 .	.	£25/£10

DASHIELL HAMMETT
(b.1894 d.1961)

American creator of tough detective fiction, his best known centring around the private eye Sam Spade.

Novels

Red Harvest, Knopf (U.S.), 1929	.	£10,000/£750
ditto, Knopf/Cassell, 1929	. . . .	£2,500/£350

The Dain Curse, Knopf (U.S.), 1929		£10,000/£500
ditto, Knopf/Cassell, 1929 .	. . .	£2,500/£250
The Maltese Falcon, Knopf (U.S.), 1930		£15,000/£500
ditto, Knopf/Cassell 1930. . .	.	£3,500/£250
The Glass Key, Knopf/Cassell, 1931		£2,500/£250
ditto, Knopf (U.S.), 1931 .	. . .	£3,000/£250
The Thin Man, Knopf (U.S.), 1934 .	.	£1,500/£175
ditto, Barker 1934	.	£1,000/£100
The Dashiell Hammett Omnibus, Knopf (U.S.), 1935 .		
. . . .		£250/£30
The Complete Dashiell Hammet, Knopf (U.S.), 1942 .		
. . . .		£150/£25
$106,000 Blood Money, Spivak (U.S.), 1943 (wraps) .		
. . . .		£150
ditto, as *Blood Money*, World (U.S.), 1943 .		£30/£10
ditto, as *The Big Knock-over*, Spivak (U.S.), 1948 (wraps)		£35
The Novels of Dashiell Hammet, Knopf (U.S.), 1965 .		
. . . .		£40/£10

Short Stories

The Adventures of Sam Spade, Spivak (U.S.), 1944 (wraps)		£100
ditto, as *They Can Only Hang You Once*, Spivak (U.S.), 1949 (wraps)		£75
The Continental Op, Spivak (U.S.), 1945 (wraps)		£75
The Return of the Continental Op, Spivak (U.S.), 1945 (wraps)		£50
Hammett Homicides, Spivak (U.S.), 1946 (wraps)		£50
Dead Yellow Women, Spivak (U.S.), 1947 (wraps)		£50
Nightmare Town, Spivak (U.S.), 1948 (wraps)		£50
The Creeping Siamese, Spivak (U.S.), 1950 (wraps)		
. . . .		£35
The Dashiell Hammett Omnibus, Cassell, 1950 .		
. . . .		£75/£15
Women in the Dark, Spivak (U.S.), 1951 (wraps)		£35
ditto, Headline, 1988		£15/£5
A Man Named Thin and Other Stories, Ferman (U.S.), 1952		£35
The Big Knockover: Selected Stories and Short Novels, Random House (U.S.), 1966	.	£10/£5
ditto, as *The Hammett Story Omnibus*, Cassell, 1966 .		
. . . .		£15/£5

THOMAS HARDY
(b.1840 d.1928)

Acknowledged as one of the great novelists, Hardy was also a prolific poet. Much of his writing is set in his native Dorset, fictionalised as Wessex.

Novels

Desperate Remedies, Tinsley Bros., 1871, (3 vols, anonymous)		£7,500
ditto, Holt (U.S.), 1874, (1 vol.)		£300
ditto, Ward & Downey, 1889, (1 vol.) . .	.	£100

Under the Greenwood Tree, Tinsley Bros., 1872, (2 vols, 'By the author of Desperate Remedies') £5,000
ditto, Tinsley Bros., 1873, (1 vol.) . . . £1,000
ditto, Holt (U.S.), 1874, (1 vol.) £300
A Pair of Blue Eyes, Tinsley Bros., 1873 (first issue, green cloth, 'c' missing in 'clouds' last line p.5, vol.2, 3 vols). £4,000
ditto, Tinsley Bros., 1873 (second issue, blue cloth. 3 vols) £1,000
ditto, Holt (U.S.), 1873, (1 vol.) £200
ditto, Henry S. King, 1877 (1 vol.) £200
Far from the Madding Crowd, Holt (U.S.), 1874, (1 vol.) £650
ditto, Smith, Elder, 1874 (2 vols). . . . £2,000
ditto, Smith, Elder, 1875 (2 vols) £1,000
ditto, Smith, Elder, 1877 (1 vol.) £200
The Hand of Ethelberta, Smith, Elder, 1876, (2 vols, 11 illustrations by George du Marier) . . £2,000
ditto, Holt (U.S.), 1876, (1 vol.) £150
ditto, Smith, Elder, 1877, (1 vol., 6 illustrations by George du Maurier) £200
The Return of the Native, Smith, Elder, 1878, (3 vols) £2,000
ditto, Holt (U.S.), 1878, (1 vol.) £150
ditto, Kegan Paul, 1880 [1879], (1 vol.) . . £200
The Trumpet-Major, Smith, Elder, 1880 (3 vols) £3,000
ditto, Holt (U.S.), 1880, (1 vol.) £250
ditto, Samson Low, 1881 (1 vol.) £200
Fellow-Townsmen, Harper (U.S.), 1880 (cloth) £750
ditto, Harper (U.S.), 1880 (wraps) . . . £450
A Laodicean, Holt (U.S.), 1881, (1 vol.) . . £450
ditto, Samson Low, 1881 (first issue without word 'or' on half-title of vol.1, 3 vols) . . . £1,000
ditto, Samson Low, 1881 (second issue with word 'or' on half-title of vol.1, 3 vols) £500
ditto, Samson Low, 1882 (1 vol) £150
Two on a Tower, Samson Low, 1882 (3 vols) £2,000
ditto, Holt (U.S.), 1882, (1 vol.) £250
ditto, Samson Low, 1883, (3 vols) . . . £1,000
ditto, Samson Low, 1883, (1 vol.) £150
The Romantic Adventures of a Milkmaid, Munro's (U.S.), 1883 (wraps). £750
The Mayor of Casterbridge, Smith Elder, 1886, (2 vols) £3,000
ditto, Holt (U.S.), 1886, (1 vol., wraps) . . £400
ditto, Samson Low, 1887, (1 vol.) £200
The Woodlanders, Macmillan, 1887, (first binding in smooth green cloth with 2 rule border on back, first issue with ad leaf at back of vol.1, 3 vols) . £1,750
ditto, Macmillan, 1887, (second binding in pebbled green cloth with 1 rule border on back, second issue without ad leaf at back of vol.1, 3 vols) . £1,000
ditto, Harper (U.S.), 1887, (1 vol.) £200
ditto, Macmillan, 1887, (1 vol.) . . . £75
Tess of the D'Urbervilles, Osgood McIlvaine, 1891, (3 vols) £3,500
ditto, Harper (U.S.), 1892, (1 vol.) £500
ditto, Osgood McIlvaine, 1892, (3 vols) . £1,000

ditto, Osgood McIlvaine, 1892, ('fifth' [third] edition, 1 vol.) £150
Jude the Obscure, Osgood McIlvaine, 1896 [1895], (1 vol.) £300
ditto, Harper (U.S.), 1896, (1 vol.) £10
The Well-Beloved, Osgood McIlvaine, 1897, (1 vol.) £125
ditto, Harper (U.S.), 1897, (1 vol.) £125
Our Exploits at West Poley, O.U.P., 1952 £150/£60

Short Stories
Wessex Tales, Macmillan, 1888, (2 vols) . £1,500
ditto, Macmillan, 1889, (1 vol.) £75
ditto, Osgood McIlvaine, 1896, (1 vol.) . . . £45
A Group of Noble Dames, Osgood McIlvaine, 1891 . . . . £150
ditto, Harper (U.S.), 1891. . . . . . . £100
Life's Little Ironies, Osgood McIlvaine, 1894 . £125
ditto, Macmillan (U.S.), 1894 . . . . . £75
A Changed Man and Other Tales, Macmillan, 1913 . . . . £50
ditto, Harper (U.S.), 1913. . . . . . . £75
Old Mrs Chundle, Crosby Gaige (U.S.), 1929 (755 numbered copies) £75

Collection Editions
Wessex Novels Edition, Osgood McIlvaine, 1895-97, (17 vols) . . . . £2,000 the set, £50-£75 each
The Writings, Autograph Edition, Harper & Bros, [1911] (153 signed copies, 20 vols) £2,500 the set
Wessex Edition, Macmillan, 1912-31, (24 vols; maroon cloth) . . . . £1,500 the set, £30 each
Melstock Edition, Macmillan, 1919-20, (37 vols, limited to 500 sets, signed by the author) £4,000 set

Magazine Serialisations
A Pair of Blue Eyes, Tinsley's Magazine, Sept 1872-July 1873 . . . . £250 (for set)
Far From the Madding Crowd, Cornhill Magazine, Jan-Sept 1874 . . . . £250 (for set)
The Hand of Ethelberta, Cornhill Magazine, July 1875-May, 1876 . . . . £250 (for set)
The Return of the Native, Belgravia, Jan-December 1878 . . . . £250 (for set)
The Trumpet Major, Good Words, Jan-December 1880 . . . . £250 (for set)
A Laodicean, Harper's, December 1880-December 1881 . . . . £250 (for set)
Two on a Tower, Atlantic Monthly, May-December 1882 . . . . £250 (for set)
The Mayor of Casterbridge, Graphic, June 1885-May 1886 . . . . £300 (for set)
The Woodlanders, Macmillan's Magazine, May 1886-April 1887 . . . . £250 (for set)
Tess of the D'Urbervilles, Graphic, July-December 1891 . . . . £300 (for set)
Jude the Obscure, Harper's, December 1894-November 1895 (first instalment as 'The Simpleton', the 'Hearts Insurgent') . . . . £200 (for set)

The **Well-Beloved**, as **The Pursuit of the Well-Beloved**, Illustrated London News, October-December 1892 . . . . . . £200 (for set)

Verse
Wessex Poems and Other Verses, Harper (U.S. & U.K.), 1898 . . . . £500
ditto, Harper (U.S. & U.K.), 1898 (presentation binding) £1,250
Poems Of The Past And The Present, Harper (U.S. & U.K.), 1902 . . . . £500
ditto, Harper (U.S. & U.K.), 1902 (presentation binding) £1,250
The Dynasts, Macmillan, 1904, 1906 [1905], 1908 .
. . . . £500
ditto, Macmillan, 1910 (1 vol.) £100
ditto, Macmillan, 1927 (525 signed large paper copies, 3 vols, tissue d/w, slipcase) . . . . £500/£400
Time's Laughingstocks and Other Verses, Macmillan, 1909 . . . . £150
Song of the Soldiers, privately printed by Clement Shorter, 1914 (single sheet, 12 copies) . . . £750
ditto, privately printed at Hove by E. Williams, 1914 (single sheet) £100
The Oxen, privately printed at Hove by E. Williams, 1915 (wraps) £150
Selected Poems, Macmillan, 1916 . . . . £150
ditto, Warner, 1921 . . . . £100
Moments of Vision and Miscellaneous Verses, Macmillan, 1917 . . . . £100
Collected Poems, Macmillan, 1919 . . . £125
Late Lyrics and Earlier with Many Other Verses, Macmillan, 1922 . . . . £125/£50
The Famous Tragedy of the Queen of Cornwall, Macmillan, 1923 . . . . £200/£75
ditto, Macmillan, 1923 (1,000 numberd copies, no d/w)
. . . . £75
Human Shows. Far Phantasies. Songs, and Trifles, Macmillan, 1925 . . . . . . £150/£65
ditto, Macmillan (U.S.), 1925 (100 numbered copies, no d/w) £150
ditto, Macmillan (U.S.), 1925 . . . . £100/£45
Yuletide in a Younger World, Faber, 1927 (wraps) .
. . . . £250
ditto, Rudge (U.S.), 1927 (27 copyright copies, wraps)
. . . . £400
Winter Words In Various Moods and Metres, Macmillan, 1928 . . . . £75/£35
ditto, Macmillan (U.S.), 1928 (500 copies, slipcase) .
. . . . £150/£125

THOMAS HARRIS
(b.1940)

Famous since the release of the film of *The Silence of the Lambs*, aficionados also recommend that *Red Dragon* should not be overlooked.

Novels
Black Sunday, Putnam (U.S.), 1975 . . . £75/£15
ditto, Hodder & Stoughton, 1975. . . . £35/£10
Red Dragon, Putnam (U.S.), 1981 . . . £50/£10
ditto, Bodley Head, 1982 . . . . . . £30/£10
The Silence of the Lambs, St Martin's Press (U.S.), 1988 . . . . £75/£10
ditto, Heinemann, 1988 . . . . . . £50/£10
Hannibal, Delacorte Press (U.S.), 1999 . . £15/£5
ditto, Heinemann, 1988 . . . . . . £10/£5

L.P. HARTLEY
(b.1895 d.1972)

Novelist and short story writer, Leslie Poles Hartley's work won a number of awards, but he is best known for *The Go-Between*, an evocative portrayal of a small boy's view of Edwardian England, which won the Heinemann Foundation Award.

Novels
Simonetta Perkins, Putnam, 1925 . . . £200/£40
ditto, Putnam (U.S.), 1925 . . . . £175/£20
The Shrimp and the Anemone, Putnam, 1944 . .
. . . . £100/£25
ditto, as **The West Window**, Putnam (U.S.), 1945 . .
. . . . £50/£10
The Sixth Heaven, Putnam, 1946 . . . £30/£5
ditto, Doubleday (U.S.), 1947 . . . . £25/£5
Eustace and Hilda, Putnam, 1947 . . . £30/£5
ditto, British Book Centre (U.S.), 1958 . . £25/£5
The Boat, Putnam, 1950 . . . . . . £50/£10
ditto, Doubleday (U.S.), 1950 . . . . £50/£10
My Fellow Devils, Barrie, 1951 . . . . £30/£5
ditto, British Book Centre (U.S.), 1959 . . £25/£5
The Go-Between, Hamilton, 1953 . . . £45/£10
ditto, Knopf (U.S.), 1954 . . . . . . £30/£5
A Perfect Woman, Hamilton, 1955 . . . £25/£5
ditto, Knopf (U.S.), 1956 . . . . . . £25/£5
The Hireling, Hamilton, 1957 . . . . £25/£5
ditto, Rinehart (U.S.), 1958 . . . . . £25/£5
Facial Justice, Hamilton, 1960 . . . . £45/£10
ditto, Doubleday (U.S.), 1961 . . . . £25/£5
The Brickfield, Hamilton, 1964 . . . . £20/£5
The Betrayal, Hamilton, 1966 . . . . £15/£5
Poor Clare, Hamilton, 1968 . . . . . £15/£5
The Love-Adept, Hamilton, 1969 . . . £15/£5
My Sister's Keeper, Hamilton, 1970 . . . £15/£5
The Harness Room, Hamilton, 1971 . . £15/£5
The Will and the Way, Hamilton, 1973 . . £10/£5

Short Stories

Night Fears and Other Stories, Putnam, 1924 . . .
. . . . £350/£50
The Killing Bottle, Putnam, 1931 . . . £150/£35
The Travelling Grave, Arkham House (U.S.), 1948 .
. . . . £65/£15
ditto, Barrie, 1951 . . . . £65/£15
A White Wand and Other Stories, Hamilton, 1954. .
. . . . £25/£5
Two for the River, Hamilton, 1961 . . . £20/£5
The Collected Stories, Hamilton, 1968 . . £15/£5
ditto, Horizon Press (U.S.), 1969 . . . . £15/£5
Mrs Carteret Receives, Hamilton, 1971 . . £10/£5

Others

The Novelist's Responsibility, Hamilton, 1967 £25/£5

JOHN HARVEY
(b.1938)

A highly respected British author of crime novels, Harvey has also written novels under various pseudonyms such as John B. Harvey, John J. McLaglen, Wilkliam S. Brady, J.D. Sandon, L.J. Coburn, J.B. Dancer, William M. James, John Hart and Jon Barton.)

'Resnick' Novels

Lonely Hearts, Viking, 1989 . . . . . £150/£25
ditto, Holt (U.S.), 1989 . . . . . £75/£15
Rough Treatment, Viking, 1990 . . . . £45/£10
ditto, Holt (U.S.), 1990 . . . . . £30/£10
Cutting Edge, Viking, 1991 . . . . . £45/£10
ditto, Holt (U.S.), 1991 . . . . . £30/£10
Off Minor, Viking, 1992 . . . . . . £85/£25
ditto, Holt (U.S.), 1992 . . . . . £30/£10
Wasted Years, Viking, 1993 . . . . . £45/£5
ditto, Holt (U.S.), 1993 . . . . . £30/£10
Cold Light, Heinemann, 1994 . . . . £15/£5
ditto, Holt (U.S.), 1994 . . . . . £15/£10
Living Proof, Heinemann, 1995 . . . . £15/£5
ditto, Holt (U.S.), 1995 . . . . . £15/£10
Easy Meat, Heinemann, 1996 . . . . £15/£5
ditto, Holt (U.S.), 1996 . . . . . £15/£10
Still Water, Heinemann, 1997 . . . . £10/£5
ditto, Holt (U.S.), 1997 . . . . . £15/£10
Last Rites, Heinemann, 1998 . . . . £10/£5

'Resnick' Short Stories

Now's The Time, Slow Dancer Press, 1999 (wraps) .
. . . . £10
ditto, Slow Dancer Press, 1999 (600 hardback copies) .
. . . . £25/£10
ditto, Slow Dancer Press, 1999 (400 signed hardback copies) . . . . £45/£25

Other Crime Fiction

Amphetamines and Pearls, Sphere, 1976 (wraps) £5
The Geranium Kiss, Sphere, 1976 (wraps) . . £5
Junkyard Angel, Sphere, 1977 (wraps) . . . £5
Neon Madman, Sphere, 1977 (wraps) . . . £5
Frame, Magnum, 1979 (wraps) £10
ditto, Severn House, [1995] . . . . . £25/£10
Blind, Magnum, 1981 (wraps) £10
Endgame, N.E.L., 1982 (pseud. James Mann, wraps) .
. . . . £5
Dancer Draws a Wild Card, Hale, 1985. . £10/£5

NATHANIEL HAWTHORNE
(b.1804 d.1864)

Hawthorne's rarest work is *Fanshawe*, which he attempted to suppress by destroying as many copies as he could obtain.

Verse
Fanshawe, Marsh & Capen (U.S.) 1828 (anonymous).
. . . . £20,000
Twice-Told Tales, American Stationers Co./John B. Russell (U.S.), 1837 (first issue with fifth story listed in Contents as at p.78, not p.77) . . . £3,000
Peter Parley's Univeral History, American Stationers Co./John B. Russell (U.S.), 1837 (anonymous, 2 vols)
. . . . £3,000
The Gentle Boy, Weeks, Jordon/Wiley & Putnam (U.S.) 1939 (wraps) £1,500
The Sister Years, Salem Gazette (U.S.) 1939 (anonymous, wraps) £1,250
Grandfather's Chair, Peabody/Wiley & Putnam (U.S.) 1841 . . . . £500
Famous Old People, Peabody (U.S.) 1841 . . £500
Liberty Tree, Peabody (U.S.) 1841 (first printing with 'Meet in a Con-' on p.25, line 2) £1,000
ditto, Peabody (U.S.) 1841 (second printing with 'Meet in Con-' on p.25, line 2) £400
The Celestial Railroad, Wilder (U.S.) 1843 (wraps) .
. . . . £3,000
ditto, Fish (U.S.) 1843 (wraps) £3,000
Mosses from an Old Manse, Wiley & Putnam (U.S.) 1846 (printer given as 'R. Craighead's Power Press' verso title page, 2 vols, wraps) . . . £2,500
ditto, Wiley & Putnam (U.S.) 1846 (1 vol., cloth) £500
The Scarlet Letter, Ticknor, Reed, & Fields (U.S.) 1850 (first edition with 'reduplicate' instead of 'repudiate' on p.21, line 20 and no preface) £5,000
ditto, Ticknor, Reed, & Fields (U.S.) 1850 (second edition with with preface) £500
ditto, Ticknor, Reed, & Fields (U.S.) 1850 (third edition with with 'Hobart and Robbins' on copyright page instead of 'Metcalf and Co.') . . . £150
True Stories from History and Biography, Ticknor, Reed, & Fields (U.S.) 1851 (first issue with 'Cambridge: Printed by Bolles & Houghton' verso title-page) £500

The House of the Seven Gables, Ticknor, Reed, & Fields (U.S.) 1851 (first printing with the last letters ('t' and 'h') of the last words in lines 1 and 2 on p.149 broken) £2,500
A Wonder Book for Boys and Girls, Ticknor, Reed, & Fields (U.S.) 1852 (first issue with design at top of spine only, not entire spine). £2,000
The Snow Image and Other Tales, Bohn's Cheap Series, 1851. . . . . £200
ditto, as The Snow Image and Other Twice-Told Tales, Ticknor, Reed, & Fields (U.S.) 1852 . £400
The Blithedale Romance, Chapman & Hall 1852 (2 vols) £400
ditto, Ticknor, Reed, & Fields (U.S.) 1852 . . £250
Life of Franklin Pierce, Ticknor, Reed, & Fields (U.S.) 1852 (wraps) £400
ditto, Ticknor, Reed, & Fields (U.S.) 1852 (cloth) £125
Tanglewood Tales, Chapman and Hall, 1853 . £500
ditto, Ticknor, Reed, & Fields (U.S.) 1853 (without 'George C. Rand' imprint on title page) . £1,000
A Rill from the Town Pump, Cash (U.S.) 1857 (wraps) £1,500
Transformation, Smith, Elder, 1860 (3 vols) . £750
ditto, as The Marble Faun, Ticknor & Fields, 1860 (first printing with 'Preface' preceeding 'Contents', 2 vols) £500
Our Old Home, Ticknor, & Fields (U.S.) 1853 (first issue with publisher's list on leaf opposite p.398). .
. . . . £150
Pansie, John Camden Hotten, [1864] . . . £300

SEAMUS HEANEY
(b.1939)

The acclaimed Irish poet who moved away from powerful nature poetry to deal with political and cultural issues. Heaney was awarded the Nobel Prize for Literature in 1995.

Verse
Eleven Poems, Festival (Belfast), 1965 (first issue, laid paper, red-violet sun, wraps) £750
ditto, Festival (Belfast), 1965 (second issue, wove paper, dark-maroon sun, wraps) . . . £450
ditto, Festival (Belfast), 1965 (third issue, grey paper, stiff green wraps) £200
Death of a Naturalist, Faber, 1966 . . . £300/£50
ditto, O.U.P. (U.S.), 1966. . . . . . £175/£35
ditto, Faber, 1969 (wraps). £35
A Lough Neagh Sequence, Phoenix Pamphlet, Poets Press, 1969 (950 copies, wraps) £100
ditto, Phoenix Pamphlet, Poets Press, 1969 (50 signed copies, wraps) £500
Door into the Dark, Faber, 1969. . . . £450/£45
ditto, O.U.P. (U.S.), 1969. . . . . . £200/£35
ditto, Faber, 1972 (wraps). £20

Night Drive: Poems, Gilbertson, 1970, (100 signed copies) £500
ditto, Gilbertson, 1970, (25 of the above containing poem in author's hand) £1,000
ditto, Crediton, 1970 (100 signed copies, wraps) £400
A Boy Driving His Father to Confession, Sceptre Press, 1970 (150 numbered copies, wraps) £125
ditto, Sceptre Press, 1970 (50 signed copies, wraps) .
. . . . £300
Land, Poem of the Month Club, 1979 (signed broadside) £75
Wintering Out, Faber, 1972 (wraps). . . . £300
ditto, Faber, 1973 . . . . £100/£20
ditto, O.U.P. (U.S.), 1973. . . . . . £100/£20
Stations, Ulsterman Publications, 1975 (wraps) £100
North, Faber, 1975 . . . . £300/£75
ditto, Faber, 1975 (wraps). £35
ditto, O.U.P. (U.S.), 1976. . . . . . £175/£35
Bog Poems, Rainbow Press, 1975 (150 signed copies, slipcase) . . . . £1,000/£850
In Their Element, Arts Council of Northern Ireland, 1977 (wraps) £35
Ugolino, Carpenter, 1978 (125 signed copies, hardback, no d/w) £500
Hedgeschool, Seluzicki/Janus Press (U.S.), 1979 (285 numbered copies signed by poet and artist, wraps) .
. . . . £400
After Summer, Gallery Press (Dublin), 1979 (250 signed copies) . . . . £250/£200
Field Work, Faber, 1979 . . . . . . £150/£20
ditto, Faber, 1979 (wraps). £25
ditto, Farrar Straus (U.S.), 1979 . . . . £150/£20
Gravities, Charlotte Press, 1979 (wraps). . . £25
Selected Poems 1965-1975, Faber, 1980 £75/£20
ditto, Faber, 1980 (wraps). £15
ditto, Farrar Straus (U.S.), 1980 . . . £50/£10
Holly, Loughcrew, 1981 (121 signed copies, wraps) .
. . . . £175
Sweeney Praises the Trees, Kelly/Winterton Press (U.S.), 1981 (110 copies, wraps) £300
Poems and a Memoir, The Limited Editions Club (U.S.), 1982 (2,000 signed copies, slipcase) . . .
. . . . £400/£350
An Open Letter, Field Day, (Derry), 1983 (wraps) £40
Sweeney Astray, Field Day, (Derry), 1983 £70/£20
ditto, Field Day, (Derry), 1983 (wraps) . . £25
ditto, Faber, 1984 . . . . £35/£10
ditto, Faber, 1984 (wraps). £15
ditto, Farrar Straus (U.S.), 1984 . . . . £25/£10
ditto, Farrar Straus (U.S.), 1984 (350 signed copies, slipcase) . . . . £200/£175
Station Island, Faber, 1984 . . . . . £35/£10
ditto, Faber, 1984 (wraps). £15
ditto, Farrar Straus (U.S.), 1984 . . . . £35/£10
Verses for a Fordham Commencement, Fordham Univ. (U.S.), 1982 (broadsheet) £200
ditto, NADJA (U.S.), 1984 (200 signed, numbered copies, wraps) £200

ditto, NADJA (U.S.), 1984 (26 signed, lettered copies on hand-made paper, boards) £350
Hailstones, Gallery Press (Dublin), 1984 (250 signed copies) . . . . £350/£200
ditto, Gallery Press (Dublin), 1984 (500 unsigned copies, wraps) £75
From the Republic of Conscience, Amnesty International, 1985 (2,000 copies, wraps) . . £20
Towards a Collaboration, Arts Council of Northern Ireland, 1986 (wraps) £20
The Haw Lantern, Faber, 1987 . . . . £65/£10
ditto, Faber, 1987 (wraps). £10
ditto, Farrar Straus (U.S.), 1987 . . . . £65/£10
ditto, Farrar Straus (U.S.), 1987 (250 signed copies, slipcase) . . . . £125/£100
An Upstairs Outlook, Linen Hall, 1989 (wraps) £20
Railway Children, Poems on the Underground, 1989 (200 copies, broadside) £65
The Fire Gaze, Cheltenham Festival of Literature, 1989 (broadside) £25
New Selected Poems 1966-87, Faber, 1990 £20/£5
ditto, Faber, 1990 (25 signed copies of 125, slipcase) .
. . . . £500/£450
ditto, Faber, 1990 (100 signed copies of 125, slipcase).
. . . . £200/£165
ditto, Faber, 1990 (wraps). £10
ditto, Farrar Straus (U.S.), 1990 . . . . £15/£5
ditto, Farrar Straus (U.S.), 1990 (200 signed copies, slipcase) . . . . £175/£150
The Place of Waiting, Scholars Press (U.S.), 1990 £10
The Tree Clock, Linen Hall, 1990 (750 copies) . .
. . . . £125/£50
ditto, Linen Hall, 1990 (100 signed copies, slipcase) .
. . . . £350/£300
The Earth House, Cheltenham Festival of Literature, 1990 (broadside) £15
Seeing Things, Faber 1991 . . . . £25/£5
ditto, Faber 1991 (250 signed copies, slipcase) . . .
. . . . £175/£150
ditto, Faber, 1991 (wraps). £10
Squarings, Hieroglyph Editions (Dublin), 1991 (100 signed copies in slipcase) £750
The Water Pause, Cheltenham Festival of Literature, 1991 (broadside) £15
Sweeney's Flight, Faber, 1992 . . . £45/£10
ditto, Farrar Straus (U.S.), 1992 . . . . £45/£10
Iron Spike, Ewart (U.S.), 1992 (100 signed copies, broadside) £100
The Air Station, Cheltenham Festival of Literature, 1992 (broadside) £15
The Gravel Walks, Lenoir Rhyne College, 1992 (wraps) £100
The Midnight Verdict, Gallery Press (Dublin), 1993 (925 copies) . . . . £45/£15
ditto, Gallery Press (Dublin), 1993 (75 signed copies) .
. . . . £250
Poet's Chair, Ewart (U.S.), 1993 (100 signed copies, broadside) £100

Keeping Going, Ewart (U.S.), 1993 (50 signed copies, boards, no d/w) £200
ditto, Ewart (U.S.), 1993 (150 signed copies, wraps) .
. . . . £125
Laments: Jan Kochanowski (1530-1584), Faber 1995 (translation, with Stanislaw Baranczak) £25/£10
ditto, Farrar Straus (U.S.), 1995 . . . . £25/£10
The Spirit Level, Faber, 1996 . . . . £15/£5
ditto, Faber, 1996 (350 numbered, signed copies, slipcase) . . . . £250/£225
ditto, Farrar Straus (U.S.), 1996 (200 signed, numbered copies with audio cassette in slipcase) . £200/£175
ditto, Farrar Straus (U.S.), 1996 (with audio cassette in slipcase) . . . . £25/£10
Opened Ground: Poems 1966-1996, Faber, 1998 . .
. . . . £15/£5
ditto, Faber, 1998 (300 signed, numbered copies in slipcase) . . . . £300/£250
ditto, Farrar Straus (U.S.), 1998 . . . £15/£5
Electric Light, Faber, 2001 . . . . . £25/£5
ditto, Faber, 2001 (300 signed, numbered copies, slipcase) . . . . £250/£225

Others
The Fire i' the Flint: Reflections on the Poetry of Gerard Manley Hopkins, British Academy/O.U.P., 1975 (wraps) £45
Robert Lowell: A Memorial Lecture and an Eulogy, privately printed, 1978 (wraps) £125
The Makings of Music: Reflections on the Poetry of Wordsworth and Yeats, Univ. of Liverpool, 1978 (wraps) £35
Preoccupations: Selected Prose 1968-1978, Faber, 1980 . . . . £75/£15
ditto, Farrar Straus (U.S.), 1980 . . . £50/£10
Among the Schoolchildren, Queen's Univ., (Belfast), 1983 (green wraps) £75
ditto, Queen's Univ., (Belfast), 1983 (blue wraps) £20
Place and Displacement, Dove Cottage, 1984 (wraps)
. . . . £25
The Government of the Tongue, Faber, 1988 £15/£5
ditto, Farrar Straus (U.S.), 1988 . . . . £15/£5
The Cure at Troy, Field Day, 1989 (500 signed copies)
. . . . £200/£125
ditto, Faber, 1989 (wraps). £5
ditto, Farrar Straus (U.S.), 1991 . . . . £25/£5
The Redress of Poetry, Clarendon Press, 1990 £15
ditto, Faber, 1995 . . . . £20/£5
ditto, Farrar Straus (U.S.), 1995 . . . £10/£5
Dylan the Durable? On Dylan Thomas, Bennington College, 1992 (1,000 numbered copies, wraps) £25
Joy or Night, Univ. College of Swansea, 1993 (wraps)
. . . . £20
Crediting Poetry, Gallery Books, 1995 (wraps) £25
Commencement Address, Univ. of North Carolina (U.S.), 1998 (100 signed copies of 500, wraps) £175
ditto, Univ. of North Carolina (U.S.), 1998 (400 unsigned copies of 500, wraps) £25

Beowulf, Faber, 1999 . . . . . . £15/£5
ditto, Faber, 1999 (300 signed, numbered copies, slipcase) . . . . £500/£400
ditto, Farrar Straus (U.S.), 2000 . . . . £25/£5

ROBERT A. HEINLEIN
(b.1907 d.1988)

An influential American science fiction writer,
Heinlein was first published in *Astounding SF*
magazine in 1939.

Novels
The Discovery of the Future, Novacious Press (U.S.),
1941 ('Limited First Edition' (200) on front wrapper,
wraps). £1,250
ditto, Novacious Press (U.S.), 1941 (adds 'Reprint
(100) under original limitation, wraps). . . £500
Rocket Ship Galileo, Scribners (U.S.), 1947 (first state
d/w published at $2.00) . . . . . . £650/£75
ditto, New English Library, 1971 (wraps) . . £10
Beyond This Horizon, Fantasy Press (U.S.), 1948 . .
. . . . £200/£45
ditto, Fantasy Press (U.S.), 1948 (500 signed, numbered copies). . . . .£750/£500
Space Cadet, Scribners (U.S.), 1948 (first state d/w
published at $2.50) . . . . £450/£45
ditto, Gollancz, 1966 . . . . £150/£35
Red Planet, Scribners (U.S.), 1949 . . . £125/£35
ditto, Gollancz, 1963 . . . . £150/£35
Sixth Column, Gnome Press (U.S.), 1949 £300/£35
ditto, Mayflower, 1962 (wraps) £10
Farmer in the Sky, Scribners (U.S.), 1950 £200/£35
ditto, Gollancz, 1962 . . . . £125/£25
The Man Who Sold the Moon, Shasta (U.S.), 1950 .
. . . . £250/£45
ditto, Shasta (U.S.), 1950 (subscriber's copy signed on
tipped-in page) . . . . £750/£500
ditto, Sidgwick & Jackson, 1953 . . . . £125/£25
Waldo and Magic Inc., Doubleday (U.S.), 1950 . .
. . . . £200/£35
Between Planets, Scribners (U.S.), 1951 £200/£45
ditto, Gollancz, 1968 . . . . £150/£35
The Green Hills of Earth, Shasta (U.S.), 1951 . . .
. . . . £250/£45
ditto, Shasta (U.S.), 1951 (subscriber's copy signed on
tipped-in page) . . . . £600/£400
ditto, Sidgwick & Jackson, 1954 . . . . £150/£35
The Puppet Masters, Doubleday (U.S.), 1951 . . .
. . . . £300/£75
ditto, Museum Press, 1953 . . . . £125/£30
Universe, Dell Books (U.S.), 1951 (wraps) . . £35
The Rolling Stones, Scribners (U.S.), 1952 £250/£45
ditto, as *Space Family Stone*, Gollancz, 1969 £125/£35
Assignment in Eternity, Fantasy Press (U.S.), 1953
(500 numbered, signed copies) . . . £400/£250

ditto, Fantasy Press (U.S.), 1953 . . . £200/£75
ditto, Museum Press, 1955 . . . . . £175/£50
Revolt in 2100, Shasta (U.S.), 1953 . . . £150/£25
ditto, Shasta (U.S.), 1953 (subscriber's copy signed on
tipped-in page) . . . . £350/£200
ditto, Gollancz, 1964 . . . . £65/£15
Starman Jones, Scribners (U.S.), 1953 . . £200/£45
ditto, Sidgwick & Jackson, 1954 . . . . £65/£15
The Star Beast, Scribners (U.S.), 1954 . . £100/£20
ditto, New English Library, 1971 . . . £65/£10
Tunnel in the Sky, Scribners (U.S.), 1955 £150/£50
ditto, Gollancz, 1965 . . . . £65/£15
Double Star, Doubleday (U.S.), 1956 . . £500/£100
ditto, Michael Joseph, 1958 . . . . . £200/£65
Time for the Stars, Scribners (U.S.), 1956 . £250/£35
ditto, Gollancz, 1963 . . . . £100/£20
Citizen of the Galaxy, Scribners (U.S.), 1957 £200/£50
ditto, Gollancz, 1969 . . . . £75/£25
The Door into Summer, Doubleday (U.S.), 1957 . .
. . . . £450/£75
ditto, Panther, 1960 (wraps) £5
ditto, Gollancz, 1967 . . . . £100/£25
Have Space Suit - Will Travel, Scribners (U.S.), 1958
. . . . £300/£50
ditto, Gollancz, 1970 . . . . £65/£20
Methuselah's Children, Gnome Press (U.S.), 1958 .
. . . . £200/£35
ditto, Gollancz, 1963 (abridged version). . £75/£20
The Robert Heinlein Omnibus, Science Fiction Book
Club, 1958 . . . . £25/£10
The Menace from Earth, Gnome Press (U.S.), 1959 .
. . . . £150/£40
ditto, Dobson, 1966 . . . . £75/£25
Starship Troopers, Putnam (U.S.), 1959 £1,000/£250
ditto, New English Library, 1961 . . . £100/£35
The Unpleasant Profession of Jonathan Hoag,
Gnome Press (U.S.), 1959 . . . . £175/£45
ditto, Dobson, 1964 . . . . £100/£25
Stranger in a Strange Land, Putnam (U.S.), 1961 (first
issue with 'C22" on p. 408 and d/w priced $4.50) .
. . . . £1,000/£100
ditto, New English Library, 1965 . . . £150/£25
Orphans of the Sky, Gollancz, 1963 . . . £350/£75
ditto, Putnam (U.S.), 1964 . . . . . £200/£45
Glory Road, Putnam (U.S.), 1963 . . . £300/£65
ditto, New English Library, 1965 . . . £150/£20
Podkayne of Mars, Putnam (U.S.), 1963 £500/£125
ditto, New English Library, 1969 . . . £35/£10
Farnham's Freehold, Putnam (U.S.), 1964 £175/£45
ditto, Dobson, 1965 . . . . £75/£25
Three by Heinlein, Doubleday (U.S.), 1965 £75/£25
ditto, as *A Heinlein Triad*, Gollancz, 1966 £35/£10
The Moon is a Harsh Mistress, Putnam (U.S.), 1966 .
. . . . £350/£45
ditto, Dobson, 1967 . . . . £75/£25
The Worlds of Robert Heinlein, Ace Books (U.S.),
1966 (wraps) £10
ditto, New English Library, 1970 (wraps) . . £10

A Robert Heinlein Omnibus, Sidgwick & Jackson, 1966 . . . . £25/£10
The Past Through Tomorrow, Putnam (U.S.), 1967 . . . . £200/£50
ditto, New English Library, 1977 (2 vols) . £100/£20
I Will Fear No Evil, Putnam (U.S.), 1970 . £125/£20
ditto, New English Library, 1971 . . . £35/£15
Time Enough For Love, Putnam (U.S.), 1973 . . . . £125/£45
ditto, New English Library, 1974 . . . £100/£35
Best of Robert Heinlein, Sidgwick & Jackson, 1973 . . . . £25/£10
The Notebooks of Lazarus Long, Putnam (U.S.), 1978 (wraps) £15
Destination Moon, Gregg Press (U.S.), 1979 (no d/w). £65
Expanded Universe, Grosset & Dunlap (U.S.), 1980 . . . . £50/£15
The Number of the Beast, New English Library, 1980 . . . . £50/£10
ditto, Fawcett (U.S.), 1980 . . . . £45/£15
ditto, Fawcett (U.S.), 1980 (wraps) . . . £10
Friday, Holt Rinehart (U.S.), 1982 . . £25/£5
ditto, Ballantine/Del Ray (U.S.), 1984 (500 signed, numbered copies, slipcase) . . . £150/£100
ditto, New English Library, 1982 . . £20/£5
Job, Ballantine/Del Ray (U.S.), 1984 . £15/£5
ditto, Ballantine/Del Ray (U.S.), 1984 (750 signed, numbered copies, slipcase) . . . . £100/£75
ditto, Ballantine/Del Ray (U.S.), 1984 (26 signed deluxe copies, slipcase) £1,000
ditto, New English Library, 1984 . . £20/£5
The Cat Who Walks Through Walls, Putnam (U.S.), 1985 (First state with line missing on p.300, erratum sheet laid in) . . . . £25/£5
ditto, Putnam (U.S.), 1984 (350 signed, numbered copies, slipcase) . . . . £200/£150
ditto, New English Library, 1986 . . £20/£5
To Sail Beyond the Sunset, Ace/Putnam (U.S.), 1987 . . . . £20/£5
ditto, Michael Joseph, 1987 . . . . £15/£5

JOSEPH HELLER
(b.1923)

Heller, an American author, is chiefly known for *Catch-22*, an anti-war satire which drew on his own experience of military service.

Novels
Catch-22, Simon & Schuster (U.S.), 1961 (d/w priced $5.95') . . . . £1,750/£200
ditto, Cape, 1962 (first issue d/w with blurb about book on back) . . . . £150/£25
ditto, Cape, 1962 (second issue d/w with comments of other authors on back) . . . . . £75/£25

ditto, Franklin Library (U.S.), 1978 (signed) . £100
ditto, Simon & Schuster (U.S.), 1994 (750 signed, numbered copies, slipcase) . . . . . £200/£125
Something Happened, Knopf (U.S.), 1974 £25/£5
ditto, Knopf (U.S.), 1974 (350 signed, numbered copies, d/w and slipcase) . . . . £150/£100
ditto, Cape, 1974 . . . . £20/£5
Good as Gold, Franklin Library (U.S.), 1979 (limited edition) £25
ditto, Franklin Library (U.S.), 1979 (signed copies from unspecified limited edition) £75
ditto, Simon & Schuster (U.S.), 1979 . . £20/£5
ditto, Simon & Schuster (U.S.), 1979 (500 signed copies, acetate d/w, slipcase) . . . . . £100/£75
ditto, Cape, 1979 . . . . £20/£5
God Knows, Knopf (U.S.), 1984 . . . . £20/£5
ditto, Knopf (U.S.), 1984 (350 signed copies, d/w and slipcase) . . . . £75/£50
ditto, Cape, 1984 . . . . £10/£5
ditto, Franklin Library (U.S.), 1984 (signed limited edition) £45
Picture This, Putnam (U.S.), 1988 . . £15/£5
ditto, Putnam (U.S.), 1988 (250 signed copies, slipcase, no d/w) . . . . £75/£50
ditto, Macmillan, 1988 . . . . . £15/£5
ditto, Macmillan, 1988 (50 proof copies) . . £50
Closing Time, Franklin Library (U.S.), 1994 (signed limited edition) £45
ditto, Simon & Schuster (U.S.), 1994 . . £15/£5
ditto, Simon & Schuster (U.S.), 1994 (750 signed, numbered copies, slipcase, no d/w). . . £65/£50
ditto, Simon & Schuster, 1994 . . . £15/£5
Portrait of an Artist as an Old Man, Simon & Schuster (U.S.), 2000 . . . . £15/£5
ditto, Simon & Schuster, 2000 . . . £15/£5

Plays
We Bombed in New Haven, Knopf (U.S.), 1968 . . . . £35/£10
ditto, Cape, 1969 . . . . £25/£5
Catch-22, French (U.S.), 1971 . . . . £25
Clevinger's Trial, French (U.S.), 1973 . . £20

Non Fiction
No Laughing Matter, Knopf (U.S.), 1986 (with Speed Vogel). . . . . £25/£5
ditto, Cape, 1986 . . . . £25/£5
Now and Then, From Coney Island to Here, Franklin Library (U.S.), 1994 (signed limited edition) . £75
ditto, Knopf, 1998 . . . . £15/£5
ditto, Simon & Schuster, 1998 . . . £15/£5

ERNEST HEMINGWAY
(b.1899 d.1961)

One of the most famous American novelists of the twentieth century, Hemingway's great successes were *A Farewell to Arms*, set during the First World War, and *For Whom the Bell Tolls* with the Spanish Civil War as its background.

Novels
The Torrents of Spring, Scribner (U.S.), 1926 . . .
. . . . £3,000/£350
ditto, Black Sun Press (Paris), 1933 (large paper edition, 125 francs, wraps) £250
ditto, Black Sun Press (Paris), 1933 (small paper edition, 10 francs, wraps) £125
ditto, Jonathan Cape, 1933 . . . . £500/£50
The Sun Also Rises, Scribner (U.S.), 1926 (first issue with 'stoppped' rather than 'stopped' on p.181, line 26, d/w with error 'In Our Times' rather than 'In Our Time'). . . . . £12,500/£3,000
ditto, Scribner (U.S.), 1926 (second issue with errors corrected). . . . . £1,500/£150
ditto, as *Fiesta*, Jonathan Cape, 1927 . . £750/£200
A Farewell to Arms, Scribner (U.S.), 1929 (510 signed copies, glassine d/w, slipcase) . . £5,000/£3,000
ditto, Scribner (U.S.), 1929 (no disclaimer on p.[x]) .
. . . . £1,000/£200
ditto, Scribner (U.S.), 1929 (with disclaimer on p.[x]) .
. . . . £500/£50
ditto, Jonathan Cape, 1929 (first issue with 'seriosu' on p.66, line 28) . . . . £400/£100
ditto, Jonathan Cape, 1929 (second issue with error corrected). . . . . £300/£45
To Have and to Have Not, Scribner (U.S.), 1937 . . .
. . . . £1,000/£75
ditto, Jonathan Cape, 1937 . . . . £175/£25
For Whom the Bell Tolls, Scribner (U.S.), 1940 (first issue d/w without photographer's name on back panel). . . . . £600/£45
ditto, Scribner (U.S.), 1940 (second issue d/w with photographer's name) . . . . . £150/£45
ditto, Jonathan Cape, 1941 . . . . £200/£15
Across the River and into the Trees, Jonathan Cape, 1950 . . . . £125/£25
ditto, Scribner (U.S.), 1950 (24 advance copies containing errors) £10,000
ditto, Scribner (U.S.), 1950 (first issue d/w with yellow lettering to spine) . . . . . . £125/£20
ditto, Scribner (U.S.), 1950 (second issue d/w with orange lettering to spine) . . . . £75/£20
The Old Man and the Sea, Scribner (U.S.), 1952 . . .
. . . . £250/£75
ditto, Scribner (U.S.), 1952 (30 sheets bound in black buckram for presentation, signature blind-stamped on front cover, spine gilt) £8,000
ditto, Jonathan Cape, 1952 . . . . . £125/£15
Islands in the Stream, Scribner (U.S.), 1970 £35/£5
ditto, Collins, 1970 . . . . £20/£5

The Garden of Eden, Scribner (U.S.), 1986 £20/£5
ditto, Hamish Hamilton, 1987 . . . . £15/£5
True at First Light, Heinemann, 1999 . . £15/£5

Short Stories
Three Stories and Ten Poems, privately printed, Contact Publishing Co., 1923 (300 copies, wraps) .
. . . . £10,000
In Our Time, Three Mountains Press (Paris), 1924 (170 copies) £10,000
ditto, Boni & Liveright (U.S.), 1925 . . £4,000/£600
ditto, Jonathan Cape, 1926 . . . . £2,000/£600
ditto, Black Sun Press (Paris), 1932 . . . . £250
Men Without Women, Scribner (U.S.), 1927 (first state weighing 15.5 ounces) . . . . . £2,000/£150
ditto, Scribner (U.S.), 1927 (second state weighing 13.8 ounces) . . . . £750/£100
ditto, Jonathan Cape, 1928 . . . . . £350/£35
Winner Take Nothing, Scribner (U.S.), 1933 . . . .
. . . . £450/£100
ditto, Jonathan Cape, 1934 . . . . . £200/£45
The Fifth Column and The First Forty-Nine Stories, Scribner (U.S.), 1938 . . . . . . £750/£50
ditto, Jonathan Cape, 1939 . . . . . £200/£35
God Rest You Merry Gentlemen, House of Books (U.S.), 1933 (300 copies, no d/w) . . £1,000
Winner Take Nothing, Scribners (U.S.), 1933 . . . .
. . . . £500/£75
ditto, Jonathan Cape, 1933 . . . . . £250/£35
The Fifth Column and the First Forty-Nine Stories, Scribners (U.S.), 1938 . . . . . £750/£75
ditto, Jonathan Cape, 1939 . . . . £100/£20
The First Forty-Nine Stories, Jonathan Cape, 1944 .
. . . . £75/£10
Two Christmas Tales, Hart Press (U.S.), 1959 (150 copies, wraps) £750
The Fifth Column and Four Unpublished Stories of the Spanish Civil War, Scribners (U.S.), 1960 . .
. . . . £45/£10
The Snows of Kilamanjaro and Other Stories, Scribners (U.S.), 1961 . . . . . £25/£10
The Short Happy Life of Francis Macomber and Other Stories, Penguin, 1963 (wraps) . . . £5
The Nick Adams Stories, Scribner (U.S.), 1972 . .
. . . . £75/£20
A Divine Gesture, A Fable, Aloe Editions (U.S.), 1974 (200 copies, wraps) £75

Others
Today is Friday, Stable Publications (U.S.), 1926 (300 numbered copies, wraps) £500
Introduction to Kiki of Montparnasse, Titus (U.S.), 1929 (25 copies, wraps) £500
Death in the Afternoon, Scribner (U.S.), 1932 . . . .
. . . . £1,000/£150
ditto, Jonathan Cape, 1932 . . . . . £250/£65
Green Hills of Africa, Scribner (U.S.), 1935 . . . .
. . . . £450/£100
ditto, Jonathan Cape, 1936 . . . . . £75/£25

The Spanish Earth, Savage (U.S.), 1938 (glassine d/w) . . . . £250/£200
The Spanish War, Fact, 1938 (card wraps) . . £100
The Fifth Column: A Play in Three Acts, Scribner (U.S.), 1940 . . . . £200/£25
ditto, Penguin, 1966 . . . . £5
ditto, Jonathan Cape, 1968 . . . . . £15/£5
Voyage to Victory, Crowell-Collier (U.S.), 1944 (wraps with d/w) . . . . £45/£20
The Essential Hemingway, Jonathan Cape, 1947 . . . . £25/£5
The Hemingway Reader, Scribner (U.S.), 1953 . . . . £25/£5
The Wild Years, Dell (U.S.), 1962 (wraps) . . £5
The Collected Poems, Library of Living Poets [Paris], [c.1955] (pirated, wraps) £150
ditto, Haskell House (U.S.), 1970 . . £25/£10
A Moveable Feast, Scribner (U.S.), 1964 . £65/£20
ditto, Jonathan Cape, 1964 . . . £75/£20
By-Line, Scribner, 1967 . . . . . £65/£15
ditto, Collins, 1968 . . . . . . £45/£15
Ernest Hemingway, Cub Reporter, Univ. of Pittsburgh Press (U.S.), 1970 . . . . . £20/£5
ditto, Univ. of Pittsburgh Press (U.S.), 1970 (200 copies) . . . . £40/£20
Ernest Hemingway's Apprenticeship, Microcard (U.S.), 1971 . . . . £20/£5
ditto, Microcard (U.S.), 1971 (200 copies) . £40/£20
Bastard Sheet Note for A Farewell to Arms, Cohn (U.S.), 1971 (93 copies, single sheet) . . . £250
Eighty-Eight Poems, Harcourt Brace (U.S.), 1980 . . . . £25/£10
Selected Letters, 1917-1961, Scribners (U.S.), 1981 . . . . £25/£10
ditto, Scribners (U.S.), 1981 (500 copies signed by editor, glassine d/w, slipcase) . . . £75/£50
ditto, Granada, 1981 . . . . . . £25/£10
The Dangerous Summer, Scribner (U.S.), 1985 £20/£5
ditto, Hamish Hamilton, 1985 . . . . £20/£5
On Writing, Granada, 1985 . . . . . £15/£5
Marlin, Big Fish Books (U.S.), 192 . . . £50/£15

G.A. HENTY

(b.1832 d.1902)

Henty was a popular nineteenth-century author of patriotic stories for boys.

A Search for a Secret, Tinsley Brothers, 1867 (3 vols, blue or green cloth) £2,000
The March to Magdala, Tinsley Brothers, 1868 . . . . £2,000
All But Lost, Tinsley Brothers, 1869 (3 vols, blue boards) £2,000
Out on the Pampas, or The Young Settlers, Griffith & Farran, 1871 [1870] (blue or brown boards) £1,000

The Young Franc-Tireurs, Griffith & Farran, 1872 [1871] (blue, red or green boards). . . . £650
The March to Coomassie, Tinsley Brothers, 1874 £500
Seaside Maidens, Tinsley Brothers, 1880 (orange boards) £625
The Young Buglars, Griffith & Farran, 1880 [1879] (red or green boards) £500
The Cornet of Horse, Sampson Low & Marston, 1881 (red boards). £500
In Times of Peril, Griffith & Farran, 1881 (red or blue boards) £700
Facing Death, Blackie, [1882] (blue or brown boards) £500
Winning His Spurs, Sampson Low & Marston, 1882 . . . . £300
Friends Though Divided, Griffith & Farran, 1883 . . . . £400
Jack Archer, Sampson Low & Marston, 1883 £400
Under Drake's Flag, Blackie, 1883 [1882] (green or brown boards) £200
ditto, as *Cast Ashore*, Blackie, 1906 . . . £45
By Sheer Pluck, Blackie, 1884 [1883] (red boards) £300
With Clive in India, Blackie, 1884 [1883] (red, brown or blue boards) £200
ditto, as *The Young Captain*, Blackie, 1906 . £50
ditto, as *Charlie Marryat*, Blackie, 1906 . . £50
The Young Colonists, Routledge, 1885 [1884] (blue and gold boards) £200
True to the Old Flag, Blackie, 1885 [1884]. . £200
In Freedom's Cause, Blackie, 1885 [1884]. . £100
ditto, as *A Highland Chief*, Blackie, 1906 . . £50
St. George For England, Blackie, 1885 [1884] £100
The Lion of the North, Blackie, 1886 [1885] (brown or green boards). £150
The Dragon and the Raven, Blackie, 1886 [1885] (brown or green boards). £200
For Name and Fame, Blackie, 1886 [1885] (brown or grey boards) £200
Through the Fray, Blackie, 1886 [1885] (brown or red boards) £150
Yarns on the Beach, Blackie, 1886 [1885] (brown or red boards) £350
The Young Carthaginian, Blackie, 1887 [1886] (blue or green boards) £150
The Bravest of the Brave, Blackie, 1887 [1886] (red or blue boards) £150
A Final Reckoning, Blackie, 1887 [1886] (blue or green boards) £100
ditto, as *Among the Bushrangers*, Blackie, 1906 £50
With Wolfe in Canada, Blackie 1887 [1886] £200
The Sovereign Reader: Scenes from the Life and Reign of Queen Victoria, Blackie, [1887] (red or purple boards) £175
In the Reign of Terror, Blackie, 1888 . . £150
Sturdy and Strong, Blackie, 1888 [1887] (red, blue or orange boards) £150
Orange and Green, Blackie 1888 [1887] (red, blue or orange boards) £100

ditto, as *Cornet Walter*, Blackie, 1906 . . . £50
Bonnie Prince Charlie, Blackie, 1888 [1887] (brown
or red boards). £100
For the Temple, Blackie, 1888 [1887] (brown, red or
blue boards) £200
Gabriel Allen MP, Spencer & Blackett, [1888] (red
boards) £250
Captain Bayley's Heir, Blackie, 1889 (red, brown or
blue boards) £100
The Cat of Bubastes, Blackie, 1889 [1888]. . £200
The Lion of St Mark, Blackie, 1889 [1888] (red, blue
or grey boards) £75
The Curse of Carne's Hold, Spencer & Blackett, 1889
(2 vols, blue boards). £500
The Plague Ship, S.P.C.K. 'Penny Library of Fiction'
series, 1889 (wraps) £600
By Pike and Dyke, Blackie, 1890 [1889] (brown or
green boards). £125
One of the 28th, Blackie, 1890 [1889] . . . £200
Tales of Daring and Danger, Blackie, 1889 [1890]
(blue or green boards) £300
With Lee in Virginia, Blackie, 1890 [1889] (brown or
blue boards) £150
Those Other Animals, Henry & Co., [1891] (green
boards) £250
By England's Aid, Blackie, 1891 [1890] (blue or
brown boards) £150
By Right of Conquest, Blackie, 1891 [1890] (green or
brown boards) £100
Maori and Settler, Blackie, 1891 . . . . £100
A Chapter of Adventures, Blackie, 1891 [1890] £1,000
A Hidden Foe, Sampson Low & Marston, [1891] (2
vols, grey boards) £2,000
The Dash for Khartoum, Blackie, 1892 [1891] £100
Held Fast for England, Blackie, 1892 [1891] (red,
grey or brown boards) £100
Redskin and Cowboy, Blackie, 1892 [1891] (red, green
or brown boards). £100
ditto, as *An Indian Raid*, Blackie, 1906. . . £50
The Ranch in the Valley, S.P.C.K. 'Penny Library of
Fiction' series, 1892 (wraps) £500
Beric the Briton, Blackie, 1893 [1892] (blue or brown
boards) £150
Condemned as Nihilist, Blackie, 1893 [1892] (brown
or blue boards) £150
In Greek Waters, Blackie, 1893 [1892] (grey, brown or
green boards). £100
Tales from the Works of G.A. Henty, Blackie, 1893
(red boards) £100
Rujub the Juggler, Chatto & Windus, 1893 (3 vols,
blue boards) £750
A Jacobite Exile, Blackie, 1894 [1893] . . . £200
Through the Sikh War, Blackie, 1894 [1893] (green
boards) £100
St Bartholomew's Eve, Blackie, 1894 [1893] (green,
blue or red boards) £100
Dorothy's Double, Chatto & Windus, 1894 (3 vols)
. . . . £750

When London Burned, Blackie, 1895 [1894] (blue
boards). £200
Cuthbert Hartington and A Woman of the Commune,
F.V. White, 1895. . . . . £200
Wulf the Saxon, Blackie, 1895 [1894] (green boards).
. . . . £75
In the Heart of the Rockies, Blackie, 1895 [1894]
(grey boards). £100
A Knight of the White Cross, Blackie, 1896 [1895]
(green boards) £150
Bears and Dacoits, Blackie, [1896] (wraps) £300
Surly Joe, Blackie, [1896] (wraps) £200
White-Faced Dick, Blackie, [1896] (limp cloth cover)
. . . . £200
Through Russian Snows, Blackie, 1896 [1895] (grey
boards). £100
The Tiger of Mysore, Blackie, 1896 [1895] (blue
boards). £100
On the Irrawaddy, Blackie, 1897 [1896] (blue boards)
. . . . £150
At Agincourt, Blackie, 1897 (grey boards) . . £150
With Cochrane the Dauntless, Blackie, 1897 (blue
boards) £100
The Queen's Cup, Chatto & Windus, 1897 (three vols,
green or blue boards) £600
With Moore at Corunna, Blackie, 1898 [1897] (green
or blue boards) £100
Colonel Thorndyke's Secret, Chatto & Windus, 1898
(pink boards). £150
With Frederick the Great, Blackie, 1898 [1897] (red
boards) £100
Under Wellington's Command, Blackie, 1899 [1898]
(blue boards). £100
· *At Aboukir and Acre*, Blackie, 1899 [1898] (red
boards) £100
Both Sides the Border, Blackie, 1899 [1898] (blue
boards) £75
The Lost Heir, James Bowden, 1899 (green boards) .
. . . . £150
On the Spanish Main, Chambers, [1899] (red wraps) .
. . . . £100
At Duty's Call, Chambers, [1899] £75
A Roving Commission, Blackie, 1900 [1899] (red
boards) £100
Won by the Sword, Blackie, 1900 [1899] (blue boards)
. . . . £75
No Surrender!, Blackie, 1900 [1899] (red boards). .
. . . . £100
Do Your Duty, Blackie, [1900] (blue or green boards)
. . . . £150
The Soul Survivors, Chambers, [1901] (red wraps) .
. . . . £100
In the Irish Brigade, Blackie, 1901 [1900] (green
boards) £100
Out With Garibaldi, Blackie, 1901 [1900] (blue
boards) £65
John Hawke's Fortune, Chapman & Hall:, Young
People's Library series, 1901 (paper cover) £65

With Buller in Natal, Blackie, 1901 (blue boards) £65
Queen Victoria, Blackie, 1901 (purple boards) £50
To Herat and Cabul, Blackie, 1902 [1901] (blue boards) £65
With Roberts in Pretoria, Blackie, 1902 [1901] (red boards) £150
At the Point of the Bayonet, Blackie, 1902 [1901] (green boards) £65
In the Hands of the Cave Dwellers, Blackie, 1903 [1902]. £150
The Treasure of the Incas, Blackie, 1903 [1902] (green boards) £75
With the British Legion, Blackie, 1903 [1902] (blue or green boards). £75
With Kitchener in the Soudan, Blackie, 1903 [1902] (red boards) £65
Through Three Campaigns, Blackie, 1904 [1903] (red boards) £65
With the Allies to Pekin, Blackie, 1904 [1903] (green boards) £65
By Conduct and Courage, Blackie, 1905 [1904] (red boards) £100
Gallant Deeds, Chambers, 1905 (white or grey boards) £65
In the Hands of the Malays, Blackie, 1905 (red boards) £65
A Soldier's Daughter, Blackie, 1906 [1905] (red, blue or green boards) £65
ditto, as *The Two Prisoners*, Blackie, 1906 [1905] £45

JAMES HERBERT
(b.1943)

Often thought of as the British version of Stephen King, Herbert may not have King's world-wide sales, but he is just as successful in the United Kingdom.

Novels
The Rats, New English Library, 1974 . . £300/£50
ditto, as *Deadly Eyes*, Signet (U.S.), 1975 (wraps) £5
ditto, (*The Rats*) New English Library, 1985, (limited edition, limitation unknown) . . . £35/£10
The Fog, New English Library, 1975 . . £175/£45
ditto, Signet (U.S.), 1975 (wraps) . . . £5
ditto, New English Library, 1988, (3,000 copies) . . . . £30/£10
The Survivor, New English Library, 1976 £75/£25
ditto, Signet (U.S.), 1977 (wraps) . . . £5
ditto, New English Library, 1988, (2,000 copies) . . . . £30/£10
Fluke, New English Library, 1977 . . £50/£15
ditto, Signet (U.S.), 1978 (wraps) . . . £5
The Spear, New English Library, 1978 . £25/£5
ditto, Signet (U.S.), 1980 (wraps) . . . £5
Lair, New English Library, 1979. . . £200/£50
ditto, Signet (U.S.), 1979 (wraps) . . . £5

ditto, New English Library, 1985, (limited edition, limitation unknown) . . . . . . £100/£25
The Dark, New English Library, 1980 . . £30/£10
ditto, Signet (U.S.), 1980 (wraps) . . . £5
ditto, New English Library, 1988, (2,000 copies) . . . . £30/£10
The Jonah, New English Library, 1981. . £25/£5
ditto, Signet (U.S.), 1981 (wraps) . . . £5
ditto, New English Library, 1985, (limited edition, limitation unknown) . . . . . . £25/£5
Shrine, New English Library, 1983 . . . £25/£5
ditto, Signet (U.S.), 1985 (wraps) . . . £5
Domain, New English Library, 1984 . . £25/£5
ditto, Signet (U.S.), 1985 (wraps) . . . £5
Moon, New English Library, 1985 . . . £20/£5
ditto, Crown (U.S.), 1985. . . . . . £15/£5
The Magic Cottage, Hodder & Stoughton, 1986 £15/£5
ditto, New American Library (U.S.), 1987 £15/£5
Sepulchre, Hodder & Stoughton, 1987 . . £15/£5
ditto, Putnam's (U.S.), 1988 . . . . . £15/£5
Haunted, Hodder & Stoughton, 1988 . . £15/£5
ditto, Hodder & Stoughton, 1988 (250 signed copies, slipcase, no d/w) . . . . £75/£50
ditto, Putnam's (U.S.), 1989 . . . . . £15/£5
Creed, Hodder & Stoughton, 1990 . . . £15/£5
Portent, Hodder & Stoughton, 1992 . . . £15/£5
ditto, Hodder & Stoughton, 1992 (pre-publication issue, with d/w) . . . . £35/£10
ditto, Harper Prism (U.S.), 1996 . . . . £15/£5
The Ghosts of Sleath, Harper Collins, 1994 £15/£5
ditto, Harper Collins, 1994, (over-sized edition, 500 signed copies) . . . . £40/£20
ditto, Harper Prism (U.S.), 1996 . . . . £15/£5
'48, Harper Collins, 1996. . . . . . £15/£5
ditto, Harper Prism (U.S.), 1996 . . . . £15/£5
Others, Macmillan, 1999. . . . . . £15/£5

Others
James Herbert's Dark Places, Harper Collins, 1983 . . . . £15/£5
The City, Pan Macmillan, 1994 (wraps). . . £5
ditto, Pan Macmillan, 1994 (1,000 copies, signed by author and artist in silver, some with flyer) . £25

From 1990 Hodder & Stoughton have published *Uniform Editions* of the above titles, each edition limited to 3,000 copies . . . . £25/£5 each

EDWARD HERON-ALLEN
(b.1861 d.1943)

A British scientist and polymath whose writings range from hard sciences to the occult. He wrote several entertaining works of weird fiction under the pseudonym of Christopher Blayre which are highly sought after by collectors.

Novels
The Princess Daphne, Belford, Clarke & Co. (U.S.), 1888 (with Selina Dolaro) £125
ditto, H.J. Drane, 1889 . . . . £125
ditto, Tartarus Press, 2001 (300 numbered copies). .
. . . . £25/£10
The Romance of a Quiet Watering-Place, Belford, Clarke & Co. (U.S.), 1888 (pseud. 'Nora Helen Warddel'). £100
Bella Demonia, Belford, Clarke & Co. (U.S.), [c.1889] (ghost written for Selina Dolaro) £75
The Vengeance of Maurice Denalguez, Belford, Clarke & Co. (U.S.), [c.1889] (ghost written for Selina Dolaro) £75

Short Stories
Kisses of Fate. A study of mere human nature, Belford, Clarke & Co. (U.S.), 1888 . . . £125
A Fatal Fiddle: the commonplace tragedy of a snob, Belford, Clarke & Co. (U.S.), 1889 . . . £150
The Purple Sapphire and other Posthumous Papers, Allan, [1921] (pseud. Christopher Blayre) £250
ditto, Allan, [1921] (10 numbered presentation copies, grey paper boards) £500
ditto, Allan, [1921] (second issue, boards with purple cloth, gilt lettering) . . . . . . £200/£75
ditto, Allan, [1921] (later issue, purple/grey cloth with black lettering) . . . . £200/£65
ditto, as *The Strange Papers of Dr. Blayre*, Allan, 1932 . . . . £200/£65
ditto, as *The Strange Papers of Dr. Blayre*, Arno Press (U.S.), 1976 . . . . £45
The Cheetah-Girl, privately printed, 1923 (pseud. Christopher Blayre, 20 signed copies) . . £1,500
ditto, Tartarus Press, 1998 (99 numbered copies) . .
. . . . £150/£100
Some Women of the University, Sorelle Nessuno, Nubiana [Stockwell], 1934 (pseud. Christopher Blayre, 100 numbered copies) £350
The Collected Strange Papers of Christopher Blayre, Tartarus Press, 1998 (pseud. Christopher Blayre). . .
. . . . £45/£20

Palmistry
Chiromancy, or the science of palmistry, Routledge & Sons, 1883 . . . . £45
A Manual of Cheirosophy, Ward, Lock, & Co., 1885 .
. . . . £25

Practical Cheirosophy. A synoptical study of the science of the hand, etc., G.P. Putnam's Sons (U.S.) 1887 . . . . £25

Translations and Commentaries
The Ruba'iyat of Omar Khayyam, H.S. Nichols, 1898 (1022 copies). £100
Some Side-lights upon Edward FitzGerald's poem 'The Ruba'iyat of Omar Khayyam.', Nichols, 1898 (wraps) £35

The Violin
Violin-Making, as it was and is, Ward, Lock, & Co., 1884 . . . . £200
ditto, Second edition, Ward, Lock & Co., [1885.] £65
ditto, Ward, Lock & Co., 1886 (deluxe edition of 25 copies for private circulation) £500

Scientific
The Foraminifera of the Clare Island District, Co. Mayo, Ireland, Dublin, 1913 . . . . £100
The Fossil Foraminifera of the Blue Marl of the Côte des Basques, Biarritz, Manchester, 1919 . . £125
Barnacles in Nature and in Myth, Humphrey Milford, 1928 . . . . £125/£65

Local History
Selsey Bill: Historic and Prehistoric, Duckworth, 1911 (2 vols) £250

HERMANN HESSE
(b.1877 d.1962)

One of the greatest literary figures of the German-speaking world, the Nazis banned his books, but he was awarded the Nobel Prize for literature in 1946.

Novels
In Sight of Chaos, Verlag Seldwyla (Zurich), 1923 (no d/w) £250
ditto, as *Demian*, Boni & Liveright (U.S.), 1923 . .
. . . . £250/£75
ditto, Peter Owen/Vision Press, 1960 (Translated by W.J. Strachan) . . . . £65/£20
Steppenwolf, Secker, 1929 (translated by Basil Creighton) . . . . £750/£150
ditto, Holt (U.S.), 1929 . . . . . £400/£100
Magister Ludi, Holt (U.S.), 1949 (translated by Mervyn Savill) . . . . £35/£10
ditto, as *The Glass Bead Game*, Holt (U.S.), 1969 (translated by Richard and Clara Winston) £35/£10
ditto, Cape, 1970 . . . . £30/£10
Siddhartha, New Directions (U.S.), 1951 (translated by Hilda Rosner). . . . . . . £40/£10
ditto, Peter Owen, 1954 . . . . . £40/£10
The Journey to the East, Peter Owen, 1954 (translated by Hilda Rosner). . . . . . . £50/£10

ditto, Noonday Press (U.S.), 1957 . . . £35/£10
Gertrude, Peter Owen, 1955 (translated by Hilda Rosner) . . . . £45/£10
ditto, Farrar Straus & Giroux (U.S.), 1969 . £45/£10
The Prodigy, Peter Owen/Vision Press, 1957 (translated by W.J. Strachan) . . . . £60/£15
Goldmund, Peter Owen, 1959 (translated by Geoffrey Dunlop) . . . . £50/£10
ditto, as *Narcissus and Goldmund*, Farrar Straus & Giroux (U.S.), 1968 (translated by Ursule Molinaro) .
. . . . £45/£10
Peter Camenzind, Peter Owen/Vision Press, 1961 (translated by W.J. Strachan) . . . £60/£15
ditto, Farrar Straus & Giroux (U.S.), 1969 (translated by Michael Roloff) . . . . . . £45/£10
Rosshalde, Farrar Straus & Giroux (U.S.), 1970 (translated by Ralph Manheim). . . £45/£10
ditto, Cape, 1971 . . . . £45/£10
Klingsor's Last Summer, Farrar Straus & Giroux (U.S.), 1970 (translated by Richard and Clara Winston) . . . . £40/£10
ditto, Cape, 1971 . *£10/£5* . . £1,000/£200
Knulp, Farrar Straus & Giroux (U.S.), 1971 (translated by Ralph Manheim) . . . . . £40/£10
ditto, Cape, 1972 . . . . £40/£10

Short Stories
Strange News from Another Star, Farrar Straus & Giroux (U.S.), 1972 (translated by Denver Lindley) .
. . . . £40/£10
ditto, Cape, 1973 . . . . £40/£10
Stories of Five Decades, Farrar Straus & Giroux (U.S.), 1975 (Translated by Ralph Manheim and Denver Lindley) . . . . £30/£10
ditto, Cape, 1974 . . . . £25/£10

Others
Poems, Farrar Straus & Giroux (U.S.), 1970, 1954 (translated by James Wright) . . . £30/£10
ditto, Cape, 1971 . . . . £25/£10
If the War Goes On..., Farrar Straus & Giroux (U.S.), 1971 (translated by Ralph Manheim) . . £40/£10
ditto, Cape, 1972 . . . . £35/£10
Wandering, Farrar Straus & Giroux (U.S.), 1972 (translated by James Wright) . . . . £50/£15
Autobiographical Writings, Farrar Straus & Giroux (U.S.), 1972, 1972 (translated by Denver Lindley) .
. . . . £30/£10
ditto, Cape, 1973 . . . . £30/£10
My Belief, Farrar Straus & Giroux (U.S.), 1974 (translated by Denver Lindley and Ralph Manheim) .
. . . . £30/£10
ditto, Cape, 1976 . . . . £30/£10
Reflections, Farrar Straus & Giroux (U.S.), 1974 (translated by Ralph Manheim) . . . . £30/£10
ditto, Cape, 1972 . . . . £35/£10
Crisis, Farrar Straus & Giroux (U.S.), 1975 (translated by Ralph Manheim) . . . . . £30/£10

PATRICIA HIGHSMITH
(b.1921 d.1995)

A cult crime writer born in Fort Worth, Texas, Highsmith began writing at the age of fifteen. She started out writing speech bubbles for comic strips such as *Superman*. Her first novel, *Strangers on a Train*, was filmed by Hitchcock in 1951. She lived in Europe during her later years and died in Switzerland.

Novels
Strangers on a Train, Harper (U.S.), 1950 £650/£125
ditto, Cresset Press, 1951 . . . . . £250/£65
The Price of Salt, Coward McCann (U.S.), 1952 (pseud. 'Claire Morgan') . . . . . £200/£50
ditto, as *Carol* , Bloomsbury, 1990 . . . £10/£5
The Blunderer, Coward McCann (U.S.), 1954 . . .
. . . . £200/£50
ditto, Cressett Press, 1956 . . . . . £175/£50
The Talented Mr Ripley, Coward McCann (U.S.), 1955 . . . . £250/£50
ditto, Cressett Press, 1957. . . . . . £150/£40
Deep Water, Harper (U.S.), 1957 . . . £75/£25
ditto, Heinemann, 1958 . . . . . £50/£20
A Game for the Living, Harper (U.S.), 1958 £50/£20
ditto, Heinemann, 1959 . . . . . £35/£15
This Sweet Sickness, Harper (U.S.), 1960 . £35/£15
ditto, Heinemann, 1961 . . . . . £25/£5
The Cry of the Owl, Harper (U.S.), 1962 £30/£10
ditto, Heinemann, 1963 . . . . . £25/£5
The Two Faces of January, Doubleday (U.S.), 1964 .
. . . . £30/£10
ditto, Heinemann, 1964 . . . . . £25/£5
The Glass Cell, Doubleday (U.S.), 1964 . £35/£10
ditto, Heinemann, 1965 . . . . . £35/£10
The Story-Teller, Doubleday (U.S.), 1965 £25/£10
ditto, as *A Suspension of Mercy*, Heinemann, 1965 .
. . . . £20/£5
Those Who Walk Away, Doubleday (U.S.), 1967 . .
. . . . £20/£5
ditto, Heinemann, 1967 . . . . . £15/£5
The Tremor of Forgery, Doubleday (U.S.), 1969 . .
. . . . £20/£5
ditto, Heinemann, 1969 . . . . . £15/£5
Ripley Under Ground, Doubleday (U.S.), 1970 £40/£5
ditto, Heinemann, 1971 . . . . . £15/£5
A Dog's Ransom, Knopf (U.S.), 1972 . . £20/£5
ditto, Heinemann, 1972 . . . . . £15/£5
Ripley's Game, Knopf (U.S.), 1974 . . . £30/£5
ditto, Heinemann, 1974 . . . . . £15/£5
Edith's Diary, Simon & Schuster (U.S.), 1977 £15/£5
ditto, Heinemann, 1977 . . . . . £15/£5
The Boy Who Followed Ripley, Heinemann, 1980 . .
. . . . £15/£5
ditto, Lippincott (U.S.), 1980. . . . . £15/£5
The People Who Knock on the Door, Heinemann, 1983 . . . . £10/£5
ditto, Mysterious Press (U.S.), [1985] (250 signed copies, slipcase, no d/w). . . . . . £25/£15

ditto, Mysterious Press (U.S.), [1985] . . £10/£5
Found in the Street, Heinemann, 1986 . . £10/£5
ditto, Atlantic Monthly Press (U.S.), 1986 £10/£5
Ripley Under Water, Bloomsbury, 1991 £15/£5
ditto, London Limited Editions, 1991 (150 signed copies, glassine d/w). £40
ditto, Knopf (U.S.), 1992 . . . . . . £15/£5
Small G: A Summer Idyll, Bloomsbury, 1995 £10/£5

Short Stories
The Snail-Watcher, Doubleday (U.S.), 1970 £20/£5
ditto, as *Eleven*, Heinemann, 1970 . . . £20/£5
Kleine Geschichten Fur Weiberfeinde, Diogenes (Germany), 1974. . . . . . . £25/£10
ditto, as *Little Tales of Misogyny*, Heinemann, 1977 .
. . . . £20/£5
ditto, as *Little Tales of Misogyny*, Mysterious Press (U.S.), [1986] (250 signed copies, slipcase, no d/w) .
. . . . £25/£15
ditto, as *Little Tales of Misogyny*, Mysterious Press (U.S.), [1986]. . . . . . . £10/£5
The Animal-Lover's Book of Beastly Murder, Heinemann, 1975 . . . . . . £20/£5
ditto, Mysterious Press (U.S.), [1986] (250 signed copies, slipcase, no d/w). . . . . £25/£15
ditto, Mysterious Press (U.S.), [1986] . £10/£5
Slowly, Slowly in the Wind, Heinemann, 1979 £20/£5
ditto, Mysterious Press, [1984] (250 signed copies, slipcase and d/w). . . . . . . £25/£15
ditto, Mysterious Press, [1984] . . . . £10/£5
The Black House, Heinemann, 1981 . . £15/£5
ditto, Mysterious Press (U.S.), [1988] (250 signed copies, slipcase, no d/w). . . . . £25/£15
ditto, Mysterious Press (U.S.), [1988] . . £10/£5
Mermaids on the Golf Course and Other Stories, Heinemann, 1985 . . . . . . £15/£5
ditto, Mysterious Press (U.S.), 1988 . . . £10/£5
The Man Who Wrote Books in His Head and Other Stories, Eurographica (Helsinki), 1986 (350 signed copies, wraps and d/w) £50
Tales of Natural and Unnatural Catastrophes, Bloomsbury, 1987 . . . . £15/£5
ditto, Atlantic Monthly Press (U.S.), 1989 £10/£5
Where the Action Is and Other Stories, Eurographica (Helsinki), 1989 (350 signed copies, wraps and d/w) .
. . . . £50
Tales of Obsession, Severn House, 1994 £10/£5

Children's
Miranda the Panda is on the Verandah, Coward McCann (U.S.), 1958 (with Doris Sanders) £50/£15

Miscellaneous
Plotting and Writing Suspense Fiction, Writer (U.S.), 1966 . . . . £25/£10
ditto, Poplar Press, 1983 . . . . . £10/£5

REGINALD HILL
(b.1936)

Although he has written a number of books with other characters, often under pseudonyms, Hill is best-known for his now televised Dalziel (pronounced 'De-al') and Pascoe novels.

'Dalziel and Pascoe Novels'
A Clubbable Woman, Collins Crime Club, 1970 . .
. . . . £500/£75
ditto, Countryman (U.S.), 1984 . . . . £25/£5
An Advancement of Learning, Crime Club, 1971 . .
. . . . £200/£25
ditto, Countryman (U.S.), 1985 . . . . £20/£5
Ruling Passion, Crime Club, 1973 . . . £200/£25
ditto, Harper (U.S.), 1977. . . . . . £45/£10
An April Shroud, Crime Club, 1975. . . £300/£35
ditto, Countryman (U.S.), 1986 . . . . £15/£5
A Pinch of Snuff, Crime Club, 1978 . . £250/£25
ditto, Harper (U.S.), 1978. . . . . . £150/£20
A Killing Kindness, Crime Club, 1980 . . £150/£20
ditto, Pantheon (U.S.), 1981 . . . . . £25/£5
Deadheads, Crime Club, 1983 . . . . £75/£10
ditto, Macmillan, 1984 . . . . . . £35/£10
Exit Lines, Crime Club, 1984 . . . . £75/£10
ditto, Macmillan (U.S.), 1985 . . . . £30/£5
Child's Play, Crime Club, 1987 . . . . £50/£10
ditto, Macmillan (U.S.), 1987 . . . . £25/£5
Under World, Crime Club, 1988 . . . £40/£10
ditto, Scribner (U.S.), 1988 . . . . . £20/£5
Bones and Silence, Crime Club, 1990 . . £15/£5
ditto, Delacorte (U.S.), 1990 . . . . . £15/£5
Recalled to Life, Scorpion Press, 1992 (99 signed, numbered copies) £100
ditto, Scorpion Press, 1992 (20 signed, lettered copies)
. . . . £200
ditto, HarperCollins, 1992 . . . . . £25/£5
ditto, Delacorte (U.S.), 1992 . . . . . £15/£5
Pictures of Perfection, Scorpion Press, 1994 (75 signed, numbered copies) £85
ditto, Scorpion Press, 1994 (20 signed, lettered copies)
. . . . £175
ditto, HarperCollins, 1994 . . . . . £20/£5
ditto, Delacorte (U.S.), 1994 . . . . . £10/£5
The Wood Beyond, Scorpion Press, 1996 (85 signed, numbered copies) £45
ditto, HarperCollins, 1996 . . . . . £10/£5
ditto, Delacorte (U.S.), 1996 . . . . . £10/£5
On Beulah Height, Scorpion Press, 1998 (85 signed, numbered copies) £45
ditto, HarperCollins, 1998 . . . . . £10/£5
ditto, Delacorte (U.S.), 1998 . . . . . £10/£5
Arms and the Women, Delacorte (U.S.), 1998 £10/£5
ditto, HarperCollins, 1998 . . . . . £10/£5

'Joe Sixsmith' Novels

Blood Sympathy, HarperCollins, 1993 . .	£30/£5
Born Guilty, HarperCollins, 1995 . . .	£25/£5
Singing the Sadness, HarperCollins, 1999 .	£15/£5

Other Novels

Fell of Dark, Crime Club, 1971	£350/£45
ditto, N.A.L. (U.S.), 1986.	£20/£5
A Fairly Dangerous Thing, Crime Club, 1972 . . .	
. . . .	£100/£15
ditto, Countryman (U.S.), 1983	£15/£5
A Very Good Hater, Crime Club, 1974 . .	£100/£15
ditto, Countryman (U.S.), 1982	£20/£5
Another Death in Venice, Crime Club, 1976	£100/£15
ditto, NAL (U.S.), 1987	£15/£5
The Spy's Wife, Collins, 1980 . . .	£45/£10
ditto, Pantheon (U.S.), 1980	£20/£5
Who Guards a Prince?, Collins, 1982 . .	£40/£5
ditto, as *Who Guards the Prince?*, Pantheon 1982 . .	
. . . .	£30/£5
Traitor's Blood, Collins, 1983	£50/£10
ditto, Countryman (U.S.), 1986	£25/£5
No Man's Land, Collins, 1985	£35/£5
ditto, St Martin's Press (U.S.), 1985 . . .	£25/£5
The Collaborators, Collins, 1987 . . .	£15/£5
ditto, Countryman (U.S.), 1989	£15/£5

Short Stories

Pascoe's Ghost, Crime Club 1979 . . .	£125/£20
There Are No Ghosts in the Soviet Union, Crime Club	
1987	£50/£10
ditto, Countryman (U.S.), 1988 . . .	£15/£5
One Small Step, Crime Club 1990 . . .	£40/£5
Brother's Keeper, Eurographica, 1992 (350 signed	
copies, wraps)	£60
Asking for the Moon, HarperCollins, 1994 .	£20/£5
ditto, Countryman (U.S.), 1996	£15/£5

Novels written as Dick Moorland

Heart Clock, Faber, 1973.	£150/£25
Albion! Albion!, Faber, 1974.	£75/£10

Novels written as Patrick Ruell

The Castle of the Demon, John Long, 1971	£25/£5
ditto, Hawthorn (U.S.), 1973	£25/£5
ditto, as *The Turning of the Tide*, Severn House, 1999	
. . . .	£15/£5
Red Christmas, Long 1972	£150/£25
ditto, Hawthorn (U.S.), 1974	£50/£10
Death Takes the Low Road, Hutchinson 1974 . . .	
. . . .	£150/£25
ditto, Mysterious Press (U.S.), 1987 . . .	£20/£5
Urn Burial, Hutchinson, 1975, ...	£75/£15
ditto, Countryman (U.S.), 1987	£15/£5
ditto, as *Beyond the Bone*, Severn House, 2000	£15/£5
The Long Kill, Methuen 1986	£25/£5
ditto, Countryman (U.S.), 1988	£20/£5
Death of a Dormouse, Methuen 1987 . .	£15/£5
ditto, Mysterious Press (U.S.), 1987 . . .	£15/£5

Dream of Darkness, Methuen 1989 . . .	£15/£5
ditto, Countryman (U.S.), 1990	£15/£5
The Only Game, Collins 1991	£15/£5
ditto, Countryman (U.S.), 1993	£15/£5

Novels written as Charles Underhill

Captain Fantom, Hutchinson, 1978 . . .	£20/£5
ditto, St Martin's Press (U.S.), 1980 . . .	£20/£5
The Forging of Fantom, Hutchinson, 1979	£200/£35

SUSAN HILL
(b.1942)

A novelist whose work frequently explores states of loneliness.

Novels

The Enclosure, Hutchinson, 1961 . . .	£125/£30
Do Me a Favour, Hutchinson 1963 . . .	£75/£20
Gentlemen and Ladies, Hamilton, 1968. .	£40/£10
ditto, Walker (U.S.), 1969	£15/£5
A Change for the Better, Hamilton 1969 .	£30/£10
I'm the King of the Castle, Hamilton, 1970.	£25/£10
ditto, Viking (U.S.), 1970.	£15/£5
Strange Meeting, Hamilton, 1971 . . .	£20/£5
ditto, Saturday Review Press (U.S.), 1972 .	£15/£5
The Bird of Night, Hamilton, 1972 . . .	£25/£10
ditto, Saturday Review Press (U.S.), 1972 .	£15/£5
In the Springtime of the Year, Hamilton, 1974	£15/£5
ditto, Saturday Review Press (U.S.), 1974 .	£10/£5
The Woman in Black, Hamilton 1983 . .	£25/£10
ditto, Godine (U.S.), 1986	£15/£5
Air and Angels, Sinclair-Stevenson, 1991 .	£10/£5
The Mist in the Mirror, Sinclair-Stevenson, 1992 . .	
. . . .	£10/£5
Mrs. de Winter, Sinclair Stevenson 1993 .	£10/£5
ditto, Morrow (U.S.), 1993	£10/£5
The Service of Clouds, Chatto & Windus 1998	£10/£5

Short Stories

The Albatross and Other Stories, Hamilton, 1971 . .	
. . . .	£20/£5
ditto, Saturday Review/Dutton (U.S.), 1971 .	£10/£5
The Custodian, Covent Garden Press, 1972 (100 of	
600 signed copies, wraps)	£35
ditto, Covent Garden Press, 1972 (500 of 600 copies) .	
. . . .	£20
A Bit of Singing and Dancing, Hamilton, 1973	£20/£5
Listening to the Orchestra, Long Barn, 1996 (wraps,	
signed)	£5

Plays

The Cold Country and other plays for radio, BBC,	
1975	£10/£5

Autobiography

The Magic Apple Tree, Hamilton 1982 . .	£15/£5

ditto, Holt, Rinehart & Winston (U.S.), 1992   £15/£5
Family, Joseph, 1989 . . . .   £10/£5
ditto, Viking (U.S.), 1990. . . . .   £10/£5

Children's
Lanterns Across the Snow, Joseph 1987   . £10/£5
ditto, Potter (U.S.), 1988 . . . . .   £10/£5
Can It Be True?, Hamilton 1988.   . . . £10/£5
ditto, Viking Kestrel (U.S.), 1998   . . . £10/£5
The Glass Angels, Walker Books 1991 . .   £10/£5
ditto, Candlewick Press (U.S.), 1991.   . . £10/£5
King of Kings, Walker Books 1993 . . .   £10/£5
Beware Beware, Walker Books 1993   . . . £10/£5
ditto, Candlewick Press (U.S.), 1993.   . . £10/£5
Christmas Collection, Candlewick Press (U.S.), 1994 .
  . . . . £15/£5
ditto, Candlewick Press (U.S.), 1994.   . . £10/£5

Others
Through the Kitchen Window, Hamilton 1984 £15/£5
ditto, Stemmer House (U.S.), 1984   . . . £10/£5
The Spirit of the Cotswolds, Josph, 1985   . £15/£5
Through the Garden Gate, Hamilton 1986 .   £15/£5
The Lighting Of The Lamps, Hamilton 1987 £15/£5
Shakespeare Country, Josph, 1987   . . . £15/£5
The Spirit of Britain, An Illustrated guide to Literary
Britain, Headline, 1994 .   . . . . . £10/£5

WILLIAM HOPE HODGSON
(b.1877 d.1918)

Hodgson was born in Essex and spent many of his earlier years at sea with the Merchant Marine. He is known for his ghost and horror stories, many of which have a maritime theme. Hodgson was killed in an artillery bombardment near Ypres in April, 1918.

The Boats of 'Glen Carrig ', Chapman & Hall, 1907 .
  . . . . £1,000
The House on the Borderland, Chapman & Hall, 1908
  . . . . £1,750
The Ghost Pirates, Stanley Paul, 1909 . .   £1,000
The Night Land, Eveleigh Nash, 1912 .   . £2,000
Poems and The Dream of X, R. Harold Paget (U.S.),
  1912 (wraps) £250
Carnacki the Ghost-Finder, Eveleigh Nash, 1913 .
  . . . . £1,000
ditto, Mycroft & Moran (U.S.), 1947   . £100/£30
Men of the Deep Waters, Eveleigh Nash, 1914   £750
The Luck of the Strong, Eveleigh Nash, 1916 .   £400
Captain Gault, Eveleigh Nash, 1917   . . . £400
ditto, Mcbride & Co. (U.S.), 1918 .   . . £200
The Calling of the Sea, Selwyn & Blount, 1920   . .
  . . . . £750/£250
The Voice of the Ocean, Selwyn & Blount, 1921   . .
  . . . . £750/£250

The House on the Borderland and Other Novels,
Arkham House (U.S.), 1946   . . . . £250/£75
Deep Waters, Arkham House (U.S.), 1967 . £125/£30
Out of the Storm, Donald Grant (U.S.), 1975   £50/£15
The Dream of X, Donald Grant (U.S.), 1977   £30/£10
Poems of the Sea, Ferret, 1977, (50 numbered large
paper copies of 500 signed by editor) . . £65/£20
ditto, Ferret, 1977, (450 copies of 500) . .   £45/£15
The Haunted 'Pampero': Uncollected Fantasies and
Mysteries, Donald Grant (U.S.), 1996 (500 numbered
copies signed by editor) . .   . . . . £30/£10
Terrors of the Sea: Unpublished and Uncollected
Fantasies, Donald M. Grant (U.S.), 1996 .   £50/£15

GEOFFREY HOUSEHOLD
(b.1900 d.1988)

Household is a pseudonym for Edward West. He is best known for his second novel, *Rogue Male*, although he wrote twenty thrillers and adventure stories. His work is characterised by an interest in the psychology of the chase.

Novels
The Third Hour, Chatto & Windus, 1937   . £75/£15
ditto, Little, Brown (U.S.), 1938 .   . . £65/£15
Rogue Male, Chatto & Windus, 1939   . . £500/£45
ditto, Little, Brown (U.S.), 1939 .   . . £350/£40
Arabesque, Chatto & Windus, 1948 . .   £35/£10
ditto, Little, Brown (U.S.), 1948 .   . . £20/£5
The High Place, Joseph, 1950   . . . £25/£5
ditto, Little, Brown (U.S.), 1950 .   . . £15/£5
A Rough Shoot, Joseph, 1951   . . . £25/£5
ditto, Little, Brown (U.S.), 1951 .   . . £15/£5
A Time to Kill, Little, Brown (U.S.), 1951 .   £25/£5
ditto, Joseph, 1952. . . . . £15/£5
Fellow Passenger, Joseph, 1955 .   . . £15/£5
ditto, Little, Brown (U.S.), 1955 .   . . £15/£5
Watcher in the Shadows, Joseph, 1960 .   £15/£5
ditto, Little, Brown (U.S.), 1960 .   . . £15/£5
Thing to Love, Joseph, 1963 .   . . . £10/£5
ditto, Little, Brown (U.S.), 1963 .   . . £10/£5
Olura, Joseph, 1965 . . . . . . £10/£5
ditto, Little, Brown (U.S.), 1965 .   . . £10/£5
The Courtesy of Death, Joseph, 1967   . . £10/£5
ditto, Little, Brown (U.S.), 1967 .   . . £10/£5
Dance of the Dwarfs, Joseph, 1968 .   . £10/£5
ditto, Little, Brown (U.S.), 1968 .   . . £10/£5
Doom's Caravan, Joseph , 1971 .   . . £10/£5
ditto, Little, Brown (U.S.), 1971 .   . . £10/£5
The Three Sentinels, Joseph, 1972 . .   £10/£5
ditto, Little, Brown (U.S.), 1972 .   . . £10/£5
The Lives and Times of Bernardo Brown, Joseph,
  1973 . . . . £10/£5
ditto, Little, Brown (U.S.), 1974 .   . . £10/£5
Red Anger, Joseph, 1975 . . . . . . £10/£5
ditto, Little, Brown (U.S.), 1976 .   . . £10/£5

Hostage: London, Joseph, 1977 . . . . £10/£5
ditto, Little, Brown (U.S.), 1977 . . . . £10/£5
The Last Two Weeks of George Rivac, Joseph, 1978 .
. . . . £10/£5
ditto, Little, Brown (U.S.), 1978 . . . . £10/£5
The Sending, Joseph, 1980 . . . . . £10/£5
ditto, Little, Brown (U.S.), 1980 . . . . £10/£5
Summon the Bright Water, Joseph, 1981 . £10/£5
ditto, Little, Brown (U.S.), 1981 . . . £10/£5
Rogue Justice, Joseph, 1982 . . . . . £10/£5
ditto, Little, Brown (U.S.), 1983 . . . . £10/£5
Face to the Sun, Joseph, 1988 . . . . £10/£5

Short Stories
The Salvation of Pisco Gabar, Chatto & Windus, 1938
. . . . £100/£15
ditto, Little, Brown (U.S.), 1940 . . . £65/£5
Tales of Adventurers, Joseph, 1952 . . . £20/£5
ditto, Little, Brown (U.S.), 1952 . . . . £15/£5
The Brides of Solomon, Joseph, 1958 . . £20/£5
ditto, Little, Brown (U.S.), 1958 . . . . £15/£5
Sabres on the Sand, Joseph, 1966 . . . £10/£5
ditto, Little, Brown (U.S.), 1966 . . . . £10/£5
The Europe That Was, David & Charles, 1979 £10/£5
ditto, St Martin's (U.S.), 1979 . . . . £10/£5
Capricorn and Cancer, Joseph, 1981 . . £10/£5
Arrows of Desire, Joseph, 1985 . . . . £10/£5
ditto, Little, Brown (U.S.), 1986 . . . . £10/£5
The Days of Your Fathers, Joseph, 1987 . £10/£5
ditto, Little, Brown (U.S.), 1987 . . . . £10/£5

Children's
The Terror of Villadonga, Hutchinson, 1936 £75/£25
ditto, as *The Spanish Cave*, Little, Brown (U.S.), 1936
(revised edition) . . . . £50/£20
The Exploits of Xenophon, Random House (U.S.),
1955 . . . . £15/£5
ditto, as *Xenophon's Adventure*, Bodley Head, 1961 .
. . . . £10/£5
Prisoner of the Indies, Bodley Head, 1967 . £10/£5
ditto, Little, Brown (U.S.), 1967 . . . . £10/£5
Escape Into Daylight, Bodley Head, 1976 . £10/£5

A. E. HOUSMAN
(b.1859 d.1936)

Housman was both a scholar and a poet. Although his output of verse was relatively small it is very highly regarded.

Verse
A Shropshire Lad, Kegan Paul, Trench, Trubner & Co., 1896 (first state with 'Shropshire' on the label 33mm wide) £1,500
ditto, Kegan Paul, Trench, Trubner & Co., 1896 (second state with 'Shropshire' on the label 37mm wide) £750

ditto, John Lane (U.S.), 1897 . . . . . £1,500
Last Poems, Grant Richards, [1922] (first issue with comma missing after 'love' and semicolon missing after 'rain' on p.52) . . . . . . £150/£25
ditto, Henry Holt (U.S.), 1922 . . . . £75/£15
A Fragment, privately printed, 1930 (37 copies, two folded leaves) £100
Three Poems, privately printed, Dept of English, Univ. College, London, 1935 . . . . . £45
[For my Funeral], C.U.P., 1936 (300 copies, two folded leaves) £40
More Poems, Cape, 1936. . . . . . £25/£10
ditto, Cape, 1936 (379 deluxe copies) . . £200/£75
ditto, Knopf (U.S.), 1936 . . . . . . £20/£10
Collected Poems, Cape, 1939 . . . . £25/£10
ditto, Henry Holt (U.S.), 1940 . . . . £25/£10
Stars, Venice, 1939 (10 copies signed by the artist, F. Prokosch, wraps). £150
The Manuscript Poems of A.E. Housman, Univ. of Minnesota Press (U.S.), 1955 . . . . £30/£15

Prose
Introductory Lecture, C.U.P., 1892 (wraps) . £350
ditto, privately printed, C.U.P., 1933 (100 copies, wraps). £100
ditto, C.U.P., 1937. . . . . £35/£10
ditto, Macmillan & C.U.P. (U.S.), 1937 . £30/£10
The Name and Nature of Poetry, C.U.P., 1933 . .
. . . . £45/£15
ditto, Macmillan (U.S.), 1933 . . . . £45/£15
Jubilee Address to King George V, C.U.P., 1935 (2 copies of 26 on vellum) £1,250
ditto, C.U.P., 1935 (24 copies of 26). . . £600
Letters to E.H. Blakeney, privately printed (18 copies)
. . . . £175
A.E.H., W.W., privately printed, 1944 (12 copies) £175
Thirty Letters to Witter Bynner, Knopf (U.S.), 1957 (700 copies) . . . . £45/£20
To Joseph Ishill, Oriole Press (U.S.), 1959 . . £25
Selected Prose, C.U.P., 1961 . . . . . £25/£10
The Confines of Criticism, C.U.P., 1969 . £30/£10
Letters, Hart-Davis, 1971. . . . . . £35/£10
ditto, Harvard Univ. Press, 1971. . £35/£10
Classical Papers, C.U.P., 1962 (3 vols) . . £50
Fifteen Letters to Walter Ashburner, Tragara Press, 1976 (125 copies) £75

ELIZABETH JANE HOWARD
(b.1923)

Howard took up writing novels and short stories after spending the war years as an Air Raid Warden in London.

Novels
The Beautiful Visit, Jonathan Cape, 1950 . £45/£15
ditto, Random House (U.S.), 1950 . . . £35/£5

The Long View, Jonathan Cape, 1956 . . £20/£5
ditto, Reynal (U.S.), 1956. . . . . . £20/£5
The Sea Change, Jonathan Cape, 1959 . . £20/£5
ditto, Harper (U.S.), 1960 . . . . . £15/£5
After Julius, Jonathan Cape, 1965 . . . £15/£5
ditto, Viking (U.S.), 1965 . . . . . £15/£5
Something in Disguise, Jonathan Cape, 1969 £15/£5
ditto, Viking (U.S.), 1970 . . . . . £10/£5
Odd Girl Out, Jonathan Cape, 1972 . . £10/£5
ditto, Viking (U.S.), 1972 . . . . . £10/£5
Getting it Right, Hamish Hamilton, 1982 . £10/£5
ditto, Viking (U.S.), 1982 . . . . . £10/£5
The Light Years, Macmillan, 1990 . . . £10/£5
ditto, Pocket Books (U.S.), 1990. . . . £10/£5
Making Time, Macmillan, 1991 . . . . £10/£5
ditto, Pocket Books (U.S.), 1992. . . . £10/£5
Casting Off, Macmillan, 1995 . . . . £10/£5
ditto, Pocket Books (U.S.), 1996. . . . £10/£5
Falling, Macmillan, 1991. . . . . . £10/£5

Short Stories
We Are For the Dark, Jonathan Cape, 1951 (with
Robert Aickman). . . . . . £350/£125
Mr Wrong, Jonathan Cape, 1975. . . . £10/£5
ditto, Viking (U.S.), 1975 . . . . £10/£5

Miscellaneous
Howard and Maschler on Food, Michael Joseph, 1987
(with Fay Maschler) . . . . . . £10/£5

As Editor
The Lover's Companion, David & Charles, 1978 . .
. . . . £15/£5
Green Shades, An Anthology of Plants, Arum, 1991 .
. . . . £10/£5

ROBERT E. HOWARD
(b.1906 d.1936)

A Texan writer of pulp fiction, his range extended
beyond his 'Conan' tales through westerns and sports
stories.

'Conan' Novels
Conan the Conqueror: The Hyperborean Age, Gnome
Press (U.S.), 1950 . . . . . . £200/£100
ditto, Boardman, 1954. . . . . . £125/£50
The Return of Conan, Gnome Press (U.S.), 1957 (by
L. Sprague de Camp & Bjorn Nyberg). . £125/£50
People of the Black Circle, Grant (U.S.), 1974 £35/£15
Red Nails, Grant (U.S.), 1975 . . . £25/£10
A Witch Shall Be Born, Grant (U.S.), 1975 £25/£10
The Hour of the Dragon, Grant (U.S.), 1989 £20/£10

'Conan' Stories
The Sword of Conan: The Hyperborean Age, Gnome
Press (U.S.), 1952 . . . . . . £200/£75

King Conan: The Hyperborean Age, Gnome Press
(U.S.), 1953 . . . . £200/£75
The Coming of Conan, Gnome Press (U.S.), 1953 .
. . . . £150/£65
Conan the Barbarian, Gnome Press (U.S.), 1954 . .
. . . . £150/£65
Tales of Conan, Gnome Press (U.S.), 1955 (with L.
Sprague de Camp) . . . . . . £125/£50
Conan the Adventurer, Lancer (U.S.), 1966 (wraps) .
. . . .£10
Conan the Usurper, Lancer (U.S.), 1967 (wraps) £10
The Tower of the Elephant, Grant (U.S.), 1975 . .
. . . . £25/£10
The Devil in Iron, Grant (U.S.), 1976 . £25/£10
Rogues in the House, Grant (U.S.), 1976 . £25/£10
Queen of the Black Coast, Grant (U.S.), 1978 £25/£10
Black Colossus, Grant (U.S.), 1979 . . £25/£10
Jewels of Gwahlur, Grant (U.S.), 1979 . £25/£10
The Pool of the Black One, Grant (U.S.), 1986 . .
. . . . £25/£10
The Conan Chronicles, Orbit, 1990 (two vols, wraps).
. . . . £10

Other Novels
Almuric, Ace (U.S.), 1964 (wraps) . . . £10
ditto, N.E.L., 1971 (wraps) £5

Other Short Stories
A Gent from Bear Creek, Herbert Jenkins, 1937 . .
. . . . £1,750/£1,000
ditto, Grant (U.S.), 1966 . . . . . £25/£5
Skull-Face and Others, Arkham House (U.S.), 1946
. . . . £500/£200
ditto, as *Skull-Face Omnibus*, Spearman, 1974 . .
. . . . £35/£20
The Dark Man and Others, Arkham House (U.S.),
1963 . . . . £145/£45
ditto, as *The Dark Man Omnibus*, Panther 1978 (two
vols, wraps) £10
The Pride of Bear Creek, Grant (U.S.), 1966 £45/£15
King Kull, Lancer (U.S.), 1967 (wraps, with Lin
Carter) £5
Bran Mak Morn, Dell (U.S.), 1969 (wraps) . £5
ditto, Sphere, 1976 (wraps) £5
ditto, as *Kull*, Grant (U.S.), 1985 (revised text) £20/£10
Wolfshead, Lancer (U.S.), 1968 (wraps) . . £5
Red Shadows, Grant (U.S.), 1968 . . . £125/£30
Red Blades of Black Cathay, Grant (U.S.), 1971 (with
Tevis Clyde Smith) . . . . . . £75/£25
Marchers of Valhalla, Grant (U.S.), 1972 . £20/£5
ditto, Sphere, 1977 (wraps) £5
The Vultures, Fictioneer (U.S.), 1973 . . £20/£10
The Sowers of the Thunder, Grant (U.S.), 1973 . .
. . . . £35/£10
ditto, Sphere, 1977 (wraps) £5
Worms of the Earth, Grant (U.S.), 1974 . £25/£10
ditto, Orbit/Futura, 1976 (wraps). . . . £5
The Incredible Adventures of Dennis Dorgan, Fax
(U.S.), 1974 . . . . £15/£5

The Lost Valley of Iskander, Fax (U.S.), 1974   £15/£5
ditto, Orbit/Futura, 1976 (wraps). £5
Tigers of the Sea, Grant (U.S.), 1974   .   .   £20/£5
ditto, Sphere, 1977 (wraps) £5
*Black Vulmea's Vengeance and Other Tales of
Pirates,* Grant (U.S.), 1976   .   .   .   .   £15/£5
The Iron Man and Other Tales of the Ring, Grant
(U.S.), 1976   .   .   .   .   £10/£5
The Swords of Shahrazar, Fax (U.S.), 1976   £10/£5
ditto, Orbit/Futura, 1976 (wraps).   .   .   .   £5
Son of the White Wolf, Fax (U.S.), 1977   .   £10/£5
ditto, Futura, 1977 (wraps) £5
Three-Bladed Doom, Futura, 1977 (wraps)   .   £5
Mayhem on Bear Creek, Fax (U.S.), 1979   .   £15/£5
The Road to Azrael, Grant (U.S.), 1979   .   £15/£5
Lord of the Dead, Grant (U.S.), 1981   .   .   £15/£5
Cthulhu: The Mythos and Kindred Horrors, Baen
(U.S.), 1987   .   .   .   .   £20/£5
Post Oaks and Sand Roughs, Grant (U.S.), 1991   .   .
.   .   .   .   £15/£5

Verse •
Always Comes Evening, Arkham House (U.S.), 1957 .
.   .   .   .   £300/£100
Etchings in Ivory: Poems in Prose, Glenn Lord (U.S.),
1968   .   .   .   .   £150/£50
Singers in the Shadows, Grant (U.S.), 1970 (500
copies)   .   .   .   .   £75/£25
Echoes from an Iron Harp, Grant (U.S.), 1972   .   .
.   .   .   .   £45/£15
Rhymes of Death, McHaney (U.S.), 1975 (600
numbered copies) £40
Shadows of Dreams, Grant (U.S.), 1991   £20/£10

L. RON HUBBARD
(b.1911 d.1986)

Although he wrote a number of very collectable
science fiction titles, L. Ron Hubbard is best-known
as the founder of Scientology.

Novels
Buckskin Brigades, Macauley (U.S.), 1937   .   .   .
.   .   .   .   £2,000/£200
ditto, Wright & Brown, [1938]   .   .   .   £500/£75
Final Blackout, Hadley Publishing (U.S.), 1948   .   .
.   .   .   .   £250/£65
ditto, New Era, 1989 .   .   .   .   .   .   £15/£5
Death's Deputy, Fantasy Publishing (U.S.), 1948   .   .
.   .   .   .   £125/£35
ditto, Fantasy Publishing/Gnome Press, 1959   £75/£25
Slaves of Sleep, Shasta (U.S.), 1938 .   .   .   £250/£75
ditto, Shasta (U.S.), 1938 (250 signed copies)   .   .
.   .   .   .   £1,250/£1000
Triton, Fantasy Publishing (U.S.), 1949 .   .   £100/£25
The Kingslayer, Fantasy Publishing (U.S.), 1949   .   .
.   .   .   .   £100/£25

Typewriter in the Sky and Fear, Gnome Press (U.S.),
1951   .   .   .   .   £150/£25
ditto, Fantasy Publishing/Gnome (U.S.), 1959   £45/£20
From Death to the Stars, Fantasy Publishing (U.S.),
1953)   .   .   .   .   £350/£65
Return to Tomorrow, Ace (U.S.), 1954 (wraps)   £10
ditto, Panther, 1957 (wraps) £5
Fear and the Ultimate Adventure, Berkley Medallion
(U.S.), 1970 (wraps). £10
Seven Steps to the Arbiter, Major Books (U.S.) 1975
(wraps) £10
Battlefield Earth, St Martin's Press (U.S.), 1982   .   .
.   .   .   .   £20/£5
ditto, Quadrant, 1984 .   .   .   .   .   .   £15/£5
Mission Earth, Bridge Publications (U.S.), 1985-87
(ten vols: 'The Invader's Plan', 'Death Quest', 'Black
Genesis', 'The Enemy Within', 'An Alien Affair',
'Fortune of Fear', 'Voyage of Vengeance', 'Disaster',
'Villainy Victorious' and 'The Doomed Planet')   .   .
.   .   .   .   £10/£5 each
ditto, New Era, 1986-88 (10 vols)   .   .   £10/£5 each
ditto, Bridge Publications (U.S.), 1987 (set)   .   £200

Short Stories
Ole Doc Methuselah, Theta Press (U.S.), 1970 £75/£25
ditto, New Era, 1993   .   .   .   .   .   .   £10/£5
Lives You Wished to Lead but Never Dared, Theta
Books (U.S.), 1978   .   .   .   .   .   .   £150/£45

Dianetics
Dianetics: The Modern Science of Mental Health,
Hermitage House, 1950   .   .   .   .   .   £400/£150

RICHARD HUGHES
(b.1900 d.1976)

Hughes is best known for *A High Wind in Jamaica,* a
story of children kidnapped by pirates. The novel was
considered unusual for its time because of its lack of
sentimentality.

Plays
The Sister's Tragedy, Blackwell, 1922 (wraps)   £100
The Sister's Tragedy and Other Plays, Heinemann,
1924 .   .   .   .   £75/£20
ditto, as *A Rabbit and a Leg, Collected Plays,* Knopf
(U.S.), 1924   .   .   .   .   .   .   £45/£10

Verse
Gipsy-Night and Other Poems, Golden Cockerell,
1922 (750 copies)   .   .   .   .   .   .   £75/£35
ditto, Will Ransom (U.S.), 1922 (63 copies)   £200
Confessio Juvenis: Collected Poems, Chatto &
Windus, 1925 (55 signed, numbered copies)   .   .   .
.   .   .   .   £200/£100
ditto, Chatto & Windus, 1925   .   .   .   £65/£20

Short Stories
A Moment of Time, Chatto & Windus, 1926 £100/£20
Burial and The Dark Child, Chatto & Windus, 1930 .
. . . . £75/£15
In The Lap of Atlas, Chatto & Windus, 1979 £25/£10
ditto, Merrimack (U.S.), 1980 . . . . £20/£10

Novels
The Innocent Voyage, Harper (U.S.), 1929 £150/£20
ditto, as *A High Wind in Jamaica*, Chatto & Windus,
1929 . . . . £50/£15
ditto, Chatto & Windus, 1929 (150 signed copies) . .
. . . . £200
In Hazard, Chatto & Windus, 1938 . . . £30/£5
ditto, Harper (U.S.), 1938. . . . . £30/£5
The Fox in the Attic, Chatto & Windus, 1961 £20/£5
ditto, Harper (U.S.), 1961. . . . . £20/£5
ditto, Harper (U.S.), 1961 (unknown number of copies
with signature on tipped-in leaf) . . . £30/£15
The Wooden Shepherdess, Chatto & Windus, 1973 .
. . . . £20/£5
ditto, Harper (U.S.), 1973. . . . . £20/£5

Children's Titles
The Spider's Palace, Chatto & Windus, 1931 £40/£10
ditto, Chatto & Windus, 1931 (110 numbered, signed
copies) £100
ditto, Harper (U.S.), 1932. . . . . £35/£10
Don't Blame Me and Other Stories, Chatto & Windus,
1940 . . . . £25/£5
ditto, Harper (U.S.), 1940. . . . . £20/£5
Gertrude's Child, Harlin Quist (U.S.), 1966 £25/£10
The Wonder Dog, Chatto & Windus, 1977 . £20/£5

Others
Richard Hughes: An Omnibus, Harper (U.S.), 1931.
. . . . £20/£5
The Administration of War Production, H.M.S.O.,
1955 (with J.D. Scott) £35

TED HUGHES
(b.1930 d.1998)

Hughes is chiefly known for his poetry which often
depicts the cruelties of the animal world, and the
malevolence of creatures of his own invention. In
1984 he was made Poet Laureate.

Verse
The Hawk in the Rain, Faber, 1957 . . . £200/£50
ditto, Harper (U.S.), 1957. . . . . £100/£35
Pike, Gehenna Press, 1959 (broadsheet, 150 signed
copies) £300
Lupercal, Faber, 1960. . . . . . £125/£45
ditto, Harper (U.S.), 1960. . . . . £75/£25
Selected Poems, Faber, 1962 (with Thom Gunn, wraps)
. . . . £35

The Burning of the Brothel, Turret Books, 1966 (75
numbered and signed copies, wraps with d/w) . .
. . . . £250/£150
ditto, Turret Books, 1966 (225 unsigned copies, wraps
with d/w) . . . . £75/£45
Recklings, Turret Books, 1966 (150 numbered and
signed copies) . . . . £200/£125
Scapegoats and Rabies, Poet & Printer, 1967 (approx.
400 copies, wraps) £50
ditto, Poet & Printer, 1967 (in portfolio with three other
poetry chapbooks published by the press, wraps) £200
ditto, Poet & Printer, 1967 (26 lettered copies for the
poet, wraps) £400
Wodwo, Faber, 1967 . . . . . . £45/£10
ditto, Harper (U.S.), 1967. . . . . £35/£10
Animal Poems, Gilbertson, 1967 (6 signed copies with
poems handwritten by Hughes). . . . £1,000
ditto, Gilbertson, 1967 (10 signed copies with three
manuscript poems) £750
ditto, Gilbertson, 1967 (20 signed copies with 1
manuscript poem) £500
ditto, Gilbertson, 1967 (63 signed, numbered copies) .
. . . . £400
Gravestones, Bartholomew, 1967 (set of 6 broadsheets,
40 sets printed) £1,500
ditto, as *Poems*, Bartholomew, 1967 (300 copies) £150
I Said Goodbye to Earth, Turret Books, 1969
(broadsheet, 75 signed copies) £150
A Crow Hymn, Sceptre Press, 1970 (21 signed copies
for sale) £250
ditto, Sceptre Press, 1970 (64 unsigned copies) £200
The Martyrdom of Bishop Farrar, Gilbertson, 1970
(signed copies, wraps) £200
ditto, Gilbertson, 1970 (rejected printing, lines 15 and
16 of the poem transposed) £125
A Few Crows, Rougemont Press, 1970 (75 signed
copies) . . . . £350/£275
ditto, Rougemont Press, 1970 (75 unsigned copies) .
. . . . £125/£75
Crow, Faber, 1970. . . . . . . £40/£10
ditto, Harper (U.S.), 1971. . . . . £25/£10
Fighting for Jerusalem, Northumberland Arts, 1970
(poster) £25
Crow Wakes, Poet & Printer, 1971 (100 copies) £100
Eat Crow, Rainbow Press, 1971 (150 signed, numbered
copies, slipcase) . . . . . . £300/£250
Poems, Rainbow Press, 1971 (with Ruth Fainlight and
Alan Sillitoe, 300 copies, numbered and signed by all
three poets, slipcase) . . . . £225/£175
Selected Poems, 1957-1967, Faber, 1972 (wraps) £10
ditto, Harper (U.S.), 1973. . . . . £50/£15
Prometheus on His Crag, Rainbow Press, 1973 (160
copies signed by Hughes and Leonard Baskin,
slipcase) . . . . £400/£325
Cave Birds, Scolar Press, 1975 (10 sheets issued in
box, 125 sets printed) £500
ditto, Faber, 1978 . . . . £25/£5
ditto, Viking (U.S.), 1978. . . . . £25/£5

The Interrogator: A Titled Vultress, Scolar Press, 1975
. . . . £25/£10
The New World, O.U.P., 1975 . . . . £25/£10
Eclipse, Sceptre Press, 1976 (50 signed copies, wraps)
. . . . £150
ditto, Sceptre Press, 1976 (200 unsigned copies, wraps)
. . . . £65
Gaudete, Faber, 1977 . . . . . . £20/£5
ditto, Harper (U.S.), 1977. . . . . £20/£5
Chiasmadon, Janus Press (U.S.), 1977 (120 signed copies, wraps) £250
Sunstruck, Sceptre Press, 1977 (100 signed copies) .
. . . . £150
ditto, Sceptre Press, 1977 (200 numbered copies) £60
A Solstice, Sceptre Press, 1978 (100 signed copies, wraps). £150
ditto, Sceptre Press, 1978 (250 numbered copies, wraps). £45
Orts, Rainbow Press, 1978 (200 numbered and signed copies, slipcase) . . . . . . £300/£250
Moortown Elegies, Rainbow Press, 1978 (6 author's copies) £1,000
ditto, Rainbow Press, 1978 (26 lettered A-Z) . £500
ditto, Rainbow Press, 1978 (143 numbered copies) .
. . . . £350
Adam and the Sacred Nine, Rainbow Press, 1979 (200 numbered and signed copies, slipcase) £300/£250
Remains of Elmet, Rainbow Press, 1979 (numbered 1-70, signed by Hughes and the artist, leather bound) .
. . . . £750
ditto, Rainbow Press, 1979 (numbered 71-180 signed by Hughes, ordinary binding) £500
ditto, Faber, 1979 . . . . £25/£10
The Threshold, Steam Press, 1979 (100 copies of 12 leaves, illustrated by Ralph Steadman, and signed by Hughes and Steadman) £400
Night Arrival of Sea-Trout, The Iron Wolf, Puma, Morrigu Press, 1979 (three broadsheets, 30 sets) £125
Brooktrout, Morrigu Press, 1979 (60 signed copies, broadsheet) £150
Pan, Morrigu Press, 1979 (60 signed copies, broadsheet) £150
Woodpecker, Morrigu Press, 1979 (60 signed copies, broadsheet) £150
Moortown, Faber, 1979 . . . . . £20/£5
ditto, Harper (U.S.), 1980. . . . . £20/£5
Wolverine, Morrigu Press, 1979, (75 signed copies, broadsheet) £125
Four Tales Told by an Idiot, Sceptre Press, 1979 (450 numbered copies with erratum slip) . . . £45
ditto, Sceptre Press, 1979 (100 signed copies with erratum slip) £125
In the Black Chapel, Victoria and Albert Museum, 1979 (poster) £35
Eagle, Morrigu Press, 1980, (75 signed copies, broadsheet) £125
Mosquito, Morrigu Press, 1980, (60 signed copies, broadsheet) £150

Catadrome, Morrigu Press, 1980, (75 signed copies, broadsheet) £125
Caddis, Morrigu Press, 1980, (75 signed copies, broadsheet) £125
Visitation, Morrigu Press, 1980, (75 signed copies, broadsheet) £125
A Primer of Birds, Gehenna Press, 1981 (250 copies numbered and signed by Hughes and artist, Leonard Baskin) £400
Selected Poems, 1957-1981, Faber, 1982 . £15/£5
ditto, as *New Selected Poems*, Harper (U.S.), 1982. .
. . . . £15/£5
River, Faber, 1983. . . . . . . £25/£5
ditto, Harper (U.S.), 1984. . . . . £20/£5
Weasels at Work, Morrigu Press, 1983 (75 signed copies, broadsheet) £100
Fly Inspects, Morrigu Press, 1983 (75 signed copies, broadsheet) £100
Mice are Funny Little Creatures, Morrigu Press, 1983 (75 signed copies, broadsheet) £100
Flowers and Insects: Some Birds and a Pair of Spiders, Faber, 1986. . . . . . . £25/£5
ditto, Knopf (U.S.), 1986 . . . . . £25/£5
Moortown Diary, Faber, 1989 . . . £20/£5
ditto, Faber, 1989 (wraps). £5
Wolf-Watching, Faber, 1989 . . . . £20/£5
ditto, Farrar, Straus, and Giroux (U.S.), 1991 £20/£5
Rain-Charm for the Duchy, Faber, 1992 . £15/£5
ditto, Faber, 1992 (280 signed copies with loose insert, 'The Unicorn', slipcase). £175
ditto, Faber, 1992 (wraps). £5
Three Books: Remains of Elmet, Cave Birds, River, Faber, 1993 . . . . £10
Elmet, Faber, 1984 . . . . . . £30/£10
Earth Dances, Old Stile Press, 1994 (250 copies, slipcase) £200
New Selected Poems, 1957-94, Faber, 1995 £15/£5
Ted Hughes Poetry, Collins Educational, 1997 £10/£5
Birthday Letters, Faber, 1998 . . . £25/£5
ditto, Faber, 1998 (300 signed copies) . . £500
ditto, Farrar Straus Giroux (U.S.), 1998 . £25/£5

Children's Verse
Meet My Folks!, Faber, 1961 . . . £75/£20
ditto, Bobbs-Merrill (U.S.), 1973. . . £30/£5
The Earth-Owl and Other Moon-People, Faber, 1963
. . . . £45/£15
ditto, as *Moon Whales and Other Moon People*, Viking (U.S.), 1976 . . . . . . £25/£5
ditto, as *Moonwhales*, Faber, 1988 . . £10/£5
Nessie the Mannerless Monster, Faber, 1964 £50/£15
ditto, as *Nessie the Monster*, Bobbs-Merrill (U.S.), 1974 . . . . £25/£5
Five Autumn Songs for Children's Voices, Gilbertson, 1968 (9 copies for sale with a verse in manuscript & a watercolour) £450
ditto, Gilbertson, 1968 (27 copies with a verse in manuscript, wraps) £250
ditto, Gilbertson, 1968 (150 signed copies, wraps) £150

ditto, Gilbertson, 1968 (312 numbered copies) . £25
Spring Summer Autumn Winter, Rainbow Press, 1974 (140 numbered and signed copies) £300
ditto, as *Season Songs*, Doubleday (U.S.), 1975 £20/£5
ditto, Faber, 1976 . . . . £20/£5
Earth-Moon, Rainbow Press, 1976 (226 signed and numbered copies, slipcase) . . . . . £200/£165
Moon-Bells and Other Poems, Chatto & Windus, 1978
. . . . £25/£5
Under the North Star, Faber, 1981 . . £40/£10
ditto, Viking (U.S.), 1981 . . . . . £35/£5
The Cat and the Cuckoo, Sunstone Press, [1987] (250 signed copies in d/w and slipcase) . . . £125/£50
ditto, Faber, 1991 . . . . £15/£5
Under the North Star and Others, Faber, 1990 £20/£5
The Mermaids Purse, Faber, 1991 . . . £15/£5
ditto, Knopf (U.S.), 2000 . . . . . . £15/£5
Collected Animal Poems, Faber, 1995 (4 vols). . .
. . . . £100/£20
ditto, Faber, 1996 (1 vol.). . . . . £15/£5

Children's Prose
How the Whale Became, Faber, 1963 . . £50/£15
ditto, Atheneum (U.S.), 1964 . . . . £35/£10
The Iron Man, Faber, 1968 . . . . . £50/£15
ditto, as *The Iron Giant*, Harper (U.S.), 1968 £45/£5
What is the Truth?, Faber, 1984 . . . . £25/£5
ditto, Harper (U.S.), 1984 . . . . . £20/£5
Ffangs the Vampire Bat and the Kiss of Truth, Faber, 1986 . . . . £20/£5
Tales of the Early World, Faber, 1988 . . £20/£5
The Iron Woman, Faber, 1993 . . . . £15/£5
ditto, Dial (U.S.), 1995 . . . . . £15/£5
Dreamfighter and Other Creation Tales, Faber, 1995 .
. . . . £15/£5
Shaggy and Spotty, Faber, 1997 . . . £15/£5

Others
Poetry in the Making, Faber, 1967 (no d/w) . £50
ditto, as *Poetry Is*, Doubleday (U.S.), 1970 . £35/£10
Seneca's Oedipus, Faber, 1969 . . . . £25/£5
ditto, Doubleday (U.S.), 1972 . . . . £20/£5
The Coming of the Kings and Other Plays, Faber, 1970 . . . . £25/£5
ditto, as *Tiger's Bones and Other Plays for Children*, Viking (U.S.), 1974 . . . . . . £20/£5
Shakespeare's Poem, Lexham Press, 1971 (75 signed copies, wraps) £125
Orpheus, Dramatic Publishing Company (U.S.), 1973 (1,023 copies, wraps) £30
Henry Williamson, Rainbow Press, 1979 (200 signed copies, wraps) £100
T.S. Eliot: A Tribute, Faber, 1987 (privately printed, 250 copies, wraps) £125
Shakespeare and the Goddess of Complete Being, Faber, 1992 . . . . £15/£5
ditto, Farrar Straus Giroux (U.S.), 1992 . . £15/£5
Winter Pollen: Occasional Prose, Faber, 1994 £20/£5
ditto, Picador (U.S.), 1995 . . . . . £15/£5

Difficulties of a Bridegroom, Faber, 1995 . £20/£5
ditto, Picador (U.S.), 1995 . . . . . £15/£5

ALDOUS HUXLEY
(b.1894 d.1963)

A novelist and short story writer, much of Huxley's work is marked by a certain despair and disgust, none more so than his great novel of the future, *Brave New World*.

Verse
The Burning Wheel, Blackwell, 1916 (wraps) . £450
Jonah, Holywell, 1917 (approx 50 signed copies, wraps) £1,500
The Defeat of Youth and Other Poems, Blackwell, 1918 (500 copies, wraps, no title page) . . £150
Leda, Chatto & Windus, 1920 . . . . £150/£75
ditto, Chatto & Windus, 1920 (160 numbered and signed copies) £250
ditto, Doran (U.S.), 1920 . . . . . £100/£45
ditto, Doran (U.S.), 1920 (361 numbered and signed copies, slipcase) . . . . . . £125/£100
Selected Poems, Blackwell, 1925 . . . . £75
ditto, Blackwell, 1925 (100 signed copies) . . £250
ditto, Appleton (U.S.), 1925 . . . . £65/£15
Arabia Infelix, Fountain Press (U.S.), Chatto & Windus, 1929 (692 signed, numbered copies, glassine d/w) . . . . £100/£75
Apennine, Slide Mountain Press (U.S.), 1930 (91 signed, numbered copies, glasine d/w) . . £350/£300
The Cicadas and Other Poems, Chatto & Windus, 1931 . . . . £65/£20
ditto, Chatto & Windus, 1931 (160 signed, numbered copies) . . . . £175/£125
ditto, Doubleday Doran (U.S.), 1931 . . £50/£15
Verses and a Comedy, Chatto & Windus, 1946. . .
. . . . £45/£15

Short Stories
Limbo, Chatto & Windus, 1920 (6 stories and a play) .
. . . . £75/£25
ditto, Doran (U.S.), 1920 . . . . . £65/£20
Mortal Coils, Chatto & Windus, 1922 . . £75/£25
ditto, Doran (U.S.), 1922 . . . . . £65/£20
Little Mexican and Other Stories, Chatto & Windus, 1924 . . . . £125/£35
ditto, as *Young Archimedes*, Doran (U.S.), 1924 . .
. . . . £75/£25
Two or Three Graces and Other Stories, Chatto & Windus, 1926. . . . . £75/£25
ditto, Doran (U.S.), 1926 . . . . . £50/£15
Brief Candles, Fountain Press (U.S.), 1930 (800 signed copies) £150
ditto, Doubleday Doran (U.S.), 1930 . . £65/£10
ditto, Chatto & Windus, 1930 . . . . £65/£15

Collected Short Stories, Chatto & Windus, 1957 . .
. . . . £20/£5
ditto, Harper (U.S.), 1957. . . . . . £20/£5

Novels
Crome Yellow, Chatto & Windus, 1921 . . £250/£75
ditto, Doran (U.S.), 1922 . . . . . . £175/£45
Antic Hay, Chatto & Windus, 1923 . . . £175/£40
ditto, Doran (U.S.), 1923 . . . . . . £100/£25
Those Barren Leaves, Chatto & Windus, 1925 £75/£15
ditto, Doran (U.S.), 1925 . . . . . . £65/£15
ditto, Doran, 1925 (250 signed, numbered copies) £200
Point Counter Point, Chatto & Windus, 1928 . .
. . . . £125/£25
ditto, Chatto & Windus, 1928 (256 signed and
numbered copies) £200
ditto, Doubleday Doran (U.S.), 1928 . . £75/£15
Brave New World, Chatto & Windus, 1932. . . .
. . . . £1,250/£150
ditto, Chatto & Windus, 1932 (324 signed numbered
copies) £1,250
ditto, Doubleday Doran (U.S.), 1932 £1,250/£150
ditto, Doubleday Doran (U.S.), 1932 (250 signed
numbered copies) £1,250
Eyeless in Gaza, Chatto & Windus, 1936 . £200/£35
ditto, Chatto & Windus, 1936 (200 signed, numbered
copies) £300
ditto, Harper (U.S.), 1936. . . . . . £125/£30
After Many a Summer, Chatto & Windus, 1939 . .
. . . . £175/£35
ditto, Harper (U.S.), 1939. . . . . . £100/£20
Time Must Have a Stop, Chatto & Windus, 1944 . .
. . . . £45/£10
ditto, Harper (U.S.), 1944. . . . . . £35/£10
Ape and Essence, Chatto & Windus, 1948 . £30/£5
ditto, Harper (U.S.), 1948. . . . . . £25/£5
The Genius and the Goddess, Chatto & Windus, 1955
. . . . £25/£5
ditto, Harper (U.S.), 1955. . . . . . £20/£5
Island, Chatto & Windus, 1962 . . . . £20/£5
ditto, Harper (U.S.), 1962. . . . . . £20/£5

Drama
The World of Light, Chatto & Windus, 1931 £75/£10
ditto, Chatto & Windus, 1931 (160 signed, numbered
copies) £150
ditto, Doubleday Doran (U.S.), 1931 . . £65/£10
The Gioconda Smile, Chatto & Windus, 1948 £35/£5
ditto, Harper (U.S.), 1948. . . . . . £30/£5

Others
On the Margin, Chatto & Windus, 1923 (first issue
with page 'vi' numbered 'v') . . . . £100/£25
ditto, Doran (U.S.), 1923 . . . . . . £50/£10
Along the Road, Chatto & Windus, 1925 . £75/£20
ditto, Doran (U.S.), 1925 . . . . . . £40/£5
ditto, Doran, 1925 (250 signed, numbered copies,
slipcase and d/w). . . . . . £200/£100

Essays New and Old, Chatto & Windus, 1926 (650
signed, numbered copies) . . . . £150/£100
ditto, Doran (U.S.), 1927 . . . . . . £45/£10
Jesting Pilate, Chatto & Windus, 1926 . . £100/£20
ditto, Doran (U.S.), 1926 . . . . . . £75/£20
Proper Studies, Chatto & Windus, 1927 . £75/£15
ditto, Chatto & Windus, 1927 (260 signed copies) £150
ditto, Doubleday Doran (U.S.), 1928 . . £65/£15
Do What You Will, Chatto & Windus, 1929 £65/£15
ditto, Doubleday Doran (U.S.), 1929 . . £45/£10
Holy Face and Other Essays, The Fleuron Press, 1929
(300 numbered copies) £175
Vulgarity in Literature, Chatto & Windus, 1930, No. 1
of the 'Dolphin's Books' . . . . £50/£115
ditto, Chatto & Windus, 1930 (260 signed, numbered
copies) £125
ditto, Doubleday Doran (U.S.), 1933 . £45/£15
Music at Night and Other Essays, Chatto & Windus,
1931 . . . . £75/£15
ditto, Chatto & Windus/Fountain Press 1931 (842
signed, numbered copies) £125
ditto, Doubleday Doran (U.S.), 1931 . . £50/£10
Rotunda, Chatto & Windus, 1932 . . £25/£10
T.H. Huxley as a Man of Letters, Macmillan, 1932
(wraps) £25
Texts and Pretexts, Chatto & Windus, 1932 (214
signed copies) £200
ditto, Chatto & Windus, 1932 . . . . £25/£5
ditto, Harper (U.S.), 1933. . . . . . £25/£5
Beyond the Mexique Bay, Chatto & Windus, 1934 .
. . . . £125/£25
ditto, Chatto & Windus, 1934 (210 signed, numbered
copies) £200
ditto, Harper (U.S.), 1934. . . . . . £75/£10
The Olive Tree and Other Essays, Chatto & Windus,
1936 . . . . £45/£10
ditto, Chatto & Windus, 1936 (160 signed, numbered
copies) £200
ditto, Harper (U.S.), 1937. . . . . . £35/£10
**What Are You Going to do About It? The Case for
Constructive Peace**, Chatto & Windus, 1936 (wraps)
. . . . £65
ditto, Harper (U.S.), 1937 (wraps) £35
Ends and Means, Chatto & Windus, 1937 . £15/£5
ditto, Chatto & Windus, 1937 (160 signed, numbered
copies) £150
ditto, Harper (U.S.), 1937. . . . . . £15/£5
The Most Agreeable Vice, Ward Ritchie Press (U.S.),
1938 (500 copies, wraps) £250
Beyond the Swarm, Ward Ritchie Press (U.S.), 1939
(300 copies, wraps) £250
Grey Eminence, Chatto & Windus, 1941 . £25/£5
ditto, Harper (U.S.), 1941. . . . . . £25/£5
The Art of Seeing, Chatto & Windus, 1942. £25/£5
ditto, Harper (U.S.), 1942. . . . . . £25/£5
The Perennial Philosophy, Chatto & Windus, 1945 .
. . . . £30/£5
ditto, Harper (U.S.), 1945. . . . . . £25/£5

Science, Liberty and Peace, Chatto & Windus, 1946 .
. . . . £15/£5
ditto, Harper (U.S.), 1946 . . . . . £15/£5
The Prisons, Trianon Press, 1949 (212 signed and numbered copies, slipcase) £250
ditto, Trianon Press, 1949 (1,000 unsigned copies) £45
ditto, Zeitlin & Ver Brugge (U.S.), 1949 (212 signed and numbered copies, slipcase) £250
Themes and Variations, Chatto & Windus, 1950 . .
. . . . £15/£5
ditto, Harper (U.S.), 1950 . . . . . £15/£5
The Devils of Loudun, Chatto & Windus, 1952 £25/£5
ditto, Harper (U.S.), 1952 . . . . . £20/£5
The Doors of Perception, Chatto & Windus, 1954 . .
. . . . £45/£10
ditto, Harper (U.S.), 1954 . . . . . £40/£10
Adonis and the Alphabet, Chatto & Windus, 1956 .
. . . . £15/£5
ditto, as *Tomorrow and Tomorrow and Tomorrow*, Harper (U.S.), 1956 . . . . . . £15/£5
Heaven and Hell, Chatto & Windus, 1956 . £25/£5
ditto, Harper (U.S.), 1956 . . . . . £10/£5
Brave New World Revisited, Chatto & Windus, 1958 .
. . . . £30/£5
ditto, Harper (U.S.), 1958 . . . . . £25/£5
Letters, Chatto & Windus, 1969 . . . . £30/£5

J. K. HUYSMANS
(b.1848 d.1907)

The dates of publication of the English translations of Huysmans' work give a distorted idea of the development of this writer. *A Rebours*, or *Against the Grain* (also translated as *Against Nature*) was not only highly sensational, but very influential, following on from his early novels which had shown a marked influence of Zola.

En Route, Kegan Paul, 1896 . . . . . £50
ditto, Dutton (U.S.), 1920 . . . . . . £25
The Cathedral, Kegan Paul, 1898 . . . . £40
Knapsack, Collier, 1907 . . . . . . £10
Against the Grain, Lieber & Lewis (U.S.), 1922 . .
. . . . £75/£25
ditto, Fortune Press, 1931 . . . . . £75/£25
St. Lydwine of Schiedam, Kegan Paul, 1923 £75/£35
The Oblate, Kegan Paul, 1924 . . . . £50/£25
Down There, Boni (U.S.), 1924 . . . . £150/£25
ditto, Fortune Press, 1930 . . . . . £75/£25
The Crowds of Lourdes, Burns & Oates, 1925 £50/£20
Downstream and Other Works, Covici (U.S.), 1927 .
. . . . £75/£30
ditto, Fortune Press, 1952 . . . . . £50/£20
Marthe, Lear (U.S.), 1948 . . . . . £30/£10
ditto, Fortune Press, 1958 . . . . . £45/£20
Grunewald, Phaidon, 1958 . . . . £45/£20

ditto, Dutton (U.S.), 1976 . . . . . . £25/£10
Parisian Sketches, Fortune Press, 1962 . . £35/£15
Emile Zola and L'Assommoir, Princeton (U.S.), 1963
. . . . £25/£10
Living Together, Fortune Press, [1971] . . £25/£10
Vatard Sisters, Univ. of Kentucky Press (U.S.), 1983 .
. . . . £20/£5
The Bievre River, Langtry Press, 1986 . . £25/£10
The Road from Decadence : From Brothel to Cloister: Selected Letters, Athlone Press, 1989 . . £20/£5
ditto, Ohio State Univ. Press, 1989 . . . £20/£5

HAMMOND INNES
(b.1913 d.1998)

Ralph Hammond Innes' thrillers have been translated into many languages, and appear in book club and wraps editions throughout the world.

Novels
The Doppelganger, Jenkins, 1936 . . . £750/£65
Air Disaster, Jenkins, 1937 . . . . . £650/£50
Sabotage Broadcast, Jenkins, 1938 . . . £650/£50
All Roads Lead to Friday, Jenkins, 1939 . £650/£50
Wreckers Must Breathe, Collins, 1940 . . £500/£45
The Trojan Horse, Collins, 1940 . . . £500/£45
Attack Alarm, Collins, 1941 . . . . . £500/£45
ditto, Macmillan (U.S.), 1942 . . . . £250/£25
Dead and Alive, Collins, 1946 . . . . £250/£25
The Lonely Skier, Collins, 1947 . . . . £125/£15
ditto, as *Fire In The Snow*, Harper (U.S.), 1947 . .
. . . . £100/£15
The Killer Mine, Collins, 1947 . . . . £75/£10
ditto, Harper (U.S.), 1947 . . . . . £50/£10
Maddon's Rock, Collins, 1948 . . . . £50/£10
ditto, as *Gale Warning*, Harper (U.S.), 1948 £45/£10
The Blue Ice, Collins, 1948 . . . . . £45/£10
ditto, Harper (U.S.), 1948 . . . . . £35/£10
The White South, Collins, 1949 . . . . £45/£10
ditto, as *Survivors*, Harpers (U.S.), 1949 . £35/£10
The Angry Mountain, Collins, 1950 . . . £35/£10
ditto, Harper (U.S.), 1950 . . . . . £35/£10
Air Bridge, Collins, 1951 . . . . . £45/£10
ditto, Knopf (U.S.), 1951 . . . . . £35/£10
Campbell's Kingdom, Collins, 1952 . . . £35/£10
ditto, Knopf (U.S.), 1952 . . . . . £25/£5
The Strange Land, Collins, 1954 . . . £25/£5
ditto, as *The Naked Land*, Knopf (U.S.), 1954 £25/£5
The Mary Deare, Collins, 1956 . . . . £25/£5
ditto, as *The Wreck of the Mary Deare*, Knopf (U.S.), 1956 . . . . £25/£5
The Land God Gave to Cain, Collins, 1958 £25/£5
ditto, Knopf (U.S.), 1958 . . . . . £25/£5
The Doomed Oasis, Collins, 1960 . . . £30/£5
ditto, Knopf (U.S.), 1960 . . . . . £25/£5

Atlantic Fury, Collins, 1962	£20/£5
ditto, Random House (U.S.), 1962 . . .	£20/£5
The Strode Venturer, Collins, 1965 . . .	£15/£5
ditto, Knopf (U.S.), 1965	£15/£5
Levkas Man, Collins, 1971	£15/£5
ditto, Knopf (U.S.), 1971	£15/£5
Golden Soak, Collins, 1973	£15/£5
ditto, Knopf (U.S.), 1973	£15/£5
North Star, Collins, 1974	£15/£5
ditto, Knopf (U.S.), 1975	£15/£5
The Big Footprints, Collins, 1977 . . .	£15/£5
ditto, Knopf (U.S.), 1977	£15/£5
Solomon's Seal, Collins, 1980	£15/£5
ditto, Knopf (U.S.), 1975	£15/£5
The Black Tide, Collins, 1982	£15/£5
ditto, Doubleday (U.S.), 1983	£15/£5
High Stand, Collins, 1985	£15/£5
ditto, Atheneum (U.S.), 1986	£15/£5
Medusa, Collins, 1988	£15/£5
ditto, Atheneum (U.S.), 1988	£15/£5
Isvik, Chapmans, 1991	£15/£5
ditto, St Martin's Press (U.S.), 1992 . .	£10/£5
The Delta Connection, Macmillan, 1996 .	£10/£5
ditto, Thorndike Press (U.S.), 1997 . . .	£10/£5

Children's (pseud. 'Ralph Hammond')

Cocos Island, Collins, 1950	£35/£10
ditto, as *Cocos Gold*, Harpers (U.S.), 1950 .	£25/£5
Isle of Strangers, Collins, 1951	£35/£10
Saracen's Tower, Collins, 1952	£35/£10
ditto, as *Cruise of Danger*, Westminster Press (U.S.), 1952	£25/£5
Black Gold on the Double Diamond, Collins, 1953 .	
. . . .	£35/£10
ditto, as *Island of Peril*, Westminster Press (U.S.), 1953	£25/£5

Non Fiction

Harvest of Journeys, Collins, 1960 . . .	£25/£5
ditto, Knopf (U.S.), 1960	£25/£5
Scandinavia, Time-Life (U.S.), 1963 . . .	£10
Sea and Islands, Collins, 1967	£10/£5
ditto, Knopf (U.S.), 1967	£10/£5
The Conquistadores, Collins, 1969 . . .	£10/£5
ditto, Collins, 1969 (deluxe leather-bound edition) .	
. . . .	£200
ditto, Knopf (U.S.), 1969	£10/£5
Hammond Innes Introduces Australia, Andre Deutsch, 1971	£10/£5
ditto, McGraw Hill (U.S.), 1971	£10/£5
The Last Voyage: Captain Cook's Lost Diary, Collins, 1979	£15/£5
ditto, Knopf (U.S.), 1979	£10/£5
Hammond Innes' East Anglia, Hodder & Stoughton, 1986	£15/£5

MICHAEL INNES
(b.1906 d.1994)

Innes is the pseudonym used by J.I.M. Stewart when writing his many detective novels. These range from the ingenious and urbane through to straightforward chase novels.

Novels

Death at the President's Lodging, Gollancz, 1936 . .	
. . . .	£750/£100
ditto, as *Seven Suspects*, Dodd, Mead (U.S.), 1936 .	
. . . .	£400/£50
Hamlet, Revenge!, Gollancz, 1937 . . .	£500/£75
ditto, Dodd, Mead (U.S.), 1938	£300/£50
Lament for a Maker, Gollancz, 1938 . .	£450/£75
ditto, Dodd, Mead (U.S.), 1938	£300/£50
Stop Press, Gollancz, 1939	£450/£75
ditto, as *The Spider Strikes*, Dodd, Mead (U.S.), 1939 .	
. . . .	£300/£50
There Came Both Mist and Snow, Gollancz, 1940 .	
. . . .	£450/£75
ditto, as *A Comedy of Terrors*, Dodd, Mead (U.S.), 1940	£300/£50
The Secret Vanguard, Gollancz, 1940 . .	£300/£25
ditto, Dodd, Mead (U.S.), 1941	£75/£25
Appleby on Ararat, Gollancz, 1941 . . .	£400/£45
ditto, Dodd, Mead (U.S.), 1941	£75/£25
The Daffodil Affair, Gollancz, 1942 . .	£250/£30
ditto, Dodd, Mead (U.S.), 1942	£75/£25
The Weight of the Evidence, Dodd, Mead (U.S.), 1943 .	
. . . .	£125/£25
ditto, Gollancz, 1944	£125/£25
Appleby's End, Gollancz, 1945 . . .	£200/£25
ditto, Dodd, Mead (U.S.), 1945	£50/£15
From London Far, Gollancz, 1946 . . .	£40/£15
ditto, as *The Unsuspected Chasm*, Dodd, Mead (U.S.), 1946	£25/£5
What Happened at Hazelwood, Gollancz, 1946 . .	
. . . .	£40/£15
ditto, Dodd, Mead (U.S.), 1946	£50/£15
A Night of Errors, Dodd, Mead (U.S.), 1947	£45/£15
ditto, Gollancz, 1948	£35/£10
The Journeying Boy, Gollancz, 1949 . .	£35/£10
ditto, as *The Case of the Journeying Boy*, Dodd, Mead (U.S.), 1949	£25/£5
Operation Pax, Gollancz, 1951	£35/£10
ditto, as *The Paper Thunderbolt*, Dodd, Mead (U.S.), 1951	£25/£5
A Private View, Gollancz, 1952	£35/£5
ditto, as *One-Man Show*, Dodd, Mead (U.S.), 1952 .	
. . . .	£25/£5
Christmas at Candleshoe, Gollancz, 1953 .	£30/£5
ditto, Dodd, Mead (U.S.), 1953	£25/£5
The Man from the Sea, Gollancz, 1955 . .	£30/£5
ditto, as *Death by Moonlight*, Dodd, Mead (U.S.), 1955	£25/£5
Old Hall, New Hall, Gollancz, 1956 . . .	£30/£5

ditto, as *A Question of Queens*, Dodd, Mead (U.S.),
1956 . . . . £25/£5
Appleby Plays Chicken, Gollancz, 1956 . £30/£5
ditto, as *Death On a Quiet Day*, Dodd, Mead (U.S.),
1957 . . . . £25/£5
The Long Farewell, Gollancz, 1958 . . . £30/£5
ditto, Dodd, Mead (U.S.), 1958 . . . . £25/£5
Hare Sitting Up, Gollancz, 1959 . . . . £30/£5
ditto, Dodd, Mead (U.S.), 1959 . . . . £25/£5
The New Sonia Wayward, Gollancz, 1960 . £30/£5
ditto, as *The Case of Sonia Wayward*, Dodd, Mead
(U.S.), 1960 . . . . £25/£5
Silence Observed, Gollancz, 1961 . . . £30/£5
ditto, Dodd, Mead (U.S.), 1961 . . . . £25/£5
A Connoisseur's Case, Gollancz, 1962 . . £30/£5
ditto, as *The Crabtree Affair*, Dodd, Mead (U.S.), 1962
. . . . £25/£5
Money from Holme, Gollancz, 1964 . . £30/£5
ditto, Dodd, Mead (U.S.), 1965 . . . . £25/£5
Appleby Intervenes, Dodd, Mead (U.S.), 1965 £20/£5
The Bloody Wood, Gollancz, 1966 . . . £25/£5
ditto, Dodd, Mead (U.S.), 1966 . . . . £20/£5
A Change of Heir, Gollancz, 1966 . . . £25/£5
ditto, Dodd, Mead (U.S.), 1966 . . . . £20/£5
Appleby at Allington, Gollancz, 1968 . . £25/£5
ditto, as *Death by Water*, Dodd, Mead (U.S.), 1968 .
. . . . £20/£5
A Family Affair, Gollancz, 1969 . . . . £25/£5
ditto, as *Picture of Guilt*, Dodd, Mead (U.S.), 1969 .
. . . . £20/£5
Death at the Chase, Gollancz, 1970 . . . £25/£5
ditto, Dodd, Mead (U.S.), 1970 . . . . £20/£5
An Awkward Lie, Gollancz, 1971 . . . £20/£5
ditto, Dodd, Mead (U.S.), 1971 . . . . £15/£5
The Open House, Gollancz, 1972 . . . £20/£5
ditto, Dodd, Mead (U.S.), 1972 . . . . £15/£5
Appleby's Answer, Gollancz, 1973 . . . £20/£5
ditto, Dodd, Mead (U.S.), 1973 . . . . £15/£5
Appleby's Other Story, Gollancz, 1974 . . £20/£5
ditto, Dodd, Mead (U.S.), 1974 . . . . £15/£5
The Mysterious Commission, Gollancz, 1974 £20/£5
ditto, Dodd, Mead (U.S.), 1974 . . . . £15/£5
The Gay Phoenix, Gollancz, 1976 . . . £20/£5
ditto, Dodd, Mead (U.S.), 1976 . . . . £15/£5
Honeybath's Haven, Gollancz, 1977 . . £15/£5
ditto, Dodd, Mead (U.S.), 1977 . . . . £10/£5
The Ampersand Papers, Gollancz, 1978 . £15/£5
ditto, Dodd, Mead (U.S.), 1978 . . . . £10/£5
Going It Alone, Gollancz, 1980 . . . . £15/£5
ditto, Dodd, Mead (U.S.), 1980 . . . . £10/£5
Lord Mullion's Secret, Gollancz, 1981 . . £15/£5
ditto, Dodd, Mead (U.S.), 1981 . . . . £10/£5
Sheikhs and Adders, Gollancz, 1982 . . £15/£5
ditto, Dodd, Mead (U.S.), 1984 . . . . £10/£5
Appleby and Honeybath, Gollancz, 1983 . £15/£5
ditto, Dodd, Mead (U.S.), 1983 . . . . £10/£5
Carson's Conspiracy, Gollancz, 1984 . . £15/£5
ditto, Dodd, Mead (U.S.), 1984 . . . . £10/£5
Appleby and the Ospreys, Gollancz, 1986 . £15/£5

ditto, Dodd, Mead (U.S.), 1986 . . . . £10/£5

Short Stories
Appleby Talking, Gollancz, 1954 . . . £200/£25
ditto, as *Dead Man's Shoes*, Dodd, Mead (U.S.), 1954
. . . . £150/£15
Appleby Talks Again, Gollancz, 1956 . . £35/£5
ditto, Dodd, Mead (U.S.), 1957 . . . . £25/£5
The Appleby File, Gollancz, 1975 . . . £20/£5
ditto, Dodd, Mead (U.S.), 1975 . . . . £15/£5

CHRISTOPHER ISHERWOOD
(b.1904 d.1986)

Isherwood is usually remembered for the novels *Mr
Norris Changes Trains* and *Goodbye to Berlin*. The
latter included the sketch 'Sally Bowles', which was
dramatised and turned into the popular musical
Cabaret.

Novels
All the Conspirators, Cape, 1928 . . £1,500/£100
ditto, New Directions (U.S.), 1958 . . . £50/£10
The Memorial, Hogarth Press, 1931 (first binding pink,
lettered blue) . . . . £350/£100
ditto, Hogarth Press, 1931 (later bindings, blue or
ochre) . . . . £250/£45
ditto, New Directions (U.S.), 1946 . . . £45/£10
Mr Norris Changes Trains, Hogarth Press, 1935 . .
. . . . £1,500/£100
ditto, as *The Last of Mr Norris*, Morrow (U.S.), 1935 .
. . . . £250/£40
Sally Bowles, Hogarth Press, 1937 . . £750/£250
Goodbye to Berlin, Hogarth Press, 1939 £1,250/£100
ditto, Random House (U.S.), 1939 . . . £400/£75
Prater Violet, Random House (U.S.), 1945 . £125/£15
ditto, Methuen, 1946 . . . . £75/£15
The World in the Evening, Random House (U.S.),
1954 . . . . £45/£10
ditto, Methuen, 1954 . . . . £25/£5
Down There on a Visit, Simon & Schuster (U.S.), 1962
. . . . £25/£5
ditto, Methuen, 1962 . . . . £15/£5
A Single Man, Simon & Schuster (U.S.), 1964 £20/£5
ditto, Methuen, 1964 . . . . £15/£5
A Meeting by the River, Simon & Schuster (U.S.),
1967 . . . . £15/£5
ditto, Methuen, 1967 . . . . £15/£5

Omnibus Editions
The Berlin Stories, New Directions (U.S.), 1945 . .
. . . . £125/£15
ditto, as *The Berlin of Sally Bowles*, Hogarth Press,
1975 . . . . £15/£5

Plays

The Dog Beneath the Skin, Faber, 1935 (with W.H. Auden) . . . . £125/£35
ditto, Random House (U.S.), 1935 . . . £75/£25
The Ascent of F6, Faber, 1936 (with W.H. Auden) . . . . £75/£20
ditto, Random House (U.S.), 1937 . . . £50/£20
On The Frontier, Faber, 1938 (with W.H. Auden). . . . . £100/£25
ditto, Random House (U.S.), 1939 . . . £75/£20

Verse

People One Ought to Know, Doubleday, 1982 £10/£5
ditto, Macmillan, 1982 . . . . . . £10/£5

Others

Lions and Shadows, Hogarth Press, 1938 (blue cloth lettered black) . . . . £500/£100
ditto, Hogarth Press, 1938 (blue cloth lettered gilt). . . . . £400/£50
ditto, New Directions (U.S.), 1948 . . . £125/£25
Journey to a War, Faber, 1939 (with W.H. Auden) . . . . £100/£35
ditto, Random House (U.S.), 1939 . . . £75/£25
The Condor and the Cows, Random House (U.S.), 1949 . . . . £45/£15
ditto, Methuen, 1949 . . . . £40/£10
Ramakrishna and His Disciples, Simon & Schuster (U.S.), 1965 . . . . £20/£5
ditto, Methuen, 1965 . . . . £20/£5
Exhumations, Simon & Schuster (U.S.), 1966 £15/£5
ditto, Methuen, 1966 . . . . £15/£5
Kathleen and Frank, Simon & Schuster (U.S.), 1971 . . . . £10/£5
ditto, Methuen, 1971 . . . . £10/£5
Frankenstein: The True Story, Avon (U.S.), 1973 (wraps) £10
Christopher and His Kind, Farrar, Strauss and Giroux (U.S.), 1976 . . . . £10/£5
ditto, Farrar, Strauss/Sylvester & Orphanos (U.S.), 1976 (100 signed copies, slipcase) . . . £250/£200
ditto, Eyre Methuen, 1977 . . . . £10/£5
My Guru and His Disciple, Farrar Straus (U.S.), 1980 . . . . £10/£5
ditto, Eyre Methuen, 1980 . . . . £10/£5
October, Twelvetrees Press (U.S.), 1980 (150 numbered, signed copies, slipcase). . . . £250
ditto, Twelvetrees Press (U.S.), 1980 (26 signed, lettered copies) £400
ditto, Twelvetrees Press (U.S.), 1980 (wraps) £20
ditto, Methuen, 1982 (1,000 copies, wraps). . £20
Diaries, Volume One: 1939-1960, Methuen, 1996. . . . . £15/£5
ditto, HarperCollins (U.S.), 1997. . . . £15/£5

KAZUO ISHIGURO
(b.1954)

A product of Malcolm Bradbury's creative writing course at the University of East Anglia, Ishiguro's slim, studied novels have become very fashionable following the successful film adaptation of *The Remains of the Day*.

Novels

A Pale View of Hills, Faber, 1982 . . . £750/£50
ditto, Putnam (U.S.), 1982 . . . . . £100/£20
An Artist of the Floating World, Faber, 1986 (2nd issue, printed by Richard Clay) . . . . £65/£10
ditto, Putnam (U.S.), 1986 . . . . . £35/£5
The Remains of the Day, Faber 1989 . . £125/£25
ditto, Knopf (U.S.), 1989 . . . . . . £50/£20
The Unconsoled, Faber 1995. . . . . £15/£5
ditto, Knopf (U.S.), 1995 . . . . . . £15/£5
When We Were Orphans, Faber 2000 . . £15/£5
ditto, Knopf (U.S.), 2000 . . . . . . £15/£5

Short Stories

Early Japanese Stories, Belmont Press, 2000 (50 signed deluxe copies of 250) £300
ditto, Belmont Press, 2000 (150 signed special copies of 250) £200
ditto, Belmont Press, 2000 (100 signed standard copies of 250) £100

HENRY JAMES
(b.1843 d.1916)

Highly regarded American (later British) author of early modernist fiction, often producing comedies of manners featuring the American abroad.

Novels

Roderick Hudson, Osgood (U.S.) 1876 [1875] (first issue) £500
ditto, Houghton Mifflin (U.S.) 1876 [1875] (second issue) £400
ditto, Macmillan, 1879 (3 vols) £2,500
The American, Osgood (U.S.), 1877 . . . £450
ditto, Ward Lock, 1877 (pirated U.K. first edition). £450
ditto, Macmillan, 1879 (authorised U.K. first edition) £400
Watch and Ward, Houghton Osgood (U.S.), 1878 (with blank leaf after p.129) £500
ditto, Houghton Osgood (U.S.), 1878 (without blank leaf) £250
ditto, Houghton Osgood (U.K.), 1878 . . £400
The Europeans, Macmillan, 1878, (2 vols). . £600
ditto, Houghton Osgood (U.S.), 1879 . . £400
Confidence, Chatto & Windus, 1880 [1879] (2 vols) £2,500

ditto, Houghton Osgood (U.S.), 1880 . . . £300
Washington Square; The Pension Beaurepas; A Bundle of Letters, Harper (U.S.), 1881 [1882] £400
ditto, Macmillan, 1881 (2 vols) £1,000
The Portrait of a Lady, Macmillan, 1881, (3 vols). .
. . . . £4,000
ditto, Houghton Mifflin (U.S.), 1882 . . . £250
The Bostonians, Macmillan, 1886, (3 vols). . £2,500
ditto, Macmillan (U.S.), 1886 . . . . . £200
The Princess Casamassima, Macmillan, 1886, (3 vols)
. . . . £2,500
ditto, Macmillan (U.S.), 1886 . . . . . £200
The Reverberator, Macmillan, 1888, (2 vols) £1,000
ditto, Macmillan (U.S.), 1888 . . . . . £200
The Tragic Muse, Houghton Mifflin (U.S.), 1890 (2 vols) £500
ditto, Macmillan, 1890, (2 vols) £500
The Other House, Heinemann, 1896, (2 vols) . £500
ditto, Macmillan (U.S.), 1896 . . . . . £100
The Spoils of Poynton, Heinemann, 1897 . . £125
ditto, Houghton Mifflin (U.S.), 1897 . . . £100
What Maisie Knew, Stone (U.S.), 1897 . . . £100
ditto, Heinemann, 1897 (tulips on front cover) . £400
ditto, Heinemann, 1897 (irises on front cover) . £100
In the Cage, Duckworth, 1898 . . . . . £50
ditto, Herbert S. Stone & Co. (U.S.), 1898 . . £50
The Awkward Age, Heinemann, 1899 . . . £75
ditto, Harper (U.S.), 1899. . . . . . . £75
The Sacred Fount, Scribners (U.S.), 1901 (2 vols) £75
ditto, Methuen, 1901 . . . . £50
The Wings of the Dove, Scribners (U.S.), 1902 (2 vols)
. . . . £200
ditto, Archibald Constable, 1902. . . . . £200
The Ambassadors, Macmillan, 1903 . . . £75
ditto, Harper (U.S.), 1903. . . . . . . £50
The Golden Bowl, Scribners (U.S.), 1905 (2 vols). .
. . . . £150
ditto, Methuen, 1905 . . . . £100
The Outcry, Methuen, 1911 . . . . . . £25
ditto, Scribners (U.S.), 1911 . . . . . . £25
The Ivory Tower, Collins, 1917 . . . . . £50
ditto, Scribner (U.S.), 1917 . . . . . . £45
The Sense of the Past, Collins, 1917 (unfinished) £25
ditto, Scribner (U.S.), 1917 . . . . . . £25

Collected Editions
The Collective Edition, Macmillan, 1883, (14 vols) .
. . . . £1,000
ditto, Macmillan, 1883, (14 vols, wraps) . . £750
The New York Edition, Scribners (U.S.), 1907-9, 1918
(26 vols) £2,500
ditto, Scribners (U.S.), 1907-9 (156 copies on handmade paper). £5,000

Short Stories
A Passionate Pilgrim, Osgood (U.S.), 1875 . £750
ditto, Macmillan, 1879 (3 vols) £500
Daisy Miller; An International Episode, Four Meetings, Macmillan, 1879 (2 vols) . . £450

The Madonna of the Future and Other Tales, Macmillan, 1879 (2 vols) £450
Tales of Three Cities, Macmillan, 1884 . . . £75
Stories Revived, Macmillan, 1885 (3 vols) . . £400
The Aspern Papers; Louis Pallant, The Modern Warning, Macmillan, 1888 (2 vols) . . . £350
A London Life; The Patagonia; The Liar; Mrs Temperley, Macmillan, 1889 (2 vols) . . . £250
ditto, Macmillan (U.S.), 1889 . . . . . . £75
The Lesson of the Master; The Marriages; The Pupil; Brooksmith; The Solution; Sir Edmund Orme, Macmillan (U.S.), 1892 . . . . £75
ditto, Macmillan, 1892 . . . . £75
The Real Thing and Other Tales, Macmillan (U.S.), 1893 . . . . £75
ditto, Macmillan, 1893 . . . . £75
The Private Life; The Wheel of Time; Lord Beaupre; The Visits; Collaboration; Owen Wingrave, Osgood McIlvane, 1893 . . . . £100
ditto, Harpers (U.S.), 1893 . . . . . . £75
Terminations; The Death of the Lion; The Coxon Fund; The Middle Years; The Altar of the Dead, Heinemann, 1895 . . . . £75
ditto, Harpers (U.S.), 1895 . . . . . . £75
Embarrassments; The Figure in the Carpet; Glasses; The Next Time; The Way it Came, Heinemann, 1896 . . . . £75
The Two Magics: The Turn of the Screw; Covering End, Heinemann, 1898 . . . . . . £150
ditto, Macmillan (U.S.), 1898 . . . . . £150
The Soft Side, Methuen, 1900 . . . . . £75
ditto, Macmillan (U.S.), 1900 . . . . . . £75
The Better Sort, Methuen, 1903 . . . . . £50
ditto, Scribners (U.S.), 1900 . . . . . . £35
The Finer Grain, Scribners (U.S.), 1910 . . £35
ditto, Methuen, 1910 . . . . £35
The Ghostly Tales of Henry James, Rutgers Univ. Press (U.S.), 1948 [1949] . . . . £25/£5
ditto, as **Stories of the Supernatural**, Barrie & Jenkins, 1971 . . . . £15/£5

Plays
Theatricals: Two Comedies—Tenants [and] **Disengaged**, Osgood McIlvaine, 1894 . . . . £100
ditto, Harpers (U.S.), 1894 . . . . . £100
Theatricals: Second Series—The Album; The Reprobate, Osgood McIlvaine, 1895 . . . £75
ditto, Harpers (U.S.), 1895 [1894] £70
The Complete Plays of Henry James, Lippincott (U.S.), 1949 . . . . £45/£15
ditto, Hart-Davis, 1949 . . . . . £45/£15

Non Fiction
French Poets and Novelists, Macmillan, 1878 . £300
Hawthorne, Macmillan, 1879 . . . . . £125
ditto, Harpers (U.S.), 1880 . . . . . . £45
Portraits of Places, Macmillan, 1883 . . . £100
ditto, Osgood (U.S.), 1884 . . . . . . £100
Partial Portraits, Macmillan, 1888 . . . . £75

Essays in London and Elsewhere, Osgood McIlvaine, 1893 . . . . £75
A Little Tour in France, Heinemann, 1900 . . £50
ditto, Heinemann, 1900 (150 copies on Japanese vellum) £350
ditto, Houghton, Mifflin (U.S.), 1900 . . . £75
ditto, Cambridge Riverside Press (U.S.), 1900 (250 numbered large paper copies) £150
William Wetmore Story and His Friends, Blackwood, 1903 (2 vols). £150
ditto, Houghton, Mifflin (U.S.), 1903 (2 vols) . £150
English Hours, Heinemann, 1905 . . . . £50
ditto, Houghton, Mifflin (U.S.), 1905 . . . £50
ditto, Cambridge Riverside Press (U.S.), 1905 (400 large paper copies) £125
The American Scene, Chapman & Hall, 1907 . £50
ditto, Scribner's (U.S.), 1946 . . . . . £45/£10
Italian Hours, Heinemann, 1909. . . . . £75
Notes on Novelists, Dent, 1914 . . . . . £40
ditto, Scribner's (U.S.), 1914 . . . . . . £40
The Middle Years, Collins, [1917] £40
ditto, Scribner's (U.S.), 1917 . . . . . . £40
Within the Rim and Other Essays, Collins, [1919] £40
The Letters of Henry James, Macmillan, 1920 (2 vols) . . . . £200/£45
ditto, Scribner's (U.S.), 1920 (2 vols) . . £200/£45
The Painter's Eye, Hart-Davis, 1956 . . £35/£10
The House of Fiction, Hart-Davis, 1957 . £30/£10

Autobiography
A Small Boy and Others, Macmillan, 1913 . . £25
ditto, Scribners (U.S.), 1913 . . . . . . £25
Notes of a Son and a Brother, Macmillan, 1914 £25
ditto, Scribners (U.S.), 1914. . . . . . . £25

M.R. JAMES
(b.1862 d.1936)

A distinguished scholar and academic, James was awarded the Order of Merit in 1930. He had a penchant for the macabre and supernatural, and is famous for his ghost stories.

Ghost Stories
Ghost Stories of an Antiquary, Edward Arnold, [1904] (catalogue dated 1904) £750
ditto, Longmans (U.S.), 1905. . . . . . £500
More Ghost Stories, Edward Arnold, 1911 . . £450
A Thin Ghost, Edward Arnold, 1919 . . . £100
A Warning to the Curious, Edward Arnold, 1925 . . . . £250/£75
Wailing Well, Mill House Press, 1928 (157 numbered copies) £650
Collected Ghost Stories, Edward Arnold, 1931 . . . . £100/£25
ditto, Longmans (U.S.), 1931. . . . . £100/£25

Two Ghost Stories: A Centenary, Ghost Story Press, 1993 (200 numbered copies) £100

Other Titles
Old Testament Legends, Longmans, 1913 . . £35
The Five Jars, Edward Arnold, 1922 . . £250/£75
ditto, Ash-Tree Press, 1995 . . . . . £75/£25
Abbeys, Great Western Railway, 1925 . . £65/£20
ditto, Doubleday (U.S.), 1926 . . . . £65/£15
Eton and Kings, William & Norgate, 1926 . . £15
Suffolk and Norfolk, Dent, 1930 . . . £30/£10
Letters to a Friend, Edward Arnold, 1956 . £25/£10

Edited/Translated by M.R. James
The Apocryphal New Testament, Clarendon Press, 1924 . . . . £30
Judith, Medici, 1928 (illustrated by W.R. Flint) £40
The Book of Tobit & The History of Susanna, Medici, 1929 . . . . £35
Hans Andersen, Forty Stories, Faber, 1930 £30/£15
The New Testament, Dent, 1934-6 (4 vols). . £45

P.D. JAMES
(b.1920)

Born in Oxford but educated at Cambridge Girl's High School, P.D. James worked in the Civil Service and did not begin writing until her forties. She is famous for her detective fiction, much of which has been successfully televised.

'Adam Dalgliesh' Novels
Cover Her Face, Faber, 1962 . . . £1,500/£250
ditto, Scribner (U.S.), 1966 . . . . . £250/£35
A Mind to Murder, Faber, 1963 . . . .£750/£200
ditto, Scribner (U.S.), 1967 . . . . . £250/£35
Unnatural Causes, Faber, 1967 . . . .£500/£100
ditto, Scribner (U.S.), 1967 . . . . £125/£20
Shroud for a Nightingale, Faber, 1971 . £250/£75
ditto, Scribner (U.S.), 1971 . . . . . £75/£15
The Black Tower, Faber, 1975 . . . .. £50/£15
ditto, Scribner (U.S.), 1974 . . . . . £20/£5
Death of an Expert Witness, Faber, 1977 . £35/£10
ditto, Scribner (U.S.), 1977 . . . . . £15/£5
A Taste for Death, Faber, 1986 . . . . £20/£5
ditto, Knopf (U.S.), 1986 . . . . . . £10/£5
Devices and Desires, Faber, 1989 . . . £15/£5
ditto, Franklin Press (U.S.), 1990 (signed) . . £45
ditto, Knopf (U.S.), 1990 . . . . . . £10/£5
Original Sin, Faber, 1994. . . . . . £20/£5
ditto, London Limited Editions, 1994 (150 signed copies, acetate d/w) . . . . £100/£90
ditto, Knopf (U.S.), 1995 . . . . . . £10/£5
A Certain Justice, Faber, 1997 . . . . £10/£5
ditto, Knopf (U.S.), 1997 . . . . . . £10/£5
Death in Holy Orders , Faber, 2001 . . . £10/£5

'Cordelia Gray' Novels
An Unsuitable Job for a Woman, Faber, 1972 . . .
. . . . £125/£25
ditto, Scribner (U.S.), 1972 . . . . . £35/£10
The Skull Beneath the Skin, Faber, 1982 . £50/£10
ditto, Scribner (U.S.), 1982 . . . . . £25/£5

Other Novels
Innocent Blood, Faber, 1980 . . . . . £35/£10
ditto, Scribner (U.S.), 1980 . . . . . £15/£5
The Children of Men, Faber, 1992 . . . £20/£5
ditto, Knopf (U.S.), 1993 . . . . . . £10/£5

Omnibus Editions
P.D. James Omnibus, Faber, 1982 . . . £15/£5
The Second P.D. James Omnibus, Faber, 1990 . .
. . . . £10/£5

Non Fiction
The Maul and the Pear Tree, Constable, 1971, (with
T.A. Critchley) . . . . £50/£20
ditto, Mysterious Press (U.S.), 1986 . . . £15/£5
Bad Language in Church, Prayer Book Society, 1988
(wraps) £10

RICHARD JEFFERIES
(b.1848 d.1887)

British essayist, novelist, and chronicler of rural life.

Novels
The Scarlet Shawl, Tinsley Bros., 1874 . . . £300
Restless Human Hearts, Tinsley Bros., 1875 (3 vols) .
. . . . £450
World's End, Tinsley Bros., 1877 (3 vols) . . £350
Greene Ferne Farm, Smith, Elder & Co., 1880 £200
The Dewy Morn, Bentley, 1884, (2 vols) . . £200
After London, or Wild England, Cassell & Co., 1885 .
. . . . £200
Amaryllis at the Fair, Sampson, Low & Co., 1887.
. . . . £125
The Early Fiction of Richard Jefferies, Simpkin,
Marshall & Co., 1896 . . . . £75
ditto, 1896 (large paper, 50 numbered copies) . £125

Short Story
T.T.T., Arthur Young, 1896 (100 copies) . . £150

Children's
Wood Magic, A Fable, Cassell, Petter & Galpin, 1881,
(2 vols) £400
Bevis, The Story of a Boy, Sampson, Low & Co.,
1882, (3 vols). £750

Non Fiction
*Reporting, Editing and Authorship: Practical Hints
for Beginners in Literature*, John Snow & Co.,
[1873]. £600
Jack Brass, Emperor of England, Pettit & Co., 1873 .
. . . . £400
*A Memoir of the Goddards of North Wilts Compiled
from Ancient Records, Registers and Family Papers*,
Simmons & Botten, [1873] £600
*Suez-cide!! or How Miss Britannia Bought a Dirty
Puddle and Lost her Sugar Plums*, John Snow, 1876
. . . . £300
*The Gamekeeper at Home, or Sketches of Natural
History & Rural Life*, Smith, Elder & Co., 1878
(anonymous) £150
Wild Life in a Southern County, Smith, Elder & Co.,
1879 (anonymous) £150
The Amateur Poacher, Smith, Elder & Co., 1879
(anonymous) £200
Hodge and His Masters, Smith, Elder & Co., 1880, (2
vols) £200
Round About a Great Estate, Smith, Elder & Co.,
1880 . . . . £150
Nature Near London, Chatto & Windus, 1883 . £100
The Story of My Heart, My Autobiography, Long-
mans, 1883 . . . . £150
Red Deer, Longmans, 1884 . . . . . £125
The Life of the Fields, Chatto & Windus, 1884 £75
The Open Air, Chatto & Windus, 1885 . . . £75
*Field and Hedgerow, Being the Last Essays of
Richard Jefferies Collected by His Widow*,
Longmans, Green & Co., 1889 . . . . £75
ditto, Longmans, Green & Co., 1889 (large paper, 200
numbered copies) £125
The Toilers of the Field, Longmans, Green & Co.,
1892 . . . . £25
ditto, Longmans, Green & Co., 1892 (large paper, 105
numbered copies) £75
*Jefferies Land, A History of Swindon and Its
Environs*, Simpkin, Marshall & Co., 1896. . £75
ditto, Simpkin, Marshall & Co., 1896 (large paper, 50
numbered copies) £100
The Hills and the Vale, Duckworth, 1909 . . £25
*The Nature Diaries and Notebooks of Richard
Jefferies, With an Essay 'A Tangle of Autumn' Now
Printed for the First Time*, Grey Walls Press, 1941 .
. . . . £35/£15
ditto, Grey Walls Press, 1941 (large paper, 105
numbered copies) £75
Chronicles of the Hedges And Other Essays, Phoenix
House, 1948 . . . . £15/£5
The Old House at Coate, Lutterworth Press, 1948
. . . . £25/£10
ditto, Harvard Univ. Press, 1948 . . . . £20/£10
*Beauty Is Immortal (Felise of the Dewy Morn), With
Some Hitherto Uncollected Essays and Manuscripts*,
Worthing Cavalcade, 1948 . . . . . £25
*Field and Farm, Essays Now Collected With Some
From Manuscripts*, Phoenix House, 1957 . £25/£10

Landscape and Labour, Moonraker Press, 1979 . . .
. . . . £10/£5
By the Brook, Eric & Joan Stevens, 1981 (170 numbered copies) £25
ditto, Eric & Joan Stevens, 1981 (20 leather bound copies in slipcase) £75
The Birth of a Naturalist, Tern Press, 1985 (300 numbered copies) £50
ditto, Tern Press, 1985 (20 leather-bound copies in slipcase) . . . . £125/£100

JEROME K. JEROME
(b.1859 d.1927)

First employed as a railway clerk at Euston Station, then as an actor, Jerome was best known as a novelist, but was also a successful dramatist and popular journalist.

Novels
Three Men in a Boat, Arrowsmith, 1889, (first issue, address: 'Quay Street') £125
ditto, Arrowsmith, 1889, (second issue, address: '11 Quay Street') £75
ditto, Holt (U.S.), 1890 . . . . . . £75
Diary of a Pilgrimage, Arrowsmith, 1891 . . £30
ditto, Holt (U.S.), 1891 . . . . . . £20
Three Men on the Bummel, Arrowsmith, 1900 £30
Paul Kelver, Hutchinson, 1902 . . . . £30
ditto, Dodd, Mead (U.S.), 1902 . . . . £20
Tommy & Co, Hutchinson, 1904. . . . £20
ditto, Dodd, Mead (U.S.), 1904 . . . . £15
They and I, Hutchinson, 1909 . . . . £20
ditto, Dodd, Mead (U.S.), 1909 . . . . £15
All Roads Lead to Calvary, Hutchinson, 1919 £15
ditto, Dodd, Mead (U.S.), 1919 . . . . £15
Anthony John, Cassell, 1923. . . . . £35/£15
ditto, Dodd, Mead (U.S.), 1923 . . . . £35/£15

Short Stories
Told After Supper, Leadenhall Press, 1891 . . £45
ditto, Holt (U.S.), 1891 . . . . . . £40
John Ingerfield and Other Stories, McClure, 1894 .
. . . . £30
ditto, Holt (U.S.), 1894 . . . . . . £25
The Observations of Henry, Arrowsmith, 1901 £25
ditto, Dodd, Mead (U.S.), 1901 . . . . £15
Tea Table Talk, Hutchinson, 1903 . . . £15
ditto, Dodd, Mead (U.S.), 1903 . . . . £15
The Passing of the Third Floor Back, Hurst & Blackett, 1907 . . . . £25
ditto, Dodd, Mead (U.S.), 1908 . . . . £25
Malvina of Brittany, Cassell, 1916 . . . £15

Plays
Barbara, Lacy, 1886 . . . . £20
Sunset, Fitzgerald (U.S.), [1888]. . . . £20

Fennel, French, [1888] £15
Woodbarrow Farm, French, [1888] £15
The Prude's Progress, French, 1895 . . . £15
Miss Hobbs, French, 1902 . . . . . £15
Fanny and the Servant Problem, Lacy, 1909 . £15
The Passing of the Third Floor Back, Hurst & Blackett, 1910 . . . . £20
The Master of Mrs Chilvers, Fisher Unwin, 1911 £10
Robina in Search of a Husband, Lacy, 1914 . £10
The Celebrity, Hodder & Stoughton, 1926 . £25/£10
The Soul of Nicholas Snyders, Hodder & Stoughton, 1927 . . . . £25/£10

Other Works
On Stage-and Off, Field & Tuer, 1885 . . . £75
ditto, Leadenhall Press, 1891 . . . . . £35
The Idle Thoughts of an Idle Fellow, Field & Tuer, 1886 . . . . £100
ditto, Holt (U.S.), 1890 . . . . . . £50
Stage-Land, Chatto & Windus, 1889 . . £25
ditto, Holt (U.S.), 1906 . . . . . . £25
Novel Notes, Leadenhall Press, 1893 . . . £35
Sketches in Lavender, Blue and Green, Longman, 1897 . . . . £25
ditto, Holt (U.S.), 1907 . . . . . . £25
The Second Thoughts of an Idle Fellow, Hurst & Blackett, 1898 . . . . £25
ditto, Dodd, Mead (U.S.), 1898 . . . . £20
American Wives and Others, Stokes (U.S.), 1904 £25
Idle Ideas in 1905, Hurst & Blackett, 1905 . £15
The Angel and the Author—and Others, Hurst & Blackett, 1908 . . . . £15
Thoughts from Jerome K. Jerome, Sesame Booklets, 1913 . . . . £10
A Miscellany of Sense and Nonsense, Arrowsmith, 1923 . . . . £15
My Life and Times, Hodder & Stoughton, 1926 . .
. . . . £35/£15
ditto, Harper (U.S.), 1926. . . . . . £35/£15

RUTH PRAWER JHABVALA
(b.1927)

Born in Cologne, Ruth Prawer Jhabvala fled with her Polish/Jewish family to England in 1939. She married an Indian architect in 1951 and moved to Delhi. Her first novel was published in 1955. She is also known for her short stories and film scripts written for the Merchant/Ivory partnership.

Novels
To Whom She Will, George Allen & Unwin, 1955. .
. . . . £75/£15
ditto as *Amrita*, Norton (U.S.), 1956 . . £45/£10
The Nature of Passion, George Allen & Unwin, 1956.
. . . . £50/£20
ditto, Norton (U.S.), 1957. . . . . . £25/£5

Esmond in India, George Allen & Unwin, 1958 . .
. . . . £50/£20
ditto, Norton (U.S.), 1958. . . . . . £25/£5
The Householder, John Murray, 1960 . . £50/£20
ditto, Norton (U.S.), 1960. . . . . . £20/£5
Get Ready for Battle, John Murray, 1962 . £40/£15
ditto, Norton (U.S.), 1963. . . . . . £15/£5
A Backward Place, John Murray, 1965 . . £25/£10
ditto, Norton (U.S.), 1965. . . . . . £15/£5
A New Dominion, John Murray, 1972 . . £25/£10
ditto, as *Travellers*, Harper & Row (U.S.), 1973 £15/£5
Heat and Dust, John Murray, 1975 . . . £25/£10
ditto, Harper (U.S.), 1976 . . . . . £20/£5
In Search of Love and Beauty, John Murray, 1983 .
. . . . £10/£5
ditto, Morrow (U.S.), 1983 . . . . . £10/£5
Three Continents, John Murray, 1987 . . £10/£5
ditto, Morrow (U.S.), 1987 . . . . . £10/£5
Poet and Dancer, John Murray, 1993 . . £10/£5
ditto, Doubleday (U.S.), 1993 . . . . £10/£5
Shards of Memory, John Murray, 1995 . . £10/£5
ditto, Doubleday (U.S.), 1995 . . . . £10/£5

Short Stories
Like Birds Like Fishes, John Murray, 1963. £35/£10
ditto, Norton (U.S.), 1964. . . . . . £20/£5
A Stronger Climate, John Murray, 1968 . £25/£10
ditto, Norton (U.S.), 1969. . . . . . £15/£5
An Experience of India, John Murray, 1971 £25/£10
ditto, Norton (U.S.), 1972. . . . . . £15/£5
How I Became a Holy Mother, John Murray, 1976 .
. . . . £10/£5
ditto, Harper (U.S.), 1976. . . . . . £10/£5
Out of India: Selected Stories, Morrow (U.S.), 1986 .
. . . . £10/£5
ditto, John Murray, 1987 . . . . . . £10/£5
*East Into Upper East: Plain Tales From New York
and New Delhi*, Murray, 1998 . . . . £10/£5
ditto, Counterpoint (U.S.), 1998 . . . . £10/£5

CAPTAIN W.E. JOHNS
(b.1893 d.1968)

In 1916 Johns joined the newly formed Royal Flying
Corps, and remained in the Air Force until 1930. He
founded the monthly *Popular Flying* magazine in
which Captain James Bigglesworth made his first
appearance.

'Biggles' Titles
The Camels Are Coming, Hamilton [1932] (pseud.
'William Earle') . . . . £1,750/£250
The Cruise of the Condor: A Biggles Story, Hamilton
[1933]. . . . . £1,500/£200
'Biggles' of the Camel Squadron, Hamilton [1934] .
. . . . £1,500/£200

Biggles Flies Again, Hamilton [1934] . £1,500/£200
ditto, Penguin, 1941 (wraps) £100
Biggles Learns to Fly, Boys' Friend Library, 1935
(wraps) £500
ditto, Brockhampton Press, 1955 (first hardback
edition) . . . . £50/£10
Biggles Flies East, O.U.P., 1935. . . £1,000/£100
Biggles Hits the Trail, O.U.P., 1935. . £1,000/£100
Biggles in France, Boys' Friend Library, 1935 (wraps)
. . . . £500
The Black Peril: A 'Biggles' Story, Hamilton [1935] .
. . . . £1,000/£100
Biggles in Africa, O.U.P., 1936 . . . £1,000/£100
Biggles & Co, O.U.P., 1936 . . . . £1,000/£100
Biggles - Air Commodore, O.U.P., 1937 £1,000/£100
Biggles Flies West, O.U.P., 1937 . . £1,000/£100
Biggles Flies South, O.U.P., 1938 . . £1,000/£100
Biggles Goes to War, O.U.P., 1938 . . £1,000/£100
Biggles Flies North, O.U.P., 1939 . . £1,000/£100
Biggles in Spain, O.U.P., 1939 . . . £1,000/£100
The Rescue Flight: A 'Biggles' Story, O.U.P., 1939 .
. . . . £1,000/£100
*Biggles in the Baltic: A Tale of the Second Great
War*, O.U.P., 1940 . . . . £750/£75
Biggles in the South Seas, O.U.P., 1940 . £750/£75
Biggles - Secret Agent, O.U.P., 1940 . . £750/£75
Spitfire Parade: Stories of Biggles in War-Time,
O.U.P., 1941 . . . . £1,000/£100
Biggles Sees it Through, O.U.P., 1941 . £600/£65
Biggles Defies the Swastika, O.U.P., 1941 . £600/£65
Biggles in the Jungle, O.U.P., 1942 . . £400/£45
Biggles Sweeps the Desert, Hodder & Stoughton, 1942
. . . . £50/£15
Biggles - Charter Pilot, O.U.P., 1943 . . £400/£45
Biggles 'Fails to Return', Hodder & Stoughton, 1943 .
. . . . £50/£15
Biggles in Borneo, O.U.P., 1943. . . . £250/£30
Biggles in the Orient, Hodder & Stoughton, 1945 . .
. . . . £40/£10
Biggles Delivers the Goods, Hodder & Stoughton,
1946 . . . . £30/£10
Sergeant Bigglesworth CID, Hodder & Stoughton,
1947 . . . . £30/£10
Biggles Hunts Big Game, Hodder & Stoughton, 1948
. . . . £30/£10
Biggles' Second Case, Hodder & Stoughton, 1948 .
. . . . £30/£10
Biggles Breaks the Silence, Hodder & Stoughton, 1949
. . . . £30/£10
Biggles Takes a Holiday, Hodder & Stoughton, 1949 .
. . . . £30/£10
Biggles Gets His Men, Hodder & Stoughton, 1950 .
. . . . £30/£10
Another Job for Biggles, Hodder & Stoughton, 1951 .
. . . . £30/£10
Biggles Goes to School, Hodder & Stoughton, 1951 .
. . . . £30/£10
Biggles Works It Out, Hodder & Stoughton, 1951 . .
. . . . £30/£10

Guide to First Edition Prices, 2002/3

Biggles - Air Detective, Marks & Spencer, 1951 (no d/w) £10
Biggles Follows On, Hodder & Stoughton, 1952 . . . . £25/£10
Biggles Takes the Case, Hodder & Stoughton, 1952 . . . . £25/£10
Biggles and the Black Raider, Hodder & Stoughton, 1953 . . . . £25/£10
Biggles in the Blue, Brockhampton Press, 1953 . . . . £35/£10
Biggles of the Special Air Police, Thames [1953] . . . . £15/£5
Biggles in the Gobi, Hodder & Stoughton, 1953 . . . . £25/£10
Biggles and the Pirate Treasure and Other Biggles Adventures, Brockhampton Press, 1954 . £35/£10
Biggles Cuts it Fine, Hodder & Stoughton, 1954 . . . . £30/£10
Biggles, Foreign Legionnaire, Hodder & Stoughton, 1954 . . . . £30/£10
Biggles, Pioneer Airfighter, Thames [1954] £15/£5
Biggles' Chinese Puzzle and Other Biggles Adventures, Brockhampton Press, 1955 . . . £45/£10
Biggles in Australia, Hodder & Stoughton, 1955 . . . . £45/£10
Biggles of 266, Thames [1956] . . . . £15/£5
Biggles Takes Charge, Brockhampton Press, 1956 . . . . £45/£10
No Rest For Biggles, Hodder & Stoughton, 1956 . . . . £45/£10
Biggles Makes Ends Meet, Hodder & Stoughton, 1957 . . . . £45/£10
Biggles of the Interpol, Brockhampton Press, 1957 . . . . £45/£10
Biggles on the Home Front, Hodder & Stoughton, 1957 . . . . £45/£10
Biggles Buries a Hatchet, Brockhampton Press, 1958 . . . . £45/£10
Biggles on Mystery Island, Hodder & Stoughton [1958]. . . . . £45/£10
Biggles Presses On, Brockhampton Press, 1958 £25/£5
Biggles at World's End, Brockhampton Press, 1959 . . . . £45/£10
Biggles' Combined Operation, Hodder & Stoughton [1959]. . . . . £45/£10
Biggles in Mexico, Brockhampton Press, 1959 £45/£10
Biggles and the Leopards of Zinn, Brockhampton Press, 1960 . . . . £45/£10
Biggles Goes Home, Hodder & Stoughton [1960] . . . . £45/£10
Biggles and the Missing Millionaire, Brockhampton Press, 1961 . . . . . . £45/£10
Biggles and the Poor Rich Boy, Brockhampton Press, 1961 . . . . £35/£5
Biggles Forms a Syndicate, Hodder & Stoughton, 1961 . . . . £45/£10
Biggles Goes Alone, Hodder & Stoughton [1962] . . . . £45/£10

Biggles Sets a Trap, Hodder & Stoughton, 1962 . . . . £45/£10
Orchids for Biggles, Hodder & Stoughton, 1962 . . . . £45/£10
Biggles and the Planet That Disappeared: A Story of the Air Police, Hodder & Stoughton, 1963 £45/£10
Biggles Flies to Work, Dean [1963] . . . £15/£5
Biggles' Special Case, Brockhampton Press, 1963 . . . . £50/£15
Biggles Takes A Hand, Hodder & Stoughton [1963] . . . . £50/£15
Biggles Takes it Rough, Brockhampton Press, 1963 . . . . £50/£15
Biggles and the Black Mask, Hodder & Stoughton, 1964 . . . . £100/£25
Biggles and the Lost Sovereigns, Brockhampton Press, 1964 . . . . £75/£10
Biggles Investigates and Other Stories of the Air Police, Brockhampton Press, 1965 . . £75/£10
Biggles and the Blue Moon, Brockhampton Press, 1965 . . . . £100/£20
Biggles and the Plot That Failed, Brockhampton Press, 1965 . . . . £100/£20
Biggles Looks Back: A Story of Biggles and the Air Police, Hodder & Stoughton, 1965 . £100/£25
Biggles Scores a Bull, Hodder & Stoughton, 1965 . . . . £125/£35
Biggles in the Terai, Brockhampton Press, 1966 . . . . £150/£45
Biggles and the Gun Runners, Brockhampton Press, 1966 . . . . £150/£45
Biggles and the Penitent Thief, Brockhampton Press, 1967 . . . . £150/£45
Biggles Sorts It Out, Brockhampton Press, 1967 . . . . £150/£45
Biggles and the Dark Intruder, Knight, 1967 (wraps) £20
ditto, Brockhampton Press, 1970. . . . £65/£15
Biggles in the Underworld, Brockhampton Press, 1968 . . . . £200/£50
The Boy Biggles, Dean, 1968 . . . . £20/£5
Biggles and the Deep Blue Sea, Brockhampton Press, 1968 . . . . £200/£50
Biggles and the Little Green God, Brockhampton Press, 1969 . . . . £200/£50
Biggles and the Noble Lord, Brockhampton Press, 1969 . . . . £200/£50
Biggles Sees Too Much, Brockhampton Press, 1970 . . . . £200/£50
Biggles of the Royal Flying Corps, Purnell, 1978 . . . . £15/£5
Biggles Does Some Homework, Wright/Schofield, 1997 (300 copies, wraps) £35
Biggles Air Ace: The Uncollected Stories, Wright, 1999 (300 copies, wraps) £35

Biggles Omnibuses
The Biggles Omnibus, O.U.P., 1938. . £1,000/£75
The Biggles Flying Omnibus, O.U.P., 1940 . . .
. . . . £1,000/£75
The Third Biggles Omnibus, O.U.P., 1941 £1,000/£75
The First Biggles Omnibus, Hodder and Stoughton,
1953 . . . . £45/£10
The Biggles Air Detective Omnibus, Hodder and
Stoughton, 1956 . . . . £45/£10
The Biggles Adventure Omnibus, Hodder and
Stoughton, 1965 . . . . £45/£10
The Bumper Biggles Book, Chancellor, 1983 £10/£5
The Best of Biggles, Chancellor, 1985 . . £10/£5

'Worrals' Books
Worrals of the W.A.A.F., Lutterworth Press, 1941 .
. . . . £50/£15
Worrals Carries On, Lutterworth Press, 1942 £40/£10
Worrals Flies Again, Hodder & Stoughton, 1942 . .
. . . . £40/£10
Worrals On the War-Path, Hodder & Stoughton, 1943
. . . . £40/£10
Worrals Goes East, Hodder & Stoughton, 1944 £35/£5
Worrals of the Islands: A Story of the War in the
Pacific, Hodder & Stoughton, 1945 . . £35/£5
Worrals in the Wilds, Hodder & Stoughton, 1947 . .
. . . . £30/£5
Worrals Down Under, Lutterworth Press, 1948 £35/£5
Worrals Goes Afoot, Lutterworth Press, 1949 £35/£5
Worrals In the Wastelands, Lutterworth Press, 1949
. . . . £35/£5
Worrals Investigates, Lutterworth Press, 1950 £35/£5

'Gimlet' Books
King of the Commandos, Univ. of London Press, 1943
. . . . £50/£10
Gimlet Goes Again, Univ. of London Press, 1944 . .
. . . . £50/£10
Gimlet Comes Home, Univ. of London Press, 1946 .
. . . . £45/£10
Gimlet Mops Up, Brockhampton Press, 1947 £40/£10
Gimlet's Oriental Quest, Brockhampton Press, 1948 .
. . . . £40/£10
Gimlet Lends a Hand, Brockhampton Press, 1949 . .
. . . . £40/£10
Gimlet Bores In, Brockhampton Press, 1950 £40/£10
Gimlet Off the Map, Brockhampton Press, 1951 . .
. . . . £40/£10
Gimlet Gets the Answer, Brockhampton Press, 1952 .
. . . . £35/£10
Gimlet Takes a Job, Brockhampton Press, 1954 . .
. . . . £35/£10

Science Fiction Titles
Kings of Space: A Story of Interplanetary
Explorations, Hodder & Stoughton, 1954 . £25/£5
Return to Mars, Hodder & Stoughton, 1955 £25/£5
Now to the Stars, Hodder & Stoughton, 1956 £25/£5
To Outer Space, Hodder & Stoughton, 1957 £25/£5

The Edge of Beyond, Hodder & Stoughton [1958]. .
. . . . £25/£5
The Death Rays of Ardilla, Hodder & Stoughton
[1959]. . . . . £25/£5
To Worlds Unknown: A Story of Interplanetary
Explorations, Hodder & Stoughton [1960] £20/£5
The Quest for the Perfect Planet, Hodder &
Stoughton, 1961 . . . . £20/£5
Worlds of Wonder: More Adventures in Space,
Hodder & Stoughton, 1962 . . . . . £20/£5
The Man Who Vanished into Space, Hodder &
Stoughton [1963] . . . . . . £20/£5

Others
Mossyface, 'The Weekly Telegraph Novel', 1922
(pseud. 'William Earle', wraps). £600
ditto, Mellifont, 1932 (wraps) £200
Modern Boys Book of Aircraft, Amalgamated Press,
1931 . . . . £50/£15
The Pictorial Flying Course, John Hamilton [1932]
(by Johns and H.M. Schofield) . . . . £250/£75
Fighting Planes and Aces, John Hamilton [1932] . .
. . . . £250/£75
The Spy Flyers, John Hamilton, 1933 . £500/£125
The Raid, John Hamilton [1935]. . . . £250/£75
The Air VC's, John Hamilton [1935] . . £250/£75
Some Milestones in Aviation, John Hamilton [1935] .
. . . . £200/£45
Blue Blood Runs Red, Newnes [1936] (pseud. 'Jon
Early') . . . . £500/£125
Modern Boy's Book of Adventure Stories, Amalgam-
ated Press, 1936 . . . . £50/£15
Ace High, Ace, 1936 . . . . . . £100/£30
Air Adventures, Ace, 1936 . . . . . £100/£30
Sky High: A 'Steeley' Adventure, Newnes [1936] .
. . . . £250/£75
Steeley Flies Again, Newnes [1936]. . . £250/£75
Flying Stories, John Hamilton, 1937 . £100/£25
Murder By Air: A 'Steeley' Adventure, Newnes [1937]
. . . . £250/£75
The Passing Show, My Garden/Newnes, 1937 . . .
. . . . £75/£20
Desert Night: A Romance, John Hamilton [1938] . .
. . . . £200/£45
The Murder at Castle Deeping: A 'Steeley' Adventure,
John Hamilton [1938] . . . . . . £400/£100
Champion of the Main, O.U.P., 1938 . £250/£75
Wings of Romance: A 'Steeley' Adventure, Newnes,
1939 . . . . £250/£75
Modern Boy's Book of Pirates, Amalgamated Press,
[1939]. . . . . £200/£50
The Unknown Quantity, John Hamilton, [1940] . .
. . . . £200/£50
Sinister Service: A Tale, O.U.P., 1942 . £100/£25
The Rustlers of Rattlesnake Valley, Nelson, 1948 . .
. . . . £25/£5
Dr Vane Answers the Call, Latimer House, 1950 . .
. . . . £100/£25
Short Sorties, Latimer House, 1950 . . . £100/£25

Sky Fever and Other Stories, Latimer House, [1953] .
. . . . £100/£25
Adventure Bound, Nelson, 1955 . . . . £10/£5
Adventure Unlimited, Nelson, 1957 . . . £10/£5
No Motive for Murder, Hodder & Stoughton [1958] .
. . . . £100/£25
The Man Who Lost His Way, Macdonald, 1959 . .
. . . . £100/£25
The Biggles Book of Heroes, Parrish, 1959 £50/£15
Adventures of the Junior Detection Club, Parrish
[1960]. . . . . £50/£15
Where the Golden Eagle Soars, Hodder & Stoughton
[1960]. . . . . £25/£5
The Biggles Book of Treasure Hunting, Parrish, 1962
. . . . £50/£15
Out of the Blue, John Hamilton [no date] . £100/£25

Illustrated by Johns
Desert Wings, by Clark Venable, John Hamilton
[1931] (real name 'Covington Clarke') . £25/£10
Aces Up, by Clark Venable, John Hamilton [1931]
(real name 'Covington Clarke'). . . . £25/£10
For Valour, by Clark Venable, John Hamilton [1931]
(real name 'Covington Clarke'). . . . £25/£10

Short Stories
Statement Against Corpses, Constable, 1964 (with
Zulfikar Ghose) . . . . £75/£25
*Aren't You Rather Young to be Writing Your
Memoirs?*, Hutchinson, 1973 . . . . . £20
Everybody Knows Somebody Who's Dead, Covent
Garden Press, 1973 (100 signed, numbered copies) .
. . . . £100/£65

Poetry
Poems, Constable, 1964 . . . . £125/£25
Poems Two, Trigram Press, 1972 (100 signed copies,
acetate d/w) . . . . £100/£75
ditto, Trigram Press, 1972 (hardback) . . £25/£10
ditto, Trigram Press, 1972 (wraps) £10
A Dublin Unicorn, Byron Press, 1975 (25 signed
copies of 250, wraps) £250
ditto, Byron Press, 1975 (225 unsigned copies of 250,
wraps) £50

Others
Street Children, Hodder & Stoughton, 1964 (with
photographs by Julia Trevelyan) . . . £25/£10
You're Human Like the Rest of Them, Penguin New
English Dramatists, 1970 (wraps) £5

B.S. JOHNSON
(b.1933 d.1973)

A controversial and experimental novelist, Johnson's
books have been purposefully issued with pages
which are black, blank, and containing holes. *The
Unfortunates* was published in the form of loose
sections to be shuffled and read in no particular order.

Novels
Travelling People, Constable, 1963 . . . £150/£45
ditto, Transworld, 1964 (wraps) £10
Albert Angelo, Constable, 1964 . . . . £125/£35
ditto, Panther, 1967 (wraps) £10
ditto, New Directions (U.S.), 1987 . . . . £10/£5
Trawl, Secker & Warburg, 1966 . . . . £75/£35
ditto, Panther, 1968 (wraps) £10
The Unfortunates, Panther [with Secker & Warburg],
1969 (27 loose sections in box) £150
House Mother Normal, Trigram Press, 1971 (26
signed, lettered copies) £200
ditto, Trigram Press, 1971 (100 signed, numbered
copies) £100
ditto, Collins, 1971 . . . . £45/£20
ditto, Quartet, 1973 (wraps) £10
ditto, Bloodaxe, 1984 (wraps) £10
ditto, New Directions (U.S.), 1987 . . . £10/£5
Christie Malry's Own Double Entry, Collins, 1973 .
. . . . £25/£5
ditto, Viking (U.S.), 1973. . . . . . £20/£5
See The Old Lady Decently, Collins, 1973 . £25/£5
ditto, Viking (U.S.), 1975. . . . . . £15/£5

JAMES JOYCE
(b.1882 d.1941)

Novelist, short story writer, poet and father of
modernism, Joyce's *Ulysses* and *Finnegan's Wake*
revolutionised narrative form and paved the way for
the modern novel.

Verse
Chamber Music, Elkin Mathews, 1907 (first state 16.2
x 11cm, thick laid endpapers, signature 'c' well
centred) £4,000
ditto, Elkin Mathews, 1907 (second state 15.8 x 11cm,
thick wove endpapers, signature 'c' poorly centred) .
. . . . £2,500
ditto, Elkin Mathews, 1907 (third state 15.9 x 10.9cm,
thin wove transparent endpapers) . . . £1,750
ditto, Cornhill Co. (U.S.), 1918 (unauthorised edition).
. . . . £150
ditto, Huebsch (U.S.), 1918 (authorised edition) £125
Pomes Penyeach, Shakespeare and Co. (Paris), 1927
(13 specially bound copies) £2,500
ditto, Shakespeare and Co. (Paris), 1927 (with tipped-in
errata slip) £300
ditto, privately printed, (U.S.), 1931 (100 copies) . .
. . . . £1,000
ditto, Faber, 1933 (wraps). £100
Collected Poems, Black Sun Press (U.S.), 1936 (800
copies, glassine d/w). . . . . £500/£400
ditto, Black Sun Press (U.S.), 1936 (50 signed copies,
tissue d/w, slipcase) . . . . . £4,000/£3,500

ditto, Black Sun Press (U.S.), 1936 (3 signed, lettered copies, tissue d/w, slipcase) £7,500
ditto, Viking (U.S.), 1937 . . . . . £350/£65

Short Stories
Dubliners, Grant Richards, 1914 . . . . £1,500
ditto, Huebsch (U.S.), 1916 . . . . . £750

Novels
A Portrait of the Artist as a Young Man, Huebsch (U.S.), 1916 . . . . £3,000
ditto, Egoist Ltd, 1916 [1917] £1,750
Ulysses, Shakespeare Press (Paris), 1922, (740 numbered copies on handmade paper, wraps) £12,000
ditto, Shakespeare Press (Paris), 1922 (100 signed, numbered copies on Dutch handmade paper, wraps) .
. . . . £50,000
ditto, Shakespeare Press (Paris), 1922 (150 copies on Velin d'Arches paper, wraps) £20,000
ditto, Egoist Press, 1922 (2,000 numbered copies with errata slip and 4-page leaflet of press notices, wraps) .
. . . . £1,750
ditto, Random House (U.S.), 1934 (first copyright printing, 100 copies) £1,000
ditto, Random House (U.S.), 1934 (second printing) .
. . . . £500/£50
ditto, Bodley Head, 1936 (900 copy edition) . . .
. . . . £2,000/£500
ditto, Bodley Head, 1936 (100 signed copies, slipcase)
. . . . £10,000/£6,500
ditto, Bodley Head, 1937 . . . . . . £250/£100
Finnegan's Wake, Faber, 1939 . . . £1,500/£250
ditto, Faber/Viking, 1939 (425 signed copies, glassine d/w, slipcase) . . . . £4,500/£4,000
ditto, Faber/Viking, 1939 (26 signed copies, glassine d/w, slipcase) £8,000
ditto, Viking (U.S.), 1939 . . . . . . £750/£50
Stephen Hero, Cape, 1944 . . . . . £250/£75
ditto, New Directions (U.S.), 1944 . . . £200/£75

Fragments
Anna Livia Plurabelle, Crosby Gaige (U.S.), 1928 (800 signed copies) £1,500
ditto, Crosby Gaige (U.S.), 1928 (50 unsigned copies on green paper) £1,500
ditto, Faber, 1930 (tissue d/w) . . . £150/£100
ditto, Faber, 1930 (wraps) £65
Tales Told of Shem and Shaun, Black Sun Press (Paris), 1929 (500 copies, wraps, slipcase) £700/£600
ditto, Black Sun Press (Paris), 1929 (100 signed copies)
. . . . £5,000
ditto, as *Two Tales of Shem and Shaun*, Faber, 1932 .
. . . . £200/£50
Haveth Childers Everywhere, Fountain Press (U.S.), 1930 (500 copies of 685, wraps with glassine d/w and slipcase) . . . . £650/£500
ditto, Fountain Press (U.S.), 1930 (75 'writer's copies of 685) £1,500

ditto, Fountain Press (U.S.), 1930 (100 signed copies of 685, glassine d/w, slipcase) £3,500
ditto, Fountain Press (U.S.), 1930 (10 signed copies of 685, glassine d/w, slipcase) £4,000
ditto, Faber, 1931 (tissue d/w) . . . £140/£125
ditto, Faber, 1931 (wraps in d/w) . . . £75/£50
The Mime of Mick Nick and the Maggies, Servire Press, 1934 (1000 copies, wraps, slipcase) £500/£400
ditto, Servire Press, 1934 (29 signed copies, wraps, slipcase) £6,500
Storiella As She is Syung, Corvinus Press, 1937 (150 numbered copies, slipcase) £2,000
ditto, Corvinus Press, 1937 (25 signed copies, slipcase)
. . . . £7,500/£7,000

Letters
The Letters Vol. I, Faber, 1957 . . . . £100/£25
ditto, Viking (U.S.), 1957 . . . . . £100/£25
The Letters Vol. II, Faber, 1966 . . . . £50/£15
ditto, Viking (U.S.), 1966 . . . . . £50/£15
The Letters Vol. III, Faber, 1966 . . . £50/£15
ditto, Viking (U.S.), 1966 . . . . . £50/£15
The Selected Letters of James Joyce, Faber, 1975 . .
. . . . £25/£10

Others
Exiles, Grant Richards, 1918 . . . . . . £500
ditto, Huebsch (U.S.), 1918 . . . . . . £250
Introducing James Joyce: A Selection of Joyce's Prose, Faber, 1942 (by T.S. Eliot) . . . £10/£5
The Critical Writings, Faber, 1959 . . . £40/£15
ditto, Viking (U.S.), 1959 . . . . . £40/£15
The Cat and the Devil, Dodd, Mead (U.S.), [1964] .
. . . . £50/£20
ditto, Faber, 1965 . . . . £50/£20

FRANZ KAFKA
(b.1883 d.1924)

A German-speaking Czech author whose name has become synonomous with the nightmarish, confused struggles of individuals against an incomprehensible system.

Novels
The Castle, Secker, 1930 (Translated by Willa and Edwin Muir) . . . . £1,000/£200
ditto, Knopf (U.S.), 1930 . . . . £750/£175
The Trial, Gollancz, 1937 (Translated by Willa and Edwin Muir) . . . . £750/£200
ditto, Knopf (U.S.), 1937 . . . . . £300/£75
America, Routledge, 1938 (Translated by Willa and Edwin Muir) . . . . £500/£100
ditto, New Directions (U.S.), 1946 . . . £100/£25

Novellas and Short Stories

The Great Wall of China, Secker, 1933 (Translated by Willa and Edwin Muir) . . . . . £500/£100

ditto, Schocken Books (U.S.), 1946 . . £100/£25

The Metamorphosis, Parton Press, 1937 (Translated by A.L. Lloyd) . . . . £2,500/£500

ditto, Vanguard Press (U.S.), 1946 . . . £250/£45

In The Penal Settlement, Secker & Warburg, 1949 (translated by Willa and Edwin Muir) . . £100/£30

Wedding Preparations in the Country, Secker & Warburg, 1954 (translated by Ernst Kaiser and Eithne Wilkins) . . . . £75/£25

Description of a Struggle, Schocken Books (U.S.), 1946 . . . . £100/£25

ditto, as *Description of a Struggle* and *The Great Wall of China*, Secker & Warburg, 1960 (with additional translations by Tania and James Stern) . . £75/£25

Others

Diaries, 1910-1913, Secker & Warburg, 1948 (translated by Joseph Kresh) . . . . . £50/£25

ditto, Schocken Books (U.S.), 1948 . . . £50/£25

Diaries, 1914-1923, Secker & Warburg, 1949 (translated by M. Greenberg and H. Arendt) . . £50/£25

ditto, Schocken Books (U.S.), 1949 . . £50/£25

Letters to Milena, Secker & Warburg, 1953 (translated by Tania and James Stern) . . . £65/£20

ditto, Schocken Books (U.S.), 1953 . . . £65/£25

Letters to Felice, Schocken Books (U.S.), 1973 (translated by James Stern and Elisabeth Duckworth) . . . . £65/£25

ditto, Secker & Warburg, 1974 . . . . £45/£20

Letters to Friends, Family and Editors, John Calder, 1978 (translated by Richard and Clara Winton) . . . . £45/£20

ditto, Schocken Books (U.S.), 1977 . . . £65/£25

ERICH KÄSTNER
(b.1899 d.1974)

A German writer in a wide range of genres, he is collected principally for his children's works, notably *Emil and the Detectives.*

Emil and the Detectives, Doubleday (U.S.), 1930 . . . . £150/£40

ditto, Cape, 1931 (illustrated by Walter Trier) . . . . £150/£40

Annaluise and Anton, Cape, 1932 . . . £100/£25

ditto, Dodd, Mead (U.S.), 1933 . . . . £75/£25

The 35th of May, Cape, 1933 . . . . £45/£15

The Flying Classroom, Cape, 1934 . . . £75/£20

Emil and the Three Twins, Cape, 1935 . . £60/£20

ditto, Franklin Watts (U.S.), 1961 . . . £25/£10

The Missing Miniature or The Adventures of a Sensitive Butcher, Knopf (U.S.), 1937 . . £40/£10

Emil, Cape, 1949 . . . . £15/£5

The Animals' Conference, D. McKay Co. (U.S.), [c.1949] . . . . £75/£10

ditto, Collins, 1955 . . . . £60/£20

Lottie and Lisa, Cape, 1950 . . . . . £65/£20

ditto, Knopf (U.S.), 1969 . . . . . . £25/£10

A Salzburg Comedy, Weidenfeld & Nicolson, 1950 . . . . £35/£10

ditto, Ungar (U.S.), 1957 . . . . . . £25/£10

Don Quixote, Messner (U.S.), [c.1957] . . £25/£25

Baron Munchhausen, Messner (U.S.), [c.1957] . . . . £25/£25

The Simpletons, Messner (U.S.), [c.1957] . £25/£25

Till Eulenspiegel the Clown, Messner (U.S.), [c.1957] . . . . £75/£20

ditto, Cape, 1967 . . . . £75/£20

Puss in Boots, Messner (U.S.), [c.1957] . . £45/£10

ditto, Cape, 1967 . . . . £45/£15

When I was a Little Boy, Cape, 1959 . . £25/£5

Let's Face It, Cape, 1963 . . . . . £20/£5

The Little Man, Cape, 1966 . . . . . £25/£10

ditto, Knopf (U.S.), 1966 . . . . . . £25/£10

The Little Man and the Little Miss, Cape, 1969 . . . . £20/£5

The Little Man and the Big Thief, Knopf (U.S.), 1969 . . . . £20/£5

JOHN KEATS
(b.1795 d.1821)

Along with Wordsworth, Keats is one of the best known and most widely read of the English Romantic poets.

Poetry

Poems, Ollier, 1817 (original boards with paper label to spine) £12,500

ditto, Ollier, 1817 (rebound) £5,000

Endymion, Taylor & Hessey, 1818 (first state with one line of errata and 2 advert leaves at end) . £7,500

ditto, Taylor & Hessey, 1818 (second state with 5 lines of errata and 5 advert leaves at end) . . £4,500

Lamia, Isabella, The Eve of St Agnes, and Other Poems, Taylor & Hessey, 1820 (with half title and 8 pages of adverts at end) £7,500

Miscellaneous

Life, Letters and Literary Remains of John Keats, Moxon, 1848 (2 vols) £400

Letters ... to Fanny Brawne, privately printed, 1878-79 (50 copies) £500

The Letters of John Keats, Reeves & Turner, 1895 . . . . £100

Anatomical and Physiological Notebook, O.U.P., 1934 (350 copies) £75

THOMAS KENEALLY
(b.1935)

An Australian novelist whose *Schindler's Ark* won the Booker Prize before being successfully filmed as *Schindler's List*.

Novels
The Place at Whitton, Cassell (Melbourne), 1964 . . . . £200/£25
ditto, Cassell, 1964 . . . . £200/£25
ditto, Walker (U.S.), 1964 . . . . . £125/£20
The Fear, Cassell (Melbourne), 1965 . . £150/£20
ditto, Cassell, 1965 . . . . £150/£20
ditto, as *By The Line*, Univ. of Queensland Press, 1989 . . . . £20/£5
ditto, as *By The Line*, Sceptre, 1992 (wraps) . £5
Bring Larks and Heroes, Cassell (Melbourne), 1967 . . . . £45/£10
ditto, Cassell, 1967 . . . . £45/£10
ditto, Viking (U.S.), 1968. . . . . . £30/£10
Three Cheers for the Paraclete, Angus & Robertson, 1968 . . . . £45/£10
ditto, Viking (U.S.), 1969. . . . . . £35/£10
The Survivor, Angus & Robertson, 1969 . £65/£15
A Dutiful Daughter, Angus & Robertson, 1971 £25/£5
ditto, Viking (U.S.), 1971. . . . . . £20/£5
The Chant of Jimmie Blacksmith, Angus & Robertson, 1972 . . . . £25/£5
ditto, Viking (U.S.), 1972. . . . . . £20/£5
Blood Red, Sister Rose, Collins, 1974 . . £25/£5
ditto, Viking (U.S.), 1974. . . . . . £20/£5
Gossip from the Forest, Collins, 1975 . . £35/£10
ditto, Harcourt Brace (U.S.), 1976 . . . £25/£5
Season in Purgatory, Collins, 1976 . . . £20/£5
ditto, Harcourt Brace (U.S.), 1977 . . . £15/£5
A Victim of the Aurora, Collins, 1977 . . £15/£5
ditto, Harcourt Brace (U.S.), 1978 . . . £15/£5
Passenger, Collins, 1979 . . . . . . £15/£5
ditto, Harcourt Brace (U.S.), 1979 . . . £15/£5
Confederates, Collins, 1979 . . . . . £15/£5
ditto, Harcourt Brace (U.S.), 1980 . . . £15/£5
Schindler's Ark, Hodder & Stoughton, 1982 £75/£20
ditto, as *Schindler's List*, Simon & Schuster (U.S.), 1982 . . . . £75/£20
The Cut-Rate Kingdom, Wildcat Press (Sydney), 1980 . . . . £40
ditto, Allen Lane, 1984 . . . . . . £15/£5
A Family Madness, Hodder & Stoughton, 1985 £15/£5
ditto, Simon & Schuster (U.S.), 1986 . . £15/£5
The Playmaker, Hodder & Stoughton, 1987 £15/£5
ditto, Simon & Schuster (U.S.), 1987 . . £15/£5
Act of Grace, Chatto & Windus, 1988 (pseud. 'William Coyle') . . . . £15/£5
Towards Asmara, Hodder & Stoughton, 1989 £15/£5
ditto, as *To Asmara*, Warner (U.S.), 1989 . £15/£5
Flying Hero Class, Hodder & Stoughton, 1991 £15/£5
ditto, Warner (U.S.), 1991 . . . . . £15/£5
Chief of Staff, Chatto & Windus, 1991 (pseud.

'William Coyle'). . . . . £15/£5
A Woman of the Inner Sea, Hodder & Stoughton, 1992 . . . . £15/£5
Jacko, The Great Intruder, Hodder & Stoughton, 1993 . . . . £15/£5
A River Town, Hodder & Stoughton, 1995 . £15/£5
Bettany's Book, Sceptre, 2000 . . . . £15/£5

Plays
Halloran's Little Boat, Penguin, 1975 (wraps) . £15
Bullie's House, Currency Press (Sydney), 1981 £20/£5

Others
Moses the Lawgiver, Harper (U.S.), 1975 . £15/£5
ditto, Collins, 1976 . . . . £15/£5
Ned Kelly and the City of the Bees, Cape, 1978 £15/£5
ditto, Godine (U.S.), 1981 . . . . . £15/£5
Outback, Hodder & Stoughton, 1983 . . £15/£5
Now and in a Time To Be, Ryan Publishing, 1991. . . . . £15/£5
Ireland, Fontana, 1992 (wraps) £5
The Place Where Souls are Born, Hodder & Stoughton, 1992. . . . . £15/£5
The Utility Player, The Des Hasler Story, Pan Macmillan (Sydney), 1993 (wraps). . . . £5
Our Republic, Heinemann (Melbourne), 1993 £10/£5
Memoirs from a Young Republic, Heinemann, 1993 . . . . £10/£5
Homebush Boy, A Memoir, Hodder & Stoughton, 1995 . . . . £10/£5
The Great Shame, A Story of the Irish in the Old World and the New, Chatto & Windus, 1999 £10/£5

JACK KEROUAC
(b.1922 d.1969)

The semi-autobiographical novelist of the Beat Generation in 1950s San Francisco.

Fiction
The Town and the City, Harcourt Brace (U.S.), 1950 (pseud. 'John Kerouac') . . . . £600/£125
ditto, Eyre & Spottiswoode, 1951 . . . £250/£50
On the Road, Viking (U.S.), 1957 . £2,000/£300
ditto, Andre Deutsch, 1958 (author photo on real flap). . . . . £600/£75
ditto, Andre Deutsch, 1958 (author photo on front flap) . . . . £300/£75
The Subterraneans, Grove Press (U.S.), 1958 . . . . £650/£50
ditto, Grove Press (U.S.), 1958 (100 numbered copies, no d/w) £400
ditto, Grove Press (U.S.), 1958 (wraps) . . . £30
ditto, Andre Deutsch, 1962 . . . . . £200/£50
The Dharma Bums, Viking (U.S.), 1958 . £200/£50
ditto, Andre Deutsch, 1959 . . . . . £75/£25
Doctor Sax: Faust Part Three, Grove Press (U.S.), 1959 . . . . £500/£75

ditto, Grove Press (U.S.), 1959 (26 signed, lettered copies) £2,000
ditto, Grove Press (U.S.), 1959 (4 signed, numbered copies) £4,000
ditto, Evergreen, 1961 (wraps) £20
ditto, Deutsch, 1977 . . . . £50/£15
Maggie Cassidy, Avon (U.S.), 1959 (wraps) . £35
ditto, Panther, 1960 (wraps) £15
ditto, Deutsch, 1974 . . . . . . £75/£15
Excerpts from Visions of Cody, New Directions (U.S.), 1959 (750 signed, numbered copies) . . . £500
ditto, Andre Deutsch, 1973 . . . . . £50/£15
Tristessa, Avon (U.S.), 1960 (wraps) . . . £15
ditto, World Distributors, 1963 (wraps) . . . £10
Book of Dreams, City Light Books (U.S.), 1961 £50
Big Sur, Farrar Straus (U.S.), 1962 . . . £125/£25
ditto, Andre Deutsch, 1963 . . . . . £75/£20
Visions of Gerard, Farrar Straus (U.S.), 1963 £100/£25
ditto, Andre Deutsch, 1964 (with *Tristessa*) £50/£15
Desolation Angels, Coward McCann (U.S.), 1965 . . . . £125/£25
ditto, Andre Deutsch, 1966 . . . . . £75/£25
Satori in Paris, Grove Press (U.S.), 1966 . £100/£20
ditto, Andre Deutsch, 1967 . . . . £25/£10
Vanity of Dulouz: An Adventurous Education, 1935-46, Coward McCann (U.S.), 1968 . . . £75/£20
ditto, Andre Deutsch, 1969 . . . . . £50/£20
Pic and the Subterraneans, Grove Press (U.S.), 1971 . . . . £45/£10
ditto, Andre Deutsch, 1973 . . . . . £40/£10
Old Angel Midnight, Unicorn Press, 1976 (wraps) £25
ditto, Midnight Press (U.S.), 1985 (wraps) . . £25
Take Care of My Ghost, Ghost Press (U.S.), 1977 (with Ginsberg, wraps) £20
ditto, Ghost Press (U.S.), 1977 (200 copies signed by Ginsberg, wraps) £100
Baby Driver: A Story About Myself, St Martin's Press (U.S.), 1981 . . . . £20/£5
ditto, Andre Deutsch, 1981 . . . . . £20/£5
San Francisco Blues, Beat Books (U.S.), 1983 £25
Two Stories, Pacific Red Car (U.S.), 1984 (100 copies, wraps) £35
The Great Western Bus Ride, Pacific Red Car (U.S.), 1984 (100 copies, wraps) £45
Celine and Other Tales, Pacific Red Car (U.S.), 1985 (100 copies, wraps) £35
The Vision of the Hooded White Angels, Pacific Red Car (U.S.), 1985 (100 copies, wraps) . . £35
Home at Christmas, Pacific Red Car (U.S.), [no date] (wraps) £25

Verse

Mexico City Blues, Grove Press (U.S.), 1959 . . . . £750/£150
ditto, Grove Press (U.S.), 1959 (26 signed, lettered copies) £1,500
ditto, Grove Press (U.S.), 1959 (4 signed, numbered copies) £2,500

Hymn - God Pray For Me, Jubilee Magazine (U.S.), [1959], (broadsheet) £45
The Scripture of the Golden Eternity, Totem Press/Corinth Books (U.S.), 1960 (wraps) . . £125
Rimbaud, City Light Books (U.S.), 1960 (broadsheet) £50
'I demand that the human race ceases multiplying its kind...', Pax #17 (U.S.), 1962 (broadsheet) . £50
Poem, Jubilee Magazine (U.S.), [1962] (broadsheet) £45
A Pun for Al Gepi, privately printed (U.S.) (100 copies, broadsheet) £50
Hugo Weber, Portents (U.S.), 1967 (200 copies, broadsheet) £45
Someday You'll be Lying, privately printed (U.S.), 1968 (broadsheet) £45
A Last Haiku, privately printed (U.S.), 1969 (broadsheet) £35
Scattered Poems, City Lights (U.S.), 1971 (wraps) £30
Trip, Trap, Grey Fox Press (U.S.), 1973 (wraps) £40
Heaven and Other Poems, Grey Fox Press (U.S.), 1977 . . . . £40

Others
Lonesome Traveller, McGraw Hill (U.S.), 1960 . . . . £100/£20
ditto, Andre Deutsch, 1962 . . . . . £50/£15
Pull My Daisy, Grove Press (U.S.), 1961 (wraps) £75
ditto, Evergreen, 1961 (wraps) £35

KEN KESEY
(b.1935)
An American novelist, Kesey volunteered, in the 1960s, for Government drug experiments. His *One flew over the Cuckoo's Nest* draws on his experience of working as an aide on a psychiatric ward in a veteran's hospital.

Novels
One Flew over the Cuckoo's Nest, Viking (U.S.), 1962 . . . . £2,000/£100
ditto, Methuen, 1963 . . . . £300/£35
Sometimes a Great Notion, Viking (U.S.), 1964 (first issue with Viking ship on half title before title page) . . . . £150/£25
ditto, Viking (U.S.), 1964 (more scarce second issue with Viking ship on half title after title page) . . . . £150/£25
ditto, Methuen, 1966 . . . . £100/£20
Demon Box, Viking (U.S.), 1986 . . . £15/£5
ditto, Methuen, 1986 . . . . £10/£5
The Further Inquiry, Viking (U.S.), 1990 . £10/£5
Sailor Song, Viking (U.S.), 1992 . . . £10/£5
ditto, Black Swan, 1993 (wraps) £5
Last Go Round, Viking (U.S.), 1994 (with Ken Babbs) . . . . £10/£5

Children's

Little Tricker the Squirrel Meets Big Double the Bear,
Viking (U.S.), 1990 . . . . . . £25/£10
Sea Lion, Viking (U.S.), 1991 . . . . £25/£10

Others

Kesey's Garage Sale, Viking (U.S.), 1973 . £25/£10
Kesey, Northwest Review Books (U.S.), 1977
(hardback, no d/w) £50
ditto, Northwest Review Books (U.S.), 1977 (wraps) .
. . . . £15
The Day After Superman Died, Lord John Press
(U.S.), 1980 (350 signed copies) £65
Caverns, by O.U. Levon, Penguin (U.S.), 1990
(Collaborative novel written by Kesey and students in
his writing class at the Univ. of Oregon, wraps) £65

KEYNOTES

A series of 33 books (34 were advertised) issued by
John Lane between 1893 and 1897. Nos. 1-21 and 23
have cover, title page and key designs by Aubrey
Beardsley; the remaining nos. have designs by Patten
Wilson.

1. *Keynotes*, by George Egerton, Mathews/Lane, 1893
(500 copies in pink wraps) £200
ditto, Mathews/Lane, 1893 (600 copies in green cloth)
. . . . £100
ditto, Roberts Bros. (U.S.), 1893 . . . . £40
2. *The Dancing Faun*, by Florence Farr, Mathews/
Lane, 1894 (1st issue, light blue cloth, key on spine in
gilt) £150
ditto, Mathews/Lane, 1894 (2nd issue, light green cloth,
key on spine in blue). £125
ditto, Roberts Bros. (U.S.), 1894 . . . . £45
3. *Poor Folk*, by Fedor [sic] Dostoievsky, Mathews/
Lane, 1894 . . . . £100
ditto, Roberts Bros. (U.S.), 1894 . . . . £40
4. *A Child of the Age*, by Francis Adams, Lane, 1894 .
. . . . £100
ditto, Roberts Bros. (U.S.), 1894 . . . . £40
5. *The Great God Pan and the Inmost Light*, by
Arthur Machen, Lane, 1894 . . . . . £225
ditto, Roberts Bros. (U.S.), 1894 . . . . £100
6. *Discords*, by George Egerton, Lane, 1894 . £100
ditto, Roberts Bros. (U.S.), 1894 . . . . £40
7. *Prince Zaleski*, by M.P. Shiel, Lane, 1895 . £300
ditto, Roberts Bros. (U.S.), 1895 . . . . £150
8. *The Woman Who Did*, by Grant Allen, Lane, 1895 .
. . . . £100
ditto, Roberts Bros. (U.S.), 1895 . . . . £40
9. *Women's Tragedies*, by H.D. Lowry, Lane, 1895 .
. . . . £100
ditto, Roberts Bros. (U.S.), 1895 . . . . £40
10. *Grey Roses*, by Henry Harland, Lane, 1895 £100
ditto, Roberts Bros. (U.S.), 1895 . . . . £40

11. *At the First Corner and Other Stories*, by H.B.
Marriott Watson, Lane, 1895 . . . . . £100
ditto, Roberts Bros. (U.S.), 1895 . . . . . £40
12. *Monochromes*, by Ella D'Arcy, Lane, 1895 £100
ditto, Roberts Bros. (U.S.), 1895 . . . . £40
13. *At the Relton Arms*, by Evelyn Sharp, Lane, 1895 .
. . . . £100
ditto, Roberts Bros. (U.S.), 1895 . . . . £40
14. *The Girl from the Farm*, by Gertrude Dix, Lane,
1895 . . . . £100
ditto, Roberts Bros. (U.S.), 1895 . . . . £40
15. *The Mirror of Music*, by Stanley V. Makower,
Lane, 1895 . . . . £100
ditto, Roberts Bros. (U.S.), 1895 . . . . £40
16. *Yellow and White*, by W. Carlton Dawe, Lane,
1895 . . . . £100
ditto, Roberts Bros. (U.S.), 1895 . . . . £40
17. *The Mountain Lovers*, by Fiona MacLeod, Lane,
1895 . . . . £100
ditto, Roberts Bros. (U.S.), 1895 . . . . £40
18. *The Woman Who Didn't*, by Victoria Crosse,
Lane, 1895 . . . . £100
ditto, Roberts Bros. (U.S.), 1895 . . . . . £40
19. *The Three Impostors*, by Arthur Machen, Lane,
1895 . . . . £225
ditto, Roberts Bros. (U.S.), 1895 . . . . £150
20. *Nobody's Fault*, by Netta Syrett, Lane, 1896 £100
ditto, Roberts Bros. (U.S.), 1895 . . . . . £40
21. *The British Barbarians*, by Grant Allen, Lane,
1895 . . . . £100
ditto, Lane/Putnams (U.S.), 1895. . . . £40
22. *In Homespun*, E. Nesbit, Lane, 1896 . . £100
ditto, Roberts Bros. (U.S.), 1896 . . . . £40
23. *Platonic Affections*, by John Smith, Lane, 1896 .
. . . . £100
ditto, Roberts Bros. (U.S.), 1896 . . . . £40
24. *Nets for the Wind*, by Una Taylor, Lane, 1896 . .
. . . . £100
ditto, Roberts Bros. (U.S.), 1896 . . . . £40
25. *Where the Atlantic Meets the Land*, by Caldwell
Lipsett, Lane, 1896 . . . . £100
ditto, Roberts Bros. (U.S.), 1896 . . . . £40
26. *In Scarlet and Grey*, by Florence Henniker
(contains 'The Spectre of the Real', by F.H. and
Thomas Hardy), Lane, 1896 . . . . . £200
ditto, Roberts Bros. (U.S.), 1896 . . . . £80
27. *Maris Stella*, by Marie Clothilde Balfour, Lane,
1896 . . . . £100
ditto, Roberts Bros. (U.S.), 1896 . . . . £40
28. *Day Books*, by Mabel E. Wotton, Lane, 1896 £100
ditto, Roberts Bros. (U.S.), 1896 . . . . £40
29. *Shapes in the Fire*, by M.P. Shiel, Lane, 1896 £300
ditto, Roberts Bros. (U.S.), 1896 . . . . £150
30. *Ugly Idol*, by Claud Nicholson, Lane, 1896. £100
ditto, Roberts Bros. (U.S.), 1896 . . . . £40
31. *Kakemonos*, by W. Carlton Dawe, Lane, 1897 . .
. . . . £100
32. *God's Failures*, by J.S. Fletcher, Lane, 1897 £100

33. *A Deliverence*, by Allan Monkhouse. Not published in Keynotes series although advertised.
34. *Mere Sentiment*, A.J Dawson, Lane, 1897 . £100

C. DALY KING
(b.1895 d.1963)

An author of detective fiction from its 'Golden Age', King's books are unconventional, enthralling and puzzling.

Novels
Obelists at Sea, Heritage, [1932]. . . £1,500/£200
ditto, Knopf (U.S.), 1933 . . . . . £1,000/£150
ditto, Collins Crime Club [no date] . . . £350/£35
Obelists En Route, Collins Crime Club, 1934 . . .
. . . . £1,250/£150
Obelists Fly High, Collins Crime Club, 1935 . . .
. . . . £1,250/£150
ditto, Smith & Haas (U.S.), 1935. . . £450/£100
Careless Corpse, Collins Crime Club, 1937. . . .
. . . . £1,000/£150
Arrogant Alibi, Collins Crime Club, 1938 . . .
. . . . £1,000/£150
ditto, Appleton (U.S.), 1939 . . . . £350/£100
Burmuda Burial, Collins Crime Club, 1940 . . .
. . . . £1,000/£150
ditto, Funk (U.S.), 1941 . . . . . £350/£100

Short Stories
The Curious Mt Tarrant, Collins Crime Club, 1935 .
. . . . £1,500/£150
ditto, Dover (U.S.), 1977 . . . . . . £15

STEPHEN KING
(b.1947)

One of the most successful of living writers, King's breakthrough was *Carrie*, a book which has now sold over 12 million copies.

Novels
Carrie, Doubleday (U.S.), 1974 (inner margin of p.199 has date code 'P6') . . . . . £750/£150
ditto, New English Library, 1974 . . £750/£150
Salem's Lot, Doubleday (U.S.), 1975 (inner margin of p.439 with date code 'Q37', first state, first issue d/w with Father 'Cody' and price $8.95) . £1,250/£125
ditto, Doubleday (U.S.), 1975 (first state second issue d/w with Father 'Cody' but price clipped and new price of $7.95 added) . . . . £750/£125

ditto, Doubleday (U.S.), 1975 (second state d/w with Father 'Callahan' and unclipped price of $7.95) . .
. . . . £400/£125
ditto, New English Library, 1976 . . . £350/£50
The Shining, Doubleday (U.S.), 1977 . . £500/£75
ditto, New English Library, 1977 . . . £250/£50
Rage, Signet/New American Library (U.S.), 1977 (pseud. 'Richard Bachman', wraps) . . . £30
ditto, New English Library, 1983 (wraps) . . £20
The Stand, Doubleday (U.S.), 1978 (d/w price $12.95)
. . . . £300/£50
ditto, New English Library, 1979 . . . £200/£50
The Dead Zone, Viking (U.S.), 1979 . . £125/£20
ditto, Macdonald & Jane, 1979 . . . . £125/£20
The Long Walk, Signet/New American Library (U.S.), 1979 (pseud. 'Richard Bachman', wraps) . . . £30
Firestarter, Phantasia Press (U.S.), 1980 (725 copies in d/w and slipcase). . . . . . . £500/£200
ditto, Phantasia Press (U.S.), 1980 (26 lettered copies, bound in asbestos) £5,000
ditto, Viking (U.S.), 1980. . . . . . £25/£10
ditto, Macdonald & Jane, 1980 . . . . £25/£10
Roadwork, Signet/New American Library (U.S.), 1981 (pseud. 'Richard Bachman', wraps) . . . £20
ditto, New English Library, 1983 (wraps) . . £15
Cujo, Viking (U.S.), 1981 . . . . . £40/£10
ditto, Mysterious Press (U.S.), 1981 (750 numbered, signed copies) . . . . £300/£150
ditto, Mysterious Press (U.S.), 1981 (lettered, signed copies) £1,000
ditto, Macdonald, 1982 . . . . . . £25/£10
The Running Man, Signet/New American Library (U.S.), 1982 (pseud. 'Richard Bachman', wraps) £25
ditto, New English Library, 1983 (wraps) . . £15
Creepshow, NAL/Plume (U.S.), 1982 (wraps) . £25
The Dark Tower: The Gunslinger, Grant (U.S.), 1982
. . . . £200/£65
ditto, Grant (U.S.), 1982 (lettered, signed edition, d/w and slipcase) . . . . . . £2,000/£1,500
ditto, Grant (U.S.), 1982 (500 numbered, signed copies, d/w and slipcase) . . . . . £1,000/£400
ditto, Sphere, 1988, (wraps) £10
Christine, Grant (U.S.), 1983 (lettered, signed edition)
. . . . £2,000
ditto, Grant (U.S.), 1983 (1,000 signed copies, slipcase)
. . . . £350/£200
ditto, Viking (U.S.), 1983. . . . . . £25/£5
ditto, Hodder & Stoughton, 1983. . . . £25/£5
Cycle of the Werewolf, Land of Enchantment (U.S.), 1983 . . . . £200/£75
ditto, Land of Enchantment (U.S.), 1983 (8 present-ation copies) £3,000
ditto, Land of Enchantment (U.S.), 1983 (250 copies, slipcase) . . . . £500/£250
ditto, Land of Enchantment (U.S.), 1983 (100 copies with original drawing, slipcase). £1,250/£1,000
ditto, New English Library, 1985 (wraps) . . £10
Selected Works, Heinemann/Octopus, 1983 £15/£5
Pet Sematary, Doubleday (U.S.), 1983 . . £20/£5

ditto, Hodder & Stoughton, 1984. . . . £20/£5

The Talisman, Viking, 1984 (with Peter Straub) . .
. . . . £20/£5

ditto, Grant (U.S.), 1984 (70 numbered copies signed by authors and artists, slipcase, 2 vols). £750/£500

ditto, Grant (U.S.), 1984 (1,200 signed, numbered copies, no d/w, slipcase, 2 vols) . . £300/£200

ditto, Viking (U.K.), 1984 . . . . £15/£5

The Eyes of the Dragon, Philtrum (U.S.), 1984 (1,000 signed copies numbered in black ink, slipcase, no d/w) . . . . £500/£400

ditto, Philtrum (U.S.), 1984 (250 signed copies numbered in red ink, slipcase, no d/w). £850/£700

ditto, Viking (U.S.), 1987. . . . . £15/£5

ditto, Macdonald, 1987 . . . . . . £15/£5

Thinner, New American Library (U.S.), 1984 (pseud. 'Richard Bachman') . . . . £45/£10

ditto, New English Library, 1985 (pseud. 'Richard Bachman') . . . . £30/£10

The Bachman Books, New American Library, 1985 (pseud. 'Richard Bachman') . . . . £20/£5

ditto, New English Library, 1986 . . . £20/£5

Silver Bullet, New American Library/Signet (U.S.), 1985 (wraps) £15

It, Hodder & Stoughton, 1986 . . . . £20/£5

ditto, Viking (U.S.), 1986. . . . . £15/£5

Misery, Viking (U.S.), 1987 . . . . £20/£5

ditto, Hodder & Stoughton, 1987. . . £15/£5

The Dark Tower II: The Drawing of the Three, Grant (U.S.), 1987 . . . . £30/£10

ditto, Grant (U.S.), 1987 (800 signed copies, d/w and slipcase) . . . . £450/£300

ditto, Grant (U.S.), 1987 (50 lettered copies, d/w and slipcase) . . . . £1,000/£750

ditto, Sphere, 1989 (wraps) £10

The Tommyknockers, Putnam (U.S.), 1987 £15/£5

ditto, Hodder & Stoughton, 1988. . . £15/£5

The Dark Half, Hodder & Stoughton, 1989 £10/£5

ditto, Viking (U.S.), 1989. . . . . £10/£5

The Stand, Doubleday (U.S.), 1990 (complete and uncut edition). . . . . £25/£5

ditto, Doubleday (U.S.), 1990 (52 signed, lettered copies) £1,500

ditto, Doubleday (U.S.), 1990 (1,250 signed copies, bound in full leather, in wooden box) . . . £750

ditto, Hodder & Stoughton, 1990. . . £25/£5

The Dark Tower III: The Wastelands, Grant (U.S.), 1991 . . . . £25/£10

ditto, Grant (U.S.), 1991 (1,250 signed copies, d/w and slipcase). . . . . £300/£200

ditto, Sphere, 1991, (wraps) £10

Needful Things, Hodder & Stoughton, [1991] £10/£5

ditto, Viking (U.S.), 1991. . . . . £10/£5

Gerald's Game, Viking (U.S.), 1992 . . £10/£5

ditto, Hodder & Stoughton, 1992. . . £10/£5

Dolores Claiborne, Book Club Associates, 1992 . .
. . . . £10/£5

ditto, Viking (U.S.), 1992. . . . . £10/£5

ditto, Hodder & Stoughton, 1992. . . £10/£5

ditto, Hodder & Stoughton, 1992 ('Special Limited Christmas Gift Edition', slipcase) . . . £100/£50

Insomnia, Ziesing (U.S.), 1994 (1,250 signed copies, d/w and case). . . . . £300/£150

ditto, Ziesing (U.S.), 1994 ('Gift edition', d/w and slipcase) . . . . £75/£45

ditto, Viking (U.S.), 1994. . . . . . £10/£5

ditto, Hodder & Stoughton, 1994. . . £10/£5

ditto, Hodder & Stoughton, 1994 (200 signed, numbered copies, slipcase, no d/w). . £250/£200

Rose Madder, Hodder & Stoughton, 1994 . £10/£5

ditto, Hodder & Stoughton, 1994 (250 signed copies, slipcase, no d/w) . . . . £200/£125

ditto, Viking (U.S.), 1995. . . . . £10/£5

The Green Mile, Penguin/Signet (U.S.), 1996 (six paperbacks) . . . . £15 the set

ditto, Penguin, 1996 (six paperbacks) . £15 the set

ditto, Penguin/Plume (U.S.), 1997 (1 vol.) . . £5

Desperation, Viking (U.S.), 1996 . . . £10/£5

ditto, Hodder & Stoughton, 1996. . . . £10/£5

Desperation and *The Regulator*, Hodder Headline, 1996 (250 sets in single slipcase, the former signed, the latter pseud. 'Richard Bachman') . £250/£200

The Dark Tower IV: Wizard and Glass, Grant (U.S.), 1997 . . . . £25/£10

ditto, Grant (U.S.), 1991 (1,200 signed copies, d/w and slipcase). . . . . £300/£200

ditto, Hodder & Stoughton, 1988, (wraps) . . £10

ditto, Hodder & Stoughton, 1988, (500 copies, no d/w) £250

Bag of Bones, Simon & Schuster/Scribner (U.S.), 1998
. . . . £10/£5

ditto, Hodder & Stoughton, 1998. . . . £10/£5

ditto, Hodder & Stoughton, 1998 (2,000 signed copies)
. . . . £50/£20

The Girl Who Loved Tom Gordon, Hodder & Stoughton, 1999 . . . . £10/£5

ditto, Scribner (U.S.), 1999 . . . . . £10/£5

Dreamcatcher, Hodder & Stoughton, 2001 . £10/£5

ditto, Scribner (U.S.), 2001 . . . . £10/£5

Short Stories

Night Shift, Doubleday (U.S.), 1978. . . . £500/£60

ditto, New English Library, 1978 . . . £250/£45

Different Seasons, Viking (U.S.), 1982 . . £25/£10

ditto, Macdonald, 1982 . . . . . . £20/£15

The Plant, Philtrum (U.S.), 1982 (200 signed copies, wraps). £1,000

ditto, Philtrum (U.S.), 1982 (26 signed, lettered copies, wraps). £1,750

The Plant - Part Two, Philtrum (U.S.), 1983 (200 copies, wraps) £1,000

ditto, Philtrum (U.S.), 1983 (26 signed, lettered copies, wraps). £1,750

Skeleton Crew, Putnam (U.S.), 1985 . . . £45

ditto, as *Stephen King's Skeleton Crew*, Scream Press (U.S.), 1985 (1,000 copies numbered in silver ink and signed by author and artist, slipcase) . £300/£200

ditto, Scream Press (U.S.), 1985, (69 leather-bound, zippered copies) £1,500
ditto, Scream Press (U.S.), 1985 (17 presentation copies) £2,000
ditto, Scream Press (U.S.), 1985 (52 lettered copies) .
. . . . £750
ditto, Putnam), 1985 . . . . . . £20/£5
ditto, Macdonald, 1985 . . . . . £20/£5
The Plant - Part Three, Philtrum (U.S.), 1985 (200 copies, wraps) £1,000
ditto, Philtrum (U.S.), 1985 (26 signed, lettered copies, wraps). £1,500
My Pretty Pony, Whitney Museum of American Art (U.S.), 1989 (250 copies) £1,750
ditto, Knopf (U.S.), 1989 . . . . . £30/£10
Dolan's Cadillac, Lord John Press (U.S.), 1989 (26 lettered, signed copies) £1,500
ditto, Lord John Press (U.S.), 1989 (100 presentation copies, quarter-bound in leather) . . . £300
ditto, Lord John Press (U.S.), 1989 (250 numbered, signed copies, quarter-bound in leather) . . £250
ditto, Lord John Press (U.S.), 1989 (1,000 numbered, signed copies, no d/w) £100
Four Past Midnight, Viking (U.S.), 1990 . £10/£5
ditto, Hodder & Stoughton, 1990. . . . £10/£5
Nightmares and Dreamscapes, Viking (U.S.), 1993 .
. . . . £10/£5
ditto, Hodder & Stoughton, 1993. . . . £10/£5
Six Stories, Philtrum (U.S.), 1997 (900 [800] signed copies, wraps) . . . . . . £10/£5

Others

Danse Macabre, Everest House (U.S.), 1981 £50/£20
ditto, Everest House (U.S.), 1981 (250 signed, numbered copies, slipcase, tissue d/w) . £450/£150
ditto, Everest House (U.S.), 1981 (signed, lettered copies, slipcase, tissue d/w) . . . £1,000/£750
ditto, Everest House (U.S.), 1981 (35 publishers copies, no slipcase or d/w) £750
ditto, Macdonald Futura, 1981 . . . £25/£10
Letters from Hell, Lord John Press (U.S.), 1988 (500 signed copies, broadside in wraps) . . . £100
Storm of the Century, Pocket Books (U.S.), 1999 (wraps) £5
ditto, Book of the Month Club (U.S.), 1999. £10/£5
Hearts in Atlantis, Hodder & Stoughton, 1999 £10/£5
ditto, Scribner (U.S.), 1999 . . . . £10/£5
On Writing, Scribner (U.S.), 2000 . . £10/£5
ditto, Hodder & Stoughton, 2000. . . £10/£5

RUDYARD KIPLING
(b.1865 d.1936)

Often considered a poet of British imperialism, Kipling's work has caused much controversy, though poems such as *If* and his 'Jungle Book' stories remain firmly entrenched in British colonial mythology.

Verse

Schoolboy Lyrics, privately printed at the 'Civil & Military Gazette' Press (Lahore), 1881 (wraps) . .
. . . . £5,000
Echoes, privately printed (Lahore), 1884 (published anonymously, with Alice Kipling, wraps) . . £2,000
Quartette, privately printed at the 'Civil & Military Gazette' Press (Lahore), 1885 (published anonymously, with his sister, mother and father, wraps) .
. . . . £2,000
Departmental Ditties, Civil and Military Gazette (Lahore), 1886 (wraps) £1,000
ditto, Thacker, Spink & Co. (Calcutta), 1886 . £250
ditto, Thackar & Co. (London), 1890 . . . £40
Barrack-Room Ballads and Other Verses, Methuen, 1892 . . . . £150
ditto, Methuen, 1892 (large paper edition, 225 copies).
. . . . £400
ditto, Methuen, 1892 (deluxe edition, 30 copies on half-vellum) £1,000
The Seven Seas, Methuen, 1896 . . . . . £35
ditto, Methuen, 1896 (large paper edition, 150 copies).
. . . . £200
ditto, Methuen, 1896 (deluxe edition, 30 copies on half-vellum) £500
An Almanac of Twelve Sports, Heinemann, 1898 [1897]. £400
Early Verse, Macmillan, 1900 . . . . . £60
The Five Nations, Methuen, 1903 . . . £45
ditto, Methuen, 1903 (large paper edition, 200 copies).
. . . . £200
ditto, Methuen, 1903 (deluxe edition, 30 copies on full vellum. £750
A Song of the English, Hodder & Stoughton, [c.1909] (30 colour plates illustrated by W. Heath Robinson) .
. . . . £100
ditto, Hodder & Stoughton, [c.1909] (deluxe edition, 500 copies signed by the artist, 30 colour plates, full vellum) £250
ditto, Hodder & Stoughton, [1912], (12 colour plates) .
. . . . £45
ditto, Hodder & Stoughton/Daily Telegraph, [1915] (16 colour plates). £65
ditto, Hodder & Stoughton, [1919] (16 colour plates) .
. . . . £45
The Dead King, Hodder & Stoughton, 1910 (illustrated by W. Heath Robinson) £50
ditto, Hodder & Stoughton, 1910 (illustrated by W. Heath Robinson, wraps). £30
Collected Verse, Doubleday Page (U.S.), 1907 (without index) £100

ditto, Doubleday Page (U.S.), 1907 (with index) £65

ditto, Doubleday Page (U.S.), 1910 (9 colour plates by W. Heath Robinson) £100

ditto, Doubleday Page (U.S.), 1910 (125 signed copies, 9 colour plates by W. Heath Robinson) . . £750

ditto, Hodder & Stoughton, 1912 (500 copies) . £150

ditto, Hodder & Stoughton, 1912 (deluxe edition, 100 copies on full vellum) £450

A History of England, O.U.P./Hodder & Stoughton, 1911 (quarto, with C.R.L. Fletcher) . . . £25

ditto, O.U.P./Hodder & Stoughton, 1911 (octavo edition for schools) £15

Songs from Books, Macmillan, 1913 . . . £25

Twenty Poems, Methuen, 1918 (wraps) . . . £20

The Years Between, Methuen, 1919 . . . . £25

ditto, Methuen, 1919 (Large Paper edition, 100 copies) £200

ditto, Methuen, 1919 (deluxe edition, 30 copies on vellum) £350

Verse: Inclusive Edition 1885-1918, Hodder & Stoughton, 1919 (3 vols) £75

ditto, Hodder & Stoughton, 1919 (deluxe edition, 100 signed sets on vellum) £750

A Kipling Anthology: Verse, Methuen, 1922 £20/£5

Songs for Youth, Hodder & Stoughton, [1924] £35/£10

A Choice of Songs, Methuen, 1925 . . . £20/£5

Sea and Sussex, Macmillan, 1926 (illustrated by Donald Maxwell) . . . . . . £50/£15

ditto, Macmillan, 1926 (500 copies on half-vellum) £250

Songs of the Sea, Macmillan, 1927 (illustrated by Donald Maxwell) . . . . . . £50/£15

ditto, Macmillan, 1927 (500 copies on half-vellum) £250

Poems 1886-1929, Macmillan, 1929 (3 vols, illustrated by Francis Dodd) . . . . £50/£20

ditto, Macmillan, 1929 (deluxe edition, 525 sets in morocco leather) £250

East of Suez, Macmillan, 1931 (illustrated by Donald Maxwell) . . . . £25/£10

Selected Poems, Methuen, 1931 . . . . £15/£5

Sixty Poems, Hodder & Stoughton, 1939 . £15/£5

Verse: Definitive Edition, Hodder & Stoughton, 1940 . . . . £25/£5

So Shall Ye Reap: Poems For These Days, Hodder & Stoughton, 1941 . . . . £15/£5

A Choice of Kipling's Verse, Faber & Faber, 1941 (edited by T.S. Eliot) . . . . . £20/£5

Children's

The Jungle Book, Macmillan, 1894 . . . . £750

ditto, Century (U.S.), 1894 . . . . . £150

The Second Jungle Book, Macmillan, 1895 . £350

ditto, Century (U.S.), 1895 . . . . . £75

'Captains Courageous', a story of the Grand Banks, Macmillan, 1897 . . . . £400

ditto, Century (U.S.), 1897 . . . . . £100

Stalky and Co., Macmillan, 1899 . . . . £200

Just So Stories for Little Children, Macmillan, 1902 . . . . £250

ditto, Doubleday Page (U.S.), 1902 . . . . £200

Puck of Pook's Hill, Macmillan, 1906 . . . £150

ditto, Doubleday Page (U.S.), 1906 (illustrated by Arthur Rackham). £200

Rewards and Fairies, Macmillan, 1910 . . . £50

Novels

The Light That Failed, Lippincott (U.S.), 1890 (12 chapters with happy ending, wraps) . . . £150

ditto, Macmillan, 1891 (15 chapters with unhappy ending!) £200

The Naulahka, a story of West and East, Heinemann, 1892 (with W. Balestier) £75

Kim, Doubleday Page (U.S.), 1901 . . . . £100

ditto, Macmillan, 1901 . . . . £75

Short Stories

Plain Tales from the Hills, Thacker Spink (Calcutta), 1888 (first issue with 24 pages of adverts at end dated 'Calcutta December 1887') £5,000

ditto, Thacker Spink (Calcutta), 1888 (second issue with 32 pages of adverts at end dated 'Calcutta December 1887'). £1,500

ditto, Macmillan, 1890 . . . . £125

Soldiers Three, A.H. Wheeler (Allahabad), 1888 (first state without cross-hatching on barrack doors on cover, wraps). £600

ditto, A.H. Wheeler (Allahabad), 1888 (second state with cross-hatching on barrack doors on cover, wraps). £300

ditto, Sampson Low, 1890. . . . . . £100

The Story of the Gadsby's, A.H. Wheeler (Allahabad), 1888 (first printing with no date on front cover, wraps). £750

ditto, A.H. Wheeler (Allahabad), 1888 (second printing with 1888 date on front cover, wraps) . . . £250

ditto, Sampson Low, 1890, ... £100

In Black and White, A.H. Wheeler (Allahabad), 1888 (wraps) £600

ditto, Sampson Low, 1890 (wraps) £300

Under the Deodars, A.H. Wheeler (Allahabad), 1888 (first state without shading around 'No.4' and 'One Rupee', wraps) £1,000

ditto, A.H. Wheeler (Allahabad), 1888 (second state with shading around 'No.4' and 'One Rupee', wraps) £300

ditto, Sampson Low, 1890 (wraps) £100

The Phantom Rickshaw and Other Tales, A.H. Wheeler (Allahabad), [1888] (first binding with 'A H Wheeler' and 'Mufid I am Press' below design on front cover, wraps) £1,000

ditto, A.H. Wheeler (Allahabad), [1888] (second binding with 'A.H. Wheeler' and 'Mayo School of Art' below design on front cover, wraps) . . £500

ditto, Sampson Low, 1890 (wraps) £400

Wee Willie Winkie and Other Child Stories, A.H. Wheeler (Allahabad), 1888 (first issue, wraps) £1,250
ditto, A.H. Wheeler (Allahabad), 1888 (second issue with Mayo School of Art on front wrapper, wraps) £750
ditto, A.H. Wheeler (Allahabad), 1888 (third issue with 96 instead of 104 pages, wraps). £250
ditto, Sampson Low, 1890 . . . . . . £100
The Courting of Dinah Shad and Other Stories, Harper (U.S.), 1890 . . . . £300
The City of Dreadful Night and Other Sketches, A.H. Wheeler (Allahabad), 1890 (suppressed edition) £1,250
ditto, as *The City of Dreadful Night and Other Places*, A.H. Wheeler (Allahabad), 1891 (unsuppressed edition) £350
ditto, Sampson Low, 1891 . . . . . £100
Life's Handicap, being stories of mine own people, Macmillan, 1891 . . . . £75
Many Inventions, Macmillan, 1893 . . . £75
Soldier Tales, Macmillan, 1896 (reprints from *The Story of the Gadsbys* and *In Black and White*) £75
The Day's Work, Doubleday & McClure (U.S.), 1898. . . . . £100
ditto, Macmillan, 1898 . . . . . . £75
The Kipling Reader, Macmillan, 1900 . . . £30
Traffics and Discoveries, Macmillan, 1904 . . £75
They, Macmillan, 1905 (from *Traffics and Discoveries*) £50
The Brushwood Boy, Macmillan, 1907 (from *The Day's Work*) £30
Actions and Reactions, Macmillan, 1909 . . £75
Abaft the Funnel, Dodge (U.S.), 1909 . . . £150
A Diversity of Creatures, Macmillan, 1917 . . £30
Land and Sea Tales for Scouts and Guides, Macmillan, 1923 . . . . £45/£20
Debits and Credits, Macmillan, 1926 . . £40/£15
Thy Servant A Dog, Told by Boots, Macmillan, 1930 . . . . £40/£15
Humorous Tales, Macmillan, 1931 . . . £40/£15
Animal Stories, Macmillan, 1932 . . £40/£15
Limits and Renewals, Macmillan, 1932 . . £40/£15
All The Mowgli Stories, Macmillan, 1933 . £75/£25
Collected Dog Stories, Macmillan, 1934 . £35/£15
Ham and the Porcupine, Doubleday Doran (U.S.), 1935 . . . . £40/£15
The Maltese Cat, Macmillan 1936 (from *The Day's Work*). . . . . £50/£15
More Selected Stories, Macmillan, 1940 . £40/£15
Twenty-One Tales, Reprint Society, 1946 . £15/£5
Ten Stories, Pan, 1947 (wraps) £5
A Choice of Kipling's Prose, Macmillan, 1952 £15/£5
Complete Works: The Sussex Edition, Macmillan, 1937-1939 (35 vols) . . . . . . £2,500 the set

C.H.B. KITCHIN
(b.1895 d.1967)

A novelist, poet and musician, it is as the author of a handful of detective novels that Kitchin is best known.

Detective Novels
Death of My Aunt, Hogarth Press, 1929 . £200/£45
ditto, Harcourt Brace (U.S.), 1930 . . . £45/£10
Crime at Christmas, Hogarth Press, 1934 . £200/£45
Death of His Uncle, Constable, 1939 . . £50/£15
ditto, Perennial (U.S.), 1984 (wraps). . . £5
The Cornish Fox, Secker & Warburg, 1949 £35/£10

Other Novels
Streamers Waving, Hogarth Press, 1925 . £150/£45
Mr Balcony, Hogarth Press, 1927 . . . £125/£30
The Sensitive One, Hogarth Press, 1921 . £100/£20
Olive E, Constable, 1937 . . . . . . £20/£10
Birthday Party, Constable, 1938. . . . £20/£10
The Auction Sale, Secker & Warburg, 1949 £25/£10
The Secret River, Secker & Warburg, 1956 £20/£5
Ten Pollitt Place, Secker & Werburg, 1957 £20/£5
The Book of Life, Davies, 1960 . . . . £15/£5
ditto, Appleton-Century-Crofts (U.S.), [1961, c1960] . . . . £15/£10
A Short Walk in Williams Park, Chatto & Windus, 1971 . . . . £10/£5

Short Stories
Jumping Joan and Other Stories, Secker & Warburg, 1954 . . . . £25/£5

Poetry
Curtains, Blackwell, 1919 (wraps) £75
Winged Victory, Blackwell, 1921 (wraps) . . £50

ARTHUR KOESTLER
(b.1905 d.1983)

A novelist and philosopher, all of Koestler's books are more or less an analysis of the turmoil in Europe in the years preceding World War Two.

Autobiography
Spanish Testament, Gollancz, 1937 . . . £175/£25
ditto, Gollancz, 1937 (Left Book Club, wraps) £35
ditto, as *Dialogue with Death*, Macmillan (U.S.), 1942 (abridged). . . . . £25/£5
Scum of the Earth, Cape, 1941 . . . . £35/£10
ditto, Macmillan (U.S.), 1941 . . . . £15/£5
Arrow in the Blue, Collins/Hamilton, 1952 . £20/£5
ditto, Macmillan (U.S.), 1952 . . . . £20/£5
The Invisible Writing, Collins/Hamilton, 1954 £20/£5
ditto, Macmillan (U.S.), 1954 . . . . £15/£5

Stranger on the Square, Hutchinson, 1984 (unfinished, by Arthur and Cynthia Koestler) . . . £10/£5
ditto, Random House (U.S.), 1984 . . . £10/£5

Novels
The Gladiators, Cape, 1939 . . . . . £75/£10
ditto, Macmillan (U.S.), 1939 . . . . £50/£10
Darkness at Noon, Cape, 1940 . . . £2,500/£450
ditto, Macmillan (U.S.), 1941 . . . . £75/£15
ditto, Franklin Library (U.S.), 1970 (signed, limited edition) £95
Arrival and Departure, Cape, 1943 . . . £35/£10
ditto, Macmillan (U.S.), 1943 . . . . £20/£5
Thieves in the Night, Macmillan, 1946 . . £20/£5
ditto, Macmillan (U.S.), 1946 . . . . £15/£5
The Age of Longing, Collins, 1951 . . . £15/£5
ditto, Macmillan (U.S.), 1951 . . . . £15/£5
The Call-Girls, Hutchinson, 1972 . . . £15/£5
ditto, Random House (U.S.), 1973 . . . £15/£5

Essays
The Yogi and the Commissar, Cape, 1945 . £25/£5
ditto, Macmillan (U.S.), 1945 . . . . £15/£5
Insight and Outlook, Macmillan, 1949 . . £15/£5
ditto, Macmillan (U.S.), 1949 . . . . £15/£5
The Trail of the Dinosaur, Collins, 1955 . £15/£5
ditto, Macmillan (U.S.), 1955 . . . . £15/£5
Reflections on Hanging, Gollancz, 1957 . £15/£5
ditto, Macmillan (U.S.), 1957 . . . . £10/£5
The Lotus and the Robot, Hutchinson, 1960 £10/£5
ditto, Macmillan (U.S.), 1961 . . . . £10/£5
Hanged by the Neck, Penguin, 1961. . . £10/£5
Drinkers of Infinity: Essays 1955-1967, Hutchinson, 1968 . . . . £10/£5
ditto, Macmillan (U.S.), 1969 . . . . £10/£5
The Lion and the Ostrich, O.U.P., 1973 . £10/£5
The Heel of Achilles: Essays, Hutchinson, 1974 . . . . £10/£5
ditto, Random House (U.S.), 1975 . . . £10/£5
Janus: A Summing Up, Hutchinson, 1978 . £10/£5
ditto, Random House (U.S.), 1978 . . . £10/£5
Bricks to Babel, Hutchinson, 1980 . . . £10/£5
ditto, Random House (U.S.), 1981 . . . £10/£5

Non Fiction
Promise and Fulfilment, Macmillan, 1949 . £20/£5
ditto, Macmillan (U.S.), 1949 . . . . £15/£5
The Sleepwalkers, Hutchinson, 1959 . . £20/£5
ditto, Macmillan (U.S.), 1959 . . . . £15/£5
The Act of Creation, Hutchinson, 1964 . . £20/£5
ditto, Macmillan (U.S.), 1964 . . . . £15/£5
The Ghost in the Machine, Hutchinson, 1967 £25/£5
ditto, Macmillan (U.S.), 1968 . . . . £15/£5
The Case of the Midwife Toad, Hutchinson, 1971 . . . . £10/£5
ditto, Random House (U.S.), 1972 . . . £15/£5
The Roots of Coincidence, Hutchinson, 1972 £15/£5
ditto, Random House (U.S.), 1972 . . . £10/£5

The Challenge of Chance, Hutchinson, 1973 (with Alister Hardy and Robert Harvie) . . . £10/£5
ditto, Random House (U.S.), 1975 . . . £10/£5
The Thirteenth Tribe, Hutchinson, 1976 . £10/£5
ditto, Random House (U.S.), 1976 . . . £10/£5

DEAN KOONTZ
(b.1945)

Koontz's writing career began in 1956 when, at the age of twenty, he won an *Atlantic Monthly* fiction competition. His world wide sales amount to close on 100 million.

Novels
Star Quest, Ace (U.S.), 1968 (with *Doom of the Green Planet* by Emil Petaja, wraps) £15
The Fall of the Dream Machine, Ace (U.S.), 1969 (with *The Star Venturers*, wraps) £25
Fear That Man, Ace (U.S.), 1969 (with *Toyman* by E.C. Tubb, wraps) £15
Anti-Man, Paperback Library (U.S.), 1970 (wraps) £20
Beastchild, Lancer (U.S.), 1970 (wraps) . . £20
Dark of the Woods and *Soft Come The Dragons*, Ace (U.S.), 1970 (wraps). £15
The Dark Symphony, Lancer (U.S.), 1970 (wraps) £25
Hell's Gate, Lancer (U.S.), 1971 (wraps) . . £20
The Crimson Witch, Curtis (U.S.), 1971 (wraps) £20
A Darkness in My Soul, Daw (U.S.), 1972 (wraps) £10
ditto, Dobson, 1979 . . . . . . £65/£20
The Flesh in the Furnace, Bantam (U.S.), 1972 (wraps) £25
Starblood, Lancer (U.S.), 1972 (wraps) . . . £15
Time Thieves, Ace (U.S.), 1972 (with *Against Arcturus* by Susan K. Putney, wraps) . . . £10
ditto, Dobson, 1977 . . . . . . £75/£25
Warlock, Lancer (U.S.), 1972 (wraps) . . . £10
Writing Popular Fiction, Writers' Digest Fiction (U.S.), 1973 . . . . £45/£15
A Werewolf Among Us, Ballantine (U.S.), 1973 (wraps) £15
The Haunted Earth, Lancer (U.S.), 1973 (wraps) £15
Hanging On, M. Evans (U.S.), 1973 . . £75/£25
ditto, Barrie & Jenkins, 1974 (wraps) . . . £10
Demon Seed, Bantam (U.S.), 1973 (wraps) . £15
ditto, Corgi, 1977 (wraps). £10
After the Last Race, Athenaeum (U.S.), 1974 £75/£25
Nightmare Journey, Putnam (U.S.), 1975 . £100/£25
Night Chills, Atheneum (U.S.), 1976 . . £100/£30
ditto, W.H. Allen, 1977 . . . . . . £75/£25
The Vision, Putnam (U.S.), 1977 . . . £80/£25
ditto, Corgi, 1980 (wraps). £10
ditto, W.H. Allen, 1988 . . . . . . £45/£15
Whispers, Putnam (U.S.), 1980 . . . . £200/£50
ditto, W.H. Allen, 1981 . . . . . . £75/£25
How To Write Best-Selling Fiction, Writers' Digest Books (U.S.), 1981 . . . . £50/£15

ditto, Popular Press (U.S.), 1981 . . . . £20/£5
Phantoms, Putnam (U.S.), 1983 . . . . £75/£25
ditto, W.H. Allan, 1983 . . . . £25/£15
Darkness Comes, W.H. Allen, 1984 . . £125/£35
ditto, as *Darkfall*, Berkeley (U.S.), 1984 . £15/£5
Twilight Eyes, Land of Enchantment (U.S.), 1985 .
. . . . £35/£15
ditto, Land of Enchantment (U.S.), 1985 (signed, illustrated collector's edition, 50 copies) . . £350
ditto, Land of Enchantment (U.S.), 1985 (signed edition, 200 copies, d/w and slipcase) . . £200/£125
ditto, W.H. Allen, 1987 . . . . . £50/£20
Strangers, Putnam (U.S.), 1986 . . . . £25/£5
ditto, W.H. Allen, 1987 . . . . . . £25/£5
Watchers, Putnam (U.S.), 1987 . . . . £20/£5
ditto, Headline, 1987 . . . . . . £20/£5
Lightning, Putnam (U.S.), 1987 . . . . £20/£5
ditto, Headline, 1988 . . . . . . £20/£5
Oddkins, Warner (U.S.), 1988 . . . . £25/£10
ditto, Headline, 1988 . . . . . . £20/£5
Midnight, Putnam (U.S.), 1989 . . . . £15/£5
ditto, Headline, 1989 . . . . . . £15/£5
Bad Place, Putnam (U.S.), 1990 . . . . £15/£5
ditto, Putnam (U.S.), 1990 (250 signed, numbered copies, d/w and slipcase) . . . £125/£75
ditto, Headline, 1990 . . . . . . £15/£5
Cold Fire, Putnam (U.S.), 1991 . . . . £10/£5
ditto, Putnam (U.S.), 1991 (750 signed, numbered copies, d/w and slipcase) . . . £100/£65
ditto, Headline, 1991 (200 signed, numbered copies) .
. . . . £125/£100
ditto, Headline, 1991 . . . . . . £10/£5
Hideaway, Putnam (U.S.), 1992 . . . . £10/£5
ditto, Putnam (U.S.), 1991 (800 signed, numbered copies, d/w and slipcase) . . . £100/£65
ditto, Headline, 1992 . . . . . . £10/£5
Dragon Tears, Putnam (U.S.), 1993 . . . £10/£5
ditto, Putnam (U.S.), 1991 (700 signed, numbered copies, d/w and slipcase) . . . £100/£65
ditto, Headline, 1993 . . . . . . £10/£5
Mr Murder, Headline, 1993 . . . . £10/£5
ditto, Putnam (U.S.), 1993 . . . . £10/£5
ditto, Putnam (U.S.), 1991 (600 signed, numbered copies, d/w and slipcase) . . . £100/£65
Winter Moon, Headline, 1994 . . . . £20/£5
ditto, Ballantine (U.S.), 1994 (wraps) . . . £5
Dark Rivers of the Heart, Charnel House, 1994 (26 signed, lettered copies, slipcase) . . . £750
ditto, Charnel House, 1994 (500 signed, numbered copies, slipcase) £250
ditto, Knopf, 1994 . . . . . . £10/£5
ditto, Headline, 1994 . . . . . . £10/£5
Icebound, Headline, 1995 . . . . £10/£5
Strange Highways, Warner (U.S.), 1995 . £10/£5
ditto, Headline, 1995 . . . . . . £10/£5
Intensity, Knopf, 1995 . . . . . £10/£5
ditto, Headline, 1995 . . . . . . £10/£5
Ticktock, Headline, 1996 . . . . . £10/£5
ditto, Ballantine (U.S.), 1996 (wraps) . . . £5

Sole Survivor, Knopf, 1997 . . . . . £10/£5
ditto, Headline, 1997 . . . . . . £10/£5
Fear Nothing, Headline, 1997 . . . . £10/£5
ditto, Cemetery Dance (U.S.), 1998 (52 signed, lettered copies) £400
ditto, Cemetery Dance (U.S.), 1998 (698 signed, numbered copies with d/w and slipcase) . £100/£40
ditto, Bantam (U.S.), 1998 . . . . . £10/£5
Seize the Night, Headline, 1998 . . . . £10/£5
ditto, Cemetery Dance (U.S.), 1998 (52 signed, lettered copies) £400
ditto, Cemetery Dance (U.S.), 1998 (698 signed, numbered copies with d/w and slipcase) . £100/£40
ditto, Bantam (U.S.), 1999 . . . . . £10/£5
False Memory, Headline, 1999 . . . . £10/£5
ditto, Cemetery Dance (U.S.), 1999 (52 signed, lettered copies) £400
ditto, Cemetery Dance (U.S.), 1999 (698 signed, numbered copies with d/w and slipcase) . £100/£40
ditto, Bantam (U.S.), 2000 . . . . . £10/£5
From the Corner of His Eye, Headline, 2000 £10/£5
ditto, Charnel House (U.S.), 2000 (26 signed, lettered copies) £400
ditto, Bantam (U.S.), 2000 . . . . . £10/£5

Titles written with Gerda Koontz
Bounce Girl, Cosmo (U.S.), 1970 . . . £30/£10
The Underground Lifestyles Handbook, Aware Press (U.S.), 1970 . . . . £25/£10
The Pig Society, Aware Press (U.S.), 1970 . £25/£10

Written as 'David Axton'
Prison of Ice, Lippincott (U.S.), 1976 . . £200/£45
ditto, W.H. Allen, 1977 . . . . . £100/£35

Written as 'Brian Coffey'
Blood Risk, Bobbs-Merrill (U.S.), 1973 . . £150/£45
ditto, Arthur Barker, 1974 . . . . . £75/£25
Surrounded, Bobbs-Merrill (U.S.), 1974 . £150/£50
ditto, Arthur Barker, 1975 . . . . . £75/£25
The Wall of Masks, Bobbs-Merrill (U.S.), 1975 . .
. . . . £100/£25
The Face of Fear, Bobbs-Merrill (U.S.), 1977 . . .
. . . . £150/£50
ditto, Peter Davis, 1978 (pseud. 'K.R. Dwyer') £75/£25
The Voice of the Night, Doubleday (U.S.), 1980 . .
. . . . £200/£65
ditto, Robert Hale, 1981 . . . . . £45/£15

Written as 'Deanna Dwyer'
The Demon Child, Lancer (U.S.), 1971 (wraps) £15
Legacy of Terror, Lance (U.S.), 1971 (wraps) £15
Children of the Storm, Lancer (U.S.), 1972 (wraps) .
. . . . £15
The Dark of Summer, Lancer (U.S.), 1972 (wraps) .
. . . . £15
Dance With the Devil, Lancer (U.S.), 1972 (wraps) .
. . . . £15

Written as 'K.R. Dwyer'
Chase, Random House (U.S.), 1972 . . . £125/£40
ditto, Arthur Barker, 1974 . . . . £75/£25
Shattered, Random House (U.S.), 1972 . . £150/£45
ditto, Arthur Barker, 1974 . . . . £75/£25
Dragonfly, Random House (U.S.), 1975 . £100/£30
ditto, Peter Davis, 1977 . . . . . . £45/£20

Written as 'John Hill'
The Long Sleep, Popular Library (U.S.), 1975 (wraps)
. . . . £15

Written as 'Leigh Nichols'
The Key to Midnight, Pocket (U.S.), 1979 (wraps) £15
ditto, Magnum, 1980 (wraps). £10
ditto, Dark Harvest (U.S.), 1989 . . . £25/£10
The Eyes of Darkness, Pocket (U.S.), 1981 (wraps) .
. . . . £10
ditto, Piatkus, 1981 . . . . . . £25/£5
ditto, Dark Harvest (U.S.), 1981 (400 signed, numbered copies, d/w and slipcase) . . £50/£35
The House of Thunder, Pocket (U.S.), 1982 (wraps) .
. . . . £10
ditto, Fontana, 1983 (wraps) £10
ditto, Dark Harvest (U.S.), 1988 (550 signed, numbered copies, d/w and slipcase) . . £50/£35
Twilight, Pocket (U.S.), 1984 (wraps) . . . £10
ditto, as *The Servants of Twilight*, Fontana, 1985 (wraps) £10
ditto, as *The Servants of Twilight*, Dark Harvest (U.S.), 1988 (450 signed copies, d/w and slipcase) .
. . . . £50/£35
The Door to December, NAL (U.S.), 1985 (wraps, pseud. 'Richard Paige') £10
ditto, Fontana, 1987 (wraps, pseud. 'Leigh Nichols') .
. . . . £10
Shadowfires, Pocket (U.S.), 1987 (wraps) . . £10
ditto, Fontana, 1987 (wraps) £10
ditto, Collins, 1987 . . . . . . £45/£20
ditto, Dark Harvest (U.S.), 1990 . . . . £10/£5

Written as 'Anthony North'
Strike Deep, Dial (U.S.), 1974 . . . . £150/£50

Written as 'Owen West'
The Funhouse, Jove (U.S.), 1980 (wraps) . . £10
ditto, Doubleday (U.S.), 1980 . . . . £15/£5
ditto, Sphere, 1981 (wraps) £10
The Mask, Jove (U.S.), 1980 (wraps) . . . £10
ditto, Coronet/Hodder, 1983 (wraps). . . £10
ditto, Headline, 1989 . . . . . . £30/£10

Written as 'Aaron Wolfe'
Invasion, Laser Books (U.S.), 1975 (wraps) . £15

PHILIP LARKIN
(b.1922 d.1985)

A poet and novelist, *XX Poems* was the first of Larkin's collections to realise his own distinctive voice, although *The Less Deceived* was his first popular success.

Verse
The North Ship, The Fortune Press, 1945 (black cloth)
. . . . £850/£200
ditto, The Fortune Press, 1945 [1965] (unauthorised second edition, maroon cloth) . . . £75/£25
ditto, Faber, 1966 . . . . £45/£15
XX Poems, privately printed, 1951 (100 copies, not for sale, wraps) £1,000
The Fantasy Poets No. 21, Fantasy Press, 1954 (300 copies) £500
The Less Deceived, Marvell Press, 1955 £450/£125
ditto, Marvell Press, 1955 (wraps) . . . £40
ditto, St Martin's Press (U.S.), 1960 . . £65/£20
The Whitsun Weddings, Faber, 1964 . . £100/£25
ditto, Random House (U.S.), 1964 . . . £65/£20
The Explosion, Poem of the Month Club, 1970 (broadsheet, 1,000 signed copies) . . . £125
High Windows, Faber, 1974 . . . . £40/£15
ditto, Farrar Straus (U.S.), 1974 . . . £25/£10
Femmes Damnées, Sycamore Press, 1978 (broadsheet)
. . . . £30
Aubade, Penstemon Press (U.S.), 1980 (250 numbered, initialed copies, wraps, in envelope) . . . £150
Collected Poems, Faber, 1988 . . . . £25/£10
ditto, Farrar Straus (U.S.), 1988 . . . . £20/£5

Novels
Jill, The Fortune Press, 1946 . . . . £1,000/£200
ditto, Faber, 1964 . . . . £75/£25
ditto, St Martin's Press (U.S.), 1964 . . . £50/£20
A Girl in Winter, Faber, 1947 . . . £1,000/£200
ditto, St Martin's Press (U.S.), 1957 . . . £75/£20

Recordings
Listen Presents Philip Larkin Reading 'The Less Deceived', Listen/The Marvell Press, 1959 . £25
ditto, Listen/The Marvell Press, 1959 (100 copies signed by the author) £100
Philip Larkin Reads and Comments on 'The Whitsun Weddings', Listen Records [1965] . . . £25
British Poets of Our Time, Philip Larkin 'High Windows': Poems Read by the Author, Argo [1975].
. . . . £25

Others
All What Jazz: A Record Diary, 1961-68, Faber, 1970
. . . . £45/£15
ditto, St Martin's Press (U.S.), 1970 . . . £25/£10
Philip Larkin Talks to Eboracum, [Eboracum, 1970] (wraps) £50

The Oxford Book of Twentieth Century English
Verse, O.U.P., 1973 (edited by Larkin) .   £25/£10
Required Writing, Miscellaneous Pieces, 1955-1982,
Faber, 1983 (wraps) £20
ditto, Farrar Straus (U.S.), 1983 .   .   .   .   £20/£5
ditto, Faber, 1984 (hardback).   .   .   .   .   £50/£15
Selected Letters of Philip Larkin, 1940-1985, Faber,
1992 .   .   .   .   £25/£10
ditto, Farrar Straus (U.S.), 1993 .   .   .   .   £15/£5

D.H. LAWRENCE
(b.1885 d.1930)

A versatile and controversial modernist writer whose
achievements have often been overshadowed by the
various court cases they have provoked, especially the
trial of *Lady Chatterly's Lover*.

Novels

The White Peacock, Duffield (U.S.), 1911 (first issue
with integral title page and copyright date 1910) .   .
.   .   .   .   £5,000
ditto, Duffield (U.S.), 1911 (second issue with tipped-
in title page and copyright date 1911) .   .   £1,250
ditto, Heinemann, 1911 (first issue with windmill
device on back cover and pages 227-30 tipped-in) .
.   .   .   .   £750
ditto, Heinemann, 1911 (second issue without windmill
device, and pages 227-30 integral) £300
The Trespasser, Duckworth, 1912 (first issue with dark
blue cloth) £750
ditto, Duckworth, 1912 (second issue with green cloth)
.   .   .   .   £500
ditto, Kennerley (U.S.), 1912.   .   .   .   .   £300
Sons and Lovers, Duckworth, 1913 (first state without
date on title page or with dated title page tipped-in) .
.   .   .   .   £600
ditto, Duckworth, 1913 (second state with dated title
page integral). £200
ditto, Kennerley (U.S.), 1913.   .   .   .   .   £250
The Rainbow, Methuen, 1915 (blue-green cloth)   .   .
.   .   .   .   £750
ditto, Methuen, 1915 (red or brown cloth)   .   .   £400
ditto, Methuen, 1915 (wraps). £400
ditto, Huebsch (U.S.), 1916 .   .   .   .   .   £250
The Lost Girl, Secker, 1920 (first issue, p.256 line 15
reads '...she was taken to her room...' and p.268
reads 'whether she noticed anything in the bedroom,
in the beds.') .   .   .   .   £1,250/£350
ditto, Secker, 1920 (second issue, p.256 line 15 reads
'...she let be.' and p.268 deletes 'in the bedroom, in
the beds.').   .   .   .   .   .   .   £1,000/£100
ditto, Seltzer (U.S.), 1921.   .   .   .   .   £500/£65
Women in Love, privately printed (U.S.), 1921 (16 or
18 signed, numbered copies of 1,250).   .   £4,000
ditto, privately printed (U.S.), 1921 (1,250 unsigned,
numbered, copies) £600

ditto, Secker, 1921.   .   .   .   .   .   .   £600/£75
ditto, Secker, 1922 (50 signed copies) .   .   .£3,000
Aaron's Rod, Seltzer (U.S.), 1922 .   .   .   £200/£45
ditto, Secker, 1922.   .   .   .   .   .   .   £200/£45
Kangaroo, Secker, 1923   .   .   .   .   .   £175/£25
ditto, Seltzer (U.S.), 1923.   .   .   .   .   £150/£25
The Boy in the Bush, Secker, 1924 (with M.L.
Skinner) .   .   .   .   £200/£45
ditto, Seltzer (U.S.), 1924.   .   .   .   .   £200/£45
The Plumed Serpent, Secker, 1926 .   .   .   £200/£45
ditto, Knopf (U.S.), 1926 .   .   .   .   .   £200/£45
Lady Chatterly's Lover, privately printed (Florence),
1928 (1,000 signed, numbered copies, plain
protective jacket).   .   .   .   .   .   £4,500/£3,000
ditto, privately printed (Florence), 1928 (second
edition, wraps) £300
ditto, privately printed (Paris), 1929 (wraps)   .   £200
ditto, Secker, 1932 (expurgated edition).   .   £750/£25
ditto, Knopf (U.S.), 1932 (expurgated edition) .   .   .
.   .   .   .   £650/£45
ditto, Grove Press (U.S.), 1959 (unexpurgated edition)
.   .   .   .   £50/£15
ditto, Penguin, 1960 (unexpurgated edition, wraps) £10
The Virgin and the Gypsy, Orioli (Florence), 1930
(810 copies, d/w and slipcase)   .   .   .   £300/£125
ditto, Secker, 1930.   .   .   .   .   .   .   £100/£25
ditto, Knopf (U.S.), 1930 .   .   .   .   .   £75/£25
Mr Noon, C.U.P., 1984   .   .   .   .   .   £15/£5
ditto, Viking (U.S.), 1985.   .   .   .   .   £10/£5

Verse

Love Poems and Others, Duckworth, 1913 .   .   £300
ditto, Kennerley (U.S.), 1913.   .   .   .   .   £150
Amores, Duckworth, 1916 (first issue with 16pps of
ads) £750
ditto, Duckworth , 1916 (second issue without ads)   .
.   .   .   .   £150
ditto, Huebsch (U.S.), 1916 .   .   .   .   .   £100
Look! We have come through!, Chatto & Windus,
1917 .   .   .   .   £150
ditto, Huebsch (U.S.), 1918 .   .   .   .   .   £150
New Poems, Secker, 1918 (wraps)   .   .   .   £100
ditto, Huebsch (U.S.), 1920 .   .   .   .   .   £75
Bay, A Book of Poems, Beaumont, 1919 .   .   £100
ditto, Beaumont, 1919 (30 signed copies)   .   £1,000
Tortoises, Seltzer (U.S.), 1921 (glassine d/w)   .   .   .
.   .   .   .   £250/£200
Birds, Beasts and Flowers, Seltzer (U.S.), 1923   .   .
.   .   .   .   £350/£100
ditto, Secker, 1923   .   .   .   .   .   .   £300£100
ditto, Cresset Press, 1923 (500 copies)   .   .   £125
The Collected Poems of D. H. Lawrence, Secker, 1928
(2 vols) .   .   .   .   £200/£65
ditto Secker, 1928 (100 signed copies, d/w and
slipcase) .   .   .   .   £1,750/£1,250
Pansies, Secker, 1929.   .   .   .   .   .   £125/£45
ditto, Secker, 1929 (250 signed copies)   .   £750/£400
ditto, Stephenson, 1929 (10 signed copies bound in
vellum, slipcase) £3,000

ditto, Stephenson, 1929 (50 signed copies bound in full leather, glassine d/w and slipcase) . . . £2,000
ditto, Stephenson, 1929 (500 signed copies, wraps, glassine d/w and slipcase) . . . . . £500/£450
ditto, privately printed [for Frieda Lawrence] (U.S.), 1954 (750 numbered copies, glassine d/w) £25/£15
ditto, privately printed [for Frieda Lawrence] (U.S.), 1954 (250 numbered copies, signed by Frieda Lawrence, glassine d/w). . . . . £50/£35
Nettles, Faber & Faber, 1930 (tissue d/w) . £125/£75
ditto, Faber & Faber, 1930 (wraps) . . . £35
The Triumph of the Machine, Faber, [1930] (wraps) .
. . . . £30
ditto, Faber, [1930] (400 numbered large paper copies)
. . . . £150
Last Poems, G. Orioli (Florence), 1932 (750 copies with d/w and slipcase . . . . . £300/£125
ditto, Secker, 1933. . . . . £100/£25
The Ship of Death, Secker, 1933 . . . £125/£60
Poems, Heinemann, 1939 (2 vols) . . . £35/£10
Fire and Other Poems, Book Club of California, 1940 (100 copies) . . . . £300/£200
The Complete Poems, Heinemann, 1957 (3 vols) . .
. . . . £50/£25
ditto, Viking (U.S.), 1964 (2 vols, slipcase) . £40/£20

Short Stories
The Prussian Officer and Other Stories, Duckworth, 1914 (first issue, blue cloth stamped in gold with 20 pages of ads) . . . . £350/£200
ditto, Duckworth, 1914 (second issue, light blue cloth stamped in dark blue with 16 pages of ads) £200/£50
ditto, Huebsch (U.S.), 1916 . . . . . £150/£35
England, My England, Seltzer (U.S.), 1922 £200/£100
ditto, Secker. 1924. . . . . £250/£75
The Ladybird, The Fox, The Captain's Doll, Secker, 1923 . . . . £100/£40
ditto, as *The Captain's Doll*, Seltzer (U.S.), 1923 . .
. . . . £100/£40
St Mawr, Secker, 1925 (contents say text begins on p.9) . . . . £200/£75
ditto, Secker, 1925 (contents corrected to say text begins on p.7) . . . . £150/£30
ditto, Knopf (U.S.), 1925 . . . . . . £150/£35
Glad Ghosts, Ernest Benn, 1926 (500 copies, wraps) .
. . . . £100
Sun, E. Archer, 1926 (100 copies, expurgated). £350
ditto, Black Sun Press (Paris), 1928 (15 signed copies in glassine d/w and gold folder ,wraps) . £2,500
ditto, Black Sun Press (Paris), 1928 (150 copies in gold folder, wraps). £1,000
Rawdon's Roof, Mathews and Marrot, 1928 (530 signed, numbered copies) . . . . £350/£225
The Woman Who Rode Away, Secker, 1928 £150/£30
ditto, Knopf (U.S.), 1928 . . . . . £125/£30
The Escaped Cock, Black Sun Press (Paris), 1929 (450 numbered copies, wraps, with tissue d/w and slipcase)
. . . . £400/£200

ditto, Black Sun Press (Paris), 1929 (50 signed copies)
. . . . £1,000/£750
ditto, as *The Man Who Died*, Secker, 1931 (2,000 copies) . . . . £200/£100
Love Among the Haystacks, Nonesuch Press, 1930 (1,600 numbered copies) . . . . £175/£100
ditto, Secker, 1930. . . . . £65/£15
ditto, Haldeman Julius (U.S.), 1941 (wraps) . £25
The Lovely Lady, Secker, 1932 [1933] . . £75/£25
ditto, Viking (U.S.), 1933. . . . . . £45/£20
The Tales of D.H.Lawrence, Secker, 1934 . £35/£10
A Modern Lover, Secker, 1934 . . . . £50/£15
ditto, Viking (U.S.), 1934. . . . . . £45/£15

Plays
The Widowing of Mrs Holroyd, Kennerley (U.S.), 1914 (500 copies) £100
ditto, Duckworth, 1914 . . . . . . £35
Touch and Go, Daniel, 1920 . . . . . £200/£35
ditto, Seltzer (U.S.), 1920. . . . . . £150/£35
David, Daniel, 1926 . . . . £100/£25
ditto, Knopf (U.S.), 1926 . . . . . . £100/£25
The Plays, Secker, 1933 . . . . . . £35/£10
A Collier's Friday Night, Secker, 1934 . . £35/£10
The Complete Plays, Heinemann, 1965 . . £25/£10
ditto, Viking (U.S.), 1965. . . . . . £25/£10

Miscellaneous
Twilight in Italy, Duckworth, 1916 . . . . £300
ditto, Huebsch (U.S.), 1916 . . . . . . £175
Movements in European History, O.U.P., 1921 (pseud. Lawrence H. Davison) £200
Sea and Sardinia, Seltzer (U.S.), 1921 . . £750/£150
ditto, Secker, 1923. . . . . . . £1,000/£200
Psychoanalysis and the Unconscious, Seltzer (U.S.), 1921 . . . . £250/£75
ditto, Secker, 1923 . . . . £200/£50
Fantasia of the Unconscious, Seltzer (U.S.), 1922 . .
. . . . £250/£65
ditto, Secker, 1923. . . . . £250/£65
Studies in Classic American Literature, Seltzer (U.S.), 1923 . . . . £250/£65
ditto, Secker, 1924 . . . . £250/£65
Reflections on the Death of a Porcupine and Further Essays, Centaur Press (U.S.), 1925 (925 copies, slipcase) . . . . £200/£150
ditto, distributed by Simpkin, Marshall, Hamilton, Kent in the UK, 1925 (475 numbered copies) . £200/£150
Mornings in Mexico, Secker, 1927 . . . £300/£75
ditto, Knopf (U.S.), 1927 . . . . . . £300/£75
The Paintings of D.H. Lawrence, The Mandrake Press, 1929 (500 copies, slipcase) . . £650/£500
ditto, The Mandrake Press, 1929 (10 signed copies on Japan paper) £5,000
Pornography and Obscenity, Faber & Faber, 1929 (wraps) £20
ditto, Faber & Faber, 1929 (cloth) . . . £75
The Story of Doctor Manente, by A.F. Grazzini, Orioli (Florence), 1929 (2 signed copies on blue paper,

translated and with an Introduction by Lawrence) .
. . . . £1,000
ditto, G. Orioli (Florence), 1929 (200 signed copies) .
. . . . £500
ditto, G. Orioli (Florence), 1929 (1,000 unsigned, numbered copies) . . . . . £125/£100
Assorted Articles, Secker, 1930 . . . . £65/£20
ditto, Knopf (U.S.), 1930 . ? . . . £65/£20
Apropos of Lady Chatterly's Lover, Mandrake Press, 1930 . . . . £35/£15
Apocalypse, Orioli (Florence), 1931 (750 copies) . .
. . . . £150/£75
ditto, Secker, 1932 (750 numbered copies) . £75/£25
ditto, Secker, 1932. . . . . . . £30/£10
ditto, Viking (U.S.), 1932. . . . . £25/£10
The Letters of D.H. Lawrence, Heinemann, 1932 . .
. . . . £100/£40
ditto, Heinemann, 1932 (525 numbered parchment bound copies) £200
ditto, Viking (U.S.), 1932. . . . . £25/£10
Etruscan Places, Secker, 1932 . . . £200/£45
Pornography and So On, Faber, 1936 . . £75/£25
Phoenix: The Posthumous Papers of D.H. Lawrence, Heinemann, 1936 . . . . . £35/£15
The Manuscripts of D.H. Lawrence, Los Angeles Public Library (U.S.), 1937 (750 copies, wraps) £25
D.H. Lawrence's Letters to Bertrand Russell, Gotham Book Mart (U.S.), 1948 (950 copies) . . £50/£20
Sex, Literature and Censorship, Twayne (U.S.), 1953 . . . . £20/£5
ditto, Heinemann, 1955 . . . . . £20/£5
Collected Letters, Heinemann, 1962. . . £40/£15
ditto, Viking (U.S.), 1962 (2 vols) . . . £30/£10
Letters to Martin Secker, privately printed, 1970 (500 numbered copies) . . . . . £45/£15
The Letters, C.U.P., 1979 (vol. I) . . . £25/£10
The Letters, C.U.P., 1981 (vol. II) . . . £25/£10

T.E. LAWRENCE
(b.1888 d.1935)

A soldier and author, Lawrence is popularly known as 'Lawrence of Arabia'. His account of the Arab Revolt, *The Seven Pillars of Wisdom*, is seen as a masterpiece by many.

The Seven Pillars of Wisdom, Oxford Edition, 1922 (8 copies) £30,000
ditto, London, 1924 (first proof copy) . . . £4,000
ditto, London, 1925, (second proof, 100 copies) £3,000
ditto, Cranwell, Subscribers' Edition, 1926 (169 copies) £30,000
ditto, Cranwell, Subscribers' Edition, 1926 (32 incomplete copies) £20,000
ditto, Doubleday Doran (U.S.), 1926 (copyright edition, 22 copies) £12,500

ditto, Jonathan Cape, 1935 (750 copies, d/w and slipcase) . . . . £1,250/£850
ditto, Jonathan Cape, 1935 . . . . £300/£125
ditto, Jonathan Cape, 1935 (60 privately issued copies) £750
ditto, Doubleday Doran (U.S.), 1935 . . £200/£50
ditto, Doubleday Doran (U.S.), 1935 (750 copies, d/w and slipcase) . . . . . £1,250/£600
Revolt in the Desert, Jonathan Cape, 1927 . £300/£50
ditto, Jonathan Cape, 1927 (315 large paper copies) .
. . . . £1,250/£750
ditto, Doubleday Doran (U.S.), 1927 . . £300/£50
ditto, Doubleday Doran (U.S.), 1927 (250 large paper copies) £1,000
The Mint, Doubleday Doran, (U.S.), 1936 (pseud. '352087 A/C Ross', U.S. copyright edition, 50 copies) £20,000
ditto, Jonathan Cape, 1955 (first unexpurgated U.K. edition, 2,000 copies, no d/w, in slipcase) £125/£100
ditto, Jonathan Cape, 1955 (first U.K. trade edition, expurgated) . . . . £25/£10
ditto, Doubleday Doran, (U.S.), 1955 (1,000 numbered copies, slipcase) . . . . . £150/£100
ditto, Doubleday Doran, (U.S.), 1957 . . £15/£5
Crusader Castles, Golden Cockerel Press, 1936 (2 vols, 1000 copies, no d/w or slipcase) . . . £800
ditto, *The Thesis*, Golden Cockerel Press, 1936 (75 copies) £1,000
ditto, *The Letters*, Golden Cockerel Press, 1936 (35 copies) £1,500
ditto, Doubleday Doran (U.S.), 1937 (copyright edition) £400
The Diary of T.E. Lawrence MCMXI, Corvinus Press, 1937 (30 copies on 'Canute' paper) . . £4,000
ditto, Corvinus Press, 1937 (40 copies on 'Medway' paper). £2,500
ditto, Corvinus Press, 1937 (130 copies on parchment-style paper) £1,750
ditto, Doubleday Doran, U.S., 1937 (copyright edition, 50 copies). £3,000
An Essay on Flecker, Corvinus Press, 1937 (26 copies, slipcase) . . . . . . £2,500/£2,000
ditto, Corvinus Press, 1937 (4 copies, vellum) . £3,500
ditto, Corvinus Press, 1937 (2 copies, leather) . £5,000
ditto, Doubleday Doran (U.S.) 1937 (copyright edition of approx 56 copies, wraps). £1,250
Two Arabic Folk Tales, Corvinus Press, 1937 (31 copies) £1,750
Secret Dispatches from Arabia, Golden Cockerel Press, 1939 (Nos. 1-30, printed on Arnold hand-made paper, bound in white pig-skin, with supplement). £2,000
ditto, Golden Cockerel Press, 1939 (nos. 31-1,000, printed on Arnold hand-made paper, bound in quarter Niger, without supplement) £400
ditto, Bellew, 1991 (revised edition). . . . £10
Men in Print, Golden Cockerel Press, 1940 (nos. 1-30, bound in full Niger, with supplement, slipcase) . .
. . . . £1,750/£1,250

ditto, Golden Cockerel Press, 1940 (nos. 31-500) £400
The Essential T.E. Lawrence, Jonathan Cape, 1951 .
. . . . £35/£10
ditto, Dutton (U.S.), 1951 . . . . . £35/£10
Evolution of a Revolt, Early Postwar Writings of T.E.
Lawrence, The Pennsylvania State Univ. Press (U.S.),
1968 . . . . £35/£15

Translations by 'J.H. Ross'
The Forest Giant, by Adrien Le Corbeau, Jonathan
Cape, 1924 . . . . £75/£25
ditto, Harper & Bros. (U.S.), 1924 (1st issue with
translator incorrectly given as L.H. Ross) . £75/£25

Translations by 'T.E. Shaw'
The Odyssey of Homer, Bruce Rogers, 1932, (530
copies, slipcase) . . . . . £1,500/£1,000
ditto, O.U.P. (U.S.), 1932 . . . . . . £75
ditto, O.U.P. (U.S.), 1932 (32 copies) . . . £500
ditto, O.U.P., 1935. . . . . . . £75/£30

Letters
Letters from T.E. Shaw to Bruce Rogers, privately
printed by Bruce Rogers, 1933 (300 copies) . £750
More Letters from T.E. Shaw to Bruce Rogers,
privately printed by Bruce Rogers, 1936 (300 copies)
. . . . £500
A Letter from T.E. Lawrence to His Mother, Corvinus
Press, 1936 (30 copies) £1,250
Letter from T.E. Shaw to Viscount Carlow, Corvinus
Press, 1936, (17 copies) £1,000
The Letters of T.E. Lawrence, Cape, 1938 . £100/£35
ditto, Doubleday Doran (U.S.), 1939 . . £45/£15
ditto, Dent, 1988 (new edition) . . . . £20/£5
T.E. Lawrence To His Biographers, Faber, 1938 (500
copies signed by Graves and Hart, 2 vols with d/ws,
in slipcase) . . . . £450/£400
ditto, Doubleday Doran, 1938 (500 copies signed by
Graves and Hart, 2 vols with d/ws, in slipcase) .
. . . . £450/£400
Eight Letters from T.E.L., privately printed [Corvinus
Press], 1939 (50 copies) £750
Selected Letters of T.E. Lawrence, World Books, 1941
. . . . £5
Shaw-Ede: T.E. Lawrence's letters to H.S. Ede, 1927-
35, Golden Cockerel Press, 1942 (nos. 1-130, bound
in full morocco, with facsimile reproductions of 5 of
the letters) £1,000
ditto, Golden Cockerel Press, 1942 (nos. 31-500) £300
The Home Letters of T.E. Lawrence and His
Brothers, Blackwell, 1954 . . . . £125/£35
ditto, Macmillan (U.S.), 1954 . . . £75/£25
From a Letter of T.E. Lawrence, Officina Bodoni,
1959 (75 copies) £150
T.E.L., Five Hitherto Unpublished Letters, privately
printed, 1975 (30 copies, wraps) . . . £150
Fifty Letters, Humanities research centre (U.S.), 1962
(wraps) £30

Letters to E.T. Leeds, Whittington Press, 1988 (650
copies, slipcase) £100

Edited by Lawrence
Minorities, Cape, 1971 . . . . . . £40/£15
ditto, Cape, 1971 (125 copies signed by C. Day-Lewis)
. . . . £300
ditto, Doubleday (U.S.), 1972 . . . . £35/£15

EDWARD LEAR
(b.1812 d.1888)

Popularly known as a nonsense poet, Lear, an
accomplished artist and travel-writer, illustrated his
own verse.

Nonsense Books
A Book of Nonsense, Thomas Maclean, 1846 (pseud.
'Derry Down Derry', 175 copies, wraps) . £10,000
ditto, Thomas Maclean, 1855 (no pseud., two volumes,
wraps). £7,500
ditto, Routledge, 1861 (enlarged edition) . . £600
ditto, Routledge, 1861 (enlarged edition) . . £600
Nonsense Songs, Stories, Botany and Alphabets,
Robert John Bush, 1871 . . . . . . £600
More Nonsense, Pictures, Rhymes, Botany, Robert
John Bush, 1872 [1874] £500
Laughable Lyrics, A Fourth Book of Nonsense
Poems, Songs, Botany, Music, etc., Robert John
Bush, 1877 . . . . £650
The Jumblies and Other Nonsense Poems, Songs,
Botany, Music, Warne, 1877 [1876] . . . £200
Nonsense Drolleries, Warne, 1889 . . . . £150
A Nonsense Birthday Book, Warne, [1894]. . £100
Nonsense Songs and Stories, Warne, 1895 . . £100
Nonsense Songs and Laughable Lyrics, Little, Brown
& Co (U.S.), 1899 . . . . £100
ditto, Peter Pauper Press (U.S.), 1935 (650 copies) £75
The Pelican Chorus and Other Nonsense Verses,
Warne, 1900 . . . . £125
Queery Leary Nonsense, Mills & Boon, 1911 . £50
Callico Pie, Warne, [1924] . . . . £75/£25
Facsimile of A Nonsense Alphabet, Warne, 1926
(1,000 numbered copies) £65
The Owl and the Pussy Cat, Warne, [1924] £75/£35
The Pobble, Hugh Sharpe, 1934 (50 copies) . £250
The Quangle Wangle's Hat, Hugh Sharp, 1933 (50
copies) £250
Edward Lear's Nonsense Songs, Chatto & Windus,
1938 . . . . £35/£15
A Book of Lear, Penguin, 1939 (wraps with d/w) .
. . . . £10/£5
Edward Lear's Nonsense Omnibus, Odhams, 1943 .
. . . . £25/£10
The Complete Nonsense of Edward Lear, Faber, 1947
. . . . £25/£10

Edward Lear's Nonsense Alphabet, Collins, [1949] .
. . . . £25/£15
A Nonsense Alphabet, H.M.S.O., 1952 . . . £10
Teapots and Quails and Other Nonsense, John
Murray, 1953 . . . . £35/£15
ditto, Harvard Univ. (U.S.), 1953 . . . £25/£10
ABC, Constable, 1965 . . . . £15/£5
A Book of Nonsense, Peter Owen, 1972 (illustrated by
Mervyn Peake) . . . . £25/£10
Bosh and Nonsense, Allen Lane, 1982 . . £15/£5

Natural History
Illustrations of the Family Psittacide, or Parrots, R.
Ackerman & E. Lear, 1832 (42 hand-coloured plates,
in original wraps) £100,000
ditto, R. Ackerman & E. Lear, 1832 (rebound) . . . .
. . . . £50,000
*Gleanings from The Menagerie and Aviary at
Knowsley Hall*, privately printed, Knowsley, 1846 .
. . . . £20,000
Tortoises, Terrapins and Turtles Drawn from Life,
Henry Sotheran & Joseph Baer, 1872 (with James de
Carle Sowerby) £2,500
The Lear Coloured Bird Book for Children, Mills and
Boon, [1912] £50
Edward Lear's Parrots, Duckworth, 1949 (12 plates) .
. . . . £75/£30
The Birds of Edward Lear, A Selection, Ariel Press,
1975 (1000 copies, 12 plates) . . . . £150/£100

Travel
Views in Rome and Its Environs, Thomas Maclean,
1841 (25 plates) £2,500
Illustrated Excursions in Italy, Thomas Maclean, 1846
(first series, 30 plates) £1,500
ditto, Thomas Maclean, 1846 (second series, 25 plates)
. . . . £1,500
Journals of a Landscape Painter in Albania, Richard
Bentley, 1851 (21 plates) £1,000
*Journals of a Landscape Painter in Southern
Calabria*, Richard Bentley, 1852 (2 maps, 20 plates) .
. . . . £500
Views in the Seven Southern Ionian Islands, E. Lear,
1863 (20 plates) £5,000
ditto, Oldham, 1979 (facsimile reprint of 1,000
numbered copies, 20 plates) . . . . £100/£65
Journals of a Landscape Painter in Corsica, Robert
John Bush, 1870 (41 plates) £500
Lear in Sicily, Duckworth, 1938 . . . £35/£15
Edward Lear's Journals, A Selection, Arthur Barker,
1952 (4 plates) . . . . £45/£20
Edward Lear's Indian Journal, Jarrolds, 1953 (9
plates) . . . . £45/£20
Edward Lear in Southern Italy, W. Kimber, 1964 (20
plates) . . . . £100/£35
Edward Lear in Greece, W. Kimber, 1965 (20 plates) .
. . . . £100/£35
Edward Lear in Corsica, W. Kimber, 1966 £100/£35

Lear's Corfu, Corfu Travel, 1965 (8 illustrations) . .
. . . . £25/£10

Letters
The Letters of Edward Lear, T. Fisher Unwin, 1907
(20 plates) £50
*Letters ... to Chichester Fortescue Lord Carlingford,
and Frances Countess Waldegrave*, Duffield (U.S.),
[1908] £45
The Later Letters of Edward Lear, T. Fisher Unwin,
1911 . . . . £25
A Letter from Edward Lear to George William Curtis,
Harvard Printing Office (U.S.), 1947 (660 copies,
wraps) £5
Selected Letters, Clarendon Press, 1988 . . £25/£10

Others
*Three Poems by Tennyson Illustrated by Edward
Lear*, Bousson, Valadon & Co., Scribner & Welford,
1889 (100 copies signed by Tennyson, 24 illustrations
by Lear) £2,500
Edward Lear on My Shelves, privately printed by
William Osgood Field, 1933 . . . . . £500

JOHN LE CARRÉ
(b.1931)

A novelist whose thrillers have examined the grey,
dubious world of Cold War spying. As the years have
passed his 'fiction' is seen to have been more and
more perceptive.

Novels
Call for the Dead, Gollancz, 1961 . . £3,000/£250
ditto, Walker (U.S.), 1962 . . . . £1,000/£100
A Murder of Quality, Gollancz, 1962 . £3,000/£250
ditto, Walker (U.S.), 1963 . . . . £1,000/£100
The Spy Who Came in from the Cold, Gollancz, 1963
. . . . £500/£45
ditto, Coward McGann (U.S.), 1963 . . . £100/£20
The Looking-Glass War, Heinemann, 1965 £50/£10
ditto, Coward McGann (U.S.), 1965 . . . £25/£5
A Small Town in Germany, Heinemann, 1968 £35/£10
ditto, Coward-McCann (U.S.), 1968 (500 signed
copies, tissue d/w) . . . . . . £200/£175
ditto, Coward McGann (U.S.), 1968 . . . £20£5
The Naive and Sentimental Lover, Hodder &
Stoughton, 1971 . . . . £25/£5
ditto, Knopf (U.S.), 1971 . . . . . £15/£5
Tinker, Tailor, Soldier, Spy, Hodder & Stoughton,
1974 . . . . £25/£5
ditto, Knopf (U.S.), 1974 . . . . . £15/£5
The Honourable Schoolboy, Franklin Center: Franklin
Library for The First Edition Society (U.S.), 1977 £75
ditto, Knopf (U.S.), 1977 . . . . . £15/£5
ditto, Hodder & Stoughton, 1977 . . . £25/£5

Smiley's People, Franklin Center: Franklin Library for
The First Edition Society (U.S.), 1979 . . £100
ditto, Hodder & Stoughton, 1980. . . . £35/£5
ditto, Knopf (U.S.), 1980 . . . . . . £15/£5
ditto, Knopf (U.S.), 1980 (signed sheet tipped-in) . .
. . . . £60/£30
The Little Drummer Girl, Knopf (U.S.), 1983 £15/£5
ditto, Knopf (U.S.), 1983 (signed sheet tipped-in) . .
. . . . £75/£40
ditto, Book of the Month Club (U.S.), 1983 (1,048
signed copies, slipcase) . . . . . . £100/£75
ditto, Hodder & Stoughton, 1983 . . . . £15/£5
A Perfect Spy, Hodder & Stoughton, 1986 . £15/£5
ditto, London Limited Editions/Hodder & Stoughton,
1986 (250 signed copies, glassine d/w) £125/£100
ditto, Knopf (U.S.), 1986 . . . . . . £15/£5
ditto, Knopf (U.S.), 1986 (signed sheet tipped-in) . .
. . . . £60/£30
The Russia House, Knopf (U.S.), 1989 . . £15/£5
ditto, Knopf (U.S.), 1989 (signed sheet tipped-in) . .
. . . . £60/£30
ditto, Hodder & Stoughton, 1989. . . . £15/£5
ditto, Hodder & Stoughton, 1989 (collector's edition,
500 copies, quarter leather, slipcase) . . £75/£50
ditto, London Limited Editions, 1989 (250 signed
copies, glassine d/w). . . . . . . £125/£75
The Secret Pilgrim, Hodder & Stoughton, 1991 £15/£5
ditto, Knopf (U.S.), 1991 . . . . . . £15/£5
ditto, Knopf (U.S.), 1991 (signed sheet tipped-in) . .
. . . . £60/£30
The Night Manager, Hodder & Stoughton, 1993 . .
. . . . £15/£5
ditto, Knopf (U.S.), 1993 . . . . . . £15/£5
ditto, Knopf (U.S.), 1993 (signed sheet tipped-in) . .
. . . . £50/£25
Our Game, Hodder & Stoughton, 1995 (1st issue) . .
. . . . £125/£50
ditto, Hodder & Stoughton, 1995 (2nd issue) £10/£5
ditto, Knopf (U.S.), 1995 . . . . . . £10/£5
The Tailor of Panama, Hodder & Stoughton, 1996 .
. . . . £10/£5
ditto, Knopf (U.S.), 1996 . . . . . . £10/£5
Single and Single, Hodder & Stoughton, 1999 £10/£5
ditto, Scribners (U.S.), 1999 . . . . . £10/£5

Collections
The Le Carré Omnibus, Gollancz, 1964 . £75/£25
The Quest for Karla, Hodder & Stoughton. 1982 . .
. . . . £25/£5
ditto, Knopf (U.S.), 1982 . . . . . . £15/£5

Others
The Clandestine Muse, Seluzicki (U.S.), 1986 (250
signed copies) £200
Vanishing England, Salem House (U.S.), 1987 (with
Gareth H. Davies) . . . . £35/£15
*Nervous Times: An Address Given at the Savoy
Hotel...*, Anglo-Israel Association, 1998 (250 signed,
numbered copies) £100

HARPER LEE
(b. 1926)

Lee's one and only novel, *To Kill a Mockingbird* is a
landmark of 20th century American literature and is
one of the best-selling novels of all time.

Novel
To Kill a Mockingbird, Lippincott (U.S.), 1960 . .
. . . . £4,000/£1,000
ditto, Heinemann, 1963 . . . . . . £450/£75

Other
Romance and High Adventure, Cather & Brown
(U.S.), 1993 (100 signed copies, wraps) . . £300

LAURIE LEE
(b.1914 d.1997)

Lee was primarily a poet, best known for his volumes
of autobiography. *Cider with Rosie* is a nostalgic
memoir of his Gloucestershire childhood.

Autobiography
Cider with Rosie, Hogarth Press, 1959 . . £75/£15
ditto, as *The Edge of Day*, Morrow (U.S.), 1960 . .
. . . . £40/£10
As I Walked Out One Midsummer Morning, Deutsch,
1969 . . . . £20/£5
ditto, Atheneum (U.S.), 1969. . . . . £10/£5
A Moment of War, Viking, 1991. . . . £10/£5
ditto, New Press (U.S.), 1991 . . . . £10/£5
Red Sky at Sunrise, Viking, 1992 (collects above
autobiographical works). . . . . . £10/£5

Verse
The Sun My Monument, Hogarth Press, 1944 £65/£25
ditto, Doubleday (U.S.), 1947 . . . . £40/£15
The Bloom of Candles, Lehmann, 1947. . £40/£15
New Poems, 1954, M. Joseph, 1954 . . . £25/£10
My Many-Coated Man, Deutsch, 1955 . . £25/£10
ditto, Coward McGann (U.S.), 1957 . . . £15/£5
Pocket Poets, Studio Vista, 1960. . . . £5
15 Poems for William Shakespeare, Trustees and
Guardians of Shakespeare's Birthplace, 1964 (wraps)
. . . . £20
Pergamon Poets 10, Pergamon Press, 1970 (wraps) £5
Selected Poems, Deutsch, 1983 (wraps). . . £5
Fish and Water, Friends of the Cheltenham Festival,
[1991] (broadsheet) £15
Boy in Ice, Turret Bookshop, [1991] (broadsheet) £40

Plays
Peasant's Priest, Friends of Canterbury Cathedral,
1947 . . . . £30/£10

The Voyage of Magellan, Lehmann, 1948 . £60/£15

Others
Land at War, H.M.S.O., 1945 (anonymous, wraps) £25
We Made a Film in Cyprus, Longman, 1947 (with Ralph Keene). . . . . £65/£25
Vassos the Goatherd: A Story of Cyprus, Pilot Press, 1947 . . . . , . . . £45/£15
An Obstinate Exile, privately printed (U.S.), 1951 (glassine d/w). . . . . . . £125/£100
A Rose for Winter: Travels in Andalusia, Hogarth Press, 1955 . . . . £50/£10
ditto, Morrow (U.S.), 1956 . . . . . £30/£10
Epstein: A Camera Study, Deutsch, 1956 . £35/£10
ditto, Deutsch, 1956 (200 signed copies, slipcase) . . . . £250/£200
Man Must Move, Rathbone, 1960 . . . £25/£10
ditto, as *The Wonderful World of Transportation*, Doubleday (U.S.), 1961 (with David Lambert) £20/£5
Atlantic Fairway, Cunard Line, [1962] (wraps) £15
The Firstborn, Hogarth Press, 1964 . . . £25/£10
ditto, Morrow (U.S.), 1964 . . . . £15/£5
Paintings and Drawings of the Gypsies of Granada, Athelnay Books (U.S.), 1969 . . . . . £10
I Can't Stay Long, Deutsch, 1975 . . . £15/£5
ditto, Atheneum (U.S.), 1976. . . . . £10/£5
Innocence in the Mirror, Morrow (U.S.), 1978 £10/£5
Two Women, Deutsch, 1983 . . . . . £10/£5

J. SHERIDAN LE FANU
(b.1814 d.1873)

Anglo-Irish writer of mystery, supernatural and historical romances.

Novels
The Cock and Anchor, Curry, Longmans, Fraser, 1845, (anonymous, 3 vols, boards) . . £1,250
ditto, as *Morley Court*, Chapman & Hall, 1873 (revised edition) £45
The Fortunes of Colonel Torlogh O'Brien, McGlashan, Orr, 1847 (anonymous) . . . £400
The House by the Church-Yard, Tinsley, 1863 (3 vols, royal blue cloth) £4,000
ditto, Tinsley, 1863 (3 vols, green cloth) . £2,500
Wylder's Hand, Bentley, 1864 (3 vols) . . £2,250
Uncle Silas, Bentley, 1864 (3 vols) . . . £2,250
Guy Deverell, Bentley, 1865 (3 vols) . . £2,000
All in the Dark, Bentley, 1866 (2 vols, claret cloth) £1,500
ditto, Bentley, 1866 (presentation copies, 2 vols, white cloth) £2,000
The Tenants of Malory, Tinsley, 1867, (3 vols) £2,000
A Lost Name, Bentley, 1868 (3 vols) . . £2,000
Haunted Lives, Tinsley, 1868, (3 vols) . . £2,000
The Wyvern Mystery, Tinsley, 1869, (3 vols) £2,500

Checkmate, Hurst & Blackett, 1871 (3 vols) £2,500
The Rose and The Key, Chapman & Hall, 1871 (3 vols) £2,000
Willing to Die, Hurst & Blackett, 1873 (3 vols) £1,500

Short Stories and Collected Editions
Ghost Stories and Tales of Mystery, McGlashan, Orr, 1851 (anonymous, red pictorial boards). . £5,000
ditto, McGlashan, Orr, 1851 (anonymous, with gold blocking to front board) £2,000
ditto, McGlashan, Orr, 1851 (anonymous, no gold blocking to front board) £600
Chronicles of Golden Friars, Bentley, 1871 (3 vols) £3,000
In A Glass Darkly, Bentley, 1872, (3 vols) . . £3,000
The Purcell Papers, Bentley, 1880, (3 vols) £2,000
The Watcher, Downey, [1894] £400
The Evil Guest, Downey, [1895]. . . . £400
Madam Crowl's Ghost, Bell, 1923 . . £400/£100
Green Tea and Other Ghost Stories, Arkham House (U.S.), 1945 . . . . £175/£45
A Strange Adventure in the Life of Miss Laura Mildmay, Home & Van Thal, 1947 . . £25/£10
Best Ghost Stories, Dover (U.S.), 1964 (wraps) £5
Ghost Stories and Mysteries, Dover (U.S.), 1975 (wraps) £5
Borrhomeo The Astrologer, Tragara Press (Edinburgh), 1985, (wraps).. . . . . . £25

Verse
The Poems of Joseph Sheridan Le Fanu, Downey, 1896 . . . . £100

RICHARD LE GALLIENNE
(b.1866 d.1947)

Generally disregarded simply because he survived the 1890s, Le Gallienne is not overlooked by all collectors of the period.

Fiction
The Student and the Body-Snatcher and Other Tales, Elkin Mathews, 1890 (with R.K. Leather). . £65
The Book-Bills of Narcissus, Frank Murray, 1891 £45
Prose Fancies, Elkin Mathews & John Lane, 1894 £10
Prose Fancies: Second Series, John Lane, 1896 £10
The Quest of the Golden Girl, John Lane, 1896 £50
The Romance of Zion Chapel, John Lane, 1898 £25
Young Lives, A Tale, Arrowsmith, 1899 . . £25
The Worshipper of the Image, John Lane, 1900 £25
Sleeping Beauty and Other Prose Fancies, John Lane, 1900 . . . . £25
The Life Romantic, Including the Love-Letters of the King, Hurst & Blackett, 1901 . . . . £25
Painted Shadows, John Lane, 1908 [1907] . . £25
Little Dinners with The Sphinx and Other Prose Fancies, John Lane, 1909 . . . . . . £25

The Maker of Rainbows, with Other Fairy-Tales and
Fables, Harper, 1912 . . . . . . £20
The Highway to Happiness, T. Werner Laurie, [1914]
. . . . £15
Pieces of Eight, Collins, 1918 . . . . . £15
Old Love Stories Retold, John Lane, 1924 . £35/£10
The Magic Seas, H. Toulmin, 1930 . . . £35/£10

Verse

My Ladies' Sonnets and Other 'Vain and
Amatorious' Verses, with Some of Graver Mood,
privately printed, 1887 . . . . £150
ditto, privately printed, 1887 (50 signed copies) £300
Volumes in Folio, Elkin Mathews, 1889 . . £125
ditto, Elkin Mathews, 1889 (250 copies) . £300
ditto, Elkin Mathews, 1889 (50 large paper copies) .
. . . . £300
English Poems, Elkin Mathews & John Lane, 1892 .
. . . . £50
A Fellowship in Song, Elkin Mathews & John Lane,
1893 (with A. Hayes and N. Gale) . . . £20
Robert Louis Stevenson: An Elegy and Other Poems,
John Lane, 1895 . . . . £10
ditto, John Lane, 1895 (500 copies) . . . £100
ditto, John Lane, 1895 (75 large paper copies) . £200
Holly and Mistletoe, Marcus Ward, 1896 (with E.
Nesbit and N. Gale) £45
Rubaiyat of Omar Khayyam: A Paraphrase, Grant
Richards, 1897 . . . . £25
Odes from the Divan of Hafiz, Duckworth, 1903 £40
Omar Repentant, Grant Richards, 1908 . . . £20
New Poems, John Lane, 1910 . . . . £10
The Lonely Dancer and Other Poems, John Lane,
1914 . . . . £10
The Silk-Hat Soldier and Other Poems, John Lane,
1915 (wraps) £20

Non Fiction

George Meredith: Some Characteristics, Elkin
Mathews, 1890 . . . . £10
The Religion of a Literary Man, Elkin Mathews &
John Lane, 1893 . . . . £10
Retrospective Reviews: A Literary Log, John Lane,
1896, 2 vols) £15
If I Were God, privately printed, 1897 . . . £30
Rudyard Kipling: A Criticism, John Lane, 1900 £25
Travels in England, Grant Richards, 1900 . . £25
The Beautiful Life of Rome, Simpkin, Marshall,
Hamilton, Kent & Co. 1900 . . . . . £10
An Old Country House, Grant Richards, 1902 . £30
October Vagabonds, John Lane, 1910 . . . £10
Attitudes and Avowals, John Lane, 1910 [1911] £10
Vanishing Roads and Other Essays, Putnam, 1915 £10
The Romantic 90s, Putnam, 1926 . . . £50/£15
From a Paris Garret, Richards Press, 1936 . £30/£10
The Cry of the Little Peoples, privately printed, 1941 .
. . . . £25

URSULA LE GUIN
(b.1929)

An American novelist, poet and critic, Le Guin is
admired for her science fiction novels and for the
'Earthsea' fantasy books for children.

Children's Titles

A Wizard of Earthsea, Parnassus Press, (U.S.), 1968
(faint vertical line or smudge on title page, d/w priced
$3.95) . . . . £1,250/£300
ditto, Parnassus Press, (U.S.), 1968 (no line or smudge,
unpriced d/w) . . . . £125/£25
ditto, Penguin Books: Puffin, 1971 (wraps, illustrated
by Ruth Robbins) £10
ditto, Gollancz, 1971 . . . . . . £150/£35
The Tombs of Atuan, Atheneum (U.S.), 1971 . . .
. . . . £125/£25
ditto, Gollancz, 1972 . . . . . . £100/£20
The Farthest Shore, Atheneum (U.S.), 1972 £100/£20
ditto, Gollancz, 1973 . . . . . . £65/£15
Very Far Away From Anywhere Else, Atheneum
(U.S.), 1976 . . . . £25/£5
ditto, as A Very Long Way from Anywhere Else,
Gollancz, 1976 . . . . £20/£5
Leese Webster, Atheneum (U.S.), 1979 . . £20/£5
ditto, Gollancz, 1981 . . . . . . £15/£5
The Beginning Place, Harper (U.S.), 1980 . £20/£5
ditto, as Threshold, Gollancz, 1980 . . £20/£5
Visit from Dr Katz, Atheneum (U.S.), 1988 (picture
book; boards). £5
ditto, Collins, 1988 . . . . £5
Catwings, Orchard (U.S.), 1988 . . . £10/£5
Catwings Return, Orchard (U.S.), 1989 . . £10/£5
Fire and Stone, Atheneum (U.S.), 1989 . . £10/£5
Tehanu, Atheneum (U.S.), 1990 . . . £10/£5
ditto, Gollancz, 1990 . . . . . . £10/£5
The Adventures of Cobbler's Rune, Cheap Street
(U.S.), 1982 (26 signed, lettered copies) . . £200
ditto, Cheap Street (U.S.), 1982 (250 signed, lettered
copies) £50
Solomon Leviathan's 931st Trip Around the World,
Cheap Street (U.S.), 1983 (26 signed, lettered copies)
. . . . £200
ditto, Cheap Street (U.S.), 1983 (250 signed, lettered
copies) £50
ditto, Philomel (U.S.), 1984 . . . . £15/£5
Fish Soup, Atheneum (U.S.), 1992 . . . £10/£5
A Ride on the Red Mare's Back, Orchard (U.S.), 1992
. . . . £10/£5
Jane On Her Own, Orchard (U.S.), 1999 . £10/£5

Novels

The Left Hand of Darkness, Ace (U.S.), 1969 (wraps,
no mention of Hugo and Nebula awards) . . £25
ditto, Walker (U.S.), 1969 . . . . £200/£35
ditto, Macdonald, 1969 . . . . . £100/£20
City of Illusions, Ace (U.S.), 1971 (wraps) . . £10
ditto, Gollancz, 1971 . . . . . . £65/£15

ditto, Garland (U.S.), 1975 (no d/w) £35
Rocannon's World, Ace (U.S.), 1966 (wraps) . £5
ditto, Tandem, 1972 (wraps) £5
ditto, Garland (U.S.), 1975 (no d/w) £35
Planet of Exile, Ace (U.S.), 1966 (wraps) . . £5
ditto, Tandem, 1972 (wraps) £5
ditto, Garland (U.S.), 1975 (no d/w) £35
The Lathe of Heaven, Scribner (U.S.), 1971 £125/£25
ditto, Gollancz, 1972 . . . . £65/£20
The Dispossessed, Harper (U.S.), [1974] . £125/£25
ditto, Gollancz, 1974 . . . . £50/£20
The Word for World is Forest, Putnam (U.S.), 1976 .
. . . . £25/£5
ditto, Gollancz, 1977 . . . . £15/£5
Malafrena, Putnam (U.S.), 1979 . . . £15/£5
ditto, Gollancz, 1980 . . . . £10/£5
The Eye of the Heron, Harper (U.S.), 1982 £15/£5
ditto, Gollancz, 1983 . . . . £10/£5
The Visionary, Capra (U.S.) 1985 (with **Wonders Hidden** by Scott Saunders, wraps) . . . £5
Always Coming Home, Harper (U.S.), 1985 £10/£5
ditto; Harper (U.S.), 1985 (unspecified number of signed copies with cassette in slipcase) . £100/£35
ditto, Gollancz, 1986 . . . . . . £10/£5
ditto, Gollancz, 1986 (100 signed copies with cassette in slipcase) . . . . £75/£35
The Telling, Harcourt Brace (U.S.), 2000 . £10/£5

Short Stories
From Elfland to Ploughkeepsie, Pendragon Press/ Oregon Press (U.S.), 1973 (26 signed hardback copies, no d/w) £250
ditto, Pendragon Press/Oregon Press (U.S.), 1973 (100 signed copies, wraps) £50
ditto, Pendragon Press/Oregon Press (U.S.), 1973 (650 trade copies, wraps) £15
The Wind's Twelve Quarters, Harper (U.S.), 1975 .
. . . . £25/£5
ditto, Gollancz, 1976 . . . . £20/£5
Orsinian Tales, Harper (U.S.), 1976 . . . £20/£5
ditto, Gollancz, 1977 . . . . . . £10/£5
The Water is Wide, Pendragon Press (U.S.), 1976 (50 signed copies, no d/w) £100
ditto, Pendragon Press (U.S.), 1976 (950 signed copies)
. . . . £15/£5
The Compass Rose, Pendragon Press/Underwood-Miller (U.S.), 1982 (550 signed copies) . £45/£25
ditto, Harper (U.S.), 1982 . . . . . . £30/£10
ditto, Gollancz, 1983 . . . . £25/£5
Gwilan's Harp, Lord John Press (U.S.), 1981 (50 signed, numbered handbound, cloth copies of 350) .
. . . . £100
ditto, Lord John Press (U.S.), 1981 (300 signed copies of 350, wraps in d/w) . . . . . £25/£10
Buffalo Gals and Other Animal Presences, Capra Press (U.S.), 1987 . . . . . . £15/£5
ditto, Gollancz, 1990 . . . . . . £10/£5
Searoad, Harper (U.S.), 1991 . . . . £10/£5
ditto, Gollancz, 1992 . . . . £10/£5

A Fisherman of the Inland Sea, Harper Prism (U.S.), 1994 (526 copies, no d/w) £25
ditto, Harper Prism (U.S.), 1994 (1,500 advance copies) . . . . £25/£10
ditto, Gollancz, 1994 . . . . £10/£5
Four Ways to Forgiveness, Easton Press, 1995 (signed limited edition) £45
ditto, Harper Prism (U.S.), 1995 . . . . £10/£5
Unlocking the Air and Other Stories, Harper (U.S.), 1996 . . . . £10/£5

Verse
Wild Angels, Capra Press (U.S.), 1973 (200 signed, numbered copies) £45
Hard Words and Other Poems, Harper (U.S.), 1981 .
. . . . £20/£5
Wild Oats and Fireweed, Harper (U.S.), 1988 £10/£5
Going Out With Peacocks and Other Poems, Harper (U.S.), 1994 (wraps) £10
The Twins, the Dream/Las Gemelas, El Sueño, Arte Publico Press (U.S.), 1996 (with Diana Bellessi, wraps) £10
Sixty Odd: New Poems, Shambhala (U.S.), 1999 £10
Walking in Cornwall: A Poem for the Solstice, Portland Press (U.S.), 1996 (wraps) . . . £25

Others
Dreams Must Explain Themselves, Algol Press (U.S.), 1973 (1,000 numbered copies, wraps) . . . £15
In The Red Zone, Lord John Press, 1983 (25 signed copies) £100
ditto, Lord John Press, 1983 (50 signed deluxe copies)
. . . . £100
ditto, Lord John Press, 1983 (150 signed copies) £50
King Dog, Capra Press (U.S.), 1986 (with Tess Gallagher, bound in with **Dostoevsky: A Screenplay** by Raymond Carver, wraps) £25
ditto, Capra (U.S.), 1985 (200 copies signed by all authors, wraps) £100
Language of the Night: Essays on Fantasy and Science Fiction, Putnam (U.S.), 1979 . . £15/£5
ditto, Women's Press, 1989 (revised edition, wraps) £5
Dancing at the Edge of the World: Thoughts on Words, Women and Places, Grove Press (U.S.), 1989
. . . . £10/£5
ditto, Gollancz, 1989 . . . . £10/£5
Findings, Ox Head Press, 1992 (26 signed, lettered copies) £125
Lorenzo Bean, Dozing, Parchment Gallery Graphics, 1998 (100 signed, numbered copies, sketch, broadsheet) £40

ROSAMOND LEHMANN
(b.1903 d.1990)

A writer whose novels often deal with the emotional development of womanhood.

Novels

Dusty Answer, Chatto & Windus, 1927 . .	£125/£20
ditto, Holt (U.S.), 1927	£40/£10
A Note in Music, Chatto & Windus, 1930 .	£35/£10
ditto, Chatto & Windus, 1930 (260 signed copies) £100	
ditto, Holt (U.S.), 1930	£20/£5
ditto, Holt (U.S.), 1930 (300 signed copies) .	£75
Invitation to the Waltz, Chatto & Windus, 1932 . .	
. . . .	£30/£10
ditto, Holt (U.S.), 1932	£15/£5
The Weather in the Streets, Collins, 1936 .	£45/£15
ditto, Reynal Hitchcock (U.S.), 1936 . .	£15/£5
The Ballad and the Source, Collins, 1944 .	£20/£5
ditto, Reynal Hitchcock (U.S.), 1945 .	£15/£5
The Echoing Grove, Collins, 1953 . . .	£25/£5
ditto, Harcourt Brace (U.S.), 1953 . . .	£20/£5
A Sea-Grape Tree, Collins, 1976 . . .	£15/£5
ditto, Harcourt Brace (U.S.), 1977 . .	£15/£5

Short Stories

The Gipsy's Baby and Other Stories, Collins, 1946 .	
. . . .	£20/£5
ditto, Reynal Hitchcock (U.S.), 1947 . .	£15/£5

Others

Letter to a Sister, Hogarth Press, 1931 (wraps)	£15
ditto, Harcourt Brace (U.S.), 1932	£10
No More Music, Collins, 1939	£25/£10
ditto, Reynal Hitchcock (U.S.), 1945 . .	£10/£5
A Man Seen Afar, Spearman, 1965 (with W. Tudor Pole)	£10/£5
The Swan in the Evening: Fragments of an Inner Life, Collins, 1967	£10/£5
ditto, Harcourt Brace (U.S.), 1967 . .	£10/£5
Letters from Our Daughters, College of Psychic Studies, 1972 (with Cynthia Hill Sandys, 2 vols) £15	

ELMORE LEONARD

Elmore Leonard had his first success in 1951 when *Argosy* magazine published his short story 'Trail of the Apache.' Despite early recognition as the writer of westerns, his crime novels have become more popular in recent years, in part due to the attentions of Hollywood. Quentin Tarantino ('Pulp Fiction') directed 'Jackie Brown,' a film based on Leonard's novel *Rum Punch*, in 1997.

The Bounty Hunters, Houghton-Mifflin (U.S.), 1953 .	
. . . .	£2,000/£300
ditto, Ballantine (U.S.), 1953 (wraps) . . .	£75

ditto, Hale, 1956	£650/£50
The Law at Randado, Houghton-Mifflin (U.S.), 1954 .	
. . . .	£1,2500/£250
ditto, Hale, 1957	£450/£50
Escape from Five Shadows, Houghton-Mifflin (U.S.), 1956	£1,000/£150
ditto, Hale, 1957	£450/£50
Last Stand at Saber River, Dell (U.S.), 1959 (wraps) .	
. . . .	£45
ditto, as *Lawless River*, Hale, 1961 . . .	£450/£50
Hombre, Ballantine (U.S.), 1961 (wraps) . .	£100
ditto, Hale, 1961	£450/£50
The Big Bounce, Fawcett Gold Medal (U.S.), 1969 (wraps)	£45
ditto, Hale, 1969	£250/£20
The Moonshine War, Doubleday (U.S.), 1969 . . .	
. . . .	£300/£65
ditto, Hale, 1970	£250/£30
Valdez is Coming, Hale, 1969	£300/£40
ditto, Fawcett Gold Medal (U.S.), 1970 (wraps) £45	
Forty Lashes Less One, Bantam (U.S.), 1972 (wraps) .	
. . . .	£25
Mr. Majestyk, Dell (U.S.), 1974 (wraps) . .	£25
Fifty-Two Pickup, Delacorte (U.S.), 1974 .	£200/£25
ditto, Secker & Warburg, 1974	£75/£25
Swag, Delacorte (U.S.), 1976.	£200/£25
ditto, Secker & Warburg, 1976	£75/£25
Unknown Man No. 89, Delacorte (U.S.), 1977 . .	
. . . .	£250/£45
ditto, Secker & Warburg, 1977	£75/£25
The Hunted, Dell (U.S.), 1977 (wraps) . . .	£25
ditto, Secker & Warburg, 1978	£75/£25
The Switch, Bantam (U.S.), 1978 (wraps) . .	£25
ditto, Secker & Warburg, 1979	£75/£25
Gunsights, Bantam (U.S.), 1979 (wraps) . .	£25
City Primeval, Arbor House (U.S.), 1980 .	£35/£10
ditto, W.H. Allen, 1981	£45/£15
Gold Coast, Bantam (U.S.), 1980 (wraps) . .	£20
ditto, W.H. Allen, 1982	£25/£10
Split Images, Arbor House (U.S.), 1981. .	£35/£10
ditto, W.H. Allen, 1983	£25/£10
Cat Chaser, Arbor House (U.S.), 1982 . .	£25/£10
ditto, Viking, 1986	£25/£10
Stick, Arbor House (U.S.), 1983	£25/£10
ditto, Allen Lane, 1984	£25/£10
LaBrava, Arbor House (U.S.), 1983 . . .	£25/£10
ditto, Viking, 1984	£25/£10
Glitz, Viking, 1985	£25/£10
ditto, Arbor House (U.S.), 1986	£25/£10
ditto, Arbor House (U.S.), 1986 (26 signed lettered copies in slipcase)	£200
ditto, Arbor House (U.S.), 1986 (500 signed copies in slipcase)	£50
Bandits, Arbor House (U.S.), 1987 . . .	£25/£10
ditto, Viking, 1987	£25/£10
Touch, Arbor House (U.S.), 1987 . . .	£20/£10
ditto, Viking, 1988	£20/£10
Freaky Deaky, Arbor House/Morrow (U.S.), 1988 .	
. . . .	£20/£10

ditto, Viking, 1988 . . . . . . £20/£10
Killshot, Arbor House/Morrow (U.S.), 1989 £15/£5
ditto, Viking, 1989 . . . . . . £15/£5
Get Shorty, Delacorte (U.S.), 1990 . . . £20/£5
ditto, Viking, 1990 . . . . . . £20/£5
Maximum Bob, Delacorte, Arbor House (U.S.), 1986, 1991 . . . . £15/£5
ditto, Viking, 1991 . . . . . . £15/£5
Rum Punch, Delacorte, Arbor House (U.S.), 1986, 1992 . . . . £30/£5
ditto, Viking, 1992 . . . . . . £30/£5
ditto, as **Jackie Brown**, Dell, Arbor House (U.S.), 1986, 1997 (wraps) £5
Pronto, Delacorte, Arbor House (U.S.), 1986, 1993 . . . . £15/£5
ditto, Viking, 1993 . . . . . . £15/£5
Out of Sight Delacorte (U.S.), 1996 . . . £15/£5
ditto, Viking, 1996 . . . . . . £15/£5
The Tonto Woman and other Western Stories, Delacorte (U.S.), 1998 . . . . . . £15/£5
ditto, Viking, 1999 . . . . . . £15/£5
Cuba Libre, Delacorte (U.S.), 1998 . . . £10/£5
ditto, Viking, 1998 . . . . . . £10/£5
Be Cool, Delacorte (U.S.), 1999 . . . . £10/£5
ditto, Viking, 1999 . . . . . . £10/£5
Pagan Babies, Delacorte (U.S.), 2000 . . £10/£5
ditto, Viking, 2000 . . . . . . £10/£5

GASTON LEROUX

(b.1868 d.1927)

Celebrated in his lifetime as an author of detective fiction, Leroux's posthumous reputation is based mainly on *The Phantom of the Opera*, the basis for Andrew Lloyd Webber's hugely successful staged musical.

Verse
The Mystery of the Yellow Room, Daily Mail Sixpenny Novels, 1908 (wraps) £30
ditto, Brentano's (U.S.), 1908 . . . . £50
ditto, Edward Arnold, 1909 . . . . £40
The Double Life, Kearney (U.S.), 1909 . . . £50
ditto, Laurie, 1910 (wraps) £15
ditto, as **The Man With the Black Feather**, Hurst & Blackett, 1912 . . . . £30
ditto, as **The Man With the Black Feather**, Small (U.S.), 1912 . . . . £30
The Perfume of the Lady in Black, Daily Mail Sixpenny Novels, 1909 (wraps). . . . £25
ditto, Brentano's (U.S.), 1908 . . . . £40
ditto, Eveleigh Nash, 1911 . . . . . £25
The Phantom of the Opera, Mills & Boon, 1911 £200
ditto, Bobbs-Merrill (U.S.), 1911 (colour plates) £450
ditto, Grosset & Dunlap, [1925] (colour plates). £200
Balaoo, Hurst & Blackett, 1913 . . . . . £35

The Secret of the Night, Eveleigh Nash, 1914 . £35
ditto, Macaulay (U.S.), 1914 . . . . . . £35
The Bride of the Sun, McBride-Nast (U.S.), 1915 £45
ditto, Hodder & Stoughton, 1918. . . . . £45
The Man Who Came Back From the Dead, Eveleigh Nash, 1916 . . . . £35
The Floating Prison, Laurie, 1922 . . . £150/£20
ditto, as **Wolves of the Sea**, Macaulay (U.S.), 1923 . . . . £150/£20
The Amazing Adventures of Carolous Herbert, Mills & Boon, 1922 . . . . £150/£20
Cheri-Bibi and Cecily, Laurie, 1923 . . . £150/£20
ditto, as **Missing Men**, Macaulay (U.S.), 1923 . . . . £150/£20
The Veiled Prisoner, Mills & Boon, 1923 . £125/£15
Cheri-Bibi, Mystery Man, John Long, 1924 £125/£15
ditto, as **The Dark Road**, Macaulay (U.S.), 1924 . . . . £100/£15
The Dancing Girl, John Long, 1925. . . £100/£15
ditto, as **Nomads of the Night**, Macaulay (U.S.), 1925. . . . . £100/£15
The Burgled Heart, John Long, 1925 . £150/£25
ditto, as **The New Terror**, Macaulay (U.S.), 1926 . . . . £150/£25
The Slave Bangle, John Long, 1925. . . £100/£15
ditto, as **The Phantom Clue**, Macaulay (U.S.), 1926 . . . . £100/£15
The Sleuth Hound, John Long, 1926 . . £100/£15
ditto, as **The Octopus of Paris**, Macaulay (U.S.), 1927 . . . . £100/£15
The Adventures of a Coquette, Laurie, 1926 £100/£15
The Masked Man, John Long, 1927. . . . £100/£15
ditto, Macaulay (U.S.), 1929 . . , , £100/£15
The Son of Three Fathers, John Long, 1927 £75/£15
ditto, Macaulay (U.S.), 1928 . . . . . £75/£15
The New Idol, John Long, 1928 . . . . £75/£15
ditto, Macaulay (U.S.), 1929 . . . . . £75/£15
The Midnight Lady, John Long, 1930 . . £65/£15
The Man of a Hundred Masks, Cassel, 1930 £65/£15
ditto, as **The Man of a Hundred Faces**, Macaulay (U.S.), 1930 . . . . £65/£15
The Haunted Chair, Dutton (U.S.), 1931 . £50/£10
The Missing Archduke, John Long, 1931 . £50/£10
Lady Helena, Laurie, 1931 . . . . . £50/£10
ditto, Dutton (U.S.), 1931. . . . . . £50/£10
The Kiss That Killed, Macaulay (U.S.), 1934 £45/£10
The Machine to Kill, Macaulay (U.S.), 1935 £45/£10
Gaston Leroux's Crime Omnibus Book, Laurie, 1935 . . . . £35/£10
The Gaston Leroux Bedside Companion, Gollancz, 1980 . . . . £10/£5

DORIS LESSING
(b.1919)

Lessing's first novel is a study of a white woman's obsession with her black servant, and is the first of many novels which suggest a fascination with the private world of the mind.

Novels

The Grass is Singing, Joseph, 1950 . . .	£350/£45
ditto, Crowel (U.S.), 1950	£200/£25
Martha Quest, Joseph, 1952	£100/£25
ditto, Simon & Schuster (U.S.), 1964 (with *A Proper Marriage*)	£25/£5
A Proper Marriage, Joseph, 1954 . . .	£45/£10
Retreat to Innocence, Joseph, 1956 . . .	£45/£10
A Ripple from the Storm, Joseph, 1958 . .	£40/£10
ditto, Simon & Schuster (U.S.), 1966 (with *Landlocked*)	£25/£5
The Golden Notebook, Joseph, 1962 . .	£150/£5
ditto. Simon & Schuster (U.S.), 1962 .	£30/£5
Landlocked, MacGibbon & Kee, 1965 . .	£40/£10
The Four-Gated City, MacGibbon & Kee, 1969	£50/£10
ditto, Knopf (U.S.), 1969	£45/£10
Briefing for a Descent into Hell, Cape, 1971	£25/£5
ditto, Knopf (U.S.), 1971	£25/£5
The Summer Before the Dark, Cape, 1973 .	£30/£5
ditto, Knopf (U.S.), 1973	£25/£5
Memoirs of a Survivor, Octagon Press, 1974	£25/£5
ditto, Knopf (U.S.), 1975	£25/£5
Re: Colonised Planet 5, Shikasta, Cape, 1979	£20/£5
ditto, Knopf (U.S.), 1979	£20/£5
The Marriages Between Zones Three, Four and Five, Cape, 1980	£20/£5
ditto, Knopf (U.S.), 1980	£15/£5
The Sirian Experiments, Cape, 1981 . .	£15/£5
ditto, Knopf (U.S.), 1981	£15/£5
The Making of the Representative for Planet 8, Cape, 1982	£15/£5
ditto, Knopf (U.S.), 1982	£15/£5
Documents Relating to the Sentimental Agents in the Volyen Empire, Cape, 1983	£15/£5
ditto, Knopf (U.S.), 1983	£15/£5
The Diary of a Good Neighbour, Cape, 1983 (pseud. 'Jane Somers')	£15/£5
ditto, Knopf (U.S.), 1983	£15/£5
If the Old Could, Cape, 1984 (pseud. 'Jane Somers')	£15/£5
ditto, Knopf (U.S.), 1984	£15/£5
The Good Terrorist, Cape, 1985	£15/£5
ditto, Knopf (U.S.), 1985	£15/£5
The Fifth Child, Cape, 1988	£15/£5
ditto, Knopf (U.S.), 1988	£15/£5
African Laughter, HarperCollins, 1992 . .	£10/£5
ditto, HarperCollins (U.S.), 1992 . . .	£10/£5
Playing the Game, HarperCollins, 1995 (graphic novel)	£10
Love, Again, Flamingo, 1996	£10/£5

ditto, HarperCollins (U.S.), 1996 . . .	£10/£5
Mara and Dann, an Adventure, HarperCollins, 1999	£10/£5
ditto, HarperCollins (U.S.), 1999 . . .	£10/£5
Ben, in the World, Flamingo, 2000 . . .	£10/£5
ditto, HarperCollins (U.S.), 2000 . . .	£10/£5

Short Stories

This was the Old Chief's Country, Joseph, 1951	£125/£25
ditto, Crowel (U.S.), 1952	£100/£20
Five: Short Novels, Joseph, 1953 . . .	£65/£10
The Habit of Loving, MacGibbon & Kee, 1957	£40/£10
ditto, Crowel (U.S.), 1958	£35/£5
A Man and Two Women, Stories, MacGibbon & Kee, 1963	£40/£10
ditto, Simon & Schuster (U.S.), 1963 . .	£35/£5
African Stories, Joseph, 1964	£40/£10
ditto, Simon & Schuster (U.S.), 1965 . .	£35/£5
The Black Madonna, Panther, 1966 (wraps) .	£10
Winter in July, Panther, 196 (wraps) . . .	£10
Nine African Stories, Longman, 1968 . .	£35/£10
The Story of a Non-Marrying Man, Cape, 1972	£25/£5
ditto, as *The Temptation of Jack Orkney*, Knopf (U.S.), 1972	£25/£5
Collected African Stories, Joseph, 1973 (2 vols, *This Was the Old Chief's Country* and *The Sun Between their Feet*)	£25/£5
Collected Stories, Cape, 1978 (2 vols, *To Room Nineteen* and *The Temptation of Jack Orkney*)	£20/£5
ditto, as *Stories*, Knopf (U.S.), 1979 . .	£20/£5
London Observed, HarperCollins, 1992 . .	£15/£5
ditto, as *The Real Thing*, HarperCollins (U.S.), 1992	£15/£5
ditto, as *The Real Thing*, Ultramarine Publishing Company (U.S.), 1992 (38 signed copies) . .	£100
ditto, Ultramarine Publishing Company (U.S.), 1992 (12 signed copies in full leather)	£150
Spies I Have Known and Other Stories, Cascade/ Collins Educational, 1995	£10/£5

Others

Going Home, Joseph, 1957	£75/£15
ditto, Ballantine (U.S.), 1968	£20/£5
A Small Personal Voice, MacGibbon & Kee, 1957	£30/£10
ditto, Dutton (U.S.), 1958	£25/£5
Fourteen Poems, Scorpion Press, 1959 (500 copies, wraps).	£50
ditto, Scorpion Press, 1959 (50 signed copies, wraps)	£250
In Pursuit of the English, A Documentary, MacGibbon & Kee, 1960	£20/£5
ditto, as *Portrait of the English*, Simon & Schuster (U.S.), 1961	£15/£5
Play with a Tiger, Joseph, 1962	£60/£10

Particularly Cats, Joseph, 1967 . . . . £35/£5
ditto, Simon & Schuster (U.S.), 1967 . . £35/£5
ditto, as *Particularly Cats... and Rufus*, Simon &
Schuster (U.S.), 1967 . . . . . . £20/£5
ditto, as *Particularly Cats and More Cats*, Joseph,
1989 . . . . £15/£5
ditto, as *Particularly Cats and Rufus the Survivor*,
Knopf (U.S.), 1991 . . . . £15/£5
ditto, as *The Old Age of El Magnificato*, Burford
Books (U.S.), 2000 . . . . . . £10/£5
ditto, as *Particularly Cats*, Flamingo, 2000 £10/£5
Prisons We Choose to Live Inside, C.B.C. (Canada),
1986 . . . . £10/£5
ditto, Joseph, 1987. . . . . £15
ditto, Simon & Schuster (U.S.), 1987 . . £15/£5
The Wind Blows Away Our Words, Picador, 1987. .
. . . . £15/£5
ditto, Vintage (U.S.), 1987 . . . . £15/£5
Conversations, Ontario Review Press (U.S.), 1994. .
. . . . £15/£5
ditto, as *Putting the Questions Differently*, Flamingo,
1996 . . . . £10/£5
Under My Skin, HarperCollins, 1994 . . £10/£5
ditto, HarperCollins (U.S.), 1994. . . . £10/£5
Walking in the Shade, HarperCollins, 1997 £10/£5
ditto, HarperCollins (U.S.), 1997. . . . £10/£5

C.S. LEWIS
(b.1898 d.1963)

Arguably best known for his children's books, Lewis
also wrote a handful of science fiction novels, and a
great number of theological works.

Children's
The Lion, The Witch and The Wardrobe, Bles, 1950 .
. . . . £2,000/£300
ditto, Macmillan (U.S.), 1950 . . . £1,000/£200
Prince Caspian: The Return to Narnia, Bles, 1951 .
. . . . £1,000/£150
ditto, Macmillan (U.S.), 1951 . . . . £500/£50
The Voyage of the 'Dawn Treader', Bles, 1952 . .
. . . . £1,000/£150
ditto, Macmillan (U.S.), 1952 . . . . £400/£50
The Silver Chair, Bles, 1953 . . . . £1,000/£150
ditto, Macmillan (U.S.), 1953 . . . . £250/£50
The Horse and His Boy, Bles, 1954 . . £1,000/£150
ditto, Macmillan (U.S.), 1954 . . . . £200/£25
The Magician's Nephew, Bles, 1955 . . £750/£150
ditto, Macmillan (U.S.), 1955 . . . . £250/£25
The Last Battle, Bles, 1956 . . . . . £750/£150
ditto, Macmillan (U.S.), 1956 . . . . £250/£25

Novels
Out of the Silent Planet, Bodley Head, 1938 . . .
. . . . £750/£100
ditto, Macmillan (U.S.), 1943 . . . . £125/£35

Perelandra, Bodley Head, 1943 . . . . £300/£75
ditto, Macmillan (U.S.), 1944 . . . . £125/£35
*That Hideous Strength: A Modern Fairy-Tale for
Grown-Ups*, Bodley Head, 1945 . . . £200/£45
ditto, Macmillan (U.S.), 1946 . . . . £100/£25
Till We Have Faces: A Myth Retold, Bles, 1956 . .
. . . . £75/£25
ditto, Harcourt Brace & Co (U.S.), 1957 . £35/£10

Short Stories
The Dark Tower and Other Stories, Collins, 1977 .
. . . . £30/£10
ditto, Harcourt, Brace (U.S.), 1977 . . . £25/£10

Verse
Spirits in Bondage, Heinemann, 1919 (pseud. 'Clive
Hamilton') . . . . £225/£40
Dymer, Dent, 1926 (pseud. 'Clive Hamilton') . £175
ditto, Dutton (U.S.), 1926. . . . . . . £150
Hamlet, the Prince or the Poem, British Academy,
1942 (wraps) £45
Poems, Bles, 1964. . . . . £50/£15
ditto, Harcourt, Brace (U.S.), 1965 . . . £25/£10
Narrative Poems, Bles, 1969 . . . . . £15/£5

Christian Titles
*The Pilgrim's Regress: An Allegorical Apology for
Christianity, Reason and Romanticism*, Dent, 1933 .
. . . . £75/£25
The Problem of Pain, Centenary Press, 1940 £50/£15
ditto, Bles, 1943 . . . . £30/£10
ditto, Macmillan (U.S.), 1943 . . . . £25/£5
The Screwtape Letters, Bles, 1942 . . . £250/£35
ditto, Saunders (U.S.), 1942 . . . . . £125/£15
*Broadcast Talks: Right and Wrong: A Clue to the
Meaning of the Universe, and What Christians
Believe*, Bles, 1942 . . . . £50/£15
*Christian Behaviour: A Further Series of Broadcast
Talks*, Bles, 1943 . . . . £100/£20
ditto, Macmillan (U.S.), 1945 . . . . £20/£5
*The Abolition of Man: or Reflections on Education
with Special Reference to the Teaching of English in
the Upper Forms of Schools*, O.U.P., 1943 £25/£10
ditto, Macmillan (U.S.), 1947 . . . . £25/£10
Beyond Personality: The Christian Idea of God, Bles,
1944 . . . . £35/£10
The Great Divorce: A Dream, Bles, 1945 . £35/£10
Miracles: A Preliminary Study, Bles, 1947. £25/£10
Vivisection, The National Anti-Vivisection Society
[1947] (wraps) £95
Mere Christianity, Bles, 1952 . . . . £15/£5
Reflections on the Psalms, Bles, 1958 . . £15/£5
ditto, Harcourt Brace (U.S.), 1958 . . . £15/£5
Shall We Lose God in Outer Space?, S.P.C.K., 1959
(wraps) £65
The Four Loves, Bles, 1960 . . . . . £15/£5
ditto, Harcourt Brace (U.S.), 1960 . . . £15/£5
The World's Last Night, Harcourt Brace (U.S.), 1960 .
. . . . £30/£10

Beyond the Bright Blur, Harcourt Brace (U.S.), 1963 .
. . . . £25/£10
Letters to Malcolm chiefly on Prayer, Bles, [1964] .
. . . . £15/£5
ditto, Harcourt Brace (U.S.), 1964 . . . £15/£5
Screwtape Proposes a Toast and Other Pieces, Bles,
1965 . . . . £15/£5
Christian Reflections, Bles, 1967 . . . £10/£5
Letters to an American Lady, Eerdmans (U.S.), 1967 .
. . . . £15/£5
The Joyful Christian, Macmillan (U.S.), 1977 £10/£5

Academic
The Allegory of Love: A Study in Medieval Tradition,
O.U.P., 1936 . . . . £45/£15
ditto, O.U.P. (U.S.), 1936 . . . . . £45/£15
Rehabilitations and Other Essays, O.U.P., 1939 . .
. . . . £40/£15
The Personal Heresy: A Controversy, O.U.P., 1939
(with E.M.W. Tillyard) . . . . . £35/£10
A Preface to Paradise Lost, O.U.P., 1942 . £35/£15
Arthurian Torso, O.U.P., 1948 (with Charles
Williams) . . . . £75/£35
ditto, O.U.P. (U.S.), 1948 . . . . . £75/£35
*English Literature in the Sixteenth Century,
Excluding Drama*, O.U.P., 1954 . . . £45/£15
ditto, O.U.P. (U.S.), 1954 . . . . . £45/£15
Studies in Words, C.U.P., 1960 . . . £15/£5
ditto, Macmillan (U.S.), 1960 . . . . £10/£5
An Experiment in Criticism, C.U.P., 1961 £35/£15
ditto, Macmillan (U.S.), 1961 . . . £30/£10
They Asked for a Paper, Bles, 1962 . . . £15/£5
The Discarded Image, C.U.P., 1964 . . . £10/£5
Of Other Worlds, Bles, 1966 . . . . £10/£5
Studies in Mediaeval and Renaissance Literature,
C.U.P., 1966 . . . . £10/£5
Spenser's Images of Life, C.U.P., 1961 . . £10/£5

Autobiography
Surprised by Joy, Bles, 1955 . . . . £35/£15
ditto, Harcourt Brace (U.S.), 1956 . . . £30/£10
A Grief Observed, Faber, 1961 (pseud. 'N.W. Clerk') .
. . . . £50/£15
ditto, Seabury (U.S.), 1963 . . . . . £25/£10

NORMAN LEWIS
(b.1908)

A travel writer and novelist, Lewis was hailed by
Graham Greene as one of the best writers of the
twentieth century.

Travel
Spanish Adventure, Gollancz, 1935 . . . £250/£35
ditto, Holt (U.S.), 1935 . . . . . £200/£20
Sand and Sea in Arabia, Routledge, 1938 . £150/£25

A Dragon Apparent, Travels In Indo-China, Cape,
1951 . . . . £65/£20
ditto, Scribner's (U.S.), 1951 . . . . £50/£10
Golden Earth, Travels In Burma, Cape, 1952 £50/£20
ditto, Scribner's (U.S.), 1952 . . . . £35/£10
The Changing Sky, The Travels of a Novelist, Cape,
1959 . . . . £45/£15
ditto, Pantheon (U.S.), 1959 . . . . £40/£10
*The Honoured Society, The Mafia Conspiracy
Observed*, Collins, 1964 . . . . . £45/£15
ditto, Putnam's (U.S.), 1964 . . . . £40/£10
Naples '44, Collins, 1978 . . . . . £45/£15
ditto, Pantheon (U.S.), 1978 . . . . £40/£10
Voices of the Old Sea, Hamish Hamilton, 1984 £25/£5
ditto, Viking (U.S.), 1985 . . . . . £20/£5
A Goddess in the Stones, Travels In India, Cape, 1991
. . . . £20/£5
ditto, Holt (U.S.), 1992 . . . . . . £20/£5
An Empire of the East, Travels In Indonesia, Cape,
1993 . . . . £15/£5
ditto, Holt (U.S.), 1993 . . . . . . £15/£5

Novels
Samara, Cape, 1949 . . . . . . £45/£10
Within the Labyrinth, Cape, 1950 . . . £30/£5
ditto, Carroll & Graf (U.S.), 1986 . . . £10/£5
A Single Pilgrim, Cape, 1953 . . . . £15/£5
ditto, Rinehart & Co. (U.S.), 1953 . . . £15/£5
The Day of the Fox, Cape, 1955 . . . £15/£5
ditto, Rinehart & Co. (U.S.), 1955 . . . £15/£5
The Volcanoes Above Us, Cape, 1957 . . £15/£5
ditto, Pantheon (U.S.), [1957] . . . . £15/£5
Darkness Visible, Cape, 1960 . . . . £15/£5
ditto, Pantheon (U.S.), 1960 . . . . £15/£5
The Tenth Year of the Ship, Collins, 1962 £15/£5
ditto, Harcourt, Brace (U.S.), 1962 . . . £15/£5
A Small War Made to Order, Collins, 1966 £15/£5
ditto, Harcourt, Brace (U.S.), 1966 . . . £15/£5
Every Man's Brother, Heinemann, 1967 . £15/£5
ditto, Morrow (U.S.), 1968 . . . . . £15/£5
Flight from a Dark Equator, Collins, 1972 £15/£5
ditto, Putnam (U.S.), 1972 . . . . . £15/£5
The Sicilian Specialist, Random House (U.S.), 1974 .
. . . . £10/£5
ditto, Collins, 1975 . . . . . . £10/£5
The German Company, Collins, 1979 . . £10/£5
The Cuban Passage, Collins, 1982 . . . £10/£5
ditto, Pantheon (U.S.), 1982 . . . . £10/£5
A Suitable Case for Corruption, Hamish Hamilton,
1984 . . . . £10/£5
ditto, as The Man in the Middle, Pantheon (U.S.),
1984 . . . . £10/£5
The March of the Long Shadows, Secker & Warburg,
1987 . . . . £10/£5

Miscellaneous
Jackdaw Cake, Hamish Hamilton, 1985 . £20/£5
ditto, as I Came, I Saw, Picador, 1994 (enlarged
edition) . . . . £10/£5

A View of the World, Eland, 1986 . . . £15/£5
The Missionaries, Secker & Warburg, 1988 £15/£5
ditto, McGraw-Hill (U.S.), 1988.. . . . £15/£5
To Run Across the Sea, Cape, 1989 . . . £10/£5
The World, The World, Cape, 1996 . . . £10/£5
ditto, Holt (U.S.), 1997. . . . . . £10/£5
The Happy Ant-Heap and Other Pieces, Cape, 1998 .
. . . . £10/£5

WYNDHAM LEWIS
(b.1882 d.1957)

Considered one of the most versatile writers of his
time, Lewis was also a painter of some importance.

Fiction
Tarr, Knopf (U.S.), 1918 (red cloth). . . . £250
ditto, Knopf (U.S.), 1918 (blue cloth) . . . £150
ditto, Egoist Press, 1918 . . . . . £150
The Wild Body, Chatto & Windus, 1927 £200/£35
ditto, Chatto & Windus, 1927 (85 signed copies) . .
. . . . £650/£200
ditto, Harcourt, Brace (U.S.), [1928]. . £125/£30
The Childermass: Section 1, Chatto & Windus, 1928 .
. . . . £200/£35
ditto, Chatto & Windus, 1928 (231 signed copies) . .
. . . . £450/£225
ditto, Covici Friede (U.S.), [1928] . . £125/£30
The Apes of God, The Arthur Press, 1930 (750 signed
copies) . . . . £300/£125
ditto, Nash & Grayson, 1931 . . . . £125/£25
ditto, Robert McBride (U.S.), 1932 . . £125/£25
Snooty Baronet, Cassell, 1932 . . £300/£100
ditto, Haskell House (U.S.), 1971 . . . £10
The Revenge for Love, Cassell, 1937 . £250/£75
ditto, Regnery (U.S.), 1952 . . . . £40/£10
The Vulgar Streak, Robert Hale, 1941 . £300/£100
ditto, Jubilee Books (U.S.), 1973. . . . £20/£5
Rotting Hill, Methuen, 1951 . . . . £75/£25
ditto, Regnery (U.S.), 1952 . . . . £40/£10
Self Condemned, Methuen, 1954 . . £75/£25
ditto, Regnery (U.S.), 1955 . . . . £40/£10
The Red Priest, Methuen, 1963 . . . £50/£15
The Roaring Queen, Secker & Warburg, 1973 £25/£10
ditto, Secker & Warburg, 1973 (130 signed by Mrs
Wyndham Lewis) . . . . . £150/£45
ditto, Liveright (U.S.), 1973 . . . £25/£10
Unlucky for Pringle, Vision Press, 1973 £25/£10
ditto, D. Lewis (U.S.), [1973] . . £20/£5
Mrs Dukes' Millions, The Coach House Press
(Canada), 1977 (in box) . . . . . £20/£5

Plays
The Ideal Giant, Privately Printed for the London
Office of the *Little Review*, 1917 . . . £1,250
Enemy of the Stars, Harmsworth, 1932 . £200/£50

Verse
One-Way Song, Faber, 1933 . . . . . £150/£25
ditto, Faber, 1933 (40 signed copies) . . £1,000

Collections
The Letters, Methuen, 1963 . . . . £45/£15
ditto, New Directions (U.S.), [1927] . . £45/£15
A Soldier of Humour and Selected Writings, New
American Library (U.S.), 1966 (wraps) . . £10
Wyndham Lewis: An Anthology of His Prose,
Methuen, 1969 . . . . . . £30/£10

Others
Timon of Athens, Benmar & Co, 1913 (portfolio of 16
loose plates) £3,000
The Caliph's Design, Egoist Press, 1919 . . £250
ditto, Black Sparrow Press (U.S.), 1986 (176 copies,
acetate d/w) £35
Fifteen Drawings, Ovid Press, 1920. . . £150
The Art of Being Ruled, Chatto & Windus, 1926 . .
. . . . £300/£75
ditto, Harpers (U.S.), 1926 . . . . £250/£50
The Lion and the Fox, Grant Richards, 1927 . .
. . . . £500/£100
ditto, Harpers (U.S.), [1927] . . . . £350/£50
Time and Western Man, Chatto & Windus, 1927 . .
. . . . £150/£45
ditto, Harcourt, Brace (U.S.), 1928 . . £50/£15
Paleface, Chatto & Windus, 1929 . . £200/£45
Hitler, Chatto & Windus, 1931 . . . £450/£125
*The Diabolical Principle and the Dithyrambic
Spectator*, Chatto & Windus, 1931. . £150/£30
Doom of Youth, Robert McBride (U.S.), 1932 . . .
. . . . £200/£30
ditto, Chatto & Windus, 1932 . . £500/£200
Filibusters in Barbary, Grayson, 1932 . £250/£65
ditto, National Travel Club (U.S.), [1927] £100/£25
Thirty Personalities and a Self-Portrait, Harmsworth,
1932 (200 signed sets, portfolio with 31 loose plates)
. . . . £750
The Old Gang and the New Gang, Harmsworth, 1933
. . . . £200/£45
ditto, Haskell House (U.S.), 1972 . . . £10
Men Without Art, Cassell, 1934 . . . £300/£45
ditto, Russell & Russell (U.S.), 1964. . £25/£10
Left Wings Over Europe, Cape, 1936 . £150/£25
ditto, Gordon Press (U.S.), 1972 . . . £20/£5
Count Your Dead: They Are Alive!, Lovat Dickson,
1937 . . . . £250/£45
ditto, Gordon Press (U.S.), 1972 . . . £20/£5
Blasting and Bombadiering, Eyre & Spottiswoode,
1937 . . . . £150/£30
ditto, Univ. of California Press (U.S.), 1967 £20/£5
The Mysterious Mr Bull, Robert Hale, 1938 £200/£30
The Jews, Are They Human, Allen & Unwin, 1939 .
. . . . £250/£35
ditto, Gordon Press (U.S.), 1972 . . . £20/£5

Wyndham Lewis The Artist, From 'Blast' to Burlington House, Laidlaw & Laidlaw, 1939. . .
. . . . £175/£45
The Hitler Cult, Dent, 1939 . . . . . £400/£100
ditto, Gordon Press (U.S.), 1972 . . . . £20/£5
America, I Presume, Howell & Soskin (U.S.), 1940 (wraps) . . . . £125/£35
Anglosaxony: A League That Works, Ryerson (Canada), 1941 . . . . £400
America and Cosmic Man, Nicholson & Watson, 1948
. . . . £100/£25
ditto, Doubleday (U.S.), 1949 . . . . £75/£20
Rude Assignment, Hutchinson, [1950] . . £100/£25
ditto, Black Sparrow Press (U.S.), 1984 . . . £35
The Writer and the Absolute, Methuen, 1952 £75/£20
ditto, Greenwood Press (U.S.), 1975 . . . £15/£5
The Demon of Progress in the Arts, Methuen, 1954 .
. . . . £50/£10
ditto, Regnery (U.S.), 1955 . . . . . £40/£10
The Human Age, Methuen, 1955-56 (2 vols) £50/£20
Wyndham Lewis on Art, Thames & Hudson, 1969. .
. . . . £50/£15
ditto, Funk & Wagnalls (U.S.), 1969. . . £45/£15
Enemy Salvoes: Selected Literary Criticism, Vision Press, 1976 . . . . £25/£10
ditto, Barnes & Noble (U.S.), 1976 . . £45/£15
Imaginary Letters, Wyndham Lewis Society, 1977 (300 copies, wraps) £35

DAVID LINDSAY
(b.1878 d.1945)

British novelist whose curious metaphysical writings are not widely known. Among devotees, however, he is considered highly original and interesting.

Novels
A Voyage to Arcturus, Methuen, 1920 (first binding, 8 page catalogue at rear) . . . . . £2,000/£500
ditto, Methuen, 1920 (second binding without catalogue at rear). . . . . . . £1,000/£350
ditto, Gollancz, 1946 . . . . . . £45/£15
ditto, Macmillan (U.S.), 1963 . . . . £30/£10
The Haunted Woman, Methuen, 1922 . £1,000/£250
ditto, Gollancz, 1947 . . . . £25/£10
ditto, Newcastle (U.S.), 1975 (wraps) . . . £10
Sphinx, John Long, 1923 . . . . . £1,000/£250
The Adventures of M. De Mailly, Melrose, 1926 . .
. . . . £200/£75
ditto, as *A Blade for Sale*, McBride (U.S.), 1927 . .
. . . . £150/£35
Devil's Tor, Putnam, 1932 . . . . £1,000/£150
The Violet Apple and The Witch, Chicago Review Press (U.S.), 1975 . . . . . . £75/£25
The Violet Apple, Sidgwick & Jackson, [1978]. . .
. . . . £35/£10

DAVID LODGE
(b.1935)

Also a professor and literary critic, Lodge's novels are the most keenly sought after titles.

Novels
The Picturegoers, MacGibbon & Kee, 1960 £275/£45
Ginger, You're Barmy, MacGibbon & Kee 1962 . .
. . . . £225/£40
ditto, Doubleday (U.S.), 1965 . . . . £50/£15
The British Museum is Falling Down, MacGibbon & Kee, 1965. . . . . £200/£35
ditto, Holt Rinehart (U.S.), 1967 . . . . £45/£15
Out of the Shelter, Macmillan, 1970. . . £75/£20
Changing Places; A Tale of Two Campuses, Secker & Warburg, 1975 . . . . £65/£15
ditto, Viking (U.S.), 1979. . . . . . £25/£10
How Far Can You Go?, Secker & Warburg, 1980 .
. . . . £65/£15
ditto, as *Souls and Bodies*, Morrow (U.S.), 1982 . .
. . . . £15/£5
Small World, Secker & Warburg, 1984 . . £25/£10
ditto, Macmillan (U.S.), 1985 . . . . £15/£5
Nice Work, Secker & Warburg, 1988 . . £15/£5
ditto, Viking, 1989 . . . . £15/£5
Paradise News, Secker & Warburg, 1991 . £10/£5
ditto, Viking (U.S.), 1992. . . . . . £10/£5
Therapy, Secker & Warburg, 1995 . . . £10/£5
ditto, Viking (U.S.), 1995. . . . . . £10/£5
Thinks, Bridgewater Press, 2001 (XII signed, Roman-numbered copies of 138) £125
ditto, Bridgewater Press, 2001 (26 signed, lettered copies) £125
ditto, Bridgewater Press, 2001 (100 signed, numbered copies) £35
ditto, Secker & Warburg, 2001 . . . . £10/£5
ditto, Viking (U.S.), 2001. . . . . . £10/£5

Short Stories and Novellas
The Man Who Wouldn't Get Up and Other Stories, Bridgewater Press, 1998 (XII signed, Roman-numbered copies of 138) £125
ditto, Bridgewater Press, 1998 (26 signed, lettered copies) £125
ditto, Bridgewater Press, 1998 (100 signed, numbered copies) £35
Home Truths, Colophon Press,, 1999 (XII signed, Roman-numbered copies of 112) . . . £125
ditto, Colophon Press, 1999 (100 signed, numbered copies) £35

Play
The Writing Game, Secker & Warburg, 1991 £10/£5
Home Truths, Secker & Warburg, 1999 (wraps) £5

Others

The Language of Fiction, Routledge, 1966 £15/£5
ditto, Columbia Univ. Press (U.S.), 1966 . £15/£5
Graham Greene, Columbia Univ. Press (U.S.), 1966
(wraps) £45
The Novelist at the Crossroads and Other Essays on Fiction and Criticism, Roudedge, 1971 £10/£5
ditto, Cornell Univ. Press (U.S.), 1971 . . £10/£5
Evelyn Waugh, Columbia Univ. Press (U.S.), 1971
(wraps) £15
Twentieth Century Literary Criticism, Longman, 1972
. . . . £10/£5
The Modes of Modern Writing: Metaphor, Metonymy and the Typology of Modern Literature, Arnold, 1977 . . . . £15/£5
ditto, Cornell Univ. Press (U.S.), 1977 . . £15/£5
Working with Structuralism: Essays and Reviews on Nineteenth and Twentieth Century Literature, Routledge, 1981 . . . . £10/£5
Write On, Secker & Warburg, 1986 . . . £15/£5
After Bakhtin: Essays on Fiction and Criticism, Routledge, 1990 . . . . £10/£5
The Art of Fiction, Viking (U.S.), 1992 . . £10/£5
The Practice of Writing, Allen Lane/Penguin Press (U.S.), 1996 . . . . £10/£5

JACK LONDON
(b.1876 d.1916)

The highly successful writer of many adventure stories, London took part in the Klondike gold rush of 1897 and used this experience as the background for much of his work.

Novels

A Daughter of the Snows, Lippincott (U.S.), 1902 .
. . . . £450
ditto, Isbister, 1904 . . . . £100
The Kempton-Wace Letters, Macmillan (U.S.), 1903 (with Anna Strunsky. 1st issue without authors names on title page) £400
ditto, Macmillan (U.S.), 1903 (2nd issue with authors names on title page) £150
ditto, Isbister, 1903 . . . . £75
The Call of the Wild, Macmillan (U.S.), 1903 . £750
ditto, Heinemann, 1903 . . . . . . £300
The Sea-Wolf, Macmillan (U.S.), 1904 (title page not a cancel, copyright notice dated 1904 only) . £4,000
ditto, Macmillan (U.S.), 1904 (title page is a cancel, copyright notices dated 1903 and 1904). . . £300
ditto, Heinemann, 1904 . . . . . . £100
The Game, Macmillan (U.S.), 1905 . . . . £200
ditto, Heinemann, 1905 . . . . . . £100
White Fang, Macmillan (U.S.), 1906 (first state with title leaf integral). £200
ditto, Macmillan (U.S.), 1906 (second state with title leaf tipped-in) £100

ditto, Methuen, 1907 . . . . £75
Before Adam, Macmillan (U.S.), 1907 . . . £200
ditto, Macmillan Colonial Library Edition, 1907 £100
ditto, Werner Laurie, [1908] £100
The Iron Heel, Macmillan (U.S.), 1908 . . . £250
ditto, Everett, [1908] £75
Martin Eden, Donohoe (U.S.), 1980. . . . £250
ditto, Macmillan (U.S.), 1909 . . . . . £200
ditto, Heinemann, 1910 . . . . . . £75
Burning Daylight, Macmillan (U.S.), 1910 (first printing, one blank leaf follows p.374) . . £200
ditto, Macmillan (U.S.), 1910 (second printing, three blank leaves follows p.374) £100
ditto, Heinemann, 1911 . . . . . . £50
Adventure, Nelson, [1911] ('First published in 1911' on copyright page) £500
ditto, Nelson, [1911] ('Published in March 1911' on copyright page) £200
ditto, Macmillan (U.S.), 1911 . . . . . £75
The Abysmal Brute, The Century Co. (U.S.), 1913 . .
. . . . £125
ditto, Newnes, [1914] £65
John Barleycorn, The Century Co. (U.S.), 1913 £125
ditto, as *John Barleycorn or Alcoholic Memoirs*, Mills & Boon, 1914 . . . . £50
The Valley of the Moon, Macmillan (U.S.), 1913 £125
ditto, Mills & Boon, 1914. . . . . . £50
The Mutiny of the Elsinor, Macmillan (U.S.), 1914 .
. . . . £250
ditto, Mills & Boon, 1915. . . . . . . £75
The Scarlet Plague, Macmillan (U.S.), 1915 . £300
ditto, Mills & Boon, 1915. . . . . . . £75
The Jacket, Mills & Boon, 1915 . . . . . £450
ditto, as *The Star Rover*, Macmillan (U.S.), 1915 £300
The Little Lady of the Big House, Macmillan (U.S.), 1916 . . . . £125
ditto, Mills & Boon, 1916. . . . . . . £50
Jerry of the Islands, Macmillan (U.S.), 1917 . £125
ditto, Mills & Boon, 1917. . . . . . . £50
Michael, Brother of Jerry, Macmillan (U.S.), 1917 .
. . . . £150
ditto, Mills & Boon, 1918. . . . . . . £50
Hearts of Three, Mills & Boon, 1918 . . . £450
ditto, Macmillan (U.S.), 1920 . . . . £250/£45
The Assassination Bureau Ltd, McGraw-Hill (U.S.), 1963 (completed by Robert L. Fish) . . £30/£10
ditto, Deutsch, 1964 . . . . . . £30/£10

Short Stories

The Son of the Wolf: Tales of the Far North, Houghton, Mifflin (U.S.), 1900 (trial bindings of either grass-green cloth stamped in silver, greenish-black cloth stamped in silver, or white buckram stamped in red) £2,000
ditto, Houghton, Mifflin (U.S.), 1900 (first printing, gray cloth stamped in silver, pagination (i-viii); no blank leaf following page (252); collation: (4), 2-22(6)) £750

ditto, Houghton, Mifflin (U.S.), 1900 (Second printing, gray cloth stamped in silver, pagination: (i-vi) blank leaf following page (252)) £300
ditto, Houghton, Mifflin (U.S.), 1900 (Third printing, as second except collation differs: 1-21(6), 22(4)) .
. . . . £200
ditto, Watt, 1900 . . . . £1,000
ditto, Isbister, 1902 . . . . £300
The God of His Fathers, & Other Stories, McClure, Philips (U.S.), 1901 . . . . £450
ditto, Isbister, 1902 . . . . £150
Children of the Frost, Macmillan (U.S.), 1902 £500
ditto, Macmillan, 1902 . . . . . . £150
The Faith of Men, and Other Stories, Macmillan (U.S.), 1904 . . . . £350
ditto, Heinemann, 1904 . . . . . . £125
Tales of the Fish Patrol, Macmillan (U.S.), 1905 £250
ditto, Heinemann, 1906 . . . . . . £50
Moon-Face, and Other Stories, Macmillan (U.S.), 1906 . . . . £250
ditto, Heinemann, 1906 . . . . . . £50
Love of Life, and Other Stories, Macmillan (U.S.), 1907 . . . . £250
ditto, Everett, [1908] £75
Lost Face, Macmillan (U.S.), 1910 . . . £250
ditto, Mills & Boon, [1915] £50
When God Laughs, and Other Stories, Macmillan (U.S.), 1911 . . . . £250
ditto, Mills & Boon, 1912. . . . . . £50
South Sea Tales, Macmillan (U.S.), 1911 . £250
ditto, Mills & Boon, 1912. . . . . . £50
The House of Pride and Other Tales of Hawaii, Macmillan (U.S.), 1912 . . . . . . £250
ditto, Mills & Boon, 1914. . . . . . £50
A Son of the Sun, Doubleday, Page & Co. (U.S.), 1912
. . . . £300
ditto, Mills & Boon, 1913. . . . . . £50
Smoke Bellew, The Century Co. (U.S.), 1912 . £250
ditto, Mills & Boon, 1913. . . . . . £50
The Night-Born, The Century Co. (U.S.), 1913 £250
ditto, Mills & Boon, 1916. . . . . . £50
The Strength of the Strong, Macmillan (U.S.), 1914 .
. . . . £250
ditto, Mills & Boon, 1917. . . . . . £50
The Turtles of Tasman, Macmillan (U.S.), 1916 £250
ditto, Mills & Boon, 1917. . . . . . £50
The Human Drift, Macmillan (U.S.), 1917. . £300
ditto, Mills & Boon, 1919. . . . . . £75
The Red One, Macmillan (U.S.), 1918 . . £250
ditto, Mills & Boon, 1919. . . . . . £50
On The Makaloa Mat, Macmillan (U.S.), 1919 £200
ditto, as **Island Tales,** Mills & Boon, 1920 £500/£75
Dutch Courage, and Other Stories, Macmillan (U.S.), 1922 . . . . £2,000/£250
ditto, Mills & Boon, 1923. . . . . £250/£50

Others
The Cruise of the Dazzler, The Century Co. (U.S.), 1902 . . . . £1,250

ditto, Hodder & Stoughton, 1906. . . . £350
The People of the Abyss, Macmillan (U.S.), 1903 (grey-blue cloth) £500
ditto, Macmillan (U.S.), 1903 (dark blue cloth) £200
ditto, Isbister, 1903 . . . . £125
War of the Classes, Macmillan (U.S.), 1905 . £200
ditto, Heinemann, 1905 . . . . . . £65
Scorn of Women, Macmillan (U.S.), 1906 (top edge gilt) £1,500
ditto, Macmillan (U.S.), 1906 (top edge not gilt) £1,000
ditto, Macmillan, 1906 . . . . . . £250
The Road, Macmillan (U.S.), 1907 (grey cloth stamped in gold) £300
ditto, Macmillan (U.S.), 1907 (cream cloth stamped in black) £200
ditto, Mills & Boon, 1914. . . . . . £100
Revolution, Kerr (U.S.), [1909] (ads on p.32 headed 'A Socialist Success', wraps) £200
ditto, Kerr (U.S.), [1909] (ads on p.32 headed 'Pocket Library of Socialism', wraps) £150
ditto, Kerr (U.S.), [1909] (ads on p.32 headed either 'Socialist periodicals' or 'Study Socialism', wraps) .
. . . . £125
ditto, Kerr (U.S.), [1909] (ads on p.32 headed 'Socialist Literature', wraps) £100
Revolution and Other Essays, Macmillan (U.S.), 1910 (maroon cloth) £350
ditto, Macmillan (U.S.), 1910 (brown cloth) £200
ditto, Mills & Boon, 1920. . . . . £100/£25
Theft: A Play in Four Acts, Macmillan (U.S.), 1910 .
. . . . £500
ditto, Macmillan, 1910 . . . . . . £150
The Cruise of the Snark, Macmillan (U.S.), 1911 £200
ditto, Mills & Boon, 1913. . . . . . £50
Jack London By Himself, Macmillan (U.S.), [1913] .
. . . . £250
ditto, Mills & Boon, 1913. . . . . . £150
The Acorn-Planter; A California Forest Play, Macmillan (U.S.), 1916 . . . . . £1,000
ditto, Mills & Boon, 1916. . . . . . £250
Letters from Jack London, The Odyssey Press (U.S.), 1965 . . . . £40/£20

Collected Editions
The Works of Jack London, Macmillan (U.S.), 1919 (21 vols) £1,000

E.C.R. LORAC
(b.1894 d.1958)

Edith Caroline Rivett is known for her 'Golden Age' detective fiction written under the pseudonyms of Lorac (Carol backwards) and Carnac.

Novels as 'E.C.R. Lorac'
The Murder on the Burrows, Sampson Low, [1931] .
. . . . £1,500/£250

ditto, Macaulay (U.S.), 1932 . . . . £500/£100
The Affair at Thor's Head, Sampson Low, [1932] .
. . . . £1,250/£250
The Greenwell Mystery, Sampson Low, [1932] . .
. . . . £1,250/£250
ditto, Macaulay (U.S.), 1934 . . . £500/£100
Death on the Oxford Road, Sampson Low, [1933] .
. . . . £1,250/£250
ditto, Macaulay (U.S.), 1934 . . . £500/£100
The Case of Colonel Marchand, Sampson Low,
[1933] . . . . £1,250/£250
ditto, Macaulay (U.S.), 1933 . . . £500/£100
Murder in St John's Wood, Sampson Low, [1934] .
. . . . £1,000/£200
ditto, Macaulay (U.S.), 1934 . . . £400/£100
Murder in Chelsea, Sampson Low, [1934] . . .
. . . . £1,000/£200
ditto, Macaulay (U.S.), 1935 . . . £400/£100
The Organ Speaks, Sampson Low, [1935] . . .
. . . . £1,000/£200
The Death of an Author, Sampson Low, [1935] . .
. . . . £1,000/£200
ditto, Macaulay (U.S.), 1937 . . . £400/£100
Crime Counter Crime, Collins Crime Club, 1936 . .
. . . . £750 /£100
Post After Post-Mortem, Collins Crime Club, 1936 .
. . . . £750/£100
A Pall for a Painter, Collins Crime Club, 1936 . .
. . . . £750/£100
Bats in the Belfry, Collins Crime Club, 1937 . .
. . . . £750/£100
ditto, Macaulay (U.S.), 1937 . . . £400/£100
These Names Make Clues, Collins Crime Club, 1937 .
. . . . £750/£100
The Devil and the CID, Collins Crime Club, 1938 .
. . . . £750/£100
Slippery Staircase. Collins Crime Club, 1938 . . .
. . . . £750/£100
John Brown's Body, Collins Crime Club, 1938 . .
. . . . £750/£100
Black Beadle, Collins Crime Club, 1939 £750/£100
Death at Dyke's Corner, Collins Crime Club, 1940 .
. . . . £500/£100
Tryst for a Tragedy, Collins Crime Club, 1940 . .
. . . . £500/£100
Case in the Clinic, Collins Crime Club, 1941 £250/£75
Rope's End, Rogue's End, Collins Crime Club, 1942 .
. . . . £150/£25
The Sixteenth Stair, Collins Crime Club, 1942. . .
. . . . £125/£25
Death Came Softly, Collins Crime Club, 1943 . . .
. . . . £125/£25
ditto, Mystery House (U.S.), 1943 . . £75/£20
Checkmate to Murder, Collins Crime Club, 1944 . .
. . . . £125/£25
ditto, Mystery House (U.S.), 1944 . . £75/£20
Fell Murder, Collins Crime Club, 1944 . £125/£25
Murder by Matchlight, Collins Crime Club, 1945 . .
. . . . £125/£25

ditto, Mystery House (U.S.), 1946 . . . £50/£15
Fire in the Thatch, Collins Crime Club, 1946 . . .
. . . . £100/£25
ditto, Mystery House (U.S.), 1946 . . . £50/£15
The Theft of the Iron Dogs, Collins Crime Club, 1946
. . . . £100/£25
ditto, as *Murderer's Mistake*, Mystery House (U.S.),
1947 . . . . £50/£15
Relative to Poison, Collins Crime Club, 1947 £100/£25
ditto, Doubleday (U.S.), 1948 . . . . £50/£15
Death Before Dinner, Collins Crime Club, 1948 . .
. . . . £100/£25
ditto, as *A Screen for Murder*, Doubleday (U.S.), 1948
. . . . £50/£15
Part for a Poisoner, Collins Crime Club, 1948 . . .
. . . . £100/£25
ditto, as *Place for a Poisoner*, Doubleday (U.S.), 1949
. . . . £50/£15
Still Waters, Collins Crime Club, 1949 . . £100/£25
Policemen on the Precinct, Collins Crime Club, 1949.
. . . . £100/£25
ditto, as *And Then Put Out the Light*, Doubleday
(U.S.), 1950 . . . . £50/£15
Accident by Design, Collins Crime Club, 1950. . . .
. . . . £100/£25
ditto, Doubleday (U.S.), 1951 . . . . £50/£15
Murder of a Martinet, Collins Crime Club, 1951 . .
. . . . £100/£25
ditto, as *I Could Murder Her*, Doubleday (U.S.), 1951
. . . . £50/£15
The Dog It Was That Died, Collins Crime Club, 1952
. . . . £75/£20
ditto, Doubleday (U.S.), 1952 . . . . £45/£15
Murder in the Millrace, Collins Crime Club, 1952 .
. . . . £75/£20
ditto, as *Speak Justly of the Dead*, Doubleday (U.S.),
1953 . . . . £45/£15
Crook o'Lune, Collins Crime Club, 1953 . £75/£20
ditto, as *Shepherd's Crook*, Doubleday (U.S.), 1953 .
. . . . £45/£15
Shroud of Darkness, Collins Crime Club, 1954 . .
. . . . £75/£20
ditto, Doubleday (U.S.), 1954 . . . . £45/£15
Let Well Alone, Collins Crime Club, 1954 £75/£20
Ask a Policeman, Collins Crime Club, 1955 £75/£20
Murder in Vienna, Collins Crime Club, 1956 £75/£20
Picture of Death, Collins Crime Club, 1957 £75/£20
Dangerous Domicile, Collins Crime Club, 1957 . .
. . . . £75/£20
Death in Triplicate, Collins Crime Club, 1958 £75/£20
ditto, as *People Will Talk*, Doubleday (U.S.), 1958 .
. . . . £35/£10
Murder on a Monument, Collins Crime Club, 1958 .
. . . . £75/£20
Dishonour Among Thieves, Collins Crime Club, 1959
. . . . £75/£20
ditto, as *The Last Escape*, Doubleday (U.S.), 1959 .
. . . . £35/£10

Novels as 'Carol Carnac'

Triple Death, Butterworth, [1936] . . £1,000/£200
Murder at Mornington, Skeffington, [1937] . . .
. . . . £1,000/£200
The Missing Rope, Skeffington, [1937] £1,000/£200
When the Devil Was Sick, Peter Davies, 1939 . . .
. . . . £750/£150
The Case of the First-Class Carriage, Peter Davies,
1939 . . . . £650/£125
Death the Diving Pool, Peter Davies, 1940 £500/£100
A Double for Detection, Macdonald, [1945] £125/£25
The Striped Suitcase, Macdonald, 1946 . . £125/£25
ditto, Doubleday (U.S.), 1947 . . . . £50/£15
Clue Sinister, Macdonald, 1947 . . . £125/£25
Over the Garden Wall, Macdonald, 1948 . £125/£25
ditto, Doubleday (U.S.), 1949 . . . . £50/£15
Upstairs, Downstairs, Macdonald, 1950 . £100/£25
ditto, as *Upstairs and Downstairs*, Doubleday (U.S.),
1950 . . . . £45/£15
Copy for Crime, Macdonald, 1950 . . . £100/£25
ditto, Doubleday (U.S.), 1951 . . . . £45/£15
It's Her Own Funeral, Collins Crime Club, 1951 . .
. . . . £100/£25
Crossed Skis, Collins Crime Club, 1952 . £100/£25
Murder As A Fine Art, Collins Crime Club, 1953 . .
. . . . £100/£25
A Policeman at the Door, Collins Crime Club, 1953 . .
. . . . £100/£25
ditto, Doubleday (U.S.), 1954 . . . . £45/£15
Impact of Evidence, Collins Crime Club, 1954 . . .
. . . . £100/£20
ditto, Doubleday (U.S.), 1954 . . . . £45/£15
Murder Among Members, Collins Crime Club, 1955 .
. . . . £100/£20
Rigging the Evidence, Collins Crime Club, 1955 . .
. . . . £100/£20
The Double Turn, Collins Crime Club, 1956 . . .
. . . . £75/£20
ditto, as *The Late Miss Trimming*, Doubleday (U.S.),
1957 . . . . £45/£15
The Burning Question, Collins Crime Club, 1957 . .
. . . . £75/£20
Long Shadows, Collins Crime Club, 1958 . £75/£20
ditto, as *Affair at Helen's Court*, Doubleday (U.S.),
1958 . . . . £45/£15
Death of a Lady Killer, Collins Crime Club, 1959 . .
. . . . £75/£20

Novels as 'Carol Rivett'

Outer Circle, Hodder & Stoughton, 1939 . £100/£25
Time Remembered, Hodder & Stoughton, 1940 . .
. . . . £100/£25

H.P. LOVECRAFT
(b.1890 d.1937)

Born in Providence, Rhode Island (U.S.), where he
lived for the rest of his life, Lovecraft is famous for
his weird fiction. Arkham House have issued revised
and corrected editions of all the major Lovecraft
stories in recent years.

Fiction

The Crime of Crimes, Harris, 1915 (mimeographed
pamphlet) £10,000
The Shunned House, The Recluse Press (U.S.), 1928
(original unbound sheets, 300 printed of which c.75
may survive) £3,000
ditto, copies bound by R.H. Barlow (U.S.), 1934/35
(c.8 may exist) £8,000
ditto, Arkham House (U.S.), 1959 (unbound sheets, 50
sets) £2,000
ditto, Arkham House (U.S.), 1961 (bound, 100 copies,
no d/w) £2,500
ditto, Arkham House (U.S.), (counterfeit edition,
1965/66) £500
The Battle That Ended the Century, Barlow (U.S.),
1934 (50 mimeographed copies, wraps) . . £750
A Sonnet – The Lovecrafter, Shepherd & Wollheim
(U.S.), 1936 (16 copies) £600
The Cats of Ulthar, Dragon-Fly Press (U.S.), 1935 (42
copies) £1,000
The Shadow Over Innsmouth, Visionary Publishing
(U.S.), 1936 (150-200 copies) . . £4,000/£2,000
H.P.L., Corwin Stickney (U.S.), 1937 (poetry, limited
to 23 copies) £1,500
A History of the Necronomicon, Rebel Press (U.S.),
1938 (wraps) £500
The Outsider and Others, Arkham House (U.S.), 1939
. . . . £1,500/£500
Fungi from Yuggoth, Evans (U.S.), 1943 (approx 65
copies, wraps) £1,000
Beyond the Wall of Sleep, Arkham House (U.S.), 1943
. . . . £1,250/£400
The Weird Shadow Over Innsmouth, Bart House
(U.S.), 1944 (wraps) £40
The Dunwich Horror and Other Weird Tales, Armed
Services Edition (U.S.), 1945 (wraps) . . . £35
Best Supernatural Stories, Tower Books (U.S.), 1945 .
. . . . £50/£15
The Dunwich Horror, Bart House (U.S.), 1945 (wraps)
. . . . £35
The Lurker at the Threshold, Arkham House (U.S.),
1945 (novel by Derleth) . . . . . £80/£25
ditto, Museum Press, 1948 . . . . . £200/£40
ditto, Gollancz, 1968 . . . . . . £40/£15
The Lurking Fear and Other Stories, Avon (U.S.),
1947 (wraps) £25
The Haunter of the Dark, Gollancz, (U.K.), 1951 . .
. . . . £50/£15
The Case of Charles Dexter Ward, Gollancz, (U.K.),
1951 . . . . £100/£40

The Curse of Yig, Arkham House (U.S.), 1953 (by Zealia B. Bishop) . . . . . . £75/£25

The Challenge from Beyond, Evans (U.S.), 1954 (with Abraham Merrit, Robert E. Howard, Frank Belknap Long, and C.L. Moore) . . . £40

The Dream Quest of Unknown Kadath, Shroud (U.S.), 1955 (50 copies bound in cloth) £250

ditto, Shroud (U.S.), 1955 (1,400+ copies in wrappers)
. . . . £60

ditto, Shroud (U.S.), 1955 (12 numbered copies clothbound by Gerry de la Ree in 1972) . . £100

The Survivor and Others, Arkham House (U.S.), 1957 (completed by Derleth) . . . . . £75/£35

The Dunwich Horror and Others, Arkham House (U.S.), 1963 . . . . £100/£30

Collected Poems, Arkham House (U.S.), 1963 . . .
. . . . £100/£25

At the Mountains of Madness, Arkham House (U.S.), 1964 . . . . £125/£25

ditto, Gollancz, (U.K.), 1966 . . . . . £65/£20

The Colour Out Of Space, Lancer, 1964 (wraps) £10

The Lurking Fear and Other Stories, Panther, 1964 (wraps) £10

Dagon and Other Macabre Tales, Arkham House (U.S.), 1965 . . . . £100/£20

ditto, Gollancz (U.K.), 1967 . . . . . £60/£20

The Dark Brotherhood, Arkham House (U.S.), 1966 .
. . . . £65/£20

Three Tales of Horror, Arkham House (U.S.), 1967 .
. . . . £75/£25

The Shadow out of Time, Gollancz, U.K., 1968 . .
. . . . £45/£15

The Prose Poems: Ex Oblivione, Memory, Nyarla-thotep, What the Moon Brings, Squires (U.S.), 1969-1970 (25 lettered copies of 125, 4 booklets in envelopes) £100

ditto, Squires (U.S.), 1969-1970 (99 numbered copies of 125, 4 booklets, in envelopes) £200

The Dream Quest of Unknown Kadath, Ballantine (U.S.), 1970 (wraps) £10

The Horror in the Museum and Other Revisions, Arkham House (U.S.), 1970 . . . . £45/£15

The Doom That Came To Sarnath, Ballantine (U.S.), 1971 (wraps) £10

The Shadow Over Innsmouth, Scholastic, 1971 (wraps) £5

The Watchers Out of Time and Others, Arkham House (U.S.), 1974 (stories completed by Derleth) .
. . . . £45/£15

Medusa: A Portrait, Oliphant Press (U.S.), 1975 (500 numbered copies in wrappers) £20

The Statement of Randolph Carter, The Strange Company (U.S.), 1976 (150 copies, unbound holographic sheets in folder) £25

ditto, The Strange Company (U.S.), 1976 (30 copies signed by the editor, unbound holographic sheets in folder). £50

Antarktos, Fantome Press (U.S.), 1977 (150 copies, wraps). £15

Herbert West: Reanimator, Necronomicon Press (U.S.), 1977 (1,000 copies, wraps) £10

The Lurking Fear, Necronomicon Press (U.S.), 1977 (550 copies, wraps) £15

Collapsing Cosmoses, Necronomicon Press (U.S.), 1977 (500 copies, wraps) £15

A Winter Wish and Other Poems, Whispers Press (U.S.), 1977 (26 copies signed and lettered in slipcase) £300

ditto, Whispers Press (U.S.), 1977 (200 signed, numbered copies in slipcase and d/w) . . £50/£25

ditto, Whispers Press (U.S.), 1977 (trade edition, 2,000 copies) . . . . £30/£15

Uncollected Prose and Poetry, Vol I, Necronomicon Press (U.S.), 1978 (wraps) £10

ditto, Vol II, Necronomicon Press (U.S.), 1980 (wraps)
. . . . £10

ditto, Vol III, Necronomicon Press (U.S.), 1982 (wraps) £10

The Colour Out Of Space, Necronomicon Press (U.S.), 1982 (400 copies, wraps) £15

The Best of H.P. Lovecraft, Del Rey/Ballantine (U.S.), 1982 (wraps) £5

The Young Folks' Ulysses, Soft Books (U.S.), 1982 (200 copies, wraps) £10

Ashes and Others, Miskatonic Univ. Press (U.S.), 1983 (wraps) £10

The Illustrated Fungi from Yuggoth, Dream House (U.S.), 1983 (wraps). £15

Saturnalia and Other Poems, Crypt of Cthulhu (U.S.), 1984 (wraps) £5

Juvenilia:, 1895-1905, Necronomicon Press (U.S.), 1984 (wraps) £5

The Festival, Necronomicon Press (U.S.), 1984 (50 copies, wraps) £20

Medusa and Other Poems, Crypt of Cthulhu (U.S.), 1986 (wraps) £10

At the Mountains of Madness, Grant (U.S.), 1990 (1,000 copies signed by the artist, leather binding) .
. . . . £75

The Fantastic Poetry, Necronomicon Press (U.S.), 1990 (wraps) £10

The Battle that Ended the Century/Collapsing Cosmoses, Necronomicon Press (U.S.), 1992 (wraps)
. . . . £10

Crawling Chaos: Selected Works 1920-1935, Creation Press, 1993 (wraps) £10

The Dream Cycle of H.P. Lovecraft, Ballantine/Del Ray (U.S.), 1995 (wraps) £5

The Transition of H.P. Lovecraft, Ballantine/Del Ray (U.S.), 1995 (wraps). £5

The Annotated H.P. Lovecraft, Dell (U.S.), 1997 (wraps) £10

Tales of H.P. Lovecraft, Ecco Press (U.S.), 1997 .
. . . . £20/£5

More Annotated of H.P. Lovecraft, Dell (U.S.), 1999 (wraps) £10

The Ancient Track, Necronomicon Press (U.S.), 2000 (250 copies) . . . . £25 *ditto*, Necronomicon Press (U.S.), 2000 (800 copies, wraps). £10

Non Fiction
Exponenets of Amateur Journalism, United Amateur Press Association (U.S.), 1915 (mimeographed pamphlet). £1,500
Looking Backward, C.W. Smith (U.S.), 1920 (c. 40 copies, mimeographed pamphlet) . . . £1,500
The Materialist Today, Driftwind Press (U.S.), 1926 (15 copies, pamphlet) £2,500
Further Criticism of Poetry, George C. Fetter (U.S.), 1932 (pamphlet) £2,000
Charleston, H.C. Koenig (U.S.), 1936 (first state, 20-25 copies, pamphlet) £2,000
ditto, H.C. Koenig (U.S.), 1936 (second state, 30-35 copies, pamphlet) £1,500
Some Current Motives and Practices, R.H. Barlow (U.S.), 1936 (50-100 copies, mimeographed pamphlet) £1,500
Notes and the Commonplace Book, Futile Press (U.S.), 1938 (no d/w) £1,500
Marginalia, Arkham House (U.S.), 1944 . £250/£75
Supernatural Horror in Literature, Abramson (U.S.), 1945 (no d/w) £50
Something About Cats, Arkham House (U.S.), 1949 . . . . £125/£45
The Lovecraft Collector's Library, S.S.R. Publications (U.S.), 1952-55 (7 vols, 75 copies). . . . £150
The Shuttered Room and Other Pieces, Arkham House (U.S.), 1959 . . . . . £125/£45
Dreams and Fancies, Arkham House (U.S.), 1962. . . . . £125/£45
Some Notes on a Nonentity, Arkham House (U.S.), 1963 (wraps) £100
Selected Letters, Volume I, Arkham House (U.S.), 1965 . . . . £30/£10
Selected Letters, Volume II, Arkham House (U.S.), 1968 . . . . £30/£10
Hail, Klarkash-Ton!, Squires, 1971 (89 copies, wraps) £35
Selected Letters Volume, III, Arkham House (U.S.), 1971 . . . . £100/£45
Ec'h-Pi-El Speaks, de la Ree (U.S.), 1972 (25 cloth bound copies, no d/w) £125
ditto, de la Ree (U.S.), 1972 (475 copies, wraps) £40
Lovecraft at Last, Carrollton Clark (U.S.), 1975 ('Collectors edition', 1,000 copies in slipcase) . . . . £100/£65
ditto, Carrollton Clark (U.S.), 1975 (2,000 copies) £50
The Occult Lovecraft, de la Ree (U.S.), 1975 (128 numbered cloth bound copies, no d/w). . £60
ditto, de la Ree (U.S.), 1975 (990 copies, wraps) £20
First Writings: Pawtuxet Valley Gleaner 1906, Necronomicon Press (U.S.), 1976 (500 numbered copies, wraps) £25
Selected Letters, Volume IV, Arkham House (U.S.), 1976 . . . . £25/£10

Selected Letters, Volume V, Arkham House (U.S.), 1976 . . . . £25/£10
The Conservative Complete 1915-1923, Necronomicon Press (U.S.), 1976 (400 copies, wraps) £25
Writings in the United Amateur 1915-1922, Necronomicon Press (U.S.), 1976 (500 numbered copies, wraps). £25
To Quebec and the Stars, Grant (U.S.), 1976 £35/£10
The Californian, Necronomicon Press (U.S.), 1977 (1,000 numbered copies, wraps) . . . £10
Writings in The Tryout, Necronomicon Press (U.S.), 1977 (1,000 numbered copies, wraps) . . £10
Memoirs of an Inconsequential Scribbler, Necronomicon Press (U.S.), 1977 (500 copies, wraps) £10
Science Versus Charlatanry, Strange Company (U.S.), 1979 (200 numbered copies, wraps) . . £25
H.P. Lovecraft in The Eyrie, Necronomicon Press (U.S.), 1979 (wraps). £5
The H.P. Lovecraft Christmas Book, Necronomicon Press (U.S.), 1984 (wraps) £5
In Defence of Dagon, Necronomicon Press (U.S.), 1985 (1,000 numbered copies, wraps) . . . £5
Uncollected Letters, Necronomicon Press (U.S.), 1986 (wraps) £5
Commonplace Book, Necronomicon Press (U.S.), 1987 (2 vols, wraps) £10
Yr Obt Servt., The Strange Company (U.S.), 1988 (200 copies, wraps) £20
European Glimpses, Necronomicon Press (U.S.), 1988 (wraps) £5
The Vivesector, Necronomicon Press (U.S.), 1990 (wraps) £5
Letters to Henry Kuttner, Necronomicon Press (U.S.), 1990 (wraps). £5
The Conservative, Necronomicon Press (U.S.), 1990 (wraps) £5
Letters to Richard Searight, Necronomicon Press (U.S.), 1992 (wraps). £5
Autobiographical Writings, Necronomicon Press (U.S.), 1992 (wraps). £5
Letters to Robert Bloch, Necronomicon Press (U.S.), 1993 (wraps). £5
Letters to Robert Bloch Supplement, Necronomicon Press (U.S.), 1993 (wraps) £5
H.P. Lovecraft in The Argosy, Necronomicon Press (U.S.), 1994 (wraps). £5
The H.P. Lovecraft Dream Book, Necronomicon Press (U.S.), 1994 (wraps). £10
Miscellaneous Writings, Arkham House (U.S.), 1995 (wraps) . . . . £20/£5

PETER LOVESEY

(b.1936)

An author of detective fiction whose early works look as if they will become very collectable.

Novels

Wobble to Death, Macmillan, 1970 . . . £150/£45
ditto, Dodd, Mead (U.S.), 1970 . . . . £75/£15
The Detective Wore Silk Drawers, Macmillan, 1971 .
. . . . £50/£10
ditto, Dodd, Mead (U.S.), 1971 . . . . £30/£5
Abracadaver, Macmillan, 1972 . . . . £50/£10
ditto, Dodd, Mead (U.S.), 1972 . . . . £25/£5
Mad Hatter's Holiday, Macmillan, 1973 . £30/£5
ditto, Dodd, Mead (U.S.), 1973 . . . . £15/£5
Invitation to a Dynamite Party, Macmillan, 1974 . .
. . . . £25/£5
ditto, as *The Tick of Death*, Dodd, Mead (U.S.), 1974 .
. . . . £15/£5
A Case of Spirits, Macmillan, 1975 . . . £20/£5
ditto, Dodd, Mead (U.S.), 1975 . . . . £15/£5
Swing, Swing Together, Macmillan, 1976 . £20/£5
ditto, Dodd, Mead (U.S.), 1976 . . . . £15/£5
Golden Girl, Cassell 1977 (pseud. 'Peter Lear') £15/£5
Waxwork, Macmillan 1978 . . . . . £15/£5
ditto, Pantheon (U.S.), 1978 . . . . . £10/£5
Spider Girl, Cassell 1980 (pseud. 'Peter Lear') £20/£5
ditto, Viking (U.S.), 1980 . . . . . . £20/£5
The False Inspector Dew, Macmillan, 1982 £10/£5
ditto, Pantheon (U.S.), 1982 . . . . . £10/£5
Keystone, Macmillan, 1983 . . . . . £15/£5
ditto, Pantheon (U.S.), 1983 . . . . . £10/£5
The Secret of Spandau, Michael Joseph, 1986 (pseud.
'Peter Lear') . . . . £15/£5
Rough Cider, Bodley Head, 1986 . . . £10/£5
ditto, Mysterious Press (U.S.), 1987 . . . £10/£5
Bertie and the Tinman, Bodley Head, 1987 £10/£5
ditto, Mysterious Press (U.S.), 1988 . . . £10/£5
On the Edge, Mysterious Press, 1989 . . £10/£5
ditto, Mysterious Press, 1989 (250 signed, numbered
proof copies, wraps) £25
ditto, Mysterious Press (U.S.), 1989 . . . £10/£5
Bertie and the Seven Bodies, Mysterious Press, 1990 .
. . . . £10/£5
ditto, Mysterious Press (U.S.), 1990 . . . £10/£5
The Last Detective, Scorpion Press, 1991 (99 signed,
numbered copies, acetate d/w) . . . . £75/£65
ditto, Scribners, 1991 . . . . £10/£5
ditto, Doubleday (U.S.), 1991 . . . . £10/£5
Diamond Solitaire, Little, Brown, 1992 . . £10/£5
ditto, Mysterious Press (U.S.), 1993 . . . £10/£5
Bertie and the Crime of Passion, Little, Brown, 1993 .
. . . . £10/£5
ditto, Mysterious Press (U.S.), 1993 . . . £10/£5
The Summons, Little, Brown, 1995 . . . £10/£5
ditto, Mysterious Press (U.S.), 1995 . . . £10/£5
Bloodhounds, Little, Brown, 1996 . . . £10/£5
ditto, Mysterious Press (U.S.), 1996 . . . £10/£5

Upon a Dark Night, Little, Brown, 1997 . £10/£5
ditto, Mysterious Press (U.S.), 1998 . . . £10/£5
Do Not Exceed the Stated Dose, Mysterious Press
(U.S.), 1998 . . . . £10/£5
ditto, Crippen & Landru, 1998 (250 signed, numbered
copies with booklet) . . . . £35/£25
ditto, Little, Brown, 1998 . . . . . . £10/£5
The Vault, Little, Brown, 1999 . . . . £10/£5

Short Stories
Butchers and Other Stories of Crime, Macmillan 1985
ditto, Mysterious Press, 1987 . . . . . £10/£5
The Staring Man and Other Stories, Eurographica
(Helsinki), 1988 (350 signed, numbered copies, wraps
with d/w) £75

MALCOLM LOWRY

(b.1909 d.1957)

Few of Lowry's books were published in his lifetime.
Under the Volcano is regarded as his best work.

Ultramarine, Cape, 1933 . . . . . £3,000/£300
ditto, Lippincott (U.S.), 1962, (revised edition) £75/£20
ditto, Cape, 1963, (revised edition) . . . £45/£15
Under the Volcano, Reynal & Hitchcock, 1947 . .
. . . . £750/£150
ditto, Cape, 1947 . . . . £350/£75
Hear Us O Lord from Heaven Thy Dwelling Place,
Lippincott (U.S.), 1961 . . . . . . £30/£10
ditto, Cape, 1962 . . . . £25/£10
Selected Poems of Malcolm Lowry, City Lights, 1962
(wraps) £25
Selected Letters of Malcolm Lowry, Lippincott (U.S.),
1965 . . . . £35/£15
ditto, Cape, 1967 . . . . £35/£15
Lunar Caustic, Grossman (U.S.), 1968 . £200/£45
ditto, Cape, 1968 . . . . £65/£15
Dark as the Grave Wherein My Friend is Laid, New
American Library (U.S.), 1968 . . . . £30/£10
ditto, Cape, 1969 . . . . £25/£10
October Ferry to Gabriola, World (U.S.), 1970 £25/£5
ditto, Cape, 1971 . . . . £20/£5
China and Kristbjotg's Story in the Black Hills, Aloe
Editions (U.S.), 1974 (150 numbered copies, wraps) .
. . . . £65
Malcolm Lowry, Psalms and Songs, New American
Library (U.S.), 1975 . . . . £45/£15
*Notes on a Screenplay for F. Scott Fitzgerald's
Tender is the Night*, Bruccoli (U.S.), 1976 £45/£10
The Collected Letters Volume One: 1926-1946, Univ.
Of Toronto Press (Canada), 1995 . . . £25/£10
*The Collected Letters of Malcolm Lowry. Volume
Two: 1946-57*, Univ. Of Toronto Press (Canada),
1995 . . . . £25/£10

ROSE MACAULAY
(b.1881 d.1958)

Macaulay is well-respected as a novelist who can combine intelligence with humour and compassion.

Novels

Abbots Verney, Murray, 1906	£75
The Furnace, Murray, 1907	£45
The Secret River, Murray, 1909	£35
The Valley Captives, Murray, 1911	£25
Views and Vagabonds, Murray, 1912 . . .	£25
ditto, H. Holt and Co (U.S.), 1912	£25
The Lee Shore, Hodder & Stoughton, 1912. .	£25
The Making of a Bigot, Hodder & Stoughton, 1914 .	
. . . .	£15
Non-Combatants and Others, Hodder & Stoughton, 1916	£15
What Not: A Prophetic Comedy, Constable, 1918	£15
Potterism: A Tragi-Farcical Tract, Collins, 1920 . .	
. . . .	£45/£15
ditto, Boni & Liveright (U.S.), [1920] . .	£45/£15
Dangerous Ages, Collins, 1921	£35/£10
ditto, Boni & Liveright (U.S.), [1921] . .	£35/£10
Mystery at Geneva, Collins, 1922 . . .	£25/£10
ditto, Boni & Liveright (U.S.), [1923] . .	£25/£10
Told By an Idiot, Collins, 1923	£20/£5
ditto, Boni & Liveright (U.S.), 1923 . . .	£20/£5
Orphan Island, Collins, 1924	£20/£5
ditto, Boni & Liveright (U.S.), [1925] . .	£20/£5
Crewe Train, Collins, 1926	£20/£5
ditto, Boni & Liveright (U.S.), 1926 . . .	£20/£5
Keeping Up Appearances, Collins, 1928 .	£20/£5
Staying With Relations, Collins, 1930 . .	£20/£5
ditto, Liveright (U.S.), [1930]	£20/£5
They Were Defeated, Collins, 1932 . . .	£20/£5
ditto, as *The Shadow Flies*, Harper & Bros (U.S.), 1934	£20/£5
Going Abroad, Collins, 1934	£20/£5
ditto, Harper & Bros (U.S.), 1934 . . .	£20/£5
I Would Be Private, Collins, 1937 . . .	£20/£5
ditto, Harper & Bros (U.S.), 1937 . . .	£20/£5
And No Man's Wit, Collins, 1940 . . .	£15/£5
ditto, Little, Brown (U.S.), 1940	£15/£5
The World My Wilderness, Collins, 1950 .	£15/£5
ditto, Little, Brown (U.S.), 1950	£15/£5
The Towers of Trebizond, Collins, 1956 .	£15/£5
ditto, Farrar, Straus (U.S.), 1957	£15/£5

Verse

The Two Blind Countries, Sidgwick & Jackson, 1914	£25
Three Days, Constable, 1919	£25
ditto, Dutton (U.S.), 1919	£25

Travel

They Went to Portugal Too, Jonathan Cape, 1946 . .	
. . . .	£20/£5

Fabled Shore: From the Pyrenees to Portugal, Hamish Hamilton, 1949	£20/£5
ditto, Farrar, Straus (U.S.), 1949	£15/£5
Pleasure of Ruins, Weidenfeld & Nicolson, 1953 . .	
. . . .	£20/£10
ditto, Walker (U.S.), [1966]	£35/£10

Others

A Casual Commentary, Methuen, 1925 . .	£15/£5
ditto, Boni & Liveright (U.S.), 1926 . . .	£15/£5
Catchwords and Claptrap, Hogarth Press, 1926	£65
Some Religious Elements in English Literature, Hogarth Press, 1931	£35/£10
ditto, Harcourt Brace (U.S.), [1931] . . .	£20/£5
Milton, Duckworth, 1934	£10
ditto, Harper & Row (U.S.), 1935 . . .	£20/£10
Personal Pleasures, Gollancz, 1935 . . .	£30/£10
ditto, Macmillan (U.S.), 1936	£20/£10
The Writings of E.M. Forster, Hogarth Press, 1938 .	
. . . .	£50/£20
ditto, Harcourt Brace (U.S.), 1938 . . .	£20/£5
Life Among the English, Collins, 1942 . .	£10/£5
Letters to a Friend: 1950 - 1952, Collins, 1961	£10/£5
ditto, Atheneum (U.S.), 1962	£10/£5
Last Letters to a Friend, 1952 - 1958, Collins, 1962 .	
. . . .	£10/£5
ditto, Atheneum (U.S.), 1963	£10/£5
Letters to a Sister, Collins, 1964	£10/£5
ditto, Atheneum (U.S.), 1964	£10/£5

GEORGE MACDONALD
(b.1824 d.1905)

A Scottish author, Macdonald is perhaps best known for his children's book *At the Back of the North Wind*, and his adult fantasy *Phantastes*

Children's

Dealings with the Fairies, Strahan, 1867 (blue cloth) .	
. . . .	£750
ditto, Strahan, 1867 (green cloth)	£500
At the Back of the North Wind, Strahan, 1871 (first issue binding bright blue pictorial cloth stamped in gold)	£2,000
ditto, Strahan, 1871 (second issue binding without gold frame)	£750
ditto, George Routledge (U.S.), [c.1871] .	£1,000
Ranald Bannerman's Boyhood, Strahan, 1871	£650
ditto, Lippincott (U.S.), 1879	£200
The Princess and the Goblin, Strahan, 1872 .	£1,000
ditto, Lippincott (U.S.), 1871	£200
Gutta Percha Willie, King, 1873	£300
The Wise Woman, Strahan, 1875	£150
The Princess and the Curdie, Chatto & Windus, 1883 .	
. . . .	£250
ditto, Lippincott (U.S.), 1883	£200
Cross Purpose and the Shadows, Blackie, 1886	£50

The Light Princess and Other Fairy Tales, Blackie, 1891 . . . . £150
ditto, Putnam (U.S.), 1893 . . . . . . £100
The Golden Key, Crowell (U.S.), [1906] . . £200
ditto, The Bodley Head, 1972 . . . . £20/£5

Verse
Within and Without: a Dramatic Poem, Longman, 1855 . . . . £1,750
ditto, Scribner, Armstrong (U.S.), 1872 . . . £150
Poems, Longman, 1857 . . . . £300
ditto, Dutton (U.S.), 1887 . . . . . . £200
The Disciple and Other Poems, Strahan, 1867 £250
ditto, Sunrise Books (U.S.), 1989 . . . £10/£5
A Threefold Cord: Poem, by Three Friends, edited by MacDonald, privately printed by Hughes, [1883]. .
. . . . £350

Translations
Twelve of the Spiritual Songs of Novalis, Strahan, 1851 . . . . £500
Exotics, Strahan, 1851 . . . . £500

Others
Phantastes; a Faerie Romance, Smith, Elder, 1858 .
. . . . £1,250
ditto, Loring (U.S.), 1870 . . . . . . £150
David Elginbrod, Hurst & Blackett, 1863 (3 vols) . .
. . . . £500
ditto, Loring (U.S.), [1863] £250
Adela Cathcart, Hurst & Blackett, 1864 (3 vols) £250
ditto, Loring (U.S.), [1864] £200
The Portent, Smith, Elder, 1864 . . . . £400
ditto, Loring (U.S.), [1864] £200
Alec Forbes of Howglen, Hurst & Blackett, 1865 (3 vols) £750
Annals of a Quiet Neighbourhood, Hurst & Blackett, 1867 (3 vols) £750
ditto, Harper (U.S.), 1867 . . . . . . £200
Unspoken Sermons, Strahan, 1867 . . . . £450
ditto, Second series, Longmans 1885 . . . £100
ditto, Third series, Longmans 1889 . . . . £100
ditto, Sunrise Books (U.S.), 1988 . . . £10/£5
Guild Court, Hurst & Blackett, 1868 (3 vols) £250
Robert Falconer, Hurst & Blackett, 1868 (3 vols) £250
ditto, Loring (U.S.), [1868] £200
The Seaboard Parish, Tinsley, 1868 (3 vols) . £200
England's Antiphon, Macmillan, [1868] . . £100
ditto, Lippincott (U.S.), [1868] £75
The Miracles of Our Lord, Strahan, 1870 . . £75
Works of Fancy and Imagination, Strahan, 1871 (10 vols, slipcase) £2,000
Wilfred Cumbermede, Hurst & Blackett, 1872 (3 vols)
. . . . £150
ditto, Scribner (U.S.), 1872 . . . . . £100
The Vicar's Daughter, Tinsley, 1872 (3 vols) . £150
ditto, Roberts (U.S.), 1872 . . . . . £100
Malcolm, King, 1875 (3 vols) £150
ditto, Lippincott (U.S.), 1877 . . . . . £100

St George and St Michael, King, 1876 (3 vols) £150
ditto, Ford & Co (U.S.), [1876] £100
Thomas Wingfold, Hurst & Blackett, 1876 (3 vols) .
. . . . £150
ditto, Routledge (U.S.), 1876 . . . . . £100
The Marquis of Losse, Hurst & Blackett, 1877 (3 vols)
. . . . £150
ditto, Lippincott (U.S.), 1877 . . . . . £100
Paul Faber, Hurst & Blackett, 1879 (3 vols) . £150
ditto, Lippincott (U.S.), 1879 . . . . . £100
Sir Gibbie, Hurst & Blackett, 1879 (3 vols) . . £150
ditto, Lippincott (U.S.), 1879 . . . . . £100
A Book of Strife, privately printed, 1880 . . £1,000
ditto, privately printed, 1882 . . . . . £750
ditto, Longman, 1889 . . . . £450
Mary Marston, Sampson, Low, 1881 (3 vols) . £150
ditto, Appleton (U.S.), 1881 . . . . . £100
Warlock O'Glen Warlock, Lothrop (U.S.) 1881 £175
ditto, Harper & Brothers (U.S.), 1881 (wraps) . £35
ditto, as *Castle Warlock*, Sampson, Low, 1882 (3 vols)
. . . . £175
Orts, Sampson Low, 1882 . . . . . . £125
Weighed and Wanting, Sampson, Low, 1882 (3 vols).
. . . . £150
ditto, Lothrop (U.S.), 1882 . . . . . . £100
The Gifts of the Child Christ, Sampson Low, 1882 (2 vols) £75
Donal Grant, Kegan Paul, 1883 (3 vols) . . £150
ditto, Lothrop (U.S.), 1883 . . . . . . £100
What's Mine's Mine, Kegan Paul, 1886 (3 vols) £200
ditto, Lothrop (U.S.), [1886] £100
Home Again, Kegan Paul, 1887 . . . . . £150
ditto, Appleton (U.S.), 1888 . . . . . £100
The Elect Lady, Kegan Paul, 1888 . . . . £150
ditto, Appleton (U.S.), 1888 . . . . . £100
There and Back, Kegan Paul, 1891 (3 vols) . £175
ditto, Lothrop (U.S.), [1891] £100
A Rough Shaking, Blackie, 1891 . . . . £150
The Flight of the Shadow, Kegan Paul, 1891 . £150
ditto, Appleton (U.S.), 1891 . . . . . £100
The Hope of the Gospel, Ward, Lock, 1892 . £50
ditto, Appleton (U.S.), 1892 . . . . . £45
Heather and Snow, Chatto & Windus, 1893 (2 vols) .
. . . . £100
ditto, Harper (U.S.), 1893 . . . . . . £50
A Dish of Orts, Sampson Low, 1893 . . . £75
Poetical Works, Chatto & Windus, 1893 (2 vols) £100
Lilith, Chatto & Windus, 1895 . . . . . £300
ditto, Ballantine Books (U.S.), [1969] (wraps) . . £5
Salted with Fire, Hurst & Blackett, 1897 . . £50
ditto, Dodd, Mead (U.S.), 1897 . . . . . £50
Far Above Rubies, Dodd, Mead (U.S.), 1899 . £50
Fairy Tales, Fifield, 1904 (five parts) . . . £125
ditto, Fifield, 1904 (1 vol.) £70

ROSS MACDONALD
(b.1915)

Macdonald is the best known of the many pseudonyms for Kenneth Millar, an American writer of detective novels, who also writes under his own name.

'Ross Macdonald' Novels

The Barbarous Coast, Knopf (U.S.), 1956 £1,000/£75
ditto, Cassell, 1957 . . . . £100/£20
The Doomsters, Knopf (U.S.), 1958 . . £750/£50
ditto, Cassell, 1958 . . . . . . £100/£15
The Galton Case, Knopf (U.S.), 1959 . £300/£40
ditto, Cassell, 1960 . . . . . . £100/£15
The Fergusson Affair, Knopf (U.S.), 1960 . £300/£40
ditto, Collins, 1961 . . . . . . £100/£15
The Wycherley Woman, Knopf (U.S.), 1961 £300/£40
ditto, Collins, 1961 . . . . . . £100/£15
The Zebra-Striped Hearse, Knopf (U.S.), 1962 . .
. . . . £125/£30
ditto, Collins, 1963 . . . . . £25/£10
The Chill, Knopf (U.S.), 1964 . . . £125/£30
ditto, Collins, 1964 . . . . . . £40/£10
The Far Side of the Dollar, Knopf (U.S.), 1965 . .
. . . . £35/£10
ditto, Collins, 1965 . . . . . £20/£10
Black Money, Knopf (U.S.), 1966 . . £35/£10
ditto, Collins, 1966 . . . . . . £25/£10
The Instant Enemy, Knopf (U.S.), 1968 . £25/£10
ditto, Collins, 1968 . . . . . . £25/£10
The Goodbye Look, Knopf (U.S.), 1969 . £20/£10
ditto, Collins, 1969 . . . . . . £15/£5
The Underground Man, Knopf (U.S.), 1971 £15/£5
ditto, Collins, 1971 . . . . . . £10/£5
Sleeping Beauty, Knopf (U.S.), 1973 . . £15/£5
ditto, Collins, 1973 . . . . . . £10/£5
The Blue Hammer, Knopf (U.S.), 1976 . £15/£5
ditto, Collins, 1976 . . . . . . £10/£5
Lew Archer, Private Investigator, Mysterious Press
(U.S.), 1977 (250 numbered, signed copies, acetate
d/w and slipcase). . . . . . . £175/£65

Other Titles as 'Ross Maconald'

On Crime Writing, Capra Press (U.S.), 1973 (250
signed, numbered copies, no d/w) £125
ditto, Capra Press (U.S.), 1973 (wraps) . . . £15
Self Portrait, Ceaselessly Into The Past, Capra Press
(U.S.), 1981 (250 signed, numbered copies, no d/w) .
. . . . £125
ditto, Capra Press (U.S.), 1981 (wraps) . . £15

'Kenneth Millar' Novels

The Dark Tunnel, Dodd, Mead (U.S.), 1944 . . .
. . . . £3,000/£250
ditto, as *I Die Slowly*, Lion, 1955, . . . £45/£10
Trouble Follows Me, Dodd, Mead (U.S.), 1946 . .
. . . . £1,500/£100
ditto, as *Night Train*, Lion, 1955. . . . £20/£5

Blue City, Knopf (U.S.), 1947 . . . . £300/£65
ditto, Cassell, 1949 . . . . . . £25/£10
The Three Roads, Knopf (U.S.), 1948 . . £300/£65
ditto, Cassell, 1950 . . . . . . £25/£10

'John Ross Macdonald' Novels

The Drowning Pool, Knopf (U.S.), 1950 £1,000/£75
ditto, Cassell, 1952 . . . . . . £125/£15
The Way Some People Die, Knopf (U.S.), 1951 . .
. . . . £750/£75
ditto, Cassell, 1953 . . . . . . £50/£15
The Ivory Grin, Knopf (U.S.), 1951 . . . £750/£75
ditto, Cassell, 1953 . . . . . . £50/£15
Meet Me at the Morgue, Knopf (U.S.), 1953 £250/£45
ditto, as *Experience with Evil*, Cassell, 1954 £25/£10
Find a Victim, Knopf (U.S.), 1954 . . . £150/£35
ditto, Cassell, 1955 . . . . . . £25/£10

'John Ross Macdonald' Short Stories

The Name is Archer, Bantam (U.S.), 1955 (wraps) £25

'John Macdonald' Novels

The Moving Target, Knopf (U.S.), 1949 . £450/£45
ditto, Cassell, 1951 . . . . . . £125/£25

IAN McEWAN
(b.1948)

The writer of obsessive, often explicit novels and short stories, McEwan was the first former student to receive recognition following attendance at Malcolm Bradbury's creative writing course at the University of East Anglia.

Short Stories

First Love, Last Rites, Cape, 1975 . . . £200/£35
ditto, Random House (U.S.), 1975 . . . £40/£10
In Between the Sheets, Cape, 1978 . . . £125/£20
ditto, Simon & Schuster (U.S.), 1979 . . £25/£5
The Short Stories, Cape, 1995 . . . . £15/£5

Novels

The Cement Garden, Cape, 1978 . . . £100/£15
ditto, Simon & Schuster (U.S.), 1978 . . £25/£5
The Comfort of Strangers, Cape, 1981 . . £40/£5
ditto, Simon & Schuster (U.S.), 1981 . . £20/£5
The Child in Time, Cape, 1987 . . . . £25/£5
ditto, London Limited Editions (150 numbered, signed
copies in glassine jacket) . . . . £75/£60
ditto, Houghton Mifflin (U.S.), 1987 . . £15/£5
The Innocent, Cape, 1990 . . . . . £20/£5
ditto, Doubleday (U.S.), 1990 . . . . £15/£5
Black Dogs, Cape, 1992 . . . . . . £15/£5
ditto, London Limited Editions, 1992 (150 numbered,
signed copies in glassine jacket) . . . £65/£50
ditto, Doubleday (U.S.), 1992 . . . . £10/£5

Enduring Love, Cape, 1997	£10/£5
ditto, Doubleday (U.S.), 1998	£10/£5
Amsterdam, Cape, 1998	£10/£5
ditto, Doubleday (U.S.), 1999	£10/£5

Children's

Rose Blanche, Cape, 1983	£30/£5
The Daydreamer, Cape, 1994	£25/£5
ditto, Harper Collins (U.S.), 1994	£15/£5

Miscellaneous

British Films at the London Film Festival, Filmways, 1979 [1980] (wraps)	£25
The Imitation Game: Three Plays for Television, Cape, 1981	£25/£5
ditto, Houghton Mifflin (U.S.), 1982	£10/£5
Or Shall We Die?, Cape, 1983	£35/£15
The Ploughman's Lunch, Methuen, 1985 (wraps)	£10
Soursweet, Faber, 1988 (wraps)	£10
A Move Abroad, Picador, 1989 (wraps)	£5

JOHN McGAHERN
(b.1934)

A novelist and short story writer whose works, wherever they are set, always refer back to the author's native Ireland.

Novels

The Barracks, Faber, 1963	£350/£75
ditto, Macmillan (U.S.), 1964	£30/£10
The Dark, Faber, 1965	£125/£25
ditto, Knopf (U.S.), 1966	£25/£10
The Leavetaking, Faber, 1974	£35/£10
ditto, Little, Brown (U.S.), 1974	£20/£5
The Pornographer, Faber, 1979	£35/£10
ditto, Harper & Row (U.S.), 1979	£15/£5
Amongst Women, Faber, 1990	£10/£5
ditto, Viking (U.S.), 1990	£10/£5

Short Stories

Nightlines, Faber, 1970	£50/£10
ditto, Little, Brown (U.S.), 1971	£20/£5
Getting Through, Faber, 1978	£35/£10
ditto, Harper & Row (U.S.), 1980	£15/£5
High Ground, Faber, 1985	£20/£5
ditto, Viking (U.S.), 1987	£10/£5
The Collected Stories, Faber, 1992	£25/£10
ditto, Knopf (U.S.), 1993	£20/£5

Plays

The Power of Darkness, Faber, 1991 (wraps)	£15

ARTHUR MACHEN
(b.1863 d.1947)

A novelist, short story writer and essayist, Machen is generally read for his tales of horror and the supernatural although his work is predominantly of a mystical cast. His *Bowmen* was the origin of the 'Angels of Mons' myth in the First World War.

Verse

Eleusinia, privately printed, 1881 (wraps)	£20,000

Novels

The Chronicle of Clemendy, Carbonnek, 1888 (250 numbered copies)	£200
ditto, privately printed Carbonnek (U.S.), 1923 (1,050 numbered, signed copies)	£75
ditto, Martin Secker, 1925 [1926], (100 signed, numbered copies)	£125
ditto, Martin Secker, 1925, (trade edition)	£65/£20
The Great God Pan, John Lane, 1894	£225
ditto, Roberts Bros (U.S.), 1894	£150
The Three Impostors, John Lane, 1895	£225
ditto, Roberts Bros (U.S.), 1895	£150
ditto, Knopf (U.S.), 1923	£45/£20
The Hill of Dreams, Grant Richards, 1907	£100
ditto, Dana Estes & Co (U.S.), 1907	£50
ditto, Martin Secker, [1922] (150 signed, numbered copies)	£250
The Great Return, The Faith Press, 1915	£100/£45
The Terror, Duckworth & Co., 1917	£150/£35
ditto, as *The Terror, A Mystery*, McBride (U.S.), [1917].	£30
The Secret Glory, Martin Secker, 1922	£100/£30
ditto, Knopf (U.S.), 1923	£75/£25
ditto, as *Chapters Five and Six of 'The Secret Glory'*, Tartarus Press, 1990 (250 numbered copies)	£35/£10
ditto, Tartarus Press, 1998 (first edition of all six chapters)	£25/£10
The Green Round, Ernest Benn, 1933	£150/£35
ditto, Arkham House (U.S.), 1968	£50/£20
ditto, Tartarus Press, 2000	£20/£5

Short Stories

The House of Souls, Grant Richards, 1906	£250
ditto, Dana Estes & Co (U.S.), 1906	£200
The Bowmen, Simpkin Marshall, 1915	£125/£45
ditto, Simpkin Marshall, 1915 (enlarged edition with silhouette)	£125/£45
ditto, Putnams (U.S.), 1915 (first issue with blue bowman)	£125/£45
ditto, Putnams (U.S.), 1915 (second issue with brown bowman)	£125/£45
The Shining Pyramid, Covici-McGee (U.S.), 1923 (875 numbered copies)	£75
Ornaments In Jade, Knopf (U.S.), 1924 (1,000 signed, numbered copies, slipcase)	£95/£75
ditto, Tartarus Press, 1997	£25/£10

The Shining Pyramid, Martin Secker, 1925 (different
from above *Shining Pyramid*) . . . . £75/£30
ditto, Martin Secker, 1925 (250 signed, numbered
copies) . . . . £200/£125
ditto, Knopf (U.S.), 1925 . . . . . . £75/£30
The Cosy Room, Rich & Cowan, 1936 . . £750/£350
The Children of the Pool, Hutchinson & Co., 1936 .
. . . .£750/£250
Ritual and Other Stories, Tartarus Press, 1992 . .
. . . . £45/£10

Essays
Strange Roads & With the Gods in Spring, The
Classic Press, 1923 . . . . £25
ditto, The Classic Press, 1924 (300 signed, numbered
copies) £100
The Grande Trouvaille: A Legend of Pentonville,
privately printed, 1923 (250 signed, numbered copies,
wraps) £75
The Collector's Craft, privately printed, 1923 (250
numbered copies, wraps) £75
ditto, privately printed, 1923 (unknown number also
signed, wraps) £150
Dog and Duck, Knopf (U.S.), 1924 . . . £65/£20
ditto, Jonathan Cape, [1924] (900 numbered copies) .
. . . . £75/£25
ditto, Jonathan Cape, [1924] (150 of above numbered
and signed) . . . . £150/£75
The Glorious Mystery, Covici-McGee (U.S.), 1924
(pictorial boards) . . . . £150/£50
Dreads and Drolls, Martin Secker, 1926 . £65/£20
ditto, Martin Secker, 1926 (100 signed, numbered
copies) . . . . £125/£75
ditto, Knopf (U.S.), 1927 . . . . . . £65/£20
Notes and Queries, Spurr & Swift, 1926 (265 signed,
numbered copies) £125
Tom O' Bedlam and His Song, The Appellicon Press
(U.S.), 1930 (200 signed copies, slipcase) £100/£75
Beneath the Barley, privately printed, 1931 (25 signed,
numbered copies, wraps) £75
The Glitter of the Brook, Postprandial Press (U.S.),
1932 (10 copies) £250
Bridles and Spurs, The Rowfant Club (U.S.), 1951
(178 numbered copies, slipcase) £200
ditto, The Rowfant Club (U.S.), 1951 (offprint of the
Preface only 25 copies) £75
A Critical Essay, privately printed (U.S.), 1953 (50
copies) £100
A Note on Poetry, Four Ducks Press (U.S.), 1959 (50
numbered copies) £100
From the London Evening News, Four Ducks Press
(U.S.), 1959 (50 numbered copies). . . . £100
The Secret of the Sangraal, Tartarus Press, 1996 (250
copies) . . . . £45/£15

Autobiography
Far Off Things, Martin Secker, 1922 (100 signed,
numbered copies) £125
ditto, Martin Secker, 1922 (trade edition) . £50/£25

ditto, Knopf (U.S.), 1923 . . . . . . £45/£15
Things Near and Far, Martin Secker, 1923 (100
signed, numbered copies) £125
ditto, Martin Secker, 1923 . . . . £75/£25
ditto, Knopf (U.S.), 1923 . . . . . £45/£15
The London Adventure, Martin Secker, 1924 £40/£20
ditto, Martin Secker, 1924 (200 signed, numbered
copies) £100
ditto, Knopf (U.S.), 1924 . . . . . . £45/£15
In the Eighties, privately printed, 1931 . . . £75
ditto, Twyn Barlwm Press, 1933 (50 numbered copies)
. . . . £40

Translations
The Heptameron, by Queen Margaret of Navarre,
privately printed [Dryden Press], 1886. . . £50
ditto, as *The Fortunate Lovers*, Redway, 1887 (a
selection of the above) £30
ditto, Scribner & Welford (U.S.), 1887 . . . £100
Fantastic Tales, or The Way to Attain, privately
printed, Carbonnek, 1889 [1890] (500 numbered
copies) £50
ditto, privately printed, Carbonnek, 1889 [1890] (large
paper issue, 50 signed, numbered copies) . . £150
ditto, privately printed Carbonnek (U.S.), 1923 (1050
numbered, signed copies) . . . . . £75/£35
The Memoirs of Casanova, privately printed, 1894 (12
vols, 1,000 copies) £300
ditto, privately printed 1894 (large paper issue, 50
numbered sets) £500
ditto, privately printed 1894 (3 numbered sets, Japanese vellum). £750
Casanova's Escape from the Leads, Casanova Society,
1925 . . . . £25/£10
ditto, Knopf (U.S.), Borzoi Pocket Books No. 28
[1925]. . . . . £25/£10

Others
The Anatomy of Tobacco, George Redway, 1884
(pseud Leolinus Siluriensis). £250
ditto, Knopf (U.S.), 1926 . . . . . . £50/£20
Don Quijote de la Mancha, George Redway, 1887
(wraps) £250
Hieroglyphics, Grant Richards, 1902 . . . £45
ditto, Kennerley (U.S), 1913 . . . . . £50
ditto, Knopf (U.S), 1923 . . . . . . £50/£20
The House of the Hidden Light, privately printed,
1904 (with A.E. Waite) £5,000
Dr. Stiggins, Francis Griffiths, 1906 . . . £45
ditto, Knopf (U.S), 1925 . . . . . . £50/£10
War and the Christian Faith, Skeffington & Son, 1918
. . . . £50
Arthur Machen, a novelist of ecstasy and sin, Walter
M. Hill (U.S.), 1918. (250 copies) . . . £150
Precious Balms, Spurr & Swift, 1924 (265 signed,
numbered copies) £100
The Canning Wonder, Chatto & Windus, 1925 . .
. . . . £65/£20

ditto, Chatto & Windus, 1925 (130 signed, numbered copies) £75
ditto, Knopf (U.S.), 1926 . . . . . £30/£10
A Preface to Casanova's Escape from the Leads, The Casanova Society, 1925 (25 copies, wraps) . £150
A Souvenir of Cadby Hall, J. Lyons and Co. Ltd, 1927 . . . . £75
Parish of Amersham, Mason, 1930 (wraps) . £35
An Introduction to J. Gawsworth: Above the River, privately printed, 1931 (12 signed, numbered copies, wraps). £250
A Few Letters from Arthur Machen, The Rowfant Club (U.S.), 1932 (170 copies) £125
ditto, Aylesford Press, 1993 (83 copies signed by Janet Machen of 333) £30
ditto, Aylesford Press, 1993 (250 copies of 333, wraps) £15
A.L.S., Four Ducks Press (U.S.), 1956 (50 numbered copies) £125
Starrett Vs. Machen, Autolycus Press (U.S.) 1977 £30
ditto, Autolycus Press (U.S.) 1977 (50 numbered copies) £60
Dreams and Visions, by Morchard Bishop, Caermaen Books, 1987 (wraps). £10
Selected Letters, The Aquarian Press, 1988 . . £10/£5

Collected Edition
The Caerleon Edition, Martin Secker, 1923 (9 vols) .
. . . . £600/£350

COLIN MACINNES
(b.1914 d.1976)

Chiefly read today for his 'London Trilogy' novels, which jauntily catch the changing mood of 1950s and 60s society.

Novels
To The Victors The Spoils, MacGibbon & Kee, 1950 .
. . . . £45/£15
June in Her Spring, MacGibbon & Kee, 1952 £45/£15
City of Spades, MacGibbon & Kee, 1957 . £30/£10
ditto, Macmillan (U.S.), 1958 . . . . £20/£5
Absolute Beginners, MacGibbon & Kee, 1959 .
. . . . £65/£15
ditto, Macmillan (U.S.), 1960 . . . . £25/£10
Mr Love and Justice, MacGibbon & Kee, 1960 . .
. . . . £30/£10
ditto, Dutton (U.S.), 1961. . . . . . £20/£5
All Day Saturday, MacGibbon & Kee, 1966 £20/£5
Sweet Saturday Night, MacGibbon & Kee, 1967 . .
. . . . £20/£5
Westward to Laughter, MacGibbon & Kee, 1969 .
. . . . £20/£5
ditto, Farrar Straus (U.S.), 1970 . . . . £15/£5
Three Years to Play, MacGibbon & Kee, 1970 £15/£5
ditto, Farrar Straus (U.S.), 1970 . . . . £10/£5

Out of the Garden, Hart-Davis MacGibbon, 1974 . . .
. . . . £10/£5

Collected Editions
Visions of London, MacGibbon & Kee, 1969 £15/£5
ditto, as *The London Novels*, Farrar Straus (U.S.), 1969 . . . . £15/£5

Essays
England, Half English, MacGibbon & Kee, 1961 . .
. . . . £30/£10
ditto, Random House (U.S.), 1962 . . . £20/£5
Posthumous Essays, Brian & O'Keefe, 1977 £15/£5
Out of the Way: Later Essays, Brian & O'Keefe, 1980
. . . . £15/£5

Others
London: City of Any Dream, Thames & Hudson, 1962
. . . . £25/£10
Australia and New Zealand, Time (U.S.), 1966 (with the editors of *Life*) . . . . . . £15/£5
Loving Them Both: A Study of Bisexuality and Bisexuals, Brian & O'Keefe, 1973 . . £25/£10
'No Novel Reader', Brian & O'Keefe, 1975 £15/£5

ALISTAIR MACLEAN
(b.1923 d.1987)

A successful popular novelist, Maclean used wartime experiences with the Royal Navy as the background to his first novel, *HMS Ulysses*. A series of naval and military thrillers followed, characterised by an attention to detail and compelling plots.

Novels
HMS Ulysses, Collins, 1955 . . . . . £50/£10
ditto, Doubleday (U.S.), 1956 . . . . £15/£5
The Guns of Navarone, Collins, 1957 . . £40/£10
ditto, Doubleday (U.S.), 1957 . . . . £30/£5
South By Java Head, Collins, 1958 . . . £20/£5
ditto, Doubleday (U.S.), 1958 . . . . £15/£5
The Last Frontier, Collins, 1959. . . . £15/£5
ditto, as *The Secret Ways*, Doubleday (U.S.), 1959 .
. . . . £15/£5
Night Without End, Collins, 1960 . . . £15/£5
ditto, Doubleday (U.S.), 1960 . . . . £15/£5
Fear is the Key, Collins, 1961 . . . . £10/£5
ditto, Doubleday (U.S.), 1961 . . . . £10/£5
The Snow on the Ben, Ward Lock, 1961 (pseud. 'Ian Stuart'), Collins, 1961 . . . . . . £10/£5
The Dark Crusader, Collins, 1961 (pseud. 'Ian Stuart')
. . . . £10/£5
ditto, as *The Blake Shrike*, Scribner (U.S.), 1961 . .
. . . . £10/£5
The Golden Rendezvous, Collins, 1962. . £10/£5
ditto, Doubleday (U.S.), 1962 . . . . £10/£5

The Satan Bug, Collins, 1962 (pseud. 'Ian Stuart') .	
. . . .	£20/£5
ditto, Scribner (U.S.), 1962	£15/£5
Ice Station Zebra, Collins, 1963	£15/£5
ditto, Doubleday (U.S.), 1963	£15/£5
When Eight Bells Toll, Collins, 1966 . .	£10/£5
ditto, Doubleday (U.S.), 1966	£10/£5
Where Eagles Dare, Collins, 1967 . . .	£30/£5
ditto, Doubleday (U.S.), 1967	£15/£5
Force 10 from Navarone, Collins, 1968 .	£25/£5
ditto, Doubleday (U.S.), 1968	£15/£5
Puppet on a Chain, Collins, 1969 . . .	£10/£5
ditto, Doubleday (U.S.), 1969	£10/£5
Caravan to Vaccares, Collins, 1970 . . .	£10/£5
ditto, Doubleday (U.S.), 1970	£10/£5
Bear Island, Collins, 1971	£10/£5
ditto, Doubleday (U.S.), 1971	£10/£5
The Way to Dusty Death, Collins, 1973 . .	£10/£5
ditto, Doubleday (U.S.), 1973	£10/£5
Breakheart Pass, Collins, 1974	£10/£5
ditto, Doubleday (U.S.), 1974	£10/£5
Circus, Collins, 1975	£10/£5
ditto, Doubleday (U.S.), 1975	£10/£5
The Golden Gate, Collins, 1976	£10/£5
ditto, Doubleday (U.S.), 1976	£10/£5
Death from Disclosure, Hale, 1976 (pseud. 'Ian Stuart')	£10/£5
Flood Tide, Hale, 1977 (pseud. 'Ian Stuart')	£10/£5
Sand Trap, Hale, 1977 (pseud. 'Ian Stuart')	£10/£5
Seawitch, Collins, 1977	£10/£5
ditto, Doubleday (U.S.), 1977	£10/£5
Goodbye, California, Collins, 1978 . . .	£10/£5
ditto, Doubleday (U.S.), 1978	£10/£5
Fatal Switch, Hale, 1978 (pseud. 'Ian Stuart')	£10/£5
A Weekend to Kill, Hale, 1978 (pseud. 'Ian Stuart') .	
. . . .	£10/£5
Athabasca, Collins, 1980	£10/£5
ditto, Doubleday (U.S.), 1980	£10/£5
River of Death, Collins, 1981	£10/£5
ditto, Doubleday (U.S.), 1982	£10/£5
Partisans, Collins, 1982	£10/£5
ditto, Doubleday (U.S.), 1983	£10/£5
Floodgate, Collins, 1983	£10/£5
ditto, Doubleday (U.S.), 1984	£10/£5
San Andreas, Collins, 1984	£10/£5
ditto, Doubleday (U.S.), 1985	£10/£5
The Lonely Sea, Collins, 1985	£10/£5
ditto, Doubleday (U.S.), 1985	£10/£5
Santorini, Collins, 1986	£10/£5

Others

All About Lawrence of Arabia, Allen, 1962	£75/£20
ditto, as *Lawrence of Arabia*, Random House (U.S.), 1961	£10/£5
Captain Cook, Collins, 1971	£10/£5
ditto, Doubleday (U.S.), 1972	£10/£5
Alistair MacLean Introduces Scotland, Deutsch, 1972	
. . . .	£10/£5

LOUIS MACNEICE
(b.1907 d.1963)

A poet often associated with Auden and Spender, MacNeice employs similar devices of irony and satire.

Verse

Blind Fireworks, Gollancz, 1929 . . . £500/£125
Poems, Faber, 1935 . . . . £200/£45
Poems, Random House (U.S.), 1937. . . £125/£25
The Earth Compels, Faber, 1938 . . . £125/£35
Autumn Journal, Faber, 1939 . . . . £150/£35
ditto, Random House (U.S.), 1939 . . . £25/£10
The Last Ditch, Cuala Press (Dublin), 1940 (450 copies, tissue d/w) . . . . . . £150/£100
ditto, Cuala Press (Dublin), 1940 (25 signed copies) .
. . . . £400
Selected Poems, Faber, 1940 . . . . . £15/£5
Poems, 1925-1940, Random House (U.S.), 1940 . .
. . . . £15/£5
Plant and Phantom, Faber, 1941 . . . £30/£10
Springboard: Poems, 1941-44, Faber, 1944 £30/£10
ditto, Random House (U.S.), 1945 . . . £20/£5
Holes in the Sky: Poems, 1944-47, Faber, 1948 . .
. . . . £25/£10
ditto, Random House (U.S.), 1949 . . . £20/£5
Collected Poems, 1925-48, Faber, 1949 . £30/£10
Ten Burnt Offerings, Faber, 1951 . . . £30/£10
ditto, O.U.P. (U.S.), 1953 . . . . . £20/£5
Autumn Sequel, Faber, 1954 . . . . . £25/£10
The Other Wing, Faber, 1954 (wraps) . . £15
Visitations, Faber, 1957 . . . . . . £20/£5
ditto, O.U.P. (U.S.), 1958 . . . . . £20/£5
Eighty-Five Poems, Faber, 1959 . . . . £20/£5
ditto, O.U.P. (U.S.), 1959 . . . . . £20/£5
Solstices, Faber, 1961 . . . . £20/£5
ditto, O.U.P. (U.S.), 1961 . . . . . £20/£5
The Burning Perch, Faber, 1963 . . . . £20/£5
ditto, O.U.P. (U.S.), 1963 . . . . . £20/£5
Selected Poems, Faber, 1964 . . . . . £10/£5
Collected Poems, Faber, 1966 . . . . £15/£5
ditto, O.U.P. (U.S.), 1967 . . . . . £10/£5

Novel

Roundabout Way, Putman, 1931 (pseud. 'Louis Malone') . . . . £250/£75

Translations

The Agamemnon of Aeschylus, Faber, 1936	£35/£10
ditto, Harcourt Brace (U.S.), 1937. . .	£25/£10
Goethe's Faust Parts I & II, Faber, 1951 .	£30/£10
ditto, O.U.P. (U.S.), 1952	£25/£10

Plays

Out of the Picture, Faber, 1937	£50/£15
ditto, Harcourt Brace (U.S.), 1938. . .	£35/£15

Christopher Columbus, Faber, 1944. . . £30/£10
The Dark Tower, Faber, 1947 . . . . £30/£10
The Mad Islands and The Administrator, Faber, 1964
. . . . £15/£5
One for the Grave, Faber, 1968 . . . . £15/£5
ditto, O.U.P. (U.S.), 1968 . . . . . £10/£5
Persons from Porlock and Other Plays, BBC, 1969 .
. . . . £15/£5

Essays
Modern Poetry: A Personal Essay, O.U.P. (U.S.),
1938 . . . . £25/£10
The Poetry of W.B. Yeats, O.U.P. (U.S.), 1941 .
. . . . £45/£15
Meet the U.S. Army, H.M.S.O., 1943 (anonymous,
wraps) £300
Varieties of Parable, C.U.P., 1965 . . . £15/£5

Children's
The Penny That Rolled Away, Putnam (U.S.), 1954 .
. . . . £75/£25
ditto, as The Sixpence That Rolled Away, Faber, 1956
. . . . £75/£25

Autobiography
The Strings are False, Faber, 1965 . . . £30/£10
ditto, O.U.P. (U.S.), 1966 . . . . . £25/£10

Others
Letters from Iceland, Faber, 1937 (with W.H. Auden).
. . . . £75/£25
ditto, Harcourt Brace (U.S.), 1937 . . . £50/£15
Zoo, Joseph, 1938 . . . . £175/£35
I Crossed the Minch, Longman, 1938 . . £175/£35
Astrology, Aldus, 1964 . . . . . . £25/£5
ditto, Doubleday (U.S.), 1964 . . . . £20/£5

NORMAN MAILER
(b.1923)

An American novelist and journalist, Mailer excels at taking real events and subjecting them to his own fictional representation.

Fiction and Non Fiction
The Naked and the Dead, Rinehart (U.S.), 1948 . .
. . . . £750/£75
ditto, Wingate, 1949 (240 numbered copies) . £300
ditto, Wingate, 1949 . . . . . . £75/£25
Barbary Shore, Rinehart (U.S.), 1951 (2 dustjackets issued simultaneously in red and black, and green and black). . . . . £125/£25
ditto, Cape, 1952 . . . . £50/£15
The Deer Park, Putnam (U.S.), 1955 . . £75/£20
ditto, Wingate, 1957 . . . . £50/£15

The White Negro, City Lights Books (U.S.) 1957 (35 cents cover price, wraps) £150
ditto, City Lights Books (U.S.) 1957 (50 cents cover price, wraps) £15
Advertisements for Myself, Putnam (U.S.), 1959 . .
. . . . £75/£15
ditto, Deutsch, 1961 . . . . . . £40/£10
The Presidential Papers, Putnam (U.S.), 1963 £40/£10
ditto, Deutsch, 1961 . . . . £30/£5
An American Dream, Dial Press (U.S.), 1965 £45/£10
ditto, Deutsch, 1965 . . . . £25/£5
Cannibals and Christians, Dial Press (U.S.), 1966 .
. . . . £40/£5
ditto, Deutsch, 1967 . . . . £30/£5
Why are We in Vietnam?, Putnam (U.S.), 1967 . . .
. . . . £40/£10
ditto, Weidenfeld & Nicholson, 1969 . . £25/£5
The Armies of the Night, NAL (U.S.), 1968 (wraps) .
. . . . £10
ditto, NAL (U.S.), 1968 . . . . . . £30/£10
ditto, Weidenfeld & Nicholson, 1968 . . £20/£5
Miami and the Siege of Chicago, World (U.S.), 1968 .
. . . . £20/£5
ditto, Weidenfeld & Nicholson, 1968 . . £20/£5
A Fire on the Moon, Little, Brown (U.S.), 1970 £20/£5
ditto, Weidenfeld & Nicholson, 1970 . . £20/£5
The Prisoner of Sex, Little, Brown (U.S.), 1971 . .
. . . . £20/£5
ditto, Weidenfeld & Nicholson, 1970 . . £20/£5
Maidstone, NAL (U.S.), 1971 (wraps) . . £15
Existential Errands, Little, Brown (U.S.), 1972 £20/£5
St. George and the Godfather, Arbor House (U.S.),
1972 . . . . £20/£5
Marilyn, Grosset & Dunlap (U.S.), 1973 (signed limited edition in slipcase) . . . £175/£145
ditto, Grosset & Dunlap (U.S.), 1973 . . £45/£20
Faith of Graffiti, Praeger Publishers (U.S.), 1974 (350 signed copies, slipcase) . . . . . £100/£75
The Fight, Little, Brown (U.S.), 1975 . . £15/£5
ditto, Hart-Davis, MacGibbon, 1975 . . . £15/£5
Some Honourable Men, Little, Brown (U.S.), 1976 .
. . . . £15/£5
Genius and Lust, Grove Press (U.S.), 1976 £25/£10
A Transit to Narcissus, Howard Fertig (U.S.), 1978 .
. . . . £100/£45
The Executioner's Song, Little, Brown (U.S.), 1979 .
. . . . £15/£5
ditto, Hutchinson , 1979 . . . . . . £15/£5
Of Women and their Elegance, Simon & Schuster (U.S.), 1980 . . . . £35/£10
ditto, Hodder & Stoughton, 1980. . . . £35/£10
Of a Small and Modest Malignancy, Lord John Press (U.S.), 1980 (300 signed, numbered copies, slipcase)
. . . . £50/£35
ditto, Lord John Press (U.S.), 1980 (100 deluxe signed, numbered copies, slipcase) . . . . . £125/£75
Pieces, Little, Brown (U.S.), 1982 (wraps) . . £10
Pontifications, Little, Brown (U.S.), 1982 (wraps) £10
Ancient Evenings, Little, Brown (U.S.), 1983 . £25/£5

ditto, Little, Brown (U.S.), 1983 (350 signed, numbered copies, slipcase) . . . . . . £100/£65
ditto, Macmillan, 1983 . . . . . . £20/£5
Tough Guys Don't Dance, Random House (U.S.),
1984 . . . . £20/£5
ditto, Franklin Library (U.S.), 1984 (signed limited
edition, slipcase) £45
ditto, Joseph, 1984. . . . . . . £15/£5
The Last Night, Targ Editions (U.S.), 1984 (250 signed
copies, tissue d/w) . . . . . . £75/£50
A Fragment from Vietnam, Eurographica (Helsinki),
1985 (350 signed, numbered copies, wraps) . £75
Conversations with Norman Mailer, Univ. Press of
Mississippi (U.S.), 1988. . . . . . £20/£5
Harlot's Ghost, Random House (U.S.), 1991 £20/£5
ditto, Joseph, 1991. . . . . . . £15/£5
Portrait of Picasso As a Young Man, Atlantic Monthly
Press (U.S.) 1995 . . . . . . £10/£5
ditto, Little, Brown & Co, 1996 . . . . £10/£5
Oswald's Tale, Franklin Library, 1995 (signed limited
edition) £40
ditto, Random House (U.S.), 1995 . . . £15/£5
ditto, Little, Brown, 1995 . . . . . . £15/£5
The Gospel According to the Son, Little, Brown
(U.S.), 1997 . . . . £10/£5
ditto, Little, Brown, 1997. . . . . . £10/£5
Time of Our Time, Random House (U.S.), 1998 . .
. . . . £10/£5
ditto, Little, Brown & Co, 1998 . . . . £10/£5

Verse
Deaths for the Ladies and Other Disasters, Putnam
(U.S.), 1962 . . . . £125/£25
ditto, Putnam (U.S.), 1962 (wraps) . . . £25
ditto, Deutsch, 1962 . . . . £10

Play
The Deer Park, Dial Press (U.S.), 1967 . . £100/£25
ditto, Dell (U.S.), 1967 (wraps) £10
ditto, Weidenfeld, 1970 . . . . . . £30/£10

THOMAS MANN
(b.1875 d.1955)

Arguably the most outstanding German writer of the
twentieth century, he received not only critical
admiration during his lifetime, but also popular
success.

Novels
Royal Highness, Sidgwick & Jackson, 1916 (translated
by A. Cecil Curtis) . . . . . . £500/£40
ditto, Knopf (U.S.), 1916. . . . . . £350/£35
Bashan and I, Collins, 1923 (translated by H.G.
Scheftauer) . . . . £150/£40
ditto, Holt (U.S.), 1923 . . . . . . £100/£25

Buddenbrooks, Knopf (U.S.), 1924 (translated by H.T.
Lowe-Porter, 2 vols) . . . . . . £300/£75
ditto, Secker, 1924 (2 vols) . . . . . £250/£50
The Magic Mountain, Knopf (U.S.), 1927 (translated
by H.T. Lowe-Porter, 2 vols) . . . . £500/£100
ditto, Knopf (U.S.), 1927 (200 signed copies) £1,000
ditto, Secker, 1927 (2 vols) . . . . . £400/£75
The Beloved Returns, Knopf (U.S.), 1940 (translated
by H.T. Lowe-Porter) . . . . . . £60/£10
ditto, Knopf (U.S.), 1940 (395 signed copies) . £250
ditto, as **Lotte in Weimar**, Secker & Warburg, 1940 .
. . . . £40/£10
Doctor Faustus, Knopf (U.S.), 1948 (translated by
H.T. Lowe-Porter) . . . . . . £50/£15
ditto, Secker & Warburg, 1949 . . . . £40/£10
The Holy Sinner, Knopf (U.S.), 1951 (translated by
H.T. Lowe-Porter) . . . . . . £25/£10
ditto, Secker & Warburg, 1952 . . . . £25/£10
Confessions of Felix Krull, Knopf (U.S.), 1955 (translated by Denver Lindley) . . . . . £25/£10
ditto, Secker & Warburg, 1955 . . . . £25/£10

**Joseph and His Brothers/
Joseph and His Bretheren Novels**
Book 1: The Tales of Jacob, Knopf (U.S.), 1934
(translated by H.T. Lowe-Porter) . . . £100/£25
ditto, Secker, 1934. . . . . £100/£25
Book 2: The Young Joseph, Knopf (U.S.), 1935
(translated by H.T. Lowe-Porter) . . . £100/£25
ditto, Secker, 1935. . . . . £100/£25
Book 3: Joseph in Egypt, Knopf (U.S.), 1938
(translated by H.T. Lowe-Porter, 2 vols) . £150/£45
ditto, Secker, 1938 (2 vols) . . . . . £150/£45
Book 4: Joseph the Provider, Knopf (U.S.), 1944
(translated by H.T. Lowe-Porter) . . . £50/£20
ditto, Secker & Warburg, 1945 . . . . £30/£10

Novellas and Short Stories
Death in Venice and Other Stories, Knopf (U.S.),
1925 (translated by Kenneth Burke) . . £250/£50
Death in Venice, Secker, 1928 (translated by H.T.
Lowe-Porter) . . . . £250/£75
ditto, Knopf (U.S.), 1930 . . . . . . £200/£45
Children and Fools, Knopf (U.S.), 1928 (translated by
H.G. Scheffauer) . . . . £150/£35
Early Sorrow, Secker, 1929 (translated by H.G.
Scheffauer) . . . . £75/£20
ditto, Knopf (U.S.), 1930 . . . . . . £75/£20
Mario and the Magician, Secker, 1930 (translated by
H.T. Lowe-Porter) . . . . £75/£25
ditto, Knopf (U.S.), 1931 . . . . . . £75/£25
Nocturnes, Equinox Cooperative Press (U.S.), 1934
(1,000 signed copies, translated by H.T. Lowe-Porter)
. . . . £250
Stories of Three Decades, Knopf (U.S.), 1936 (translated by H.T. Lowe-Porter) . . . . . £45/£15
ditto, Secker & Warburg, 1936 . . . . £45/£15
The Transposed Heads, Knopf (U.S.), 1941 (translated
by H.T. Lowe-Porter) . . . . . . £45/£15

ditto, Secker & Warburg, 1941 . . . . £45/£15
The Tables of the Law, Knopf (U.S.), 1945 (translated
by H.T. Lowe-Porter) . . . . . £45/£15
ditto, Secker & Warburg, 1947 . . . . £45/£15
The Black Swan, Knopf (U.S.), 1954 (translated by
Willard R. Trask) . . . . £25/£10
ditto, Secker & Warburg, 1954 . . . . £25/£10

Poetry
A Christmas Poem, Equinox Cooperative Press (U.S.),
1932 (translated by Henry Hart) £250

Non Fiction
Three Essays, Knopf (U.S.), 1929 (translated by H.T.
Lowe-Porter) . . . . £50/£20
ditto, Secker, 1932. . . . . . . £45/£15
A Sketch of My Life, Harrison (Paris), 1930 (695
numbered copies, translated by H.T. Lowe-Porter) .
. . . . £200
ditto, Knopf (U.S.), 1960 . . . . . £25/£10
ditto, Secker & Warburg, 1961 . . . . £25/£10
Past Masters and Other Papers, Secker, 1933 (Translated by H.T. Lowe-Porter) . . . . £45/£15
ditto, Knopf (U.S.), 1933 . . . . . £45/£15
An Exchange of Letters, Friends of Europe, 1937
(translated by H.T. Lowe-Porter) £35
ditto, Knopf (U.S.), 1937 . . . . . . £25
ditto, Overlook Press (U.S.), 1938 (350 copies). £45
Freud, Goethe, Wagner, Knopf (U.S.), 1937 (translated by H.T. Lowe-Porter and R. Mathias-Reil) . .
. . . . £50/£20
The Coming Victory of Democracy, Knopf (U.S.),
1938 (translated by Agnes E. Meyer) . . £40/£15
ditto, Secker & Warburg, 1938 . . . . £25/£10
This Peace, Knopf (U.S.), 1938 (translated by H.T.
Lowe-Porter) . . . . £45/£15
This War, Knopf (U.S.), 1940 (translated by Eric
Sutton) . . . . £25/£10
ditto, Secker & Warburg, 1940 . . . . £25/£10
Order of the Day, Knopf (U.S.), 1942 (translated by
H.T. Lowe-Porter, Agnes E. Meyer and Eric Sutton) .
. . . . £50/£20
Listen Germany!, Knopf (U.S.), 1943 . . £35/£10
Essays of Three Decades, Knopf (U.S.), 1947
(translated by H.T. Lowe-Porter) . . . £35/£10
ditto, Secker & Warburg, 1947 . . . . £35/£10
Last Essays, Knopf (U.S.), 1959 (translated by R. & C.
Winston and T. & J. Stern) . . . . £25/£10
ditto, Secker & Warburg, 1959 . . . . £25/£10
Letters to Paul Amann, Wesleyan Univ. Press (U.S.),
1960 (translated by R. & C. Winston) . . £25/£10
ditto, Secker & Warburg, 1961 . . . . £25/£10
The Genesis of a Novel, Knopf (U.S.), 1961 (translated
by R. & C. Winston). . . . . . £25/£10
ditto, Secker & Warburg, 1961 . . . . £25/£10
The Letters of Thomas Mann, 1889-1955, Secker &
Warburg, 1970 (translated by R. & C. Winston, 2
vols) . . . . £35/£15
ditto, Knopf (U.S.), 1971 (2 vols) . . . £35/£15

KATHERINE MANSFIELD
(b.1888 d.1923)

Katherine Mansfield was born in New Zealand, where
her work was first published, but she moved to
England in 1908 in pursuit of a literary career. Best
known for her elegant short stories, Mansfield died of
tuberculosis at the age of 35.

Fiction
In a German Pension, Stephen Swift, 1911 . . .
. . . . £1,750/£500
ditto, Constable, 1926 (new edition) . . . £30/£10
ditto, Knopf (U.S.), 1926 . . . . . £45/£15
Prelude, Hogarth Press, 1918 (wraps with design by
Fergusson) £1,500
ditto, Hogarth Press, 1918 (wraps with design by
Fergusson) £1,250
ditto, as **The Aloe**, Constable, 1930 (750 copies,
revised version, edited by J.M. Murry). . £250/£75
ditto, Knopf (U.S.), 1930 (975 numbered copies) . .
. . . . £175/£50
Je ne Parle pas Francais, Heron Press, 1919 (100
copies) £1,000
Bliss and Other Stories, Constable, 1920 (p13
numbered '3') . . . . £500/£65
ditto, Knopf (U.S.), 1923 . . . . . £300/£35
The Garden Party and Other Stories, Constable, 1922
(1st issue, 'sposition' for 'position' on p.103, red d/w,
blue lettering, 25 copies) . . . . £1,250/£500
ditto, Constable, 1922 (2nd issue) . . . £125/£30
ditto, Verona Press, 1947 (alternative selection of
stories, lithos by Marie Laurencin, slipcase) . . .
. . . . £750/£650
ditto, Knopf (U.S.), 1922 . . . . . £75/£20
The Doves' Nest and Other Stories, Constable, 1923
(1st issue, verso of title page blank, 25 copies) . . .
. . . . £1,250/£800
ditto, Constable, 1923 (2nd issue) . . . £200/£25
ditto, Knopf (U.S.), 1923 . . . . . £75/£20
Something Childish and Other Stories, Constable,
1924 (1st issue, verso of title page blank, 34 copies) .
. . . . £1,000/£550
ditto, Constable, 1924 (2nd issue) . . . £300/£35
ditto, as **The Little Girl and Other Stories**, Knopf
(U.S.), 1924 . . . . £250/£30
The Collected Stories of Katherine Mansfield,
Constable, 1946 . . . . £50/£20
Selected Stories of Katherine Mansfield, O.U.P.
Worlds Classics, 1953 (edited and with an
introduction by D.M. Davin) . . . . £15/£5
Thirty-Four Short Stories, Collins, 1957 . £10/£5
The Stories of Katherine Mansfield, O.U.P., 1985
(edited by A. Alpers) . . . . . . £15/£5

Other Works
Poems, Constable, 1923 . . . . . £150/£30

ditto, Knopf, 1924 . . . . £125/£25
ditto, Constable, 1930 (enlarged edition) . £25/£10
The Journal of Katherine Mansfield, Constable, 1927
. . . . £45/£10
ditto, Knopf (U.S.), 1927 . . . . . £45/£10
ditto, Constable, 1954 (revised and enlarged, edited by
J.M. Murry) . . . . £25/£10
The Letters of Katherine Mansfield, Constable, 1928
(2 vols, edited by J.M. Murry) . . . . £40/£15
Novels and Novelists, Constable, 1930 (edited by J.M.
Murry) . . . . £35/£15
ditto, Knopf (U.S.), 1930 . . . . . . £35/£15
Reminiscences of Tolstoy, Chekhov and Gorky,
Hogarth Press, 1934 (translation with Virginia Woolf
and S.S. Koteliansky) £30
To Stanislaw Wyspianski, privately printed, 1938
(poem, limited to 100 copies) £125
The Scrapbook of Katherine Mansfield, Constable,
1939 (edited by J.M. Murry) . . . £35/£10
ditto, Knopf (U.S.), 1940 . . . . . . £30/£15
*Katherine Mansfield's Letters to John Middleton
Murry, 1913-1922*, Constable, 1951 . . £30/£10
ditto, Knopf (U.S.), 1951 . . . . . £30/£10
Katherine Mansfield, Letters and Journals, Allen
Lane, 1977 (edited and with and introduction by C.K.
Stead) . . . . £15/£5
The Urewera Notebook, O.U.P., 1978 (edited by Ian
Gordon) . . . . £15/£5
*The Collected Letters of Katherine Mansfield Vol 1,
1903-1917*, O.U.P., 1984 (edited by Vincent
O'Sullivan and Margaret Scott). . . . £10/£5
ditto Vol.2, 1918-1919, O.U.P., 1987 . . £10/£5
The Critical Writings of Katherine Mansfield,
Macmillan, 1986 . . . . . . £10/£5

CAPTAIN FREDERICK MARRYAT
(b.1792 d.1848)

Although he was known early in his writing career for
adult novels, drawing on his experiences at sea, he is
perhaps best remembered for his books for children,
including *Masterman Ready* and *Children of the New
Forest.*

Novels
*The Naval Officer, or Scenes and Adventures in the
Life of Frank Mildmay*, Colburn, 1829 (3 vols,
anonymous) £400
ditto, Carey & A. Hart (U.S.), 1833 (2 vols) . £250
The King's Own, Colburn & Bentley, 1830 (3 vols, 'by
the author of The Naval Officer') . . . £300
ditto, D. Estes (U.S.), 1896 . . . . . £50
Newton Forster, or The Merchant Service, James
Cochrane, 1832 (3 vols, 'by the author of The King's
Own'). £300

ditto, Lane (U.S.), 1837 (2 vols) £200
Peter Simple, Saunders & Otley, 1834 (3 vols, 'by the
author of *Newton Forster, The King's Own*, etc.') .
. . . . £350
ditto, Lane (U.S.), 1837 (2 vols) £200
Jacob Faithful, Saunders & Otley, 1834 (3 vols, 'by
the author of *Peter Simple, The King's Own*, etc.') .
. . . . £400
ditto, Munro (U.S.), 1878 . . . . . . £50
Japhet In Search of a Father, Saunders & Otley, 1836
(3 vols, 'by the author of *Peter Simple, Jacob Faithful*, etc.') £300
ditto, Munro (U.S.), 1877 . . . . . . £50
Mr Midshipman Easy, Saunders & Otley, 1836 (3
vols, 'by the author of *Japhet In Search of a Father,
Peter Simple, Jacob Faithful*, etc.') . . . £200
ditto, Appleton (U.S.), 1866 . . . . . £50
Snarleyyow, or The Dog Fiend, Colburn, 1837 (3 vols,
'by the author of *Peter Simple, Frank Mildmay*, etc.')
. . . . £300
ditto, Carey & A. Hart (U.S.), 1837 (2 vols) . £200
The Phantom Ship, Colburn, 1839 (3 vols). £1,000
ditto, Munro (U.S.), 1877 . . . . . . £100
Poor Jack, Longman etc., Jan-Dec 1840 (12 parts) .
. . . . £300
ditto, Longman etc., 1840 . . . . . . £200
ditto, Munro (U.S.), 1878 . . . . . . £50
Masterman Ready, or The Wreck of the Pacific,
Longman etc (3 vols, vol.1 1841, vols 2&3 1842) .
. . . . £200
ditto, Appleton (U.S.), 1843 (3 vols). . . £125
Josph Rushbrook, or The Poacher, Longman etc,
1841 (3 vols, 'by the author of *Peter Simple* etc.') .
. . . . £200
ditto, D. Estes (U.S.), 1895 . . . . . £25
Percival Keene, Colburn, 1842 (3 vols) . . . £200
ditto, Wilson (U.S.), 1842. . . . . . £150
*Narrative of the Travels and Adventures of Monsieur
Violet in California, Sonora and Western Texas*,
Longmans etc., 1843 (3 vols) £400
ditto, as *The Travels and Romantic Adventures of
Monsieur Violet, among the Snake Indians and Wild
Tribes of the Great Western Prairies*, Longman etc,
1843 . . . . £300
ditto, Harper (U.S.), 1843. . . . . . £200
The Settlers in Canada, Longman etc, 1844 (2 vols) .
. . . . £175
ditto, D. Estes (U.S.), 1898 . . . . . £25
The Mission, or Scenes in Africa, Longmans etc, 1845
(2 vols) £200
The Privateersman, or One Hundred Years Ago,
Longman etc, 1846 (2 vols). £200
ditto, Munro (U.S.), 1877. . . . . . £50
The Children of the New Forest, Hurst, [1847] (2 vols)
. . . . £1,000
ditto, D. Estes (U.S.), 1898 . . . . . £45
The Little Savage, Hurst (2 vols, vol.1 1848, vol.2
1849) £200
ditto, Munro (U.S.), 1877 . . . . . . £50

Valerie: An Autobiography, Colburn, 1849 (2 vols) .
. . . . £175
ditto, Munro (U.S.), 1881 . . . . £50

Short Stories
The Pacha of Many Tales, Carey & A. Hart (U.S.),
1834 ('by the author of *Peter Simple, Jacob Faithful*,
etc.', 2 vols) £250
ditto, Saunders & Otley, 1835 (3 vols) . . . £250
The Pirate and The Three Cutters, Longman etc, 1836
. . . . £200
ditto, Lane (U.S.), 1837 . . . . £150

Others
*A Code of Signals for the Use of Vessels Employed in
the Merchant Service*, J. M. Richardson, 1818 £250
*Suggestions for the Abolition of the Present System of
Impressment in the Naval Service*, Richardson, 1822
(64 page booklet, withdrawn) £500
Birman Empire: Views Taken At and Near Rangoon,
Kingsbury/Clay, 1825-6 (3 parts in portfolio, and 2
booklets) £450
Diary in America: with Remarks on its Institutions,
Longman etc, 1839 (3 vols) £200
ditto, Carey & A. Hart (U.S.), 1839 . . . . £200
A Diary in America: Part Second, Longman etc, 1839
(3 vols) £250
Olla Porida, Longman etc, 1840 (3 vols 'by the author
of *Peter Simple* etc.') £250

NGAIO MARSH
(b.1899 d.1982)

A Kiwi writer of detective fiction whose novels are
considered amongst the best of the genre. She was
awarded the O.B.E. in 1948 and made a D.B.E. in
1966.

Novels
A Man Lay Dead, Bles, 1934 . . . £1,750/£200
ditto, Sheridan (U.S.), 1942 . . . . £250/£45
Enter a Murderer, Bles, 1935 . . . £1,500/£150
ditto, Pocket Books (U.S.), 1942 . . . £250/£45
The Nursing Home Murder, Bles, 1935 (with H.
Jellett) . . . . £1,250/£150
ditto, Sheridan (U.S.), 1941 . . . . £175/£25
Death in Ecstasy, Bles, 1936 . . . £1,000/£125
ditto, Sheridan (U.S.), 1941 . . . . £150/£25
Vintage Murder, Bles, 1937 . . . £750/£100
ditto, Sheridan (U.S.), 1940 . . . . £150/£25
Artists in Crime, Bles, 1938 . . . £750/£100
ditto, Furman (U.S.), 1938 . . . . £125/£25
Death in a White Tie, Bles, 1938 . . £500/£50
ditto, Ferman (U.S.), 1938 . . . . £125/£20
Overture to Death, Collins, 1939 . £1,000/£125
ditto, Furman (U.S.), 1939 . . . . £125/£20

Death at the Bar, Collins, 1940 . . . . £350/£45
ditto, Little, Brown (U.S.), 1940 . . . . £75/£15
Death of a Peer, Little, Brown (U.S.), 1940 £75/£25
ditto, as *Surfeit of Lampreys*, Collins, 1941 £350/£40
Death and the Dancing Footman, Little, Brown
(U.S.), 1941 . . . . £65/£15
ditto, Collins, 1942 . . . . . . £150/£25
Colour Scheme, Little, Brown (U.S.), 1943 . £45/£15
ditto, Collins, 1943 . . . . . . £75/£20
Died in the Wool, Collins, 1945 . . . £150/£20
ditto, Little, Brown (U.S.), 1945 . . . £65/£15
Final Curtain, Collins, 1947 . . . . £150/£20
ditto, Little, Brown (U.S.), 1947 . . . £50/£15
Wreath for Riviera, Little, Brown (U.S.), 1949. . .
. . . . £45/£10
ditto, as *Swing Brother Swing*, Collins, 1949 £75/£15
Opening Night, Collins, 1951 . . . . £65/£10
ditto, as *Night at the Vulcan*, Little, Brown (U.S.),
1951 . . . . £45/£10
Spinsters in Jeopardy, Little, Brown (U.S.), 1953 . .
. . . . £45/£10
ditto, Collins, 1954 . . . . . . £65/£10
Scales of Justice, Collins, 1955 . . . . £50/£10
ditto, Little, Brown (U.S.), 1955 . . . £45/£10
Death of a Fool, Little, Brown (U.S.), 1956 £40/£10
ditto, as *Off with His Head*, Collins, 1957 £40/£10
Singing in the Shrouds, Little, Brown (U.S.), 1958 .
. . . . £35/£10
ditto, Collins, 1959 . . . . . . £35/£10
False Scent, Little, Brown (U.S.), 1959 . . £35/£10
ditto, Collins, 1960 . . . . . . £35/£10
Hand in Glove, Little, Brown (U.S.), 1962 £30/£10
ditto, Collins, 1962 . . . . . . £30/£10
Dead Water, Little, Brown (U.S.), 1963 . £30/£10
ditto, Collins, 1964 . . . . . . £30/£10
Killer Dolphin, Little, Brown (U.S.), 1966 . £30/£10
ditto, as *Death at the Dolphin*, Collins, 1967 £30/£10
Clutch of Constables, Collins, 1968 . . . £30/£10
ditto, Little, Brown (U.S.), 1969 . . . £30/£10
When in Rome, Collins, 1970 . . . . £25/£10
ditto, Little, Brown (U.S.), 1971 . . . £25/£10
Tied up in Tinsel, Collins, 1972 . . . £25/£10
ditto, Little, Brown (U.S.), 1972 . . . £25/£10
Black as He's Painted, Collins, 1974 . . £25/£10
ditto, Little, Brown (U.S.), 1974 . . . £25/£10
Last Ditch, Collins, 1977 . . . . . £25/£10
ditto, Little, Brown (U.S.), 1977 . . . £25/£10
Grave Mistake, Collins, 1978 . . . . £20/£5
ditto, Little, Brown (U.S.), 1978 . . . £20/£5
Photo-Finish, Collins, 1980 . . . . £15/£5
ditto, Little, Brown (U.S.), 1980 . . . £15/£5
Light Thickens, Little, Brown (U.S.), 1982 . £15/£5
ditto, Collins, 1982 . . . . . . £15/£5

W. SOMERSET MAUGHAM
(b.1874 d.1965)

For many years Maugham was better known as a playwright than a novelist. He is also an acknowledged master of the short story.

Novels

Liza of Lambeth, T. Fisher Unwin, 1897 . . £350
ditto, Heinemann, 1947 (1,000 signed, numbered copies) . . . . £300/£100
The Making of a Saint, Page (U.S.), 1998 . . £250
ditto, T. Fisher Unwin, 1898 . . . . . £250
The Hero, Hutchinson, 1901 . . . . . £250
Mrs Craddock, Heinemann, 1902 . . . . £150
ditto, Doran (U.S.), 1920 . . . . . . £250/£45
The Merry-Go-Round, Heinemann, 1904 . . £125
The Bishop's Apron, Chapman & Hall, 1906 . £125
The Explorer, Heinemann, 1908 . . . . £125
ditto, Baker and Taylor (U.S.), 1909 . . . £75
The Magician, Heinemann, 1908 . . . . £125
ditto, Duffoeld and Co. (U.S.), 1909 . . . £100
Of Human Bondage, Doran (U.S.), 1915 . . £500
ditto, Heinemann, 1915 . . . . . £500
The Moon and Sixpence, Heinemann, 1919 . £100
ditto, Doran (U.S.), 1919 (author's name misspelled as 'Maughan' on cover) £100
The Painted Veil, Doran (U.S.), 1925 . . £500/£40
ditto, Doran (U.S.), 1925 (250 signed copies) . £250
ditto, Heinemann, 1925 . . . . . £500/£40
Cakes and Ale, Heinemann, 1930 . . £200/£20
ditto, with 'The Skeleton in the Cupboard', Heinemann, [1954] (eightieth birthday edition, 1,000 signed copies) £250
ditto, Doubleday (U.S.), 1930 . . . £200/£20
The Narrow Corner, Heinemann, 1932 . . £150/£15
ditto, Doubleday (U.S.), 1932 . . . . £150/£15
Theatre, Doubleday (U.S.), 1937 . . . . £75/£15
ditto, Heinemann, 1937 . . . . . £75/£15
Christmas Holiday, Heinemann, 1939 . . £75/£15
ditto, Doubleday (U.S.), 1939 . . . . £75/£15
Up at the Villa, Heinemann, 1941 . . . £45/£15
ditto, Doubleday (U.S.), 1941 . . . . £45/£15
The Razor's Edge, Doubleday (U.S.), 1944 (750 signed, numbered copies) . . . £300/£100
ditto, Doubleday (U.S.), 1944 . . . . £30/£10
ditto, Heinemann, 1944 . . . . . £300/£45
Then and Now, Heinemann, 1946 . . . £30/£10
ditto, Doubleday (U.S.), 1946 . . . . £30/£10
Catalina, Heinemann, 1948 . . . . . £30/£10
ditto, Doubleday (U.S.), 1948 . . . . £30/£10

Short Stories

Orientations, T. Fisher Unwin, 1899 . . . £200
The Trembling of a Leaf, Doran (U.S.), 1921 . . .
. . . . £150/£25
ditto, Heinemann, 1921 . . . . . £150/£25
The Casuarina Tree, Heinemann, 1926 . . £200/£35
Ashenden, Heinemann, 1928 . . . . £1,000/£50

ditto, Doubleday (U.S.), 1928 . . . . £750/£50
First Person Singular, Doran (U.S.), 1931 . £75/£10
ditto, Heinemann, 1931 . . . . . £75/£10
Ah King, Heinemann, 1933 . . . . £75/£10
ditto, Doubleday (U.S.), 1933 . . . . £75/£10
Cosmopolitans, Doran (U.S.), 1936 . . . £50/£10
ditto, Heinemann, 1936 . . . . . £50/£10
The Mixture as Before, Heinemann, 1940 . £50/£10
ditto, Doubleday (U.S.), 1940 . . . . £50/£10
Creatures of Circumstance, Heinemann, 1947 £50/£10
ditto, Doubleday (U.S.), 1947 . . . . £50/£10
Quartet, Heinemann, 1948 . . . . . £25/£10
ditto, Doubleday (U.S.), 1949 . . . . £25/£10
Trio, Heinemann, 1950 . . . . . £25/£10
ditto, Doubleday (U.S.), 1950 . . . . £25/£10
Encore, Heinemann, 1952 . . . . . £25/£10
ditto, Doubleday (U.S.), 1952 . . . . £25/£10

Plays

A Man of Honour, Chapman and Hall, 1903 (150 copies, wraps) £500
ditto, Dramatic Publishing Company (U.S.), [1912] (wraps) £75
Lady Frederick, Heinemann, 1912 . . . £75
Jack Straw, Heinemann, 1912 . . . . £75
Mrs Dot, Heinemann, 1912 . . . . . £75
Penelope, Heinemann, 1912 . . . . . £75
The Explorer, Heinemann, 1912 . . . . £75
ditto, Dramatic Publishing Company (U.S.), [1912] (wraps) £75
The Tenth Man, Heinemann, 1913 . . . . £75
ditto, Dramatic Publishing Company (U.S.), [1913] (wraps) £75
Landed Gentry, Heinemann, 1913 . . . £75
Smith, Heinemann, 1913 . . . . . £75
ditto, Dramatic Publishing Company (U.S.), [1913] (wraps) £75
The Land of Promise, 1913 . . . . . £75
The Unknown, Heinemann, 1920 . . . £75
The Circle, Heinemann, 1921 . . . . £75
ditto, Doran (U.S.), [1921] £75
Caesar's Wife, Heinemann, 1922 . . . £75
East of Suez, Heinemann, 1922 (no d/w) . . £75
ditto, Heinemann, 1922 (wraps) £45
ditto, Doran (U.S.), 1922 . . . . . £50
Our Betters, Heinemann, 1923 . . . . £75
Home and Beauty, Heinemann, 1923 . . £100
The Unattainable, Heinemann, 1923 . . £75
Loaves and Fishes, Heinemann, 1924 . . £75
The Letter, Doran (U.S.), 1925 . . . £75/£45
ditto, Heinemann, 1927 . . . . . £75
The Constant Wife, Doran (U.S.), 1926 . £75/£45
ditto, Heinemann, 1927 . . . . . £75
The Sacred Flame, Heinemann, 1928 . £100/£25
ditto, Doubleday (U.S.), 1928 . . . £75/£25
The Breadwinner, Heinemann, 1930 . £50/£15
ditto, Doubleday (U.S.), 1931 . . . £50/£15
For Services Rendered, Heinemann, 1932 . £45/£10
Sheppey, Heinemann, 1933 . . . . £40/£10

The Noble Spaniard, Evans Brothers, 1953.　£25/£10

Travel
The Land of the Blessed Virgin, Heinemann, 1905　.
. . . . £200
On a Chinese Screen, Heinemann, 1922　£150/£25
ditto, Doran (U.S.), 1922 . . . . . . £150/£25
The Gentleman in the Parlour, Heinemann, 1930 . .
. . . . £100/£25
ditto, Doubleday (U.S.), 1930　. . . . £100/£25
Don Fernando, Heinemann, 1935　. . . £100/£15
ditto, Heinemann, 1935 (175 signed, numbered copies)
. . . . £350
ditto, Doubleday (U.S.), 1935　. . . . £100/£15

Essays
Books and You, Heinemann, 1940　. . . £40/£15
ditto, Doubleday (U.S.), 1940　. . . . £40/£15
The Writer's Point of View, C.U.P., 1951 (wraps) £15
The Vagrant Mood, Heinemann, 1952　.　£25/£10
ditto, Heinemann, 1952 (500 signed copies)　. £250
ditto, Doubleday (U.S.), 1953　. . . . £25/£10
Ten Novels and Their Authors, Heinemann, 1954　.
. . . . £25/£10

Others
The Summing Up, Heinemann, 1938　.　£45/£10
ditto, Doubleday (U.S.), 1938　. . . . £45/£10
ditto, Doubleday (U.S.), 1954 (391 signed, numbered
copies) £225
France at War, Heinemann, 1940 (wraps)　. . £20
ditto, Doubleday (U.S.), 1940　. . . . £40/£10
Strictly Personal, Doubleday (U.S.), 1941 (515 signed,
numbered copies)　. . . . . . . £225
ditto, Heinemann, 1942　. . . . . . £25/£10
A Writer's Notebook, Heinemann, 1949　£20/£5
ditto, Heinemann, 1949 (1,000 signed copies)　. £200
ditto, Doubleday (U.S.), 1949　. . . . £20/£5
ditto, Doubleday (U.S.), 1949 (1,000 signed copies)　.
. . . . £200

ARTHUR MILLER
(b.1915)

An American playwright who is perhaps best known for *The Death of a Salesman*, about the unsuccessful businessman Willy Loman, and *The Crucible* which relates the Salem witch trials to the era of McCarthyism in the USA.

Plays
All My Sons, Reynal & Hitchcock (U.S.), 1947　. .
. . . . £250/£40
Death of a Salesman, Viking (U.S.), 1949　£450/£35
ditto, Cresset, 1949　. . . . . . . £100/£20
The Crucible, Viking (U.S.), 1953　. . . £300/£30
ditto, Cresset, 1956　. . . . . . . £100/£20

A View from the Bridge and A Memory of Two Mondays, Viking (U.S.), 1955 . . . . £45/£10
ditto, Cresset, 1957 . . . . £45/£10
Collected Plays, Viking (U.S.), 1957　.　£45/£10
ditto, Cresset, 1958　. . . . . . . £45/£10
After the Fall, Viking (U.S.), 1964　. . . £25/£10
ditto, Viking (U.S.), 1964 (500 signed copies, glassine
d/w and slipcase). . . . . . . £125/£75
ditto, Secker & Warburg. 1964　. . . . £25/£10
Incident at Vichy, Viking (U.S.), 1965　. . £50/£10
ditto, Secker & Warburg. 1966　. . . . £30/£10
The Price, Viking (U.S.), 1968　. . . . £30/£10
ditto, Secker & Warburg. 1968　. . . . £25/£10
The Portable Arthur Miller, Viking (U.S.), 1971 (ed.
Harold Clurman). . . . . £15/£5
The Creation of the World and Other Business,
Viking (U.S.), 1973 . . . . £20/£5
The Archbishop's Ceiling, Dramatists Play Service
(U.S.), 1976 (wraps) £10
ditto, Methuen, 1984 . . . . £10/£5
The Theater Essays of Arthur Miller, Viking (U.S.),
1978 (ed. Robert A. Martin)　. . . . £15/£5
The American Clock, Viking (U.S.), 1980　£15/£5
Collected Plays, Franklin (U.S.), 1980 (signed copies).
. . . . £75
Collected Plays: Volume II, Viking (U.S.), 1981　. .
. . . . £15/£5
Elegy for a Lady, Dramatists Play Service (U.S.), 1984
(wraps) £10
ditto, Methuen, 1984 . . . . £10/£5
Some Kind of Love Story, Dramatists Play Service
(U.S.), 1984 (wraps). £10
Playing for Time, Dramatic Publishing (U.S.), 1985
(wraps) £10
*Danger: Memory! Two Plays: 'I Can't Remember
Anything' and 'Clara'*, Grove (U.S.), 1987 £25/£10
ditto, Methuen, 1986 . . . . £10/£5
The Golden Years, Dramatists Play Service (U.S.),
1990 (wraps) £10
ditto, Methuen, 1989 . . . . £10/£5
The Last Yankee, Dramatists Play Service (U.S.), 1991
(wraps) £10
ditto, Methuen, 1993 (wraps). £5
The Ride Down Mt. Morgan, Viking Penguin (U.S.),
1992 (wraps) £5
ditto, Stephens (U.S.), 1991 (200 signed, numbered
copies) £75
Broken Glass, Viking Penguin (U.S.), 1994 (wraps) £5
ditto, Methuen, 1994 (wraps). £5
The Last Yankee and Broken Glass, Fireside (U.S.),
1994 . . . . £10/£5

Novels
Focus, Reynal (U.S.), 1945 . . . . . £100/£20
ditto, Gollancz, 1945 . . . . £40/£10
The Misfits, Viking (U.S.), 1961. . . . £125/£25
ditto, Secker & Warburg. 1961　. . . . £45/£15

Short Stories
I Don't Need You Anymore, Viking (U.S.), 1967 . .
. . . . £20/£5
ditto, Secker & Warburg. 1967 . . . £20/£5
'The Misfits' and Other Stories, Scribner (U.S.), 1987
. . . . £25/£10
Homely Girl, A Life, Viking (U.S.), 1992 (100 signed
copies of 1,200, slipcase, 2 vols) . . £300/£250
ditto, Viking (U.S.), 1992 (1,100 signed copies of
1,200, slipcase, 2 vols) . . . . . £100/£75
Homely Girl, A Life, and Other Stories, Viking (U.S.),
1995 . . . . £10/£5

Others
Situation Normal, Reynal (U.S.), 1944 . . £125/£25
An Enemy of the People, Viking (U.S.), 1951
(adaptation of play by Henrik Ibsen) . . £20/£5
On Social Plays, Viking (U.S.), 1955 (introduction to
View from the Bridge, wraps) £75
Jane's Blanket, Crowell-Collier (U.S.), 1963 £250/£35
ditto. Macmillan, 1963 . . . . . £250/£35
In Russia, Viking, 1969 (with Inge Morath) £20/£5
ditto. Secker & Warburg. 1969 . . . £20/£5
In the Country. Viking, 1977 (with Inge Morath) .
. . . . £20/£5
ditto, Secker & Warburg. 1977 . . . £20/£5
Chinese Encounters. Farrar. Straus (U.S.), 1979 (with
Inge Morath) . . . . £15/£5
ditto, Secker & Warburg. 1979 . . . £15/£5
Salesman in Beijing, Viking (U.S.), 1984 . £15/£5
ditto, Methuen, 1984 . . . . . . £15/£5
Timebends: A Life, Franklin (U.S.), 1987 (signed
copies) £35
ditto, Grove (U.S.), 1987 . . . . . £10/£5
ditto, Methuen, 1987 . . . . . . £10/£5

HENRY MILLER
(b.1891 d.1980)

The American Miller made his name by writing The
Tropic of Cancer which describes the promiscuous
lifestyle he witnessed while living in Paris. It was the
first of many of his books to be suppressed in both
America and England because of their sexual
frankness.

Fiction
The Tropic of Cancer, Obelisk Press (Paris), 1934
(first printing, copies issued in printed green and
white wrappers) £4,000
ditto, Obelisk Press (Paris), 1934 (second printing,
issued in plain wrappers with an illustrated dust
jacket) £4,000
ditto, Medvsa (U.S.), 1940 (no d/w) . . . £200
ditto, Grove Press (U.S.), 1961 (100 signed copies, no
d/w) £1,250
ditto, Grove Press (U.S.), 1961 . . . . £75/£20

ditto, Calder, 1963. . . . . £45/£15
Black Spring, Obelisk (Paris), 1936 (wraps) £1,000
ditto, Grove (U.S.), 1963 . . . . . . £25/£10
ditto, Calder, 1965. . . . . £25/£10
The Tropic of Capricorn, Obelisk Press (Paris), 1939
(60 francs price on spine, errata slip tipped in, wraps)
. . . . £1,500
ditto, Grove Press (U.S.), 1961 . . . . £75/£20
ditto, Calder, 1964. . . . . £45/£15
Sexus, Obelisk (Paris), 1949 (2 vols, 3,000 numbered
copies, no d/ws) £150
ditto, Calder, 1969. . . . . £45/£10
Plexus, Correa (Paris), 1952 (100 numbered copies, in
French, d/w) . . . . £1,450/£1,000
ditto, Correa (Paris), 1952 (wraps) . . . £250
ditto, Olympia (Paris), 1953 (2 vols, wraps). . £250
ditto, Weidenfeld & Nicolson, 1963 . . . £50/£15
Nexus, Obelisk (Paris), 1960 (wraps) . . . £50
ditto, Weidenfeld & Nicolson, 1964 . . . £45/£10
Sexus, Plexus, Nexus, Grove (U.S.), 1965 (3 vols,
slipcase) . . . . £100/£75

Plays
Scenario (A Film with Sound), Obelisk (Paris), 1937
(200 signed copies, wraps) £1,000
*Just Wild About Harry: A Melo Melo in Seven
Scenes*, New Directions (U.S.), 1963 . . £45/£15
ditto, MacGibbon & Gee, 1964 . . . . £25/£10

Others
What Are You Going to Do About Alf?, Lecram-
Servant (Paris), 1935 (wraps) £1,500
ditto, Porter (U.S.), 1944 (wraps) . . . £45
ditto, Turret , 1971 (100 sgned copies) . £150/£100
ditto, Turret , 1971. . . . . . . £65/£15
Aller Retour New York, Obelisk (Paris), 1935 (150
signed copies, wraps) £1,000
ditto, privately printed by Ben Abramson (U.S.), 1945
(500 copies, no d/w) £65
Money and How it Gets that Way, Booster (Paris),
1938 (with author's holograph limitation and copyright note, 495 copies, wraps) £650
ditto, Booster (Paris), 1938 (without author's holograph
limitation and copyright note, 495 copies, wraps). .
. . . . £200
Max and the White Phagocytes, Obelisk (Paris), 1938
(wraps) £500
The Cosmological Eye, New Directions (U.S.), 1939
(photo of eye inset on front cover, d/w spine lettered
white, priced $2.50) . . . . . . £350/£45
ditto, Editions Poetry London, 1945 . . . £150/£35
The World of Sex, Abrahamson (U.S.), 1940 (250
copies) . . . . £250/£175
ditto, Abrahamson (U.S.), 1940 (no d/w) . . £40
ditto, Grove (U.S.), 1965 . . . . . . £35/£10
ditto, Calder, 1970. . . . . £35/£10
The Collosus of Maroussi, Colt (U.S.), 1941 £200/£35
ditto, Colt (U.S.), 1941 (100 signed copies, no d/w) .
. . . . £1,000

ditto, Secker & Warburg, 1942 . . . . £125/£25
The Wisdom of the Heart, New Directions (U.S.), 1941 . . . . £75/£15
ditto, Editions Poetry London, 1947 . . . £45/£15
Sunday After the War, New Directions (U.S.), 1944 .
. . . . £75/£15
ditto, Editions Poetry London, 1945 . . . £45/£15
The Air-Conditioned Nightmare, New Directions (U.S.), 1945 . . . . £75/£15
ditto, Secker & Warburg, 1947 . . . . £65/£15
Maurizius Forever, Colt Press (U.S.), 1946 (500 copies, plain brown d/w) . . . £175/£125
Remember to Remember, New Directions (U.S.), 1947 (first state with title pages divided by frontispiece photograph of author) . . . . . . £100/£25
ditto, Grey Walls Press, 1952 . . . . . £75/£25
The Smile at the Foot of the Ladder, Duell, Sloan, and Pearce (U.S.), 1948 . . . . £75/£20
ditto, MacGibbon & Kee, 1966 . . . . £35/£10
The Books in My Life, Owen, 1952 . . . £100/£25
ditto, New Directions (U.S.), 1952 . . . £100/£25
Nights of Love and Laughter, Signet/New American Library (U.S.), 1955 (wraps) £10
The Time of the Assassins: A Story of Rimbaud, New Directions (U.S.), 1956 (no d/w) £50
ditto, Neville Spearman, 1956 . . . £125/£30
Quiet Days in Clichy, Olympia (Paris), 1956 (wraps) .
. . . . £500
ditto, Grove (U.S.), 1965 (wraps) . . . £25
ditto, Calder, 1966 . . . . £30/£10
A Devil in Paradise, Signet/New American Library (U.S.), 1956 (wraps) £10
ditto, New English Library, 1963 (wraps) . . £10
Big Sur and the Oranges of Hieronymous Bosch, New Directions (U.S.), 1957 . . . . . £100/£20
ditto, Heinemann, 1958 . . . . . £75/£20
The Henry Miller Reader, New Directions (U.S.), 1959 (ed. Lawrence Durrell) . . . . £35/£10
ditto, as *The Best of Henry Miller*, Heinemann, 1960 .
. . . . £35/£10
Reunion in Barcelona, The Scorpion Press, 1959 (50 signed copies of 500) £150
ditto, The Scorpion Press, 1959 (450 unsigned copies of 500) £35
To Paint Is to Love Again, Cambia (U.S.), 1960 . .
. . . . £35/£10
Stand Still Like Hummingbird, New Directions (U.S.), 1962 . . . . £30/£10
Henry Miller on Writing, New Directions (U.S.), 1964 (wraps) £15
Insomnia: Or, the Devil at Large, Loujon (U.S.), 1971 (200 of 385 signed, numbered copies in box) £1,250
ditto, Loujon (U.S.), 1971 (unboxed copies) . £750
My Life and Times, Playboy (U.S.), 1971 . £25/£10
ditto, Pall Mall Press, 1972 . . . . £25/£10
On Turning Eighty: Journey to an Antique Land: Forward to the 'Angel is My Watermark', Capra (U.S.), 1972 (200 signed, numbered copies, no d/w) .
. . . . £125

ditto, Capra (U.S.), 1972 (wraps). £15
Reflections on the Death of Mishima, Capra (U.S.), 1972 (200 signed, numbered copies, no d/w) . £100
ditto, Capra (U.S.), 1972 (wraps). £15
First Impressions of Greece, Capra (U.S.), 1973 (250 signed, numbered copies, no d/w) £100
ditto, Capra (U.S.), 1973 (wraps). £15
Henry Miller's Book of Friends: A Tribute to Friends of Long Ago, Capra (U.S.), 1976 (250 signed, numbered copies, no d/w) £125
ditto, Capra (U.S.), 1976 (26 signed, numbered copies with original artwork by author) £500
ditto, Capra (U.S.), 1976 (wraps). . . £25/£15
ditto, W.H. Allen, 1978 . . . . . £25/£10
Mother, China, and the World Beyond, Capra (U.S.), 1977 (250 signed, numbered copies, no d/w) . £100
ditto, Capra (U.S.), 1977 (wraps). £15
Gliding Into the Everglades, Lost Pleiade Press (U.S.), 1977 (250 signed, numbered copies, no d/w) . £100
ditto, Lost Pleiade Press (U.S.), 1977 (wraps) . £25
My Bike and Other Friends, Capra (U.S.), 1978 (250 signed, numbered copies) . . . . . £125/£75
ditto, Capra (U.S.), 1978 . . . . . £25/£10
Joey, Capra (U.S.), 1979 (250 signed, numbered copies) . . . . £100/£75
ditto, Capra (U.S.), 1979 (wraps). £25
The World of Lawrence: A Passionate Appreciation, Capra (U.S.), 1979 (250 signed, numbered copies) .
. . . . £125/£75
ditto, Capra (U.S.), 1979 . . . . . £25/£10
ditto, John Calder, 1980 . . . . . £25/£10
The Paintings of Henry Miller: Paint as You Like and Die Happy, Chronicle Books (U.S.), 1982 (wraps) .
. . . . £50
Opus Pistorum, Grove (U.S.), 1983 . . £30/£10
Crazy Cock, Grove (U.S.), 1991 . . . . £25/£10
ditto, HarperCollins, 1992 . . . . £15/£5
The Complete Book of Friends, Allison & Busby, 1988 . . . . £20/£5
Moloch: Or This Gentile World, Grove (U.S.), 1992 .
. . . . £15/£5
ditto, HarperCollins, 1993 . . . . £15/£5

ABRAHAM MERRITT
(b.1884 d.1943)

The author of exotic fantasies which are often more extreme than those of Edgar Rice Burroughs, he was a popular contributor to the pre-World War Two American pulp magazines.

Novels
The Moon Pool, Putnam's (U.S.), 1919 . . £650/£100
The Ship of Ishtar, Putnam's (U.S.), 1926 . £500/£75
Seven Footprints to Satan, Boni & Liveright (U.S.), 1928 . . . . £250/£35
ditto, Richards, 1928 . . . . £225/£35

The Face in the Abyss, Liveright (U.S.), 1931 . . .
. . . . £500/£75
Dwellers in the Mirage, Liveright (U.S.), 1932. . .
. . . . £750/£100
ditto, Skeffington, [1933]. . . . . £500/£75
Thru the Dragon Glass, ARRA (U.S.), 1932 (wraps) .
. . . . £65
ditto, as *Through the Dragon Glass*, Doreal (U.S.),
1948 (wraps) £40
Burn Witch Burn!, Liveright (U.S.), 1932 . £500/£75
ditto, Methuen, 1934. . . . . . . £250/£45
Creep, Shadow, Doubleday, Doran, (U.S.), 1934 . .
. . . . £350/£50
ditto, as *Creep, Shadow, Creep!*, Methuen, 1935 . .
. . . . £75/£20
Three Lines of Old French, Bizarre (U.S.), 1937
(wraps) £100
ditto, Doreal (U.S.), 1948 (wraps) . . . £40
The Story Behind the Story, privately printed by the
American Weekly (U.S.), 1942 (no d/w) . . £35
The Metal Monster, Avon (U.S.), 1946 (wraps) £20
ditto, Hyperion (U.S.), 1974 (no d/w) . . .£50
The Fox Woman/The Blue Pagoda, New Collectors
(U.S.), 1946 (with Hannes Bok. Nude woman
illustration) £45
ditto, New Collectors (U.S.), 1946 (with Hannes Bok.
Nude man illustration) £40
The Black Wheel, New Collectors (U.S.), 1947
(completed by Hannes Bok). £35
The Drone Man, Doreal (U.S.), 1948 (wraps) . £40
Rhythm of the Spheres, Doreal (U.S.), 1948 (wraps) .
. . . . £40
The People of the Pit, Doreal (U.S.), 1948 (wraps) .
. . . . £40
The Woman of the Wood, Doreal (U.S.), 1948 (wraps)
. . . . £40
Short Stories, Doreal (U.S.), 1948 (wraps) . . £300
The Fox Woman & Other Stories, Avon (U.S.), 1949
(wraps) £20
ditto, Eshbach (U.S.), 1949 (300 copies of Avon sheets
bound in black cloth with white d/w) . £200/£100
ditto, Eshbach (U.S.), 1949 (bound in light blue cloth
with white d/w) . . . . . . £250/£150
Seven Footprints to Satan/Burn Witch Burn!,
Liveright (U.S.), 1952 . . . . . £25/£10
Dwellers in the Mirage/The Face in the Abyss,
Liveright (U.S.), 1953 . . . . . £25/£10
The Challenge from Beyond, Evans (U.S.), 1954 (with
H.P. Lovecraft, Robert E. Howard, Frank Belknap
Long, and C.L. Moore) £40
Reflections in the Moon Pool, Train (U.S.), 1985 . .
. . . . £15/£5

A.A. MILNE
(b.1882 d.1956)

Milne was a freelance journalist in London, then
assistant editor of *Punch*, before becoming a full-time
writer from 1918. He is famous for his plays and
children's books, although he also wrote novels, short
stories, poetry and essays.

Children's Titles
Once on a Time: A Fairy Story, Hodder & Stoughton,
1917 (illustrated by H.M. Brock) £45
ditto, Hodder & Stoughton, [1925] (illustrated by
Charles Robinson) . . . . £125/£25
When We Were Very Young, Methuen, 1924 (verse,
illustrated by E.H. Shepard). . . . £2,500/£750
ditto, Methuen, 1924 (verse, illustrated by E.H.
Shepard, 100 numbered copies, signed by the author
and artist) . . . . £4,500/£3,000
ditto, Dutton (U.S.), 1924 (100 numbered copies,
signed by the author and artist) . . £2,500/£1,750
ditto, Dutton (U.S.), 1924 (400 deluxe copies) . . .
. . . . £750/£450
ditto, Methuen, 1974 (300 numbered copies, signed by
Christopher Milne) . . . .£300/£150
Vespers: A Poem, Methuen, [1924] (illustrated by E.H.
Shepard, music by H. Fraser-Simson) . £125/£45
Fourteen Songs, Methuen, 1924 (illustrated by E.H.
Shepard, music by H. Fraser-Simson) . . £175/£65
*Make-Believe: A Children's Play in a Prologue and
Three Acts*, Methuen, 1925 . . . . £75/£25
A Gallery of Children, Stanley Paul, 1925 (illustrated
by H. Willebeek le Mair) . . . . £200/£65
ditto, Stanley Paul, 1925 (500 numbered copies, signed
by the author) . . . .£500/£300
The King's Breakfast, Methuen, 1925 (illustrated by
E.H. Shepard, music by H. Fraser-Simson £175/£50
Winnie-the-Pooh, Methuen, 1926 (stories, illustrated
by E.H. Shepard) . . . . . . £500/£200
ditto, Methuen, 1926 (deluxe edition: red, green or blue
leather binding, in slipcase) . . . £1,750/£750
ditto, Methuen, 1926 (350 copies, signed by the author
and artist, d/w and slipcase) . . . £3,500/£1,750
ditto, Methuen, 1926 (20 special copies, signed by the
author and artist) £6,000
ditto, Dutton (U.S.), 1926 (200 numbered copies,
signed by the author and artist) . . £2,500/£1,750
ditto, Dutton (U.S.), 1926. . . . . £450/£175
ditto, Methuen, 1973 (illustrated in colour by E.H.
Shepard) . . . . £40/£15
ditto, Methuen, 1976 (stories, illustrated by E.H.
Shepard, 300 numbered copies, signed by Christopher
Milne). . . . .£300/£150
*Teddy Bear and Other Songs From 'When We Were
Very Young'*, Methuen, 1926 (illustrated by E.H.
Shepard, music by H. Fraser-Simson) . £175/£50
ditto, Methuen, 1926 (100 numbered copies copies,
signed by the author and artist and composer, d/w and
slipcase) £500

Now We Are Six, Methuen, 1927 (verse, illustrated by
E.H. Shepard) . . . . £250/£75
ditto, Methuen, 1927 (deluxe edition: red, blue or green
leather binding, in slipcase) . . . . £500/£200
ditto, Methuen, 1927 (200 numbered copies, signed by
the author and artist). £2,000
ditto, Methuen, 1927 (20 special copies, signed by the
author and artist) £3,500
ditto, Dutton (U.S.), 1927 (200 signed copies) . . .
. . . . £1,750/£1,000
ditto, Dutton (U.S.), 1928. . . . . £200/£75
ditto, Methuen, 1976 (300 numbered copies, signed by
Christopher Milne) . . . . . £400/£150
Songs from 'Now We Are Six', Methuen, 1927 (music
by H. Fraser-Simson) . . . . . £175/£45
ditto, Methuen, 1927 (100 signed copies) . . £650
More Very Young Songs, Methuen, 1928 . £175/£60
ditto, Methuen, 1928 (100 numbered copies, signed by
the author and artist and composer, d/w and slipcase)
. . . . £500
The House at Pooh Corner, Methuen, 1928 (stories,
illustrated by E.H. Shepard). . . . .£450/£175
ditto, Methuen, 1928 (350 numbered copies, signed by
the author and artist). . . . £3,500/£1,750
ditto, Methuen, 1928 (20 special copies, signed by the
author and artist) £6,000
ditto, Methuen, 1928 (deluxe edition: red, green or blue
leather binding, in slipcase) £2,000
ditto, Dutton (U.S.), 1928 (250 numbered copies,
signed by the author and artist) . . £1,750/£1,000
ditto, Dutton (U.S.), 1928. . . . . £200/£75
ditto, Methuen, 1974 (illustrated in colour by E.H.
Shepard) . . . . £45/£20
The Christopher Robin Calendar 1929, Methuen
'Ephemerides' series, [1928] (verse, illustrated by
E.H. Shepard) £75
The Christopher Robin Story Book, Methuen, 1928
(selections from *When We Were Very Young*, *Now We
Are Six*, *Winnie-the-Pooh* and *The House at Pooh
Corner*, new preface by the author) . . £225/£65
The Hums of Pooh, Methuen, 1929 (illustrated by E.H.
Shepard, music by H. Fraser-Simson) . . £175/£45
ditto, Methuen, 1929 (100 numbered copies, signed by
the author and artist and composer, d/w and slipcase)
. . . . £500
*Toad of Toad Hall: A Play Taken from Kenneth
Grahame's 'The Wind in the Willows'*, Methuen,
1929 . . . . £100/£25
ditto, Methuen, 1929 (200 numbered copies, signed by
Kenneth Grahame and A. A. Milne) . £1,000/£500
Tales of Pooh, Methuen: 'Modern Classics' series,
[1930], (selections from *Winnie-The-Pooh* and *The
House at Pooh Corner*, illustrated by E.H. Shepard) .
. . . . £150/£65
The Christopher Robin Birthday Book, Methuen, 1930
(selections from *When We Were Very Young*, *Now We
Are Six*, *Winnie-the-Pooh* and *The House at Pooh
Corner*, illustrated by E.H. Shepard) . . £125/£50

The Christopher Robin Verses, Methuen, 1932
(contains *When We Were Very Young* and *Now We
Are Six*, illustrated by E.H. Shepard) . . £75/£25
Introducing Winnie-the-Pooh, Methuen, 1947 £75/£35
The World of Pooh, Methuen, 1958 . . £75/£35
The World of Christopher Robin, Methuen, 1959 . .
. . . . £75/£35
*Prince Rabbit and The Princess Who Could Not
Laugh*, Ward Lock, 1966 (illustrated by Mary
Shepard) . . . . £35/£15
The Pooh Story Book, Methuen, 1967 . . £50/£20
The Christopher Robin Verse Book, Methuen, 1969
(illustrated by E.H. Shepard) . . . . £50/£20

Adult Titles: Fiction

Mr Pim, Hodder & Stoughton, 1921, (novel) £75/£25
The Red House Mystery, Methuen, 1922 (novel) . .
. . . . £500/£150
The Secret and Other Stories, Methuen/Fountain Press
(U.S.), 1929 (742 signed copies) £200
Chloe Marr, Methuen, 1946 . . . . £25/£10
Birthday Party and Other Stories, Dutton (U.S.), 1948.
. . . . £25/£10
ditto, Methuen, 1949 . . . . . . £25/£10
A Table Near the Band, Methuen, 1950 (stories) . .
. . . . £35/£15

Plays

First Plays, Chatto & Windus, 1919 (contains 'Wurzel-
Flummery', 'The Lucky One', 'The Boy Comes
Home', 'Belinda' and 'The Red Feathers') £25/£10
Second Plays, Chatto & Windus, 1921 (contains
'Make-Believe', 'Mr Pim Passes By', 'The Camberley
Triangle', 'The Romantic Age' and 'The
Stepmother') . . . . £25/£10
Three Plays, Putnam (U.S.), 1922 (contains 'The
Dover Road', 'The Truth about Blayds' and 'The
Great Broxopp') . . . . £25/£10
ditto, Chatto & Windus, 1923 . . . . £25/£10
Success, Chatto & Windus, 1923 . . . £25/£10
The Man in the Bowler Hat, French (U.K./U.S.), 1923
. . . . £15
Four Plays, Chatto & Windus, 1926 (contains 'To
Have the Honour, Meet the Prince', 'Ariadne',
'Portrait of a Gentleman in Slippers' and 'Success') .
. . . . £25/£10
More Plays, Chatto & Windus, 1935 (contains 'The
Ivory Doors', 'The Fourth Wall' and 'Other People's
Lives') . . . . £20/£5
Four Plays, Penguin, 1939 (contains 'To Have the
Honour', 'Belinda', 'The Dover Road' and 'Mr Pim
Passes By', wraps) £5
The Ugly Duckling, French, 1941 . . . £10
Before the Flood, French (U.K./U.S.), 1951 . £5

Verse

For the Luncheon Interval: Cricket and Other Verses,
Methuen, 1925 (wraps) £35
Behind the Lines, Methuen, 1940 . . . £25/£10

The Norman Church, Methuen, 1948 . . £25/£10	

Others

Lovers in London, Alston Rivers, 1905 . . . £75
The Day's Play, Methuen, 1910 (sketches) . . £15
The Holiday Round, Methuen, 1912 (sketches) £15
Once a Week, Methuen, 1914 . . . . £10
Happy Days, George H. Doran (U.S.), 1915 . £10
Not That It Matters, Methuen, 1919 . . . £10
If I May, Methuen, 1920 . . . . . . £30/£10
The Sunny Side, Methuen, 1921 . . . £30/£10
The Ascent of Man, Ernest Benn, 1928 . . £30/£10
By Way of Introduction, Methuen, 1929 . £30/£10
ditto, Dutton (U.S.), 1929 (166 signed, large paper
copies) £250
Those Were the Days, Methuen, 1929 . £30/£10
Two People, Methuen, 1931 . . . . £30/£10
Four Days Wonder, Methuen, 1933 . . £30/£10
Peace with Honour, Methuen, 1934 . £25/£10
Miss Elizabeth Bennett, Chatto & Windus, 1936 . .
. . . . £30/£10
It's Too Late Now, Methuen, 1939 . . . £30/£10
War With Honour, Macmillan, 1940 . . £25/£10
War Aims Unlimited, Methuen, 1941 (wraps) . £15
The Pocket Milne, Dutton (U.S.),1941 . . £25/£10
ditto, Methuen, 1942 . . . . . . £20/£5
Year In, Year Out, Methuen, 1952 . . . £25/£10

GLADYS MITCHELL
(b.1901 d.1983)

From the Golden Age of Detective Fiction, Mitchell's unconventional sleuth, Beatrice Adela Lestrange Bradley was already elderly when she made her first appearance in 1929. Her last case is recorded in 1984, by which time she may have been 125 years old.

Novels

Speedy Death, Gollancz, 1929 . . . . £500/£75
ditto, Dial Press (U.S.), 1929 . . . . £400/£75
The Mystery of a Butcher's Shop, Gollancz, 1929 . .
. . . . £500/£75
ditto, Dial Press (U.S.), 1930 . . . . £350/£45
The Longer Bodies, Gollancz, 1930 . . . £300/£45
The Saltmarsh Murders, Gollancz, 1932 . £350/£35
ditto, Macrae-Smith (U.S.), 1933 . . . £300/£30
Death at the Opera, Grayson, 1934 . . . £300/£30
ditto, as *Death in the Wet*, Macrae-Smith (U.S.), 1934
. . . . £200/£30
The Devil at Saxon Wall, Grayson, 1935 . £200/£35
Dead Men's Morris, Joseph, 1936 . . . £200/£35
Come Away Death, Joseph, 1937 . . . £200/£35
St Peter's Finger, Joseph, 1938 . . . . £150/£30
ditto, St Martin's Press (U.S.), 1987 . . . £15/£5
Printer's Error, Joseph, 1939 . . . . £150/£25
Brazen Tongue, Joseph, 1940 . . . . £150/£25

Hangman's Curfew, Joseph, 1941 . . . £150/£25
When Last I Died, Joseph, 1941 . . . . £150/£30
ditto, Knopf (U.S.), 1942 . . . . . . £125/£10
Laurels are Poison, Joseph, 1942 . . . £150/£30
The Worsted Viper, Joseph, 1943 . . . £150/£30
Sunset Over Soho, Joseph, 1943 . . . . £125/£20
My Father Sleeps, Joseph, 1944 . . . . £125/£15
The Rising of the Moon, Joseph, 1945 . . £125/£15
ditto, St Martin's Press (U.S.), 1985 . . . £15/£5
Here Comes a Chopper, Joseph, 1946 . . £125/£15
Death and the Maiden, Joseph, 1947 . . £125/£15
The Dancing Druids, Joseph, 1948 . . . £125/£15
ditto, St Martin's Press (U.S.), 1986 . . . £10/£5
Tom Brown's Body, Joseph, 1949 . . . £125/£15
Groaning Spinney, Joseph, 1950 . . . . £100/£10
The Devil's Elbow, Joseph, 1951 . . . £100/£10
The Echoing Strangers, Joseph, 1952 . . £75/£10
Merlin's Furlong, Joseph, 1953 . . . . £75/£10
Faintly Speaking, Joseph, 1954 . . . . £75/£10
ditto, St Martin's Press (U.S.), 1986 . . . £10/£5
Watson's Choice, Joseph, 1955 . . . . £50/£10
ditto, McKay (U.S.), 1976 . . . . . £10/£5
Twelve Horses and The Hangman's Noose, Joseph,
1956 . . . . £50/£10
ditto, British Book Centre (U.S.), 1958 . . £15/£5
ditto, as *Hangman's Noose*, Severn House, 1983 . .
. . . . £10/£5
The Twenty-Third Man, Joseph, 1957 . . £50/£10
Spotted Hemlock, Joseph, 1958 . . . . £50/£10
ditto, St Martin's Press (U.S.), 1985 . . . £10/£5
The Man Who Grew Tomatoes, Joseph, 1959 £50/£10
ditto, British Book Centre (U.S.), 1959 . . £15/£5
Say it with Flowers, Joseph, 1960 . . . £40/£5
ditto, London House (U.S.), 1960 . . . £15/£5
The Nodding Canaries, Joseph, 1961 . . £40/£5
My Bones Will Keep, Joseph, 1962 . . . £35/£5
ditto, British Book Centre (U.S.), 1962 . . £10/£5
Adders on the Heath, Joseph, 1963 . . . £35/£5
ditto, British Book Centre (U.S.), 1963 . . £10/£5
Death of a Delfy Blue, Joseph, 1964 . . . £35/£5
ditto, British Book Centre (U.S.), 1965 . . £10/£5
ditto, as *Death in Amsterdam*, Severn House, 1990 .
. . . . £10/£5
Pageant of a Murder, Joseph, 1965 . . . £35/£5
ditto, British Book Centre (U.S.), 1965 . . . £10/£5
The Croaking Raven, Joseph, 1966 . . . £35/£5
Skeleton Island, Joseph, 1967 . . . . £35/£5
Three Quick and Five Dead, Joseph, 1968 . £15/£5
Dance to Your Daddy, Joseph, 1969 . . . £35/£5
Gory Dew, Joseph, 1970 . . . . . . £35/£5
Lament for Letto, Joseph, 1971 . . . . £35/£5
A Nearse on May-Day, Joseph, 1972 . . £35/£5
The Murder of Busy Lizzie, Joseph, 1973 . £25/£5
A Javelin for Jonah, Joseph, 1974 . . . £25/£5
Winking at the Brim, Joseph, 1975 . . . £25/£5
ditto, McKay (U.S.), 1977 . . . . . £10/£5
Convent on Styx, Joseph, 1975 . . . . £25/£5
Late, Late in the Evening, Joseph, 1976 . £25/£5
Noonday and Night, Joseph, 1977 . . . £25/£5

Fault in the Structure, Joseph, 1977	£25/£5
Wraiths and Changelings, Joseph, 1978	£25/£5
Mingled with Venom, Joseph, 1978	£25/£5
Nest of Vipers, Joseph, 1979	£20/£5
The Mudflats of the Dead, Joseph, 1979	£20/£5
Uncoffin'd Clay, Joseph, 1980	£20/£5
ditto, St Martin's Press (U.S.), 1981	£10/£5
The Whispering Knights, Joseph, 1980	£20/£5
The Death-Cap Dancers, Joseph, 1981	£20/£5
ditto, St Martin's Press (U.S.), 1981	£10/£5
Lovers, Make Moan, Joseph, 1982	£15/£5
Here Lies Gloria Mundy, Joseph, 1982	£15/£5
ditto, St Martin's Press (U.S.), 1983	£10/£5
Death of a Burrowing Mole, Joseph, 1982	£15/£5
The Greenstone Griffins, Joseph, 1983	£15/£5
Cold, Lone and Still, Joseph, 1983	£10/£5
No Winding Sheet, Joseph, 1984	£10/£5
The Crozier Pharoahs, Joseph, 1984	£10/£5

Novels written as 'Stephen Hockaby'

Marsh Hay, Grayson, 1933	£150/£25
Seven Stars and Orion, Grayson, 1934	£125/£25
Gabriel's Hold, Grayson, 1935	£125/£25
Shallw Brown, Joseph, 1936	£100/£10
Grand Master, Joseph, 1939	£100/£10

Novels written as 'Malcolm Torre'

Heavy as Lead, Joseph, 1966	£25/£5
Late and Cold, Joseph, 1967	£25/£5
Your Secret Friend, Joseph, 1968	£25/£5
Churchyard Salad, Joseph, 1969	£25/£5
Shades of Darkness, Joseph, 1970	£25/£5
Bismark's Herrings, Joseph, 1971	£25/£5

MARGARET MITCHELL
(b.1900 d.1949)

Gone With the Wind was the result of ten years work, a distillation of all of the American Civil War stories Mitchell had heard. Her 1000 page novel won the Pulitzer Prize, has sold over 25 million copies and is translated into 27 different languages.

Gone With the Wind, Macmillan (U.S.), 1936 (d/w with *Gone With the Wind* listed in second column of book list on back panel)	£4,000/£200
ditto, Macmillan (U.S.), 1936 (d/w with *Gone With the Wind* listed at top of list in first column on back panel)	£750/£200
ditto, Macmillan, 1936	£300/£75

NAOMI MITCHISON
(b.1897 d.1999)

A novelist with a long career, her works of the 1920s and 30s are held in highest esteem, especially those which evoke classical Greece and Rome. Mitchison also wrote a great deal of fiction for children.

Novels

The Conquered, Cape, 1923	£125/£45
ditto, Harcourt Brace (U.S.), 1923	£100/£25
Cloud Cuckoo Land, Cape, 1925	£40/£15
ditto, Harcourt Brace (U.S.), 1926	£35/£15
The Corn King and the Spring Queen, Cape, 1931	£30/£15
ditto, Harcourt Brace (U.S.), [n.d.]	£25/£10
We Have Been Warned, Constable, 1935	£30/£15
ditto, The Vanguard Press (U.S.) [1936].	£25/£10
Beyond this Limit, Cape, 1935	£40/£15
The Blood of the Martyrs, Constable, 1939.	£25/£5
ditto, McGraw-Hill (U.S.), 1939	£25/£5
The Bull Calves, Cape, 1947	£25/£5
Lobsters on the Agenda, Gollancz, 1952	£15/£5
Behold Your King, Muller, 1957.	£15/£5
Memoirs of a Spacewoman, Gollancz, 1962	£15/£5
When We Become Men, Collins, 1965	£15/£5
Cleopatra's People, Heinemann, 1972	£15/£5
Solution Three, Dobson, 1973	£15/£5
ditto, Warner (U.S.), 1975 (wraps)	£5
Not By Bread Alone, Marion Boyars, 1983	£15/£5
Early in Orcadia, R. Drew, 1987	£10/£5
The Oath Takers, Bainain Books, 1991	£10/£5
Sea-Green Ribbons, Bainain Books, 1991	£10/£5

Short Stories

When the Bough Breaks and Other Stories, Cape, 1924	£35/£10
ditto, Harcourt Brace (U.S.), 1924	£25/£10
Black Sparta, Greek Stories, Cape, 1928	£30/£10
ditto, Harcourt Brace (U.S.), [n.d.]	£25/£10
Barbarian Stories, Cape, 1929	£30/£10
ditto, Harcourt Brace (U.S.), 1929	£30/£10
The Powers of Light, Pharos, 1932	£30/£10
Images of Africa, Canongate, 1980	£10/£5
What Do You Think of Yourself? Scottish Short Stories, P. Harris, 1982	£10/£5
Beyond this Limit, Selected Shorter Fiction, Scottish Academic Press, 1986	£10/£5

Short Stories and Poetry

The Delicate Fire, Cape, 1933	£30/£10
ditto, Harcourt Brace (U.S.), 1933	£30/£10
The Fourth Pig, Constable, 1936	£15/£5
Five Men and a Swan, Allen & Unwin, 1957	£15/£5
A Girl Must Live, R. Drew, 1990	£10/£5

Poetry

The Laburnum Branch, Cape, 1920	£35/£10
ditto, Harcourt Brace (U.S.), 1920	£25/£10

The Alban Goes Out, Raven Press, 1939 (wraps) £50
The Cleansing of the Knife and Other Poems,
Canongate, 1978 . . . . £10/£5

Plays
The Price of Freedom, Cape, 1931 . . . £25/£5
As It Was in the Beginning, Cape, 1939 . £10/£5
Spindrift, French, 1951 (wraps) £5

Children's
Nix-Nought-Nothing, Cape, 1928 . . . £20/£5
The Hostages and Other Stories, Cape, 1930 £20/£5
ditto, Harcourt Brace (U.S.), [1931] . . . £20/£5
Boys and Girls and Gods, Watts, 1931 . . £20/£5
Kate Crackernuts, Alden Press, 1931 . . £20/£5
An End and a Beginning and Other Plays, Constable,
1937 . . . . £15/£5
ditto, as *Historical Plays for Schools*, Constable, 1939
(2 vols) . . . . £15/£5
Nix-Nought-Nothing and Elfin Hill, Cape, 1948 . .
. . . . £15/£5
The Big House, Faber, 1950 . . . . £15/£5
Travel Light, Faber, 1952. . . . . £15/£5
Graeme and the Dragon, Faber, 1954 . . £15/£5
The Swan's Road, Naldrett Press, 1954 . . £15/£5
The Land the Ravens Found, Collins, 1955 £15/£5
To The Chapel Perilous, Allen & Unwin, 1955 £15/£5
Little Boxes, Faber, 1956 . . . . . £15/£5
The Far Harbour, Collins, 1957 . . . £15/£5
Judy and Lakshmi, Collins, 1959 . . £15/£5
The Rib of the Green Umbrella, Collins, 1960 £50/£20
The Young Alexander the Great, Max Parrish, 1960 .
. . . . £10/£5
ditto, Roy (U.S.), [1961, c1960] . . . . £10/£5
Karensgaard: The Story of a Danish Farm, Collins,
1961 . . . . £10/£5
The Young Alfred the Great, Max Parrish, 1962 . .
. . . . £10/£5
ditto, Roy (U.S.), [1963] . . . . . £10/£5
The Fairy Who Couldn't Tell a Lie, Collins, 1963. .
. . . . £10/£5
Alexander the Great, Longman, 1964 . . £10/£5
Henny and Crispies, Department of Education (New
Zealand), 1964 . . . . £10/£5
A Mochudi Family, Department of Education (New
Zealand), 1965 . . . . £10/£5
Ketze and the Chief, Nelson, 1965 . . . £10/£5
Friends and Enemies, Collins, 1966 . . £10/£5
ditto, John Day Co. (U.S.), [1968] . . . £10/£5
Highland Holiday, Department of Education (New
Zealand), 1967 . . . . £10/£5
The Big Surprise, Kaye & Ward, 1967 . . £10/£5
African Heroes, Bodley Head, 1968. . . £10/£5
Don't Look Back, Kaye & Ward, 1969 . . £10/£5
The Family at Ditlabeng, Collins, 1969. . £10/£5
ditto, Farrar, Straus & Giroux (U.S.), [1970] £10/£5
Sun and Moon, Bodley Head, 1970 . . . £10/£5
ditto, Nelson (U.S.), [1973] . . . . £10/£5

Sunrise Tomorrow: A Story of Botswana, Collins,
1973 . . . . £10/£5
ditto, Farrar, Straus & Giroux (U.S.), [1973] £10/£5
The Danish Teapot, Kaye & Ward, 1973 . £10/£5
Snake, Collins, 1976 . . . . . . £10/£5
The Little Sister, O.U.P. (South Africa), 1976 . £10/£5
The Wild Dogs, O.U.P. (South Africa), 1977 £10/£5
The Brave Nurse, and Other Stories, OUP (South
Africa), 1977 . . . . £10/£5
The Two Magicians, Dobson, 1978 (with G.R.
Mitchison) . . . . £10/£5
The Vegetable War, Hamish Hamilton, 1980 £10/£5
The Sea Horse, Hamish Hamilton, 1980 . £10/£5

Non Fiction
Anna Comnena, Howe, 1926 . . . . £10/£5
Comments on Birth Control, Faber, 1930 . £10/£5
Naomi Mitchison's Vienna Diary, Gollancz, 1934. .
. . . . £20/£5
ditto, Smith and Haas (U.S.), 1934 . . £20/£5
The Home and Changing Civilisation, Bodley Head,
1934 . . . . £20/£5
Socrates, Hogarth Press, 1937 (with Richard
Crossman) . . . . £20/£5
The Moral Basis of Politics, Constable, 1938 £10/£5
ditto, Kennikat Press (U.S.), [1971] . . . £10/£5
Man and Herring, A Documentary, Serif Books, 1949
(with Denis Macintosh) . . . . . £15/£5
Highlands and Islands, Unity Publishing, 1954 £15/£5
Other People's Worlds, Secker & Warburg, 1958 . .
. . . . £10/£5
A Fishing Village on the Clyde, O.U.P., 1960 (with
George Patterson) . . . . . . £10/£5
Presenting Other People's Children, Hamlyn, 1961 .
. . . . £10/£5
Return to the Fairy Hill, Heinemann, 1966. £10/£5
ditto, John Day Co. (U.S.), [1966] . . . £10/£5
Ketse and the Chief, Nelson (U.S.), [1967] . £10/£5
The Africans, Blond, 1970 . . . . £10/£5
A Life for Africa, Bram Fischer, Merlin Press, 1973 .
. . . . £10/£5
Small Talk, Memories of an Edwardian Childhood,
Bodley Head, 1973 . . . . . . £15/£5
Oil for the Highlands?, Fabian Society, 1974 (wraps).
. . . . £5
All Change Here, Girlhood and Marriage, Bodley
Head, 1975 . . . . £10/£5
Sittlichkeit, Birkbeck College, [1975] (wraps) . . £5
You May Well Ask, A Memoir 1920-1940, Gollancz,
1979 . . . . £10/£5
Images of Africa, Canongate, 1980 . . . £10/£5
Mucking Around, Five Continents over Fifty Years,
Gollancz, 1981 . . . . £10/£5
Margaret Cole, 1883-1980, The Fabian Society, 1982
(wraps) £5
*Among You Taking Notes, The Wartime Diary of
Naomi Mitchison*, 1939-1945, Gollancz, 1985 £10/£5
Saltaire Self-Portraits, Saltire Society, 1986 (wraps) .
. . . . £5

MARY RUSSELL MITFORD
(b.1787 d.1855)

Our Village is Mitford's classic, although it is only one book among verse, sketches, novels and short stories. She supported her father through her writing after he had ruined the family through his extravagance.

Verse

Poems, Longman, Hurst, Rees and Orme, 1810   £800
Christina, Valpy & Rivington, 1811. . . . £75
Watlington Hill, A.J. Valpy, 1812 (wraps) . . £75
Narrative Poems on the Female Character in the
  Various Relations of Life, Vol.1, Rivington, 1813 .
  . . . . £75
Dramatic Scenes, Sonnets and Other Poems, Geo. B
  Whittaker, 1827 . . . . £50

Sketches

Our Village, G. & W.B. Whittaker, 1824, (5 vols) £400
ditto, E. Bliss (U.S.), 1826 (3 vols) . . . £250
Belford Regis, Bentley, 1835 (3 vols) . . £150

Novels

Atherton and Other Tales, Hurst & Blackett, 1854 (3
  vols) £100
ditto Ticknor and Fields (U.S.), 1854 (3 vols) . £75

Plays

Julian, a tragedy in five acts, W.B. Gilley (U.S.), 1823
  . . . . £50
Foscari, Whittaker, 1826, ... £45
Foscari and Julian, Whittaker, 1827. . . . £35
Charles I, John Duncombe, 1834 . . . . £35
Sadak and Kalasrade, Lyceum Opera House, 1835 .
  . . . . £75
Dramatic Works, Hurst & Blackett, 1854 (2 vols) £50

Short Stories

American Stories, First Series, Whittaker, Treacher,
  1831 (3 vols) £175
Country Stories, Saunders & Otley, 1837 . . £75
ditto, Macmillan (U.S.), 1896 . . . . £45

Others

Lights and Shadows of American Life, Colborn &
  Bentley, Treacher, 1832 (3 vols) £200
Recollections of a Literary Life; or, Books, Places,
  and People, R. Bentley, 1852 (3 vols) . . £200
The Life of Mary Russell Mitford, related in a
  selection from her letters to her friends, R. Bentley,
  1870 (3 vols) £75
Memoirs and Letters of Charles Boner, with letters of
  Mary Russell Mitford to him..., R. Bentley, 1871 (2
  vols) £45

The Friendships of Mary Russell Mitford, Hurst and
  Blackett, 1882 (2 vols) £45
ditto, Harper & Brothers (U.S.), 1882 . . . £45
Elizabeth Barrett to Miss Mitford; the unpublished
  letters..., Murray, 1954 . . . . . £25/£10
ditto, Yale Univ. Press (U.S.), 1954 . . . £25/£10

NANCY MITFORD
(b. 1904 d.1973)

Although she was also a biographer, Mitford's satirical novels of aristocratic life are her most appreciated works.

Novels

Highland Fling, Hamish Hamilton, 1931 . £75/£35
Christmas Pudding, Butterworth, 1932 . . £75/£25
Wigs on the Green, Hamish Hamilton, 1935 £75/£25
Pigeon Pie: A Wartime Receipt, Hamish Hamilton,
  1940 . . . . £45/£20
ditto, British Book Centre (U.S.), 1959 . £35/£10
The Pursuit of Love, Hamish Hamilton, 1945 £65/£15
ditto, Random House (U.S.), 1946 . . . £40/£10
Love in a Cold Climate, Hamish Hamilton, 1949 . .
  . . . . £45/£15
ditto, Random House (U.S.), 1949 . . . £35/£10
The Blessing, Hamish Hamilton, 1951 . . £25/£10
ditto, Random House (U.S.), 1951 . . . £25/£10
Don't Tell Alfred, Hamish Hamilton, 1960 . £25/£10
ditto, Harper (U.S.), 1960 . . . . . £25/£10

Biography

Madame de Pompadour, Hamish Hamilton, 1954 . .
  . . . . £25/£10
ditto, Random House (U.S.), 1941 . . . £25/£10
Voltaire in Love, Hamish Hamilton, 1957 . £25/£10
ditto, Harper (U.S.), 1957 . . . . . £25/£10
The Sun King: Louis XIV at Versailles, Hamish
  Hamilton, 1966 . . . . £20/£5
ditto, Harper (U.S.), 1966 . . . . . £20/£5
ditto, Arcadia Press, 1970 (265 signed copies) . £75
Frederick the Great, Hamish Hamilton, 1970 £20/£5
ditto, Harper (U.S.), 1970 . . . . . £20/£5

Play

The Little Hut, Hamish Hamilton, 1951. . £35/£15
ditto, Random House (U.S.), 1953 . . . £25/£10

Essays

The Water Beetle, Hamish Hamilton, 1962 £35/£10
ditto, Harper (U.S.), 1962 . . . . . £30/£10

Translation

The Princess de Cleves, by Madame de Lafayette,
  Hamish Hamilton, 1950 . . . . . . £35

Editor
The Ladies of Alderley, Chapman & Hall, 1938 . .
. . . . £45/£15
The Stanleys of Alderley, Chapman & Hall, 1939
. . . . £45/£15
Noblesse Oblige, Hamish Hamilton, 1956 . £40/£15
ditto, Harper (U.S.), 1956 . . . . . £30/£10

NICHOLAS MONSARRAT
(b.1910 d.1979)

Although more than simply the author of sea stories, Monsarrat's great achievements are the novel *The Cruel Sea*, and his history of seafaring, *Master Mariner*.

Novels
Think of Tomorrow, Hurst & Blackett, 1934 £50/£15
At First Sight, Hurst & Blackett, 1935 . . £50/£15
The Whipping Boy, Jarrolds, 1936 . . . £25/£10
This is the Schoolroom, Cassell, 1939 . . £25/£10
ditto, Knopf (U.S.), 1940 . . . . . . £25/£10
The Cruel Sea, Cassell, 1951. . . . . £40/£10
ditto, Knopf (U.S.), 1951 . . . . . . £30/£10
The Story of Esther Costello, Cassell, 1953. £25/£10
ditto, Knopf (U.S.), 1951 . . . . . . £25/£10
Castle Garac, Knopf (U.S.), 1955 . . . £15/£5
ditto, Pan, 1968 (wraps) £5
The Tribe That Lost It's Head, Cassell, 1956 £15/£5
ditto, Sloane (U.S.), 1956 . . . . . . £15/£5
The Nylon Pirates, Cassell, 1960 . . . £15/£5
ditto, Sloane (U.S.), 1960 . . . . . . £15/£5
The White Rajah, Cassell, 1961 . . . . £15/£5
ditto, Sloane (U.S.), 1961 . . . . . . £15/£5
The Time Before This, Cassell, 1962 . . £15/£5
ditto, Sloane (U.S.), 1962 . . . . . . £15/£5
Smith and Jones, Cassell, 1963 . . . . £15/£5
ditto, Sloane (U.S.), 1963 . . . . . . £15/£5
A Fair Day's Work, Cassell, 1964 . . . £15/£5
ditto, Sloane (U.S.), 1964 . . . . . . £15/£5
Something to Hide, Cassell, 1965 . . . £15/£5
ditto, Sloane (U.S.), 1966 . . . . . . £15/£5
The Pillow Fight, Cassell, 1965 . . . . £15/£5
ditto, Sloane (U.S.), 1965 . . . . . . £15/£5
Richer Than All His Tribe, Cassell, 1968 . £15/£5
ditto, Morrow (U.S.), 1969 . . . . . £15/£5
The Kapillan of Malta, Cassell, 1973 . . £15/£5
ditto, Morrow (U.S.), 1974 . . . . . £15/£5
The Master Mariner, Volume 1: Running Proud,
Cassell, 1978 . . . . £15/£5
ditto, Morrow (U.S.), 1979 . . . . . £15/£5
The Master Mariner, Volume 2: Drunken Ship,
Cassell, 1980 . . . . £15/£5
ditto, Morrow (U.S.), 1981 . . . . . £15/£5

Short Stories
Depends What You Mean By Love, Cassell, 1947 . .
. . . . £25/£10
ditto, Knopf (U.S.), 1948 . . . . . . £25/£10
ditto, as *HMS Marlborough Will Enter Harbour*,
Panther, 1956 (wraps) £5
HMS Marlborough Will Enter Harbour, Cassell, 1952
(wraps) . . . . £10/£5
The Ship That Died of Shame, Cassell, 1959 £15/£5
ditto, Sloane (U.S.), 1959 . . . . . . £15/£5
Monsarrat At Sea, Cassell, 1975. . . . £10/£5
ditto, Morrow (U.S.), 1976 . . . . . £10/£5

Autobiography
My Brother Denys: A Memoir, Cassell, 1948 £25/£10
ditto, Knopf (U.S.), 1949 . . . . . . £25/£10
H.M. Corvette, Cassell, 1942 (wraps) . . £10
ditto, Lippincott (U.S.), 1943 . . . . £30/£10
East Coast Corvette, Cassell, 1943 (wraps) . . £10
ditto, Lippincott (U.S.), 1943 . . . . £30/£10
Corvette Command, Cassell, 1944 (wraps) . . £10
Three Corvettes, Cassell, 1945 . . . . £25/£10
H.M. Frigate, Cassell, 1948 (wraps). . . £10
Canada Coast To Coast, Cassell, 1955 . . £20/£5
Life is a Four Letter Word, Volume 1: Breaking In,
Cassell, 1966 . . . . £15/£5
Life is a Four Letter Word, Volume 2: Breaking Out,
Cassell, 1970 . . . . £15/£5
Breaking In, Breaking Out, Morrow, 1971 . £15/£5

Other
To Stratford, With Love, McLelland & Stewart
(Canada), 1963 (wraps) £10

BRIAN MOORE
(b.1921)

An Irish author of novels which deal powerfully with the torments of guilt and sexual obsession in relation to Catholicism.

Novels
Wreath for a Redhead, Harlequin (Canada), 1951
(pseud. 'Michael Bryan', wraps) £200
ditto, as *Sailor's Leave*, Pyramid Books (U.S.), 1953
(wraps) £45
The Executioners, Harlequin (Canada), 1951 (pseud.
'Michael Bryan', wraps). £75
French For Murder, Fawcett (U.S.), 1954 (pseud.
'Bernard Mara', wraps) £50
ditto, L. Miller & Sons, 1956 (pseud. 'Bernard Mara',
wraps). £50
A Bullet for My Lady, Fawcett (U.S.), 1955 (pseud.
'Bernard Mara', wraps) £50
ditto, L. Miller & Sons, 1956 (pseud. 'Bernard Mara',
wraps). £50
Judith Hearne, Deutsch, 1955 . . . . £750/£100

ditto, as *The Lonely Passion of Judith Hearne*, Little, Brown (U.S.), 1956 . . . . . . £12/£25
ditto, McClelland & Stewart (Canada), 1964 (wraps) .
. . . . £35
This Gun for Gloria, Dell (U.S.), 1956 (pseud. 'Bernard Mara', wraps) £45
ditto, L. Miller & Sons, 1956 (pseud. 'Bernard Mara', wraps). £35
Intent to Kill, Dell (U.S.), 1956 (pseud. 'Michael Bryan', wraps) £45
ditto, Eyre & Spottiswoode, 1956 (pseud. 'Michael Bryan') . . . . £150/£45
The Feast of Lupercal, Little, Brown (U.S.), 1957 .
. . . . £75/£25
ditto, Deutsch, 1958 . . . . . . £50/£20
ditto, as *A Moment of Love*, Longacre, 1960 £25/£10
Murder in Majorca, Dell (U.S.), 1957 (pseud. 'Michael Bryan', wraps). £45
ditto, Eyre & Spottiswoode, 1958 (pseud. 'Michael Bryan') . . . . £65/£20
The Luck of Ginger Coffey, Little, Brown (U.S.), 1960
. . . . £75/£25
ditto, McClelland & Stewart (Canada), 1960 £75/£10
ditto, Deutsch, 1960 . . . . . . £45/£15
An Answer from Limbo, Little, Brown (U.S.), 1962 .
. . . . £50/£20
ditto, McClelland & Stewart (Canada), 1962 £50/£10
ditto, Deutsch, 1963 . . . . . . £40/£15
The Emperor of Ice-Cream, Viking Press (U.S.), 1965
. . . . £30/£10
ditto, McClelland & Stewart (Canada), 1965 £30/£10
ditto, Deutsch, 1966 . . . . . . £25/£10
I Am Mary Dunne, McClelland & Stewart (Canada), 1968 . . . . £25/£10
ditto, Viking Press (U.S.), 1968 . . . . £25/£10
ditto, Cape, 1968 . . . . £25/£10
Fergus, Holt Rinehart (U.S.), 1970 . . . £20/£5
ditto, McClelland & Stewart (Canada), 1970 £20/£5
ditto, Cape, 1971 . . . . £20/£5
Catholics, McClelland & Stewart (Canada), 1972 . .
. . . . £20/£5
ditto, Cape, 1972 . . . . £20/£5
ditto, Holt Rinehart (U.S.), 1973 . . . . £10/£5
The Great Victorian Collection, Farrar Straus (U.S.), 1975 . . . . £20/£5
ditto, McClelland & Stewart (Canada), 1975 £20/£5
ditto, Cape, 1975 . . . . £20/£5
The Doctor's Wife, Farrar Straus (U.S.), 1976 £20/£5
ditto, McClelland & Stewart (Canada), 1976 £20/£5
ditto, Cape, 1976 . . . . £20/£5
The Mangan Inheritance, Farrar Straus (U.S.), 1979
. . . . £20/£5
ditto, McClelland & Stewart (Canada), 1979 £20/£5
ditto, Cape, 1979 . . . . £20/£5
The Temptation of Eileen Hughes, Farrar Straus (U.S.), 1981 . . . . £20/£5
ditto, McClelland & Stewart (Canada), 1981 £20/£5
ditto, Cape, 1981 . . . . £20/£5
Cold Heaven, Holt Rinehart (U.S.), 1983. . £20/£5

ditto, McClelland & Stewart (Canada), 1983 £20/£5
ditto, Cape, 1983 . . . . £20/£5
Black Robe, Dutton (U.S.), 1985. . . . £25/£5
ditto, McClelland & Stewart (Canada), 1985 £25/£5
ditto, Cape, 1985 . . . . £25/£5
ditto, Cape, 1985 (50 numbered, signed copies, bound by Kenny's of Galway, slipcase) . . . £100/£75
The Color of Blood, Dutton (U.S.), 1987 . £10/£5
ditto, McClelland & Stewart (Canada), 1987 £10/£5
ditto, as *The Colour of Blood*, Cape, 1987 . £15/£5
Lies of Silence, Bloomsbury, 1990 . . . £15/£5
ditto, London Limited Editions, 1990 (250 numbered, signed copies, acetate d/w) . . . . . £65/£55
ditto, McClelland & Stewart (Canada), 1990 £15/£5
ditto, Doubleday (U.S.), 1990 . . . . £10/£5
No Other Life, Bloomsbury, 1993 . . . £10/£5
ditto, Knopf (Canada), 1993 . . . . . £15/£5
ditto, Doubleday (U.S.), 1993 . . . . £10/£5
The Statement, Knopf (Canada), 1995 . . £15/£5
ditto, Bloomsbury, 1995 . . . . . . £10/£5
ditto, Dutton (U.S.), 1996 . . . . . £10/£5
The Magician's Wife, Knopf (Canada), 1997 £10/£5
ditto, Bloomsbury, 1997 . . . . . . £10/£5
ditto, Dutton (U.S.), 1998 . . . . . £10/£5

Short Stories
Two Stories, California State Univ. (U.S.), 1978 (300 signed, numbered copies) £60
ditto, California State Univ. (U.S.), 1978 (26 lettered copies) £100

Others
Canada, Time Life International (U.S.), 1965 . £15
The Revolution Script, McClelland & Stewart (Canada), 1971 . . . . £20/£5
ditto, Holt Rinehart (U.S.), 1971 . . . . £15/£5
ditto, Cape, 1971 . . . . £15/£5
Autobiography, Partridge Press, 1995 . . £10/£5

WILLIAM MORRIS
(b.1834 d.1896)

Poet, artist and socialist, Morris excelled in many of the fields in which he attempted to combat ugliness, no more so than in book production through his private press, the Kelmscott Press.

The Defence of Guinevere and Other Poems, Bell & Daldy, 1858 . . . . £500
ditto, Bell & Daldy, 1875 . . . . £100
ditto, Bell & Daldy, 1875 (25 large paper copies) £350
ditto, Kelmscott Press, 1892 (300 copies) . . £750
ditto, Kelmscott Press, 1892 (10 copies on vellum). .
. . . . £5,000
The Life and Death of Jason, Bell & Daldy, 1867. .
. . . . £250
ditto, Bell & Daldy, 1867 (25 large paper copies) £450

ditto, Kelmscott Press, 1895 (200 copies) . £2,000
The Earthly Paradise, F.S. Ellis, 1868-70 (4 parts, 1 &
2 together) £300
ditto, F.S. Ellis, 1868-70 (25 large paper copies) £500
ditto, Kelmscott Press, 1896-97 (225 copies, 8 vols) .
. . . . £1,750
ditto, Kelmscott Press, 1896-97 (6 copies on vellum, 8
vols) £6,500
The Story of Grettir the Strong, F.S. Ellis, 1869
(translated by Morris & Magnusson) . . . £250
ditto, F.S. Ellis, 1869 (25 large paper copies) . £450
The Story of Volsangs and Niblungs, F.S. Ellis 1870
(translated by Morris & Magnusson) . . . £250
ditto, F.S. Ellis, 1870 (25 large paper copies) . £450
Love is Enough, Ellis & White 1873 [1872] . £400
ditto, Kelmscott Press, 1897 [1898] (300 copies) . .
. . . . £1,750
Three Northern Love Stories and Other Tales, Ellis &
White, 1873 (translated by Morris & Magnusson) .
. . . . £200
ditto, F.S. Ellis, 1873 (large paper copies) . £350
The Aenids of Virgil, Done into English Verse, Ellis &
White, 1876 (translation, 2 vols) . . . £250
ditto, Ellis & White, 1876 (25 large paper copies, 2
vols) £450
*The Story of Sigurd the Volsung, and the Fall of the
Niblungs*, Ellis & White, 1877 [1876] . . £250
ditto, Ellis & White, 1877 [1876] (25 large paper
copies) £450
ditto, Kelmscott Press, 1898 (160 copies) . £1,000
Hopes and Fears for Art, Ellis & White, 1882 . £75
ditto, Ellis & White, 1882 (large paper copies) . £250
Chants for Socialists, Socialist League, 1884 . £75
Pilgrims of Hope, privately printed by H. Buxton
Forman, 1886. . . . . £250
The Odyssey of Homer, Done into English Verse,
Reeves & Turner 1887 (translation, 2 vols) . £100
The Aims of Art, The Commonweal, 1887 . . £30
The Tables Turned, The Commonweal, 1887 . £40
Signs of Change, Reeves & Turner 1888 . £50
True and False Society, Socialist League, 1888
(wraps) £75
A Dream of John Ball, and A King's Lesson, Reeves
& Turner, 1888 . . . . £75
ditto, Reeves & Turner, 1888 (large paper copies) £250
ditto, Kelmscott Press, 1892 (300 copies) . £1,000
ditto, Kelmscott Press, 1892 (11 copies on vellum). .
. . . . £5,000
*A Tale of the House of the Wolfings and All the
Kindreds of the Mark*, Reeves & Turner, 1889 £75
ditto, Reeves & Turner, 1888 (100 large paper copies).
. . . . £250
The Roots of the Mountains, Reeves & Turner, 1889
[1890]. £75
News From Nowhere, Roberts Bros (U.S.), 1890 £75
ditto, Reeves & Turner, 1891 . . . . . £75
ditto, Reeves & Turner, 1891 (wraps) . . . £75
ditto, Reeves & Turner, 1888 (250 large paper copies).
. . . . £250

ditto, Kelmscott Press, 1892 (300 copies) . . £750
ditto, Kelmscott Press, 1892 (10 copies on vellum). .
. . . . £6,000
The Story of Gunnlaug the Worm Tounge, Chiswick
Press, 1891 (75 copies, translated by Morris & Magnusson) £750
The Story of the Glittering Plain, Reeves & Turner/
Kelmscott Press, 1891 (200 copies, slipcase) £1,500
ditto, Kelmscott Press, 1891 (6 copies on vellum) . .
. . . . £5,000
ditto, Kelmscott Press, 1894 (250 copies, illustrated by
Walter Crane) £2,000
ditto, Kelmscott Press, 1894 (7 copies on vellum) . .
. . . . £6,000
Poems by the Way, Reeves & Turner, 1891. . £75
ditto, Reeves & Turner, 1891 (100 large paper copies).
. . . . £250
ditto, Kelmscott Press, 1891 (300 copies) . . £750
ditto, Kelmscott Press, 1891 (13 copies on vellum). .
. . . . £4,000
The Order of Chivalry & L'Ordene de Chevalerie,
Kelmscott Press, 1892 [1893] (225 copies, the latter
translated by Morris). £1,000
Gothic Architecture, Kelmscott Press, 1893 (1,500
copies) £250
A Tale of King Florus and the Fair Jehane, Kelmscott
Press, 1893 (350 copies, translated by Morris) £500
Socialism: It's Growth and Outcome, Swan Sonnen-
schein, 1893 (350 copies, translated by Morris) £500
Of the Friendship of Amis and Amilie, Kelmscott
Press, 1894 (500 copies, translated by Morris) £300
The Tale of the Emperor Coustans and of Oversea,
Kelmscott Press, 1894 (with E. Belfort Bax) . £300
The Wood Beyond the World, Kelmscott Press, 1894
(350 copies) £1,250
ditto, Kelmscott Press, 1894 (8 copies on vellum) . .
. . . . £5,000
A Tale of Beowulf, Kelmscott Press, 1895 (300 copies,
translated by Morris). £1,250
Child Christopher and Goldilind the Fair, Kelmscott
Press, 1895 (600 copies, 2 vols) . . . £500
ditto, Kelmscott Press, 1895 (12 copies on vellum). .
. . . . £2,000
Old French Romances, George Allen, 1896
(translation) £50
The Well at the World's End, Kelmscott Press, 1896
(350 copies) £1,750
The Water of the Wondrous Isles, Kelmscott Press,
1897 (250 copies) £1,500
ditto, Kelmscott Press, 1897 (6 copies on vellum) . .
. . . . £6,000
The Sundering Flood, Kelmscott Press, 1897 (300
copies) £1,000
ditto, Kelmscott Press, 1897 (10 copies on vellum). .
. . . . £5,000
*A Note By William Morris on His Aims in Founding
the Kelmscott Press*, Kelmscott Press, 1896 (525
copies) £600

JOHN MORTIMER
(b.1923)

A playwright and barrister, Mortimer was called to the Bar in 1948 and became a QC in 1966. Rumpole, his fictional, incorrigible barrister, has been successfully and popularly televised.

Novels

Charade, Bodley Head, 1947.	£50/£15
ditto, Viking (U.S.), 1986.	£10/£5
Rumming Park, Lane, 1948	£50/£15
Answer Yes or No, Lane, 1950	£35/£10
ditto, as *The Silver Hook*, Morrow (U.S.), 1950 £30/£5
Like Men Betrayed, Collins, 1953	£30/£5
ditto, Lippincott (U.S.), 1954.	£25/£5
The Narrowing Stream, Collins, 1954	£25/£5
ditto, Viking (U.S.), 1989.	£15/£5
Three Winters, Collins, 1956.	£25/£5
Will Shakespeare: The Untold Story, Hodder, 1977 .	
	£20/£5
ditto, Delacourt (U.S.), 1978 .	£15/£5
Paradise Postponed, Viking, 1985	£15/£5
ditto, Viking (U.S.), 1985.	£15/£5
Summer's Lease, Viking, 1988	£25/£5
ditto, Viking (U.S.), 1988.	£20/£5
ditto, Franklin Library (U.S.), 1988 (signed limited edition)	£35
ditto, London Limited Editions, 1990 (250 signed copies)	£35
Titmuss Regained, Viking, 1990.	£15/£5
ditto, Viking (U.S.), 1990.	£10/£5
Dunster, Viking, 1992	£10/£5
ditto, Viking (U.S.), 1993.	£10/£5
Felix in the Underworld, Viking, 1997 .	£10/£5
ditto, Viking (U.S.), 1997.	£10/£5
The Sound of Trumpets, Viking, 1998	£10/£5
ditto, Viking (U.S.), 1999.	£10/£5

Stories

Rumpole of the Bailey, Penguin, 1978 (wraps)	£20
ditto, Penguin (U.S.), 1980 (wraps)	£10
ditto, Armchair Detective Library (U.S.), 1991 (100 signed copies, slipcase)	£45
The Trials of Rumpole, Penguin, 1979 (wraps)	£10
ditto, Penguin (U.S.), 1981 (wraps)	£10
Rumpole's Return, Penguin, 1980 (wraps) .	£10
ditto, Penguin (U.S.), 1982 (wraps)	£10
Rumpole for the Defence, Penguin, 1982 (wraps)	£5
Rumpole and the Golden Thread, Penguin (U.S.), 1983 (wraps)	£10
Rumpole's Last Case, Penguin, 1987 (wraps) .	£10
ditto, Penguin (U.S.), 1988 (wraps)	£10
Rumpole and the Age of Miracles, Penguin, 1988 (wraps)	£10
ditto, Penguin (U.S.), 1989 (wraps)	£10

Rumpole à la Carte, Viking, 1990	£20/£5
ditto, Viking (U.S.), 1990.	£15/£5
Rumpole on Trial, Viking, 1992.	£15/£5
ditto, Penguin (U.S.), 1992	£15/£5
Rumpole and the Angel of Death, Viking, 1995	
	£10/£5
ditto, Penguin (U.S.), 1996	£10/£5

Plays

Three Plays, Elek, 1958	£30/£10
ditto, Grove Press (U.S.), 1962	£20/£5
The Wrong Side of the Park, Heinemann, 1960 £20/£5
Lunch Hour, French, 1960 (wraps)	£10
Lunch Hour and Other Plays, Methuen, 1960 £20/£5
Two Stars For Comfort, Methuen, 1962	£15/£5
A Flea in Her Ear, French, 1967 (wraps)	£5
ditto, French (U.S.), 1967 (wraps)	£5
The Judge, Methuen, 1967	£10/£5
Five Plays, Methuen, 1970	£10/£5
Come As You Are: Four Short Plays, Methuen, 1971 .	
	£10/£5
A Voyage Round My Father, Methuen, 1971	£20/£5
Knightsbridge, French, 1973 (wraps)	£5
Collaborations, Methuen, 1973	£10/£5
The Fear of Heaven, French, 1978 (wraps)	£5
Heaven and Hell, French, 1978 (wraps)	£5
Edwin and Other Plays, Penguin, 1984 (wraps)	£5
Three Boulevard Farces, Penguin, 1985 (wraps)	£5

Collected Editions

Rumpole, Allen Lane, 1980	£10/£5
Regina v. Rumpole, Allen Lane, 1981	£10/£5
The First Rumpole Omnibus, Penguin, 1983	£10/£5
The Second Rumpole Omnibus, Viking, 1987	£10/£5
ditto, Penguin (U.S.), 1988	£10/£5
The Rapstone Chronicles, Viking, 1991	£10/£5

Autobiography

Clinging to the Wreckage, Weidenfeld & Nicolson, 1982	£15/£5
ditto, Ticknor & Fields (U.S.), 1982 .	£15/£5
Murderers and Other Friends, Viking, 1994	£10/£5
ditto, Viking (U.S.), 1994.	£10/£5

Others

With Love and Lizards, Joseph, 1957 (written with Penelope Mortimer)	£30/£10
No Moaning at the Bar, Bles, 1957 (pseud. 'Geoffrey Lincoln')	£35/£10
In Character, Allen Lane, 1983 .	£15/£5
Character Parts, Viking, 1986	£15/£5

IRIS MURDOCH
(b.1919 d.1999)

An novelist and philosopher. Murdoch employed a blend of realism and symbolism in her highly regarded novels.

Novels

Under the Net, Chatto & Windus, 1954 .	. £500/£100
ditto, Viking (U.S.), 1954 .	. £125/£25
The Flight from the Enchanter, Chatto & Windus, 1956 .	. £300/£75
ditto, Viking (U.S.), 1956 .	£65/£15
The Sandcastle, Chatto & Windus, 1957	. £200/£65
ditto, Viking (U.S.), 1957 .	£50/£15
The Bell, Chatto & Windus, 1958	. £150/£25
ditto, Viking (U.S.), 1958 .	£20/£5
A Severed Head, Chatto & Windus, 1961	. £75/£20
ditto, Viking (U.S.), 1961 .	£20/£5
An Unofficial Rose, Chatto & Windus, 1962	£35/£10
ditto, Viking (U.S.), 1962 .	£20/£5
The Unicorn, Chatto & Windus, 1963 .	£25/£10
ditto, Viking (U.S.), 1963 .	£15/£5
The Italian Girl, Chatto & Windus, 1964 .	£25/£10
ditto, Viking (U.S.), 1964 .	£15/£5
The Red and the Green, Chatto & Windus, 1965 .	. £20/£5
ditto, Viking (U.S.), 1965 .	£15/£5
The Time of the Angels, Chatto & Windus, 1966 .	. £20/£5
ditto, Viking (U.S.), 1966 .	£15/£5
The Nice and the Good, Chatto & Windus, 1968 .	. £20/£5
ditto, Viking (U.S.), 1968 .	£15/£5
Bruno's Dream, Chatto & Windus, 1969 .	£20/£5
ditto, Viking (U.S.), 1969 .	£15/£5
A Fairly Honourable Defeat, Chatto & Windus, 1970 .	. £20/£5
ditto, Viking (U.S.), 1970 .	£15/£5
An Accidental Man, Chatto & Windus, 1971	£20/£5
ditto, Viking (U.S.), 1972 .	£15/£5
The Black Prince, Chatto & Windus, 1973 .	£20/£5
ditto, Viking (U.S.), 1973 .	£15/£5
The Sacred and Profane Love Machine, Chatto & Windus, 1974 .	. £20/£5
ditto, Viking (U.S.), 1974 .	£15/£5
A Word Child, Chatto & Windus, 1975 .	£20/£5
ditto, Viking (U.S.), 1975 .	£15/£5
Henry and Cato, Chatto & Windus, 1976 .	£20/£5
ditto, Viking (U.S.), 1976 .	£15/£5
The Sea, the Sea, Chatto & Windus, 1978 .	£20/£5
ditto, Viking (U.S.), 1978 .	£15/£5
Nuns and Soldiers, Chatto & Windus, 1980	£15/£5
ditto, Viking (U.S.), 1981 .	£10/£5
The Philosopher's Pupil, Chatto & Windus, 1983 . .	. £15/£5
ditto, Viking (U.S.), 1983 .	£10/£5
The Good Apprentice, Chatto & Windus, 1985	£15/£5

ditto, London Limited Editions, 1985 (250 signed copies, glassine d/w).	£75/£65
ditto, Viking (U.S.), 1985 .	£10/£5
The Book and the Brotherhood, Chatto & Windus, 1987 .	£10/£5
ditto, Viking (U.S.), 1988 .	£10/£5
ditto, Franklin Library (U.S.), 1988 (signed limited edition) .	£75
The Message to the Planet, Chatto & Windus, 1989 .	£10/£5
ditto, London Limited Editions, 1989 (150 signed copies, glassine d/w).	£75/£65
ditto, Viking (U.S.), 1990 .	£10/£5
Green Knight, Chatto & Windus, 1993 . .	£10/£5
ditto, Viking (U.S.), 1994 .	£10/£5
Jackson's Dilemma, Chatto & Windus, 1995	£10/£5
ditto, Viking (U.S.), 1995 .	£10/£5

Plays

A Severed Head, Chatto & Windus, 1964 (with J. Priestley) .	. £50/£20
The Italian Girl, French, 1969 (with James Saunders) .	£40
The Three Arrows and The Servants and the Snow: Two Plays, Chatto & Windus, 1973 . .	£65/£10
ditto, Viking (U.S.), 1974 .	£25/£5
Acastos: Two Platonic Dialogues, Chatto & Windus, 1986 .	£15/£5
ditto, Viking (U.S.), 1987 .	£15/£5
Three Plays, Chatto & Windus, 1989 .	£10
Joanna Joanna, A Play in Two Acts, Colophon Press, 1994 (12 signed copies, leather, slipcase) . .	£200
ditto, Colophon Press, 1994 (143 signed copies)	£90
One Alone, Colophon Press, 1995 (26 lettered, signed copies) .	£125
ditto, Colophon Press, 1995 (200 signed copies, pbk) .	£30

Verse

A Year of Birds, Compton Press, 1978 (350 signed, numbered copies, no d/w) .	£100
Something Special, Four Poems and a Story, Eurographica (Helsinki), 1990 (350 signed, numbered copies, wraps in d/w) .	£100/£75

Others

Sartre: Romantic Rationalist, Bowes & Bowes, 1953 .	. £150/£30
ditto, Yale Univ. Press (U.S.), 1953 . . .	£75/£20
The Sovereignty of Good, CUP, 1967 (wraps) .	£65
ditto, Routledge, 1971 (containing extra essays) . .	£65/£25
ditto, Schocken Books (U.S.), 1971 . . .	£15/£5
The Fire and the Sun: Why Plato Banished the Artists, O.U.P., 1977 .	. £25/£10
Reynolds Stone, Warren Editions, 1981 (300 signed copies of 750, wraps) .	£100
ditto, Warren Editions, 1981 (unsigned copies of 750, wraps) .	£30

The Existential Political Myth, Delos Press, 1989 (45 signed copies of 270, wraps, slipcase) . . . £75
ditto, Delos Press, 1989 (225 numbered copies of 270, wraps, slipcase). £45
Metaphysics as a Guide to Morals, Chatto & Windus, 1992 . . . . £20/£5
ditto, Allen Lane (U.S.), 1993 . . . . £10/£5
Existentials and Mystics, Delos Press, 1993 (100 signed copies of 500, wraps, slipcase) . . . £50
ditto, Delos Press, 1993 (400 numbered copies of 500, wraps). £35
ditto, Allen Lane (U.S.), 1998 . . . . £10/£5

VLADIMIR NABOKOV
(b.1899 d.1977)

A naturalised American novelist, short story writer and poet, Nabokov's first published works were written in his native Russian and were critically acclaimed. During the second half of his career, he achieved a somewhat notorious success with *Lolita*.

Novels
Camera Obscura, Long, 1936 (pseud. Vladamir Nabokoff-Sirin, translated by Winifred Roy) . . .
. . . . £12,000/£1,500
ditto, as *Laughter in the Dark*, Bobbs Merrill (U.S.), 1938 (pseud. Vladamir Nabokoff, revised edition) .
. . . . £1,000/£250
Despair, Long, 1937 (pseud. Vladamir Nabokoff-Sirin)
. . . . £12,000/£1,250
ditto, Putnam (U.S.), 1966 (revised edition). £100/£35
ditto, Weidenfeld , 1966 (revised edition) . £100/£35
The Real Life of Sebastian Knight, New Directions (U.S.), 1941 (woven red burlap, no d/w) . £450
ditto, New Directions (U.S.), 1941 (smooth red cloth) .
. . . . £200/£75
ditto, Editions Poetry, 1945 . . . . . £200/£25
Bend Sinister, Holt (U.S.), 1947 . . . . £150/£50
ditto, Weidenfeld, 1960 . . . . . . £100/£35
Lolita, Olympia Press (Paris), 1955 (2 vols, 'Francs: 900' on back cover, wraps) £2,000
ditto, Putnam (U.S.), 1958 (dustwrapper bears only distinction between trade and book club copies) . .
. . . . £200/£35
ditto, Weidenfeld, 1959 . . . . . . £125/£40
Pnin, Doubleday (U.S.), 1957 . . . . £150/£45
ditto, Heinemann, 1957 . . . . . . £125/£35
Invitation to a Beheading, Putnam (U.S.), 1959 . .
. . . . £75£15
ditto, Weidenfeld, 1960 . . . . . . £50/£15
Pale Fire, Putnam (U.S.), 1962 . . . . £125/£35
ditto, Weidenfeld, 1962 . . . . . . £100/£15
The Gift, Putnam (U.S.), 1963 . . . . £35/£15
ditto, Weidenfeld, 1963 . . . . . . £35/£15
The Defence, Weidenfeld, 1964 . . . . £35/£15
ditto, as *The Defense*, Putnam (U.S.), 1964 . £35/£15

The Eye, Phaedra (U.S.), 1965 . . . . £35/£15
King, Queen, Knave, McGraw-Hill (U.S.), 1968 . .
. . . . £35/£15
ditto, Weidenfeld, 1968 . . . . . . £35/£15
Ada, McGraw-Hill (U.S.), 1969 . . . . £25/£10
ditto, Weidenfeld, 1969 . . . . . . £25/£10
Mary, McGraw-Hill (U.S.), 1970 . . . £20/£5
ditto, Weidenfeld, 1971 . . . . . . £20/£5
Glory, McGraw-Hill (U.S.), 1971 . . . £20/£5
ditto, Weidenfeld, 1972 . . . . . . £20/£5
Transparent Things, McGraw-Hill (U.S.), 1972 . .
. . . . £20/£5
ditto, Weidenfeld, 1973 . . . . . . £20/£5
Look at the Harlequins!, McGraw-Hill (U.S.), 1974 .
. . . . £20/£5
ditto, Weidenfeld, 1975 . . . . . . £20/£5
The Enchanter, Harper (U.S.), 1986 . . £20/£5

Short Stories
Nine Stories/Direction Two, New Directions (U.S.), 1947 (wraps) £150
Nabokov's Dozen, Doubleday (U.S.), 1958 . £100/£35
ditto, Heinemann, 1959 . . . . . . £75/£25
ditto, as *Spring in Fialta*, Popular Library (U.S.), 1959 (wraps) £20
Nabokov's Quartet, Phaedra (U.S.), 1966 . £25/£10
ditto, Weidenfeld, 1967 . . . . . . £25/£10
A Russian Beauty and Other Stories, McGraw-Hill (U.S.), 1973 . . . . £25/£10
ditto, Weidenfeld, 1973 . . . . . . £25/£10
Tyrants Destroyed and Other Stories, McGraw-Hill (U.S.), 1975 . . . . £20/£10
ditto, Weidenfeld, 1975 . . . . . . £20/£10
Details of a Sunset and Other Stories, McGraw-Hill (U.S.), 1976 . . . . £20/£10
ditto, Weidenfeld, 1976 . . . . . . £20/£10

Collected Edition
Nabokov's Congeries, Viking Press (U.S.), 1968 . .
. . . . £15/£5

Verse
Poems, Doubleday (U.S.), 1959 . . . . £175/£45
ditto, Weidenfeld, 1961 . . . . . . £100/£35
Poems and Problems, McGraw-Hill (U.S.), 1971 . .
. . . . £50/£20
ditto, Weidenfeld, 1972 . . . . . . £45/£15

Plays
The Waltz Invention, Phaedra (U.S.), 1966 £25/£10
Lolita: A Screenplay, McGraw-Hill (U.S.), 1974 . .
. . . . £25/£10
The Man from the USSR and Other Plays, Harcourt Brace (U.S.), 1984 . . . . £20/£5
ditto, Weidenfeld, 1985 . . . . . . £20/£5

Others

Nikolai Gogol, New Directions (U.S.), 1944 (first issue, tan cloth with brown lettering, 5 titles listed on verso of half title, d/w with $1.50 price) . £225/£45

ditto, New Directions (U.S.), 1944 (second issue, tan cloth with blue lettering, 14 titles listed on verso of half title, d/w with $2.00 price and 14 titles on rear flap) . . . . £100/£35

ditto, Editions Poetry, 1947 . . . . . £100/£35

Three Russian Poets, New Directions (U.S.), 1944 (grey paper baoards, grey d/w with brown lettering, at '$1.00') . . . . £125/£45

ditto, New Directions (U.S.), 1944 (tan stapled wraps with blue-grey d/w lettered in brown, at '$.50') . . . . £75/£15

Strong Opinions, McGraw-Hill (U.S.), 1973 £25/£10

ditto, Weidenfeld, 1974 . . . . . . £20/£5

The Nabokov/Wilson Letters:, 1940-1971, Harper & Row (U.S.), 1979 . . . . . £15/£5

ditto, Weidenfeld, 1979 . . . . . £15/£5

Lectures on Literature, Harcourt Brace (U.S.), 1980 . . . . £20/£5

ditto, Weidenfeld, 1980 . . . . . £15/£5

Lectures on Russian Literature, Harcourt Brace (U.S.), 1981 . . . . £20/£5

ditto, Weidenfeld, 1982 . . . . . £15/£5

Lectures on Don Quixote, Harcourt Brace (U.S.), 1983 . . . . £20/£5

ditto, Weidenfeld, 1983 . . . . . £15/£5

Autobiography

Conclusive Evidence: A Memoir, Harper (U.S.), 1951 . . . . £200/£50

ditto, as *Speak, Memory: A Memoir*, Gollancz, 1951 (first issue blue-green cloth, black stamping, no *Daily Mail* device on spine or at bottom of front flap . . . . £300/£50

ditto, Gollancz, 1951 (second issue blue cloth, gilt stamping, with *Daily Mail* device on spine and at bottom of front flap . . . . . £150/£20

ditto, as *Speak, Memory: An Autobiography*, Putnam (U.S.), 1966 (revised edition) . . . . £50/£20

ditto, as *Speak, Memory: An Autobiography*, Weidenfeld, 1967 (revised edition). . . £25/£10

Selected Letters, 1940-1977, Harcourt Brace (U.S.), 1989 . . . . £20/£5

SHIVA NAIPAUL
(b.1945 d.1985)

A Trinidadian novelist, Shiva Naipaul's three novels effectively mix satire and compassion.

Novels

Fireflies, Deutsch, 1970 . . . . . £100/£20

ditto, Knopf (U.S.), 1971 . . . . . £45/£15

The Chip-Chip Gatherers, Deutsch, 1973 . £50/£20

ditto, Knopf (U.S.), 1973 . . . . . £25/£5

A Hot Country, Hamilton, 1983 . . . £15/£5

ditto as *Love and Death in a Hot Country*, Viking (U.S.), 1984 . . . . £10/£5

Short Stories

The Adventures of Gurudeva, Deutsch, 1976 £30/£10

Travel

North of South: An African Journey, Deutsch, 1978 . . . . £25/£5

ditto, Simon & Schuster (U.S.), 1979 . . £15/£5

Black and White, Hamilton, 1980 . . . £15/£5

ditto, as *Journey to Nowhere: A New World Tragedy*, Simon & Schuster (U.S.), 1981 . . . . £10/£5

Beyond the Dragon's Mouth, Hamilton, 1984 £15/£5

ditto, Viking (U.S.), 1985 . . . . . £10/£5

An Unfinished Journey, Hamilton, 1986 . £15/£5

ditto, Viking (U.S.), 1987 . . . . . £10/£5

V.S. NAIPAUL
(b.1932)

A distinguished Trinidadian novelist, V.S. Naipaul uses such twentieth century uncertainties as imperialism and colonialism as the motivation behind his work.

Novels

The Mystic Masseur, Deutsch, 1957 . . . £300/£65

ditto, Vanguard Press (U.S.), 1959 . . . £125/£15

The Suffrage of Elvira, Deutsch, 1958 . £400/£100

A House for Mr Biswas, Deutsch, 1961 . . £400/£75

ditto, McGraw-Hill (U.S.), 1962 . . . . £100/£15

Mr Stone and the Knights Companion, Deutsch, 1963 . . . . £125/£35

ditto, Macmillan (U.S.), 1964 . . . £50/£15

The Mimic Men, Deutsch, 1967 . . . . £75/£20

ditto, Macmillan (U.S.), 1967 . . . £40/£15

In a Free State, Deutsch, 1971 . . . £65/£20

ditto, Knopf (U.S.), 1971 . . . . . £25/£10

Guerrillas, Deutsch, 1975 . . . . . £20/£5

ditto, Knopf (U.S.), 1975 . . . . . £15/£5

A Bend in the River, Deutsch, 1979 . . . £20/£5

ditto, Knopf (U.S.), 1979 . . . . . £15/£5

The Enigma of Arrival, Viking, 1987 . . £15/£5

ditto, Knopf (U.S.), 1987 . . . . . £10/£5

A Way in the World: A Sequence, Heinemann , 1994 . . . . £15/£5

ditto, Knopf (U.S.), 1994 (advance copy, signed, in slipcase) . . . . £45/£25

ditto, Knopf (U.S.), 1994 . . . . . £10/£5

Short Stories

Miguel Street, Deutsch, 1959 . . . . . £300/£50

ditto, Vanguard Press (U.S.), 1960 . . . £125/£25
A Flag on the Island, Deutsch, 1967 . . £40/£15
ditto, Macmillan (U.S.), 1968 . . . . £35/£10

Others
The Middle Passage, Deutsch, 1962. . . £150/£20
ditto, Macmillan (U.S.), 1963 . . . . £65/£20
An Area of Darkness, Deutsch, 1964 . . £65/£20
ditto, Macmillan (U.S.), 1965 . . . £50/£15
The Loss of El Dorado, Deutsch, 1969 . . £35/£10
ditto, Knopf (U.S.), 1970 . . . . . £25/£10
The Overcrowded Barracoon, Deutsch, 1972 £45/£15
ditto, Knopf (U.S.), 1972 . . . . . £35/£10
India: A Wounded Civilisation, Deutsch, 1977. . .
. . . . £35/£10
ditto, Knopf (U.S.), 1977 . . . . . £25/£10
The Return of Eva Peron: with The Killings in Trinidad, Deutsch, 1980 . . . . . £20/£5
ditto, Knopf (U.S.), 1980 . . . . . £15/£5
Congo Diaries, Sylvester & Orphanos, 1980 (300 signed, numbered copies, no d/w) . . . £75
Among the Believers: An Islamic Journey, Deutsch, 1981 . . . . £20/£5
ditto, Franklin Library (U.S.), 1981 (signed limited edition) £45
ditto, Knopf (U.S.), 1981 . . . . . £15/£5
Finding the Centre: two narratives, Deutsch, 1984 .
. . . . £15/£5
ditto, Knopf (U.S.), 1984 . . . . . £15/£5
A Turn in the South, Viking, 1989 . . . £15/£5
ditto, Knopf (U.S.), 1989 . . . . . £15/£5
ditto, Franklin Library (U.S.), 1989 (signed limited edition) £40
India: A Million Mutinies Now, Heinemann, 1990 .
. . . . £15/£5
ditto, London Limited Editions (150 signed, numbered copies) £50
ditto, Viking (U.S.), 1991 . . . . . £10/£5
Conversations with V.S.Naipaul, Univ. Press of Mississippi (U.S.), 1995 . . . . . £20/£5
Beyond Belief: Islam Excursions Among the Converted Peoples, Little, Brown, 1998 . £15/£5
ditto, Random House (U.S.), 1998 . . . £10/£5
Between Father and Son: Family Letters, Little, Brown, 1999 . . . . £10/£5
ditto, Knopf (U.S.), 2000 . . . . . £10/£5

VIOLET NEEDHAM
(b.1876 d.1967)

A children's author, Violet Needham was 63 before her first book was published.

The Black Riders, Collins, 1939 . . . . £75/£20
The Emerald Crown, Collins, 1940 . . . £75/£20
The Stormy Petrel, Collins, 1942 . . . £75/£20

The Horn of Merlyns, Collins, 1943. . . £45/£10
The Woods of Windri, Collins, 1944 . . £45/£10
The House of the Paladin, Collins, 1945 . £35/£10
The Changeling of Monte Lucio, Collins, 1946 . .
. . . . £35/£10
The Bell of the Four Evangelists, Collins, 1947 . .
. . . . £35/£10
The Boy in Red, Collins, 1948 . . . . £35/£10
The Betrayer, Collins, 1950 . . . . . £35/£10
Pandora of Parrham Royal, Collins, 1951 . £75/£20
The Avenue, Collins, 1952 . . . . . £45/£10
How Many Miles to Babylon, Collins, 1953 £65/£20
Adventures at Hampton Court, Lutterworth Press, 1954 . . . . £65/£15
Richard and the Golden Horse Shoe, Collins, 1954 .
. . . . £75/£20
The Great House of Estraville, Collins, 1955 £75/£20
The Secret of the White Peacock, Collins, 1956 . .
. . . . £75/£20
Adventures at Windsor Castle, Lutterworth Press, 1957
. . . . £65/£15
The Red Rose of Ruvina, Collins, 1957 . . £75/£20

KAY NIELSEN
(b.1886 d.1957)

A Danish illustrator, Nielsen moved to London in 1911, and was commissioned to illustrate Quiller-Couch's *In Powder and Crinoline* by Hodder & Stoughton, followed by a series of 'Gift Books'.

In Powder and Crinoline, Old Fairy Tales, retold by Sir Arthur Quiller-Couch, Hodder & Stoughton, [1913] £6,000
ditto, Hodder & Stoughton, [1913] (large paper edition) £1,250
ditto, Hodder & Stoughton, [1913] (deluxe edition, 500 signed copies) £3,000
ditto, as *Twelve Dancing Princesses and Other Fairy Tales*, George H. Doran (U.S.) [1923] . . £450
East of the Sun and West of the Moon, Old Tales from the North, retold by Peter C. Asbjörnsen and Jorgen Moe, Hodder & Stoughton, [1914]. . £2,000
ditto, Hodder & Stoughton, [1914] (deluxe edition, 500 signed copies) £5,000
ditto, George H. Doran (U.S.) [1914] . . £1,000
Hans Andersen's Fairy Tales, Hodder & Stoughton, [1924]. . . . . £1,500/£750
ditto, Hodder & Stoughton, [1924] (deluxe edition, approx 250 of 500 signed copies, issued with d/w) .
. . . . £3,500/£1,500
ditto, Hodder & Stoughton, [1924] (deluxe edition, approx 250 of 500 signed copies, white velum binding) £2,500
ditto, Doran (U.S.), 1924 . . . . . £1,000/£250

Hansel and Gretel and Other Stories, Hodder & Stoughton, [1925] £750
ditto, Hodder & Stoughton, [1925] (600 signed copies, cream buckram binding). £3,000
ditto, Doran (U.S.), [1925] £600
ditto, Doran (U.S.), [1925] (600 signed copies) £2,500
Red Magic: A Collection of the World's Best Fairy Tales from all Countries, edited by Romer Wilson, Cape, 1930 . . . . £750/£250

PATRICK O'BRIAN
(b.1914)

Born in Ireland, O'Brian suffered from a severe illness for which 'sea-voyages' were prescribed, resulting in a life-long love of the sea. His 'Jack Aubrey' series of novels deal with the larger-than-life hero's naval career.

Novels
Three Bear Witness, Secker & Warburg, 1952 . . . . £600/£75
ditto, as *Testimonies*, Harcourt, Brace & Co. (U.S.), [1952]. . . . . £350/£35
ditto, as *Testimonies*, Harper Collins, 1994 . £20/£5
The Catalans, Harcourt, Brace & Co. (U.S.), [1953] . . . . £750/£75
ditto, as *The Frozen Flame*, Hart-Davis, 1953 . . . . £650/£75
Richard Temple, Macmillan, 1962 . . . £250/£35
Master and Commander, Lippincott (U.S.), 1969 . . . . £300/£65
ditto, Collins, 1970 . . . . . . £750/£125
Post Captain, Collins, 1972 . . . . . £500/£45
ditto, Lippincott (U.S.), 1972. . . . . £250/£35
H.M.S. Surprise, Collins, 1973 . . . . £350/£45
ditto, Lippincott (U.S.), 1973 . . . . . £150/£35
The Mauritius Command, Collins, 1977 . £300/£45
ditto, Stein & Day (U.S.), 1978 . . . . £150/£35
Desolation Island, Collins, 1978. . . . £275/£40
ditto, Stein & Day (U.S.), 1979 . . . . £125/£25
The Fortune of War, Collins, 1979 . . . £225/£40
ditto, Norton (U.S.), 1991 (wraps) . . . £25
The Surgeon's Mate, Collins, 1980 . . . £500/£65
ditto, Norton (U.S.), 1992 (wraps) . . . £25
The Ionian Mission, Collins, 1981 . . . £400/£50
ditto, Norton (U.S.), 1992 (wraps) . . . £20
Treason's Harbour, Collins, 1983 . . . £250/£45
ditto, Norton (U.S.), 1992 (wraps) . . . £20
The Far Side of the World, Collins, 1984 . £200/£40
ditto, Norton (U.S.), 1992 (wraps) . . . £20
The Reverse of the Medal, Collins, 1986 . £175/£35
ditto, Norton (U.S.), 1992 (wraps) . . . £20
The Letter of Marque, Collins, 1988 . . £150/£35
ditto, Norton (U.S.), 1991. . . . . . £25/£10
The Thirteen-Gun Salute, Collins, 1989 . £145/£35

ditto, Norton (U.S.), 1991. . . . . . £25/£10
The Nutmeg of Consolation, Collins, 1991 [1990]. . . . . £100/£25
ditto, Norton (U.S.), 1991. . . . . £25/£10
Clarissa Oakes, Harper Collins, 1992 . . £65/£20
ditto, as *The Truelove*, Norton (U.S.), 1992 £25/£10
The Wine-Dark Sea, Harper Collins, 1993 . £50/£15
ditto, Norton (U.S.), 1993. . . . . . £15/£5
The Commodore, Harper Collins, 1994 . £50/£15
ditto, Norton (U.S.), 1994. . . . . . £15/£5
ditto, Norton (U.S.), 1994 (200 signed, numbered copies, slipcase) . . . . £150/£125
The Yellow Admiral, Norton (U.S.), 1996 . £20/£5
ditto, Harper Collins, 1997 . . . . . £25/£5
The Hundred Days, Harper Collins, 1998 . £20/£5
ditto, Norton (U.S.), 1998. . . . . . £15/£5

Short Stories
The Last Pool and Other Stories, Secker & Warburg, 1950 . . . . £750/£100
The Walker and Other Stories, Harcourt, Brace & Co. (U.S.), [1955]. . . . . £150/£45
ditto, as *Lying in the Sun and Other Stories*, Hart-Davis, 1956 (slightly different contents) . £175/£50
The Chian Wine and Other Stories, Collins, 1974 . . . . £125/£30
Collected Short Stories, Harper Collins, 1994 £50/£15
ditto, as *The Rendezvous and Other Stories*, Norton (U.S.), 1994 . . . . £40/£15

Children's
The Road to Samarcand, Hart-Davis, 1954 £250/£35
The Golden Ocean, Hart-Davis, 1956 . . £350/£45
ditto, John Day (U.S.), 1957 . . . . . £250/£35
The Unknown Shore, Hart-Davis, 1959 . . £175/£40

Non Fiction
Men-Of-War, Collins, 1974 . . . . . £75/£20
ditto, Norton (U.S.), 1995. . . . . . £25/£10
Pablo Ruiz Picasso: A Biography, Collins, 1976 . . . . £75/£25
ditto, as *Picasso: Pablo Ruiz Picasso: A Biography*, Putnam (U.S.), [1976] . . . . . £75/£25
Joseph Banks: A Life, Collins Harvill, 1987 £65/£20
ditto, Godine (U.S.), 1992 . . . . . £35/£10

Translations
The Quicksand War, by Lucian Bodard, Faber, 1967 . . . . £75/£20
The Italian Campaign, by Michael Mohart, Weidenfeld, 1967 . . . . £75/£20

Editor
A Book of Voyages, Home & Van Thal, 1947 . . . . £350/£75

EDNA O'BRIEN
(b.1932)

An Irish novelist and short story writer, often concentrating on the position of women in society. Her novels are a blend of bleakness and quiet joy.

Novels

The Country Girls, Hutchinson, 1960	.	£75/£15
ditto, Knopf (U.S.), 1960 .	.	£45/£10
The Lonely Girl, Cape, 1962 .	.	£40/£10
ditto, Random House (U.S.), 1962	.	£30/£10
Girls in Their Married Bliss, Cape, 1964	.	£20/£5
ditto, Houghton Mifflin (U.S.), 1968	.	£15/£5
August is a Wicked Month, Cape, 1965 .	.	£20/£5
ditto, Simon & Schuster (U.S.), 1965	.	£15/£5
Casualties of Peace, Cape, 1966 .	.	£25/£5
ditto, Simon & Schuster (U.S.), 1967	.	£15/£5
A Pagan Place, Weidenfeld, 1970	.	£20/£5
ditto, Knopf (U.S.), 1970 .	.	£15/£5
Night, Weidenfeld, 1972 .	.	£15/£5
ditto, Knopf (U.S.), 1973 .	.	£15/£5

Johnnie, I Hardly Knew You, Weidenfeld, 1977 .
. . . . £15/£5
ditto, as *I Hardly Knew You*, Doubleday (U.S.), 1978 .
. . . . £10/£5
The High Road, Weidenfeld, 1988 . . . £15/£5
ditto, London Limited Editions, 1988 (150 signed copies, tissue d/w) . . . . . . £50/£40
ditto, Farrar Straus (U.S.), 1988 . . . £10/£5
Time and Tide, Viking, 1992. . . . . £10/£5
ditto, Farrar Straus (U.S.), 1992 . . . £10/£5
House of Splendid Isolation, Weidenfeld, 1994 £10/£5
ditto, Farrar Straus (U.S.), 1994 . . . £10/£5
Down by the River, Weidenfeld, 1995 . . £10/£5
ditto, Farrar Straus (U.S.), 1997 . . . £10/£5

Short Stories

The Love Object, Cape, 1968. . . . . £30/£5
ditto, Knopf (U.S.), 1969 . . . . . £25/£5
A Scandalous Woman, Weidenfeld, 1974 . £15/£5
ditto, Harcourt Brace (U.S.), 1974 . . . £10/£5
Mrs Reinhardt and Other Stories, Weidenfeld, 1978 .
. . . . £15/£5
ditto, as *A Rose in the Heart*, Doubleday (U.S.), 1979.
. . . . £10/£5
Returning, Weidenfeld, 1982 . . . . £15/£5
A Fanatic Heart, Weidenfeld, 1985 . . . £10/£5
ditto, Franklin Library (U.S.), (signed, limited edition)
. . . . £20
ditto, Farrar Straus (U.S.), 1984. . . . £10/£5
Lantern Slides, Weidenfeld, 1990 . . . £10/£5
ditto, Farrar Straus (U.S.), 1990 . . . £10/£5

Collected Editions

The Collected Edna O'Brien, Collins, 1978 £15/£5
Some Irish Loving, Weidenfeld, 1979 . . £15/£5
ditto, Harper (U.S.), 1979. . . . . . £10/£5

The Country Girls Trilogy and Epilogue, Farrar Straus (U.S.), 1986 . . . . £10/£5
ditto, Cape, 1987 . . . . £10/£5

Children's

The Dazzle, Hodder & Stoughton, 1981. . £15/£5
Christmas Treat, Hodder & Stoughton, 1982 £10/£5
Tales for Telling: Irish Folk and Fairy Stories, Pavilion, 1986 . . . . £10/£5
ditto, Atheneum (U.S.), 1986 . . . . £10/£5

Plays

A Pagan Place, Faber, 1973 . . . . £25/£10
Virginia, Hogarth Press, 1981 . . . . £10
ditto, Harcourt Brace (U.S.), 1981 . . . £10

Others

Zee & Co, Weidenfeld, 1971 . . . . £30/£10
Mother Ireland, Weidenfeld, 1976 . . £15/£5
ditto, Harcourt Brace (U.S.), 1976 . . £15/£5
Arabian Days, Horizon Press (U.S.), 1977 . £10/£5
ditto, Quartet, 1977 . . . . . . £10/£5
James and Nora, Lord John Press (US), 1981 (26 signed, lettered copies of 276, slipcase) . £75/£65
ditto, Lord John Press (U.S.), 1981 (250 signed, numbered copies of 276) . . . . £50/£40

FLANN O'BRIEN
(b.1911 d.1966)

An Irish novelist and journalist, his first novel, *At Swim-Two-Birds*, was hailed by many as a masterpiece in the tradition of Joyce's *Ulysses*.

Novels

At Swim-Two-Birds, Longmans, 1939 (black cloth) .
. . . . £3,000/£200
ditto, Pantheon (U.S.), 1939 . . . . £200/£25
An Beal Bocht, The National Press, 1941 (pseud. 'Myles na gCopaleen', wraps) £400
ditto, translated as *The Poor Mouth*, Hart-Davis MacGibbon, 1973 (illustrated by Ralph Steadman) .
. . . . £75/£15
ditto, Hart-Davis MacGibbon, 1973 (130 copies signed by Ralph Steadman) £500
ditto, Viking (U.S.), 1974 . . . . £45/£10
The Hard Life: An Exegesis of Squalor, MacGibbon & Kee, 1961 . . . . . . £100/£20
ditto, Pantheon (U.S.), 1962 . . . . £50/£15
The Dalkey Archive, MacGibbon & Kee, 1964. . .
. . . . £80/£15
ditto, Macmillan (U.S.), 1965 . . . £45/£10
The Third Policeman, MacGibbon & Kee, 1967 . .
. . . . £75/£15
ditto, Walker & Co (U.S.), 1967. . . . £45/£10

Others

Cruiskeen Lawn, Irish Times (Dublin), 1943 (pseud. 'Myles na gCopaleen', wraps) £200
Faustus Kelly, Cahill (Dublin), 1943 (wraps) . £500
The Best of Myles, a Selection from 'Cruiskeen Lawn', MacGibbon & Kee, 1968 . . . £75/£15
ditto, Walker & Co (U.S.), 1968 . . . . £45/£10
Stories and Plays, Hart-Davis MacGibbon, 1973 .
. . . . £50/£10
ditto, Viking (U.S.), 1976. . . . . . £45/£10
Further Cuttings from 'Cruiskeen Lawn', Hart-Davis MacGibbon, 1976 . . . . . £40/£10
ditto, Dalkey Archive Press (U.S.), 2000 . . £5
The Various Lives of Keats and Chapman and The Brother, Hart-Davis MacGibbon, 1976 . £40/£10
The Hair of the Dogma: A Further Selection from 'Cruiskeen Lawn', Hart-Davis MacGibbon, 1977 .
. . . . £40/£10
A Flann O'Brien Reader, Viking (U.S.), 1978 £25/£10
Myles Away from Dublin, Granada, 1985 . £20/£10

LIAM O'FLAHERTY
(b.1896 d.1984)

Irish novelist and short story writer.

Novels

Thy Neighbour's Wife, Cape, 1923 . . . £200/£30
ditto, Boni & Liveright, (U.S.), 1924 . . £125/£25
The Black Soul, Cape, 1924 . . . . £125/£25
ditto, Boni & Liveright (U.S.), 1924 . . . £45/£15
The Informer, Cape, 1925 . . . . . £250/£50
ditto, Knopf (U.S.), 1925 . . . . . . £150/£40
Mr Gilhooey, Cape, 1926 . . . . . . £50/£20
ditto, Harcourt Brace (U.S.), 1927 . . £45/£15
The Assassin, Cape, 1928 . . . . . £75/£15
ditto, Cape, 1928 (150 signed, numbered copies) . .
. . . . £150
ditto, Harcourt Brace (U.S.), 1928 . . . £50/£10
The House of Gold, Cape, 1929 . . . . £75/£15
ditto, Harcourt Brace (U.S.), 1929 . . . £35/£10
Return of the Brute, Mandrake Press, 1929 £150/£25
ditto, Harcourt Brace (U.S.), 1930 . . . £100/£15
The Puritan, Cape, 1931 [1932] . . . . £75/£15
ditto, Harcourt Brace (U.S.), 1932 . . . £50/£20
The Ecstasy of Angus, Joiner & Steele, 1931 £75/£15
ditto, Joiner & Steele, 1931 (365 signed copies, glassine d/w) . . . . £125/£100
Skerrett, Gollancz, 1932 . . . . . . £65/£10
ditto, Long & Smith (U.S.), 1932 . . . £40/£10
The Martyr, Gollancz, 1933 . . . . . £65/£15
ditto, Macmillan (U.S.), 1933 (expurgated edition)
. . . . £40/£10
Hollywood Cemetery, Gollancz, 1935 . £250/£30
Famine, Gollancz, 1937 . . . . . . £75/£20
ditto, Random House (U.S.), 1937 . . . £50/£15
Land, Gollancz, 1946 . . . . . . £25/£10

ditto, Random House (U.S.), 1946 . . . £20/£5
Insurrection, Gollancz, 1950 . . . . . £25/£10
ditto, Little, Brown (U.S.), 1951 . . . . £20/£5
The Wilderness, Wolfhound Press (Dublin), 1979 . .
. . . . £15/£5
ditto, Wolfhound Press (Dublin), 1979 (50 signed, numbered copies) £50
ditto, Dodd, Mead (U.S.), 1986 . . . . £10/£5

Short Stories

Spring Sowing, Cape, 1924 . . . . . £75/£25
ditto, Knopf (U.S.), 1926 . . . . . £50/£15
The Tent, Cape, 1926 (blue cloth) . . . £50/£20
ditto, Cape, 1926 (dark green cloth) . . . £40/£15
The Fairy Goose and Two Other Stories, Crosby Gaige (U.S.) & Faber & Gwyer (U.K.), 1927 (1,190 signed copies) . . . . . . £40/£15
ditto, Crosby Gaige (U.S.) & Faber & Gwyer (U.K.), 1928 (12 signed copies on blue handmade paper). .
. . . . £150
ditto, Crosby Gaige (U.S.) & Faber & Gwyer (U.K.), 1928 (12 signed copies on green handmade paper) .
. . . . £150
Red Barbara and Other Stories, Crosby Gaige (U.S.) & Faber & Gwyer (U.K.), 1928 (600 signed, numbered copies) £75
ditto, Crosby Gaige (U.S.) & Faber & Gwyer (U.K.), 1928 (9 signed copies on grey handmade paper) . .
. . . . £150
The Mountain Tavern and Other Stories, Cape, 1929.
. . . . £45/£15
ditto, Harcourt Brace (U.S.), 1929 . . . £45/£15
The Wild Swan and Other Stories, Joiner & Steele: 'Furnival Books', 1932 (550 signed copies) £75/£50
The Short Stories of Liam O'Flaherty, Cape, 1937 .
. . . . £15/£5
Two Lovely Beasts, Gollancz, 1948 . . . £15/£5
ditto, Devin-Adair (U.S.), 1950 . . . £10/£5
Duil, Sainseal & Dill, 1953 (Gaelic) . . . £15/£5
The Stories of Liam O'Flaherty, Devin-Adair (U.S.), 1956 . . . . £15/£5
The Pedlar's Revenge, Wolfhound Press (Dublin) 1976 . . . . £20/£5

Pamphlets

Civil War, E. Archer, 1925 (100 signed copies, wraps)
. . . . £150
The Terrorist, E. Archer, 1926 (100 signed copies) .
. . . . £150
Darkness: A Tragedy in Three Acts, E. Archer, 1926 .
. . . . £100
ditto, E. Archer, 1926 (12 copies with cast-list) £150
The Child Of God, E. Archer, 1926 (100 signed copies, wraps). £125
ditto, E.Archer (25 signed large paper copies) . £200
A Tourist's Guide to Ireland, Mandrake Press, [1929]
. . . . £75/£50
Joseph Conrad, E. Lahr: 'Blue Moon Booklet', 1930 .
. . . . £25

ditto, E. Lahr: 'Blue Moon Booklet', 1930 (100 large paper copies) £45
A Cure for Unemployment, E. Lahr: 'Blue Moon Booklet', 1931 . . . . £25
ditto, E. Lahr: 'Blue Moon Booklet', 1931 (100 large paper copies) £45
ditto, E. Lahr/Julian Press (U.S.), 1931 . . . £25

Others
The Life of Tim Healy, Cape, 1927 . . . £45/£10
ditto, Harcourt Brace (U.S.), 1927 . . . £35/£10
Two Years, Cape, 1930 . . . . . £20/£5
I Went to Russia, Cape, 1931 . . . . £20/£5
ditto, Harcourt Brace (U.S.), 1931 . . . £20/£5
Shame the Devil, Grayson & Grayson, 1934 £20/£5
ditto, Grayson & Grayson, 1934 (single page from original manuscript bound in) . . . . £65/£45

EUGENE O'NEILL
(b.1888 d.1953)

An American playwright whose experimental work has been a major influence on modern American theatre.

Plays
Thirst and Other One-Act Plays, Gorham Press (U.S.), 1914 . . . . £1,500/£400
Before Breakfast, Frank Shay (U.S), 1916 (wraps) .
. . . . £200
The Moon of the Caribees and Six Other Plays of the Sea, Boni & Liveright (U.S.), 1919 £1,000/£200
ditto, Cape, 1923 . . . . . . £50/£10
Gold, Boni & Liveright (U.S.), 1920 [1921] £300/£75
Beyond the Horizon, Boni & Liveright (U.S.), 1921 .
. . . . £500/£100
ditto, Cape, 1924 . . . . . £250/£35
The Emperor Jones, Diff'ent, The Straw, Boni & Liveright (U.S.), 1921 . . . . . £500/£75
ditto, Cape, 1922 . . . . . . £250/£35
ditto, Boni & Liveright (U.S.), 1928 (775 signed, numbered copies, illustrated, d/w and slipcase) .
. . . . £300/£175
The Hairy Ape, Anna Christi, The First Man, Boni & Liveright (U.S.), 1922 . . . . . £500/£75
ditto, as *The Hairy Ape and Other Plays*, Cape, 1923 .
. . . . £150/£35
Anna Christi,Cape, 1923 . . . . . £200/£25
ditto, Boni & Liveright (U.S.), 1930 (775 signed, numbered copies, illustrated, d/w and slipcase) . .
. . . . £250/£175
ditto, Boni & Liveright (U.S.), 1930 (12 signed copies in morocco with original lithograph) . . £1,000
All God's Chillun' Got Wings, Welded, Boni & Liveright (U.S.), 1924 . . . . . £350/£50
ditto, Cape, 1925 . . . . . . £200/£25

Desire Under the Elms, Boni & Liveright (U.S.), 1925
. . . . £550/£50
ditto, Cape, 1925 . . . . £75/£15
The Great God Bown, The Fountain, The Moon of the Caribees and Other Plays, Boni & Liveright (U.S.), 1926 . . . . £400/£50
ditto, Cape, 1926 . . . . £200/£25
Marco Millions, Boni & Liveright (U.S.), 1927 . .
. . . . £200/£30
ditto, Boni & Liveright (U.S.), 1927 (450 signed copies, slipcase) . . . . . . £200/£150
ditto, Cape, 1927 . . . . £75/£15
Lazarus Laughed, Boni & Liveright (U.S.), 1927 . .
. . . . £200/£30
ditto, Boni & Liveright (U.S.), 1927 (775 signed copies, slipcase) . . . . . . £200/£150
Dynamo, Boni & Liveright (U.S.), 1929 . £75/£15
ditto, Boni & Liveright (U.S.), 1929 (775 signed copies, slipcase) . . . . . . £200/£150
Mourning Becomes Electra, Boni & Liveright (U.S.), 1931 . . . . £100/£45
ditto, Boni & Liveright (U.S.), 1931 (550 signed copies, slipcase) . . . . . . £250/£175
ditto, Boni & Liveright (U.S.), 1931 (50 signed presentation copies) £350
ditto, Cape, 1932 . . . . . . £100/£20
Strange Interlude, Boni & Liveright (U.S.), 1933 . .
. . . . £250/£25
ditto, Boni & Liveright (U.S.), 1933 (775 signed copies, slipcase) . . . . . . £200/£150
Ah, Wilderness!, Random House (U.S.), 1933 . .
. . . . £150/£25
ditto, Random House (U.S.), 1933 (325 signed copies, slipcase) . . . . £300/£250
Days Without End, Random House (U.S.), 1934 . .
. . . . £100/£25
ditto, Cape, 1934 . . . . . . £40/£10
The Iceman Cometh, Random House (U.S.), 1946. .
. . . . £100/£25
ditto, Cape, 1947 . . . . . . £45/£15
Lost Plays of Eugene O'Neill, New Fathoms Press (U.S.), 1950 . . . . £75/£15
A Moon for the Misbegotten, Random House (U.S.), 1952 . . . . £100/£15
ditto, Cape, 1953 . . . . . . £25/£10
Nine Plays by Eugene O'Neill, Modern Library (U.S.), 1954 . . . . £75/£15
Long Day's Journey Into Night, Yale Univ Press (U.S.), 1956 . . . . £150/£25
ditto, Cape, 1956 . . . . . . £30/£10
A Touch of the Poet, Yale Univ. Press (U.S.), 1957 .
. . . . £75/£15
ditto, Cape, 1957 . . . . . . £25/£5
Hughie, Yale Univ. Press (U.S.), 1959 . £75/£10
ditto, Cape, 1962 . . . . . . £25/£5
More Stately Mansions, Yale Univ. Press (U.S.), 1964
. . . . £75/£15
The Calms of Capricorn, Tichnor & Fields (U.S.), 1982 . . . . £25/£10

Eugene O'Neill: The Unfinished Plays, Continuum (U.S.), 1988 . . . . £15/£5
The Unknown O'Neill, Yale Univ, Press (U.S.), 1988.
. . . . £15/£5
Eugene O'Neill: Complete Plays, Library of America (U.S.), 1988 . . . . £20/£5

Others
A Bibliography of the Works of Eugene O'Neill and The Collected Poems of Eugene O'Neill, Random House (U.S.), 1931 . . . . . £75/£10
Inscriptions: Eugene O'Neill to Carlotta Monterey O'Neill, Yale Univ. Press (U.S.), 1960 (limited edition in slipcase) £200
Poems: 1912-1944, Yale Univ. Press (U.S.), 1979 . .
. . . . £15/£5
Work Diary: 1924-1943, Yale Univ. Press (U.S.), 1981
. . . . £15/£5
Eugene O'Neill At Work: Newly Released Ideas for Plays, Ungar (U.S.), 1981 . . . . £15/£5
The Theatre We Worked For: The Letters of Eugene O'Neill to Kenneth MacGowran, Yale Univ. Press (U.S.), 1982 . . . . £75/£10
Love, Admiration and respect: The O'Neill-Commins Correspondence, Duke Univ. Press (U.S.), 1986 . .
. . . . £50/£10
As Ever, Gene: The Letters of Eugene O'Neill to George Jean Nathan, Fairleigh Univ. Press (U.S.), 1987 . . . . £15/£5
Selected Letters of Eugene O'Neill, Yale Univ. Press (U.S.), 1988 . . . . £35/£10

JOE ORTON
(b.1933 d.1967)

Orton's black farces are a skilful blend of the crude and the clever. His irreverence and ear for comic dialogue are unique.

Plays
Entertaining Mr Sloane, Hamish Hamilton, 1964 . .
. . . . £125/£25
ditto, Grove Press (U.S.), 1965 (wraps) . . . £25
Loot, Methuen, 1967 . . . . . . £35/£10
ditto, Methuen, 1967 (wraps). £10
ditto, Grove Press (U.S.), 1968 . . . . £10
Crimes of Passion, Methuen, 1967 . . . £25/£10
ditto, Methuen, 1967 (wraps). £10
ditto, Grove Press (U.S.), 1968 . . . . £10
What the Butler Saw, Methuen, 1969 . . £25/£10
ditto, Methuen, 1969 (wraps). £10
ditto, Grove Press (U.S.), 1969 . . . . £10
Funeral Games and The Good and Faithful Servant, Methuen, 1970 . . . . . . £25/£10
ditto, Methuen, 1970 (wraps). £10
Joe Orton: The Complete Plays, Eyre Methuen, 1976.
. . . . £15/£5

ditto, Grove Press (U.S.), 1977 . . . . . £10

Screenplay
Up Against It, Eyre Methuen, 1979 . . . £20/£5
ditto, Grove Press (U.S.), 1979 . . . . £15/£5

Novel
Head to Toe, Blond, 1971 . . . . . £45/£10
ditto, St Martins Press (U.S.), 1971 . . . £30/£10

Others
The Orton Diaries, Methuen, 1986 . . . £15/£5
ditto, Harper & Row (U.S.), 1986 . . . £10/£5

GEORGE ORWELL
(b.1903 d.1950)

A left-wing novelist, essayist and journalist, Orwell, a pseudonym for Eric Blair, is famous for his bleak political satires *Animal Farm* and *Nineteen Eighty Four*.

Novels
Burmese Days, Harper (U.S.), 1934 . . £2,500/£200
ditto, Gollancz, 1935 . . . . . £3,000/£300
A Clergyman's Daughter, Gollancz, 1935 . . . .
. . . . £4,000/£400
ditto, Harper (U.S.), 1936. . . . £2,500/£200
Keep the Aspidistra Flying, Gollancz, 1936 . . .
. . . . £2,500/£200
ditto, Harcourt Brace (U.S.), 1956 . . £75/£15
Coming Up for Air, Gollancz, 1939 . . £1,500/£150
ditto, Harcourt Brace (U.S.), 1950 . . £75/£25
Animal Farm, Secker, 1945 . . . £1,500/£100
ditto, Harcourt Brace (U.S.), 1946 . . £75/£25
Nineteen Eighty-Four, Secker, 1949 (red d/w) . .
. . . . £1,000/£50
ditto, Secker, 1949 (green d/w) . . . £650/£50
ditto, Harcourt Brace (U.S.), 1949 (red d/w) £250/£25
ditto, Harcourt Brace (U.S.), 1949 (blue d/w) £125/£25

Non Fiction
Down and Out in Paris and London, Gollancz, 1933 .
. . . . £3,000/£250
ditto, Harper (U.S.), 1933. . . . £1,250/£200
The Road to Wigan Pier, Gollancz, 1937 (Left Book Club Edition). £50
ditto, Gollancz, 1937 . . . . £1,000/£125
ditto, Gollancz, 1937 (200 copies of the Left Book Club Edition bound separately, without the preface) .
. . . . £200
ditto, Supplementary Left Book Club Edition (part one only, plus photographs) £200
ditto, Harcourt Brace (U.S.), 1958 . . £50/£15
Homage to Catalonia, Secker, 1938. . £2,000/£175
ditto, Harcourt Brace (U.S.), 1952 . . £50/£15

The Lion and the Unicorn, Secker, 1941 (Searchlight Books, No.1) . . . . £75/£20
James Burnham and the Managerial Revolution, Socialist Book Centre, 1946 (wraps) . . . £200

Essays
Inside the Whale, Gollancz, 1940 . . £1,000/£75
Critical Essays, Secker, 1946. . . . . £75/£15
ditto, as *Dickens, Dali and Others*, Reynal (U.S.), 1946 . . . . £50/£15
The English People, Collins, 1947 . . . £35/£10
Shooting an Elephant, Secker, 1950 . . £45/£10
ditto, Harcourt Brace (U.S.), 1950 . . . £40/£10
Such, Such Were the Joys, Harcourt Brace (U.S.), 1953 . . . . £50/£15
ditto, as *England, Your England*, Secker, 1953 . . . . £45/£15
The Decline of the English Murder and Other Essays, Penguin, 1965 (wraps) £10
The War Broadcasts, BBC/Duckworth, 1985 £15/£5
The War Commentaries, BBC/Duckworth, 1985 . . . . £15/£5

Selected and Collected Editions
The Orwell Reader, Harcourt Brace (U.S.), 1956 . . . . £35/£10
Selected Essays, Penguin, 1957 (wraps). . . £10
Selected Writings, Heinemann, 1958 . . £15/£5
The Collected Essays, Journalism and Letters, Secker, 1968 (4 vols) . . . . . £150/£45
ditto, Harcourt Brace (U.S.), 1968 (4 vols) . £145/£40
The Penguin Complete Longer Non-fiction of George Orwell, Penguin, 1983 (wraps) £5

JOHN OSBORNE
(b.1929 d.1994)

The author of *Look Back in Anger*, which won the 1956 Evening Standard Award for Best Play, is well known for his 'kitchen sink' dramas.

Plays
Look Back in Anger, Faber, 1957 . . . £60/£15
ditto, Criterion (U.S.), 1957 . . . . . £30/£10
The Entertainer, Faber, 1957 . . . £40/£10
ditto, Criterion (U.S.), 1958 . . . . . £20/£5
Epitaph for George Dillon, Faber, 1958 (with Anthony Creighton) . . . . £25/£10
ditto, Criterion (U.S.), 1958 . . . . . £10/£5
The World of Paul Slickey, Faber, 1959 . £25/£10
ditto, Criterion (U.S.), 1961 . . . . . £10/£5
A Subject of Scandal and Concern, Faber, 1961 . . . . £35/£15
Luther, Faber, 1961 . . . . £25/£10
ditto, Dramatic Publishing Co. (U.S.), 1961 £10/£5
Plays for England, Faber, 1963 . . . . £25/£10
ditto, Criterion (U.S.), 1964 . . . . . £10/£5

Inadmissible Evidence, Faber, 1965. . . £25/£10
ditto, Grove Press (U.S.), 1965 . . . . £10/£5
A Patriot for Me, Faber, 1966 . . . . £25/£10
ditto, Random House (U.S.), 1970 . . . £10/£5
Time Present and *Hotel in Amsterdam*, Faber, 1968 . . . . £20/£5
The Right Prospectus, Faber, 1970 . . . £15/£5
Very Like a Whale, Faber, 1971 . . . . £15/£5
West of Suez, Faber, 1971 . . . . . £15/£5
The Gift of Friendship, Faber, 1972. . . £15/£5
A Sense of Detachment, Faber, 1973 . . £15/£5
The End of Me Old Cigar, Faber, 1975 . . £15/£5
Watch It Come Down, Faber, 1975 . . . £15/£5
You're Not Watching Me, Mummy, and *Try a Little Tenderness*, Faber, 1978 . . . . . £15/£5
A Better Class of Person and *God Rot Tunbridge Wells*, Faber, 1985 . . . . £15/£5
Dejavu, Faber, 1992. . . . . £10/£5

Autobiography
A Better Class of Person, Faber, 1981. . . £20/£5
ditto, Dutton (U.S.), 1981. . . . . . £10/£5
Almost a Gentleman: An Autobiography, Vol II, 1955 -1966, Faber, 1991 . . . . . £15/£5

Translations/Adaptations
A Bond Honoured, Faber 1966 (from Lope de Vega's *La Fianza Satisfecha*) . . . . . £15/£5
Hedda Gabler, Faber 1972 (Ibsen) . . . £10/£5
The Picture of Dorian Gray: A Moral Entertainment, Faber, 1973 (Oscar Wilde) . . . . £10/£5
A Place Calling Itself Rome, Faber, 1973 (based on Shakespeare's *Coriolanus*) . . . . . £10/£5
Strindberg's 'The Father' and *Ibsen's 'Hedda Gabler'*, Faber, 1989. . . . . . . £10/£5

Others
Look Back in Anger, Four Square Books, 1960 (novelisation by John Burke, wraps) . . . £5
The Entertainer, Four Square Books, 1960 (novelisation by John Burke, wraps) . . . £5
Tom Jones: A Film Script, Faber, 1964. . £20/£5
ditto, Grove Press (U.S.), 1964 . . . . £10/£5
Damn You, England: Collected Prose, Faber, 1994 . . . . £10/£5

WILFRED OWEN
(b.1893 d.1918)

Owen suffered trench fever and concussion in World War One and was diagnosed 'shell-shocked.' While waiting to return to the trenches he drafted and revised his best poems, but was killed in action only a week before the Armistice.

Verse
Poems, Chatto & Windus, 1920 . . . £1,500/£200
ditto, Huebsch (U.S.), n.d. [1921] . . . £750/£150

The Poems of Wilfred Owen, Chatto & Windus 1931 .
. . . . £200/£50
ditto, Viking (U.S.), 1931. . . . . . £45/£15
Thirteen Poems, Gehenna Press (U.S.), 1956
(illustrated by Shahn and Baskin, 400 copies signed
by Baskin, no d/w) £250
ditto, Gehenna Press (U.S.), 1956 (35 copies with
portrait proof, signed by both artists) . . £1,000
The Collected Poems of Wilfred Owen, Chatto &
Windus, 1963. . . . . £30/£10
ditto, New directions (U.S.), 1964 . . . £25/£10
The Complete Poems and Fragments, Chatto &
Windus, 1983 (2 vols, d/ws and slipcase) . £75/£45
ditto, Norton (U.S.), 1984 (2 vols, d/ws and slipcase) .
. . . . £75/£45

Others
Collected Letters, O.U.P., 1967 . . . . £125/£50

THOMAS LOVE PEACOCK
(b.1785 d.1866)

Although he also wrote poetry, Peacock is
remembered as the author of a number of unique, if
odd novels.

Poetry
Palmyra and Other Poems, Richardson, 1806 . £600
The Genius of the Thames, Hookham, 1810 . £300
The Philosophy of Melancholy, Hookham, 1812 £300
Sir Hornbook, or Childe Launcelot's Expedition,
Sharpe & Hailes, 1814 (anonymous) . . £1,000
The Round Table, or King Arthur's Feast, John
Arliss, 1817 (anonymous) £1,000
Rhododaphne, or The Thessalian Spell, Hookham,
1818 (anonymous) £300
ditto, Carey & Son (U.S.), 1818 . . . . £100
Paper Money Lyrics, Reynell, 1837 (100 copies,
anonymous) £500

Novels
Headlong Hall, Hookham, 1816 (anonymous) . £600
Melincourt, Hookham, 1817 (anonymous, 3 vols) . .
. . . . £750
Nightmare Abbey, Hookham, 1818 ('By the Author of
Headlong Hall') £750
Maid Marian, Hookham, 1822 ('By the Author of
Headlong Hall') £500
The Misfortunes of Elphin, Hookham, 1829 ('By the
Author of Headlong Hall') £250
Crotchet Castle, Hookham, 1831 ('By the Author of
Headlong Hall') £500
Gryll Grange, Parker, Son, & Bourn, 1861
(anonymous) £250

Others
Gl'Ingannati, The Deceived and Aelia Laelia Crispis,
Chapman & Hall, 1862 (translated by Peacock) . .
. . . . £100
Memoirs of Shelley, Frowde, 1909 . . . . £40
The Works of Thomas Love Peacock, Richard
Bentley, 1875 (3 vols) £200

MERVYN PEAKE
(b.1911 d.1968)

Peake's strength in both his writing and drawing is in
the creation of atmosphere through often grotesque
detail. Some of his verse is of the nonsense school.

Verse by Peake
Shapes and Sounds, Chatto & Windus, 1941 £200/£50
Rhymes Without Reason, Eyre & Spottiswoode, 1944
. . . . £100/£30
The Glassblowers, Eyre & Spottiswoode, 1950 . .
. . . . £75/£25
The Rhyme of the Flying Bomb, Dent, 1962 £40/£10
Poems and Drawings, Keepsake Press, 1965 (150
copies, wraps) £200
A Reverie of Bone, Rota, 1967 (320 copies, wraps with
d/w) . . . . £100/£50
Selected Poems, Faber, 1972 . . . . . £25/£10
A Book of Nonsense, Owen, 1972 . . . £25/£10
ditto, Dufour (U.S.), 1975 . . . . . £20/£10
Twelve Poems, 1939-1960, Bran's Head, 1975 (350
numbered copies, wraps with glassine dw) £175/£150
Swans Die and Towers Fall, Grasshopper Press, 1973
(100 copies, broadside) £125

Novels by Peake
Titus Groan, Eyre & Spottiswoode, 1946 . £200/£25
ditto, Reynal and Hitchcock (U.S.), 1946 . £75/£15
Gormenghast, Eyre & Spottiswoode, 1950 . £125/£20
ditto, Weybright & Talley, (U.S.), 1967 . £15/£5
Mr Pye, Heinemann, 1953 . . . . . £50/£15
Titus Alone, Eyre & Spottiswoode, 1959 . £75/£20
ditto, Weybright & Talley, (U.S.), 1967 . £15/£5
Boy in Darkness, Wheaton, 1976 (wraps) . . £30
ditto, Hodder, 1996 . . . . £15/£5

Children's Books by Peake
Captain Slaughterboard Drops Anchor, Country Life,
1939 . . . . £1,500/£1,000
ditto, Eyre & Spottiswoode, 1945 . . . £300/£75
ditto, Macmillan, (U.S.), 1967 . . . £30/£10
Letters from a Lost Uncle from Polar Regions, Eyre &
Spottiswoode, 1948 . . . . £75

Other Books by Peake
The Craft of the Lead Pencil, Wingate, 1946 . £60
The Drawings of Mervyn Peake, Grey Walls Press,
1949 . . . . £75/£35

Figures of Speech, Gollancz, 1954 . . . £50/£20
The Drawings of Mervyn Peake, Davis-Poynter, 1974
. . . . £30/£10
Mervyn Peake: Writings and Drawings, Academy,
1974 . . . . £20/£10
ditto, St Martin's Press (U.S.), 1974 . . . £20/£10
Peake's Progress: Selected Writings and Drawings,
John Lane, 1979 . . . . . . £20/£10
ditto, Overlook Press (U.S.), 1981 . . . £20/£10

Books Illustrated by Peake
Ride a Cock-Horse, and other nursery rhymes, Chatto
& Windus 1940 . . . . £350/£75
ditto, Transatlantic (U.S.), 1944 . . . . £250/£45
The Hunting of the Snark, An agony in eight fits, by
Lewis Carroll, Chatto & Windus, 1941 (yellow
boards) . . . . £75/£20
ditto, by Lewis Carroll, Chatto & Windus, 1941 (large
format, pink boards) . . . . . . £125/£35
*The Adventures of The Young Soldier in search of
The Better World*, by C[yril] E[dwin] M[itchinson]
Joad, Faber & Faber 1943 . . . . £45/£10
ditto, Arco (U.S.), 1944 . . . . . £40/£10
All This and Bevin Too, by Quentin Crisp, Nicholson
& Watson, 1943 (wraps) £150
ditto, Mervyn Peake Society, 1978 (40 copies signed
by Crisp) £200
The Rime of the Ancient Mariner, by Samuel Taylor
Coleridge, Chatto & Windus, 1943 . . £45/£15
*Prayers and Graces, A little book of extraordinary
piety*, by Allan M. Laing, Gollancz, 1944 . £50/£15
Witchcraft in England, by Christina Hole, Batsford
1945 . . . . £50/£10
ditto, Scribner's Sons (U.S.), 1947 . . £45/£10
*Alice's Adventures in Wonderland and Through the
Looking-Glass*, by Lewis Carroll, Zephyr Books
(Sweden), 1946 (wraps with d/w) . . £200/£75
ditto, Allan Wingate 1954 . . . . £450/£150
ditto, Schocken (U.S.), 1979 . . . . £25/£10
Quest for Sita, by Maurice Collis, Faber, 1946 (500
copies) . . . . £250/£175
ditto, John Day (U.S.), 1947 . . . . £75/£45
Household Tales, by Brothers Grimm, Eyre &
Spottiswoode, 1946 . . . . . . £100/£35
ditto, Schocken (U.S.), 1979 . . . . £25/£10
Dr Jekyll & Mr Hyde, by Robert Louis Stevenson, The
Folio Society, 1948 . . . . . . £45/£10
ditto, Duchesne 1948 . . . . . £45/£10
Treasure Island, by Robert Louis Stevenson, Eyre &
Spottiswoode, 1949 . . . . . . £45/£10
ditto, Schocken (U.S.), 1979 . . . . £25/£10
ditto, Schocken (U.S.), 1979 (wraps) . . . £5
Thou Shalt Not Suffer a Witch and Other Stories, by
Dorothy K. Haynes, Methuen, 1949 . . £75/£25
The Swiss Family Robinson, by Johann R. Wyss,
Heirloom Library, [1949] . . . . £35/£10
ditto, Chanticleer Press Inc. (U.S.), [1950] . £35/£10
The Book of Lyonne, by [Henry] Burgess Drake,
Falcon Press, 1952 . . . . . . £450/£45

ditto, British Book Centre (U.S.), 1952 . . £350/£35
The Young Blackbird, by E[rnest] Clephan Palmer,
Allan Wingate, 1953 . . . . . . £45/£10
The Wonderful Life & Adventures of Tom Thumb, by
Paul Britten Austin, Radiotjänst (Radio Sweden) 1954
(2 vols, wraps) £125
Men: A Dialogue Between Women, by Allegra Sander,
Cresset Press, 1955 (translated by Vyvyan Holland) .
. . . . £30/£10
Under the Umbrella Tree, The Oxford English Course
for Secondary Schools, by H[enry] B[urgess] Drake,
Oxford Univ. Press, 1957 . . . . £20
*More Prayers and Graces, A second little book of
unusual piety*, by Allan M. Laing, Gollancz, 1957 .
. . . . £40/£15
The Pot of Gold and Two Other Tales, by Aaron
Judah, Faber 1959 . . . . . . £30/£10
Droll Stories, by Honoré de Balzac, The Folio Society,
1961 (translated by Alec Brown, slipcase) . £20/£10
Meryyn Peake/Oscar Wilde, by Oscar Wilde, Gordon,
Spilstead, 1980 (200 numbered copies, slipcase) .
. . . . £100/£75
ditto, Sidgwick & Jackson, 1980 . . . £15/£5
Sketches from Bleak House, Methuen, 1983 £25/£10

ELLIS PETERS
(b.1913 d.1995)

Edith Pargeter has written many books under her own
name and such pseudonyms as Jolyon Carr and Peter
Benedict. However, it is as Ellis Peters that she is best
known. As Peters she has given the world a literary
sleuth who is also a Benedictine monk, the now
televised Brother Cadfael.

Brother Cadfael Novels
A Morbid Taste for Bones: A Mediaeval Whodunnit,
Macmillan, 1977 . . . . £1,000/£75
ditto, Morrow (U.S.), 1978 . . . . £450/£35
One Corpse Too Many, Macmillan, 1979 . £500/£75
ditto, Morrow (U.S.), 1980 . . . . £250/£25
Monk's Hood, Macmillan, 1980 . . . £400/£75
ditto, Morrow (U.S.), 1981 . . . . £100/£15
Saint Peter's Fair, Macmillan, 1981 . £300/£50
ditto, Morrow (U.S.), 1981 . . . . £100/£15
The Leper of Saint Giles, Macmillan, 1981. £250/£40
ditto, Morrow (U.S.), 1982 . . . . £100/£15
The Virgin in the Ice, Macmillan, 1982 . £200/£25
ditto, Morrow (U.S.), 1983 . . . . £75/£15
The Sanctuary Sparrow, Macmillan, 1983 . £175/£20
ditto, Morrow (U.S.), 1983 . . . . £65/£10
The Devil's Novice, Macmillan, 1983 . . £175/£20
ditto, Morrow (U.S.), 1984 . . . . £65/£10
Dead Man's Ransom, Macmillan, 1984. . £100/£15
ditto, Morrow (U.S.), 1984 . . . . £50/£10
The Pilgrim of Hate, Macmillan, 1984 . . £100/£15
ditto, Morrow (U.S.), 1984 . . . . £40/£5
An Excellent Mystery, Macmillan, 1985 . £100/£15

ditto, Morrow (U.S.), 1986 . . . . . £30/£5
The Raven in the Foregate, Macmillan, 1986 £75/£10
ditto, Morrow (U.S.), 1986 . . . . . £20/£5
The Rose Rent, Macmillan, 1986 . . . £50/£10
ditto, Morrow (U.S.), 1986 . . . . . £20/£5
The Hermit of Eyton Forest, Headline, 1987 £40/£10
ditto, Mysterious Press (U.S.), 1988 . . £20/£5
The Confession of Brother Haluin, Headline, 1988 .
. . . . £40/£10
ditto, Mysterious Press (U.S.), 1989 . . . £20/£5
The Heretic's Apprentice, Headline, 1989 . £35/£10
ditto, Mysterious Press (U.S.), 1990 . . . £20/£5
The Potter's Field, Headline, 1989 . . . £25/£10
ditto, Mysterious Press (U.S.), 1990 . . . £20/£5
The Summer of the Danes, Headline, 1991. £25/£10
ditto, Mysterious Press (U.S.), 1990 . . . £20/£5
The Holy Thief, Headline, 1992 . . . . £20/£5
ditto, Mysterious Press (U.S.), 1993 . . . £20/£5
Brother Cadfael's Penance, Headline, 1994 £15/£5
ditto, Headline, 1994 (97 signed, numbered uncorrected proof copy, wraps) £100

Brother Cadfael Short Stories
A Rare Benedict, Headline, 1988 . . £35/£5
ditto, Mysterious Press (U.S.), 1989 . . . £25/£5

The 'Felse' Series
Death and the Joyful Woman, Collins, 1961 £250/£25
ditto, Doubleday (U.S.), 1961 . . . . £100/£25
Flight of a Witch, Collins, 1964 . . . . £200/£25
ditto, Mysterious Press (U.S.), 1991 . . . £20/£5
A Nice Derangement of Epitaphs, Collins, 1965 .
. . . . £175/£25
ditto, as **Who Lies Here?**, Morrow (U.S.), 1966 .
. . . . £125/£25
The Piper on the Mountain, Collins, 1966 . £75/£15
ditto, Morrow (U.S.), 1966 . . . . . £45/£10
Black is the Colour of My True-Love's Heart, Collins,
1967 . . . . £50/£15
ditto, Morrow (U.S.), 1967 . . . . £45/£10
The Grass Widow's Tale, Collins, 1968 . £75/£15
ditto, Morrow (U.S.), 1968 . . . . £45/£10
The House of Green Turf, Collins, 1969 . £50/£10
ditto, Morrow (U.S.), 1969 . . . . £30/£10
Mourning Raga, Macmillan, 1969 . . . £50/£10
ditto, Morrow (U.S.), 1970 . . . . £20/£5
The Knocker on Death's Door, Macmillan, 1970 . .
. . . . £45/£10
ditto, Morrow (U.S.), 1971 . . . . £20/£5
Death to the Landlords!, Macmillan, 1972 . £35/£10
ditto, Morrow (U.S.), 1972 . . . . £20/£5
City of Gold and Shadows, Macmillan, 1973 £30/£10
ditto, Morrow (U.S.), 1974 . . . . £20/£5
Rainbow's End, Macmillan, 1978 . . . £30/£10
ditto, Morrow (U.S.), 1979 . . . . £20/£5

Novels by Edith Pargeter
Hortensius, Friend of Nero, Lovat Dickson, 1936 (125
signed copies) . . . . . £500/£250

ditto, Greystone Press (U.S.), 1937 . . . £200/£35
Iron-Bound, Lovat Dickson, 1936 . . . £450/£50
The City Lies Foursquare, Heinemann, 1939 £175/£25
ditto, Reynall & Hitchcock (U.S.), 1939. . £125/£25
Ordinary People, Heinemann, 1941 . . . £100/£15
She Goes to War, Heinemann, 1942 . . . £100/£15
The Eighth Champion of Christendom, Heinemann,
1945 . . . . £75/£15
Reluctant Odyssey, Heinemann, 1946 . . £75/£15
Warfare Accomplished, Heinemann, 1947 . £75/£15
By Firelight, Heinemann, 1948 . . . . £50/£15
The Fair Young Phoenix, Heinemann, 1948 £45/£15
Lost Children, Heinemann, 1942 . . . £45/£15
Fallen into the Pit, Heinemann, 1951 . . £45/£15
Holiday with Violence, Heinemann, 1952 . £45/£15
This Rough Magic, Heinemann, 1953 . . £45/£15
Most Loving Mere Folly, Heinemann, 1953 £45/£15
The Soldier at the Door, Heinemann, 1954 . £45/£15
A Means of Race, Heinemann, 1956 . . £45/£15
The Heaven Tree, Heinemann, 1960 . . £40/£15
ditto, Doubleday (U.S.), 1960 . . . . £25/£5
The Green Branch, Heinemann, 1962 . . £35/£10
The Scarlet Seed, Heinemann, 1963 . . £35/£10
A Bloody Field by Shrewsbury, Macmillan, 1972 . .
. . . . £35/£10
ditto, Viking (U.S.), 1973 . . . . . £25/£25
Sunrise in the West, Macmillan, 1974 . . £35/£10
The Dragon at Noonday, Macmillan, 1975 . £35/£10
The Hounds of Sunset, Macmillan, 1976 . £35/£10
Afterglow and Nightfall, Macmillan, 1977 . £35/£10
The Marriage of Meggotta, Macmillan, 1979 £35/£10
ditto, Viking (U.S.), 1979 . . . . . £25/£25

Short Stories by Edith Pargeter
The Assize of the Dying, Heinemann, 1958 £75/£15
ditto, Doubleday (U.S.), 1958 . . . £45/£10
The Lily Hand, Heinemann, 1965 . . . £100/£15

Novels by Ellis Peters
Death Mask, Collins, 1959 . . . . . £200/£35
ditto, Doubleday (U.S.), 1960 . . . . £125/£25
The Will and the Deed, Collins, 1960 . . £125/£20
ditto, as **Where There's a Will**, Doubleday (U.S.), 1960
. . . . £100/£15
Funeral of Figaro, Collins, 1962 . . . £75/£15
ditto, Morrow (U.S.), 1964 . . . . £45/£10
The Horn of Roland, Macmillan, 1974 . . £65/£15
ditto, Morrow (U.S.), 1974 . . . . £40/£10
Never Pick Up Hitchhikers!, Macmillan, 1976 . . . .
. . . . £50/£10
ditto, Morrow (U.S.), 1976 . . . . £30/£10

Novels by Jolyon Carr
Murder in the Dispensary, Herbert Jenkins, 1938 . .
. . . . £250/£45
ditto, Post Mortem Books (U.S.), 1999 (350 signed,
numbered copies, no d/w) £25
Freedom for Two, Herbert Jenkins, 1938 . £250/£45
Death Comes by Post, Herbert Jenkins, 1940 £250/£45

Masters of the Parachute Mail, Herbert Jenkins, 1940
. . . . £250/£45

Novels by John Redfern
The Victim Needs a Nurse, Jarrolds, 1940 . £250/£45

Others
The Coast of Bohemia, Heinemann, 1950 (by Edith Pargeter) . . . . £100/£25
Shropshire, A Memoir of the English Countryside, Macdonald, 1990. . . . . £30/£10
ditto, Mysterious Press (U.S.), 1993 . . . £35/£10
Strongholds and Sanctuaries, Sutton, 1993 £35/£10

HAROLD PINTER
(b.1930)

A playwright who created, in his best work, a 'comedy of menace'; claustrophobic situations in which there is an indefinable threat hanging over the characters.

Plays
The Birthday Party, Encore Publishing, [1959] (wraps)
. . . . £150
The Birthday Party and Other Plays, Methuen, 1960 .
. . . . £65/£10
The Caretaker, Encore Publishing, 1960 (wraps) £100
ditto, Methuen, 1960 . . . . . . £50/£10
A Night Out, French, 1961 (wraps) £20
ditto, Grove Press (U.S.), 1967 . . . . £25/£5
A Slight Ache and Other Plays, Methuen, 1961 . .
. . . . £40/£10
The Birthday Party and The Room, Grove Press (U.S.), 1961 (wraps) £25
The Collection, French, 1962 . . . . . £15
Three Plays, Grove Press (U.S.), 1962 . . £15/£5
The Lover, Dramatists Play Service (U.S.), 1965 £15
The Dwarfs and Eight Review Sketches, Dramatists Play Service (U.S.), 1965 (wraps) . . £15
The Homecoming, Methuen, 1965 . . £15/£5
ditto, Grove Press (U.S.), 1966 . . . . £10/£5
ditto, Karnac, 1969 (200 signed, numbered copies) £65
The Collection and The Lover, Methuen, 1966 £15/£5
Tea Party, Methuen, 1965 . . . . £15/£5
ditto, Vanista (Zagreb), 1965 (280 numbered copies) .
. . . . £50
ditto, Grove Press (U.S.), 1966 . . . . £10/£5
Tea Party and Other Plays, Methuen, 1967 £10/£5
Early Plays, Grove Press (U.S.), 1967 (wraps) £25/£10
Landscape, Pendragon Press, 1968 (2,000 numbered copies) £45
Landscape and Silence, Methuen, 1969. . £15/£5
ditto, Grove Press (U.S.), 1970 . . . . £10/£5
Old Times, Eyre Methuen, 1971 . . . £15/£5
ditto, Karnac, 1971 (150 signed, nubered copies) £75
ditto, Grove Press (U.S.), 1971 . . . . £10/£5
No Man's Land, Eyre Methuen, 1975 . . £15/£5

ditto, Karnac, 1975 (150 signed, numbered copies, glassine d/w) £65
ditto, Grove Press (U.S.), 1975 . . . . £10/£5
Betrayal, Eyre Methuen, 1978 . . . . £15/£5
ditto, Karnac, 1978 (150 signed, numbered copies) £65
ditto, Grove Press (U.S.), 1979 . . . . £10/£5
The Hothouse, Eyre Methuen, 1980. . . £15/£5
ditto, Grove Press (U.S.), 1989 . . . . £10/£5
Family Voices, Next Editions/Faber & Faber, 1980 (spiral bound in wraps) £10
Other Places, Methuen, 1982 . . . . £15/£5
ditto, Grove Press (U.S.), 1983 . . . . £10/£5
One for the Road, Methuen, 1985 . . . £15/£5
Mountain Language, Faber, 1988 . . . £15/£5
ditto, Grove Weidenfeld, (U.S.), 1988 . . £10/£5
The Heat of the Day, Faber, 1989 . . . £15/£5
ditto, Grove Weidenfeld, (U.S.), 1990 . . £10/£5
Party Time, Faber, 1991 . . . . . £15/£5
ditto, Grove Weidenfeld, (U.S.), 1993 . . . £5
Moonlight, Faber, 1993 . . . . . £10/£5
Ashes to Ashes, Faber, 1996 (wraps) . . . £5

Verse
Poems, Enitharmon Press, 1968 (200 signed copies, no d/w) £100
ditto, Enitharmon Press, 1971 (2nd edition, enlarged, 100 signed copies) £75
Poems and Prose, 1949-1977, Grove Press, 1978 . .
. . . . £10/£5
ditto, Eyre Methuen, 1978 . . . . . £10/£5
I Know The Place, Greville Press, 1979 (500 signed copies, no d/w) £50
11 Early Poems, Greville Press, 1992 (wraps) . £10

Novel
The Dwarfs, Faber, 1990 . . . . . £15/£5
ditto, London Limited Editions, 1990 (150 signed copies) £100
ditto, Grove Weidenfeld (U.S.), 1990 . £15/£5

Others
The Homecoming: Images, by Harold Cohen, Cohen, 1968 (175 copies) £75
ditto, Cohen, 1968 (25 copies, additional set of plates, slipcase) . . . . £175/£125
Mac, Pendragon Press, 1968 (2,000 numbered copies, no d/w) £30
Five Screenplays, Methuen, 1971 . . . £15/£5
ditto, Methuen, 1971 (wraps). £5
ditto, Karnac, 1971 (150 signed, numbered copies) £75
ditto, Grove (U.S.), 1973 . . . . . £10/£5
Monologue, Covent Garden Press, 1973 . £25/£10
ditto, Covent Garden Press, 1973 (100 signed copies in slipcase) . . . . £125/£100
The Proust Screenplay, Grove Press (U.S.), 1977 . .
. . . . £10/£5
ditto, Eyre Methuen, 1978 . . . . . £10/£5
The French Lieutenant's Woman, A Screenplay, Cape, 1981 . . . . £20/£5

ditto, Little, Brown (U.S.), 1981 . . . . £20/£5
ditto, Little, Brown (U.S.), 1981 (360 signed, numbered copies, slipcase) . . . . . £125/£75
The French Lieutenant's Woman and Other Screenplays, Methuen, 1982 . . . . £15/£5
The Comfort of Strangers and Other Screenplays, Faber, 1990 . . . . £15/£5
Various Voices - Prose, Poetry, Politics 1948-1998, Faber, 1998 . . . . £15/£5
ditto, Grove, (U.S.), 1998 . . . . . . £15/£5

SYLVIA PLATH
(b.1932 d.1963)

American poet whose poems display an ironic tone and an undercurrent of terror. Married to Ted Hughes, she committed suicide in 1963.

Verse
Sculptor, Grecourt Review, 1959 (25 copies, wraps) £1,000
A Winter Ship, Tragara Press (Edinburgh), 1960 (anonymous leaflet) £1,250
The Colossus and Other Poems, Heinemann, 1960 . . . . £1,000/£150
ditto, Knopf (U.S.), 1962 . . . . . £150/£45
ditto, as **The Colossus**, Heinemann, 1967 . £15/£5
Ariel, Faber, 1965 . . . . £150/£20
ditto, Harper (U.S.), 1966 . . . . . £100/£15
Uncollected Poems, Turret Books, 1965 (150 copies, wraps) £300
Wreath for a Bridal, Sceptre Press, 1970 (150 copies, wraps) £100
Million Dollar Month, Sceptre Press, 1971 (150 copies, wraps) £100
Fiesta Melons: Poems, Rougemont Press, 1971 (75 copies of 150, signed by Ted Hughes) . . £275/£200
ditto, Rougemont Press, 1971 (75 unsigned copies of 150) . . . . £150/£100
Child, Rougemont Press, 1971 (325 copies, wraps with d/w) . . . . £75/£35
Crystal Gazer, Rainbow Press, 1971 (300 copies, slipcase) . . . . £200/£125
ditto, Rainbow Press, 1971 (80 morocco bound copies) £750
ditto, Rainbow Press, 1971 (20 vellum bound copies) £1,000
Lyonesse, Rainbow Press, 1971 (300 copies bound in quarter leather) £150
ditto, Rainbow Press, 1971 (90 copies bound in full calf) £750
ditto, Rainbow Press, 1971 (10 bound in vellum) £1,000
Crossing the Water, Faber, 1971 . . . . £30/£10
ditto, Harper (U.S.), 1971 . . . . . £20/£5
Winter Trees, Faber, 1971 . . . . £25/£10
ditto, Harper (U.S.), 1972 . . . . . £15/£5

Pursuit, Rainbow Press, 1973 (100 copies) . . . . £1,000/£750
Two Poems, Sceptre Press, [1980] (225 of 300 copies, wraps) £30
ditto, Sceptre Press, [1980] (75 'especial' of 300 copies, wraps) £75
Two Uncollected Poems, Anvil Press, 1980 (450 copies, wraps) £25
Collected Poems, Faber, 1981 . . . . £20/£5
ditto, Harper (U.S.), 1981 . . . . . . £10/£5
Dialogue Over a Ouija Board, Rainbow Press, 1981 (140 copies) £125

Novel
The Bell Jar, Heinemann, 1963 (pseud. 'Victoria Lucas') . . . . £1,500/£450
ditto, Faber, 1966 (as 'Sylvia Plath') . . £50/£15
ditto, Harper, (U.S.), 1971 (as 'Sylvia Plath') £40/£10

Plays
Three Women, Turret Books, 1968 (180 copies, glassine d/w) . . . .£300/£200

Children's
The Bed Book, Faber, 1976 . . . . . £125/£30
ditto, Harper (U.S.), 1976 . . . . . £75/£15

Others
The Art of Sylvia Plath: A Symposium, Faber, 1970 . . . . £60/£20
Letters Home, Harper (U.S.), 1975 . . . £20/£5
ditto, Faber, 1976 . . . . £20/£5
Johnny Panic and the Bible of Dreams and Other Writings, Faber, 1977 . . . . £25/£5
Johnny Panic and the Bible of Dreams: Short Stories, Prose and Diary Excerpts, Harper (U.S.), 1979 . . . . £20/£5
The Magic Mirror: A Study of the Doublein Two of Dostoevsky's Novels, Embers Handpress, 1989 (50 copies, 'Oxford Hollow' binding, slipcase) £200/£150
ditto, Embers Handpress, 1989 (176 copies, in d/w) . . . . £125/£65

EDGAR ALLAN POE
(b.1809 d.1849)

An American poet and short story writer, Poe is best known for often anthologised horror tales such as 'The Fall of the House of Usher'. 'The Murder in the Rue Morgue' signalled the birth of the detective fiction genre.

Verse
Tamerlane and Other Poems, Calvin F.S. Thomas (U.S.), 1827 ('by a Bostonian', wraps) . £150,000
ditto, Redway, 1884 (100 copies) £1,750

Al AAraaf, Tamerlane and Minor Poems, Hatch & Dunning (U.S.), 1829 . . . . . . £50,000
Poems, Elam Bliss (U.S.), 1831 (claims wrongly to be the second edition) £20,000
The Raven and Other Poems, Wiley & Putnam (U.S.), 1845 (first issue with 'T.B. Smith, Stereotyper' on copyright page, wraps) £50,000
ditto, Wiley & Putnam, 1845 (cloth). . . £40,000

Fiction
The Narrative of Arthur Gordon Pym of Nantucket, Harper Bros. (U.S.), 1838 (anonymous) . . £3,000
ditto, Wiley & Putnam, 1838 (cloth). . . . £2,000
Tales of the Grotesque and Arabesque, Lea & Blanchard (U.S.), 1840 (page 213 wrongly numbered, 2 vols). £15,000
ditto, Lea & Blanchard (U.S.), 1840 (page 213 correctly numbered, 2 vols) £10,000
ditto, Lea & Blanchard (U.S.), 1840 (page 213 correctly numbered, 1 vol.) £7,000
The Murders in the Rue Morgue, and the Man that was Used Up, William H. Graham (U.S.), 1843 (wraps) £15,000
The Tales, Wiley & Putnum (U.S.), 1845 (wraps) . .
. . . . £30,000
ditto, Wiley & Putnam, 1845 . . . . . £15,000
Eureka, A Prose Poem, Putnam (U.S.), 1848 . £2,500

Others
The Conchologist's First Book, Haswell, Barrington & Baswell (U.S.), 1839 (coloured plates). . . £1,500
ditto, Haswell, Barrington & Baswell (U.S.), 1839 (uncoloured plates) £1,000
ditto, 1840 (2nd edition) £250
Mesmerism, 'In Articulo Mortis', Short & Co., 1846 (wraps) £1,500

BEATRIX POTTER
(b.1866 d.1943)

British author and illustrator. *The Tale of Peter Rabbit* was first written down in a letter to the son of one of her governesses. It was later privately printed in an edition of 250 copies, the first of a highly successful series of books for the very young.

The Tale of Peter Rabbit, privately printed, [1901] (250 copies, flat spine) £50,000
ditto, privately printed, 1902 (200 copies, round spine)
. . . . £25,000
ditto, Warne, [1902] (trade edition, cloth) . £4,000
ditto, Warne, 1902 (trade edition, boards) . £2,000
ditto, Warne, 1902 (deluxe edition) . . . £5,000
ditto, Warne, 1993 (boxed set containing facsimiles of the 1901 first edition, the first Warne cloth-bound edition of 1902, and the original 'Peter Rabbit' letter from Beatrix Potter, 750 numbered sets) . . £125

The Tailor of Gloucester, privately printed, 1902 (500 copies) £5,000
ditto, Warne, 1903 (trade edition) £1,000
ditto, Warne, 1903 (deluxe edition) . . . £5,000
ditto, Warne, 1903 (art cloth binding) . . . £3,000
ditto, Warne, 1968 (facsimile of the original manuscript and illustrations, 1,500 numbered copies in box) . . . . £75/£45
ditto, Warne, 1969 (facsimile of the original manuscript) £45
The Tale of Squirrel Nutkin, Warne, 1903 . . £500
ditto, Warne, 1903 (deluxe edition) . . . £4,000
ditto, Warne, 1903 (art cloth binding) . . . £3,000
The Tale of Benjamin Bunny, Warne, 1904 . £500
ditto, Warne, 1904 (deluxe edition) . . . £3,500
The Tale of Two Bad Mice, Warne, 1904 . . £300
ditto, Warne, 1904 (deluxe edition) . . . £3,500
The Tale of Mrs Tiggy-Winkle, Warne, 1905 . £500
ditto, Warne, 1905 (deluxe edition) . . . £4,000
The Pie and the Patty Pan, Warne, 1905 (large format)
. . . . £450
ditto, Warne, 1905 (deluxe edition) . . . £2,500
The Tale of Mr Jeremy Fisher, Warne, 1906 . £200
ditto, Warne, 1906 (deluxe edition) . . . £2,500
The Story of a Fierce Bad Rabbit, Warne, 1906 (panorama) £500
The Story of Miss Moppet, Warne, 1906, (panorama) .
. . . . £500
The Tale of Tom Kitten, Warne, 1907 . . . £300
ditto, Warne, 1907 (deluxe edition) . . . £2,500
The Tale of Jemima Puddle-Duck, Warne, 1908 . .
. . . . £350
ditto, Warne, 1908 (deluxe edition) . . . £2,500
The Roly-Poly Pudding, Warne, 1908 (large format) .
. . . . £300
ditto, as *The Tale of Samuel Whiskers*, Warne, [1926]
. . . . £125
The Tale of the Flopsy Bunnies, Warne, 1909 . £300
ditto, Warne, 1909 (deluxe edition) . . . £2,500
Ginger and Pickles, Warne, 1909 (large format) £200
The Tale of Mrs Tittlemouse, Warne, 1910. . £225
ditto, Warne, 1910 (deluxe edition) . . . £2,500
Peter Rabbit's Painting Book, Warne, [1911] . £300
The Tale of Timmy Tiptoes, Warne, 1911 . . £250
ditto, Warne, 1911 (deluxe edition) . . . £2,250
The Tale of Mr Tod, Warne, 1912 . . . . £250
The Tale of Pigling Bland, Warne, 1913 . . £250
Appley Dapply's Nursery Rhymes, Warne, 1917 £300
Tom Kitten's Painting Book, Warne, 1917 . . £250
The Tale of Johnny Town-Mouse, Warne, [1918]. . .
. . . . £200
Cecily Parsley's Nursery Rhymes, Warne, 1922, (small format) £450
Jemima Puddle-Duck's Painting Book, Warne, [1925]
. . . . £200
Peter Rabbit's Almanac for 1929, Warne, [1928] . .
. . . . £350
The Fairy Caravan, McKay (U.S.), 1929 . . £125
ditto, Warne, 1952. . . . . . . £100/£50

The Tale of Little Pig Robinson, Warne, [1930] (large format) . . . . £350/£200
Sister Anne, McKay (U.S.), 1932 . . . . £125
Wag-By-Wall, Warne, [1944] (100 copies) . . £300
Jemima Puddle-Duck's Painting Book, From the Original Designs by B. Potter, Warne [1954] £50
Jeremy Fisher's Painting Book, From the Original Designs by B. Potter, Warne, [1954] . . . £50
Peter Rabbit's Painting Book, From the Original Designs by B. Potter, Warne, [1954] . . . £50
Tom Kitten's Painting Book, From the Original Designs by B. Potter, Warne, [1954] . . . £50
The Tale of the Faithful Dove, Warne, [1955] (100 copies, illustrated by Marie Angel). . . . £1,000
The Sly Old Cat, Warne, 1971 (issued with d/w) . . . . £20/£5
The Tale of Tupenny, Warne, 1973 (illustrated by Marie Angel). . . . . £10/£5

EZRA POUND
(b.1885 d.1972)

An American poet, Pound is generally acknowledged as one of the prime movers of modern poetry.

Verse
Verse
A Lume Spento, Antonini (Venice), 1908 (150 copies, wraps). £30,000
ditto, New Directions (U.S.), 1965 (acetate d/w) . . . . £45/£15
ditto, Faber, 1965 . . . . £20/£5
A Quinzane for this Yule, Pollock & Co, 1908 (100 copies, wraps) £20,000
ditto, printed for Elkin Mathews, 1908 (100 copies, wraps). £10,000
Personae, Elkin Mathews, 1909 (500 copies) . £500
ditto, Boni & Liveright (U.S.), 1926. . £1,000/£125
Exultations, Elkin Mathews, 1909 (500 copies) £400
Provenca, Small Maynard (U.S.), [1910] (200 copies, tan boards stamped in dark brown). . . . £500
ditto, Small Maynard (U.S.), [1917] (later issue, tan boards stamped in green) £100
Canzoni, Elkin Mathews, 1911 (grey cloth, author's name on cover) £400
ditto, Elkin Mathews, 1911 (brown boards, without author's name on cover). £200
Ripostes, Stephen Swift, 1912 . . . . £500
ditto, Small Maynard (U.S.), 1913 . . . . £250
Lustra, Elkin Mathews, [1916] (200 numbered copies, unexpurgated version for private circulation) £1,000
ditto, Elkin Mathews, 1916 (expurgated trade edition). £600
ditto, Knopf (U.S.), 1917 . . . . . £1,250/£400
Pavannes and Divisions, Knopf (U.S.), 1918 (first binding, blue cloth stamped in gold) . . . £150

ditto, Knopf (U.S.), 1918 (later bindings stamped in green). £100
ditto, Peter Owen, 1960 . . . . . £35/£10
Quia Pauper Amavi, The Egoist, [1919] (100 signed copies, handmade paper) £2,250
ditto, The Egoist, [1919] (10 signed copies, roman numerals). £5,000
ditto, The Egoist, [1919] £400
The Fourth Canto, Ovid Press, 1919 (40 copies for private circulation) £6,000
Hugh Selwyn Mauberley, Ovid Press, 1920 (165 unsigned copies) £2,500
ditto, Ovid Press, 1920 (35 signed copies) . £5,000
Umbra, Elkin Mathews, 1920 . . . . £400/£150
ditto, Elkin Mathews, 1920 (100 signed copies) £2,500
ditto, Elkin Mathews, 1920 (signed, lettered copies) £5,000
Poems, 1918-21, Boni & Liveright (U.S.), 1921 . . . . £500/£175
Indiscretions; Or, Une Revue de Deux Mondes, Three Mountains Press, 1923 (300 numbered copies) £750
ditto, Three Mountains Press, 1923 (300 numbered copies, unbound sheets) £300
A Draft of XVI Cantos, Three Mountains Press, 1925 (90 copies) £1,500
A Draft of Cantos 12-27, Three Mountain Press, 1928 . . . . £500
Selected Poems, Faber, 1928 (100 signed copies) £2,000
ditto, Faber, 1928 . . . . £350/£100
A Draft of XXX Cantos, Hours Press, 1930 (200 unsigned copies). £1,500
ditto, Hours Press, 1930 (10 signed copies) . £7,500
ditto, Farrar & Rinehart (U.S.), 1933 ('shit' on page 62). £1,000
ditto, Farrar & Rinehart (U.S.), 1933 ('sh-t' on page 62). . . . . £250/£45
ditto, Faber, 1933 . . . . £175/£35
Imaginary Letters, Black Sun Press (Paris), 1930 (50 signed copies on Japanese vellum, wraps with glassine d/w and slipcase) . . . £2,500/£2,000
ditto, Black Sun Press (Paris), 1930 (300 copies, wraps with glassine d/w and slipcase) . . . . £500/£350
Eleven New Cantos: XXXI-XLI, Farrar & Rineheart (U.S.), 1934 . . . . £150/£40
ditto, as *Draft of Cantos XXXI-XLI*, Faber, 1935 . . . . £125/£30
Homage to Sextus Propertius, Faber, 1934 £150/£45
The Fifth Decad of Cantos, Faber, 1937 . £150/£45
ditto, Farrar & Rinehart (U.S.), 1937 . . £100/£25
ditto, New Directions (U.S.), 1940 . . £100/£25
Cantos LII-LXXI, Faber, 1940 . . . . £200/£45
ditto, New Directions (U.S.), 1940 (500 copies with envelope and pamphlet). . . . . . £200/£75
ditto, New Directions (U.S.), 1940 (500 copies without envelope and pamphlet). . . . . . £100/£35
The Pisan Cantos, New Directions (U.S.), 1948 . . . . £250/£65
ditto, Faber, 1949 . . . . £250/£50

Section: Rock-Drill, Pesce d'Oro (Milan), 1955   £200
ditto, New Directions (U.S.), 1956   .   .   .   £45/£15
ditto, Faber, 1957   .   .   .   .   £45/£15
Diptych Rome-London, New Directions (U.S.), 1957
   (125 signed copies in slipcase)   .   .   .   £1,000/£650
ditto, Faber, 1957 (50 signed copies in slipcase)   .   .
   .   .   .   .   £1,250/£1,000
ditto, Vanni Scheiwiller (Italy), 1957 (25 signed copies
   in slipcase)   .   .   .   .   .   .   £2,000/£1,750
Thrones, Pesce d'Oro (Milan), 1959 (300 copies) £125
ditto, New Directions (U.S.), 1959   .   .   .   £45/£15
ditto, Faber, 1960   .   .   .   .   .   .   £45/£15
The Cantos, Faber, 1964 (all 109 cantos)   .   £45/£10
Cavalcanti Poems, New Directions (U.S.), [1966] (200
   signed copies, glassine d/w, slipcase)   £1,500/£1,250
ditto, Faber, (1966) (190 signed copies in slipcase).   .
   .   .   .   .   £1,000/£850
Drafts and Fragments of Cantos CX-CXVII, New
   Directions (U.S.), 1969   .   .   .   .   .   £45/£15
ditto, New Directions (U.S.), 1969 (200 signed,
   numbered copies, slipcase)   .   .   .   .   £500/£400
ditto, Stone Wall Press (U.S.), 1969 (10 signed,
   numbered copies, slipcase)   .   .   .   £1,000/£850
ditto, Faber, 1970 (200 signed, numbered copies,
   slipcase)   .   .   .   .   £300/£250
ditto, Faber, 1970   .   .   .   .   .   .   £40/£15

Others
The Spirit of Romance, Dent, 1910   .   .   .   .   £300
ditto, Dutton (U.S.), 1910.   .   .   .   .   .   £200
Cathay, Elkin Mathews, 1915 (wraps)   .   .   £350
Gaudier-Brzeska, Bodley Head, 1916 (with design on
   front cover) £500
ditto, Bodley Head, 1916 (without design on front
   cover). £250
ditto, Lane (U.S.), 1916   .   .   .   .   .   .   £350
Instigations, Boni & Liveright (U.S.), 1920   .   .   .
   .   .   .   .   £1,000/£200
Antheil and the Treatise on Harmony, Three
   Mountains Press (Paris), 1924 (360 copies, wraps)   .
   .   .   .   .   £500
ditto, Three Mountains Press (Paris), 1924 (40 copies,
   Arches paper, wraps) £1,000
ditto, Contact Editions/Three Mountains Press (Paris),
   1924 (unsold copies of above, wraps)   .   .   £300
ditto, Pascal Covici (U.S.), 1927   .   £200/£50
How to Read, Harmsworth, 1931   .   .   £225/£35
ABC of Economics, Faber, 1933.   .   .   £150/£35
ditto, New Directions (U.S.), 1940   .   .   £75/£25
ABC of Reading, Routledge, 1934   .   .   £150/£35
ditto, Yale Univ. Press (U.S.), 1934   .   .   £100/£25
Make it New, Faber, 1934   .   .   .   £150/£35
ditto, Yale Univ. Press (U.S.), 1935   .   .   £100/£25
Social Credit, Nott, [1935 or 37?] (wraps)   .   £150
Polite Essays, Faber, 1937   .   .   .   .   £150/£35
ditto, New Directions (U.S.), 1940   .   .   £100/£25
Guide to Kulchur, Faber, 1938   .   .   £150/£35
ditto, New Directions (U.S.), 1938   .   .   £100/£25
Patria Mia, Seymour, 1950   .   .   .   .   £100/£25

ditto, Owen (U.S.), 1962   .   .   .   .   .   £45/£15
The Letters of Ezra Pound, Harcourt Brace (U.S.),
   1950   .   .   .   .   £50/£10
ditto, Faber, 1951   .   .   .   .   .   .   £45/£10
The Translations of Ezra Pound, Faber, 1953 £50/£15
ditto, New Directions (U.S.), 1953   .   .   .   £50/£15
Literary Essays of Ezra Pound, Faber, 1954   £40/£10
ditto, New Directions (U.S.), 1954   .   .   £40/£10
**Impact, Essays on Ignorance and the Decline of
American Civilisation**, Regenery (U.S.), 1960   .   .
   .   .   .   .   £35/£10
Pound/Joyce, New directions (U.S.), 1967   .   £25/£10
ditto, Faber, 1968   .   .   .   .   .   .   £25/£10
Selected Prose, 1909-65, Faber, 1973   .   .   £25/£10
ditto, New Directions (U.S.), 1975   .   .   £25/£10
An Autobiographical Outline, NADJA, 1980 (200
   copies, wraps) £45
Pound/Ford, Faber, 1982.   .   .   .   .   £25/£10

ANTHONY POWELL
(b.1905)

As a novelist Powell is best known for the series of
novels having the general title *Dance to the Music of
Time*.

'Dance to the Music of Time' Novels
A Question of Upbringing, Heinemann, 1951   .   .   .
   .   .   .   .   £500/£100
ditto, Scribner (U.S.), 1951   .   .   .   .   £100/£25
A Buyer's Market, Heinemann, 1952   .   .£600/£100
ditto, Scribner (U.S.), 1953   .   .   .   .   £95/£25
The Acceptance World, Heinemann, 1955   .   £250/£35
ditto, Farrar Straus (U.S.), 1956   .   .   .   £45/£15
At Lady Molly's, Heinemann, 1957   .   .   £75/£20
ditto, Little, Brown (U.S.), 1958   .   .   .   £30/£10
Casanova's Chinese Restaurant, Heinemann, 1960   .
   .   .   .   .   £75/£15
ditto, Little, Brown (U.S.), 1960   .   .   .   £30/£10
The Kindly Ones, Heinemann, 1962.   .   .   £50/£15
ditto, Little, Brown (U.S.), 1962   .   .   .   £15/£5
The Valley of Bones, Heinemann, 1964.   .   £50/£15
ditto, Little, Brown (U.S.), 1964   .   .   .   £15/£5
The Soldier's Art, Heinemann, 1966   .   .   £35/£10
ditto, Little, Brown (U.S.), 1966   .   .   .   £15/£5
The Military Philosophers, Heinemann, 1968 £35/£10
ditto, Little, Brown (U.S.), 1969   .   .   .   £15/£5
Books Do Furnish a Room, Heinemann, 1971 £30/£10
ditto, Little, Brown (U.S.), 1971   .   .   .   £10/£5
Temporary Kings, Heinemann, 1973   .   .   £25/£10
ditto, Little, Brown (U.S.), 1963   .   .   .   £10/£5
Hearing Secret Harmonies, Heinemann, 1975 £25/£10
ditto, Little, Brown (U.S.), 1975   .   .   .   £10/£5
All twelve *Dance to the Music of Time* novels   £2,500

Other Novels

Afternoon Men, Duckworth, 1931 . . £2,500/£300
ditto, Holt (U.S.), 1932 . . . . . £2,000/£300
Venusberg, Duckworth, 1932 . . . £1,750/£300
ditto, as *Venusberg & Agents and Patients*, Periscope/
Holliday (U.S.), 1952 . . . . . £100/£15
From a View to a Death, Duckworth, 1933. . . .
. . . . £1,500/£250
ditto, as *Mr Zouch: Superman*, Vanguard Press, 1934
. . . . £250/£45
ditto, Little, Brown (U.S.), 1964 . . . . £20/£5
Agents and Patients, Duckworth, 1936 . £1,250/£200
ditto, Holliday (U.S.), 1952 . . . . £20/£5
What's Become of Waring, Cassell, 1939 £750/£175
ditto, Little, Brown (U.S.), 1963 . . . £20/£5
O, How the Wheel Becomes It, Heinemann, 1983 . . .
. . . . £20/£5
ditto, Holt Rinehart (U.S.), 1983 . . . £10/£5
The Fisher King, Heinemann, 1985 . . . £30/£5
ditto, Norton (U.S.), 1986. . . . . £10/£5

Autobiography

Infants of the Spring, Heinemann, 1976 . £20/£5
ditto, Holt Rinehart (U.S.), 1976 . . . £10/£5
Messengers of the Day, Heinemann, 1978 . £20/£5
ditto, Holt Rinehart (U.S.), 1978 . . . £10/£5
Faces in My Time, Heinemann, 1980 . . £20/£5
ditto, Holt Rinehart (U.S.), 1981 . . . £10/£5
The Strangers all are Gone, Heinemann, 1982 £20/£5
ditto, Holt Rinehart (U.S.), 1983 . . . £10/£5

Others

Caledonia: A Fragment, privately printed, 1934 (100
copies) £2,500
John Aubrey and His Friends, Heinemann, 1948 . .
. . . . £45/£10
ditto, Scribner (U.S.), 1949 . . . . £40/£10
The Garden of God and The Rest I'll Whistle,
Heinemann, 1971 . . . . . £25/£5
ditto, Little, Brown (U.S.), 1971. . . . £10/£5
*Under Review, Further Writings on Writers, 1946-
1989*, Heinemann, 1991 . . . . £10/£5
ditto, Univ. of Chicago (U.S.), 1991 . . £10/£5
Journals, 1982-1986, Heinemann, 1995 . £10/£5
Journals, 1987-1989, Heinemann, 1996 . £10/£5
A Reference for Mellors, Moorhouse and Sorensen,
1994 (26 signed copies of 326, quarter goatskin,
slipcase) £450
ditto, Moorhouse and Sorensen, 1994 (100 signed
copies of 326) £200
ditto, Moorhouse and Sorensen, 1994 (200 copies of
326, wraps) £45

JOHN COWPER POWYS
(b.1872 d.1963)

Novelist, poet and essayist, Powys's romances are
very highly rated by his readers, although his work
has never received much general literary recognition.

Novels

Wood and Stone, A Romance, G.A. Shaw (U.S.), 1915
. . . . £75
ditto, Heinemann, [1917] £50
Rodmoor, A Romance, G.A. Shaw, 1916 . . £75
Ducdame, Doubleday Page (U.S.), 1925 . £150/£30
ditto, Grant Richards, 1925 . . . . £150/£30
Wolf Solent, Simon & Schuster (U.S.), 1929 (2 vols,
slipcase) . . . . £125/£25
ditto, Jonathan Cape, 1929 (1 vol.) . . . £125/£25
A Glastonbury Romance, Simon & Schuster (U.S.),
1932 . . . . £75/£25
ditto, Simon & Schuster (U.S.), 1932 (204 signed,
numbered copies, no d/w) £300
ditto, John Lane, 1929 (1 vol.) . . . . £75/£25
Weymouth Sands, Simon & Schuster (U.S.), 1934 .
. . . . £75/£25
ditto, as *Jobber Skald*, John Lane, 1935 (revised text) .
. . . . £45/£15
ditto, Jonathan Cape, 1963 (unexpurgated version) .
. . . . £15/£5
Maiden Castle, Simon & Schuster (U.S.), 1936 . . .
. . . . £45/£10
ditto, Cassell, 1937 . . . . £45/£10
Morwyn, or The Vengeance of God, Cassell, 1937 .
. . . . £75/£25
Owen Glendower, Simon & Schuster (U.S.), 1940 (2
vols) . . . . £75/£25
ditto, John Lane, 1941 (1 vol.) . . . . £75/£25
Porius, Macdonald, 1951 . . . . . £25/£10
ditto, Macdonald, 1951 (200 signed copies). . £75
ditto, Philosophical Library (U.S.), 1952 . £25/£10
The Inmates, Macdonald, 1952 . . . . £25/£10
Atlantis, Macdonald, 1954 . . . . . £25/£10
The Brazen Head, Macdonald, 1956 . . £25/£10
All or Nothing, Macdonald, 1960 . . . £25/£10
Real Wraiths, Village, 1974 (wraps). . . . £5
You and Me, Village, 1975 (wraps) £5
After My Fashion, Picador, 1980 (wraps) . . £5
Three Fantasies, Carcanet, 1985. . . . £10/£5

Short Stories

The Owl, the Duck and - Miss Rowe! Miss Rowe!,
Black Archer Press (U.S.), 1930 (250 signed copies,
slipcase) . . . . £150/£125
Up and Out, Macdonald, 1957 . . . . £25/£10

Verse

Corinth, privately printed, 1891 ('English Verse' on
front cover, wraps) £2,000
Odes and Other Poems, Rider & Co., 1896. . £350
Poems, Rider & Co., 1899 . . . . . £250

Wolf's Bane, Rhymes, G.A. Shaw (U.S.), 1916   £35
Mandragora, Poems, G.A. Shaw, 1917 .   .   .   £50
Samphire, Poems, T. Selzer (U.S.), 1922   .   £75/£35
Lucifer, A Poem, Macdonald, 1956 (560 signed, numbered copies, acetate d/w) .   .   .   . £135/£100
John Cowper Powys: A Selection from His Poems, Macdonald, 1964. .   .   .   . £20/£10

Others
The War and Culture, G.A. Shaw (U.S.), 1914 (boards) £50
ditto, G.A. Shaw (U.S.), 1914 (wraps) .   .   .   £45
ditto, as *The Menace of German Culture*, 1915   £50
Visions and Revisions, G.A. Shaw (U.S.), 1915 .   .
.   .   .   . £25/£10
Confessions of Two Brothers, Manas Press (U.S.), 1916 (with Llewelyn Powys) .   .   .   . £75/£25
One Hundred Best Books, G.A. Shaw (U.S.), 1916 .
.   .   .   . £50/£10
Suspended Judgements, Essays on Books and Sensations, G.A. Shaw (U.S.), 1916 .   . £75/£20
The Complex Vision, Dodd, Mead (U.S.), 1920 .   .
.   .   .   . £25/£10
The Art of Happiness, Haldeman-Julius, 1923 (wraps)
.   .   .   .   £10
Psychoanalysis and Morality, Jessica Colbert (U.S.), 1923 (500 numbered copies) £50
ditto, Random House, 1925 (approximately 50 copies of the above were rebound and signed by J.C. Powys)
.   .   .   .   £150
The Religion of a Sceptic, Dodd, Mead (U.S.), 1925 (1,000 copies) .   .   .   . £25/£10
The Secret of Self-Development, Haldeman-Julius, 1926 (wraps) £15
The Art of Forgetting the Unpleasant, Haldeman-Julius, 1928 (wraps) £15
The Meaning of Culture, Norton (U.S.), 1929   £20/£5
ditto, Cape, 1930 .   .   .   .   £15/£5
In Defence of Sensuality, Simon & Schuster (U.S.), 1930 .   .   .   . £45/£10
ditto, Gollancz, 1930 .   .   .   .   .   . £35/£10
Debate! 15. Modern Marriage a Failure?, Discussion Guild (U.S.), 1930 (with Bertrand Russell)   £1,000
Dorothy M. Richardson, Joiner & Steele, 1931 .
.   .   .   . £40/£10
ditto, Joiner & Steele, 1931 (60 signed, numbered copies) .   .   .   . £125/£75
A Philosophy of Solitude, Simon & Schuster (U.S.), 1933 .   .   .   . £20/£5
Autobiography, Simon & Schuster (U.S.), 1934 £20/£5
ditto, Bodley Head, 1934 .   .   .   .   . £20/£5
The Art of Happiness, Simon & Schuster (U.S.), 1935 (not the 1923 version) .   .   .   .   . £25/£10
ditto, The Bodley Head, 1935 .   .   .   . £25/£10
Enjoyment of Literature, Simon & Schuster (U.S.), 1938 .   .   .   .   .·.   .   .   .   . £25/£10
ditto, as *The Pleasures of Literature*, Cassell, 1938 (contains one extra essay) .   .   .   . £25/£10
Mortal Strife, Jonathan Cape, 1941 .   . £25/£10

The Art of Growing Old, Jonathan Cape, 1944 £25/£10
Dostoievsky, John Lane, 1946 .   .   .   . £25/£10
Pair Dadeni, or The Cauldron of Rebirth, Druid Press, 1946 .   .   .   . £25/£10
Obstinate Cymric, Essays 1935-47, Druid Press, 1947 .   .   .   . £40/£15
Rabelais, John Lane, 1948 .   .   .   .   . £20/£5
ditto, Philosophical Library (U.S.), 1951 (500 copies) .
.   .   .   .   £15
In Spite Of, A Philosophy for Everyman, Macdonald, 1952 .   .   .   . £20/£5
ditto, Philosophical Library (U.S.), 1953 .   £15/£5
The Letters of John Cowper Powys to Louis Wilkinson, 1935-1956, Macdonald, 1958 .   £20/£5
Homer and the Aether, Macdonald, 1959 .   £15/£5
Letters to Nicholas Ross, Bertram Rota, 1971 .   £10

LLEWELYN POWYS
(b.1884 d.1939)

Although he wrote three novels, the author's reputation rests upon his collected essays, many detailing his observations of Africa.

Novels
Black Laughter, Harcourt Brace (U.S.), 1924 £45/£15
ditto, Grant Richards, 1925 .   .   .   . £45/£15
The Verdict of Bridlegoose, Harcourt Brace (U.S.), 1926 .   .   .   . £35/£10
ditto, Jonathan Cape, 1927 (900 signed, numbered copies) .   .   .   . £40/£25
Apples Be Ripe, Harcourt Brace (U.S.), 1930 £50/£20
ditto, Longman, 1930 .   .   .   .   . £50/£20

Essays
Ebony and Ivory, American Library Service (U.S.), 1923 .   .   .   . £35/£10
ditto, Grant Richards, 1923 .   .   .   . £35/£10
Thirteen Worthies, American Library Service (U.S.), 1923 .   .   .   . £35/£10
ditto, Grant Richards, 1924 .   .   .   . £35/£10
Honey and Gall, Haldeman-Julius (U.S.), 1924 (wraps)
.   .   .   .   £10
Cup Bearers of Wine and Hellebore, Haldeman-Julius (U.S.), 1924 (wraps) £10
The Cradle of God, Harcourt Brace (U.S.), 1929 .
.   .   .   . £25/£10
ditto, Cape, 1924 .   .   .   .   .   . £25/£10
The Pathetic Fallacy, Longmans Green, 1930 £15/£5
Impassioned Clay, Longmans Green (U.S.), 1931 .
.   .   .   . £65/£25
ditto, Longmans Green, 1930. .   .   . £50/£15
Now that the Gods are Dead, Equinox Press (U.S.), 1932 (400 signed copies) £175
ditto, Bodley Head, 1949 .   .   .   . £25/£10
Glory of Life, Golden Cockerel Press, 1934 (277 numbered copies) £500

ditto, Golden Cockerel Press, 1934 (2 copies on vellum) £5,000
ditto, John Lane, 1938. . . . . . . £65/£15
Earth Memories, John Lane, 1934 . . . £35/£15
ditto, Simon & Schuster (U.S.), 1938 . . £25/£10
Damnable Opinions, Watts, 1935 . . . £20/£5
Dorset Essays, Bodley Head, 1935 . . . £30/£10
The Twelve Months, Bodley Head, 1936 . £25/£10
ditto, Bodley Head, 1936 (100 signed copies) . £200
Somerset Essays, Bodley Head, 1937 . . £25/£10
A Baker's Dozen, Trovillion Press (U.S.), 1940 (493 signed, numbered copies, in slipcase) . . £75/£45
ditto, Bodley Head, 1941 . . . . . . £20/£10
Old English Yuletide, Trovillion Press (U.S.), 1940 (202 numbered copies, signed by the printers, in slipcase) . . . . £125/£100
Swiss Essays, Bodley Head, 1947 . . . £20/£10
Somerset and Dorset Essays, Bodley Head, 1957 . .
. . . . £20/£10

Autobiography

Skin for Skin, Harcourt Brace (U.S.), 1925 . £30/£10
ditto, Jonathan Cape, 1927 (900 signed, numbered copies) . . . . £40/£25
Love and Death, Bodley Head, 1939 . . £25/£10
ditto, Simon & Schuster (U.S.), 1941 . . £20/£5

Others

Henry Hudson, John Lane, 1927 (1000 copies) . .
. . . . £45/£15
ditto, Harper & Brothers (U.S.), 1928 . £25/£10
Out of the Past, Grey Bow Press, 1928 (25 copies) .
. . . . £150
A Pagan's Pilgrimage, Harcourt Brace (U.S.), 1931 .
. . . . £30/£10
The Life and Times of Anthony A. Wood, Wishart & Co., 1932 . . . . £30/£10
Rats in the Sacristy, Watts & Co., 1937 . . £25/£10
The Book of Days, Golden Cockerel Press, 1937 (300 copies) £200
ditto, Golden Cockerel Press, 1937 (nos. 1-55 bound in red leather & signed by artist) £300
ditto, Golden Cockerel Press, 1937 (nos. 1-5 on lamb's vellum, bound in red leather & signed by artist) . .
. . . . £1,250
The Letters of Llewelyn Powys, Bodley Head, 1943 .
. . . . £25/£10
Advice to a Young Poet, Letters Between Llewelyn Powys and Kenneth Hopkins, Bodley Head, 1949 (issued as a volume in the Uniform Edition of the Works of Llewelyn Powys) . . . . . £20/£10
So Wild a Thing, Letters to Gamel Woolsey, Ark Press, 1973 . . . . £15

T.F. POWYS
(b.1875 d.1953)

The author of a number of eccentric novels which offer a highly personal and idiosyncratic view of both God and human nature.

Novels

Black Bryony, Chatto & Windus, 1923 . . £50/£10
ditto, Knopf (U.S.), 1923 . . . . . £40/£10
Mark Only, Chatto & Windus, 1924. . . £50/£10
ditto, Knopf (U.S.), 1924 . . . . . . £40/£10
Mr Tasker's Gods, Chatto & Windus, 1925. £50/£10
ditto, Knopf (U.S.), 1925 . . . . . . £40/£10
Mockery Gap, Chatto & Windus, 1925 . . £45/£10
ditto, Knopf (U.S.), 1925 . . . . . £35/£10
Innocent Birds, Chatto & Windus, 1926 . £45/£10
ditto, Knopf (U.S.), 1926 . . . . . £35/£10
Mr Weston's Good Wine, Chatto & Windus, 1927 (660 copies) . . . . £200/£65
ditto, Viking (U.S.), 1928. . . . . £40/£10
ditto, Chatto & Windus, 1928. . . . . £40/£10
Kindness in a Corner, Chatto & Windus, 1930. . .
. . . . £40/£10
ditto, Chatto & Windus, 1930 (206 signed, numbered copies) £65
ditto, Viking (U.S.), 1930. . . . . £35/£5
Unclay, Chatto & Windus, 1931 . . . £40/£10
ditto, Chatto & Windus, 1931 (large paper edition of 160 copies) £65
ditto, Viking (U.S.), 1932. . . . . £35/£5
The Market Bell, Brynmill, 1990 . . . £20/£5

Short Stories

The Left Leg, Chatto & Windus, 1923 . . £50/£10
ditto, Knopf U.S.), 1923 . . . . . £40/£10
A Stubborn Tree, privately printed, 1926 (100 copies)
. . . . £125
Feed My Swine, E. Archer, 1926 (100 copies) . £75
A Strong Girl, E. Archer, 1926 (100 copies) . £75
What Lack I Yet?, E. Archer, 1926 . . . £35
ditto, E. Archer, 1926 (100 signed, numbered copies) .
. . . . £100
ditto, E. Archer, 1926 (25 signed, numbered copies on Japanese vellum). £200
The Rival Pastors, E. Archer, 1927 (100 signed, numbered copies, in envelope) . . . . £75/£50
The House with the Echo, Chatto & Windus, 1928 .
. . . . £45/£10
ditto, Chatto & Windus, 1928 (206 numbered, signed copies) £145
ditto, Viking (U.S.), 1929. . . . . £35/£5
The Dewpond, Elkin Matthews, 1928 (530 signed, numbered copies) . . . . . . £50/£25
Fables, Viking Press, (U.S.), 1929 . . £35/£10
ditto, Chatto & Windus, 1929 (750 signed copies) . .
. . . . £75/£30
Christ in a Cupboard, Blue Moon Booklets no. 5, 1930 (500 numbered, signed copies, wraps) . . . £35

ditto, Blue Moon Booklets no. 5, 1930 (100 small-format copies 'for presentation', wraps) . . £30
The Key of the Field, Furnival Books no.1, 1930 (550 signed copies) . . . . . . £125/£50
The White Paternoster, Chatto & Windus, 1930 . .
. . . . £35/£10
ditto, Chatto & Windus, 1930 (310 copies) . . £145
ditto, Viking, 1931 . . . . £35/£10
Uriah on the Hill, Minority Press, 1930 (wraps, in envelope) . . . . £30/£15
Uncle Dottery, Douglas Cleverdon, 1930 (350 numbered, signed copies) . . . . £300/£200
ditto, Douglas Cleverdon, 1930 (nos. 1-50, containing extra set of plates) £1,250
The Only Penitent, Chatto & Windus, 1931 £30/£10
ditto, Chatto & Windus, 1931 (large paper edition of 160 signed, numbered copies) £65
When Thou Wast Naked, Golden Cockerel Press, 1931 (edition of 500 numbered, signed copies) . . £150
The Tithe Barn, privately printed, 1932 (350 signed, numbered copies) £45
ditto, privately printed, 1932 (50 copies on Japanese vellum, bound in white buckram) £150
The Two Thieves, Chatto & Windus, 1932 . £50/£15
ditto, Chatto & Windus, 1932 (85 signed, numbered copies) £115
ditto, Viking, 1933 . . . . . . £25/£10
Captain Patch, Chatto & Windus, 1935 . . £35/£10
Make Thyself Many, Grayson & Grayson, 1935 (285 signed, numbered copies) . . . . £125/£45
Goat Green, Golden Cockerel Press, 1937 (150 signed, numbered copies, slipcase) . . . £200/£125
ditto, Golden Cockerel Press, 1937 . . £45/£15
Bottle's Path, Chatto & Windus, 1946 . . £25/£10
God's Eyes A-Twinkle, Chatto & Windus, 1947 . .
. . . . £25/£10
Rosie Plum, And Other Stories, Chatto & Windus, 1966 . . . . £15/£5
Two Stories, Brimmell, 1967 (525 numbered copies) .
. . . . £100
ditto, Brimmell, 1967 (25 numbered copies on hand-made paper, signed by Reynolds Stone) £500/£450
Three Short Stories, Dud Noman Press, 1971 (150 numbered copies, acetate d/w) . . . . £35/£30

Others
An Interpretation of Genesis, privately printed, 1907 (100 copies) £400
ditto, Chatto & Windus, 1929 (490 signed copies, slipcase) . . . . £125/£75
ditto, Viking (U.S.), 1929 (260 signed copies, slipcase)
. . . . £125/£75
The Soliloquy of a Hermit, G.A. Shaw (U.S.), 1916 .
. . . . £75
ditto, as *The Soliloquies of a Hermit*, Melrose, 1918.
. . . . £35

TERRY PRATCHETT
(b.1948)

Author of the hugely successful 'Discworld' novels, which began with *The Colour of Magic*.

Discworld Novels
The Colour of Magic, Colin Smythe, 1983 (with or without alternative reviews pasted on to flap) . . .
. . . . £5,000/£500
ditto, St Martin's Press (U.S.), 1983 . . . £300/£30
ditto, Colin Smythe, 1989 (new edition) . £50/£15
The Light Fantastic, Colin Smythe, 1986 £2,000/£250
ditto, NAL/Signet (U.S.), 1988 (wraps) . . . £10
Equal Rites, Gollancz/Colin Smythe, 1987 . . . .
. . . . £1,000/£150
ditto, NAL/Signet (U.S.), 1988 (wraps) . . . £10
Mort, Gollancz/Colin Smythe, 1987 . . . £250/£25
ditto, NAL/Signet (U.S.), 1989 (wraps) . . . £10
Sourcery, Gollancz/Colin Smythe, 1988 . £200/£20
ditto, NAL/Signet (U.S.), 1989 (wraps) . . . £10
Wyrd Sisters, Gollancz, 1988 . . . . . £125/£15
ditto, NAL/Roc (U.S.), 1990 (wraps) . . . £5
Pyramids, Gollancz, 1989 . . . . £75/£15
ditto, NAL/Roc (U.S.), 1989 (wraps) . . . £5
Guards! Guards!, Gollancz, 1989 . . . £50/£10
Eric, Gollancz, 1990 (large format) . . . £45/£10
ditto, NAL/Roc (U.S.), 1995 (wraps) . . . £5
Moving Pictures, Gollancz, 1990 . . £45/£10
ditto, NAL/Roc (U.S.), 1992 (wraps) . . . £5
Reaper Man, Gollancz, 1991 . . . . £35/£10
ditto, NAL/Roc (U.S.), 1992 (wraps) . . . £5
Witches Abroad, Gollancz, 1991 . . . . £35/£10
ditto, NAL/Roc (U.S.), 1993 (wraps) . . . £5
Small Gods, Gollancz, 1992 . . . . £25/£5
HarperCollins (U.S.), 1994 . . . £20/£5
Lords and Ladies, Gollancz, 1992 . . . £25/£5
ditto, HarperPrism (U.S.), 1995 (wraps) . . . £5
Men at Arms, Gollancz, 1993 . . . £25/£5
ditto, HarperPrism (U.S.), 1996 . . . £15/£5
Soul Music, Gollancz, 1994 . . . . £20/£5
ditto, HarperPrism (U.S.), 1995 . . . £10/£5
Interesting Times, Gollancz, 1994 . . . £15/£5
ditto, HarperPrism (U.S.), 1997 . . . £10/£5
Maskerade, Gollancz, 1995 . . . . £15/£5
ditto, HarperPrism (U.S.), 1997 . . . £10/£5
Feet of Clay, Gollancz, 1996 . . . . £10/£5
ditto, HarperPrism (U.S.), 1996 . . . £10/£5
Hogfather, Gollancz, 1996 . . . £10/£5
ditto, HarperPrism (U.S.), 1998 . . . £10/£5
Jingo, Gollancz, 1997 . . . . . £10/£5
ditto, HarperPrism (U.S.), 1998 . . . £10/£5
Last Continent, Doubleday, 1998 . . . £10/£5
ditto, HarperPrism (U.S.), 1999 . . . £10/£5
Carpe Jugulum, Doubleday, 1998 . . . £10/£5
ditto, HarperPrism (U.S.), 1999 . . . £10/£5
The Fifth Elephant, Doubleday, 1999 . . £10/£5
ditto, HarperCollins (U.S.), 2000 . . . £10/£5
Truth, Doubleday, 2000 . . . . . £10/£5

ditto, HarperCollins (U.S.), 2000. . . . £10/£5

The Bromeliad Trilogy
Truckers, Doubleday, 1989 . . . . . £20/£5
ditto, Delacorte Press (U.S.), 1990 . . . £20/£5
Diggers, Doubleday, 1990 . . . . . £15/£5
ditto, Delacorte Press (U.S.), 1991 . . . £15/£5
Wings, Doubleday, 1990 . . . . . . £15/£5
ditto, Delacorte Press (U.S.), 1991 . . . £15/£5
The Bromeliad, Delacorte (U.S.), 1991 . . £15/£5
ditto, Doubleday, 1998 . . . . . . £15/£5

Johnny Maxwell Novels
Only You Can Save Mankind, Doubleday, 1992 . .
. . . . £20/£5
Johnny and the Dead, Doubleday, 1993 . £15/£5
Johnny and the Bomb, Doubleday, 1996 . £15/£5
The Johnny Maxwell Trilogy, Science Fiction Book
Club (U.S.), 1996 (with poster). . . . £15/£5

Others
The Carpet People, Colin Smythe, 1971 . £600/£75
The Dark Side of the Sun, Colin Smythe, 1976 . .
. . . . £500/£65
ditto, St Martin's Press (U.S.), 1976 . . £60/£10
ditto, Doubleday, 1994 . . . . . £10/£5
ditto, Doubleday, 1994 (500 signed copies). £50/£25
STRATA, Colin Smythe, 1981 . . . . .£450/£100
ditto, St Martin's Press (U.S.), 1981 . . £50/£10
ditto, Doubleday, 1994 . . . . . £10/£5
ditto, Doubleday, 1994 (500 signed copies). £50/£25
The Unadulterated Cat, Gollancz, 1986 (wraps) £15
Good Omens, Gollancz, 1990 (with Neil Gaiman) . .
. . . . £30/£5
ditto, Workman (U.S.), 1990 . . . . . £30/£5

ANTHONY PRICE
(b.1928)

A crime novelist and journalist, Price won the Crime
Writers Association's Silver Dagger award with his
first book, *The Labyrinth Makers*, and later the Gold
Dagger with *Other Paths to Glory*.

Novels
The Labyrinth Makers, Gollancz, 1970 . . £300/£50
ditto, Doubleday (U.S.), 1971 . . . . £45/£10
The Alamut Ambush, Gollancz, 1971 . . £100/£25
ditto, Doubleday (U.S.), 1972 . . . . £25/£5
Colonel Butler's Wolf, Gollancz 1972 . . £75/£20
ditto, Doubleday (U.S.), 1973 . . . . £25/£5
October Men, Gollancz, 1973 . . . . £75/£15
ditto, Doubleday (U.S.), 1974 . . . . £25/£5
Other Paths to Glory, Gollancz, 1974 . . £75/£15
ditto, Doubleday (U.S.), 1975 . . . . £25/£5

Our Man in Camelot, Gollancz, 1975 . . £75/£15
ditto, Doubleday (U.S.), 1976 . . . . £25/£5
War Game, Gollancz, 1976 . . . . . £65/£10
ditto, Doubleday (U.S.), 1977 . . . . £25/£5
The '44 Vintage, Gollancz, 1978 . . . £65/£10
ditto, Doubleday (U.S.), 1979 . . . . £20/£5
Tomorrow's Ghost, Gollancz, 1979 . . . £50/£10
ditto, Doubleday (U.S.), 1979 . . . . £12/£5
The Hour of the Donkey, Gollancz, 1980 . £45/£10
Soldier No More, Gollancz, 1981 . . . £35/£10
ditto, Doubleday (U.S.), 1982 . . . . £15/£5
The Old Vengeful, Gollancz, 1982 . . . £20/£5
ditto, Doubleday (U.S.), 1983 . . . . £15/£5
Gunner Kelly, Gollancz, 1983 . . . . £20/£5
ditto, Doubleday (U.S.), 1984 . . . . £15/£5
Sion Crossing, Gollancz, 1984 . . . . £15/£5
ditto, Mysterious Press (U.S.), 1985 . . . £10/£5
ditto, Mysterious Press (U.S.), 1985 (26 signed, lettered
copies, slipcase) . . . . £45/£20
ditto, Mysterious Press (U.S.), 1985 (250 signed,
numbered copies, slipcase) . . . . . £35/£15
Here Be Monsters, Gollancz, 1985 . . . £15/£5
ditto, Mysterious Press (U.S.), 1986 . . . £10/£5
ditto, Mysterious Press (U.S.), 1986 (26 signed, lettered
copies, slipcase) . . . . £50/£20
ditto, Mysterious Press (U.S.), 1986 (250 signed
numbered copies, slipcase) . . . . . £35/£15
For the Good of the State, Gollancz, 1986 . £15/£5
ditto, Mysterious Press (U.S.), 1987 . . . £10/£5
ditto, Mysterious Press (U.S.), 1987 (26 signed, lettered
copies, slipcase) . . . . £45/£20
ditto, Mysterious Press (U.S.), 1987 (250 signed,
numbered copies, slipcase) . . . . . £35/£15
A New Kind of War, Gollancz, 1987 . . £15/£5
ditto, Mysterious Press (U.S.), 1988 . . . £10/£5
A Prospect of Vengeance, Gollancz, 1988 . £10/£5
ditto, The Armchair Detective (U.S.), 1990 . £10/£5
ditto, The Armchair Detective (U.S.), 1990 (100 signed
copies, slipcase) . . . . £30/£15
The Memory Trap, Gollancz 1989 . . . £10/£5
ditto, The Armchair Detective (U.S.), 1991 . £10/£5
ditto, The Armchair Detective (U.S.), 1991 (100 signed
copies, slipcase) . . . . £30/£15

Non Fiction
The Eyes of the Fleet, Hutchinson, 1990 . £10/£5
ditto, Norton (U.S.), 1996. . . . . . £10/£5

J.B. PRIESTLEY
(b.1894 d.1984)

Priestley was born in Bradford, the son of an elementary schoolmaster, and became a clerk after leaving school. He served with distinction in the West Riding and Devonshire Regiments during the First World War, afterwards studying politics and history at Cambridge. His output was prodigious, including many non fiction titles.

Novels

Adam in Moonshine, Heinemann, 1927. . £75/£30
ditto, Harpers (U.S.), 1927 . . . . £75/£30
Benighted, Heinemann, 1927. . . . £125/£30
ditto, as *The Old Dark House*, Harpers, 1928 £125/£30
Farthing Hall (with Hugh Walpole), Macmillan, 1929
. . . . £50/£10
ditto, Doubleday, Doran (U.S.), 1929 . . £50/£10
The Good Companions, Heinemann, 1929 . £50/£15
ditto, Harpers (U.S.), 1929 . . . . . £50/£10
Angel Pavement, Heinemann, 1930 . . £50/£15
ditto, Heinemann, 1930 (1,025 signed copies, slipcase)
. . . . £65/£45
ditto, Harpers (U.S.), 1930 . . . . £50/£10
Faraway, Heinemann, 1932 . . . . £45/£10
ditto, Harpers (U.S.), 1932 . . . . £45/£10
Wonder Hero, Heinemann, 1933. . . £45/£10
ditto, Heinemann, 1933 (175 signed, numbered copies)
. . . . £75
ditto, Harpers (U.S.), 1933 . . . . £45/£10
The Walk in the City: The Lovers in the Stone Forest,
Heinemann, 1936 . . . . £25/£10
ditto, Harpers (U.S.), 1936 . . . . £25/£5
The Doomsday Men: An Adventure, Heinemann, 1938
. . . . £50/£10
ditto, Harpers (U.S.), 1938 . . . . £50/£10
Let the People Sing, Heinemann, 1939 . £25/£10
ditto, Harpers (U.S.), 1940 . . . . £25/£5
Black-Out in Gretley: A Story of - and for - Wartime,
Heinemann, 1942 . . . . £25/£10
ditto, Harpers (U.S.), 1942 . . . £255/£5
Daylight on Saturday: A Novel about an Aircraft
Factory, Heinemann, 1943 . . . £25/£10
ditto, Harpers (U.S.), 1943 . . . . £25/£10
Three Men in New Suits, Heinemann, 1945 £20/£5
ditto, Harpers (U.S.), 1945 . . . . £20/£5
Bright Day, Heinemann, 1946 . . . £20/£5
ditto, Harpers (U.S.), 1946 . . . . £20/£5
Jenny Villiers: A Story of the Theatre, Heinemann,
1947 . . . . £20/£5
ditto, Harpers (U.S.), 1947 . . . . £20/£5
Festival at Farbridge, Heinemann, 1951 . £20/£5
ditto, as *Festival*, Harpers (U.S.), 1951 . £20/£5
The Magicians, Heinemann, 1954 . . £15/£5
ditto, Harpers (U.S.), 1954 . . . . £15/£5
Low Notes on a High Level: A Frolic, Heinemann,
1954 . . . . £15/£5
ditto, Harpers (U.S.), 1954 . . . . £15/£5

Saturn Over the Water, Heinemann, 1961 . £15/£5
ditto, Doubleday (U.S.), 1961 . . . . £15/£5
The Shapes of Sleep: A Topical Tale, Heinemann,
1962 . . . . £10/£5
ditto, Doubleday (U.S.), 1962 . . . . £10/£5
Sir Michael and Sir George, Heinemann, 1964 £10/£5
ditto, Little, Brown (U.S.), 1965 . . . £10/£5
Lost Empires, Heinemann, 1965 . . . £20/£5
ditto, Little, Brown (U.S.), 1965 . . . £20/£5
Salt is Leaving: A Detective Story, Heinemann, 1966 .
. . . . £10/£5
ditto, Harpers (U.S.), 1975 . . . . £10/£5
It's an Old Country, Heinemann, 1967 . . £10/£5
ditto, Little, Brown (U.S.), 1967 . . . £10/£5
The Image Men, Heinemann, 1968-9 (2 vols, *Out of*
Town and *London End*). . . . . £20/£5
ditto, Little, Brown (U.S.), 1969 (1 vol.) . £10/£5
Found, Lost, Found or The English Way of Life,
Heinemann, 1976. . . . . . £10/£5
ditto, Hall (U.S.), 1976 . . . . . £10/£5

Short Stories

The Town Major of Miraucourt, Heinemann, 1930 .
. . . . £40/£5
ditto, Heinemann, 1930 (525 copies signed by the
author, in slipcase) . . . . . £75/£50
Albert Goes Through, Heinemann, 1933 . £25/£10
ditto, Harpers (U.S.), 1933 . . . . £25/£5
Going Up (stories and sketches), Heinemann, 1933 .
. . . . £25/£5
The Other Place, Heinemann, 1953 . . £25/£5
ditto, Harpers (U.S.), [1954] . . . . £20/£5
The Thirty-First of June: A tale of true love, enter-
prise and Progress in the Arthurian and ad-atomic
ages, Heinemann, 1961 . . . . £15/£5
ditto, Doubleday (U.S.), 1962 . . . . £10/£5
Snoggle: A Story for Anybody Between 9 and 90,
Heinemann, 1971 . . . . . £10/£5
ditto, Harcourt Brace (U.S.), [1972] . . £10/£5
The Carfit Crisis and Two Other Stories, Heinemann,
1975 . . . . £10/£5
ditto, Stein & Day (U.S.), 1976 . . . £10/£5

V. S. PRITCHETT
(b.1900 d.1997)

A writer and critic, Pritchett's books range widely through many genres encompassing travel, essays, short stories, novels and memoirs.

Novels

Clare Drummer, Benn, 1929. . . . . £175/£45
Shirley Sanz, Gollancz, 1932. . . . £150/£35
ditto, as *Elopement into Exile*, Little, Brown (U.S.),
1932 . . . . £35/£10
Nothing Like Leather, Chatto & Windus, 1935 . . .
. . . . £125/£30

ditto, Macmillan (U.S.), 1935 . . . . £25/£10
Dead Man Leading, Chatto & Windus, 1937 £75/£20
ditto, Macmillan (U.S.), 1937 . . . . £30/£10
Mr Beluncle, Chatto & Windus, 1951 . . £50/£15
ditto, Harcourt Brace (U.S.), 1951 . . . £25/£5

Short Stories
The Spanish Virgin and Other Stories, Benn, 1930 .
. . . . £300/£45
You Make Your Own Life, Chatto & Windus, 1938 .
. . . . £250/£35
It May Never Happen and Other Stories, Chatto &
Windus, 1945. . . . . £75/£15
ditto, Reynal (U.S.), 1947. . . . . . £50/£10
Collected Stories, Chatto & Windus, 1956 . £40/£10
The Sailor, The Sense of Humour and Other Stories,
Knopf (U.S.), 1956 . . . . . . £25/£5
When My Girl Comes Home, Chatto & Windus, 1961
. . . . £25/£5
ditto, Knopf (U.S.), 1961 . . . . . . £15/£5
The Key to My Heart, Chatto & Windus, 1963 £25/£5
ditto, Random House (U.S.), 1964 . . . £15/£5
The Saint and Other Stories, Penguin, 1966 (wraps) .
. . . . £5
Blind Love and Other Stories, Chatto & Windus, 1969
. . . . £15/£5
ditto, Random House (U.S.), 1970 . . . £10/£5
The Camberwell Beauty and Other Stories, Chatto &
Windus, 1974. . . . . £15/£5
Selected Stories, Chatto & Windus, 1978 . £10/£5
ditto, Random House (U.S.), 1978 . . . £10/£5
On the Edge of the Cliff, Random House (U.S.), 1979
. . . . £10/£5
ditto, Chatto & Windus, 1980 . . . . £10/£5
Collected Stories, Random House (U.S.), 1982 £10/£5
ditto, Chatto & Windus, 1982 . . . . £10/£5
More Collected Stories, Random House (U.S.), 1983 .
. . . . £10/£5
ditto, Chatto & Windus, 1983 . . . . £10/£5
*The Other Side of the Frontier, A V.S. Pritchett
Reader*, Clark, 1984 (wraps) £5
A Careless Widow and Other Stories, Chatto &
Windus, 1989. . . . . £10/£5
ditto, Random House (U.S.), 1989 . . . £10/£5
Complete Short Stories, Chatto & Windus, 1990 . .
. . . . £10/£5
ditto, as *Complete Collected Stories*, Random House
(U.S.), 1991 . . . . £10/£5

Autobiography
A Cab at the Door, Chatto & Windus, 1968 £10/£5
ditto, Random House (U.S.), 1968 . . . £10/£5
Midnight Oil, Chatto & Windus, 1971 . . £10/£5
ditto, Random House (U.S.), 1972 . . . £10/£5

Biography
Balzac, Chatto & Windus, 1973 . . . . £15/£5
ditto, Knopf (U.S.), 1973 . . . . . . £15/£5

*The Gentle Barbarian, The Life and Work of
Turgenev*, Chatto & Windus, 1977. . . £15/£5
ditto, Random House (U.S.), 1977 . . . £15/£5
Chekhov, Hodder & Stoughton, 1988 . . £15/£5
ditto, Random House (U.S.), 1988 . . . £15/£5

Others
Marching Spain, Benn, 1928 . . . . £300/£45
ditto, Left Book Club, 1928 (wraps) . . . £45
In My Good Books, Chatto & Windus, 1942 £25/£10
The Living Novel, Chatto & Windus, 1946 . £25/£10
ditto, Reynal (U.S.), 1947. . . . . . £25/£10
Build the Ships, HMSO, 1947 (wraps) . . £25
*Why Do I Write?: An Exchange of Views Between
Elizabeth Bowen, Graham Greene, and V.S.
Pritchett*, Marshall, 1948 . . . . . £100/£25
Books in General, Chatto & Windus, 1953 . £20/£5
ditto, Harcourt Brace (U.S.), 1954 . . . £20/£10
The Spanish Temper, Chatto & Windus, 1954 £20/£5
ditto, Knopf (U.S.), 1954 . . . . . . £20/£5
London Perceived, Chatto & Windus, 1962
(photographs by Evelyn Hofer). . . . £25/£10
ditto, Harcourt Brace (U.S.), 1962 . . . £25/£10
Foreign Faces, Chatto & Windus, 1964 . £15/£5
New York Proclaimed, Chatto & Windus, 1965
(photographs by Evelyn Hofer). . . . £20/£5
ditto, Harcourt Brace (U.S.), 1965 . . . £20/£5
The Working Novelist, Chatto & Windus, 1965 . .
. . . . £15/£5
Dublin, A Portrait, Bodley Head, 1967 . . £20/£5
ditto, Harper & Row (U.S.), 1967 (photographs by
Evelyn Hofer) . . . . £20/£5
George Meredith and English Comedy, Random
House (U.S.), 1969 . . . . . . £10/£5
ditto, Chatto & Windus, 1970 . . . . £10/£5
Autobiography, English Association, 1977 (wraps) £5
The Myth Makers, Chatto & Windus, 1979 . £10/£5
ditto, Random House (U.S.), 1979 . . . £10/£5
The Tale Bearers, Chatto & Windus, 1980 . £10/£5
ditto, Random House (U.S.), 1980 . . . £10/£5
The Turn of the Years, Russell, 1982 (illustrated by
Reynolds Stone, glassine wraps) . . . £20/£5
ditto, Russell, 1982 (150 copies signed by author and
artist) . . . . £125/£100
ditto, Random House (U.S.), 1982 . . . £20/£5
ditto, Random House (U.S.), 1982 (500 copies signed
by author and artist, slipcase) . . . £100/£75
A Man of Letters, Chatto & Windus, 1985 . £10/£5
ditto, Random House (U.S.), 1985 . . . £10/£5
At Home and Abroad, Chatto & Windus, 1989 £10/£5
ditto, North Point Press (U.S.), 1989. . . £10/£5
Lasting Impressions, Chatto & Windus, 1990 £10/£5
ditto, Random House (U.S.), 1990 . . . £10/£5
Complete Essays, Chatto & Windus, 1991 . £10/£5

MARCEL PROUST
(b.1871 d.1922)

The subject of Proust's work is his own past, which he recreates through an evocation of its smell, taste and sound.

À la Recherche du Temps Perdu
Swann's Way, Chatto & Windus, 1922 (translated by C.K. Scott Moncrieff, 2 vols) . . . . £150/£50
ditto, Thomas Seltzer (U.S.), 1922 (2 vols) . £75/£25
Within a Budding Grove, Chatto & Windus, 1924 (translated by C.K. Scott Moncrieff, 2 vols) £125/£35
ditto, Thomas Seltzer (U.S.), 1924 (2 vols) . £75/£25
The Guermantes Way, Chatto & Windus, 1925 (translated by C.K. Scott Moncrieff, 2 vols) £125/£35
ditto, Thomas Seltzer (U.S.), 1925 (2 vols) . £75/£25
Cities of the Plain, Alfred A. Knopf, 1925 (translated by C.K. Scott Moncrieff, 2230 numbered copies, 2 vols) . . . . £100/£35
ditto, Boni (U.S.), 1927 (2000 numbered copies, 2 vols) . . . . £100/£50
The Captive, Alfred A. Knopf, 1929 (translated by C.K. Scott Moncrieff, 2 vols) . . . . £100/£35
ditto, Boni (U.S.), 1929 . . . . . . £75/£25
The Sweet Cheat Gone, Alfred A. Knopf, 1930 (translated by C.K. Scott Moncrieff) . . £50/£20
ditto, Boni (U.S.), 1930 . . . . . . £75/£25
ditto, as *Albertine Gone*, Chatto & Windus, 1989 (translated by Terence Kilmartin) . . £15/£5
Time Regained, Chatto & Windus, 1931 (1,300 numbered copies, translated by Stephen Hudson) .
. . . . £75/£20
Remembrance of Things Past, Chatto & Windus/ Alfred A. Knopf, 1922-31 (12 vols) . £1,000/£300

Others
47 Unpublished Letters from Marcel Proust to Walter Berry, Black Sun Press (U.S.), 1930 (200 numbered copies, wraps) £250
Marcel Proust: A Selection from His Miscellaneous Writings, Allan Wingate, 1948 (translated by Gerard Hopkins) . . . . £25/£10
Letters to a Friend, The Falcon Press, 1949 £25/£10
Pleasures and Regrets, Crown (U.S.), 1948 £35/£10
ditto, Dobson, 1950 (translated by Louise Varese) . . .
. . . . £35/£10
Letters of Marcel Proust, Random House (U.S.), 1949 (translated by Mina Curtis) . . . . £25/£10
ditto, Chatto & Windus, 1950 . . . . £25/£10
The Letters of Marcel Proust to Antoine Bibescu, Thames and Hudson, [1953] (translated by Gerard Hopkins) . . . . £25/£10
ditto, Thames & Hudson, [1953] (500 copies signed by translator) . . . . £50/£20
Jean Santeuil, Weidenfeld & Nicolson, 1955 (translated by Gerard Hopkins) . . . £40/£10
ditto, Simon & Schuster (U.S.), 1956 . £40/£10
Letters to His Mother, Rider, 1956 . . £25/£10

ditto, Citadel (U.S.), 1957 . . . . . £25/£10
By Way of Saint-Beuve, Chatto & Windus, 1958 (translated by Sylvia Townsend Warner) . £40/£20
On Reading, Macmillan (U.S.), 1971 . . £15/£5
ditto, Souvenir Press, 1972 (translated by Jean Autret and William Burford) . . . . . £15/£5
Selected Letters: 1880-1903, Collins, 1983 (translated by Ralph Manheim) . . . . . . £15/£5
ditto, Doubleday (U.S.), 1983 . . . £15/£5
On Reading Ruskin, Yale Univ. Press (U.S.), 1987 .
. . . . £15/£5
Selected Letters, Volume II: 1904-1909, Collins, 1989 (translated by Terence Kilmartin) . . . £15/£5
ditto, O.U.P. (U.S.), 1989 . . . . . £15/£5

BARBARA PYM
(b.1913 d.1980)

The author of delicate, sad comedies, often set against a background of middle-class churchgoing characters.

Novels
Some Tame Gazelle, Cape, 1950 . . . £300/£75
ditto, Dutton (U.S.), 1983 . . . . . £15/£5
Excellent Women, Cape, 1952 . . . £225/£45
ditto, Dutton (U.S.), 1978 . . . . . £20/£5
Jane and Prudence, Cape, 1953 . . . £225/£45
ditto, Dutton (U.S.), 1981 . . . . . £10/£5
Less Than Angels, Cape, 1955 . . . £200/£45
ditto, Vanguard (U.S.), 1957 . . . . £35/£10
A Glass of Blessings, Cape, 1959 . . £175/£40
ditto, Dutton (U.S.), 1980 . . . . . £10/£5
No Fond Return of Love, Cape, 1961 . £150/£40
ditto, Dutton (U.S.), 1982 . . . . . £10/£5
Quartet in Autumn, Macmillan, 1977 . . £35/£10
ditto, Dutton (U.S.), 1978 . . . . . £20/£5
The Sweet Dove Died, Macmillan, 1978 . £30/£5
ditto, Dutton (U.S.), 1979 . . . . . £10/£5
A Few Green Leaves, Macmillan, 1980 . . £25/£5
ditto, Dutton (U.S.), 1980 . . . . . £10/£5
An Unsuitable Attachment, Macmillan, 1982 £25/£5
ditto, Dutton (U.S.), 1982 . . . . . £10/£5
Crampton Hodnet, Macmillan, 1985 . . £15/£5
ditto, Dutton (U.S.), 1985 . . . . . £10/£5
An Academic Question, Macmillan, 1986 . £10/£5
ditto, Dutton (U.S.), 1986 . . . . . £10/£5
Civil to Strangers, Macmillan, 1987 . . £10/£5
ditto, Dutton (U.S.), 1988 . . . . . £10/£5

Journals
A Very Private Eye, Macmillan, 1984 . . £15/£5
ditto, Dutton (U.S.), 1984 . . . . . £10/£5

ELLERY QUEEN

'Ellery Queen' was the pseudonym for Frederic Dannay and Manfred B. Lee, cousins who entered a detective prize story contest with *The Roman Hat Mystery*. This was the beginning of their successful writing career, and the career of their fictional detective, Ellery Queen. They also penned a handful of 'Barnaby Ross' novels. 'Ellery Queen' novels by other writers have also been included.

Novels

The Roman Hat Mystery, Stokes (U.S.), 1929 . . .
. . . . £4,000/£400
ditto, Gollancz, 1929 . . . . . . £450/£75
The French Powder Mystery, Stokes (U.S.), 1930 . .
. . . . £2,000/£150
ditto, Gollancz, 1930 . . . . . . £350/£45
The Dutch Shoe Mystery Stokes (U.S.), 1931 . . .
. . . . £1,500/£150
ditto, Gollancz, 1931 . . . . . . £250/£35
The Greek Coffin Mystery, Stokes (U.S.), 1932 . .
. . . . £1,500/£150
ditto, Gollancz, 1932 . . . . . . £250/£35
The Egyptian Cross Mystery, Stokes (U.S.), 1932 . .
. . . . £1,500/£150
ditto, Gollancz, 1933 . . . . . . £250/£35
The American Gun Mystery, Stokes (U.S.), 1933 . .
. . . . £1,000/£75
ditto, Gollancz, 1933 . . . . . . £200/£35
ditto, as *Death at the Rodeo*, Mercury, 1951 £45/£10
The Ellery Queen Omnibus, Gollancz, 1934 £75/£20
The Siamese Twin Mystery, Stokes (U.S.), 1933 . .
. . . . £1,000/£75
ditto, Gollancz, 1934 . . . . . . £150/£20
The Chinese Orange Mystery, Stokes (U.S.), 1934 .
. . . . £500/£50
ditto, Gollancz, 1934 . . . . . . £150/£20
The Spanish Cape Mystery, Stokes (U.S.), 1935 . .
. . . . £1,000/£100
ditto, Gollancz, 1935 . . . . . . £150/£20
Halfway House, Stokes (U.S.), 1936 . £450/£35
ditto, Gollancz, 1936 . . . . . . £150/£20
The Door Between, Stokes (U.S.), 1937. . £450/£35
ditto, Gollancz, 1937 . . . . . . £150/£20
The Devil To Pay, Stokes (U.S.), 1938 . £450/£35
ditto, Gollancz, 1938 . . . . . . £150/20
The Four of Hearts, Stokes (U.S.), 1938 . £450/£35
ditto, Gollancz, 1939 . . . . . . £150/£20
The Dragon's Teeth, Stokes (U.S.), 1939 . £450/£35
ditto, Gollancz, 1939 . . . . . . £150/£20
ditto, as *The Virgin Heiress*, Pocket Books, 1954 £20
Calamity Town, Gollancz, 1942 . . . . £250/£20
ditto, Little, Brown (U.S.), 1942 . . . £75/£15
There Was an Old Woman, Little, Brown (U.S.), 1943
. . . . £250/£20
ditto, Gollancz, 1944 . . . . . . £75/£15
ditto, as *The Quick and the Dead*, Pan, 1961 . £10

The Murderer is a Fox, Little, Brown (U.S.), 1945 .
. . . . £100/£15
ditto, Gollancz, 1945 . . . . . . £50/£10
Ten Days' Wonder, Little, Brown (U.S.), 1948 £75/£15
ditto, Gollancz, 1948 . . . . . . £50/£10
Cat of Many Tails, Little, Brown (U.S.), 1949 £75/£15
ditto, Gollancz, 1949 . . . . . . £45/£10
Double, Double, Little, Brown (U.S.), 1950 £65/£10
ditto, Gollancz, 1950 . . . . . . £45/£10
The Origin of Evil, Little, Brown (U.S.), 1951 £65/£10
ditto, Gollancz, 1951 . . . . . . £45/£10
The King is Dead, Little, Brown (U.S.), 1952 £50/£10
ditto, Gollancz, 1952 . . . . . . £45/£10
The Scarlet Letters, Little, Brown (U.S.), 1953. . .
. . . . £50/£10
ditto, Gollancz, 1953 . . . . . . £40/£10
The Glass Village, Little, Brown (U.S.), 1954 £45/£10
ditto, Gollancz, 1954 . . . . . . £35/£5
Inspector Queen's Own Case, Simon & Schuster
(U.S.), 1956 . . . . £45/£10
ditto, Gollancz, 1956 . . . . . . £35/£5
The Finishing Stroke, Simon & Schuster (U.S.), 1958
. . . . £45/£10
ditto, Gollancz, 1958 . . . . . . £35/£5
The Player on the Other Side, Random House (U.S.),
1963 . . . . £30/£5
ditto, Gollancz, 1963 . . . . . . £25/£5
And on the Eighth Day, Random House (U.S.), 1964 .
. . . . £25/£5
ditto, Gollancz, 1964 . . . . . . £20/£5
The Fourth Side of the Triangle, Random House
(U.S.), 1965 . . . . £25/£5
ditto, Gollancz, 1965 . . . . . . £20/£5
A Study in Terror, Lancer (U.S.), 1966 . . £15
ditto, as *Sherlock Holmes Versus Jack the Ripper*,
Gollancz, 1967 . . . . £150/£35
Face to Face, NAL (U.S.), 1967. . . . £25/£5
ditto, Gollancz, 1967 . . . . . . £20/£5
The House of Brass, NAL (U.S.), 1968. . £25/£5
ditto, Gollancz, 1968 . . . . . . £20/£5
Cop Out, World (U.S.), 1969. . . . £15/£5
ditto, Gollancz, 1969 . . . . . . £15/£5
The Last Woman in His Life, World (U.S.), 1970 . .
. . . . £15/£5
ditto, Gollancz, 1970 . . . . . . £15/£5
A Fine and Private Place, World (U.S.), 1971 £15/£5
ditto, Gollancz, 1971 . . . . . . £15/£5
Four Men Called John, Gollancz, 1976 . £15/£5

'Ellery Queen' Short Stories

The Adventures of Ellery Queen, Stokes (U.S.), 1934 .
. . . . £450/£35
ditto, Gollancz, 1935 . . . . . . £150/£20
The New Adventures of Ellery Queen, Stokes (U.S.),
1940 . . . . £450/£35
ditto, Gollancz, 1940 . . . . . . £150/£20
The Case Book of Ellery Queen Gollancz, 1949 . .
. . . . £45/£10
Calendar of Crime, Little, Brown (U.S.), 1952 £45/£10

ditto, Gollancz, 1952 . . . . . . £35/£10
QBI: Queen's Bureau of Investigation, Little, Brown
(U.S.), 1955 . . . . £35/£10
ditto, Gollancz, 1955 . . . . . . £25/£10
Queen's Full, Random House (U.S.), 1965 . £15/£5
ditto, Gollancz, 1966 . . . . . . £15/£5
QED: Queen's Experiments in Detection, Gollancz,
1969 . . . . £15/£5

'Ellery Queen' Non Fiction Titles
Queen's Quorum, Little, Brown (U.S.), 1951 £100/£25
ditto, Gollancz, 1953 . . . . . . £65/£20
In the Queen's Parlour, Gollancz, 1957 . £20/£5

'Barnaby Ross' Titles
The Tragedy of X, Viking (U.S.), 1932 . . £150/£35
ditto, Cassell & Co., 1932. . . . . . £150/£35
The Tragedy of Y, Viking (U.S.), 1932 . . £150/£35
ditto, Cassell & Co., 1932. . . . . . £150/£35
The Tragedy of Z, Viking (U.S.), 1933 . . £150/£35
ditto, Cassell & Co., 1933. . . . . . £150/£35
Drury Lane's Last Case, Viking (U.S.), 1933 . . .
. . . . £150/£35
ditto, Cassell & Co., 1933. . . . . . £150/£35

JONATHAN RABAN
(b.1942)

Raban's early works are academic, but he now has a
considerable reputation as a travel writer.

Travel Titles
Soft City, Hamish Hamilton, 1974 . . . £30/£5
ditto, Dutton (U.S.), 1974. . . . . . £25/£5
Arabia Through the Looking Glass, Collins, 1979 .
. . . . £25/£5
ditto, as **Arabia A Journey Through the Labyrinth**,
Simon & Schuster (U.S.), 1979. . . . £20/£5
Old Glory, Collins, 1981 . . . . . . £20/£5
ditto, Simon & Schuster (U.S.), 1981 . . £15/£5
Coasting, Collins, 1986 . . . . . . £15/£5
ditto, Simon & Schuster (U.S.), 1987 . . £10/£5
Hunting Mr Heartbreak, Collins, 1990 . . £10/£5
ditto, Harper Collins (U.S.), 1991 . . . £10/£5
Passage to Juneau, Picador, 1999 . . . £10/£5
ditto, Pantheon (U.S.), 1999 . . . . . £10/£5

Novels
Foreign Land, Collins, 1985 . . . . . £25/£5
ditto, Viking (U.S.), 1985. . . . . . £20/£5
Bad Land, Picador, 1996 . . . . . . £10/£5
ditto, Pantheon (U.S.), 1996 . . . . . £10/£5

Academic Titles
The Technique of Modern Fiction, Arnold, 1968 . .
. . . . £100/£25

ditto, Univ. of Notre Dame Press (U.S.), 1968 (wraps).
. . . . £10
Huckleberry Finn, Arnold, 1968 . . . £50/£10
Society of the Poem, Harrap, 1971 . . . £25/£5

Others
For Love and Money, Collins, 1987. . . £50/£5
ditto, Harper & Row (U.S.), 1989 . . . £10/£5
God, Man and Mrs Thatcher, Chatto & Windus
(wraps) £10

ARTHUR RACKHAM
(b.1867 d.1939)

A highly successful illustrator, Rackham's early gift
books are his most sought after titles, especially in
deluxe editions.

To the Other Side, by Thomas Rhodes, George Philip,
1893 (wraps, also illustrated by Alfred Bryan) £300
The Dolly Dialogues, by Anthony Hope, Westminster
Gazette Library: Volume One, [July] 1894 (wraps,
first issue with 'Dolly' running head) . . . £200
ditto, Westminster Gazette Library: Volume One,
[July] 1894 (wraps, second issue with 'The Dolly
Dialogues' running head) £125
ditto, Westminster Gazette Library: Volume One,
[August] 1894 (cloth edition) £125
The Illustrated Guide to Wells-next-the-Sea, by
Lingwood Lemmon, Jarrolds, [1894] (wraps) . £350
ditto, Jarrolds, [1894] (first cloth issue, date on title
page) £175
Sunrise-Land - Rambles in Eastern England, by Mrs
Alfred Berlyn, Jarrolds, 1894 (mauve pictorial cloth)
. . . . £200
ditto, Jarrolds, 1894 (cheaper edition, white boards) .
. . . . £100
The Zankiwank and the Bletherwitch, Dent, 1896. .
. . . . £2,000
ditto, Dutton (U.S.), 1896. . . . . . £2,000
The Money Spinner and Other Character Notes, by
Henry Seaton Merriman and S.G. Tallentyre, Smith
Elder, 1896 . . . . £150
**In the Evening of His Days - A Study of Mr Gladstone
in Retirement**, Westminster Gazette, 1896 . £125
The Grey Lady, by Henry Seatom Merriman, Smith
Elder, 1897 . . . . £250
**Two Old Ladies, Two Foolish Fairies and a Tom Cat,
The Surprising Adventures of Tuppy and Tue**,
Cassell, 1897 . . . . £250
Charles O'Malley, The Irish Dragoon, by Charles
Lever, Service & Paton, 1897 . . . . £200
Evelina, by Frances Burney, George Newnes, 1898
(first issue with one page advert at rear) . . £150
ditto, by Frances Burney, George Newnes, 1898
(second issue with two page advert at rear) . £45

The Ingoldsby Legends, [by R.H. Barham], J.M. Dent, 1898 (gilt lettering on cover and spine) . . £250
ditto, J.M. Dent, 1907 (second edition, revised and enlarged, 560 signed copies) £1,250
ditto, J.M. Dent, 1907 (trade edition of above) . £65
East Coast Scenery, by William J. Tate, Jarrolds, 1899
. . . . £150
Feats on the Fjord, by Harriet Martineau, J.M. Dent, 1898 (blue leather edition) £100
ditto, J.M. Dent, 1898 (blue cloth edition) . . £65
ditto, as *Feats on the Fjord and Merdhin,* Dent: Everyman Library, [1910] £35
Tales from Shakespeare, by Charles and Mary Lamb, J.M. Dent, 1899 (blue leather edition) . . . £75
ditto, J.M. Dent, 1899 (blue cloth edition) . . £45
ditto, J.M. Dent, 1909 (deluxe second edition, revised and enlarged, 750 signed copies) . . . £1,000
ditto, J.M. Dent, 1909 (trade edition of above) . £100
ditto, Dutton (U.S.), 1909. . . . . . . £75
Gulliver's Travels, by Jonathan Swift, J.M. Dent, 1900 (blue leather edition). £50
ditto, J.M. Dent, 1900 (blue cloth edition) . . £40
ditto, J.M. Dent, 1909 (deluxe second edition, revised and enlarged, 750 signed copies with extra plate). .
. . . . £1,250
ditto, J.M. Dent, 1909 (trade edition of above) . £125
Fairy Tales of the Brothers Grimm, Freemantle, 1900
. . . . £200
ditto, Lippincott (U.S.), [1902] £150
ditto, Constable, 1909 (deluxe second edition, revised and enlarged, 750 signed copies) . . . £3,000
ditto, Constable, 1909 (trade edition of the above) . .
. . . . £750
ditto, as *Hansel & Gretel and Other Tales* and *Snowdrop and Other Tales,* by the Brothers Grimm, Constable, 1920 (2 vols, dark blue cloth) . . . .
. . . . £500/£250 each
ditto, Dutton (U.S.), 1920 (2 vols as above) . . .
. . . . £500/£250 each
The Argonauts of the Amazon, by C.R. Kenyon, W. & R. Chambers, 1901 (light blue cloth) . . . £75
ditto, Dutton (U.S.), 1901. . . . . . . £75
More Tales of the Stumps, Horace Bleackley, Ward Lock, 1902 . . . . £150
Brains and Bravery, Being Stories told by ..., W. & R. Chambers, [1903] (red or blue cloth) . . . £125
ditto, W & R Chambers, 1903 (later edition, green cloth) £100
The Grey House on the Hill, by Hon. Mrs Greene, Thomas Nelson, [1903] £65
Littledom Castle and Other Tales, by Mrs M.H. Speilmann, George Routledge, 1903 . . . £200
The Greek Heroes, Cassell, 1903 (limp green buckram) £100
Two Years Before the Mast, by Richard Henry Dana, Collins, [1904] £65
Where Flies the Flag, by Henry Harbour, Collins [1904]. £75

Molly Bawn, by Mrs Hungerford, George Newnes: Newnes Sixpenny Novels, [1904] (wraps) . . £125
Red Pottage, by Mary Cholmondeley, George Newnes: Newnes Sixpenny Novels, [1904] (wraps) . . £125
The Peradventures of Private Pagett, by Major W.P. Drury, Chapman & Hall, 1904 . . . . . £125
Rip van Winkle, by Washington Irving, Heinemann, 1905 (deluxe edition, 250 signed copies) . £2,250
ditto, Heinemann, 1905 (trade edition) . . . £350
Peter Pan in Kensington Gardens, by J.M. Barrie, Hodder & Stoughton, 1906 (deluxe edition, 500 signed copies) £3,000
ditto, Hodder & Stoughton, 1906 (trade edition) . .
. . . . £1,500
ditto, Scribner (U.S.), 1906. . . . . . £1,250
The Peter Pan Portfolio, Hodder & Stoughton, [1912] (500 boxed portfolios, signed by publishers) £10,000
Puck of Pook's Hill, by Rudyard Kipling, Doubleday (U.S.), 1906 . . . . £200
Good Night, by Eleanor Gates, Thomas Y. Crowell (U.S.), [1907]. £100
Alice's Adventures in Wonderland, by Lewis Carroll, William Heinemann, [1907] (deluxe edition of 1,130 copies) £1,500
ditto, William Heinemann, [1907] (trade edition) £150
ditto, Doubleday (U.S.), [1907] (550 signed copies) .
. . . . £1,500
ditto, Doubleday (U.S.), [1907] (trade edition) £150
The Land of Enchantment, by Alfred E. Bonser, Cassell, 1907 (first binding, green cloth). . £175
ditto, Cassell, 1907 (second binding, cocoa cloth) £100
A Midsummer's Night Dream, by William Shakespeare, William Heinemann, 1908 (deluxe edition, 1,000 signed copies) £1,500
ditto, William Heinemann, 1908 (trade edition) £350
ditto, Doubleday (U.S.), 1908 . . . . . £250
ditto, by William Shakespeare, Limited Editions Club (U.S.), 1939 (deluxe 1,950 copies) £500
ditto, Weidenfeld & Nicholson, 1977 (includes 6 previously unpublished plates) . . . . £15/£100
Undine, by De La Motte Fouque, William Heinemann, 1909 (deluxe edition, 1,000 signed copies) £1,250
ditto, William Heinemann, 1909 (trade edition) £200
ditto, Doubleday (U.S.), 1909 . . . . . £200
The Book of Betty Barber, by Maggie Browne, Duckworth, [1910] £500
ditto, Badger (U.S.), 1914. . . . . . . £200
The Bee Blowaways, by Agnes Grozier Herbertson, Cassell, [1910] £650
Stories of King Arthur, by A.L. Haydon, Cassell, 1910
. . . . £75
The Rhinegold and The Valkyrie, by Richard Wagner, William Heinemann, 1910 (deluxe edition, 1,150 signed copies. £1,000
ditto, William Heinemann, 1910 (trade edition) £200
ditto, Doubleday (U.S.), 1910 (deluxe edition, 1,150 signed copies. £1,000
ditto, Doubleday (U.S.), 1910 (trade edition) . £200

Siegfried and The Twilight of the Gods, by Richard Wagner, William Heinemann, 1911 (deluxe edition, 1,150 signed copies £1,000
ditto, William Heinemann, 1911 (trade edition) £200
ditto, as *The Ring of the Nibelung*, William Heinemann, 1939 (two Warner editions in one) . .
. . . . £150/£75
Aesop's Fables, William Heinemann, 1912 (deluxe edition, 1,450 signed copies. £1,250
ditto, William Heinemann, 1912 (trade edition) £150
Mother Goose: The Old Nursery Rhymes, William Heinemann, 1913 (deluxe edition, 1,130 signed copies £1,250
ditto, William Heinemann, 1913 (trade edition) £200
ditto, Century (U.S.), 1913 . . . . . . £200
Arthur Rackham's Book of Pictures, William Heinemann, 1913 (deluxe edition, 1,030 signed copies) £1,000
ditto, William Heinemann, 1913 (trade edition) £250
ditto, William Heinemann, 1913 (30 inscibed copies with original drawing) £4,000
ditto, Century Co. (U.S.), 1913 . . . . £250
A Christmas Carol, by Charles Dickens, Heinemann, 1915 (olive green cloth) £200
ditto, Heinemann, 1915 (deluxe edition, 525 signed copies, full vellum) £1,250
ditto, Heinemann, 1915 (publishers special binding, brown leather) £300
ditto, Lippincott (U.S.), 1915. . . . . . £200
The Allies' Fairy Book, by various, Heinemann, 1916 (slate blue cloth) £125
ditto, Heinemann, 1916 (deluxe 525 signed copies, blue cloth) £500
Little Brother and Little Sister, by the Brothers Grimm, Constable, 1917 (light green cloth) . £250
ditto, (deluxe 525 signed copies, including one signed colour plate laid in, light grey cloth) . . £1,750
ditto, Dodd, Mead (U.S.), 1917 . . . . £250
The Romance of King Arthur, And his Knights of the Round Table, by Thomas Malory and Alfred Pollard, Macmillan, 1917 (dark blue cloth) £300
ditto, Macmillan, 1917 (deluxe 500 signed copies, full vellum) £1,500
ditto, Macmillan (U.S.), 1917 . . . . £250
ditto, Macmillan (U.S.), 1917 (deluxe 250 signed copies, full vellum) £1,500
English Fairy Tales, by Flora Annie Steel, Macmillan, 1918 (red cloth) £150
ditto, Macmillan, 1918 (deluxe edition limited to 500 signed copies, full vellum) £1,000
ditto, Macmillan (U.S.), 1918 . . . . . £150
The Springtide of Life: Poems of Childhood, by Algernon Charles Swinburne, Heinemann, 1918 (green cloth) £100
ditto, Heinemann, 1918 (deluxe 765 signed copies, vellum-backed cream boards) £750
ditto, Heinemann, 1918 (publishers special binding of dark green mottled leather) £125

ditto, Heinemann, 1918 [1925] (later issue, as trade edition but top edge not gilt) £30
ditto, Lippincott (U.S.), 1918. . . . . . £100
Snickerty Nick and the Giant, by Julia Ellsworth Ford, Moffat, Yard & Co (U.S.), 1919 . . . . £500
ditto, Suttonhouse (U.S.), 1933 (new edition, with music by C.A. Ridgeway) £150
Some British Ballads, by various, Constable [1919] (light blue cloth) £125
ditto, Constable [1919] (575 deluxe signed copies, vellum-backed cream boards) £650
ditto, Constable (with 'Heinemann' at the foot of the spine) [1924] . . . . . . £100/£35
Cinderella, by Charles Perrault, Heinemann, 1919 (pictorial boards). £150
ditto, Heinemann, 1919 (deluxe 'paper' 525 signed copies, printed on handmade paper, green boards with tan cloth spine) £650
ditto, Heinemann, 1919 (deluxe 'vellum' 325 signed copies, printed on Japanese vellum, vellum-backed cream boards) £1,000
The Sleeping Beauty, by Charles Perrault, Heinemann, 1920 (pictorial boards with red cloth backstrip) . .
. . . .£300/£150
ditto, Heinemann, 1920 (deluxe 625 signed copies, vellum-backed cream boards) £650
Irish Fairy Tales, by James Stephens, Macmillan, 1920 (green cloth) . . . .£350/£200
ditto, Macmillan, 1920 (deluxe 520 signed copies, vellum-backed white boards) £1,000
ditto, Macmillan (U.S.), 1920 . . . . £350/£200
Comus, by John Milton, Heinemann [1921] (green cloth) . . . .£500/£150
ditto, Heinemann [1921] (deluxe 550 signed copies, vellum-backed cream boards) £500
A Dish of Apples, by Eden Phillpotts, Hodder & Stoughton, 1921 (grey cloth) . . . £250/£100
ditto, Hodder & Stoughton, 1921 (deluxe 500 copies signed by author and artist, cream buckram) . £600
ditto, Hodder & Stoughton, 1921 (55 copies on Batchelor's Kelmscott paper) £1,500
A Wonder Book, by Nathaniel Hawthorne, Hodder & Stoughton [1922] (red cloth) . . . £300/£150
ditto, Hodder & Stoughton [1922] (deluxe 600 signed copies, cream buckram) £1,000
ditto, Doran (U.S.) [1922] . . . . £300/£150
Where the Blue Begins, by Christopher Morley, Heinemann [1925] (blue cloth) . . . .£250/£100
ditto, Heinemann [1925] (deluxe 175 signed copies) .
. . . . £1,000
ditto, Doubleday (U.S.), 1922 [1925] . .£250/£100
ditto, Doubleday (U.S.), 1922 [1925] (100 signed copies) £1,500
Poor Cecco, by Margery Williams Bianco, George H. Doran (U.S.), 1925 (deluxe 105 copies signed by the author, slipcase) . . . . . . £4,000/£3,500
ditto, George H. Doran (U.S.), 1925 (1st issue with pictorial endpapers) . . . . . £400/£250

ditto, George H. Doran (U.S.), 1925 (2nd issue with plain endpapers) . . . . £250/£100
ditto, Chatto & Windus, 1925 [May, 1926] (yellow cloth) . . . . £300/£150
A Road to Fairyland, by Erica Fay, Putnams, 1926 (colour frontispiece only, U.K. issued in grey cloth with blue lettering, U.S. issued in red cloth with gilt lettering) . . . . £250/£150
The Tempest, by William Shakespeare, Heinemann/ Doubleday, 1926 (olive green or grey-black cloth) . . . . £300/£150
ditto, Heinemann/ Doubleday, 1926 (deluxe 520 signed copies, vellum-style boards with vellum spine) £1,250
The Lonesomest Doll, by Abbie Farwell Brown, Houghton Mifflin (U.S.), 1928 . . . £300/£200
The Legend of Sleepy Hollow, by Washington Irving, Harrap, 1928 (green cloth) . . . £225/£125
ditto, Harrap, 1928 (deluxe 375 signed copies, full vellum) £1,000
ditto, Harrap, 1928 (publisher's special binding, grey or brown leather) £250
ditto, McKay (U.S.), 1928 . . . £225/£125
The Vicar of Wakefield, by Oliver Goldsmith, Harrap, 1929 (dark green cloth) . . . . . £250/£100
ditto, Harrap, 1929 (deluxe 775 signed copies, full vellum) £750
ditto, Harrap, 1929 (publisher's special binding, olive persian morocco). £250
ditto, McKay (U.S.), 1929 (200 signed copies) . £750
ditto, McKay (U.S.), 1929 . . . £250/£100
The Chimes, by Charles Dickens, with an introduction by Edward Wagenknecht, Limited Editions Club (U.K./U.S.), 1931 (6 full-page and 14 smaller black and white drawings, 1,500 copies signed by the artist, tan buckram in pictorial slipcase) . . £450/£350
The Night Before Christmas, by Clement C. Moore, Harrap, 1931 (wraps with d/w) . . . £100/£65
ditto, Harrap, 1931 (deluxe 550 signed copies, limp vellum in slipcase) . . . . . £1,000/£800
ditto, Lippincott (U.S.), 1931. . . . £100/£65
The Compleat Angler, by Izaak Walton, Harrap, 1931 (dark blue cloth) . . . . £400/£200
ditto, Harrap, 1931 (deluxe 775 signed copies, full vellum) £1,000
ditto, Harrap, 1931 (10 copies with signed watercolour, full vellum) £4,000
ditto, Harrap, 1931 (publisher's special binding, dark green or brown leather) £400
ditto, McKay (U.S.), 1931 . . . £400/£200
Fairy Tales, by Hans Andersen, Harrap, 1932 (rose-red cloth) . . . . £300/£150
ditto, Harrap, 1932 (deluxe 525 signed copies, full vellum) £1,250
ditto, Harrap, 1932 (publisher's special binding, full morocco) £300
ditto, McKay (U.S.), 1932 . . . £300/£150
The King of the Golden River, by John Ruskin, Harrap, 1932 (wraps with d/w) . . . . £100/£65

ditto, Harrap, 1932 (deluxe 570 signed copies, limp vellum) £650
ditto, Harrap, 1932 (9 copies with original drawing) £4,000
ditto, Lippincott (U.S.), 1932. . . . . £100/£65
Goblin Market, by Christina Rossetti, Harrap, 1933 (wraps with d/w) . . . . £200/£75
ditto, Harrap, 1933 (deluxe 410 signed copies, limp vellum, slipcase). . . . . . £650/£500
ditto, Harrap, 1933 (10 copies with drawing) . £6,000
ditto, Lippincott (U.S.), 1933. . . . . £150/£75
The Arthur Rackham Fairy Book, by various, Harrap, 1933 (red cloth) . . . . . . £250/£125
ditto, Harrap, 1933 (deluxe 460 signed copies, full vellum) £750
ditto, Harrap, 1933 (10 signed copies with original watercolour, full vellum) £10,000
ditto, Lippincott (U.S.), 1933. . . . £250/£125
The Pied Piper of Hamelin, by Robert Browning, Harrap, 1934 (wraps with d/w) . . . . £125/£60
ditto, Harrap, 1934 (deluxe 410 signed copies, limp vellum) £1,000
ditto, Lippincott (U.S.), 1934. . . . . £125/£50
Tales of Mystery and Imagination, by Edgar Allan Poe, Harrap, 1935 (grey-black cloth) . £350/£200
ditto, Harrap, 1935 (deluxe 460 signed copies, full vellum) £1,000
ditto, Harrap, 1935 (publisher's special binding, dark blue morocco) £400
ditto, Lippincott (U.S.), 1935. . . . £350/£200
Peer Gynt, by Henrik Ibsen, Harrap, 1936 (orange-brown cloth) . . . . £300/£150
ditto, Harrap, 1936 (deluxe 460 signed copies, full vellum) £850
ditto, Harrap, 1936 (publisher's special binding, green morocco) £250
ditto, Lippincott (U.S.), 1936. . . . £300/£150
The Wind in the Willows, by Kenneth Grahame, Limited Editions Club (U.S.), 1940 (deluxe 2,020 copies, signed by the designer Bruce Rogers, cloth-backed patterned boards) £1,500
ditto, Heritage Press (U.S.), 1940 (blue-mauve cloth) . . . . £175/£75
ditto, Methuen, 1950 (green cloth) . . £175/£75
ditto, Methuen, 1951 (deluxe 500 copies, full white calf) £1,000

Haddon Hall Library Titles
Wild Life in Hampshire Highlands, by George A.B. Dewar, Dent, 1899 . . . . £50
ditto, Dent, 1899 (deluxe edition) . . . £125
Our Gardens, by S. Reynolds Hole, Dent, 1899 £40
ditto, Dent, 1899 (deluxe edition, signed by Hole) £125
Fly Fishing, by Sir Edward Grey, Dent, 1899 . £75
ditto, Dent, 1899 (deluxe edition) . . . £250
Our Forests and Woodlands, by John Nisbet, Dent, 1900 . . . . £35
ditto, Dent, 1900 (deluxe edition) . . . £125
Hunting, by J. Otho Paget, Dent, 1900 . . £50

ditto, Dent, 1900 (deluxe edition) £175
Outdoor Games, Cricket & Golf, by Hon R.H.
Lyttelton, Dent, 1901 . . . . £75
ditto, Dent, 1901 (deluxe edition) £175
Bird Watching, by Edmund Selous, Dent, 1901. £50
ditto, Dent, 1901 (deluxe edition) £125
Shooting, by Alexander Innes Shand, Dent, 1902. £50
ditto, Dent, 1902 (deluxe edition) £175
Farming, by W.M. Todd, Dent, 1903 . . . £35
ditto, Dent, 1903 (deluxe edition) £125

ANN RADCLIFFE
(b.1764 d.1823)

Despite her inability to bring any of her characters to
life, Radcliffe excelled in her descriptions of scenes
of mystery and terror. The best known writer of the
Gothic school, without whom there would probably
be no Frankenstein or Dracula, she nevertheless
rationalized all of her supernatural manifestations
until the final novel, *Gaston de Blondeville*.

Novels
The Castles of Athlin and Dunbayne, Hookham, 1789
(anonymous) £2,500
A Sicilian Romance, Hookham & Carpenter, 1790
(anonymous) £3,000
The Romance of the Forest, Hookham, 1791 (3 vols,
'By the Authoress of 'A Sicilian Romance,', &c...') .
. . . . £2,500
*The Mysteries of Udolpho, a Romance; interspersed
with some pieces of poetry*, Robinson, 1794 (4 vols).
. . . . £2,000
*The Italian, or the Confessional of the Black
Penitents*, Cadell & Davies, 1797 (3 vols). . £250
Gaston de Blondeville, and *St Alban's Abbey, A
Metrical Tale*, Colburn, 1826 (4 vols) . . . £600

Poetry
The Poems of Mrs A. Radcliffe, Bounden, 1815 . .
. . . . £1,000
The Poems of Mrs Ann Radcliffe, Smith, 1816 £750
The Poetical Works of Ann Radcliffe, Colburn &
Bentley, 1834. . . . . £500

Travel
A Journey Made in the Summer of 1794..., Robinson,
1795 . . . . £1,000

ARTHUR RANSOME
(b.1884 d.1967)

Author of the much loved 'Swallows and Amazons'
series of books for children, Arthur Ransome also
wrote for adults.

'Swallows and Amazons' Titles
Swallows and Amazons, Cape, 1930 . £2,000/£200
ditto, Lippincott (U.S.), 1931 . . . . . £500/£25
Swallowdale, Cape, 1931 . . . . . £1,250/£65
ditto, Lippincott (U.S.), 1932. . . . . £200/£35
Peter Duck, Cape, 1932 . . . . . £1,000/£45
ditto, Lippincott (U.S.), 1933 . . . . . £200/£35
Winter Holiday, Cape, 1933 . . . . £1,000/£45
ditto, Lippincott (U.S.), [1934] . . . . £200/£35
Coot Club, Cape, 1934 . . . . . £1,000/£45
ditto, Lippincott (U.S.), 1935. . . . . £200/£35
Pigeon Post, Cape, 1936 . . . . . . £450/£40
ditto, Lippincott (U.S.), 1937. . . . . £150/£35
We Didn't Mean to Go to Sea, Cape, 1937 . £350/£35
ditto, Macmillan (U.S.), 1938 . . . . £150/£35
Secret Water, Cape, 1939. . . . . . £300/£40
ditto, Macmillan (U.S.), 1940 . . . . £150/£35
The Big Six, Cape, 1940 . . . . . . £250/£35
ditto, Macmillan (U.S.), 1941 . . . . £150/£30
Missee Lee, Cape, 1941 . . . . . . £250/£35
ditto, Macmillan (U.S.), 1942 . . . . £150/£30
The Picts and the Martyrs, or Not Welcome At All.
Cape, 1943 . . . . £145/£30
ditto, Macmillan (U.S.), 1943 . . . . £125/£25
Great Northern, Cape, 1947 . . . . . £125/£30
ditto, Macmillan (U.S.), 1948 . . . . £100/£25

Other Children's Titles
Pond and Stream, Treherne, 1906 . . . . £150
The Child's Book of the Seasons, Treherne, 1906 £150
The Things in Our Garden, Treherne, 1906 . £150
Highways and Byways in Fairyland, Pinafore Library,
[1906]. £175
The Imp and the Elf and the Ogre, Nisbet, 1910 £150
The Hoofmarks of the Faun, Martin Secker, 1911 .
. . . . £150
Old Peter's Russian Tales, T. C. & E. C. Jack, 1916 .
. . . . £150
ditto, Nelson (U.S.), [1938] . . . . £75/£25
Aladdin, Nisbet, [1919] £150
ditto, Nisbet, [1919] (250 signed copies) . £1,000

Adult Titles
The Souls of the Streets, Brown Langham, 1904 £400
The ABC of Physical Culture, Drane, 1904 . £45
The Stone Lady, Brown Langham, 1905 . . £100
Bohemia in London, Chapman & Hall, 1907 . £100
ditto, Dodd, Mead (U.S.), 1907 . . . . £75
A History of Storytelling, Jack, 1909 . . £75
Edgar Allan Poe, Secker, 1910 . . . . £100
Oscar Wilde, Secker, 1912 . . . . . £75
ditto, Mitchell Kennerley (U.S.), 1913 . . £75

Portraits and Speculations, Macmillan, 1913 . £50
The Elixir of Life, Methuen, 1915 . . . . £75
Six Weeks in Russia in 1919, Allen & Unwin, 1919
(wraps) £100
The Crisis in Russia, Allen & Unwin, 1921 £125/£50
ditto, Huebsch (U.S.), 1921 . . . . . £100/£30
The Soldier and Death, J. C. Wilson, 1921 . . £45
Racundra's First Cruise, Allen & Unwin, 1923. . .
. . . . £450/£100
ditto, Huebsch (U.S.), 1923 . . . . £450/£100
The Chinese Puzzle, Allen & Unwin, 1927 . £150/£45
Rod and Line, Cape, 1929 . . . . £400/£100
Mainly About Fishing, A. & C. Black, 1959 . . .
. . . . £300/£100
The Autobiography of Arthur Ransome, Cape, 1976
. . . . £20/£5

ditto, Constable, 1926 . . . . £75/£20
ditto, Houghton Miflin (U.S.), 1926 . . . £75/£20
ditto, Faber, 1947 (engravings by Reynolds Stone). .
. . . . £75/£20
Illustrators of the Sixties, Faber & Gwyer, 1928 . .
. . . . £150/£100
Walter de la Mare, A Critical Study, Faber, 1929 . .
. . . . £50/£20
ditto, Holt (U.S.), 1929 . . . . . . £45/£20
Private Road, Faber, 1940 . . . . . £45/£15
Retrospective Adventures, Faber, 1941 . . £35/£10
Notes and Impressions, The Mourne Press, 1942 £50
Poems from the Greek Anthology, Faber, 1943 £25/£5
The Milk of Paradise, Faber, 1946 . . . £25/£5
*The Suppressed Dedication and Envoy of The Garden
God*, D'Arch Smith, [1970's?] (105 numbered copies,
wraps). £45

FORREST REID
(b.1875 d.1947)

An author whose evocations of his native Ulster landscape, and youth, are tinged with the supernatural.

Novels
The Kingdom of Twilight, Fisher Unwin, 1904 £250
The Garden God, David Nutt, 1905 . . . . £300
The Bracknels, Edward Arnold, 1911 . . . £100
ditto, as *Denis Bracknel*, Faber, 1947 revised edition).
. . . . £20/£5
Following Darkness, Edward Arnold, 1912 . £100
The Gentle Lover, Edward Arnold, 1913 . . £100
At the Door of the Gate, Edward Arnold, 1915 . £100
The Spring Song, Edward Arnold, 1916 . . £100
ditto, Houghton Miflin (U.S.), 1917 . . . £75
Pirates of the Spring, Talbot Press/Fisher Unwin, 1919
[1920]. £100
ditto, Houghton Miflin (U.S.), 1920 . . . £200/£65
Pender Among the Residents, Collins, 1922 £200/£75
ditto, Houghton Miflin (U.S.), 1923 . . . £100/£35
Demophon, Collins, 1927 . . . . . £200/£50
Uncle Stephen, Faber, 1931 . . . . . £60/£20
Brian Westby, Faber, 1934 . . . . . £60/£20
The Retreat, Faber, 1936 . . . . . . £60/£20
Peter Waring, Faber, 1937 . . . . . £60/£20
Young Tom, Faber, 1944 . . . . . . £35/£10
Tom Barber, Pantheon (U.S.), 1955 (contains *Uncle
Stephen, Young Tom* and *The Retreat*) . . £15/£5

Short Stories
A Garden by the Sea, Talbot Press/Fisher Unwin, 1918
. . . . £125

Others
W.B. Yeats, A Critical Study, Secker, 1915 . . £50
ditto, Dodd, Mead (U.S.), 1915 . . . . . £50
Apostate, Constable, 1926 (50 signed copies) . £300

RUTH RENDELL
(b.1930)

A novelist and short story writer, Rendell is popularly known for the Wexford detective stories and novels. Other fiction written under her own name Ruth rendell explores wider issues of criminal maladjustment, while the 'Barbara Vine' books tend to investigate darker psychological motivation.

'Wexford' Novels
From Doon with Death, Long, 1964 . £2,000/£150
ditto, Doubleday (U.S.), 1965 . . . . £350/£30
A New Lease of Death, Long, 1967 . . . £750/£45
ditto, Doubleday (U.S.), 1967 . . . . £150/£15
Wolf to the Slaughter, Long, 1967 . . . £750/£45
ditto, Doubleday (U.S.), 1968 . . . . £150/£15
The Best Man to Die, Long, 1969 . . . £500/£35
ditto, Doubleday (U.S.), 1970 . . . . £75/£15
A Guilty Thing Surprised, Hutchinson, 1970 £350/£25
ditto, Doubleday (U.S.), 1970 . . . . £60/£10
No More Dying, Then, Hutchinson, 1971 . £175/£25
ditto, Doubleday (U.S.), 1972 . . . . £35/£10
Murder Being Once Done, Hutchinson, 1972 . .
. . . . £175/£20
ditto, Doubleday (U.S.), 1972 . . . . £35/£10
Some Lie and Some Die, Hutchinson, 1973 £150/£15
ditto, Doubleday (U.S.), 1973 . . . . £30/£10
Shake Hands for Ever, Hutchinson, 1975 . £125/£15
ditto, Doubleday (U.S.), 1975 . . . . £30/£10
A Sleeping Life, Hutchinson, 1978 . . . . £65/£5
ditto, Doubleday (U.S.), 1978 . . . . £15/£5
Put on by Cunning, Hutchinson, 1981 . . £50/£5
ditto, as *Death Notes*, Pantheon (U.S.), 1981 £10/£5
The Speaker of Mandarin, Hutchinson, 1983 £30/£5
ditto, Pantheon (U.S), 1983 . . . . . £10/£5
An Unkindness of Ravens, Hutchinson, 1985 £25/£5
ditto, Pantheon (U.S.), 1985 . . . . . £10/£5
The Veiled One, Hutchinson, 1988 . . . £20/£5

ditto, Pantheon (U.S.), 1988 . . . . . £10/£5
Kissing the Gunner's Daughter, Hutchinson, 1992 .
. . . . £15/£5
ditto, Warner (U.S.), 1992 . . . . £10/£5
Simisola, Hutchinson, 1994 . . . . £15/£5
ditto, Crown (U.S.), 1995 . . . . . . £10/£5
Road Rage, Hutchinson, 1997 . . . . £15/£5
ditto, Scorpion Press, 1997 (99 signed copies) . £75

Omnibus Editions
A Wexford Omnibus, Hutchinson, 1988 . £15/£5
A Second Wexford Omnibus, Hutchinson, 1989 . .
. . . . £10/£5
The Third Wexford Omnibus, Hutchinson, 1989 . .
. . . .£10/£5
The Fourth Wexford Omnibus, Hutchinson, 1990. .
. . . . £10/£5
Wexford Omnibus 5, Hutchinson, 1991 . . £10/£5

Other Novels
To Fear a Painted Devil, Long, 1965 . . £750/£100
ditto, Doubleday (U.S.), 1965 . . . £150/£15
Vanity Dies Hard, Long, 1965 . . . . £650/£45
ditto, as **In Sickness and in Health**, Doubleday (U.S.),
1966 . . . . £100/£15
The Secret House of Death, Long, 1968 . £750/£45
ditto, Doubleday (U.S.), 1969 . . . £100/£15
One Across, Two Down, Hutchinson, 1971 . £350/£25
ditto, Doubleday (U.S.), 1971 . . . . £50/£10
The Face of Trespass, Hutchinson, 1974 . £150/£15
ditto, Doubleday (U.S.), 1974 . . . . £25/£10
A Demon in My View, Hutchinson, 1976 . £75/£15
ditto, Doubleday (U.S.), 1977 . . . . £25/£10
A Judgement in Stone, Hutchinson, 1977 . £35/£10
ditto, Doubleday (U.S.), 1978 . . . . £10/£5
Make Death Love Me, Hutchinson, 1979 . £30/£10
ditto, Doubleday (U.S.), 1979 . . . . £10/£5
The Lake of Darkness, Hutchinson, 1980 . £25/£10
ditto, Doubleday (U.S.), 1980 . . . . £10/£5
Master of the Moor, Hutchinson, 1981 . . £20/£5
ditto, Pantheon (U.S.), 1982 . . . . £10/£5
The Killing Doll, Hutchinson, 1984 . . . £20/£5
ditto, Pantheon (U.S.), 1984 . . . . £10/£5
The Tree of Hands, Hutchinson, 1984 . . £20/£5
ditto, Pantheon (U.S.), 1985 . . . . £10/£5
Live Flesh, Hutchinson, 1986 . . . . £20/£5
ditto, Pantheon (U.S.), 1986 . . . . . £10/£5
A Dark Adapted Eye, Viking, 1986 (pseud. 'Barbara
Vine') . . . . £20/£5
ditto, Bantam (U.S.), 1986 . . . . . £5
A Warning to the Curious, Hutchinson, 1987 £20/£5
A Fatal Inversion, Viking, 1987 (pseud. 'Barbara
Vine') . . . . £15/£5
ditto, Bantam (U.S.), 1987 . . . . . £5
Heartstones, Hutchinson, 1987 . . . . £15/£5
ditto, Harper (U.S.), 1987 . . . . . £10/£5
Talking to Strange Men, Hutchinson, 1987 . £15/£5
ditto, Harper (U.S.), 1987 . . . . . £10/£5

The House of Stairs, Viking, 1989 (pseud. 'Barbara
Vine') . . . . £15/£5
ditto, Crown (U.S.), 1989 . . . . . £10/£5
The Bridesmaid, Hutchinson, 1989 . . £15/£5
ditto, Mysterious Press (U.S.), 1989 . . . £10/£5
Gallowglass, Viking, 1990 (pseud. 'Barbara Vine') .
. . . . £15/£5
ditto, Crown (U.S.), 1990 . . . . . £10/£5
Going Wrong, Hutchinson, 1990. . . £15/£5
ditto, Mysterious Press (U.S.), 1990 . . . £10/£5
King Solomon's Carpet, Viking, 1991 (pseud. 'Barbara
Vine') . . . . £15/£5
ditto, Crown (U.S.), 1992 . . . . . £10/£5
Asta's Book, Viking, 1993 (pseud. 'Barbara Vine') .
. . . . £15/£5
ditto, Scorpion Press, 1993 (99 signed copies) . £75
The Crocodile Bird, Hutchinson, 1993 . . £10/£5
ditto, London Limited Editions, 1993 (150 signed
copies, glassine d/w) . . . . . . £75/£65
ditto, Crown (U.S.), 1993 . . . . . £10/£5
No Night is Too Long, Viking, 1994 . . £10/£5
ditto, Harmony (U.S.), 1994 . . . . . £10/£5
The Brimstone Wedding, Harmony (U.S.), 1995
(pseud. 'Barbara Vine') . . . . . £10/£5
ditto, Viking, 1996 . . . . £10/£5
The Keys to the Street, Hutchinson, 1996 . £10/£5
ditto, Crown (U.S.), 1996 . . . . . . £10/£5
The Chimney Sweeper's Boy, Viking, 1998 £10/£5
ditto, Harmony (U.S.), 1998 . . . . . £10/£5
A Sight for Sore Eyes, Hutchinson, 1998 . £10/£5
ditto, Crown (U.S.), 1998 . . . . . . £10/£5
ditto, Scorpion Press, 1998 (99 signed copies) . £75
Grasshopper, Harmony (U.S.), 2000 (pseud. 'Barbara
Vine') . . . . £10/£5
ditto, Viking, 2000 . . . . £10/£5

Short Stories
The Fallen Curtain and Other Stories, Hutchinson,
1976 . . . . £100/£25
ditto, Doubleday (U.S.), 1976 . . . . £50/£15
Means of Evil and Other Stories, Hutchinson, 1979 .
. . . . £30/£10
The Fever Tree and Other Stories, Hutchinson, 1982 .
. . . . £40/£10
ditto, Pantheon (U.S.), 1983 . . . . £20/£5
The New Girlfriend and Other Stories, Hutchinson,
1985 . . . . £20/£5
ditto, Pantheon (U.S.), 1986 . . . . £10/£5
Three Cases for Inspector Wexford, Eurographica
(Helsinki), 1986 (350 signed copies, wraps) . £75
Collected Short Stories, Hutchinson, 1987 . £10/£5
ditto, Pantheon (U.S.), 1988 . . . . . £10/£5
The Copper Peacock and Other Stories, Hutchinson,
1991 . . . . £15/£5
ditto, Mysterious Press (U.S.), 1991 . . . £10/£5
Blood Lines, Hutchinson, 1995 . . . £10/£5
ditto, Crown (U.S.), 1996 . . . . . . £10/£5

Non Fiction
Matters of Suspense, Eurographica (Helsinki), 1986
(350 signed copies, wraps) £75
Ruth Rendell's Suffolk, Muller, 1989 . . £25/£5
Undermining the Central Line, Chatto & Windus,
1989 (with Colin Ward, signed, wraps) . . £35
ditto, Chatto & Windus, 1989 (unsigned copies) £10

JEAN RHYS
(b.1890 d.1979)

Powerfully clear and imaginative writing peoples
Rhys's novels with strong female characters, although
the protagonists are often lonely and lacking in
direction.

Novels
Postures, Chatto & Windus, 1928 . . £1,000/£100
ditto, as Quartet, Simon & Schuster, 1929 . £750/£75
After Leaving Mr Mackenzie, Cape, 1931 . £600/£75
ditto, Knopf (U.S.), 1931 . . . . . £400/£45
Voyage in the Dark, Constable, 1934 . . £500/£65
ditto, Morrow (U.S.), 1935 . . . . . £400/£45
Good Morning, Midnight, Constable, 1939. £400/£50
ditto, Harper & Row (U.S.), [1970] . . . £20/£5
Wide Sargasso Sea, Deutsch, 1966 . . £75/£15
ditto, Norton (U.S.), 1966. . . . . £45/£5

Short Stories
The Left Bank and Other Stories, Cape, 1927 .
. . . . £600/£75
ditto, Harper (U.S.), 1927. . . . . £400/£50
Tigers Are Better Looking, Deutsch, 1968 . £50/£15
ditto, Harper (U.S.), 1974. . . . . £15/£5
Sleep It Off Lady, Deutsch, 1976 . . £15/£5
ditto, Harper (U.S.), 1976. . . . . £15/£5

Translation
Perversity, by Francis Carco, Covici (U.S.), 1928
(translation credited to Ford Madox Ford but in fact
Jean Rhys). . . . . . . £500/£100

Others
My Day, Three Pieces, Frank Hallman (U.S.), 1975
(wraps) £10
ditto, Frank Hallman (U.S.), 1975 (750 copies)£65/£30
ditto, Frank Hallman (U.S.), 1975 (26 signed, lettered
copies) £175
Letters, 1931-1966, Deutsch, 1984 . . £15/£5
ditto, Viking (U.S.), 1984. . . . . £15/£5
Smile Please, An Unfinished Biography, Deutsch,
1979 . . . . £15/£5
ditto, Harper (U.S.), 1980. . . . . £15/£5

ANNE RICE
(b.1941)

Interview with the Vampire started life as a cult bestseller and found itself two decades later as a
Hollywood film.

The Vampire Chronicles
Interview with the Vampire, Knopf (U.S.), 1976 . .
. . . . £600/£45
ditto, Knopf/Borzoi (U.S.), 1976 (full leather edition) .
. . . . £200
ditto, Macdonald/Raven Books, 1976 . . £150/£15
The Vampire Lestat, Knopf (U.S.), 1985 . £150/£35
ditto, Futura Books, 1986 (wraps) . . . £5
ditto, Macdonald, 1987 (first hardback) . . £45/£10
The Queen of the Damned, Knopf (U.S.), 1988 . .
. . . . £45/£10
ditto, Ultramarine Press (U.S.), 1988 (150 signed,
numbered copies) £250
ditto, Macdonald, 1988 . . . . . £45/£10
The Tale of the Body Thief, Knopf (U.S.), 1992 .
. . . . £25/£5
ditto, Chatto & Windus, 1992 . . . . £20/£5
Memnoch the Devil, Knopf (U.S.), 1995 . £15/£5
ditto, Trice (U.S.), 1995 (26 signed, lettered copies) .
. . . . £250
ditto, Trice (U.S.), 1995 (50 signed copies in full
leather). £200
ditto, Trice (U.S.), 1995 (425 signed, numbered
copies). £100
ditto, Chatto & Windus, 1995 . . . . £15/£5
Pandora, Knopf (U.S.), 1998. . . . . £10/£5
ditto, Trice (U.S.), 1998 (26 signed, lettered copies,
bound in full leather) £500
ditto, Trice (U.S.), 1998 (50 signed, deluxe copies,
quarterbound in leather). £200
ditto, Trice (U.S.), 1998 (250 signed, numbered copies)
. . . . £75
ditto, Chatto & Windus, 1998 . . . . £10/£5
The Vampire Armand, Knopf (U.S.), 1998 . £10/£5
ditto, Trice (U.S.), 1998 (26 signed, lettered copies,
bound in full leather) £500
ditto, Trice (U.S.), 1998 (50 signed, deluxe copies,
quarterbound in leather). £200
ditto, Trice (U.S.), 1998 (250 signed, numbered copies)
. . . . £75
ditto, Chatto & Windus, 1998 . . . . £10/£5
Vittorio the Vampire, Knopf (U.S.), 1999 . £10/£5
ditto, Trice (U.S.), 1999 (250 signed, numbered copies)
. . . . £75
ditto, Franklin Library (U.S.), 1999 (signed copies) £35
ditto, Chatto & Windus, 1999 . . . . £10/£5
Merrick, Franklin Library (U.S.), 2000 (signed copies)
. . . . £35
ditto, Knopf (U.S.), 2000 . . . . . £10/£5
ditto, Chatto & Windus, 2000 . . . £10/£5

The Witch Chronicles
The Witching Hour, Knopf (U.S.), 1990 . £20/£5
ditto, Chatto & Windus, 1991 . . . . £15/£5
Lasher, Knopf (U.S.), 1993 . . . . £20/£5
ditto, Chatto & Windus, 1993 . . . . £15/£5
Taltos, Lives of the Mayfair Witches, Knopf (U.S.),
1994 . . . . £20/£5
ditto, Trice (U.S.), 1994 (500 signed, numbered
copies). £200
ditto, Chatto & Windus, 1994 . . . £15/£5

Ghost Novels
Servant of the Bones, Knopf (U.S.), 1996 . £50/£5
ditto, Trice (U.S.), 1996 (26 signed, lettered copies) .
. . . . £250
ditto, Trice (U.S.), 1996 (50 signed copies in full
leather) £200
ditto, Trice (U.S.), 1996 (425 signed, numbered copies)
. . . . £100
ditto, Chatto & Windus, 1996 . . . £30/£5
Violin, Chatto & Windus, 1997 . . . £45/£10
ditto, Trice (U.S.), 1997 (26 signed, lettered copies) .
. . . . £250
ditto, Trice (U.S.), 1997 (50 signed copies in full
leather) £200
ditto, Trice (U.S.), 1997 (325 signed, numbered copies)
. . . . £100
ditto, Knopf (U.S.), 1997 . . . . . £45/£10

Historical Novels
The Feast of All Saints, Simon & Schuster (U.S.),
1979 . . . . £100/£25
ditto, Arrow, 1991 (wraps) £5
Cry to Heaven, Knopf (U.S.), 1982 . . £60/£10
ditto, Chatto & Windus, 1990 . . . £40/£10
The Mummy, or Ramses the Damned, Ballantine
Books (U.S.), 1989 . . . . . . £150/£25
ditto, Ballantine Books (U.S.), 1989 (wraps) . £10
ditto, Chatto & Windus, 1989 . . . £150/£25

Novels as Anne Rampling
Exit to Eden, Arbor House (U.S.), 1985. . £65/£15
ditto, Macdonald, 1986 . . . . £45/£10
Belinda, Arbor House (U.S.), 1986 . . . £40/£10
ditto, Macdonald, 1987 . . . . . £25/£5

Novels as A.N. Roquelaure
The Claiming of Sleeping Beauty, Dutton (U.S.), 1983
. . . . £150/£35
ditto, Future Books, 1987 (wraps) . . . £5
ditto, Macdonald, 1988 . . . . . £25/£5
Beauty's Punishment, Dutton (U.S.), 1984 . £200/£35
ditto, Futura Books, 1987 (wraps) . . . £10
Beauty's Release, Dutton (U.S.), 1985 . £125/£35
ditto, Future Books, 1988 (wraps) . . . £10

FRANK RICHARDS
(b.1876 d.1961)

Under the pseudonym of 'Frank Richards', Charles
Hamilton created the everlasting, rotund schoolboy,
Billy Bunter.

Billy Bunter of Greyfriars School, Skilton, 1947 . .
. . £75/£15
Billy Bunter's Banknote, Skilton, 1948 . £60/£10
Billy Bunter's Barring-Out, Skilton, 1948 . £50/£10
Billy Bunter's Christmas Party, Skilton, 1949 £50/£10
Billy Bunter in Brazil, Skilton, 1949 . . £50/£10
Bessie Bunter of Cliff House School, Skilton, 1949
(pseud. 'Hilda Richards') . . . . £45/£10
Billy Bunter's Benefit, Skilton, 1950 . . £50/£10
Billy Bunter among the Cannibals, Skilton, 1950 . .
. . £45/£10
Billy Bunter's Postal Order, Skilton, 1951 . £45/£10
Billy Bunter Butts In, Skilton, 1951 . . . £45/£10
Billy Bunter and the Blue Mauritius, Skilton, 1952 .
. . £50/£10
Billy Bunter's Beanfeast, Cassell, 1952 . £45/£10
Billy Bunter's Brain-Wave, Cassell, 1953 . £45/£10
Billy Bunter's First Case, Cassell, 1953 . £45/£10
Billy Bunter the Bold, Cassell, 1954 . . £30/£5
Bunter Does His Best, Cassell, 1954 . . £30/£5
Billy Bunter's Double, Cassell, 1955 . . £30/£5
Backing Up Billy Bunter, Cassell, 1955 . £30/£5
Lord Billy Bunter, Cassell, 1956 . . . £25/£5
The Banishing of Billy Bunter, Cassell, 1956 £25/£5
Billy Bunter's Bolt, Cassell, 1957 . . . £25/£5
Billy Bunter Afloat, Cassell, 1957 . . £25/£5
Billy Bunter's Bargain, Cassell, 1958 . . £20/£5
Billy Bunter the Hiker, Cassell, 1958 . . £20/£5
Bunter Out of Bounds, Cassell, 1959 . . £20/£5
Bunter Comes for Christmas, Cassell, 1959 £20/£5
Bunter the Bad Lad, Cassell, 1960 . . . £20/£5
Bunter Keeps It Dark, Cassell, 1960 . . £20/£5
Billy Bunter's Treasure-Hunt, Cassell, 1961 £20/£5
Billy Bunter at Butlins, Cassell, 1961 . . £20/£5
ditto, Butlins Beaver Club edition, 1961 . £15/£5
Bunter the Ventriloquist, Cassell, 1961 . £20/£5
Bunter the Caravanner, Cassell, 1962 . . £20/£5
Billy Bunter's Bodyguard, Cassell, 1962 . £20/£5
Big Chief Bunter, Cassell, 1963 . . . £20/£5
Just Like Bunter, Cassell, 1963 . . . . £20/£5
Bunter the Stowaway, Cassell, 1964 . . £20/£5
Thanks to Bunter, Cassell, 1964 . . . . £20/£5
Bunter the Sportsman, Cassell, 1965 . . £20/£5
Bunter's Last Fling, Cassell, 1965 . . . £20/£5

W. HEATH ROBINSON
(b.1872 d.1944)

A British author and illustrator, Robinson did not find his own distinctive style until *The Adventures of Uncle Lubin*. He is popularly known for his illustrations of preposterous inventions.

Written and Illustrated by Heath Robinson

The Adventures of Uncle Lubin, Grant Richards, 1902
. . . . £1,000
ditto, Grant Richards, 1925 (new edition) . £100/£35
The Child's Arabian Nights, Grant Richards, 1903
. . . . £300
Bill the Minder, Constable, 1912 . . . . £450
ditto, Constable, 1912 (380 signed copies bound in vellum) £1,250
ditto, Holt (U.S.), 1912 . . . . . . £400
Peter Quip in Search of a Friend, S.W. Partridge [1922]. £1,000
Some Frightful War Pictures, Duckworth, 1915 £150
ditto, Duckworth, 1915 (wraps) £150
Hunlikely, Duckworth, 1916 . . . . . £150
The Saintly Hun, Duckworth, [1917] (wraps) . £150
Flypapers, Duckworth, 1919 (wraps) . . . £175
Get On With It, Duckworth, [1920] (with J. Birch, wraps) £200
A Jamboree of Laughter, Jones, [1920] (wraps) £150
The Home Made Car, Duckworth, [1921] (wraps). .
. . . . £150
Motor Mania, The Motor Owner, [1921] (wraps) . .
. . . . £175
Quaint and Selected Pictures, Duckworth, [1922] (with J. Birch, wraps) £200
Humours of Golf, Methuen, [1925] (pictorial boards) .
. . . . £250
The Heath Robinson Calendar, Delgardo, 1933-36 .
. . . . £75 each
Absurdities, Hutchinson, [1934] £150
ditto, Hutchinson, [1934] (deluxe edition) . . £250
ditto, Hutchinson, [1934] (250 signed copies) . £400
Railway Ribaldry, G.W.R., 1935 (wraps) . . £100
My Line of Life, Blackie, 1938 . . . . £150/£60
Let's Laugh, A Book of Humorous Inventions, Hutchinson, [1939] . . . . £75/£25
Heath Robinson at War, Methuen, 1942 . £200/£75
The Penguin Heath Robinson, Penguin, 1966 (wraps)
. . . . £10
Inventions, Duckworth, 1973 . . . . . £15/£5
The Gentle Art of Advertising, Duckworth, 1979 . .
. . . . £15/£5
Great British Industries, Duckworth, 1985 . £10/£5

Illustrated by Heath Robinson

Danish Fairy Tales and Legends, by H. C. Andersen, Bliss Sands & Co., 1897. . . . . . £100
The Life and Exploits of Don Quixote, by Cervantes, Bliss Sands & Co., 1897. . . . . . £100

The Pilgrim's Progress, by John Bunyan, Bliss Sands & Co., 1897 . . . . £60
The Giant Crab and Other Tales from Old India, by W.H.D. Rouse, Nutt, 1897 . . . . . £350
The Queen's Story Book, edited by L. Gomme, Constable, 1898 . . . . £60
The Arabian Nights Entertainments, Newnes/ Constable, 1899 . . . . £100
Fairy Tales from Hans Christian Andersen, Dent, 1899 . . . . £150
The Talking Thrush, by W.H.D. Rouse, Dent, 1899 .
. . . . £300
The Poems of Edgar Allan Poe, Bell, 1900. . £250
ditto, Bell, 1900 (75 copies on Japanese vellum) £750
Tales for Toby, by A.R. Hope, Dent, 1900 . . £45
The Adventures of Don Quixote, by Cervantes, Dent, 1902 . . . . £75
Mediaeval Stories, by H. Schuck, Sands, 1902 . £65
The Surprising Travels and Adventures of Baron Munchausen, by R.E. Raspe, Grant Richards, 1902 .
. . . . £150
Tales from Shakespeare, by C. and M. Lamb, Sands, [1902]. £100
Rama and the Monkeys, edited by G Hodgson, Dent, 1903 . . . . £100
The Works of Mr Francis Rabelais, Grant Richards, 1904 (2 vols) £250
Stories from Chaucer, edited by J.H. Kelman, Jack [1905] £25
Two Memoirs of Barry Lydon and Men's Wives, by W.M. Thackeray, Caxton, [1906] £65
Stories from the Iliad, edited by Jeanie Lang, Jack [1906]. £25
Stories from the Odyssey, edited by Jeanie Lang, Jack [1906]. £25
The Monarchs of Merry England, by Roland Carse, Alf Cooke [1907] (4 vols, wraps) £200
More Monarchs of Merry England, by Roland Carse, T. Fisher Unwin [1908] £175
Twelfth Night, by W. Shakespeare, Hodder & Stoughton [1908] £200
ditto, Hodder & Stoughton [1908] (350 signed copies, bound in vellum). £650
A Song of the English, by Rudyard Kipling, Hodder & Stoughton, [c.1909] (30 colour plates). . . £100
ditto, Hodder & Stoughton, [c.1909] (deluxe edition, 500 copies signed by the artist, 30 colour plates, full vellum) £250
ditto, Hodder & Stoughton, [1912], (12 colour plates) .
. . . . £45
ditto, Hodder & Stoughton/Daily Telegraph, [1915] (16 colour plates). £65
ditto, Hodder & Stoughton, [1919] (16 colour plates) .
. . . . £45
The Collected Verse of Rudyard Kipling, Doubleday Page (U.S.), 1910 (9 colour plates). . . . £100
ditto, Doubleday Page (U.S.), 1910 (125 signed copies)
. . . . £750

The Dead King, by Rudyard Kipling, Hodder & Stoughton, 1910 . . . . £50
ditto, Hodder & Stoughton, 1910 (wraps) . . £30
Hans Andersen's Fairy Tales, Constable, 1913 £500
ditto, Constable, 1913 (100 signed copies, bound in vellum) £1,750
A Midsummer Night's Dream, by W. Shakespeare, Constable, 1914 . . . . . . £350
ditto, Constable, 1914 (150 of 250 signed copies bound in green boards) £1,250
ditto, Constable, 1914 (100 of 250 copies bound in vellum) £2,000
The Water Babies, by Charles Kingsley, Constable, 1915 . . . . £100
ditto, Houghton Mifflin (U.S.), 1915 . . . £75
Peacock Pie, by Walter de la Mare, Constable, 1916 . . . . £75
ditto, Holt (U.S.), 1924 . . . . . £100/£20
Old Time Stories, by C. Perrault, Constable, 1921 . . . . £300/£200
Topsy Turvey Tales, by E.S. Munro, John Lane, 1923 . . . . £300/£150
The Incredible Adventures of Professor Branestawm, by Norman Hunter, John Lane, 1933 . £250/£75
Balbus, A Latin Reading Book, by G.M. Lyne, E. Arnold, 1934 . . . . £75/£25
Heath Robinson's Book of Goblins, Hutchinson [1934]. . . . . £400/£200
Once Upon A Time, by L.M.C. Clopet, Muller, 1934 . . . . £250/£125
How to Live in a Flat, by K.R.G. Browne, Hutchinson, [1936]. . . . . . . £125/£35
How to be a Perfect Husband, by K.R.G. Browne, Hutchinson, [1937] . . . . . £125/£35
How to Make a Garden Grow, by K.R.G. Browne, Hutchinson, [1938] . . . . . £125/£35
How to be a Motorist, by K.R.G. Browne, Hutchinson, [1939]. . . . . . . £125/£35
Mein Rant, by Richard F. Patterson, Blackie, 1940 . . . . £100/£30
How to make the Best of Things, by Cecil Hunt, Hutchinson, [1940] . . . . . . £75/£20
How to Build a New World, by Cecil Hunt, Hutchinson, [1941] . . . . . . £75/£20
How to Run a Communal Home, by Cecil Hunt, Hutchinson, [1943] . . . . . . £75/£20

SAX ROHMER
(b.1886 d.1959)

Rohmer was the pseudonym for Arthur Ward. Many of his exotic thrillers follow the devilish exploits of the sinister Dr Fu Manchu.

Fu Manchu Novels
The Mystery of Fu Manchu, Methuen, 1913 £300

ditto, as *The Insidious Dr Fu Manchu*, McBride (U.S.), 1913 . . . . £150
The Return of Dr Fu Manchu, McBride (U.S.), 1916 . . . . £150
ditto, as *The Devil Doctor*, Methuen, 1916 . £125
The Si-Fan Mysteries, Methuen, 1917 . . £100
ditto, as *The Hand of Fu Manchu*, McBride (U.S.), 1917 . . . . £100
The Daughter of Fu Manchu, Crime Club (U.S.), 1931 . . . . £250/£35
ditto, Cassell, 1931 . . . . . . £250/£35
The Mask of Fu Manchu, Crime Club (U.S.), 1932 . . . . £500/£100
ditto, Cassell, 1933 . . . . . . £500/£100
Fu Manchu's Bride, Crime Club (U.S.), 1933 . . . . £400/£75
ditto, as *The Bride of Fu Manchu* Cassell, 1933 . . . . £400/£75
The Trail of Fu Manchu, Crime Club (U.S.), 1934 . . . . £200/£25
ditto, Cassell, 1934 . . . . . . £400/£30
President Fu Manchu, Crime Club (U.S.), 1936 . . . . £200/£25
ditto, Cassell, 1936 . . . . . . £250/£25
The Drums of Fu Manchu, Crime Club (U.S.), 1939 . . . . £350/£75
ditto, Cassell, 1939 . . . . . . £350/£75
The Island of Fu Manchu, Crime Club (U.S.), 1941 . . . . £750/£35
ditto, Cassell, 1941 . . . . . . £750/£35
Shadow of Fu Manchu, Crime Club (U.S.), 1948 . . . . £200/£30
ditto, Jenkins, 1949 . . . . . . £300/£30
Re-Enter Dr Fu Manchu, Fawcett (U.S.), 1957 (wraps) £20
ditto, Herbert Jenkins, 1957 . . . . £300/£20
Emperor Fu Manchu, Herbert Jenkins, 1959 £150/£20
ditto, Fawcett (U.S.), 1959 (wraps) £20
The Wrath of Fu Manchu, Tom Stacey, 1973 £65/£15
ditto, Daw (U.S.), 1975 (wraps) £10

Omnibus Editions
The Book of Fu Manchu, Hurst & Blackett, 1929 . . . . £500/£100
ditto, McBride (U.S.), 1929 (different contents) . . . . £500/£100
The Golden Scorpion Omnibus, Grosset & Dunlap (U.S.), 1938 . . . . £100/£25
The Sax Rohmer Omnibus, Grosset & Dunlap (U.S.), 1938 . . . . £100/£25

Other Novels
10.30 Folkestone Express, Lloyds Home Novels No. 41 [no date] £1,000
The Sins of Severac Bablon, Cassell, 1914 . £150
ditto, Bookfinger (U.S.), 1967 (no d/w) . . . £20
The Yellow Claw, McBride (U.S.), 1915 . . £30
ditto, Methuen, 1915 . . . . £45
Brood of the Witch Queen, Pearson, 1918 . . £50

ditto, Doubleday (U.S.), 1924 . . . . . £30
The Orchard of Tears, Methuen, 1919 . . . £75
ditto, Bookfinger (U.S.), 1970 (no d/w) . . . £20
The Quest of the Sacred Slipper, Pearson, 1919 £40
ditto, Doubleday (U.S.), 1919 . . . . . £40
Dope, Cassell, 1919 . . . . £35
ditto, McBride (U.S.), 1919 . . . . . £35
The Golden Scorpion, Methuen, 1919 . . . £35
ditto, McBride (U.S.), 1920 . . . . £600/£35
The Green Eyes of Bast, Cassell, 1920 . £500/£30
ditto, McBride (U.S.), 1920 . . . . £400/£30
Bat-Wing, Cassell, 1921 . . . . . £200/£30
ditto, as **Bat Wing**, Doubleday (U.S.), 1921. £200/£30
Fire-Tongue, Cassell, 1921 . . . . £500/£30
ditto, Doubleday (U.S.), 1922 . . . . £500/£30
Grey Face, Cassell, 1924 . . . . . £200/£30
ditto, Doubleday (U.S.), 1924 . . . £200/£30
Yellow Shadows, Cassell, 1925 . . . £250/£40
ditto, Doubleday (U.S.), 1926 . . . £250/£40
Moon of Madness, Doubleday (U.S.), 1927 £250/£40
ditto, Cassell, 1927 . . . . . . £250/£40
She Who Sleeps, Doubleday (U.S.), 1928 . £250/£40
ditto, Cassell, 1928 . . . . . . £250/£40
The Emperor of America, Crime Club (U.S.), 1929 .
. . . . £300/£50
ditto, Cassell, 1929 . . . . . . £300/£50
The Day the World Ended, Crime Club (U.S.), 1930 .
. . . . £250/£40
ditto, Cassell, 1930 . . . . . . £250/£40
Yu'an Hee See Laughs, Crime Club (U.S.), 1932 .
. . . . £250/£40
ditto, Cassell, 1932 . . . . . . £250/£40
The Bat Flies Low, Crime Club (U.S.), 1935 £300/£50
ditto, Cassell, 1935 . . . . . . £300/£50
White Velvet, Doubleday (U.S.), 1936 . . £250/£40
ditto, Cassell, 1936 . . . . . . £250/£40
Seven Sins, McBride (U.S.), 1943 . . . £150/£35
ditto, Cassell, 1944 . . . . . . £150/£35
Hangover House, Random House (U.S.), 1914 . .
. . . . £125/£20
ditto, Herbert Jenkins, 1950 . . . . . £125/£20
Nude in Mink, Fawcett (U.S.), 1950 (wraps) . £25
ditto, as **Sins of Sumuru**, Herbert Jenkins, 1951 . .
. . . . £125/£20
ditto, Bookfinger (U.S.), 1977 (no d/w) . . . £20
Sinister Madonna, Fawcett (U.S.), 1950 (wraps) £20
ditto, Herbert Jenkins, 1956 . . . . . £125/£20
Wulfheim, Jarrolds, 1950 (pseud. 'Michael Furey') .
. . . . £150/£35
ditto, Bookfinger (U.S.), 1972 (no d/w) . . . £20
Samura, Fawcett (U.S.), 1951 (wraps) . . . £20
ditto, as **Slaves of Sumuru**, Herbert Jenkins, 1952
(different ending) . . . . . . £125/£20
ditto, Bookfinger (U.S.), 1979 (no d/w) . . . £20
Fire Goddess, Fawcett (U.S.), 1952 (wraps) . £25
ditto, as **Virgin in Flames**, Herbert Jenkins, 1953 . .
. . . . £125/£20
ditto, Bookfinger (U.S.), 1978 (no d/w) . . . £20
The Moon is Red, Herbert Jenkins, 1954 . £125/£20

ditto, Bookfinger (U.S.), 1976 (no d/w) . . . £20
Return of Samura, Fawcett (U.S.), 1954 (wraps) £20
ditto, as **Sand and Satin**, Herbert Jenkins, 1955 . .
. . . . £125/£20
ditto, Bookfinger (U.S.), 1978 (no d/w) . . . £20

Short Stories
The Exploits of Captain O'Hagan, Jarrolds, 1916 . .
. . . . £400
ditto, Bookfinger (U.S.), 1968 (no d/w) . . . £20
Tales of Secret Egypt, Methuen, 1918 . . . £350
ditto, McBride (U.S.), 1919 . . . . . £300
The Dream Detective, Jarrolds, 1920 . £750/£200
ditto, Doubleday (U.S.), 1925 . . . £500/£100
The Haunting of Low Fennel, Pearson, 1920 . . .
. . . . £750/£125
Tales of Chinatown, Cassell, 1922 . . . £650/£75
ditto, Doubleday (U.S.), 1922 . . . £650/£75
Tales of East and West, Cassell, 1932 . £350/£75
ditto, Crime Club (U.S.), 1933 . . . £200/£25
Salute to Bazarada, Cassell, 1939 . . £125/£25
Egyptian Nights, Hale, 1944 (text presented as novel) .
. . . . £125/£25
ditto, as **Bim-Bashi Baruk of Egypt**, McBride (U.S.),
1944 (text presented as short stories) . £125/£25
The Secret of Holm Peel, and Other Strange Stories,
Ace (U.S.) 1970 (wraps) £10

Non Fiction Titles
Pause!, Greening, 1910 (anonymous) . . . £500
Little Tich, Greening, 1911 . . . . . £500
The Romance of Sorcery, Methuen, 1914 . . £400
ditto, Dutton (U.S.), 1915 . . . . . . £300

FREDERICK ROLFE
(BARON CORVO)
(b.1860 d.1913)

The author of a number of almost indigestible semi-
autobiographical novels, Rolfe had an unbelievably
self-destructive paranoia. He is read for his Toto tales
and for the minor classic *Hadrian the Seventh*. Sadly,
he only really reached the level of genius in his
vituperative letters to self-created enemies.

Tarcissus: The Boy Martyr of Rome, privately printed,
1880 [1881] (wraps) £2,000
Stories Toto Told Me, Bodley Head, 1898 (wraps) . .
. . . . £300
The Attack on St. Winefride's Well, privately printed
[1898] (anonymous, wraps) £500
In His Own Image, Bodley Head, 1901 (first printing
with 1 advert leaf at end) £100
ditto, Knopf (U.S.), 1925 . . . . . £65/£20
Chronicles of the House of Borgia, Grant Richards,
1901 . . . . £200

ditto, Dutton (U.S.), 1901. . . . . . . £150

Hadrian the Seventh, Chatto & Windus, 1904 (first issue purple cloth with title and drawing stamped in white) £250

ditto, Chatto & Windus, 1904 (second issue with title and drawing blind stamped). £200

ditto, Knopf (U.S.), 1925 . . . . . £75/£20

Don Tarquinio, Chatto & Windus, 1905 (first binding violet cloth) £100

ditto, Chatto & Windus, 1905 (second binding red cloth) £100

Don Renato, An Ideal Content, Francis Griffiths, 1909 . . . . £400

ditto, Chatto & Windus, 1963 (200 large paper copies in slipcase) . . . . £125/£75

ditto, Chatto & Windus, 1963 . . . . £40/£15

The Weird of the Wanderer, by Prospero and Caliban, William Rider, 1912. . . . . . . £250

The Bull Against the Enemy of the Anglican Race, Corvine Society, 1929 (50 copies, wraps) . . £200

Hubert's Arthur, by Prospero and Caliban, Cassell, 1935 . . . . £175/£50

The Desire and Pursuit of the Whole, Cassell [1934] (first binding, dark green cloth) . . £175/£65

ditto, Cassell [1934] (second binding, light green cloth, no d/w) £25

ditto, New Directions (U.S.), 1953 . . . £15/£5

Three Tales of Venice, The Corvine Press [1950] (150 numbered copies) £300

Amico di Sandro, A Fragment of a Novel, The Peacocks Press, 1951 (150 numbered copies) £350

Letters to Grant Richards, The Peacocks Press, 1951 (200 numbered copies, no d/w) £200

The Cardinal Prefect of Propaganda, Nicholas Vane, 1957 (262 copies) £150

Nicholas Crabbe, Chatto & Windus, 1958 . £35/£10

ditto, Chatto & Windus, 1958 (215 numbered, large paper copies in slipcase). . . . . £125/£100

ditto, New Directions (U.S.), 1958 . . . £15/£5

The Centenary Edition of the Letters of Frederick William Rolfe, Nicholas Vane, 1959 . . . £200

Letters to Pirie Gordon and Leonard Moore, Nicholas Vane, 1959-60 (350 copies, 2 vols) . . £200

A Letter to Father Beauclerk, Tragara Press (Edinburgh), 1960 (20 copies) £200

Letters to Leonard Moore, Cecil & Amelia Woolf, 1960 (260 numbered copies) £100

Letters of Baron Corvo to Kenneth Grahame, The Peacocks Press, 1962 (40 copies) . . . £200

Without Prejudice - One Hundred Letters from Frederick William Rolfe, Baron Corvo to John Lane, privately printed for Allen Lane, 1963 (600 copies) £150

A Letter to a Small Nephew Named Claude, Iowa City, 1964 (134 copies) £150

Letters to James Walsh, Bertram Rota, 1972 (500 copies) £75

Ballade of Boys Bathing, Tragara Press (Edinburgh), 1972 (200 numbered copies) £75

Collected Poems of Fr Rolfe, Baron Corvo, Cecil & Amelia Woolf, 1974 . . . . . . £20/£5

ditto, Cecil & Amelia Woolf, 1974 (200 numbered copies) £75

The Reverse Side of the Coin, Tragara Press (Edinburgh), 1974 (95 copies) £75

The Venice Letters, Cecil & Amelia Woolf, 1974 . . . . £100/£25

The Armed Hands, and Other Stories, Cecil & Amelia Woolf, 1974 . . . . £20/£5

ditto, Cecil & Amelia Woolf, 1974 (200 numbered copies) £75

Aberdeen Interval, Tragara Press (Edinburgh), 1975 (140 copies) £65

Different Aspects: Frederick William Rolfe and the Foreign Office, Tragara Press (Edinburgh), 1977 (125 copies) £50

Frederick Rolfe and 'The Times' 4-12 Feb, 1901, Tragara Press (Edinburgh), 1975 (175 copies) £45

Letters to Harry Bainbridge, Enitharmon Press, 1977 (350 of 395 copies) £40

ditto, Enitharmon Press, 1977 (45 numbered copies of 395) £150

Miscellaneous

The Rubaiyat of Umar Khaiyam, John Lane, 1903 (translated by Rolfe). £150

Agricultural and Pastoral Prospects of South Africa, by Col. Owen Thomas, Archibald Constable, 1904 (ghost-written by Rolfe) £100

J.K. ROWLING

Rowling's series of books about a young wizard, Harry Potter, is not only a modern publishing phenomenon in terms of the huge sales of her books, but because of the prices commanded by the first edition of her first title.

Harry Potter and the Philosopher's Stone, Bloomsbury, 1997 (laminated boards, no d/w, 500 copies) £15,000

ditto, Bloomsbury, 1997 (proofs, wraps, 200 copies) £4,000

ditto, Bloomsbury, 1999 (collector's edition, no d/w) £250

ditto, as **Harry Potter and the Sorcerer's Stone**, Levine/Scholastic (U.S.), 1998 . . £2,000/£1,500

ditto, Levine/Scholastic (U.S.), 2000 (collector's edition, no d/w) £75

Harry Potter and the Chamber of Secrets, Bloomsbury, 1998 . . . . £2,000/£1,500

ditto, Bloomsbury, 1999 (collector's edition, no d/w) £100

ditto, Levine/Scholastic (US), 1999 . . . £75/£25

Harry Potter and the Prisoner of Azkaban,
Bloomsbury, 1999 (first issue with 'Joanne Rowling'
on verso title page) . . . . . £2,000/£1,600
ditto, Bloomsbury, 1999 (collector's edition, no d/w) .
. . . . £1,500
ditto, Levine/Scholastic (US), 1999 . . . £40/£10
Harry Potter and the Goblet of Fire, Bloomsbury,
2000 . . . . £20/£5
ditto, Bloomsbury, 2000 (collector's edition, no d/w) .
. . . . £75
ditto, Levine/Scholastic (US), 2000 . . . £20/£5
ditto, Levine/Scholastic (US), 2000 (25 copies with
original artwork and certificate) . £2,000/£1,950

RUPERT
see Mary Tourtel

SALMAN RUSHDIE
(b.1947)

Salman Rushdie, purveyor of post-modernist pyro-
technics, was born in Bombay but migrated to Britain
in 1965. His writing is often described as *magic
realism*, and has brought him great literary respect.

Novels
Grimus, Gollancz, 1975 . . . . . £250/£35
ditto, Overlook Press (U.S.), 1979 . . . £150/£20
Midnight's Children, Knopf (U.S.), 1981 . £500/£35
ditto, Cape, 1981 . . . . £450/£45
Shame, Cape, 1983 . . . . . . £25/£10
ditto, Knopf (U.S.), 1983 . . . . . £25/£5
The Satanic Verses, Viking, 1988 . . . £75/£20
ditto, Viking, 1988 (100 arabic numbered copies) £500
ditto, Viking (U.S.), 1988 . . . . £35/£10
ditto, Penguin, 1988 (suppressed edition, wraps) £350
The Moor's Last Sigh, Cape, 1995 . . . £15/£5
ditto, Cape, 1995 (200 signed copies, no d/w) . £100
ditto, Cape, 1995 (2,500 copies in slipcase with
facsimilie signature) . . . . . . £65/£45
ditto, Pantheon (U.S.), 1995 . . . . £10/£5
ditto, Pantheon (U.S.), 1995 (1,000 signed advance
reading copies, wraps, in slipcase) . . . £75/£50
The Ground Beneath Her Feet, Cape, 1999 . £15/£5
ditto, Cape, 1999 (150 signed copies, full leather
bound, in slipcase) . . . . . . £200/£150
ditto, Holt (U.S.), 1999 . . . . . £10/£5

Children's
Haroun and the Sea of Stories, Granta, 1990 £15/£5
ditto, Granta, 1990 (251 signed copies) . . £150
ditto, Viking (U.S.), 1991 . . . . . £10/£5

Short Stories
Two Stories, privately printed, 1989 (60 signed copies
of 72) £750
ditto, privately printed, 1989 (12 specially bound,
signed copies of 72) £1,750
East, West, Cape, 1994 . . . . . £15/£5
ditto, Pantheon (U.S.), 1994 .. . . . £10/£5

Others
The Jaguar Smile: A Nicaraguan Journey, Picador,
1987 . . . . £10/£5
ditto, Viking (U.S.), 1987. . . . . £10/£5
Is Nothing Sacred?, Granta, 1990 . . . £10/£5
Imaginary Homelands: Essays and Criticism, Granta,
1991 . . . . £10/£5
ditto, Viking (U.S.), 1991. . . . . £10/£5
The Wizard of Oz, B.F.I., 1992 (wraps) . . . £15

VITA SACKVILLE-WEST
(b.1892 d.1962)

The Land brought Vita Sackville-West recognition,
winning her the Hawthornden prize. A writer of both
poetry and prose, she was also a passionate gardener.
It is said the she was the model for Virginia Woolf's
Orlando.

Novels
Heritage, Collins, 1919 . . . . . . £500/£75
ditto, Doran (U.S.), 1919 . . . . . £250/£45
The Dragon in Shallow Waters, Collins, 1921 .
. . . . £300/£125
Challenge, Doran (U.S.), 1923 . . . £250/£125
Grey Wethers, Heinemann, 1923. . . . £225/£65
Seducers in Equador, Hogarth Press, 1924 £200/£45
ditto, Doran (U.S.), 1925 . . . . . £100/£25
The Edwardians, Hogarth Press, 1930 . £200/£45
ditto, Hogarth Press, 1930 (125 signed copies, no d/w)
. . . . £450
ditto, Doran (U.S.), 1930 . . . . . £100/£20
All Passion Spent, Hogarth Press, 1931 . £300/£50
ditto, Doran (U.S.), 1931 . . . . . £150/£20
Family History, Hogarth Press, 1932 . £150/£45
ditto, Doubleday Doran (U.S.), 1932 . £75/£20
The Death of Noble Godavary and Gottfried Kunstler,
Benn, 1932 (wraps) £30
The Dark Island, Hogarth Press, 1934 . £200/£45
ditto, Doran (U.S.), 1934 . . . . . £75/£20
Grand Canyon, Michael Joseph, 1942 . £65/£20
ditto, Doran (U.S.), 1942 . . . . . £45/£15
Devil at Westease, Doubleday Doran (U.S.), 1947 .
. . . . £175/£45
The Easter Party, Michael Joseph, 1953 . £35/£15
ditto, Doubleday (U.S.), 1953 . . . £25/£10
No Signposts in the Sea, Michael Joseph, 1961 .
. . . . £25/£10
ditto, Doubleday (U.S.), 1961 . . . . £15/£5

Short Stories
The Heir, privately printed, [1922] (100 signed copies)
. . . . £350
ditto, Heinemann, 1922 . . . . . . £200/£50
Thirty Clocks Strike the Hour and Other Stories,
Doubleday Doran (U.S.), 1934 . . . . £125/£45

Verse
Chatterton, privately printed, 1909 (wraps) . £3,000
Constantinople, Eight Poems, privately printed,
Complete Press, 1915 (wraps) £350
Poems of West and East, John Lane, 1917 . £125
Orchard and Vineyard, John Lane, 1921 £300/£125
The Land, Heinemann, 1926 . . . . . £200/£35
ditto, Heinemann, 1926 (125 copies, slipcase) . . .
. . . . £650/£500
ditto, Doubleday (U.S.), 1927 . . . . £150/£25
King's Daughter, Hogarth Press, 1929 . £100/£30
ditto, Doubleday (U.S.), 1930 . . . . £75/£25
Sissinghurst, Hogarth Press, 1931 (500 signed,
numbered copies, hand-printed by the Woolfs, no
d/w) £300
Invitation to Cast Out Care, Faber, 1931 . £50/£20
ditto, Faber, 1931 (200 copies) £125
V. Sackville-West, Benn, 1931 . . . . £10
Collected Poems, Volume One, Hogarth Press, 1933 .
. . . . £100/£35
ditto, Hogarth Press, 1933 (150 copies) . . £250
ditto, Doubleday (U.S.), 1934 . . . . £75/£25
Solitude, Hogarth Press, 1938 . . . . £75/£25
Selected Poems, Hogarth Press, 1941 . £45/£15
The Garden, Michael Joseph, 1946 . . . £60/£20
ditto, Michael Joseph, 1946 (750 signed copies, plain
d/w) . . . . £250/£100
ditto, Doubleday (U.S.), 1946 . . . . £50/£20

Travel
Passenger to Tehran, Hogarth Press, 1926 £300/£75
Twelve Days, Hogarth Press, 1928 . . . £300/£50
ditto, Doubleday (U.S.), 1928 . . . . £200/£35

Gardening
Some Flowers, Cobden-Sanderson, 1937 . £75/£30
Country Notes, Michael Joseph, 1939 . £75/£30
ditto, Harper (U.S.), 1940 . . . . . £40/£10
Country Notes in Wartime, Hogarth Press, 1940 . .
. . . . £65/£15
ditto, Doubleday Doran (U.S.), 1941 . . £50/£10
In Your Garden, Michael Joseph, 1951 . £45/£15
Hidcote Manor Garden, Country Life, 1952 £30/£10
In Your Garden Again, Michael Joseph, 1953 £45/£15
More For Your Garden, Michael Joseph, 1955 . .
. . . . £35/£10
Even More For Your Garden, Michael Joseph, 1958 .
. . . . £35/£10
A Joy of Gardening, Harper & Row (U.S.), 1958 . .
. . . . £25/£10
ditto, Harper (U.S.), 1958 . . . . . £25/£10

V. Sackville-West's Garden Book, Michael Joseph,
1968 . . . . £20/£5
ditto, Atheneum (U.S.), 1968 . . . . . £15/£5
The Illustrated Garden Book, Michael Joseph, 1986 .
. . . . £15/£5
ditto, Atheneum (U.S.), 1986 . . . . . £15/£5

Historical and Biographical
Knole and the Sackvilles, Heinemann, 1922 £400/£35
ditto, Doran (U.S.), [1924] . . . . . £250/£35
Aphra Benn, The Incomparable Astrea, Gerald Howe,
1927 . . . . £100/£35
ditto, Viking (U.S.), 1928 . . . . . £75/£30
Andrew Marvell, Faber, 1929 . . . . . £65/£20
ditto, Faber, 1929 (75 signed copies) . . . £200
Saint Joan of Arc, Cobden-Sanderson, 1936 £45/£15
ditto, Cobden-Sanderson, 1936 (120 copies) . £150
ditto, Doubleday (U.S.), 1936 . . . . £35/£10
Joan of Arc, Hogarth Press, 1937 . . . £65/£10
Pepita, Hogarth Press, 1937 . . . . £100/£15
ditto, Doubleday (U.S.), 1937 . . . . £35/£10
English Country Houses, Collins, 1941 . £35/£10
ditto, Random House (U.S.), 1949 . . . £15/£5
The Eagle and the Dove, Michael Joseph, 1943 . .
. . . . £30/£10
ditto, Doubleday (U.S.), 1944 . . . . £30/£10
Daughter of France, Michael Joseph, 1959 £30/£10
ditto, Doubleday (U.S.), 1959 . . . . £30/£10

Others
The Diary of the Lady Anne Clifford, Heinemann,
1923 (edited by V. Sackville-West) . . £150/£40
Rilke, Hogarth Press, 1931 (translation) . . £75/£20
The Women's Land Army, Michael Joseph, 1944 . .
. . . . £65/£15
Nursery Rhymes, Dropmore Press, 1947 (550 copies)
. . . . £150/£45
ditto, Dropmore Press, 1947 (25 signed copies of the
above) . . . . £1,000/£750
ditto, Joseph, 1950 . . . . £50/£15
Faces: Profiles of Dogs, Harvill Press, 1961 £25/£10
Dearest Andrew, Letters to Andrew Reiber, 1951-62,
Michael Joseph, 1979 . . . . . £20/£10
ditto, Scribners (U.S.), 1979 . . . . . £15/£5
Letters from V. Sackville-West to Virginia Woolf,
Michael Joseph, 1984 . . . . . £20/£5
ditto, Morrow (U.S.), 1985 . . . . . £15/£5

SAKI
(b.1870 d.1916)

Saki was a pseudonym adopted by H.H. Munro for his predominantly humorous novels and short stories. Although his writing is whimsical and satirical, some critics have noted the darker undercurrent of an alienated outsider.

Novels
The Unbearable Bassington, John Lane, 1912 . £65
When William Came, John Lane, 1913 .   .   . £50
The Collected Novels and Plays, John Lane/Bodley Head, 1933. .   .   .   . £35/£15

Short Stories
Reginald, Methuen, 1904. .   .   .   .   .   . £150
Reginald in Russia and Other Sketches, Methuen, 1910 .   .   .   . £100
The Chronicles of Clovis, John Lane, 1911. . £100
Beasts and Superbeasts, John Lane, 1914 . . £100
The Toys of Peace, John Lane/Bodley Head, 1919. .
.   .   .   . £40
The Square Egg and Other Sketches. John Lane/ Bodley Head, 1924 .   .   .   .   .   . £125/£40
The Collected Short Stories, John Lane/Bodley Head, 1930 .   .   .   . £25/£10

Others
The Rise of the Russian Empire, Grant Richards, 1900
.   .   .   . £75
The Westminster Alice, Westminster Gazette, 1902 (wraps) £200
ditto, Westminster Gazette, 1902 (boards) . . £150

J.D. SALINGER
(b.1919)

Essentially a one-novel novelist, the author of *The Catcher in the Rye* was born in New York. He now lives in Cornish, New Hampshire.

Novels
The Catcher in the Rye, Little, Brown (U.S.), 1951 .
.   .   .   . £3,000/£150
ditto, Hamish Hamilton, 1951 .   .   . . £300/£65

Short Stories
Nine Stories, Little, Brown (U.S.), 1953 £1,000/£100
ditto, as *For Esme - With Love and Squalor and Other Stories*, Hamish Hamilton, 1953 . . £200/£35
Franny and Zooey, Little, Brown (U.S.), 1961 £75/£20
ditto, Heinemann, 1963 .   .   .   .   . £35/£10
Raise High the Roof Beam, Carpenters and Seymour: An Introduction, Little, Brown (U.S.), 1963 (first issue with no dedication page) .   .   . £400/£300

ditto, Little, Brown (U.S.), 1963 (second issue with dedication page before half title) .   .   . £100/£15
ditto, Heinemann, 1963 .   .   .   .   . £40/£10
The Complete and Uncollected Short Stories of J.D. Salinger, no publisher named, 1974 (2 vols, wraps, first vol. saddle-stitched and the second vol. perfect bound, pirated edition) £450

SARBAN
(b.1910 d.1989)

Pseudonym used by John W. Wall, a diplomat for many years stationed in the Middle-East.

Ringstones and other stories, Davies, 1951   £125/£30
ditto, Coward-McCann (U.S.), [1951] .   . £100/£30
ditto, Tartarus Press, 2000 (350 copies) .   £30/£10
The Sound of His Horn, Davies, 1952 .   . £200/£35
ditto, Ballantine (U.S.), 1960 (wraps) .   .   . £10
ditto, Tartarus Press, 1999 (350 numbered copies) . .
.   .   .   . £40/£10
The Doll Maker, Davies, 1953 .   .   . . £300/£50
ditto, Ballantine (U.S.), 1960 (wraps) .   .   . £10
ditto, Tartarus Press, 1999 (250 numbered copies) . .
.   .   .   . £75/£20

SIEGFRIED SASSOON
(b.1886 d.1967)

A poet and author of autobiography and semi-autobiographical novels, his *Memoirs of a Fox-Hunting Man* won both the Hawthenden and Tait Black Memorial Prizes.

Novels
Memoirs of a Fox-Hunting Man, Faber, 1928 (anonymous) .   .   .   . £200/£50
ditto, Faber, 1929 (300 signed, numbered copies, illustrated) .   .   .   .   .   . £1,250/£1,000
ditto, Faber, 1929 (illustrated) .   .   .   . £100/£50
ditto, Coward McCann (U.S.), 1929 .   .   . £75/£10
Memoirs of an Infantry Officer, Faber, 1930 £100/£25
ditto, Faber, 1930 (750 signed copies) .   .   . £200
ditto, Coward McCann (U.S.), 1930 .   .   . £75/£15
ditto, Faber, 1931 (illustrated by Freedman, 320 signed copies, d/w and slipcase) .   .   .   . £750/£500
ditto, Faber, 1931 (illustrated by Freedman, 12 signed copies) £1,500
Sherston's Progress, Faber, 1936 .   .   . £100/£20
ditto, Faber, 1936 (300 signed copies) .   .   . £200
ditto, Doubleday (U.S.), 1936 .   .   .   . £65/£10
The Complete Memoirs of George Sherston, Faber, 1937 .   .   .   . £25/£10
ditto, Doubleday (U.S.), 1937 .   .   .   . £25/£10

Verse
An Ode for Music, privately printed, 1912 (50 copies)
. . . . £1,000
The Daffodil Murderer, Richmond, 1913 (wraps) £400
The Old Huntsman, Heinemann, 1917 (with errata
slip) £100
ditto, Dutton (U.S.), 1917. . . . . . £100
Counter-Attack, Heinemann, 1918 (wraps) . . £250
ditto, Heinemann, 1918 . . . . . . £125
ditto, Dutton (U.S.), 1918. . . . . . £100
The War Poems of Siegfried Sassoon, Heinemann,
1919 . . . . £75
Recreations, privately printed, 1923 (75 copies of 81).
. . . . £500
ditto, privately printed, 1923 (6 copies of 81) . £750
Selected Poems, Heinemann, 1925 . . . £65/£20
Satirical Poems, Heinemann, 1926 . . £300/£50
ditto, Viking (U.S.), 1926. . . . . £200/£45
Nativity, Faber, 1927 (350 numbered copies, wraps) .
. . . . £35
ditto, Faber, 1927 (wraps) £15
ditto, William Edwin Rudge (U.S.), 1927 (27 copies to
secure copyright). £125
The Heart's Journey, Heinemann and Crosby Gaige
(U.S.), 1928 (590 signed copies) . . .£200/£125
ditto, Heinemann and Crosby Gaige (U.S.), 1928 (9
copies on green paper) £600
ditto, Heinemann, 1928 . . . . . £75/£20
ditto, Harper (U.S.), 1929 . . . . . £45/£15
To My Mother, Faber, 1928 . . . . £40/£15
ditto, Faber, 1928 (500 signed large paper copies) £125
In Sicily, Faber, 1930 . . . . . . £40/£15
ditto, Faber, 1928 (110 signed copies) . . £150
Poems by Pinchbeck Lyre, Duckworth, 1931 (glassine
d/w) . . . . £55/£50
To the Red Rose, Faber, 1931(wraps) . . £25
ditto, Faber, 1931 (400 signed copies) . . £125
Prehistoric Burials, Knopf (U.S.), 1932 (Borzoi Chap
Book) £35
The Road to Ruin, Faber, 1933 . . . £60/£15
Vigils, [Douglas Cleverdon], 1934 (272 signed copies,
Niger morocco) £200
ditto, Heinemann, 1935 . . . . . £60/£15
ditto, Viking (U.S.), 1936. . . . . £40/£10
Rhymed Ruminations, Faber, 1940 . . £35/£10
ditto, Viking (U.S.), 1941. . . . . £25/£10
Poems Newly Selected, Faber, 1940 . . £25/£10
Collected Poems, Faber, 1947 . . . . £40/£15
ditto, Viking (U.S.), 1949. . . . . £30/£10
Sequences, Faber, 1956 . . . . . £30/£10
ditto, Viking (U.S.), 1957. . . . . £25/£10
Collected Poems, 1908-1956, Faber, 1961 . £20/£10
An Octave, privately printed, 1966 (350 copies, wraps,
slipcase) . . . . £75/£50

Others
The Old Century and Seven More Years, Faber, 1938.
. . . . £65/£20
ditto, Viking (U.S.), 1939. . . . . £35/£10

The Weald of Youth, Faber, 1941 . . . £40/£10
ditto, Viking (U.S.), 1942. . . . . £25/£10
Siegfried's Journey, Faber, 1945 . . . £35/£10
ditto, Viking (U.S.), 1946. . . . . £15/£5
Meredith, Constable, 1948 . . . . £20/£10
ditto, Viking (U.S.), 1948. . . . . £20/£10
The Path to Peace, Stanbrook Abbey Press, 1960 (500
copies, quarter vellum) £250
*Something About Myself by Siegfried Sassoon, aged
11*, Stanbrook Abbey Press, 1966 (350 copies, wraps)
. . . . £50
Diaries, 1920-1922, Faber, 1981. . . . £20/£10
Diaries, 1915-1918, Faber, 1983. . . . £20/£10
Diaries, 1923-1925, Faber, 1984. . . . £20/£10
*Siegfried Sassoon: Letters to Max Beerbohm with a
Few Answers*, Faber, 1986 . . . . . £20/£5

THE SAVOY

After leaving *The Yellow Book*, Aubrey Beardsley
joined with Arthur Symons to produce, *The Savoy*,
published by Leonard Smithers. Smithers later bound
and published sets of all 8 issues in pictorial cloth in 3
volumes.

No.1, January 1896 (including Christmas card). £100
No.2, April, 1896 . . . . £75
No.3, July, 1896 . . . . £75
No.4, August, 1896 . . . . . . £75
No.5, September, 1896 . . . . . . £75
No.6, October, 1896 . . . . . . £75
No.7, November 1896. . . . . . £75
No.8, December 1896. . . . . . £75

All 8 issues, 3 vols. £1,500

DOROTHY L. SAYERS
(b.1893 d.1957)

Principally a writer of detective fiction, Sayers'
novels follow the exploits of Lord Peter Wimsey.

Novels
Whose Body?, Boni & Liveright (U.S.), 1923 (first
issue without 'Inc.' after Boni & Liveright on title
page) . . . . £2,500/£350
ditto, Unwin, 1923. . . . . . £1,500/£350
Clouds of Witness, Unwin, 1926. . . £1,500/£200
ditto, as *Clouds of Witnesses*, Dial Press (U.S.), 1927 .
. . . . £1,000/£150
Unnatural Death, Benn, 1927 . . . £1,500/£200
ditto, as *The Dawson Pedigree*, Dial Press (U.S.), 1928
. . . . £1,000/£200
The Unpleasantness at the Bellona Club, Benn, 1928.
. . . . £2,000/£200

ditto, Payson & Clarke (U.S.), 1928 . . £750/£150
The Documents in the Case, Benn, 1930 (with Robert
  Eustace) . . . . £750/£45
ditto, Brewer (U.S.), 1930 . . . . . £500/£35
Strong Poison, Gollancz, 1930 . . . . £750/£75
ditto, Brewer (U.S.), 1930 . . . . . £600/£45
The Five Red Herrings, Gollancz, 1931 . £750/£75
ditto, as **Suspicious Characters**, Brewer (U.S.), 1931 .
  . . . . £600/£45
Have His Carcase, Gollancz, 1932 . . . £750/£45
ditto, Brewer (U.S.), 1932 . . . . . £500/£35
Murder Must Advertise, Gollancz, 1933 . £750/£45
ditto, Harcourt (U.S.), 1933 . . . . . £500/£35
The Nine Tailors, Gollancz, 1934 . . . £750/£35
ditto, Harcourt (U.S.), 1934 . . . . . £500/£35
Gaudy Night, Gollancz, 1935 . . . . £650/£35
ditto, Harcourt (U.S.), 1936 . . . . . £450/£35
Busman's Honeymoon, Harcourt (U.S.), 1937 . . .
  . . . . £450/£35
ditto, Gollancz, 1937 . . . . £450/£35
Thrones, Dominations, Hodder & Stoughton, 1998
  (completed by Jill Paton Walsh) . . £25/£10
ditto, St Martin's Press (U.S.), 1998 . . £25/£10

Short Stories
Lord Peter Views the Body, Gollancz, 1928 . . .
  . . . . £1,000/£75
ditto, Payson & Clarke (U.S.), 1929 . . £650/£50
Hangman's Holiday, Gollancz, 1933 . £650/£35
ditto, Harcourt (U.S.), 1933 . . . . £450/£30
In the Teeth of the Evidence, Gollancz, 1940 £500/£35
ditto, Harcourt (U.S.), 1940 . . . . . £450/£30
ditto, Gollancz, 1972 (3 additional stories) . £20/£5
**Lord Peter, A Collection of All the Lord Peter Wimsey
Stories**, Harper & Row (U.S.), 1972 . £25/£10
ditto, Harper & Row (U.S.), 1972 (adds 'Talboys') .
  . . . . £25/£10
Talboys, Harper & Row (U.S.), 1972 (wraps) . £50
Striding Folly, New English Library, 1973 (wraps) £10

Collaborations
The Floating Admiral, Hodder and Stoughton, [1931]
  . . . . £600/£125
ditto, Doubleday (U.S.), 1932 . . . £450/£30
Ask a Policeman, Arthur Barker, [1933] £500/£100
ditto, Morrow (U.S.), 1933 . . . . . £450/£65
The Scoop and **Behind the Screen**, Gollancz, 1983 .
  . . . . £25/£10
No Flowers by Request, Gollancz, 1984 . £25/£10

Verse
OP. 1, Blackwell, 1916 (wraps) £400
Catholic Tales and Christian Songs, Blackwell, 1918
  (wraps and d/w) . . . . . £1500/£100

Plays
Busman's Honeymoon, Gollancz, 1937 . £400/£75
ditto, Gollancz, 1937 (wraps) £150
ditto, Harcourt Brace (U.S.), 1937 . . £300/£65

The Zeal of Thy House, Gollancz, 1937 . £35/£10
ditto, Harcourt Brace (U.S.), 1937 . . £30/£10
The Devil to Pay, Gollancz, 1937 . . . £35/£15
ditto, Harcourt Brace (U.S.), 1941 . . £25/£10
He that Should Come, Gollancz, 1939 (wraps in d/w).
  . . . . £20/£10
The Man Born to be King, Gollancz, 1943 . £60/£15
ditto, Harpers (U.S.), 1943 . . . . . £25/£10
The Just Vengeance, Gollancz, 1946 . . £35/£10
ditto, Gollancz, 1946 (wraps). £15
Four Sacred Plays, Gollancz, 1948 . . £15/£5
The Emperor Constantine, Gollancz, 1951 . £20/£5

Essays
Begin Here, Gollancz, 1940 . . . . . £75/£25
ditto, Harcourt (U.S.), 1941 . . . . . £35/£10
The Mind of the Maker, Methuen, 1941 . £25/£10
ditto, Harcourt (U.S.), 1941 . . . . . £15/£5
Unpopular Opinions, Gollancz, 1946 . £25/£10
ditto, Harcourt (U.S.), 1947 . . . . . £15/£5
Creed or Chaos and Other Essays, Methuen, 1947 .
  . . . . £15/£5
ditto, Harcourt (U.S.), 1949 . . . . £15/£5
Introductory Papers on Dante, Methuen, 1954. .
  . . . . £50/£15
ditto, Harpers (U.S.), 1955 . . . . £45/£10
Further Papers on Dante, Methuen, 1957 . £45/£10
ditto, Harpers (U.S.), 1957 . . . . . £45/£10
The Poetry of Search and the Poetry of Statement,
  Gollancz, 1963 . . . . . . £15/£5
Christian Letters to a Post-Christian World, William
  Eerdmans (U.S.), 1969 . . . . . £15/£5
A Matter of Eternity, William Eerdmans (U.S.), 1973 .
  . . . . £15/£5
ditto, Mowbray, 1973 . . . . £15/£5
Wilkie Collins: A Critical and Bibliographical Study,
  University of Toledo (U.S.), 1977 . . . £20/£5

Children's
Even the Parrot, Methuen, 1944 . . . . £40/£10

Others
Papers Relating to the Family of Wimsey, privately
  printed, Humphrey Milford, [1936] (approximately
  500 copies, wraps) £300
**Account of Lord Mortimer Wimsey, Hermit of the
Wash**, 'Printed by M. Bryan, 1816' [O.U.P., 1937]
  (250 copies, wraps) £450
The Wimsey Family, A Fragmentary History,
  Gollancz, 1977 . . . . £35/£10

PAUL SCOTT
(b.1920 d.1978)

Scott only received proper recognition for his writing when in 1977 he won the Booker Prize with *Staying On*. Not until after his death, in the early 1980s, did he achieve wide popular recognition when his 'Raj' books were filmed as *The Jewel in the Crown*.

'The Raj Quartet'

The Jewel in the Crown, Heinemann, 1966		£150/£35
ditto, Morrow (U.S.), 1966		£45/£10
The Day of the Scorpion, Heinemann, 1988		£100/£25
ditto, Morrow (U.S.), 1968		£35/£10
The Towers of Silence, Heinemann, 1971		£75/£20
ditto, Morrow (U.S.), 1972		£25/£5
A Division of the Spoils, Heinemann, 1975		£75/£20
ditto, Morrow (U.S.), 1975		£25/£5

Other Novels

Johnnie Sahib, Eyre & Spottiswoode, 1952		£150/£25
The Alien Sky, Eyre & Spottiswoode, 1953		£75/£20
ditto, as *Six Days In Marapore*, Doubleday (U.S.), 1953		£35/£5
A Male Child, Eyre & Spottiswoode, 1956		£50/£15
ditto, Dutton (U.S.), 1957		£35/£10
The Mark of the Warrior, Eyre & Spottiswoode, 1956		£50/£15
ditto, Morrow (U.S.), 1958		£20/£5
The Chinese Love Pavilion, Eyre & Spottiswoode, 1960		£25/£10
ditto, as *The Love Pavilion*, Morrow (U.S.), 1962		£20/£5
The Birds of Paradise, Eyre & Spottiswoode, 1962		£25/£10
ditto, Morrow (U.S.), 1962		£20/£5
The Bender, Secker & Warburg, 1963		£25/£10
ditto, Morrow (U.S.), 1963		£20/£5
The Corrida at San Feliu, Secker & Warburg, 1964		£25/£10
ditto, Morrow (U.S.), 1964		£20/£5
Staying On, Heinemann, 1977		£75/£15
ditto, Morrow (U.S.), 1977		£35/£5

Poetry

I, Gerontius, Favil Press, 1941 (wraps)		£400

Others

After the Funeral, Whittington Press/Heinemann, 1979 (200 copies signed by illustrator)		£125
My Appointment with the Muse: Essays 1961-1975, Heinemann, 1986		£25/£10

ANNA SEWELL
(b.1820 d.1878)

Black Beauty was Anna Sewell's only novel, written in an attempt to encourage the better treatment of horses.

Black Beauty: His Grooms and Companions. The Autobiography of a Horse, Jarrold, 1877		£3,500
ditto, American Humane Education Society (U.S.), 1890 (orange printed wraps)		£600
ditto, American Humane Education Society (U.S.), 1890 (buff boards)		£500

TOM SHARPE
(b.1928)

Tom Sharpe became a full-time novelist in 1971 with the publication of *Riotous Assembly*. His books have been filmed, with varying degrees of success.

Novels

Riotous Assembly, Secker & Warburg, 1971		£200/£25
ditto, Viking (U.S.), 1971		£65/£15
Indecent Exposure, Secker & Warburg, 1973		£150/£20
ditto, Atlantic Monthly Press (U.S.), 1973 (wraps)		£10
Porterhouse Blue, Secker & Warburg, 1974		£150/£20
ditto, Prentice-Hall (U.S.), 1974		£65/£15
Blott on the Landscape, Secker & Warburg, 1975		£45/£10
ditto, Random House (U.S.), 1985		£10/£5
Wilt, Secker & Warburg, 1976		£35/£10
ditto, Random House (U.S.), 1984		£10/£5
The Great Pursuit, Secker & Warburg, 1977		£20/£5
ditto, Harper (U.S.), 1978		£15/£5
The Throwback, Secker & Warburg, 1978		£20/£5
ditto, Random House (U.S.), 1985		£10/£5
The Wilt Alternative, Secker & Warburg, 1979		£20/£5
ditto, Random House (U.S.), 1984		£10/£5
Ancestral Vices, Secker & Warburg, 1980		£20/£5
ditto, St Martin's Press (U.S.), 1980		£15/£5
Vintage Stuff, Secker & Warburg, 1982		£20/£5
ditto, Random House (U.S.), 1985		£10/£5
Wilt on High, Secker & Warburg, 1984		£15/£5
ditto, Random House (U.S.), 1985		£10/£5
Granchester Grind, A Porterhouse Chronicle, Secker & Warburg, 1995		£10/£5
The Midden, Deutsch/Secker & Warburg, 1996		£10/£5
ditto, Overlook (U.S.), 1997		£10/£5

GEORGE BERNARD SHAW
(b.1856 d.1950)

Primarily a playwright, Shaw's dramatic works are often satirical attacks on convention and cant. His many other writings are also highly political. In 1925 he was awarded the Nobel Prize for Literature, but he later declined offers of a peerage and the Order of Merit.

Novels

Cashel Byron's Profession, The Modern Press, 1886, (wraps) £750
ditto, Stone (U.S.) 1901 . . . . . . £100
An Unsocial Socialist, Swan, Sonnenschein, Lowrey & Co., 1887 (first state with Shaw's first novel given incorrectly as 'The Confessions of Bryn Cashel's...' and publisher's name spelt wrong on spine) £1,000
ditto, Swan, Sonnenschein, Lowrey & Co., 1887 (second state with errors corrected). . . . £500
ditto, Brentano's (U.S.) 1900 . . . . . £35
Love Among the Artists, Stone (U.S.), 1905 . £250
ditto, Constable, 1914 . . . . £100
The Irrational Knot, Archibald Constable, 1905 £50
ditto, Brentano's (U.S.) 1905 . . . . . £40
Immaturity, Constable, 1931 . . . . £65/£15
Unfinished Novel, Constable, 1958 (950 copies) . . . . £30/£20

Plays

Widowers' Houses, Henry and Co, 1893 . £750
Plays Pleasant and Unpleasant, Grant Richards, 1898 (2 vols) £100
ditto, Brentano's (U.S.) 1905 (2 vols) . . . £65
Three Plays for Puritans, Grant Richards, 1901 £50
John Bull's Other Island, and *Major Barbara*, Constable and Company, 1907 (also contains 'How He Lied to Her Husband') £30
Man and Superman, Constable, 1903 . . . £30
ditto, Brentano's (U.S.) 1905 . . . . . £25
The Doctor's Dilemma, Getting Married, and *The Shewing-Up of Blanco Posnet*,Constable & Co, 1911 . . . . £25
ditto, Brentano's (U.S.) 1911 . . . . . £25
Pygmalion, privately printed, 1912 (title page reads 'Rough Proof-Unpublished', wraps) . . £750
Androcles and the Lion, privately printed, 1913 (50 copies, title page reads 'Rough Proof-Unpublished', wraps). £500
Androcles and the Lion, Overruled, Pygmalion, Constable, 1916 . . . . £25
ditto, Brentano's (U.S.) 1916 . . . . . £25
Misalliance, The Dark Lady of the Sonnets, and *Fanny's First Plays*, Constable, 1914 . . . £25
ditto, Brentano's (U.S.) 1914 . . . . . £25
Heartbreak House, Great Catherine, and *Playlets of the War*, Constable, 1919 . . . . . £25
ditto, Brentano's (U.S.) 1919 . . . . . £20

Back to Methuselah. A Metabiological Pentateuch, Brentano's (U.S.) 1921 . . . . . . £50/£15
ditto, Constable, 1922 . . . . £50/£15
Saint Joan: a chronicle play in six scenes and an epilogue, Constable, 1924 . . . . £200/£30
ditto, Constable, 1924 (750 copies, with sketches by C. Ricketts) . . . . £500/£150
ditto, Brentano's (U.S.) 1924 . . . . £150/£45
The Apple Cart, a political extravaganza, Constable, 1930 . . . . £65/£15
ditto, Brentano's (U.S.) 1931 . . . . . £50/£10
Too True To Be Good, Village Wooing, and *On the Rocks*, Constable, [1934] . . . . £45/£15
ditto, Dodd, Mead (U.S.) 1934 . . . . £35/£10
The Simpleton of the Unexpected Isles, The Six of Calais, and *The Six Millionairess*, Constable, 1936 . . . . £40/£10
ditto, Dodd, Mead (U.S.) 1936 . . . . £35/£10
'In Good King Charles's Golden Days', Constable 1939 . . . . £35/£10
ditto, Dodd, Mead (U.S.) 1947 . . . . £25/£10
Buoyant Billions, Constable 1949 (1,000 numbered copies of 1025) £35
ditto, Constable, 1949 (25 lettered copies of 1025). £200
Buoyant Billions, Farfetched Fables, and *Shakes Versus Shav*, Constable, 1950 . . . . £25/£10

Political Writings

A Manifesto, Fabian Society Tract No. 2, 1884 (wraps) £100
To Provident Landlords and Capitalists, Fabian Society Tract No. 3, 1885 (anonymous, wraps) £75
The True Radical Programme, Fabian Society Tract No. 6, 1887 (anonymous, wraps) £75
Fabian Essays in Socialism, Fabian Society, 1889 . . . . £100
ditto, Browm (U.S.) 1904 . . . . . . £75
Anarchism Versus State Socialism, Henry Seymour, 1889 . . . . £75
What Socialism Is, Fabian Society Tract No. 13, 1890 (anonymous, wraps). £75
The Legal Eight Hours Question, R. Forder, 1891 (wraps) £75
Fabian Election Manifesto, Fabian Society Tract No. 40, 1892 (anonymous, wraps) £100
The Fabian Society: What it has Done, etc, Fabian Society Tract No. 41, 1892 (wraps) . . . £75
Vote! Vote! Vote!, Fabian Society Tract No. 43, 1892 (anonymous) (wraps) £75
The Impossibilities of Anarchism, Fabian Society Tract No. 45, 1893 (wraps) £75
A Plan of Campaign for Labour, Fabian Society Tract No. 49, 1894 (wraps) £75
Report on Fabian Policy, Fabian Society Tract No. 70, 1896 (anonymous, wraps) £50
Women as Councillors, Fabian Society Tract No. 93, 1900 (wraps) £75

Fabianism and the Empire: A Manifesto, Grant Richards, 1900 (wraps) £100
Socialism for Millionaires, Fabian Society Tract No. 107, 1901 (wraps) £50
Common Sense of Municipal Trading, Constable, 1904 . . . . £50
Election Address, Fabian Society, 1904 (wraps) £50
Fabianism and the Fiscal Question, Fabian Society Tract No. 116, 1904 (wraps) £35
Is Free Trade Alive or Dead?, George Standring, 1906
. . . . £75
Rent and Value, Fabian Society Tract No. 142, 1909 (wraps) £35
Socialism and Superior Brains, Fabian Society Tract No. 146, 1910 (wraps) £45
ditto, Lane (U.S.) 1910 . . . . £45
The Case for Equality, Address to the Political & Economic Circle National Liberal Club, 1913 (wraps)
. . . . £35
Common Sense about The War, 'New Statesman' supplement, 1914 (wraps) £75
How to Settle the Irish Question, Talbot and Constable (Dublin), 1917 (first issue blue wraps) . . . £100
ditto, Talbot and Constable (Dublin), 1917 (second issue green wraps) £65
Peace Conference Hints, Constable, 1919 (wraps) £35
Socialism and Ireland, 'New Commonwealth' supplement, 1919 (wraps) £25
Ruskin's Politics, Ruskin Centenary Council, 1921 £50
A Discarded Defence of Roger Casement, privately printed by Clement Shorter, 1922 (25 copies) . £200
The Unprotected Child & The Law, The Six Point Group, [1923] (wraps) £65
Bernard Shaw and Fascism, Favil Press, 1927 . £15
The Intelligent Woman's Guide to Socialism, Constable, 1928 ('were' for 'was' line 5, p.442) . . .
. . . . £150/£25
ditto, Brentano's (U.S.) 1928 . . . . . £100/£20
The League of Nations, Fabian Society Tract No. 226, 1929 (wraps) £35
Bernard Shaw and Karl Marx, Random House, 1930 (575 copies, slipcase) . . . . . £65/£50
A Little Talk on America, Friends of the Soviet Union, 1931, (50 copies). £100
The Black Girl in Search of God, Constable, 1932 .
. . . . £45/£10
ditto, Dodd, Mead (U.S.) 1933 . . . . £35/£10
A Political Madhouse in America and Nearer Home, Constable, 1933 . . . . £75
The Future of Political Science in America, Dodd, Mead (U.S.), 1933 . . . . . . £65/£20
Are We Heading for War?, Labour Party, 1934 (wraps) £30
Everybody's Political What's What?, Constable, 1944
. . . . £45/£10
ditto, Dodd, Mead (U.S.) 1944 . . . . £35/£10
Fabian Essays, C. Allen & Unwin, 1948 . .£20/£5
Shaw on Censorship, Shavian Tract No. 3, 1955 £25
The Matter with Ireland, Hart-Davis, 1962 £25/£10

ditto, Hill & Wang (U.S.), 1962 . . . . £25/£10
The Road to Equality, Beacon Press (U.S.), 1971 . .
. . . . £20/£5

Other Prose
Quintessence of Ibsenism, Walter Scott, 1891 . £125
ditto, Brentano's (U.S.) 1904 . . . . . £35
ditto, Constable, 1913 (extended edition) . . £25
On Going to Church, Roycraft Printing Shop (U.S.), 1896 . . . . £100
ditto, Roycraft Printing Shop (U.S.), 1896 (26 copies on Japanese vellum) £1,000
The Perfect Wagnerite, Grant Richards, 1898 . £125
ditto, Stone (U.S.) 1899 . . . . £50
Dramatic Opinions and Essays, Constable, 1907 (2 vols) £30
Statement of the Evidence in Chief of G.B.S. Before the Joint Select Committee on Stage Plays, privately printed, 1909 . . . . £200
Nine Answers, privately printed by Jerome Kern (U.S.), 1923 (62 copies) £200
ditto, privately printed by Jerome Kern (U.S.), 1923 (150 copies) £100
Music in London 1890-94, Constable, 1931 (3 vols) .
. . . . £100/£45
Prefaces, Constable, 1934 . . . . . . £30/£10
London Music in 1888-1889, Dodd, Mead (U.S.), 1937 (pseud. 'Bassetto'). . . . . £45/£15
Sixteen Self-Sketches, Constable, 1949 . . £35/£10
ditto, Dodd, Mead (U.S.) 1949 . . . . £35/£10
How to Become a Musical Critic, Hart-Davis, 1960 .
. . . . £25/£10
ditto, Hill & Wang (U.S.), [1961] . . . £25/£10
Shaw on Shakespeare, Dutton (U.S.), 1961 £25/£10
ditto, Cassell, 1962 . . . . £25/£10
Shaw on Religion, Constable, 1967 . . . £20/£5
ditto, Dodd, Mead (U.S.) [1967] . . . . £20/£5
The Diaries, 1885-1897, Pennsylvania State Univ. Press, 1986 (2 vols) . . . . . . £30/£10

MARY SHELLEY
(1797-1851)

Famous for *Frankenstein* of course, but her few other works are also keenly sought by collectors. There is apparently some doubt about her authorship of the first title.

Verse
Mounseer Nongtonpaw, Baldwin, Juvenile Series, 1808 (wraps) £5,000
ditto, Baldwin, Juvenile Series, 1808 (rebound) . . .
. . . . £1,000

Fiction
Frankenstein, or, the Modern Prometheus, Lackington, Hughes, Harding, Mayor & Jones, 1818,

(anonymous, original boards, paper labels, 3 vols) .
. . . . £75,000
ditto, Lackington, Hughes, Harding, Mayor & Jones,
1818, (rebound, 3 vols) £20,000
ditto, Whitaker, 1823 (second edition, 2 vols) . £5,000
ditto, Carey, Lea and Blanchard (U.S.), 1833 £20,000
Valperga, or the Life and Adventures of Castruccio,
Prince of Lucca, Whittaker, 1823 (3 vols) £1,000
The Last Man, Colburn, 1826 ('By the Author of
Frankenstein,' 3 vols) £2,000
The Fortunes of Perkin Warbeck, Colburn and
Bentley, 1830 (3 vols) £2,000
Lodore, Bentley, 1835 ('By the Author of
Frankenstein' 3 vols) £1,000
ditto, Wallis & Newell (U.S.), 1835 . . . £1,000
Falkner, Sanders and Ottley, 1837 ('The Author of
'Frankenstein;' 'The Last Man,' &c.' 3 vols) . £600
ditto, Harper (U.S.), 1837. . . . . . £600
Mathilde, 1959 (unfinished) . . . . £30/£10
Collected Tales and Stories, Johns Hopkins Univ.
Press (U.S.), [1976] . . . . . . £30/£10

Others
History of a Six Weeks' Tour, Hookham, 1817
(anonymous, co-written by Percy Bysshe Shelley) .
. . . . £1,250
Lives of the Most Eminent Literary and Scientific
Men of Italy, Spain, and Portugal, Longman, 1835-
37 (3 vols, with others, published as part of *The*
Cabinet of Biography) £100
Lives of the Most Eminent Literary and Scientific
Men of France, Longman, 1838-39 (2 vols, with
others, published as part of *The Cabinet of*
Biography) £100
Rambles in Germany and Italy, 1840, 1842 and 1843,
Moxon, 1844 (2 vols) £250

M.P. SHIEL
(b.1865 d.1947)

The author of fantasy and science fiction, Matthew
Phipps Shiel's short stories are rather luxuriant. His
'Prince Zaleski' tales, for example, offer a detective
far more decadent than that other drug-taking dilet-
tante, Sherlock Holmes.

Short Stories
Prince Zaleski, John Lane, 1895. . . . . £300
ditto, Roberts Brothers (U.S.), 1895 . . . £150
Shapes in the Fire, John Lane, 1896 . . . £300
ditto, Roberts Brothers (U.S.), 1896 . . . £150
The Pale Ape, T. Werner Laurie, [1911] . £350
Here Comes the Lady, The Richards Press, [1928]. .
. . . . £250/£65
The Invisible Voices, The Richards Press, 1935 (with
John Gawsworth) . . . . . . £250/£65
ditto, Vanguard Press (U.S.), 1936 . . . £200/£50

The Best Short Stories of M.P. Shiel, Gollancz 1948 .
. . . . £45/£15
Xélucha and Others, Arkham House (U.S.), 1975 . .
. . . . £20/£5
Prince Zaleski and Cummings King Monk, Mycroft &
Moran (U.S.), 1977 . . . . . . £20/£5

Novels
The Rajah's Sapphire, Ward, Lock & Bowden, 1896 .
. . . . £300
ditto, Highflyer Press (U.S.), 1981 (no d/w). . £45
The Yellow Danger, Grant Richards, 1898 . . £150
ditto, R.F. Fenno & Co. (U.S.), 1899 . . . £125
Contraband of War, Grant Richards, 1899 . . £125
ditto, The Gregg Press (U.S.), 1968 (no d/w) . £20
Cold Steel, Grant Richards, 1899 . . . . £125
ditto, Brentano's (U.S.), 1900 . . . . . £125
ditto, Gollancz, 1929 (revised edition, 105 signed
copies, half vellum) £300
The Man Stealers, Hutchinson & Co., 1900 . £125
ditto, Lippincott (U.S.), 1900. . . . . £100
The Lord of the Sea, Grant Richards, 1901. . £150
ditto, Frederick A. Stokes Co. (U.S.), 1901 . £125
ditto, Gollancz, 1929 (revised edition, 105 signed
copies, half vellum) £300
The Purple Cloud, Chatto & Windus, 1901. . £300
ditto, Gollancz, 1929 (revised edition, 105 signed
copies, half vellum) £350
ditto, Vanguard Press (U.S.), 1930 (revised) £45/£10
The Weird o' It, Grant Richards, 1902 . . . £300
Unto the Third Generation, Chatto & Windus, 1903 .
. . . . £250
The Evil That Men Do, Ward, Lock & Co. Ltd, 1904
. . . . £250
The Lost Viol, Edward J. Clode (U.S.), 1905 (first
issue with Edward J. Clode on spine) . . £200
ditto, Edward J. Clode (U.S.), 1905 (second issue with
E.J. Clode on spine) £100
ditto, Ward, Lock & Co. Ltd, 1905 (copyright edition)
. . . . £350
ditto, Ward, Lock & Co. Ltd, 1908 . . . £75
The Yellow Wave, Ward, Lock & Co. Ltd, 1905
(authors name spelt 'Sheil' on title page) . £200
ditto, Ward, Lock & Co. Ltd., 1905 (authors name spelt
correctly on title page) £75
ditto, Thomas Langton (Canada), 1905 (authors name
spelt 'Sheil' on title page) £75
The Last Miracle, T. Werner Laurie, 1906 [1907] £100
The White Wedding, T. Werner Laurie, [1908]. £75
The Isle of Lies, T. Werner Laurie, [1909] . . £75
This Knot of Life, Everett & Co., [1909] . . £100
The Dragon, Grant Richards, 1913 (advance copy,
green cloth) £200
ditto, Grant Richards, 1913 . . . . . £65
ditto, Edward J. Clode (U.S.), 1914 . . . £65
ditto, as *The Yellow Peril*, Gollancz, 1929 (revised
edition, 105 signed copies, half vellum) . £250
Children of the Wind, Grant Richards, 1923 £250/£50
ditto, Knopf (U.S.), 1923 . . . . . £175/£40

How The Old Woman Got Home, The Richards Press,
1927 . . . . £150/£40
ditto, Vanguard Press (U.S.), 1928 . . . £100/£20
Dr Kranski's Secret, The Vanguard Press (U.S.), 1929
. . . . £150/£25
ditto, Jarrolds, 1930 . . . . . . £100/£25
The Black Box, The Vanguard Press (U.S.), 1930 .
. . . . £150/£25
ditto, The Richards Press, 1931 . . . £100/£25
Say Au R'Voir But Not Goodbye, Ernest Benn Ltd,
1933 (wraps) £40
This Above All, The Vanguard Press (U.S.), 1933 .
. . . . £75/£20
ditto, as *Above All Else*, Lloyd Cole, 1943 . £65/£15
The Young Men Are Coming, Allen & Unwin, 1937 .
. . . . £65/£20
ditto, Vanguard Press (U.S.), 1937 . . . £65/£20

Others
*Richards Shilling Selection from Edwardian Poets -
M.P. Shiel*, The Richards Press, 1936 (wraps) £40
Science, Life and Literature, Williams & Norgate Ltd,
1950 . . . . £25/£10

NEVIL SHUTE
(b.1899 d.1961)

A popular novelist, and scientist, Shute's *On the
Beach*, about the survivors of a nuclear holocaust, is
arguably his most important work.

Novels
Marazan, Cassell, 1926 . . . . £1,000/£100
ditto, Ballantine (U.S.), 1970 (wraps) . . . £5
So Disdained, Cassell, 1926 . . . . . £750/£75
ditto, as *The Mysterious Aviator*, Houghton Mifflin
(U.S.), 1928 . . . . £750/£75
Lonely Road, Heinemann, 1932 . . . £650/£75
ditto, Ballantine (U.S.), 1970 (wraps) . . . £5
Ruined City, Heinemann, 1938 . . . £650/£75
ditto, as *Kindling*, Morrow (U.S.), 1938 . £650/£75
What Happened to the Corbetts, Heinemann, 1939 .
. . . . £500/£50
ditto, as *Ordeal*, Morrow (U.S.), 1939 . £500/£50
An Old Captivity, Heinemann, 1940 . . £200/£25
ditto, Morrow (U.S.), 1940 . . . . £200/£25
Landfall, Heinemenn, 1940 . . . . £100/£25
ditto, Morrow (U.S.), 1940 . . . . £100/£25
Pied Piper, Heinemann, 1942 . . . £60/£15
ditto, Morrow (U.S.), 1942 . . . . £50/£15
Pastoral, Heinemann, 1944 . . . . £60/£15
ditto, Morrow (U.S.), 1944 . . . . £50/£15
Most Secret, Heinemann, 1945 . . . £60/£15
ditto, Morrow (U.S.), 1945 . . . . £50/£15
The Chequer Board, Heinemann, 1947 . . £50/£10
ditto, Morrow (U.S.), 1947 . . . . £40/£10
No Highway, Heinemann, 1948 . . . £50/£10

ditto, Morrow (U.S.), 1948 . . . . £40/£10
A Town Like Alice, Heinemann, 1950 . . £75/£15
ditto, as *Legacy*, Morrow (U.S.), 1950 . . £40/£10
Round the Bend, Heinemann, 1951 . . . £30/£10
ditto, Morrow (U.S.), 1951 . . . . £30/£10
The Far Country, Heinemann, 1952 . . . £30/£10
ditto, Morrow (U.S.), 1952 . . . . £30/£10
In the Wet, Heinemann, 1953 . . . . £30/£10
ditto, Morrow (U.S.), 1953 . . . . £30/£10
Requiem for a Wren, Heinemann, 1955 . . £40/£5
ditto, as *The Breaking Wave*, Morrow (U.S.), 1955 .
. . . . £35/£5
Beyond the Black Stump, Heinemann, 1956 £30/£5
ditto, Morrow (U.S.), 1956 . . . . £25/£5
On the Beach, Heinemann, 1957 . . . £30/£5
ditto, Morrow (U.S.), 1957 . . . . £25/£5
The Rainbow and the Rose, Heinemann, 1958 £20/£5
ditto, Morrow (U.S.), 1958 . . . . £20/£5
Trustee from the Toolroom, Heinemann, 1960 £20/£5
ditto, Morrow (U.S.), 1960 . . . . £20/£5
Stephen Morris, Heinemann, 1961 . . . £20/£5
ditto, Morrow (U.S.), 1961 . . . . £20/£5

Autobiography
Slide Rule, Heinemann, 1954 . . . . £65/£10
ditto, Morrow (U.S.), 1954 . . . . £65/£10

Drama
Viland the Good, Heinemann, 1946 . . . £75/£15
ditto, Morrow (U.S.), 1946 . . . . . £75/£15

ALAN SILLITOE
(b.1928)

A novelist and poet, Sillitoe's reputation rests
principally on *Saturday Night and Sunday Morning*.

Novels
Saturday Night and Sunday Morning, Allen, 1958 .
. . . . £125/£25
ditto, Knopf (U.S.), 1958 . . . . £75/£15
The General, Allen, 1960 . . . . . £25/£5
ditto, Knopf (U.S.), 1960 . . . . £20/£5
Key to the Door, Macmillan, 1961 . . . £20/£5
ditto, Knopf (U.S.), 1961 . . . . £20/£5
The Death of William Posters, Macmillan, 1965 .
. . . . £15/£5
ditto, Knopf (U.S.), 1965 . . . . . £15/£5
A Tree on Fire, Macmillan, 1967 . . . £15/£5
ditto, Knopf (U.S.), 1967 . . . . £15/£5
A Start in Life, Allen, 1970 . . . . £15/£5
ditto, Scribner (U.S.), 1971 . . . . £15/£5
Travels in Nihilon, Allen, 1971 . . . £15/£5
ditto, Scribner (U.S.), 1972 . . . . £15/£5
Raw Material, Allen, 1972 . . . . . £15/£5
ditto, Scribner (U.S.), 1973 . . . . £15/£5
Flame of Life, Allen, 1974 . . . . £15/£5

The Widower's Son, Allen, 1976 . . . £15/£5
ditto, Harper (U.S.), 1977 . . . . . £15/£5
The Storyteller, Allen, 1979 . . . . £15/£5
ditto, Simon & Schuster (U.S.), 1980 . . £15/£5
Her Victory, Granada, 1982 . . . . . £15/£5
ditto, Watts (U.S.), 1982 . . . . . . £15/£5
The Lost Flying Boat, Granada, 1983 . . £10/£5
ditto, Little, Brown (U.S.), 1983 . . . . £10/£5
Down from the Hill, Granada, 1984 . . . £10/£5
Life Goes On, Granada, 1985 . . . . £10/£5
Out of the Whirlpool, Hutchinson, 1987 . £10/£5
ditto, Harper (U.S.), 1988 . . . . . . £10/£5
The Open Door, Grafton, 1989 . . . . £10/£5
Last Loves, Grafton, 1990 . . . . . £10/£5
Leonard's War – A Love Story, Harper Collins, 1991 .
. . . . £10/£5
Snowstop, Harper Collins, 1993 . . . . £10/£5
The Broken Chariot, Flamingo, 1998 . . £10/£5

Verse
Without Beer or Bread, Outpost Publications, 1957
(wraps) £200
The Rats and Other Poems, Allen, 1960 . £25/£10
A Falling out of Love and Other Poems, Allen, 1964 .
. . . . £15/£5
Love in the Environs of Voronezh, Macmillan, 1968 .
. . . . £10/£5
ditto, Doubleday (U.S.), 1968 . . . . £10/£5
Poems, Rainbow Press, 1971 (with Ted Hughes and
Ruth Fainlight, 300 copies, numbered and signed by
all three poets, slipcase) . . . . . £225/£175
Shaman and Other Poems, Turret Books, 1973 (500
signed copies) . . . . £35/£20
Barbarians and Other Poems, Turret Books, 1973
(500 signed copies) . . . . . . £35/£20
From Canto Two of 'The Rats', published by the
author, 1973 (wraps). £15
Storm: New Poems, Allen, 1974. . . . £25/£10
Snow on the North Side of Lucifer, Sceptre Press,
1979 (150 copies, wraps) £25
ditto, Allen, 1979 . . . . . . £20/£5
More Lucifer, Booth, 1980 (125 numbered copies,
wraps). £25
Sun Before Departure: Poems, 1974-1984, Granada,
1984 . . . . £10/£5
Tides and Stone Walls, Grafton, 1986 . . £10/£5
Three Poems, Worlds Press, 1988 . . . . £20
Shylock The Writer, Turret, 1991 (broadside) . £30
The Mentality of the Picaresque Hero, Turret, 1993
(500 copies, wraps) £25

Stories
The Loneliness of the Long Distance Runner, Allen,
1959 . . . . £150/£50
ditto, Knopf (U.S.), 1959 . . . . . £100/£25
The Ragman's Daughter, Allen, 1963 . . £25/£5
ditto, Knopf (U.S.), 1963 . . . . . £20/£5
Guzman Go Home, Macmillan, 1968 . . £20/£5
ditto, Doubleday (U.S.), 1968 . . . . £15/£5

Men, Women, and Children, Allen, 1973 . £15/£5
ditto, Scribner (U.S.), 1974 . . . . . £15/£5
The Second Chance and Other Stories, Cape, 1981 .
. . . . £10/£5
ditto, Simon & Schuster (U.S.), 1981 . . £10/£5
The Far Side of the Street, W.H. Allen, 1988 £15/£5
Collected Stories, Flamingo, 1995 . . . £15/£5
Ron Delph and His Fight with King Arthur, Clarion
Tales, 1996 (150 copies) £40
ditto, Clarion Tales, 1996 (wraps) £20
Alligator Playground, A Collection of Short Stories,
Flamingo, 1997 . . . . £15/£5

Plays
All Citizens are Soldiers, Macmillan, 1969 (adaptation
with Ruth Fainlight) . . . . . . £25/£10
ditto, Dufour (U.S.), 1969 . . . . . . £10
Three Plays, Allen, 1978 . . . . . . £10/£5

Children's
The City Adventures of Marmalade Jim, Macmillan,
1967 . . . . £15
Big John and the Stars, Robson, 1977 . . . £10
The Incredible Fencing Fleas, Robson, 1978 . £10
Marmalade Jim at the Farm, Robson, 1982 . £10
Marmalade Jim and the Fox, Robson, 1984 . £10

Others
Chopin's Winter In Majorca, By Luis Ripoll, Mossen
Allcover (Spain), 1955 (translated by Sillitoe) £5
The Road to Volgograd, Allen, 1964 . . £20/£5
ditto, Knopf (U.S.), 1964 . . . . . . £15/£5
Mountains and Caverns, Allen, 1975 . . £15/£5
The Saxon Shore Way, Hutchinson, 1983 . £15/£5
Alan Sillitoe's Nottinghamshire, Grafton, 1987 £10/£5
Every Day of the Week: An Alan Sillitoe Reader, W.
H. Allen, 1987 . . . . £10/£5
Life Without Armour, HarperCollins, 1995 . £10/£5
Leading the Blind, Picador, 1995 . . . £10/£5

GEORGES SIMENON
(b.1903 d.1989)

Born in Belgium, Simenon's literary output was
prodigious, and much of it has not been translated
into English. He is known especially for his Inspector
Maigret novels.

Maigret Novels
The Crime of Inspector Maigret, Covici (U.S.), 1932 .
. . . . £1,000/£150
ditto, as Introducing Inspector Maigret, Hurst and
Blackett, 1933 . . . . £750/£75
The Strange Case of Peter the Lett, Covici (U.S.),
1933 . . . . £400/£50
The Crossroads Murders, Covici (U.S.), 1933 . . .
. . . . £400/£50

Inspector Maigret Investigates, Hurst and Blackett, 1933 (the two above titles) . . . . . £450/£45

The Triumph of Inspector Maigret, Hurst and Blackett, 1934 . . . . £450/£45

The Patience of Maigret, George Routledge & Sons, 1939 . . . . £125/£25

ditto, Harcourt Brace (U.S.), 1940 . . . £125/£25

Maigret Travels South, George Routledge & Sons, 1940 . . . . £100/£20

ditto, Harcourt Brace (U.S.), 1940 . . . £100/£20

Maigret Abroad, George Routledge & Sons, 1940 . . . . £100/£20

ditto, Harcourt Brace (U.S.), 1940 . . . £100/£20

Maigret to the Rescue, George Routledge & Sons, 1940 . . . . £100/£20

ditto, Harcourt Brace (U.S.), 1941 . . . £100/£20

Maigret Keeps a Rendez-Vous, George Routledge & Sons, 1940 . . . . £75/£20

ditto, Harcourt Brace (U.S.), 1941 . . . £75/£20

Maigret Sits It Out, George Routledge & Sons, 1941 .

. . . . £75/£20

ditto, Harcourt Brace (U.S.), 1941 . . . £75/£20

Maigret and M. L'Abbé, George Routledge & Sons, 1941 . . . . £75/£20

ditto, Harcourt Brace (U.S.), 1942 . . . £75/£20

Maigret on Holiday, Routledge and Kegan Paul, 1950

. . . . £25/£5

ditto, as *No Vacation for Maigret*, Doubleday (U.S.), 1953 . . . . £25/£5

Maigret Right and Wrong, Hamish Hamilton, 1954 .

. . . . £25/£5

Maigret and the Strangled Stripper, Doubleday (U.S.), 1954 . . . . £20/£5

Maigret and the Killers, Doubleday (U.S.), 1954 . .

. . . . £20/£5

ditto, as *Maigret and the Gangsters*, Hamish Hamilton, 1974 . . . . £20/£5

Maigret and the Young Girl, Hamish Hamilton, 1955 .

. . . . £25/£5

ditto, as *Inspector Maigret and the Dead Girl*, Doubleday (U.S.), 1955 . . . . . £25/£5

The Fugitive, Doubleday (U.S.), 1955 . . £25/£5

Maigret and the Burglar's Wife, Hamish Hamilton, 1955 . . . . £25/£5

ditto, Doubleday (U.S.), 1956 . . . . £25/£5

Inspector Maigret in New York's Underworld, Doubleday (U.S.), 1956 . . . . . £25/£5

Maigret's Revolver, Hamish Hamilton, 1956 £25/£5

ditto, Harcourt Brace (U.S.), 1984 . . . £10/£5

My Friend Maigret, Hamish Hamilton, 1956 £25/£5

ditto, as *The Methods of Maigret*, Doubleday (U.S.), 1957 . . . . £25/£5

Maigret Goes to School, Hamish Hamilton, 1957 . .

. . . . £25/£5

ditto, Harcourt Brace (U.S.), 1988 . . . £10/£5

Maigret's Little Joke, Hamish Hamilton, 1957 £25/£5

ditto, as *None of Maigret's Business*, Doubleday (U.S.), 1958 . . . . £25/£5

Maigret and the Old Lady, Hamish Hamilton, 1958

. . . . £25/£5

Maigret's First Case, Hamish Hamilton, 1958 £25/£5

Maigret has Scruples, Hamish Hamilton, 1959 £25/£5

Maigret and the Reluctant Witnesses, Hamish Hamilton, 1959 . . . . £25/£5

ditto, Harcourt Brace (U.S.), 1989 . . . £10/£5

Madame Maigret's Own Case, Doubleday (U.S.), 1959 . . . . £25/£5

ditto, as *Madame Maigret's Friend*, Hamish Hamilton, 1960 . . . . £25/£5

Maigret Takes a Room, Hamish Hamilton, 1960 . .

. . . . £25/£5

ditto, as *Maigret Rents a Room*, Doubleday (U.S.), 1961 . . . . £25/£5

Maigret in Court, Hamish Hamilton, 1961 . £25/£5

ditto, Harcourt Brace (U.S.), 1983 . . . £10/£5

Maigret Afraid, Hamish Hamilton, 1961 . £25/£5

ditto, Harcourt Brace (U.S.), 1983 . . . £15/£5

Maigret in Society, Hamish Hamilton, 1962 £25/£5

Maigret's Failure, Hamish Hamilton, 1962 £25/£5

Maigret's Memoirs, Hamish Hamilton, 1963 £25/£5

ditto, Harcourt Brace (U.S.), 1985 . . . £15/£5

Maigret and the Lazy Burglar, Hamish Hamilton, 1963 . . . . £25/£5

Maigret's Special Murder, Hamish Hamilton, 1964 .

. . . . £25/£5

ditto, as *Maigret's Dead Man*, Doubleday (U.S.), 1964 . . . . £25/£5

Maigret and the Saturday Caller, Hamish Hamilton, 1964 . . . . £25/£5

ditto, Harcourt Brace (U.S.), 1991 . . . £10/£5

Maigret Loses His Temper, Hamish Hamilton, 1965 .

. . . . £25/£5

ditto, Harcourt Brace (U.S.), 1974 . . . £20/£5

Maigret Sets a Trap, Hamish Hamilton, 1965 £25/£5

ditto, Harcourt Brace (U.S.), 1972 . . . £20/£5

Maigret on the Defensive, Hamish Hamilton, 1966 .

. . . . £25/£5

ditto, Harcourt Brace (U.S.), 1981 . . . £15/£5

Maigret and the Headless Corpse, Hamish Hamilton, 1967 . . . . £25/£5

ditto, Harcourt Brace (U.S.), 1968 . . . £25/£5

Maigret and the Nahour Case, Hamish Hamilton, 1967 . . . . £25/£5

ditto, Harcourt Brace (U.S.), 1982 . . . £10/£5

Maigret's Pickpocket, Hamish Hamilton, 1968 £25/£5

ditto, Harcourt Brace (U.S.), 1968 . . . £25/£5

Maigret Has Doubts, Hamish Hamilton, 1968 £25/£5

ditto, Harcourt Brace (U.S.), 1982 . . . £10/£5

Maigret In Vichy, Harcourt Brace (U.S.), 1968 £25/£5

ditto, as *Maigret Takes the Waters*, Hamish Hamilton, 1969 . . . . £25/£5

Maigret and the Minister, Hamish Hamilton, 1969 .

. . . . £20/£5

ditto, as *Maigret and the Calame Report*, Harcourt Brace (U.S.), 1969 . . . . . . £20/£5

Maigret Hesitates, Hamish Hamilton, 1970 £20/£5

ditto, Harcourt Brace (U.S.), 1970 . . . £20/£5

Maigret's Boyhood Friend, Hamish Hamilton, 1970 .
. . . . £20/£5
ditto, Harcourt Brace (U.S.), 1970 . . . £20/£5
Maigret and the Wine Merchant, Hamish Hamilton,
1971 . . . . £20/£5
ditto, Harcourt Brace (U.S.), 1975 . . . £20/£5
Maigret and the Killer, Hamish Hamilton, 1971 £20/£5
ditto, Harcourt Brace (U.S.), 1971 . . . £20/£5
Maigret and the Madwoman, Hamish Hamilton, 1972
. . . . £20/£5
ditto, Harcourt Brace (U.S.), 1972 . . . £20/£5
Maigret and the Flea, Hamish Hamilton, 1972 £20/£5
ditto, as *Maigret and the Informer*, Harcourt Brace
(U.S.), 1973 . . . . £20/£5
Maigret and Monsieur Charles, Hamish Hamilton,
1973 . . . . £20/£5
Maigret and the Dosser, Hamish Hamilton, 1973 . .
. . . . £20/£5
ditto, as *Maigret and the Bum*, Harcourt Brace (U.S.),
1973 . . . . £20/£5
Maigret and the Millionaires, Hamish Hamilton, 1974
. . . . £20/£5
ditto, Harcourt Brace (U.S.), 1974 . . . £20/£5
Maigret and the Loner, Hamish Hamilton, 1975 20/£5
ditto, Harcourt Brace (U.S.), 1975 . . . £20/£5
Maigret and the Man on the Boulevard, Hamish
Hamilton, 1975 . . . . £20/£5
ditto, as *Maigret on the Bench*, Harcourt Brace (U.S.),
1975 . . . . £20/£5
Maigret and the Black Sheep, Hamish Hamilton, 1976
. . . . £20/£5
ditto. Harcourt Brace (U.S.), 1976 . . . £20/£5
Maigret and the Ghost, Hamish Hamilton, 1976 . .
. . . . £20/£5
ditto, as *Maigret and the Apparition*, Harcourt Brace
(U.S.), 1976 . . . . £20/£5
Maigret and the Spinster, Hamish Hamilton, 1977 .
. . . . £20/£5
ditto, Harcourt Brace (U.S.), 1977 . . . £20/£5
Maigret and the Hotel Majestic, Hamish Hamilton,
1977 . . . . £20/£5
ditto, Harcourt Brace (U.S.), 1978 . . . £20/£5
Maigret in Exile, Hamish Hamilton, 1978 . £15/£5
ditto, Harcourt Brace (U.S.), 1979 . . . £15/£5
Maigret and the Toy Village, Hamish Hamilton, 1978
. . . . £15/£5
ditto, Harcourt Brace (U.S.), 1979 . . . £15/£5
Maigret's Rival, Hamish Hamilton, 1979 . £15/£5
ditto, Harcourt Brace (U.S.), 1980 . . . £15/£5
Maigret in New York, Hamish Hamilton, 1979 £15/£5
Maigret and the Coroner, Hamish Hamilton, 1980 .
. . . . £15/£5
Maigret and the Mad Killers, Doubleday (U.S.), 1980
. . . . £15/£5
Maigret and the Death of a Harbor-Master, Harcourt
Brace (U.S.), 1989 . . . . £15/£5
Maigret and the Fortuneteller, Harcourt Brace (U.S.),
1989 . . . . £15/£5

Maigret and the Flemish Shop, Harcourt Brace (U.S.),
1990 . . . . £15/£5
Maigret and the Tavern by the Seine, Harcourt Brace
(U.S.), 1990 . . . . £15/£5

Maigret Short Stories
Maigret's Christmas, Hamish Hamilton, 1976 £20/£5
ditto, Harcourt Brace (U.S.), 1977 . . . £20/£5
Complete Maigret Short Stories, Hamish Hamilton,
1976 . . . . £20/£5
Maigret's Pipe, Hamish Hamilton, 1977 . £20/£5
ditto, Harcourt Brace (U.S.), 1978 . . . £20/£5

Other Novels
The Disintegration of J.P.G. George, Routledge &
Sons, 1937 . . . . £300/£75
In Two Latitudes, George Routledge & Sons, 1942 .
. . . . £125/£25
Affairs of Destiny, George Routledge & Sons, 1942 .
. . . . £75/£20
ditto, Harcourt Brace (U.S.), 1944 . . . £75/£20
The Man who Watched the Trains Go By, George
Routledge & Sons, 1942. . . . . . £70/£15
ditto, Reynal & Hitchcock (U.S.), 1946 . . £45/£10
Havoc by Accident, George Routledge & Sons, 1943 .
. . . . £70/£15
ditto, Harcourt Brace (U.S.), 1943 . . . £65/£15
Escape in Vain, George Routledge & Sons, 1943 . .
. . . . £65/£15
ditto, Harcourt Brace (U.S.), 1944 . . . £65/£15
On the Danger Line, George Routledge & Sons, 1944
. . . . £65/£15
ditto, Harcourt Brace (U.S.), 1944 . . . £65/£15
The Shadow Falls, George Routledge & Sons, 1945 .
. . . . £65/£15
ditto, Harcourt Brace (U.S.), 1945 . . . £65/£15
The Lost Moorings, George Routledge & Sons, 1946 .
. . . . £45/£10
ditto, as *Blind Alley*, Routledge & Kegan Paul, 1946 .
. . . . £45/£10
Black Rain, Reynal & Hitchcock (U.S.), 1947 £45/£10
ditto, Routledge & Kegan Paul, 1949 . . £45/£10
First Born, Reynal & Hitchcock (U.S.), 1947 £45/£10
Magnet of Doom, George Routledge & Sons, 1948 .
. . . . £45/£10
Chit of a Girl, Routledge & Kegan Paul, 1949 . . .
. . . . £45/£10
A Wife at Sea, Routledge & Kegan Paul, 1949 . . .
. . . . £45/£10
The Snow Was Black, Prentice-Hall (U.S.), 1950 . .
. . . . £35/£10
ditto, as *The Stain on the Snow*, Routledge & Kegan
Paul, 1953 . . . . £35/£10
Strange Inheritance, Routledge & Kegan Paul, 1950 .
. . . . £35/£10
Poisoned Relations, Routledge & Kegan Paul, 1950 .
. . . . £35/£10
The Strangers in the House, Routledge & Kegan Paul,
1951 . . . . £35/£10

ditto, Doubleday (U.S.), 1954 . . . . £25/£5
The Window over the Way, Routledge & Kegan Paul, 1951 . . . . £35/£10
The Heart of a Man, Prentice-Hall (U.S.), 1951 . . . . £35/£10
Act of Passion, Prentice-Hall (U.S.), 1952 . £35/£10
ditto, Routledge & Kegan Paul, 1953 . . £35/£10
The House by the Canal, Routledge & Kegan Paul, 1952 . . . . £35/£10
The Burgomaster of Furnes, Routledge & Kegan Paul, 1952 . . . . £35/£10
The Trial of Bébé Donge, Routledge & Kegan Paul, 1952 . . . . £35/£10
Aunt Jeanne, Routledge & Kegan Paul, 1953 . . . . £35/£10
ditto, Harcourt Brace (U.S.), 1983 . . . £10/£5
The Girl in his Past, Prentice-Hall (U.S.), 1953 . . . . £35/£10
ditto, Hamish Hamilton, 1976 . . . £10/£5
Four Days in a Lifetime, Prentice-Hall (U.S.), 1953 . £35/£10
ditto, Hamish Hamilton, 1977 . . . £10/£5
Belle, New American Library (U.S.), 1954 £35/£10
Across the Street, Routledge & Kegan Paul, 1954 . . . . £35/£10
ditto, Harcourt Brace (U.S.), 1992 . . . £10/£5
Ticket of Leave, Routledge & Kegan Paul, 1954 . . . . £35/£10
Tidal Wave, Doubleday (U.S.), 1954 . £35/£10
ditto, as *Violent Ends*, Hamish Hamilton, 1954 (drops one story) . . . . £30/£10
Destinations: The Hitchhiker and The Burial of Monsieur Bouvet, Doubleday (U.S.), 1955 £30/£10
Danger Ahead, Hamish Hamilton, 1955 . £30/£10
A Sense of Guilt, Hamish Hamilton, 1955 (contains *Chez Krull* and *The Heart of a Man*) £30/£10
The Magician and The Widow, Doubleday (U.S.), 1955 . . . . £35/£10
ditto, as *The Magician* only, Hamish Hamilton, 1974 . . . . £10/£5
Witnesses And The Watchmaker, Doubleday (U.S.), 1956 . . . . £35/£10
The Judge and the Hatter, Hamish Hamilton, 1956 (contains *The Witnesses* and *The Hatter's Ghosts*) . . . . £25/£5
ditto, as *The Hatter's Phantoms*, Harcourt Brace (U.S.), 1976 (single novel only) . . . £10/£5
The Sacrifice, Hamish Hamilton, 1956 . . £25/£5
The Little Man from Archangel, Hamish Hamilton, 1957 . . . . £25/£5
The Stowaway, Hamish Hamilton. 1957 £25/£5
The Son, Hamish Hamilton, 1958 . . £20/£5
Inquest on Bouvet, Hamish Hamilton, 1958 £20/£5
The Negro, Hamish Hamilton, 1959 . . £20/£5
Striptease, Hamish Hamilton, 1959 . . £20/£5
ditto, Harcourt Brace (U.S.), 1989 . . . £10/£5
In Case of Emergency, Doubleday (U.S.), 1958 £15/£5
ditto, Hamish Hamilton, 1960 . . . £15/£5
Sunday, Hamish Hamilton, 1960. . . . £15/£5

ditto, Harcourt Brace (U.S.), 1966 (with *The Little Man from Archangel*) . . . . £15/£5
The Premier, Hamish Hamilton, 1961 . . £15/£5
The Widower, Hamish Hamilton, 1961 . . £15/£5
ditto, Harcourt Brace (U.S.), 1982. . . £15/£5
The Fate of the Malous, Hamish Hamilton, 1962 . . . . £15/£5
Pedigree, Hamish Hamilton, 1962 . . . £15/£5
ditto, London House (U.S.), 1963 . . . £15/£5
Account Unsettled, Hamish Hamilton, 1962 £15/£5
A New Lease of Life, Hamish Hamilton, 1963 £15/£5
The Iron Staircase, Hamish Hamilton, 1963 £15/£5
ditto, Harcourt Brace (U.S.), 1977 . . . £10/£5
The Patient, Hamish Hamilton, 1963 . . £15/£5
ditto, as *The Bells of Bicetre*, Harcourt Brace (U.S.), 1964 . . . . £15/£5
The Accomplices, Harcourt Brace (U.S.), 1964 £15/£5
ditto, Hamish Hamilton, 1966 . . . £15/£5
The Train, Hamish Hamilton, 1964 . . £15/£5
The Door, Hamish Hamilton, 1964 . . £15/£5
ditto, Harcourt Brace (U.S.), 1964 . . . £15/£5
The Blue Room, Harcourt Brace (U.S.), 1964 £15/£5
ditto, Hamish Hamilton, 1965 . . . £15/£5
Three Beds in Manhattan, Doubleday (U.S.), 1964 . . . . £15/£5
ditto, Hamish Hamilton, 1976 . . . £10/£5
The Man with the Little Dog, Hamish Hamilton, 1965 . . . . £15/£5
ditto, Harcourt Brace (U.S.), 1989 . . . £10/£5
The Little Saint, Harcourt Brace (U.S.), 1965 £15/£5
ditto, Hamish Hamilton, 1966 . . . £15/£5
The Cat, Harcourt Brace (U.S.), 1967 . . £10/£5
ditto, Hamish Hamilton, 1972 . . . £10/£5
The Confessional, Hamish Hamilton, 1967. . £15/£5
ditto, Harcourt Brace (U.S.), 1968 . . . £15/£5
Monsieur Monde Vanishes, Hamish Hamilton, 1967 . . . . £15/£5
ditto, Harcourt Brace (U.S.), 1977 . . . £15/£5
The Old Man Dies, Harcourt Brace (U.S.), 1967 . . . . £10/£5
ditto, Hamish Hamilton, 1968 . . . £15/£5
The Neighbours, Hamish Hamilton, 1968 . £15/£5
The Prison, Hamish Hamilton, 1969 . . £15/£5
ditto, Harcourt Brace (U.S.), 1969 . . . £15/£5
Big Bob, Hamish Hamilton, 1969 . . . £15/£5
ditto, Harcourt Brace (U.S.), 1981 . . . £10/£5
The Man on the Bench in the Barn, Hamish Hamilton, 1970 . . . . £10/£5
ditto, Harcourt Brace (U.S.), 1970 . . . £10/£5
November, Hamish Hamilton, 1970 . . . £10/£5
ditto, Harcourt Brace (U.S.), 1970 . . . £10/£5
The Rich Man, Hamish Hamilton, 1971 . £10/£5
ditto, Harcourt Brace (U.S.), 1971 . . . £10/£5
Teddy Bear, Hamish Hamilton, 1971 . . £10/£5
ditto, Harcourt Brace (U.S.), 1972 . . . £10/£5
The Disappearance of Odile, Hamish Hamilton, 1972 . . . . £10/£5
ditto, Harcourt Brace (U.S.), 1972 . . . £10/£5
The Glass Cage, Hamish Hamilton, 1973 . £10/£5

ditto, Harcourt Brace (U.S.), 1973 . . . £10/£5
The Innocents, Hamish Hamilton, 1973. . £10/£5
ditto, Harcourt Brace (U.S.), 1974 . . . £10/£5
The Venice Train, Hamish Hamilton, 1974. . £10/£5
ditto, Harcourt Brace (U.S.), 1974 . . . £10/£5
Betty, Harcourt Brace (U.S.), 1974 . . . £10/£5
ditto, Hamish Hamilton, 1975 . . . £10/£5
The Others, Hamish Hamilton, 1975 . . £10/£5
The House on Quai Notre Dame, Harcourt Brace (U.S.), 1975 . . . . £10/£5
The Bottom of the Bottle, Hamish Hamilton, 1977. . £10/£5
The Girl with a Squint, Hamish Hamilton, 1978 . . . . £10/£5
ditto, Harcourt Brace (U.S.), 1978 . . . £10/£5
The Family Lie, Hamish Hamilton, 1978 . £10/£5
ditto, Harcourt Brace (U.S.), 1978 . . . £10/£5
The Night Club, Hamish Hamilton, 1979 . £10/£5
ditto, Harcourt Brace (U.S.), 1979 . . . £10/£5
The Grandmother, Harcourt Brace (U.S.), 1980 £10/£5
ditto, Harcourt Brace (U.S.), 1980 . . . £10/£5
The Delivery, Harcourt Brace (U.S.), 1981 . £10/£5
ditto, Harcourt Brace (U.S.), 1981 . . . £10/£5
The Long Exile, Hamish Hamilton, 1983 . £10/£5
ditto, Harcourt Brace (U.S.), 1983 . . . £10/£5
The Lodger, Harcourt Brace (U.S.), 1983 . £10/£5
ditto, Harcourt Brace (U.S.), 1983 . . . £10/£5
The Reckoning, Hamish Hamilton, 1984 . £10/£5
ditto, Harcourt Brace (U.S.), 1984 . . £10/£5
The Couple from Poitiers, Hamish Hamilton, 1985 . . . . £10/£5
ditto, Harcourt Brace (U.S.), 1985 . . . £10/£5
Justice, Harcourt Brace (U.S.), 1985 . . £10/£5
The Outlaw, Hamish Hamilton, 1986 . . £10/£5
ditto, Harcourt Brace (U.S.), 1987 . . . £10/£5
Maigret and the YellowDog, Harcourt Brace (U.S.), 1987 . . . . £10/£5
Uncle Charles, Hamish Hamilton, 1988. . £10/£5
ditto, Harcourt Brace (U.S.), 1987 . . . £10/£5
The Rules of the Game, Harcourt Brace (U.S.), 1989 . . . . £10/£5
ditto, Hamish Hamilton, 1989 . . . . £10/£5
Donadieu's Will, Harcourt Brace (U.S.), 1991 £10/£5

Collected Editions
African Trio, Hamish Hamilton, 1979 . . £15/£5
ditto, Harcourt Brace (U.S.), 1979 . . . £15/£5
The White Horse Inn, Hamish Hamilton, 1980 £15/£5
ditto, Harcourt Brace (U.S.), 1980 . . . £20/£5

Other Short Stories
The Little Doctor, Hamish Hamilton, 1978 . £10/£5
ditto, Harcourt Brace (U.S.), 1981 . . . £10/£5

Autobiography
When I was Old, Harcourt Brace (U.S.), 1971 £25/£5
ditto, Hamish Hamilton, 1972 . . . . £25/£5
Letters to my Mother, Hamish Hamilton, 1976 £25/£5
ditto, Harcourt Brace (U.S.), 1976 . . . £25/£5

Intimate Memoirs, Hamish Hamilton, 1984 £25/£5
ditto, Harcourt Brace (U.S.), 1984 . . . £25/£5

EDITH SITWELL
(b.1887 d.1964)

A poet and critic, Edith Sitwell co-founded the anthology *Wheels* with her brothers Osbert and Sacheverell in 1916, as a revolt against contemporary poetry. A penchant for experimentation and an eccentric and outrageous dress-sense made her a well-known literary figure.

Verse
The Mother and Other Poems, Blackwell, 1915 (500 copies) £250
Twentieth Century Harlequinade and Other Poems, Blackwell, 1916 (with Osbert Sitwell, 500 copies, wraps) £250
Clown's Houses, Blackwell, 1918 (750 copies, wraps) £150
The Wooden Pegasus, Blackwell, 1920 (750 copies) . . . . £150/£45
Facade, Favil Press, 1922 (150 signed copies, wraps) . . £450
Bucolic Comedies, Duckworth, 1923 . . £50/£15
The Sleeping Beauty, Duckworth, 1924. . £65/£20
ditto, Knopf, 1924 . . . . £50/£15
Troy Park, Duckworth, 1925 . . . . . £65/£20
ditto, Knopf, 1925 . . . . £45/£15
Poor Young People, The Fleuron, 1925 (with Osbert & Sacheverell Sitwell, 375 numbered copies) £150/£65
The Augustan Books of Modern Poetry: Edith Sitwell, Benn, 1926 . . . . £10
Elegy on Dead Fashion, Duckworth, 1926 (225 signed copies) . . . . £200/£100
Rustic Elegies, Duckworth, 1927 . . . £65/£15
ditto, Knopf, 1927. . . . . £45/£15
Popular Song, Faber & Gwyer, 1928 (wraps) . £15
ditto, Faber & Gwyer, 1928 (500 signed, numbered copies) £65
Five Poems, Duckworth, 1928 (275 copies) £150/£45
Gold Coast Customs and Other Poems, Duckworth, 1929 . . . . £45/£10
ditto, Houghton Mifflin Co. (U.S.), 1929 £45/£10
In Spring, privately printed, 1931 (290 signed copies). £65
Jane Barston, 1719-1746, Faber, 1931 (wraps) £15
ditto, Faber, 1931 (250 signed copies) . . . £50
Epithalamium, Duckworth, 1931 (900 copies, wraps) £20
ditto, Duckworth, 1931 (100 signed copies). . £50
Five Variations on a Theme, Duckworth, 1933 . . . . £40/£10
Street Songs, Macmillan, 1942 . . . . £25/£10
Green Song and Other Poems, Macmillan, 1944 . . . . £25/£10
ditto, Vanguard Press (U.S.), 1946 . . . . £50

The Shadow of Cain, John Lehmann, 1947.   £20/£5
Poor Men's Music, Fore Publications, 1950 (wraps) .
. . . .   £10
Gardeners and Astronomers, Macmillan, 1953 £20/£5
ditto, Vanguard Press (U.S.), 1953 . . .   £20/£5
The Outcasts, Macmillan, 1962 . . . .   £20/£5
ditto, as *Music and Ceremonies*, Vanguard Press
(U.S.), 1963 . . . .   £20/£5

Collected Verse
Collected Poems, Duckworth, 1930 . . . £100/£25
ditto, Duckworth, 1930 (320 signed copies). £300/£75
Selected Poems, Duckworth, 1936 . . .   £45/£15
Poems Old and New, Faber, 1940 . .   £25/£10
The Song of the Cold, Macmillan, 1945 .   £15/£5
ditto, Vanguard Press (U.S.), 1948 . . .   £15/£5
The Canticle of the Rose, Macmillan, 1949.   £15/£5
ditto, Vanguard Press (U.S.), 1949 . . .   £15/£5
Façade and Other Poems, 1920-1935, Duckworth,
1950 . . . .   £15/£5
Selected Poems, Penguin, 1952 (wraps). . .   £5
Collected Poems, Vanguard Press (U.S.), 1954 £20/£5
ditto, Duckworth, 1957 . . . . .   £20/£5
The Pocket Poets, Vista, 1960 (wraps) . .   £5

Autobiography
Taken Care Of, Hutchinson, 1965 . . .   £15/£5
ditto, Atheneum (U.S.), 1965. . . . .   £15/£5
•
Others
Poetry and Criticism, Hogarth Press, 1925 (wraps) £45
ditto, Holt (U.S.) 1926 . . . . . .   £35
Alexander Pope, Faber, 1930 . . . .   £30/£10
ditto, Faber, 1930 (220 signed copies, d/w and slipcase)
. . . . £300/£125
ditto, Cosmopolitan Book Corp (U.S.), 1930   £30/£10
The Pleasures of Poetry, Duckworth, 1930, 1931,1932
(3 vols) . . . . £150/£50
Bath, Faber, 1932 . . . .   £35/£10
ditto, Harrison Smith (U.S.) 1932 . . .   £35/£10
The English Eccentrics, Faber, 1933 . . £150/£45
ditto, Vanguard Press (U.S.), 1957 . . .   £25/£10
Aspects of Modern Poetry, Duckworth, 1934   £20/£5
Victoria of England, Faber, 1936 . . .   £75/£15
ditto, Houghton Mifflin (U.S.), 1936 . .   £30/£10
I Live Under a Black Sun, Gollancz, 1937 .   £75/£20
ditto, Doubleday (U.S.), 1938 . . . .   £65/£15
*Trio: Dissertations on Some Aspects of National
Genius*, Macmillan, 1938 (with Osbert and Sachev-
erell Sitwell) . . . .   £40/£10
English Women, Collins, 1942 . . . .   £25/£10
A Poet's Notebook, Macmillan, 1943 . .   £15/£5
ditto, Little, Brown (U.S.), 1950 . . . .   £15/£5
Fanfare for Elizabeth, Macmillan, 1946 .   £15/£5
ditto, Macmillan (U.S.), 1946 . . . .   £15/£5
The Queens and the Hive, Macmillan, 1962   £15/£5
ditto, Little, Brown (U.S.), 1962 . . . .   £15/£5
Selected Letters, Macmillan, 1970 . . .   £10/£5
ditto, Vanguard Press (U.S.), 1970 . . .   £10/£5

OSBERT SITWELL
(b.1892 d.1969)

A poet and novelist, Osbert, brother to Edith and
Sacheverell also wrote a number of volumes of family
memoirs.

Verse
Twentieth Century Harlequinade and Other Poems,
Blackwell, 1916 (with Edith Sitwell, 500 copies,
wraps) £250
The Winstonburg Line, Hendersons, 1919 (wraps)
. . . .   £125
Argonaut and Juggernaut, Chatto & Windus, 1919 .
. . . .   £25
ditto, Knopf (U.S.), 1920 . . . . .   £65/£20
At the House of Mrs Kinfoot, Favil Press, 1921 (11
signed copies, wraps) £250
Out of the Flame, Grant Richards, 1923 .   £50/£15
Poor Young People, The Fleuron, 1925 (with Edith &
Sacheverell Sitwell, 375 numbered copies) £150/£65
Winter the Huntsman, The Poetry Bookshop, 1927 .
. . . .   £15
England Reclaimed, Duckworth, 1927 .   £45/£10
ditto, Duckworth, 1927 (165 signed copies). £125/£65
ditto, Little, Brown (U.S.), 1949 . . .   £45/£10
Miss Mew, Mill House Press, 1929 (101 signed copies)
. . . .   £125
Collected Satires and Poems, Duckworth, 1931 . .
. . . .   £30/£10
ditto, Duckworth, 1931 (110 signed copies)   £100/£65
Three-Quarter Length Portrait of Michael Arlen,
Heinemann, 1931 (520 signed copies) .   £150/£40
*Three-Quarter Length Portrait of the Viscountess
Wimborne*, Cambridge, 1931 (57 signed copies) £150
Mrs Kimber, Macmillan, 1937 (500 copies)   £65/£25
Selected Poems, Old and New, Duckworth, 1943 . .
. . . . £20/£5
Four Songs of the Italian Earth, Banyan Press (U.S.),
1945 (260 copies, wraps) £75
Demos the Emperor, Macmillan, 1949 (wraps).   £10
ditto, Macmillan, 1949 (500 signed copies, wraps) £35
Wrack at Tidesend, Macmillan, 1952 . .   £20/£5
ditto, Caedmon Publishers (U.S.), 1953 . .   £20/£5
On the Continent, Macmillan, 1958 . . .   £20/£5
Poems About People, Duckworth, 1965. .   £20/£5

Autobiography
Left Hand, Right Hand!, Little, Brown (U.S.), 1944
. . . .   £20/£5
ditto, Macmillan, 1945 . . . . . .   £20/£5
The Scarlet Tree, Little, Brown (U.S.), 1946   £15/£5
ditto, Macmillan, 1946 . . . . . .   £15/£5
Great Morning, Little, Brown (U.S.), 1947 .   £15/£5
ditto, Macmillan, 1948 . . . . . .   £15/£5
Laughter in the Next Room, Little, Brown (U.S.),
1948 . . . .   £15/£5

ditto, Macmillan, 1949 . . . . . . £15/£5
Noble Essences, Macmillan, Little, Brown (U.S.), 1950
. . . . £15/£5
ditto, 1950 . . . . £15/£5

Others
Who Killed Cock Robin?, C.W. Daniel, 1921 (wrapper pasted to spine) £100
ditto, C. W. Daniel, 1921 (wrapper pasted to baords) .
. . . . £75
Triple Fugue, Grant Richards, 1924 . . . £50/£20
ditto, Doran (U.S.), 1925 . . . . . £45/£10
Discursions on Travel, Art and Life, Grant Richards, 1925 . . . . £25/£10
ditto, Doran (U.S.), [1925] . . . . . £25/£10
Before the Bombardment, Duckworth, 1926 £25/£10
ditto, Doran (U.S.), 1926 . . . . . £25/£10
All At Sea, Duckworth, 1927 (with Sacheverell Sitwell)
. . . . £50/£15
ditto, Doran (U.S.), 1928 . . . . . £50/£15
The People's Album of London Statues, Duckworth, 1928 . . . . £35/£10
ditto, Duckworth, 1928 (116 signed copies). . £60
The Man Who Lost Himself, Duckworth, 1929 . .
. . . . £30/£10
ditto, Coward-McCann (U.S.), 1930 . . . £30/£10
Dumb Animal and Other Stories, Duckworth, 1930 .
. . . . £25/£10
ditto, Duckworth, 1930 (110 signed copies) £75/£45
ditto, Lippincott (U.S.), 1931 . . . . . £25/£10
Dickens, Chatto & Windus, 1932 . . . £25/£10
ditto, Chatto & Windus, 1932 (110 signed copies) £125
Winters of Content, Duckworth, 1932 . . £35/£10
ditto, Lippincott (U.S.), 1932 . . . . . £25/£10
Miracle on Mount Sinai, Duckworth, 1933 £50/£10
Brighton, Faber, 1935 (with Margaret Barton) £30/£10
Penny Foolish, A Book of Tirades and Panegyrics, Macmillan, 1935 . . . . £35/£10
Those Were the Days: Panorama with Figures, Macmillan, 1938 . . . . £15/£5
Trio: Dissertations on Some Aspects of National Genius, Macmillan, 1938 (with Edith and Sacheverell Sitwell) . . . . £40/£10
Escape with Me: An Oriental Sketch Book, Macmillan, 1939 . . . . £35/£10
ditto, Harrison-Hilton (U.S.), 1940 . . . £30/£10
Open the Door!, Macmillan, 1941 . . . £30/£10
ditto, Smith & Durrell (U.S.), 1941 . . . £25/£10
A Place of One's Own, Macmillan, 1941 . £25/£10
Gentle Caesar, Macmillan, 1942 (with R. J. Minney) .
. . . . £25/£10
Sing High! Sing Low!, Macmillan, 1944 . £20/£5
A Letter to My Son, Home & Van Thal, 1944 (wraps with d/w) . . . . £15/£5
The True Story of Dick Whittington: A Christmas Story for Cat Lovers, Home & Van Thal, 1945 . .
. . . . £30/£10
Alive - Alive-Oh! and Other Stories, Pan, 1947 (wraps)
. . . . £5

The Novels of George Meredith and Some Notes on the English Novel, O.U.P., 1947 (wraps) . . £5
Death of a God and Other Stories, Macmillan, 1949 .
. . . . £15/£5
Collected Stories, Duckworth/Macmillan, 1952 £15/£5
ditto, Harper (U.S.), 1953 . . . . . . £15/£5
The Four Continents, Macmillan, 1954. . £15/£5
ditto, Harper (U.S.), 1954. . . . . . £15/£5
Fee Fi Fo Fum! A Book of Fairy Stories, Macmillan, 1959 . . . . £25/£10
A Place of One's Own and Other Stories, Icon, 1961 (wraps) £5
Tales My Father Taught Me, Hutchinson, 1962 . .
. . . . £20/£5
ditto, Little, Brown (U.S.), [1962] . . . £15/£5
Pound Wise, Hutchinson, 1963 . . . . £15/£5
ditto, Little, Brown (U.S.), [1963] . . . £15/£5
Queen Mary and Others, Joseph, 1974 . . £15/£5
ditto, John Day (U.S.), 1975 . . . . . £15/£5

SACHEVERELL SITWELL
(b.1897 d.1988)

A more 'traditional' poet than his brother Osbert and sister Edith, Sacheverell's most important writings were on art and music criticism.

Verse
The People's Palace, Blackwell, 1918 (400 copies, wraps). £150
Doctor Donne and Gargantua, First Canto, Favil Press, 1921 (101 signed, numbered copies, wraps) .
. . . . £125
The Hundred and One Harlequins, Grant Richards, 1922 . . . . £50/£20
The Parrot, The Poetry Bookshop, 1923 . . £35
The Thirteenth Caesar and Other Poems, Grant Richards, 1924 . . . . £65/£25
Exalt the Eglantine and Other Poems, The Fleuron, 1924 (370 copies) . . . . . . £125/£50
Poor Young People, The Fleuron, 1925 (with Osbert & Edith Sitwell, 375 numbered copies) . £150/£65
The Cyder Feast and Other Poems, Duckworth, 1927.
. . . . £35/£15
ditto, Duckworth, 1927 (165 signed copies). £125/£50
ditto, Doran (U.S.), 1927 . . . . . . £50/£15
The Augustan Books of Modern Poetry: Sacheverell Sitwell, Benn, 1928 . . . . £10
Two Poems, Ten Songs, Duckworth, 1929 (275 signed copies) £125
Dr Donne & Gargantua: The First Six Cantos, Duckworth, 1930. . . . . . . £25/£10
ditto, Duckworth, 1930 (215 signed copies). . £125
Canons of Giant Art: Twenty Torsos in Heroic Landscapes, Faber, 1933 . . . . £35/£10
Collected Poems, Duckworth, 1936 . . . £20/£5
Selected Poems, Duckworth, 1948 . . . £10/£5

Autobiography
Journey to the Ends of Time, Cassell, 1959 £20/£5
ditto, Random House (U.S.), 1959 . . £20/£5

Others
Southern Baroque Art, Grant Richards, 1924 £45/£15
All Summer in a Day, Duckworth, 1926 . £35/£10
ditto, Doran (U.S.), 1926 . . . . . £35/£10
All At Sea, Duckworth, 1927 (with Sacheverell Sitwell)
. . . . £50/£15
ditto, Doran (U.S.), 1928 . . . . . £50/£15
German Baroque Art, Duckworth, 1927 . £40/£15
ditto, Doran (U.S.), 1928 . . . . £40/£15
A Book of Towers and Other buildings of Southern Europe, Etchells & Macdonald, 1928 (350 numbered copies) £175
The Gothick North, Duckworth, 1929/30, (3 vols: *The Visit of the Gypsies; These Sad Ruins; The Fair-Haired Victory*) . . . . £125/£50
ditto, Houghton Mifflin (U.S.), 1929 (1 vol) £30/£10
ditto, Duckworth, 1938, (1 vol.) . . . £30/£10
Beckford and Beckfordism, An Essay, Duckworth, 1930 (265 signed copies) £65
Far from My Home: Stories Long and Short, Duckworth, 1931. . . . . . . £25/£10
ditto, Duckworth, 1931 (110 signed copies). . £85
Spanish Baroque Art, Duckworth, 1931 . £30/£10
Mozart, Peter Davies, 1932 . . . . £25/£10
ditto, Appleton (U.S.), 1932 . . . . £25/£10
Liszt, Faber, 1934 . . . . £20/£10
ditto, Houghton Mifflin (U.S.), 1934 . . £20/£10
Touching the Orient: Six Sketches, Duckworth, 1934
. . . . £35/£10
A Background for Domenico Scarlatti, 1685-1757, Faber, 1935 . . . . £25/£10
Dance of the Quick and the Dead, Faber, 1936 . .
. . . . £65/£20
ditto, Houghton Mifflin (U.S.), 1937 . . £25/£10
Conversation Pieces, Batsford, 1936 . . £65/£20
ditto, Scribner (U.S.), 1937 . . . . £65/£20
Narrative Pictures, Batsford, 1937 . . £75/£25
ditto, Scribner (U.S.), 1938 . . . . £65/£20
La Vie Parisienne: A Tribute to Offenbach, Faber, 1937 . . . . £25/£10
ditto, Houghton Mifflin (U.S.), 1938 . . £25/£10
Trio: Dissertations on Some Aspects of National Genius, Macmillan, 1938 (with Osbert and Edith Sitwell) . . . . £40/£10
Roumanian Journey, Batsford, 1938 . . £25/£5
Edinburgh, Faber, 1938 . . . . . £25/£10
German Baroque Sculpture, Duckworth, 1938 . .
. . . . £50/£20
The Romantic Ballet in Lithographs of the Time, Faber, 1938 . . . . £125/£65
Old Fashioned Flowers, Country Life, 1939 £100/£30
ditto, Scribner (U.S.), 1939 . . . . £5/£20
Mauretania: Warrior, Man and Woman, Duckworth, 1940 . . . . £40/£10

Poltergeists, Faber, 1940 . . . . . £45/£15
ditto, University Books (U.S.), 1959 . . . £20/£10
Sacred and Profane Love, Faber, 1940 . £25/£10
Valse des Fleurs, Faber, 1941 . . . £20/£10
ditto, Fairfax Press, 1980 (60 signed, numbered with roman numerals, deluxe copies of 400) . . £10
ditto, Fairfax Press, 1980 (340 copies of 400) . £10
Primitive Scenes and Festivals, Faber, 1942 £40/£10
The Homing of the Winds and Other Passages in Prose, Faber, 1942 . . . . . £25/£5
Splendours and Miseries, Faber, 1943 . . £25/£10
British Architects and Craftsmen, Batsford, 1945 . .
. . . . £25/£10
ditto, Scribner (U.S.), 1946 . . . . £25/£10
The Hunters and the Hunted, Macmillan, 1947 . .
. . . . £30/£10
ditto, Macmillan (U.S.), 1947 . . . . £25/£10
The Netherlands, Batsford, 1948 . . . £25/£10
Morning, Noon & Night in London, Macmillan, 1948
. . . . £20/£5
Theatrical Figures in Porcelain, Curtain Press, 1949 .
. . . . £40/£20
Spain, Batsford, 1950 . . . . . . £30/£10
Cupid and the Jacaranda, Macmillan, 1952 £25/£5
Truffle Hunt, Robert Hale, 1953. . . . £20/£5
Fine Bird Books, Collins, 1953 (with Handasyde Buchanan and James Fisher) . . £500/£350
ditto, Collins, 1953 (295 signed copies, slipcase) . .
. . . . £1,250/£750
ditto, Atlantic Monthly Press (U.S.), 1990 . £25/£10
Portugal and Madeira, Batsford, 1954 . . £20/£5
Selected Works, Bobbs-Merrill (U.S.), 1953 £25/£5
Selected Works, Robert Hale, 1955 (different selection from above title) . . . . £25/£5
Great Flower Books, Collins, 1956 . £400/£200
ditto, Collins, 1956 (with Wilfrid Blunt and Patrick M. Synge, 295 signed copies, slipcase) . £1,000/£750
ditto, Witherby, 1990 . . . . . . £25/£10
ditto, Atlantic Monthly Press (U.S.), 1990 . £25/£10
Denmark, Batsford, 1956. . . . . . £30/£10
ditto, Hastings House (U.S.), 1956 . . . £30/£10
Arabesque and Honeycomb, Robert Hale, 1957 . .
. . . . £30/£10
ditto, Random House (U.S.), 1958 . . . £20/£5
Malta, Batsford, 1958. . . . . . . £35/£10
Bridge of the Brocade Sash, Weidenfeld & Nicolson, 1959 . . . . £25/£10
ditto, World (U.S.), 1959 . . . . . £25/£10
Golden Wall and Mirador: From England to Peru, Weidenfeld & Nicolson, 1961 . . . £35/£10
ditto, World (U.S.), 1961 . . . . . £25/£10
The Red Chapels of Banteai Srei, Weidenfeld & Nicolson, 1962 . . . . £35/£15
Monks, Nuns and Monasteries, Weidenfeld & Nicolson, 1965 . . . . £30/£10
ditto, Holt, Rinehart and Winston (U.S.), 1965 £25/£10
Southern Baroque Revisited, Weidenfeld & Nicolson, 1967 . . . . £35/£10

ditto, as Baroque and Rococo, Putnam's (U.S.), 1967 .
. . . . £35/£10
Gothic Europe, Weidenfeld & Nicolson, 1969 £20/£5
ditto, Holt, Rinehart & Winston (U.S.), 1969 £20/£5
For Want of the Golden City, Thames and Hudson,
1973 . . . . £20/£5
ditto, John Day (U.S.), 1973 . . . . . £20/£5

CLARK ASHTON SMITH
(b.1893 d.1961)

An American poet and author of fantasy fiction, Clark
Ashton Smith was a member of the circle of writers
surrounding H.P. Lovecraft. His work is recognisable
by its rich vocabulary.

The Star-Treader and Other Poems, A.M. Robertson
(U.S.), 1912 . . . . £200
Odes and Sonnets, The Book Club of California
(U.S.), 1918 (500 numbered copies, wraps) . £300
Ebony and Crystal, Auburn Journal Press (U.S.), 1922
(500 signed, numbered copies) £300
Sandalwood, privately printed (U.S.), 1925 (250
signed, numbered copies, wraps) . . . £350
The Immortals of Mercury, Stellar Publishing
Corporation (U.S.), 1932 (wraps) . . . £100
The Double Shadow and Other Fantasies, Auburn
Journal Press (U.S.), 1933 (wraps) . . . £200
The White Sybil, Fantasy Publications (U.S.), 1935
(wraps) £125
Nero and Other Poems, Futile Press (U.S.), 1937 £175
Out of Space and Time, Arkham House (U.S.), 1942 .
. . . . £750/£150
ditto, Spearman, 1971. . . . . . . £45/£15
Lost Worlds, Arkham House (U.S.), 1944 . £200/£75
ditto, Spearman, 1971. . . . . . . £40/£10
Genius Loci and Other Tales, Arkham House (U.S.),
1948 . . . . £95/£35
ditto, Spearman, 1972. . . . . . . £40/£10
The Ghoul and the Seraph, Gargoyle Press (U.S.),
1950 (85 numbered copies, wraps) £300
The Dark Chateau, Arkham House (U.S.), 1958 . .
. . . . £350/£125
Spells and Philtres, Arkham House (U.S.), 1958 . .
. . . . £300/£125
Abominations of Yondo, Arkham House (U.S.), 1960 .
. . . . £100/£35
ditto, Spearman, 1972. . . . . . . £40/£10
Hesperian Fall, Clyde Beck (U.S.), 1961 (wraps) . .
. . . . £150
Poems in Prose, Arkham House (U.S.), 1964 £125/£40
Tales of Science and Sorcery, Arkham House (U.S.),
1964 . . . . £100/£30
Other Dimensions, Arkham House (U.S.), 1970 . .
. . . . £65/£25
Selected Poems, Arkham House (U.S.), 1971 £100/£30

Planets and Dimensions, Mirage (U.S.), 1973 (500
numbered copies) . . . . £65/£25
ditto, Mirage (U.S.), 1973 (wraps) £30
Grotesques and Fantastiques, De la Ree (U.S.), 1973
(500 numbered copies, wraps) £25
ditto, De la Ree (U.S.), 1973 (50 hardback copies) £75
Klarkash-Ton and Monstro Ligriv, De la Ree (U.S.),
1974 (500 numbered copies, wraps) . . . £25
The Black Book, Arkham House (U.S.), 1979 . £50
A Rendezvous in Averoigne, Arkham House (U.S.),
1988 . . . . £35/£10

STEVIE SMITH
(b.1902 d.1971)

A poet and novelist, Smith often illustrated her work
with naive line drawings somewhat in the style of
Edward Lear.

Novel
Novel on Yellow Paper, Cape, 1936 . . . £350/£40
ditto, Morrow (U.S.), 1937 . . . . . £150/£35
Over the Frontier, Cape, 1939 . . . £150/£35
The Holiday, Chapman & Hall, 1949 . . £125/£30
ditto, Smithers (U.S.), 1950 . . . . . £100/£25

Verse
A Good Time was Had by All, Cape, 1937 £200/£40
Tender Only to One, Cape, 1938. . . . £100/£25
Mother, What is Man?, Cape, 1942 . . . £100/£25
Harold's Leap, Chapman & Hall, 1950 . . £50/£15
Not Waving but Drowning, Deutsch, 1957 . £100/£25
Selected Poems, Longman, 1962 . . . . £35/£10
ditto, New directions (U.S.), 1964 (wraps) . . £10
The Frog Prince and Other Poems, Longman, 1966 .
. . . . £35/£10
ditto, as **The Best Beast**, Knopf, 1969 . £35/£10
Francesca in Winter, Poem of the Month Club, 1970
(signed broadsheet) £40
Two in One, Longman, 1971. . . . . £25/£10
Scorpion and Other Poems, Longman, 1971 £25/£10
Collected Poems, Lane, 1975. . . . . £75/£10
ditto, O.U.P. (U.S.), 1976. . . . . . £40/£10

Others
Cats in Colour, Batsford, 1959 . . . . £20/£5
ditto, Viking (U.S.), 1959. . . . . . £15/£5
Me Again: Uncollected Writings, Virago, 1981 £20/£5
ditto, Farrar Straus (U.S.), 1982 . . . . £15/£5
Stevie Smith: A Selection, Faber, 1983 . . £10/£5
ditto, Faber (U.S.), 1982 . . . . . . £10/£5

C.P. SNOW
(b.1905 d.1980)

Possessing a Ph.D in Chemistry, C.P. Snow wrote a number of technical papers before becoming well known for his detective novels, the first of which was published in 1932. He was awarded a CBE in 1943 and a knighthood in 1957. He accepted a Life Peerage in 1964.

'Strangers and Brothers' Titles
Strangers and Brothers, Faber, 1940 (later re-titled
   George Passant) . . . . £400/£75
ditto, Scribner (U.S.), 1960 . . . . . . £35/£10
The Light and the Dark, Faber, 1947 . . £40/£10
ditto, Macmillan (U.S.), 1948 . . . . £20/£5
Time of Hope, Faber, 1949 . . . . . £40/£10
ditto, Macmillan (U.S.), 1950 . . . . £20/£5
The Masters, Macmillan, 1951 . . . . £25/£10
ditto, Macmillan (U.S.), 1951 . . . . £20/£5
The New Men, Macmillan, 1954. . . . £15/£5
ditto, Scribner (U.S.), 1954 . . . . . £10/£5
Homecomings, Macmillan, 1956 . . . £25/£10
ditto, as *Homecoming*, Scribner (U.S.), 1956 £15/£5
The Conscience of the Rich, Macmillan, 1958 £15/£5
ditto, Scribner (U.S.), 1958 . . . . . £15/£5
The Affair, Macmillan, 1960 . . . . . £15/£5
ditto, Scribner (U.S.), 1960 . . . . . £10/£5
Corridors of Power, Macmillan, 1964 . . £15/£5
ditto, Scribner (U.S.), 1964 . . . . . £10/£5
The Sleep of Reason, Macmillan, 1968 . £15/£5
ditto, Scribner (U.S.), 1969 . . . . . £10/£5
Last Things, Macmillan, 1970 . . . . £10/£5
ditto, Scribner (U.S.), 1970 . . . . . £10/£5
Strangers and Brothers, Macmillan, 1972 (omnibus
   edition) . . . . £15/£5

Other Novels
Death Under Sail, Heinemann, 1932 . . £450/£65
ditto, Scribner (U.S.), 1959 . . . . . £200/£25
New Lives for Old, Gollancz, 1933 (anonymous) .
   . . . . £250/£65
The Search, Gollancz, 1934 . . . . £125/£30
ditto, Bobbs-Merrill (U.S.), 1935. . . £65/£15
The Malcontents, Macmillan, 1972 . . . £10/£5
ditto, Scribner (U.S.), 1972 . . . . . £10/£5
In Their Wisdom, Macmillan, 1974 . . . £10/£5
ditto, Scribner (U.S.), 1974 . . . . . £10/£5
A Coat of Varnish, Macmillan, 1979 . . £10/£5
ditto, Scribner (U.S.), 1979 . . . . . £10/£5
ditto, Franklin Library (U.S.), 1979 . . . £25

Others
Richard Aldington, Heinemann, [1938] (wraps) £35
Two Cultures and the Scientific Revolution, C.U.P.,
   1959 (wraps) £20
ditto, C.U.P. (U.S.), 1959 . . . . . . £15/£5
Science and Government, Harvard Univ. Press (U.S.),
   1961 . . . . £10/£5

Variety of Men, Macmillan, 1968 . . . £15/£5
ditto, Scribner (U.S.), 1968 . . . . . £15/£5
The State of Siege, Scribner (U.S.), 1969 . £10/£5
Public Affairs, Macmillan, 1971. . . . £10/£5
ditto, Scribner (U.S.), 1971 . . . . . £10/£5
Trollope, Macmillan, 1975 . . . . . £15/£5
ditto, Scribner (U.S.), 1975 . . . . . £10/£5
The Realists, Macmillan, 1978 . . . . £10/£5
ditto, Scribner (U.S.), 1978 . . . . . £10/£5
The Physicists, Macmillan, 1981. . . . £10/£5
ditto, Little, Brown (U.S.), 1981 . . . . £10/£5

ALEXANDER SOLZHENITSYN
(b.1918)

Since being deported from Russia Solzhenitsyn has lost some of his mystique, although none of his reputation as a fine writer.

Novels
One Day in the Life of Ivan Denisovich, Praeger
   (U.S.), 1963 . . . . £100/£25
ditto, Dutton (U.S.), 1963. . . . . . £75/£20
ditto, Gollancz, 1963 . . . . £75/£20
We Never Make Mistakes: Two Short Novels, Univ. of
   South Carolina (U.S.), 1963. . . . £100/£25
The First Circle, Harper & Row, 1968 . . £25/£10
ditto, Collins, 1968 . . . . £25/£10
Cancer Ward, Dial Press (U.S.), 1968 (1 vol.) £35/£10
ditto, Bodley Head, 1968-1969 (2 vols) . . £65/£20
August 1914, Bodley Head, 1972 . . . £35/£10
ditto, Farrar Straus (U.S.), 1972 . . . . £35/£10
The Gulag Archipelago, Harper (U.S.), 1974 £15/£5
ditto, Collins, 1974 . . . . £15/£5
The Gulag Archipelago, 2, Harper (U.S.), 1975 . .
   . . . . £10/£5
ditto, Collins, 1975 . . . . £10/£5
The Gulag Archipelago, 3, Harper (U.S.), 1976 £10/£5
ditto, Collins, 1978 . . . . £10/£5

Plays
The Love-Girl and the Innocent, Bodley Head, 1969 .
   . . . . £20/£5
ditto, Farrar Straus (U.S.), 1970 . . . . £15/£5
Candle in the Wind, Univ. of Minnesota (U.S.), 1973 .
   . . . . £15/£5
ditto, Bodley Head/O.U.P., 1973 . . . . £15/£5
Victory Celebrations, Bodley Head, 1983 . £10/£5
Prisoners, Bodley Head, 1983 . . . . £10/£5
Three Plays, Farrar Straus (U.S.), 1986. . £15/£5

Others
Stories and Prose Poems, Bodley Head, 1971 £15/£5
ditto, Farrar Straus (U.S.), 1971 . . . . £15/£5
'One Word of Truth ...', Bodley Head, 1972 (wraps)
   . . . . £15

ditto, as *A World Split Apart*, Harper (U.S.), 1979
. . . . £10/£5
Letter to Soviet Leaders, Index on Censorship, 1974
(wraps) £5
ditto, Harper (U.S.), 1974. . . . . £10/£5
From under the Rubble, Little, Brown (U.S.), 1975 .
. . . . £10/£5
ditto, Collins, 1975 . . . . £10/£5
Lenin in Zurich, Farrar Straus (U.S.), 1976. £10/£5
ditto, Bodley Head, 1976 . . . . . . £10/£5
Warning to the Western World, Bodley Head/BBC,
1976 (wraps) £10
ditto, as **Speeches to the Americans**, Farrar Straus,
1976 . . . . £10/£5
Alexander Solzhenitsyn Speaks to the West, Bodley
Head, 1979 . . . . £10/£5
The Mortal Danger, Bodley Head, 1980 . £10/£5
ditto, Harper (U.S.), 1980. . . . . £10/£5
The Oak and the Calf, Harper (U.S.), 1980. £10/£5
ditto, Bodley Head, 1980 . . . . . £10/£5

Verse
Prussian Nights, Collins/Harvill, 1977 . . £15/£5
ditto, Farrar Straus (U.S.), 1977 . . . . £15/£5

MURIEL SPARK
(b.1918)

A novelist, poet and short story writer, Spark's first
novel, *The Comforters* was very well received. All of
her novels are written with elegance and detachment,
and are full of black humour and irony.

Novels
The Comforters, Macmillan, 1957 . . . £250/£35
ditto, Lippincott (U.S.), 1957. . . . . £125/£25
Robinson, Macmillan, 1958 . . . . . £150/£30
ditto, Lippincott (U.S.), 1958. . . . . £75/£20
Memento Mori, Macmillan, 1959 . . . £125/£30
ditto, Lippincott (U.S.), 1959. . . . . £75/£20
The Ballad of Peckham Rye, Macmillan, 1960. . .
. . . . £75/£20
ditto, Lippincott (U.S.), 1960. . . . . £30/£10
The Bachelors, Macmillan, 1960 . . . £45/£15
ditto, Lippincott (U.S.), 1961. . . . . £15/£5
The Prime of Miss Jean Brodie, Macmillan, 1961. .
. . . . £150/£25
ditto, Lippincott (U.S.), 1962. . . . . £75/£20
The Girls of Slender Means, Macmillan, 1963 £45/£10
ditto, Knopf (U.S.), 1963 . . . . . £15/£5
The Mandelbaum Gate, Macmillan, 1965 . £20/£5
ditto, Knopf (U.S.), 1965 . . . . . £15/£5
The Public Image, Macmillan, 1968 . . £20/£5
ditto, Knopf (U.S.), 1968 . . . . . £15/£5
The Driver's Seat, Macmillan, 1970. . . £20/£5
ditto, Knopf (U.S.), 1970 . . . . . £15/£5
Not to Disturb, Macmillan, 1971. . . . £20/£5

ditto, Observer Books, 1971 (500 signed copies,
glassine d/w) . . . . . . £125/£100
ditto, Viking (U.S.), 1972. . . . . . £15/£5
The Hothouse by the East River, Macmillan, 1973 .
. . . . £15/£5
ditto, Viking (U.S.), 1973. . . . . . £15/£5
The Abbess of Crewe: A Modern Morality Tale,
Macmillan, 1974 . . . . . . £15/£5
ditto, Viking (U.S.), 1974. . . . . . £15/£5
The Takeover, Macmillan, 1976 . . . . £15/£5
ditto, Viking (U.S.), 1976. . . . . . £10/£5
Territorial Rights, Macmillan, 1979. . . £10/£5
ditto, Coward McGann (U.S.), 1979 . . . £10/£5
Loitering With Intent, Bodley Head, 1981 . £10/£5
ditto, Coward McGann (U.S.), 1981. . . £10/£5
The Only Problem, Bodley Head, 1984 . . £10/£5
ditto, Franklin Library (U.S.), 1984 (signed edition) .
. . . . £35
ditto, Coward McGann (U.S.), 1984 . . . £10/£5
A Far Cry from Kensington, Constable, 1988 £10/£5
ditto, London Limited Editions, 1988 (150 signed,
numbered copies, glassine d/w). . . £65/£50
ditto, Houghton Mifflin (U.S.), 1988 . . £10/£5
Symposium, Constable, 1990. . . . . £10/£5
ditto, Houghton Mifflin (U.S.), 1990 . . £10/£5
Reality and Dreams, Constable, 1996 . . £10/£5
ditto, Houghton Mifflin (U.S.), 1990 . . £10/£5

Omnibus Editions
The Muriel Spark Omnibus, Constable, 1993 (vol. 1).
. . . . £10/£5
The Muriel Spark Omnibus, Constable, 1994 (vol. 2).
. . . . £10/£5
The Muriel Spark Omnibus, Constable, 1996 (vol. 3).
. . . . £15/£5

Verse
Out of a Book, Millar & Burden, [1933] (broadside,
pseud. 'Muriel Camberg') £1,000
The Fanfarlo, Hand & Flower Press, 1952 (first issue,
wraps printed in red). £75
ditto, Hand & Flower Press, 1952 (second issue, wraps
printed in blue) £50
Collected Poems I, Macmillan, 1967 . . £25/£10
ditto, Knopf (U.S.), 1968 . . . . . £25/£10
Going Up to Sotheby's and Other Poems, Granada,
1982 (wraps) £10

Short Stories
The Go-Away Bird and Other Stories, Macmillan,
1958 . . . . £175/£35
ditto, Lippincott (U.S.), 1960. . . . . £45/£15
The Seraph and the Zambesi, Lippincott (U.S.), 1960
(privately printed, wraps) £45
Collected Stories, Macmillan, 1967 . . . £20/£5
ditto, Knopf (U.S.), 1968 . . . . . £15/£5
Bang-Bang You're Dead and Other Stories, Granada,
1982, (wraps). £10

The Stories of Muriel Spark, Dutton (U.S.), 1985 . . . . £10/£5
ditto, Bodley Head, 1987 . . . . . £10/£5
The Portobello Road and Other Stories, Eurographica (Helsinki), 1990 (350 signed copies, wraps) . £75
Harper and Wilton, Colophon Press, 1996 (100 signed copies of 110) £75
ditto, Colophon Press, 1996 (10 roman numbered copies for the author, signed, of 110) . . . £450

Children's
The Very Fine Clock , Knopf (U.S.), 1968 . £45/£20
ditto, Macmillan, 1969 . . . . . £25/£10
French Window, Colophon Press, 1993 (105 signed copies) £60
ditto, Colophon Press, 1994 (12 signed copies, leather) £150

Plays
Voices at Play, Macmillan, 1961 . . . . £25/£5
ditto, Lippincott (U.S.), 1962 . . . . £10/£5
Doctors of Philosophy, Macmillan, 1963 . £25/£5
ditto, Knopf (U.S.), 1966 . . . . . £10/£5

Others
Reassessment, Reassessment Pamphlet No.1, [1948], (single sheet, folded). £500
Child of Light: A Reassessment of Mary Wollstone-craft Shelley, Tower Bridge, 1951 . . £100/£25
ditto, Folcroft Library Editions (U.S.), 1976 £20/£5
Emily Brontë: Her Life and Work, Owen, 1953 (with Derek Stanford) . . . . £75/£20
ditto, Coward McGann (U.S.), 1966 . . . £25/£5
John Masefield, Nevill, 1953 . . . £45/£10
ditto, Folcroft Library Editions (U.S.), 1977 £20/£5
The Essence of the Brontës, Owen, 1993 £15/£5

Autobiography
Curriculum Vitae: A Volume of Autobiography, Constable, 1992 . . . . £10/£5
ditto, Houghton Mifflin (U.S.), 1993 . . £10/£5

STEPHEN SPENDER
(b.1909 d.1995)

Early in his poetic career Spender displays a lyricism which he did not continue. In later years he put more of his energies into critical works.

Verse
Nine Experiments by S.H.S.: Being Poems Written at the Age of Eighteen, hand-printed by Spender, 1928 (wraps) £50,000
Twenty Poems, Blackwell, 1930 (75 signed copies of 135, wraps) £600
ditto, Blackwell, 1930 (55 unsigned copies of 135, wraps). £400

Poems, Faber, 1933 . . . . £125/£25
ditto, Random House (U.S.), 1934 . . . £100/£20
Vienna, Faber, 1934 . . . . . . £125/£25
ditto, Random House (U.S.), 1935 . . . £100/£15
The Still Centre, Faber, 1939. . . . . £75/£15
Selected Poems, Faber, 1940 . . . . £30/£10
Ruins and Visions, Faber, 1942 . . . . £35/£10
ditto, Random House (U.S.), 1942 . . . £25/£10
Spiritual Exercises, Curwen Press, 1943 (125 copies, wraps) £250
Poems of Dedication, Faber, 1947 . . . £30/£10
ditto, Random House (U.S.), 1947 . . . £25/£10
The Edge of Being, Faber, 1949 . . . . £30/£10
ditto, Random House (U.S.), 1949 . . . £25/£10
Sirmione Peninsula, Faber, 1954 (wraps) . . £25
Collected Poems, 1928-1953, Faber, 1955 . £25/£10
ditto, Random House (U.S.), 1955 . . . £25/£10
Inscriptions, Poetry Book Society, 1958 (wraps) £20
Selected Poems, Random House (U.S.), 1964 £15/£5
ditto, Faber, 1965 . . . . £15/£5
The Generous Days, Faber, 1971 . . . £20/£5
ditto, Random House (U.S.), 1971 . . . £20/£5
Recent Poems, Anvil Press Poetry, 1978 (400 signed copies, wraps) £40
Dolphins, Faber, 1994 . . . . . . £15/£5
ditto, Faber, 1994 (150 signed copies) . . £75
ditto, St Martin's Press (U.S.), 1994 . . £15/£5

Novels
The Backward Son, Hogarth Press, 1940 . £150/£40
The Temple, Faber, 1988 . . . . . . £15/£5
ditto, Grove Press (U.S.), 1988 . . . . £15/£5

Short Stories
The Burning Cactus, Faber, 1936 . . . £50/£15
ditto, Random House (U.S.), 1936 . . . £45/£15
Engaged in Writing and The Fool and The Princess, Hamish Hamilton, 1958 . . . . . . £25/£5
ditto, Farrar Straus (U.S.), 1958 . . . £25/£5

Plays
Trial of a Judge, Faber, 1938 . . . . £35/£10
ditto, Random House (U.S.), 1938 . . . £30/£10
Danton's Death, Faber, 1939 (adaptation with Goronwy Rees) . . . . £35/£10
Oedipus Trilogy, Faber, 1985 . . . . £15/£5
ditto, Random House (U.S.), 1985 . . . £15/£5

Prose
The Destructive Element, Cape, 1935 . . £100/£25
ditto, Houghton Mifflin (U.S.), 1935 . . £100/£25
Forward from Liberalism, Gollancz, 1937 . £50/£15
ditto, Left Book Club, 1937 (wraps) . . . £25
ditto, Random House (U.S.), 1937 . . . £25/£10
The New Realism: A Discussion, Hogarth Press, 1939 (wraps) £30
Life and the Poet, Secker & Warburg, 1942 £20/£5
Citizens in War - And After, Harrap, 1945 . £50/£10

European Witness: Impressions of Germany in, 1945,
Hamish Hamilton, 1946 . . . . . £20/£5
ditto, Reynal & Hitchcock (U.S.), 1946 . . £20/£5
Poetry Since 1939, Longmans, Green, 1946 (wraps) .
. . . . £15
World Within World, Hamish Hamilton, 1951 £15/£5
ditto, Harcourt Brace (U.S.), 1951 . . . £10/£5
Learning Laughter, A Study of Children in Israel,
Weidenfeld & Nicolson, 1952 . . . £15/£5
ditto, Harcourt Brace (U.S.), 1953 . . . £15/£5
The Creative Element, Hamish Hamilton, 1953 .
. . . . £10/£5
ditto, British Book Center (U.S.), 1954 . £10/£5
The Making of a Poem, Hamish Hamilton, 1955 . .
. . . . £20/£5
The Struggle of the Modern, Hamish Hamilton, 1963 .
. . . . £15/£5
ditto, Univ. of California Press (U.S.), 1954 £15/£5
The Year of the Young Rebel, Weidenfeld &
Nicolson, 1969 . . . . . . £15/£5
ditto, Random House (U.S.), 1969 . . . £10/£5
*Love-Hate Relations: A Study of Anglo-American
Sensibilities*, Hamish Hamilton, 1974 . . £10/£5
ditto, Random House (U.S.), 1974 . . . £10/£5
T.S. Eliot, Fontana, 1975 (wraps) . . . £5
ditto, Viking (U.S.), 1976 . . . . £20/£5
*The Thirties and After: Poetry, Politics and People,
1933-75*, Fontana, 1975 (wraps) . . . £5
ditto, Random House (U.S.), 1978 . . . £10/£5
Letters to Christopher, Black Sparrow Press (U.S.),
1980 . . . . £20
ditto, Black Sparrow Press (U.S.), 1980 (200
numbered, signed copies) £35
China Diary, Thames & Hudson, 1982 . . £30/£10
ditto, Abrams (U.S.), 1982 . . . . £15/£5
Journals, 1939-83, Faber, 1985 . . . . £10/£5
ditto, Random House (U.S.), 1986 . . . £10/£5

Others

*W.H. Auden, A Memorial Address Delivered at Christ
Church Cathedral, Oxford on 27 October, 1973*,
Faber, 1975 (wraps) £75
W.H. Auden, A Tribute, Weidenfeld & Nicholson,
1975 . . . . £15/£5
ditto, Macmillan (U.S.), 1975 . . . . £10/£5

GERTRUDE STEIN
(b.1874 d.1946)

Although an American woman of letters, Stein lived
in France from 1903 until her death.

Fiction
*Three Lives: Stories of the Good Anna, Melanctha,
and the Gentle Lena*, The Grafton Press (U.S.), 1909
. . . . £750
ditto, John Lane (U.S.), 1909 (300 copies with sheets
from the above edition) £500
ditto, Bodley Head, 1920 . . . . . £250/£5
*The Making of Amencans, Being a History of a
Family's Progress*, Contact Editions/The Three
Mountains Press (Paris), [1925] (400 of 500 copies,
wraps) £750
ditto, Boni (U.S.), 1925 (100 of 500 copies) £1,000
*A Book Concluding with As a Wife Has a Cow: A
Love Story*, Galerie Simon (Paris), 1926 (102 signed
copies, wraps) £2,000
ditto, Galerie Simon (Paris), 1926 (10 signed copies on
Japanese vellum signed copies, wraps) . . £10,000
Lucy Church Amiably, Imprimerie Union (Paris), 1930
. . . . £250/£175
ditto, Something Else Press (U.S.), 1969 (100 of 500
copies) . . . . £30/£10
Ida: A Novel, Random House (U.S.), 1941 . £100/£25
Brewsie and Willie, Random House (U.S.), 1946 . .
. . . . £35/£10
Blood on the Dining Room Floor, Banyan Press
(U.S.), 1948 (26 copies, glassine d/w and slipcase)
. . . . £300/£250
ditto, Banyan Press (U.S.), 1948 (600 copies, glassine
d/w and slipcase) . . . . . . £175/£150
Things as They Are: A Novel in Three Parts, Banyan
Press (U.S.), 1950 (26 copies, glassine d/w) . . .
. . . . £300/£250
ditto, Banyan Press (U.S.), 1950 (490 copies, glassine
d/w) . . . . £150/£125
Mrs. Reynolds, and Five Early Novelettes, Yale Univ.
Press (U.S.) 1952 . . . . . . £25/£10
A Novel of Thank You, Yale Univ. Press (U.S.) 1958 .
. . . . £25/£10

Plays
Geography and Plays, Four Seas (U.S.), 1922 (first
binding with lettering on front cover) . . £300
ditto, Four Seas (U.S.), 1922 (second binding without
lettering on front cover) £200
A Village: Are You Ready Yet Not Yet, Editions de la
Galerie Simon (Paris), 1928 (90 signed copies, wraps)
. . . . £1,250
Operas and Plays, Plain Edition (Paris), 1932 (wraps,
slipcase) £350
Four Saints in Three Acts, Random House (U.S.),
1934 (music by Virgil Thomson) . . . £50/£20
A Wedding Bouquet: Ballet, J. & W. Chester, Ltd,
1936 (music by Lord Berners, wraps) . . . £150

In Savoy; or Yes Is for a Very Young Man, Pushkin
Press, 1946 (wraps) £30
The Mother of Us All, Music Press (U.S.), 1947 (music
by Virgil Thomson, wraps) £100
Last Operas and Plays, Rinehart (U.S.), 1949 £30/£10

Verse and Prose Poems
Tender Buttons: Objects, Food, Rooms, Claire Marie
(U.S.), 1914 . . . . £750
Have They Attacked Mary. He Giggled, Temple
(U.S.), 1917 (200 copies, red wraps) . . . £500
*Before the Flowers of Friendship Fade Friendship
Faded*, Plain Edition (Paris), 1931 (120 signed
copies, wraps) £1,000
Two (Hitherto Unpublished) Poems, Banyan Press/
Gotham Book Mart (U.S.), 1914 (wraps) . . £125
Stanzas in Meditation and Other Poems (1929-1933),
Yale Univ. Press (U.S.) 1956 . . . . £25/£10

Other Titles
Portrait of Mabel Dodge, Galileiana (Florence), 1912
(300 copies, wraps) £1,000
Composition as Explanation, Hogarth Press, 1926 .
. . . . £125
An Elucidation, Transition (Paris), 1927 (wraps) £125
Useful Knowledge, Payson & Clarke (U.S.), 1928 . .
. . . . £250/£30
ditto, John Lane/Bodley Head, 1929 . . . £200/£30
An Acquaintance with Description, Seizen Press, 1929
(225 signed copies) £750
Dix Portraits, Éditions de la Montagne (Paris), [1930]
(illustrated by Picasso and others, 10 signed copies) .
. . . . £2,000
ditto, Éditions de la Montagne (Paris), [1930] (25
signed copies) £1,250
ditto, Éditions de la Montagne (Paris), [1930] (65
signed copies) £1,000
ditto, Éditions de la Montagne (Paris), [1930] (402
signed copies) £250
How to Write, Plain Edition (Paris), 1931 . . £125
The Autobiography of Alice B. Toklas, Harcourt Brace
(U.S.), 1933 . . . . £300/£30
ditto, Bodley Head, 1933 . . . . £200/£30
*Matisse, Picasso, and Gertrude Stein, with Two
Shorter Stories*, Plain Edition (Paris), 1933 (wraps
with glassine d/w and slipcase . . . £275/£225
Portraits and Prayers, Random House (U.S.), 1934
(cellophane d/w) . . . . . £200/£150
Lectures in America, Random House (U.S.), 1935 (top
edge stained grey, with frontispiece) . . £250/£65
ditto, Random House (U.S.), 1935 (top unstained, no
frontispiece) . . . . £200/£15
Narration: Four Lectures, Univ. of Chicago Press
(U.S.), 1935 . . . . £200/£45
ditto, Univ. of Chicago Press (U.S.), 1935 (120 signed
copies in slipcase) . . . . . £650/£500
*The Geographical History of America, or, The
Relation of Human Nature to the Human Mind*,
Random House (U.S.), 1936 . . . £1,000/£250

Everybody's Autobiography, Random House (U.S.),
1937 . . . . £150/£25
ditto, Heinemann, 1938 . . . . . £100/£15
Picasso, Librairie Floury (Paris), 1938 (wraps) . £150
ditto, Batsford, 1938 . . . . . £100/£25
ditto, Scribners (U.S.), 1939 . . . . £75/£20
The World Is Round, Young Scott (U.S.), 1939
(illustrated by Clement Hurd) . . . £150/£35
ditto, Young Scott (U.S.), 1939 (350 signed copies,
slipcase) . . . . £500/£400
ditto, Batsford, 1939 . . . . . £100/£25
Paris France, Scribners (U.S.), 1940 . . £100/£25
ditto, Batsford, 1940 . . . . . £75/£20
What Are Masterpieces, Conference Press (U.S.), 1940
. . . . £100/£25
ditto, Conference Press (U.S.), 1940 (50 signed copies)
. . . . £750/£500
Wars I Have Seen, Random House (U.S.), 1945 . .
. . . . £35/£10
ditto, Batsford, 1945 . . . . . . £25/£10
The Stein First Reader, and Three Plays, Fridberg,
1946 . . . . £30/£10
ditto, Houghton Mifflin, 1948 . . . £30/£10
Selected Writings, Random House (U.S.), 1946 . .
. . . . £25/£10
Four in America, Yale Univ. Press, 1947 . £45/£15
Literally True, Holland (U.S.), 1947 (folded leaflet) .
. . . . £30
*Two: Gertrude Stein and Her Brother and Other
Early Portraits (1908-1912)*, Yale Univ. Press, 1951.
. . . . £45/£15
Bee Time Vine and Other Pieces (1913-1927), Yale
Univ. Press, 1953 . . . . . £45/£15
As Fine as Melanctha (1914-1930), Yale Univ. Press,
1954 . . . . £45/£15
Painted Lace and Other Pieces (1914-1937), Yale
Univ. Press, 1955 . . . . . £45/£15
To Bobchen Haas, Warren Press (U.S.), 1956 (second
state after suppression of first state, folded card) £25
Alphabets and Birthdays, Yale Univ. Press, 1957 . .
. . . . £45/£15
On Our Way, Simon & Schuster (U.S.), 1959 (100
copies, wraps) £50
Fernhurst, Q.E.D., and Other Early Writings, Boni &
Liveright (U.S.), 1972 . . . . . £25/£10
ditto, Peter Owen, 1972 . . . . . £25/£10
A Primer for the Gradual Understanding of Stein,
Black Sparrow Press (U.S.), 1971 (60 copies,
slipcase) £200
ditto, Black Sparrow Press (U.S.), 1971 (500 copies) .
. . . . £75/£50
Reflections on the Atomic Bomb, Black Sparrow Press
(U.S.), 1974 (50 copies, with a copy of *Literally True*)
. . . . £75/£45
ditto, Black Sparrow Press (U.S.), 1974 (750 copies)
. . . . £50/£20
Dear Sammy: Letters from Stein and Alice B. Toklas,
Houghton Mifflin (U.S.), 1977 . . . £25/£10

JOHN STEINBECK
(b.1902 d.1968)

An American novelist, *The Grapes of Wrath* is perhaps his best known work, and was later made into a classic film. He was awarded the Nobel Prize for Literature in 1962.

Novels

Cup of Gold, McBride (U.S.), 1929 (first issue, top edges stained blue and 'First published August, 1929' on copyright page) . . . . . £5,000/£750
ditto, Covici-Friede (U.S.), 1929 (second issue, using McBride sheets, maroon cloth) . . . £500/£750
ditto, Heinemann, 1937 . . . . . £750/£150
The Pastures of Heaven, Brewer (U.S.), 1932 . .
. . . . £2,750/£500
ditto, Allan, 1933 . . . . £750/£150
To a God Unknown, Ballou (U.S.), 1933 £4,500/£750
ditto, Heinemann, 1935 . . . . . £750/£150
Tortilla Flat, Covici Friede (U.S.), 1935 £1,000/£150
ditto, Covici Friede (U.S.), 1935 (500 advance review copies in wraps) £750
ditto, Heinemann, 1935 . . . . . £750/£125
In Dubious Battle, Covici Friede (U.S.), 1936 . .
. . . . £750/£150
ditto, Covici Friede (U.S.), 1936 (99 signed, numbered copies, tissue d/w and black slipcase) £3,000/£2,500
ditto, Heinemann, 1936 . . . . . £400/£65
Of Mice and Men, Covici Friede (U.S.), 1937 (first state with line ending 'pendula' on page 9 and a dot between the numbers on page 88) . £1,500/£500
ditto, Covici Friede (U.S.), 1937 (second state with line ending 'loosely' on page 9 and no dot between the numbers on page 88). . . . . £250/£150
ditto, Heinemann, 1937 . . . . . £250/£45
The Grapes of Wrath, Viking (U.S.), 1939 . . . .
. . . . £1,500/£200
ditto, Heinemann, 1939 . . . . . £200/£35
The Moon is Down, Viking (U.S.), 1941 (first state with large dot between 'talk' and 'this' on p.112, line 11). . . . . £150/£65
ditto, Viking (U.S.), 1941 (second state with large dot removed) . . . . £50/£15
ditto, Heinemann, 1942 . . . . £65/£20
Cannery Row, Viking (U.S.), 1945 (first issue, buff cloth) . . . . £650/£75
ditto, Viking (U.S.), 1945 (second issue, yellow cloth).
. . . . £200/£25
ditto, Heinemann, 1945 . . . . . £25/£5
The Wayward Bus, Viking (U.S.), 1947. . £125/£20
ditto, Heinemann, 1947 . . . . . £75/£15
The Pearl, Viking (U.S.), 1947 . . . £100/£20
ditto, Heinemann, 1948 . . . . . £35/£10
Burning Bright, Viking (U.S.), 1950 . £100/£15
ditto, Heinemann, 1951 . . . . . £25/£5
East of Eden, Viking (U.S.), 1952 . . £400/£75

ditto, Viking (U.S.), 1952 (1,500 signed, numbered copies) . . . . £1,250/£850
ditto, Heinemann, 1952 . . . . . £100/£25
Sweet Thursday, Viking (U.S.), 1954 . . £65/£15
ditto, Heinemann, 1954 . . . . . £45/£10
The Short Reign of Pippin IV: A Fabrication, Viking (U.S.), 1957 . . . . £40/£10
ditto, Heinemann, 1957 . . . . . £30/£5
The Winter of Our Discontent, Viking (U.S.), 1961 .
. . . . £20/£10
ditto, Heinemann, 1961 . . . . . £30/£5

Short Stories

Saint Katy the Virgin, Covici Friede (U.S.), 1936 (199 signed, numbered copies, glassine d/w) £1,250/£1,000
The Red Pony, Covici Friede (U.S.), 1937 (699 signed copies, slipcase) . . . . . £1,250/£1,000
ditto, Covici Friede (U.S.), 1937 (signed, lettered copies, slipcase) . . . . . £2,000/£1,800
ditto, Viking (U.S.), 1945 (enlarged edition, slipcase no d/w) . . . . £125/£100
The Long Valley, Viking (U.S.), 1938 . £250/£35
ditto, Heinemann, 1939 . . . . . £150/£25
How Edith McGillcuddy Met R.L.S., Rowfant Club (U.S.), 1943 (152 copies) . . £1,500/£1,250

Plays

Of Mice and Men, Covici Friede (U.S.), 1937 . . .
. . . . £750/£150

Screenplay

The Forgotten Village, Viking (U.S.), 1941 £1230/£20
Viva Zapata!, Edizioni Filmcritica (Italy), 1952 £25
ditto, Viking (U.S.), 1975 (wraps) £25
ditto, Yolla Bolly Press (U.S.), 1991 (190 numbered copies signed by the artist, slipcase) . £600
ditto, Yolla Bolly Press (U.S.), 1991 (40 signed deluxe copies signed by the artist, with *Zapata The Man, The Myth, And The Mexican Revolution*, also signed) .
. . . . £1,250
ditto, Heinemann , 1991 . . . . . £75/£25

Others

Sea of Cortez: A Leisurely Journal of Travel and Research, Viking, 1941 (with Edward F. Ricketts) .
. . . . £500/£50
ditto, Viking, 1941 (advance proof copy, wraps) . .
. . . . £1,000
ditto, as *The Log from the Sea of Cortez*, Viking, 1951
. . . . £200/£20
ditto, as *The Log from the Sea of Cortez*, Heinemann, 1958 . . . . £75/£15
Bombs Away: The Story of a Bomber Team, Viking, 1942 . . . . £125/£20
A Russian Journal, Viking, 1948 . . . £75/£20
ditto, Heinemann, 1949 . . . . . £50/£15
Once There Was a War, Viking (U.S.), 1958 £75/£20
ditto, Heinemann, 1959 . . . . . £50/£15

Travels With Charley in Search of America, Viking
(U.S.), 1962 . . . . £40/£10
ditto, Heinemann, 1962 . . . . . £35/£10
Speech Accepting the Nobel Prize for Literature,
Viking (U.S.), 1962 (wraps) £75
America and Americans, Viking, 1966 . £35/£10
ditto, Heinemann, 1966 . . . . . £35/£10
The Acts of King Arthur and His Noble Knights,
Farrar Straus (U.S.), 1976 . . . . £10/£5
ditto, Heinemann, 1977 . . . . £10/£5

COUNT ERIC STENBOCK
(b.1860 d.1895)

The most self-conscious of all 1890s decadents,
Stenbock impressed his contemporaries by his
personality and wealth rather than by his morbidly
sensitive and self-financed poetry and prose.

Verse
Love, Sleep and Dreams, Shrimpton & Son/Simpkin
Marshall & Co., 1881[?]. £1,000
Myrtle, Rue and Cypress, privately printed by
Hatchards, 1883 . . . . . . £850
ditto, Hermitage Books, 1992 (60 numbered copies) .
. . . . £45
The Shadow of Death, The Leadenhall Press, 1893 .
. . . . £850
On the Freezing of the Baltic Sea, privately printed for
Timothy d'Arch Smith, 1961 . . . . £50

Short Stories
Studies of Death: Romantic Tales, David Nutt, 1894 .
. . . . £1,000
ditto, Durtro Press, 1996 [1997] . . . £75
The True Story of a Vampire, Tragara Press
(Edinburgh), 1989 (reprinted from Studies of death,
110 numbered copies) £45
The Child of the Soul, Durtro Press, 1999 . . £45

ROBERT LOUIS STEVENSON
(b.1850 d.1894)

A novelist, essayist and poet, many of Stevenson's
romances have become classics of English literature,
although such novels as *Treasure Island* and
Kidnapped are often relegated to the category of
children's fiction.

Fiction
New Arabian Nights, Chatto & Windus, 1882 (2 vols)
. . . . £750
ditto, Holt (U.S.), 1882 . . . . . £200

Treasure Island, Cassell, 1883 (first issue with 'Dead
Man's Chest' not capitalized on pp. 2 and 7; with
'rain' for 'vain' in the last line p.40; the 'a' not
present in line 6, p.63; the '8' etc) . . £5,000
ditto, Roberts Bros (U.S.), 1884 . . £1,000
Prince Otto, Chatto & Windus, 1885 . . . £250
ditto, Scribner (U.S.), 1902 . . . . . £100
The Dynamiter, More New Arabian Nights, Longmans
Green & Co., 1885 (with Fanny van de Grift
Stevenson, boards) £250
ditto, Longmans Green & Co., 1885 (with Fanny van
de Grift Stevenson, wraps) £275
ditto, Holt (U.S.), 1885 . . . . . £200
The Strange Case of Dr Jekyll and Mr Hyde, Scribner
(U.S.), 1886 (wraps). £2,500
ditto, Scribner (U.S.), 1886 (boards). . . £1,750
ditto, Longmans Green & Co., 1886 (wraps, first issue
with date on upper cover changed by hand to 1886) .
. . . . £3,000
ditto, Longmans Green & Co., 1886 (boards) £2,000
Kidnapped, Cassell, 1886 (with folding frontispiece
map, first issue with 'business' in line 11, p.40) £750
ditto, Cassell, 1886 (with folding frontispiece map,
second issue with 'pleasure' in line 11, p.40) . £450
ditto, Scribners (U.S.), 1886 (boards, with folding
frontispiece map, 8 pages of ads) . . . £500
ditto, Scribners (U.S.), 1886 (wraps, no ads) . £300
The Merry Men and Other Tales, Chatto & Windus,
1887 . . . . £150
ditto, Scribners (U.S.), 1887 . . . . £150
The Black Arrow, Scribners (U.S.), 1888 (wraps) £350
ditto, Scribners (U.S.), 1888 (boards) . . £150
ditto, Cassell, 1888 (wraps) £250
ditto, Cassell, 1888 (boards) £150
The Master of Ballantrae, Cassell, 1889 . . £250
ditto, Scribners (U.S.), 1889 (boards) . . £200
ditto, Scribners (U.S.), 1889 (wraps). . . £200
The Wrong Box, Longmans Green & Co., 1889 (with
L. Osbourne) £125
ditto, Scribners (U.S.), 1889 . . . . £125
The Wrecker, Cassell, 1892 (with L. Osbourne) £100
ditto, Scribners (U.S.), 1892 . . . . . £75
Three Plays, D. Nutt, 1892 (with W. Henley) . £75
ditto, D. Nutt, 1892 (with W. Henley, 30 copies on
Japanese vellum). £500
ditto, D. Nutt, 1892 (with W. Henley, 100 on Dutch
handmade paper). £250
Catriona, Cassell, 1893 . . . . . £150
Island Nights' Entertainments, Sribners (U.S.), 1893 .
. . . . £125
ditto, Cassell, 1893 . . . . . . £125
The Ebb-Tide, Stone & Kimball (U.S.), 1894 . £45
ditto, Heinemann, 1894 (with L. Osbourne). . £45
Valima Letters, Methuen, 1895 . . . . £50
Weir of Hermiston, Chatto & Windus, 1896 . £50
ditto, Scribners (U.S.), 1896 . . . . . £45
St. Ives, Scribners (U.S.), 1897 (with Quiller Couch) .
. . . . £75
ditto, Heinemann, 1898 (with Quiller Couch) . £50

Verse

A Child's Garden of Verses, Longmans Green & Co.,
1885 . . . . £1,500
ditto, Scribners (U.S.), 1885 . . . . . £750
Underwoods, Chatto & Windus, 1887 . . . £50
ditto, Scribners (U.S.), 1887 . . . . . £50
Ballads, Scribners (U.S.), 1890 . . . . . £50
ditto, Chatto & Windus, 1890 . . . . . £50
Songs of Travel and Other Verses, Chatto & Windus,
1896 . . . . £40
Verses by R.L.S., privately printed, The De Vinne
Press (U.S.), 1912 (100 presentation copies) . £300

Non Fiction

The Pentland Rising, Elliot, 1866 (anonymous, wraps)
. . . . £2,500
The Charity Bazaar, privately printed, 1868 (signed,
wraps). £750
ditto, privately printed, 1868 (unsigned, wraps) £500
An Inland Voyage, Kegan Paul, 1878 . . . £750
ditto, Roberts Bros (U.S.), 1883 . . . . . £250
Edinburgh: Picturesque Notes, Seeley & Co., 1879 .
. . . . £200
Travels With a Donkey in the Cevennes, Kegan Paul,
1879 . . . . £400
ditto, Roberts Bros (U.S.), 1879 . . . . £250
Virginibus Puerisque, Kegan Paul, 1881 . . £150
ditto, Scribners (U.S.), 1887 . . . . . . £75
*The Graver and the Pen, or Scenes from Nature with
Appropriate Verses by ....*, Osbourne & Co, 1882
(wraps) £500
Familiar Studies of Men and Books, Chatto &
Windus, 1882. . . . . £125
ditto, Chatto & Windus, 1882 (100 large paper copies)
. . . . £150
The Silverado Squatters, Chatto & Windus, 1883 (first
issue lacking 'his' on penultimate line, p.140) £250
Memories and Portraits, Chatto & Windus, 1887 £50
ditto, Scribners (U.S.), 1887 . . . . . . £35
Memoir of Fleeming Jenkin, Scribners (U.S.), 1887 .
. . . . £45
ditto, Longmans, 1912 . . . . £25
Father Damien, An Open Letter, privately printed,
(Australia,) 1890 (wraps, 25 copies) . . . £1,500
ditto, privately printed (Edinburgh), 1890 (unbound
sheets in portfolio, 30 copies) £750
ditto, Chatto & Windus, 1890 (wraps) . . . £300
In the South Seas, Cassell (copyright edition), 1890 .
. . . . £1,000
ditto, Edinburgh edition, 1896 (with 15 of 35 letters) .
. . . . £75
ditto, Scribners (U.S.), 1896 . . . . . . £75
ditto, Chatto & Windus, 1900 . . . . . £35
Across the Plains, Chatto & Windus, 1892 . £100
ditto, Chatto & Windus, 1892 (100 large paper copies)
. . . . £200
ditto, Allen Press (U.S.), 1950 (200 copies). . £150
A Footnote to History, Cassell, 1892 . . . £40
ditto, Scribners (U.S.), 1892 . . . . . . £40

The Amateur Emigrant, Stone & Kimball (U.S.), 1895
. . . . £25
Essays of Travel, Chatto & Windus, 1905 . . £20
ditto, Scribners (U.S.), 1905 . . . . . . £20
Essays in the Art of Writing, Chatto & Windus, 1905 .
. . . . £20
ditto, Scribners (U.S.), 1905 . . . . . . £20
Lay Morals and Other Papers, Chatto & Windus, 1911
. . . . £20
ditto, Scribners (U.S.), 1915 . . . . . . £15
Records of a Family of Engineers, Chatto & Windus,
1912 . . . . £15

BRAM STOKER
(b.1847 d.1912)

Born and educated in Dublin, Stoker was the author
of a number of novels of mystery and romance, the
most famous of which was *Dracula*.

Novels

The Snake's Pass, Sampson Low, 1891 [1890] £750
ditto, Harpers (U.S.), 1890 . . . . . . £750
The Watter's Mou', De Vinne & Co. (U.S.), 1894 . .
. . . . £350
ditto, Constable, 1895. . . . . £350
The Shoulder of Shasta, Constable, 1895 . . £500
Dracula, Constable, 1897 (first issue integral blank leaf
at rear and no advertisement) . . . £10,000
ditto, Constable, 1897 (second issue with ad. for
Shoulder of Shasta on p.392) £6,000
ditto, Doubleday & McClure (U.S.), 1899 . £2,000
Miss Betty, Pearson, 1898 . . . . . . £400
The Mystery of the Sea, Doubleday (U.S.), 1902 £300
ditto, Heinemann, 1902 . . . . £300
The Jewel of the Seven Stars, Doubleday, Page, 1902.
Heinemann, 1903 . . . . £400
The Man, Heinemann, 1905 . . . . . . £350
ditto, Century (U.S.), 1905 . . . . . . £200
Lady Athyne, Heinemann, 1908 . . . . . £300
ditto, Reynolds (U.S.), 1908 . . . . . . £200
The Lady of the Shroud, Heinemann, 1909. . £350
The Lair of the White Worm, Rider, 1911 . . £350

Short Stories

Under the Sunset, Sampson Low, 1882 [1881]. £300
Snowbound, Collier, 1908 (wraps) £75
Dracula's Guest and Other Weird Stories, Routledge,
1914 . . . . £300
ditto, Hillman-Curl (U.S.), 1937 . . . . £200
The Dualists, Tragara Press (Edinburgh), 1986,
(wrappers) £35

Non Fiction

The Duties of the Clerks of Petty Sessions in Ireland,
John Falconer, 1879 . . . . £200

A Glimpse of America, Sampson Low, 1886, (wraps) .
. . . . £65
Personal Reminiscences of Henry Irving, Heinemann,
1906, (two vols) £75
ditto, Macmillan (U.S.), 1906 . . . . . £75
Famous Impostors, Sidgwick and Jackson, 1910 . .
. . . . £100
ditto, Sturgis & Walton (U.S.), 1910. . . . £100

TOM STOPPARD
(b.1937)

A prolific playwright, Stoppard was born in
Czechoslovakia, taken to Singapore as an infant, and
finished his education in England.

Plays
Rosencrantz and Guildenstern are Dead, Faber, 1967
. . . . £250/£50
ditto, Faber, 1967 (wraps). £40
ditto, Grove Press (U.S.), 1967 . . . £200/£25
The Real Inspector Hound, Faber, 1968 . £200/£45
ditto, Faber, 1968 (wraps). £25
ditto, Grove Press (U.S.), 1969 (wraps) . . . £20
Enter a Free Man, Faber, 1968 . . . £150/£35
ditto, Faber, 1968 (wraps). £25
ditto, Grove Press (U.S.), 1972 (wraps) . . . £20
*Albert's Bridge and If You're Glad I'll be Frank: Two
Plays for Radio*, Faber, 1969 (wraps) . . . £35
After Magritte, Faber, 1971 (wraps). . . . £50
ditto, Grove Press (U.S.), 1972 (wraps) . . . £15
Jumpers, Faber, 1971. . . . . . . £75/£20
ditto, Faber, 1971 (wraps). £30
ditto, Grove Press (U.S.), 1972 . . . £35/£10
*Artist Descending a Staircase and Where Are They
Now?: Two Plays for Radio*, Faber, 1973 . £45/£15
Travesties, Faber, 1975 . . . . . . £60/£15
ditto, Faber, 1975 (wraps). £20
ditto, Grove Press (U.S.), 1975 . . . . £15
Dirty Linen and New-Found-Land, Ambiance/Almost
Free Playscript, 1976 . . . . £25
ditto, Inter Action, 1976 (1,000 signed, numbered
copies, wraps) £40
ditto, Grove Press (U.S.), 1976 . . . . £35/£10
ditto, Faber, 1976 . . . . £10
The Fifteen Minute Hamlet, French, 1976 (wraps) £25
Albert's Bridge & Other Plays, Grove Press (U.S.),
1977 . . . . £20/£5
Every Good Boy Deserves Favour and *Professional
Foul*, Faber, 1978 . . . . £50/£15
ditto, Faber, 1978 (wraps). £15
ditto, Grove Press (U.S.), 1978 . . . £25/£10
Night and Day, Faber, 1978 . . . . . £40/£10
ditto, Grove Press (U.S.), 1979 . . . . £25/£10
Undiscovered Country, Faber, 1980 (wraps) . £45
Dogg's Hamlet, Cahoot's Macbeth, Inter-Action, 1979
(2,000 numbered copies, wraps) £35

ditto, Faber, 1980 . . . . £20
On the Razzle, Faber, 1981 (wraps) £20
The Real Thing, Faber, 1982. . . . . . £15
ditto, Faber, 1982 (500 signed copies, broadside) £125
ditto, Faber (U.S.), 1984 (revised edition) . £20/£5
The Dog It was That Died and Other Plays, Faber,
1983 . . . . £15
Four Plays for Radio, Faber, 1984 . . . . £10
Squaring the Circle, Faber, 1984 . . . . £10
ditto, Faber (U.S.), 1985 (wraps). £10
Rough Crossing, Faber, 1985 . . . . . £10
Hapgood, Faber, 1988 . . . . £10
Radio Plays 1964-1983, Faber, 1990 . . . £10
In the Nation State, Faber, 1991. . . . . £10
Television Plays, 1965-84, Faber, 1993 . . £35/£10
Indian Ink, Faber, 1995 . . . . . . £30/£10
ditto, Faber, 1995 (wraps). £10

Novels
Lord Malquist and Mr Moon, Blond, 1966 . £75/£15
ditto, Knopf (U.S.), 1968 . . . . . . £25/£10

Others
Rosencrantz and Guildenstern Are Dead: The Film,
Faber, 1991 . . . . £15

DAVID STOREY
(b.1933)

A novelist and playwright, much of Storey's writing
considers the problems of working class characters as
they move into middle class surroundings and/or a
mid-life crisis.

Novels
This Sporting Life, Longmans, 1960 . . £175/£30
ditto, Macmillan (U.S.), 1960 . . . . £65/£10
Flight into Camden, Longmans, 1961 . . £100/£20
ditto, Macmillan (U.S.), 1961 . . . . £45/£10
Radcliffe, Longmans, 1963 . . . . . £40/£10
ditto, Coward McGann (U.S.), 1964 . . . £25/£5
Pasmore, Longman, 1972 . . . . . £15/£5
ditto, Dutton (U.S.), 1974. . . . . . £10/£5
A Temporary Life, Lane, 1973 . . . . £15/£5
ditto, Dutton (U.S.), 1974. . . . . . £10/£5
Saville, Cape, 1976 . . . . £20/£5
ditto, Harper (U.S.), 1977. . . . . . £10/£5
A Prodigal Child, Cape, 1981 . . . . £15/£5
ditto, Dutton (U.S.), 1982. . . . . . £10/£5
Present Times, Cape, 1984 . . . . . £15/£5
A Serious Man, Cape, 1998 . . . . . £10/£5

Plays
The Restoration of Arnold Middleton, Cape, 1967. .
. . . . £20/£5
In Celebration, Cape, 1969 . . . . . £20/£5
ditto, Grove Press (U.S.), 1975 . . . . £10/£5

The Contractor, Cape, 1970	£15/£5
ditto, Random House (U.S.), 1971 . . .	£10/£5
Home, Cape, 1970.	£15/£5
ditto, Random House (U.S.), 1971 . . .	£10/£5
The Changing Room, Cape, 1972 . . .	£10/£5
ditto, Random House (U.S.), 1972 . . .	£10/£5
The Farm, Cape, 1973	£10/£5
Cromwell, Cape, 1973	£10/£5
Life Class, Cape, 1975	£10/£5
Mother's Day, Cape, 1977	£10/£5
Early Days, Penguin, 1980	£10
Sisters, Penguin, 1980.	£10
The March on Russia, French, 1989 . . .	£10

Humour

Edward, Lane, 1973	£10/£5

Verse

Storey's Lives: Poems, 1951-1991, Cape, 1992	£15/£5

GILES LYTTON STRACHEY
(b.1880 d.1932)

Lytton Strachey was educated at Liverpool and Cambridge Universities and became a prominent member of the Bloomsbury Group. Best known for biographies, he also wrote poetry, reviews and essays.

Landmarks in French Literature, Williams and Norgate, 1912 (first issue with top edge stained green and 8 pages of ads)	£75
ditto, Holt (U.S.), 1912	£15
Eminent Victorians, Chatto & Windus, 1918 .	£45
ditto, Putnam (U.S.), 1918	£25
Queen Victoria, Chatto & Windus, 1921	£75/£25
ditto, Harcourt (U.S.), 1921	£45/£15
Books and Characters, Chatto & Windus, 1922 .	
. . . .	£45/£15
ditto, Harcourt (U.S.), 1922	£25/£10
Pope: The Leslie Stephen Lecture, C.U.P., 1925 . .	
. . . .	£30/£10
ditto, Harcourt (U.S.), 1926	£25/£10
Elizabeth and Essex, Chatto & Windus, 1928	£35/£10
ditto, Harcourt Brace/Crosby Gaige (U.S.), 1928 . .	
. . . .	£20/£5
ditto, Harcourt Brace/Crosby Gaige (U.S.), 1928 (1,060 signed copies)	£50
Portraits in Miniature, Chatto & Windus, 1931 . .	
. . . .	£30/£10
ditto, Chatto & Windus, 1931 (260 signed copies)	£125
ditto, Harcourt (U.S.), 1931	£15/£5
Characters and Commentaries, Chatto & Windus, 1933	£45/£15
ditto, Harcourt (U.S.), 1933	£30/£10
Virginia Woolf and Lytton Strachey: Letters, Hogarth Press, 1956	£65/£20
ditto, Harcourt (U.S.), 1956	£25/£10

Spectatorial Essays, Chatto & Windus, 1964	£15/£5
ditto, Harcourt (U.S.), 1965	£10/£5
Ermyntrude and Esmeralda, Blond, 1969 (17 illustrations by Erte)	£45/£15
ditto, Stein & Day (U.S.), 1969	£25/£10
Lytton Strachey by Himself, Heinemann, 1971 (edited Michael Holroyd)	£15/£5
ditto, Holt, Rhinehart & Winston (U.S.), 1971	£10/£5
Lytton Strachey: The Really Interesting Question, Weidenfeld & Nicholson, 1972 (edited Paul Levy) . .	
. . . .	£15/£5
ditto, Coward, McCann (U.S.), 1973. . .	£15/£5
The Shorter Strachey, O.U.P., 1980 (edited Michael Holroyd)	£10/£5

MONTAGUE SUMMERS
(b.1880 d.1948)

A strange but scholarly character, Summers published many books on the supernatural as well as 17th century theatre and the Gothic novel.

Major Works

The Marquis de Sade, The British Society for the Study of Sex Psychology, 1920 (wraps) . .	£50
The History of Witchcraft and Demonology, Kegan Paul, 1926	£125/£50
ditto, Knopf (U.S.), 1926	£100/£35
The Geography of Witchcraft, Kegan Paul, 1927 . .	
. . . .	£100/£35
ditto, Knopf (U.S.), 1927	£100/£35
Essays in Petto, Fortune Press, [1928] . .	£125/£65
ditto, Fortune Press, [1928] (70 numbered copies)	£200
The Discovery of Witches, Cayme Press, 1928 (wraps)	£50
The Vampire: His Kith and Kin, Kegan Paul, 1928 .	
. . . .	£100/£30
ditto, University Books (U.S.), 1966. . .	£25/£10
The Vampire in Europe, Kegan Paul, 1929.	£100/£30
ditto, Dutton (U.S.), 1929.	£100/£30
The Werewolf, Kegan Paul, 1933 . . .	£200/£45
ditto, Dutton (U.S.), 1934.	£175/£40
The Restoration Theatre, Kegan Paul, 1934	£45/£20
ditto, Macmillan (U.S.), 1934	£35/£20
A Bibliography of the Restoration Drama, Fortune Press [1935]	£25/£10
ditto, Fortune Press [1935] (250 copies) . .	£45/£35
ditto, Fortune Press [1943] (revised and enlarged edition)	£25/£10
The Playhouse of Pepys, Kegan Paul, 1935	£40/£15
ditto, Macmillan (U.S.), 1935	£35/£15
A Popular History of Witchcraft, Kegan Paul, 1937 .	
. . . .	£65/£25
ditto, Dutton (U.S.), 1937.	£65/£25
The Gothic Quest, Fortune Press, [1938] (950 copies, no d/w)	£150

A Gothic Bibliography, Fortune Press [1940] (750 copies) £150
ditto, Russell & Russell (U.S.), 1964 (no d/w) . £50
Witchcraft and Black Magic, Rider, [1946] £45/£20
ditto, Causeway (U.S.), 1974 . . . . £25/£10
The Physical Phenomena of Mysticism, Rider, [1950] . . . . £35/£15
The Galanty Show: An Autobiography, Cecil Woolf, 1980 . . . . £25/£5
Letters to an Editor, Tragara Press (Edinburgh), 1986 (145 numbered copies, wraps) £25

Others
Antinous and Other Poems, Sisley's [1907] . £250
The Source of Southerne's The Fatal Marriage, C.U.P., 1916 (wraps) £45
The Double Dealer, [Incorporated Stage Society], [1916] (wraps) £35
Orrey's The Tragedy of Zoroastres, C.U.P., 1917 (wraps) £45
Love for Love, [Incorporated Stage Society], [1917] (wraps) £35
A Great Mistress of Romance, Royal Society of Literature, [1917] (wraps) £45
The Way of the World, [Incorporated Stage Society], [1918] (wraps) £35
Jane Austen: An Appreciation, Royal Society of Literature, [1918] (wraps) £45
The Provok'd Wife, Incorporated Stage Society, [1919] (wraps) £35

GRAHAM SWIFT
(b.1949)

A novelist whose acclaim was based largely on *Waterland* until *Last Orders* won the 1996 Booker Prize.

Novels
The Sweet-Shop Owner, Allen Lane, 1980 . £300/£45
ditto, Washington Square(U.S.), 1985 (wraps) . £10
Shuttlecock, Allen Lane, 1981 . . . . £250/£30
ditto, Washington Square(U.S.), 1985 (wraps) . £10
Waterland, Heinemann, 1983 . . . £75/£10
ditto, Poseidon (U.S.), 1984 . . . . £20/£5
Out of This World, Viking, 1988 . . £25/£5
ditto, Poseidon (U.S.), 1988 . . . . £15/£5
Ever After, Picador, 1992 . . . £15/£5
ditto, Knopf (U.S.), 1992 . . . . £10/£5
Last Orders, Picador, 1996 . . . £15/£5
ditto, Knopf (U.S.), 1996 . . . . £10/£5

Short Stories
Learning to Swim and Other Stories, London Magazine Editions, 1982 . . . . £125/£25
ditto, Poseidon (U.S.), 1982 . . . . £20/£5

A.J.A. SYMONS
(b.1900 d.1941)

A biographer, bibliographer and book collector, Symons' masterpiece is *The Quest for Corvo.*

A Bibliography of the First Editions of Books by William Butler Yeats, First Edition Club, 1924 (500 copies) . . . . £65/£30
Frederick Baron Corvo, Sette of Odd Volumes, 1927 (199 copies, wraps) £100
Emin: The Governor of Equatoria, The Fleuron, 1928 (300 copies) £45
ditto, Falcon Press, 1950 . . . . . £20/£5
An Episode in the Life of the Queen of Sheba Redicovered by A.J.A. Symons, privately printed, 1929 (150 copies, wraps) £100
H.M. Stanley, Duckworth, 1933 . . . £25/£10
ditto, Falcon Press, 1950 . . . . . £15/£5
The Quest for Corvo, Cassell, 1934 . . . £75/£20
ditto, Macmillan (U.S.), 1934 . . . £50 £15
The Nonesuch Century; An Appraisal. Nonesuch Press, 1936 (750 copies). £500 £375
Essays and Biographies, Cassell, 1969 (edited by Julian Symons) £15 £5
A.J.A. Symons to Wyndham Lewis: Twenty-Four Letters, Tragara Press, 1982 (120 copies, wraps) £35
Two Brothers: Fragments of a Correspondence, Tragara Press, 1985 (105 copies, wraps) . £35
ditto, Tragara Press, 1985 (25 copies, signed by Julian Symons, wraps) £60

JULIAN SYMONS
(b.1912 d.1994)

A novelist and critic, Symons' speciality is detective fiction. He co-founded the Crime Writers Association in 1953.

Novels
The Immaterial Murder Case, Gollancz, 1945 . . . . £100/£25
ditto, Macmillan (U.S.), 1957 . . . £40/£15
A Man Called Jones, Gollancz, 1947 . . £35/£10
Bland Beginning, Gollancz, 1949 . . . £35/£20
ditto, Harper (U.S.), 1949 . . . . . £25/£10
The 31st of February, Gollancz, 1950 . £35/£20
ditto, Harper (U.S.), 1950 . . . . . £15/£5
The Broken Penny, Gollancz, 1952 . . £35/£10
ditto, Harper (U.S.), 1953 . . . . . £15/£5
The Narrowing Circle, Gollancz, 1954 . £35/£10
ditto, Harper (U.S.), 1954 . . . . . £15/£5
The Paper Chase, Collins, 1956 . . . £25/£5
ditto, as *Bogue's Fortune*, Harper (U.S.), 1957 £20/£5
The Colour of Murder, Collins, 1957 . . £25/£5

ditto, Harper (U.S.), 1957. . . . . . £15/£5
The Gigantic Shadow, Collins, 1958 . . £25/£5
ditto, as **Pipe Dream**, Harper, 1958 . . . £15/£5
The Progress of a Crime, Collins, 1960. . £25/£5
ditto, Harper (U.S.), 1960. . . . . . £15/£5
The Killing of Francie Lake, Collins, 1962. £25/£5
ditto, as **The Plain Man**, Harper, 1962 . . £10/£5
The End of Solomon Grundy, Collins, 1964 £20/£5
ditto, Harper (U.S.), 1964. . . . . . £10/£5
The Belting Inheritance, Collins, 1965 . . £15/£5
ditto, Harper (U.S.), 1965. . . . . . £10/£5
The Man Who Killed Himself, Collins, 1967 £15/£5
ditto, Harper (U.S.), 1967. . . . . . £10/£5
The Man Whose Dreams Came True, Collins, 1969 .
. . . . £15/£5
ditto, Harper (U.S.), 1969. . . . . . £10/£5
The Man Who Lost His Wife, Collins, 1971 £15/£5
ditto, Harper (U.S.), 1971. . . . . . £10/£5
The Players and the Game, Collins, 1971 . £15/£5
ditto, Harper (U.S.), 1972. . . . . . £10/£5
The Plot Against Roger Rider, Collins, 1973 £15/£5
ditto, Harper (U.S.), 1973. . . . . . £10/£5
A Three Pipe Problem, Collins, 1975 . . £15/£5
ditto, Harper (U.S.), 19725. . . . . £10/£5
The Blackheath Poisonings, Collins, 1978 . £15/£5
ditto, Harper (U.S.), 1979. . . . . . £10/£5
Sweet Adelaide, Collins, 1980 . . . . £15/£5
ditto, Harper (U.S.), 1980. . . . . . £10/£5
The Detling Murders, Macmillan, 1982. . £15/£5
ditto, as **The Detling Secret**, Viking, 1983 . £10/£5
The Name of Annabel Lee, Macmillan, 1983 £15/£5
ditto, Viking (U.S.), 1983. . . . . . £10/£5
The Criminal Comedy of the Contented Couple,
Macmillan, 1985. . . . . . . £15/£5
ditto, as **A Criminal Comedy**, Viking (U.S.), 1986 . .
. . . . £10/£5
The Kentish Manor Murders, Macmillan, 1988 £15/£5
ditto, Viking (U.S.), 1988. . . . . . £10/£5
Death's Darkest Face, Macmillan, 1990 . £15/£5
ditto, Viking (U.S.), 1990. . . . . . £10/£5
Something Like a Love Affair, Macmillan, 1992 . .
. . . . £15/£5
ditto, Mysterious Press (U.S.), 1992 . . . £10/£5
Playing Happy Families, Macmillan, 1994 . £15/£5
ditto, Mysterious Press (U.S.), 1995 . . . £10/£5
A Sort of Virtue, Macmillan, 1996 . . . £10/£5

Omnibus
The Julian Symons Omnibus, Collins, 1966 £10/£5

Stories
Murder, Murder, Fontana, 1961 (wraps) . . £10
Francis Quarles Investigates, Panther, 1965 (wraps) .
. . . . £10
The Tigers of Subtopia and Other Stories, Macmillan,
1981 . . . . £15/£5
ditto, Viking (U.S.), 1983. . . . . . £10/£5
Somebody Else and Other Stories, Eurographica
(Helsinki), 1990 (wraps). £35

Portraits of the Missing, Deutsch, 1991. . £15/£5
Murder Under the Mistletoe, Severn House, 1993 .
. . . . £10/£5
The Man Who Hated Television and Other Stories,
Macmillan, 1995. . . . . . . £10/£5

Poems
Confusions About X, Fortune Press, [1939] £100/£25
The Second Man, Routledge, 1943 . . . £50/£15
The Object of an Affair and Other Poems, Tragara
Press, 1974 (25 signed copies, wraps) . . . £75
ditto, Tragara Press, 1974 (65 copies, wraps) . £45
The Thirties and the Nineties, Carcanet, 1990 (wraps)
. . . . £5

Others
A.J.A. Symons: His Life and Speculations, Eyre &
Spottiswoode, 1950 . . . . £40/£15
Thomas Carlyle. The Life and Times of a Prophet,
Gollancz Ltd., 1951 . . . . . . £15/£5
Horatio Bottomley: A Biography, The Cresset Press,
1955 . . . . £15/£5
The General Strike, The Cresset Press, 1957 £25/£10
The Thirties. A Dream Revolved, The Cresset Press,
1960 (wraps) £35
Reasonable Doubt: Some Criminal Cases, The Cresset
Press, 1960 . . . . £25/£10
The Detective Story in Britain, Longmans, Green &
Co., 1962 (wraps) £10
Buller's Campaign, The Cresset Press, 1963 £25/£10
Critical Occasions, Hamish Hamilton, 1966 £25/£10
**England's Pride: The Story of the Gordon Relief
Expedition**, Hamish Hamilton, 1965 . . £25/£10
Portrait of an Artist: Conan Doyle, Whizzard Press/
Andre Deutsch, 1979 . . . . . . £25/£10
ditto, Mysterious Press (U.S.), 1979 . . . £25/£10
The Modern Crime Story, Tragara Press, 1980 (125
signed copies, wraps) £45
ditto, Eurographica (Helsinki), 1988 (350 signed
copies, wraps) £35
1948 and 1984, Tragara Press, 1984 (135 copies,
wraps). £35
Two Brothers: Fragments of a Correspondence,
Tragara Press, 1985 (105 copies, wraps) . . £35
ditto, Tragara Press, 1985 (25 copies, signed by Julian
Symons, wraps) £60
Makers of the New, Deutsch, 1987 . . . £10/£5
ditto, Random House (U.S.), 1987 . . . £10/£5
Oscar Wilde: A Problem in Biography, Yellow Barn
Press (U.S.), 1988 (200 copies). £65

W.M. THACKERAY
(b.1811 d.1863)

Charlotte Brontë's favourite author, Thackeray's most famous work is *Vanity Fair*.

Novels

Vanity Fair: A Novel Without a Hero, Bradbury & Evans, 1848 (20 parts in 19; yellow wraps)   £4,000
ditto, Bradbury & Evans, 1848 (first book edition, made up of the original parts; with the woodcut [later suppressed] of Lord Steyne on page 336) . £2,500
ditto, Harper & Bros (U.S.), 1848 . . . £1,500
The History of Pendennis, His Fortunes and Misfortunes, His Friends and His Greatest Enemy, Bradbury & Evans, 1850 (24 parts in 23; yellow wraps). £2,000
ditto, Bradbury & Evans, 1849[-50] (2 vols) £1,250
ditto, Harper & Bros (U.S.), 1855 . . £1,500
The History of Henry Esmond, Esq. A Colonel In the Service of Her Majesty Q. Anne. Written by Himself, Smith Elder, 1852 (3 vols) . . . £500
ditto, Harper & Bros (U.S.), 1852 (wraps) . £300
The Newcomes: Memoirs of a Most Respectable Family, Bradbury & Evans, 1853-55 (24 parts in 23, yellow wraps) £1,250
ditto, Bradbury & Evans, 1854[-55] (2 vols) . £750
ditto, Harper & Bros (U.S.), 1855 . . £100
The Memoirs of Barry Lyndon, Esq., of The Kingdom of Ireland, Appleton (U.S.), 1853 (2 vols). £1,500
ditto, Bradbury & Evans, 1856 (wraps) . . £500
The Virginians: A Tale of the Last Century, Bradbury & Evans, 1859 (24 parts, yellow wraps) . £750
ditto, Bradbury & Evans, 1858[-59] (2 vols) . £500
ditto, Harper & Bros (U.S.), 1859 . . . £100
Lovel the Widower, Harper & Bros (U.S.), 1860 £250
ditto, Smith Elder, 1861 . . . . . £250
The Adventures of Philip on His Way Through the World; Shewing Who Robbed Him, Who Helped Him, and Who Passed Him By, Smith Elder, 1862 (3 vols) £400
ditto, Harper & Bros (U.S.), 1862 . . . £65
Denis Duval, Smith Elder, 1867 . . . . £250

Christmas Books

Mrs Perkins's Ball, Chapman & Hall, [1847] (pseud. 'Mr M.A. Titmarsh'). £400
'Our Street', Chapman & Hall, 1848 (pseud. 'Mr M.A. Titmarsh', wraps) £400
Doctor Birch and His Young Friends, Chapman & Hall, 1849 (pseud. 'Mr M.A. Titmarsh', wraps) £400
The Kicklebury's on the Rhine, Chapman & Hall, 1850 (pseud. 'Mr M.A. Titmarsh') . . . £400
The Rose and the Ring, or, The History of Prince Gigilo and Prince Bulbo: A Fireside Pantomime for Great and Small Children, Chapman & Hall, 1855 (pseud. 'Mr M.A. Titmarsh') £500
Christmas Books, Chapman & Hall, 1857 . . £250

Tales and Sketches

The Yellowplush Papers, Harper & Bros. (U.S.), 1848 (brown boards with brown cloth spine) . £1,000
ditto, Harper & Bros (U.S.), 1848 (green cloth wraps). £1,500
Comic Tales and Sketches, Hugh Cunningham, 1841 (pseud. 'Mr Michael Angelo Titmarsh'; no reference to *Vanity Fair*) £750
The Book of Snobs, Punch Office, 1848 (wraps) £350
ditto, Appleton (U.S.), 1852 . . . . . £100
The Great Hoggarty Diamond, Harper & Bros (U.S.), 1848 (first issue with '82 Cliff Street' on title page, wraps). £1,500
The History of Samuel Titmarsh and the Great Hoggarty Diamond, Bradbury & Evans, 1849 £350
Rebecca and Rowena: A Romance Upon Romance, Chapman & Hall, 1850 (pseud. 'Mr Michael Angelo Titmarsh') £350
A Shabby Genteel Story, Appleton (U.S.), 1852 £350
ditto, Bradbury & Evans, 1857 (wraps) . . £350
The Fatal Boots and *Cox's Diary*, Bradbury & Evans, 1855 (wraps) £350
The Little Dinner at Timmins's and *The Bedford-Row Conspiracy*, Bradbury & Evans, 1856 (wraps) £350
The Memoirs of Mr Charles J. Yellowplush and *The Diary of C. Jeames de la Pluche, Esq.*, Bradbury & Evans, 1856 (wraps). £350
The Fitz-Boodle Papers and *Men's Wives*, Bradbury & Evans, 1857 (wraps). £350

Non Fiction

The Paris Sketch Book, John Macrone, 1840 (pseud. 'Mr Titmarsh', 2 vols) £750
The Irish Sketch Book, John Macrone, 1843 (pseud. 'Mr Titmarsh', 2 vols) £750
Notes of a Journey from Cornhill to Grand Cairo, By Way of Lisbon, Athens, Constantinople, and Jerusalem, Chapman & Hall, 1846 (pseud. 'Mr M.A. Titmarsh') £500
ditto, Wiley & Putnam. (U.S.), 1846. . . £300
The English Humorists of the Eighteenth Century: A Series of Lectures Delivered in England, Scotland and the United States of America, Smith Taylor, 1853 . . . . £250
ditto, Harper & Bros (U.S.), 1853 . . . £150
The Four Georges: Sketches of Manners, Morals, Court and Town Life, Harper Bros (U.S.), 1860 £250
ditto, Smith Elder, 1861 . . . . . . £250
The Roundabout Papers, Smith Elder, 1863 . £250
ditto, Harper & Bros (U.S.), 1863 . . . £150

Collected Editions

The Works of William Makepeace Thackeray, Smith Elder 'Library Edition', 1869-86 (24 vols) . £500
The Works of William Makepeace Thackeray, Smith Elder/Ritchie Edition, 1898-99 (24 vols) . . £400
The Oxford Thackeray, O.U.P./Saintsbury Edition, O.U.P, [1908] (17 vols) £250

The Works of William Makepeace Thackeray, Smith
Elder 'Centenary Biographical Edition', 1910-11 (26
vols) £750

PAUL THEROUX
(b.1941)

An American novelist and travel writer, Theroux first
came to the attention of the critics with the
publication of *The Great Railway Bazaar* and *The Old
Patagonian Express*.

Novels

Waldo, Houghton Mifflin (U.S.), 1967 . £150/£35
ditto, Bodley Head, 1968 .   .   .   .   .   £75/£20
Fong and the Indians, Houghton Mifflin (U.S.), 1968
  .   .   .   .   £125/£35
ditto, Hamish Hamilton, 1976 .   .   .   £65/£20
Girls at Play, Houghton Mifflin (U.S.), 1969 £100/£20
ditto, Bodley Head, 1969 .   .   .   .   £45/£15
Murder in Mount Holly, Ross, 1969   £2,000/£300
Jungle Lovers, Houghton Mifflin (U.S.), 1971 £75/£20
ditto, Bodley Head, 1971 .   .   .   .   .   £75/£20
Saint Jack, Bodley Head, 1973 .   .   £35/£10
ditto, Houghton Mifflin (U.S.), 1973 .   £35/£10
The Black House, Hamish Hamilton, 1974 .   £25/£5
ditto, Houghton Mifflin (U.S.), 1974 .   £20/£5
The Family Arsenal, Hamish Hamilton, 1976 £25/£5
ditto, Houghton Mifflin (U.S.), 1976 .   £25/£5
Picture Palace, Hamish Hamilton, 1978 .   £20/£5
ditto, Houghton Mifflin (U.S.), 1978 .   £20/£5
The Mosquito Coast, Hamish Hamilton, 1981 £20/£5
ditto, Houghton Mifflin (U.S.), 1982 .   £15/£5
ditto, Houghton Mifflin (U.S.), 1982 (350 signed
  copies, slipcase) .   .   .   .   .   £100/£65
Doctor Slaughter, Hamish Hamilton, 1984 .   £15/£5
ditto, as *Half Moon Street*, Houghton Mifflin (U.S.),
  1984 .   .   .   .   £15/£5
O-Zone, Hamish Hamilton, 1986 .   .   £15/£5
ditto, Putnam (U.S.), 1986 .   .   .   £10/£5
My Secret History, Hamish Hamilton, 1989 £10/£5
ditto, London Limited Editions, 1989 (150 signed,
  numbered copies) £75
ditto, Putnam (U.S.), 1989 .   .   .   £10/£5
Doctor Demarr, Hutchinson, 1990 .   .   £10/£5
Chicago Loop, Hamish Hamilton, 1990 .   .   £10/£5
ditto, Random House (U.S.), 1991 .   .   £10/£5
Millroy the Magician, Hamish Hamilton, 1993 £10/£5
ditto, Random House (U.S.), 1994 .   .   £10/£5
My Other Life, Hamish Hamilton, 1996.   .   £10/£5
ditto, Houghton Mifflin (U.S.), 1996 .   £10/£5
Kowloon Tong, Hamish Hamilton, 1997 .   £10/£5
ditto, Houghton Mifflin (U.S.), 1997 .   £10/£5
ditto, Franklin Library (U.S.), 1998 (1,350 signed
  copies) £40

Short Stories

Sinning with Annie and Other Stories, Houghton
  Mifflin (U.S.), 1972 .   .   .   .   .   £75/£20
ditto, Hamish Hamilton, 1975   .   .   .   £25/£10
The Consul's File, Hamish Hamilton, 1977   £20/£5
ditto, Houghton Mifflin (U.S.), 1977 .   .   £15/£5
World's End, Hamish Hamilton, 1980 .   £10/£5
ditto, Houghton Mifflin (U.S.), 1980 .   £10/£5
The London Embassy, Hamish Hamilton, 1982 £10/£5
ditto, Houghton Mifflin (U.S.), 1983 .   £10/£5
Collected Stories, Viking (U.S.), 1997 .   £10/£5

Travel

The Great Railway Bazaar: By Train Through Asia,
  Hamish Hamilton, 1975 .   .   .   .   £100/£25
ditto, Houghton Mifflin (U.S.), 1975 .   £65/£20
*The Old Patagonian Express: By Train Through the
  Americas*, Hamish Hamilton, 1979.   .   £20/£5
ditto, Houghton Mifflin (U.S.), 1979 .   £20/£5
The Kingdom by the Sea, Hamish Hamilton, 1983.   .
  .   .   .   .   £10/£5
ditto, Houghton Mifflin (U.S.), 1983 .   £10/£5
ditto, Houghton Mifflin (U.S.), 1983 (250 signed,
  numbered copies, slipcase) .   .   .   £50/£35
Sailing through China, Russell, 1984 (150 [400]
  signed copies, glassine d/w).   .   .   £75/£65
ditto, Houghton Mifflin (U.S.), 1984 .   £10/£5
Patagonia Revisited, Russell, 1985 (with Bruce
  Chatwin) .   .   .   .   .   .   £25/£10
ditto, Russell, 1985 (250 copies, cellophane d/w) .   .
  .   .   .   .   £200/£165
ditto, Houghton Mifflin (U.S.), 1986 .   £20/£10
ditto, as *Nowhere Is a Place*, Sierra Club (U.S.), 1991
  .   .   .   .   £20/£10
Sunrise with Seamonsters, Hamish Hamilton, 1985 .
  .   .   .   .   £10/£5
ditto, Houghton Mifflin (U.S.), 1985 .   £10/£5
The Imperial Way, Hamish Hamilton, 1985 (with
  Steve McCurry) .   .   .   .   .   £10/£5
ditto, Houghton Mifflin (U.S.), 1985 .   £10/£5
Riding the Iron Rooster: By Train Through China,
  Hamish Hamilton, 1988 .   .   .   .   £10/£5
ditto, Putnam (U.S.), 1988 .   .   .   £10/£5
The Happy Isles of Oceana: Paddling the Pacific,
  Hamish Hamilton, 1992 .   .   .   .   £10/£5
ditto, Putnam (U.S.), 1992 .   .   .   £10/£5
Pillars of Hercules, Hamish Hamilton, 1995 £10/£5
ditto, Putnam (U.S.), 1995 .   .   .   £10/£5
Fresh Air Fiend. Travel Writings, 1985–2000,
  Houghton Mifflin (U.S.), 2000 .   .   .   £15/£5

Others

V.S. Naipaul: An Introduction to his Work, Deutsch,
  1972 .   .   .   .   £1,000/£150
ditto, Africana (U.S.), 1972 .   .   .   £1,250/£150
A Christmas Card, Hamish Hamilton, 1978   £10/£5
ditto, Houghton Mifflin (U.S.), 1978 .   .   £10/£5

London Snow, Russell, 1979 (450 signed copies, glassine d/w) . . . . £100/£85
ditto, Hamish Hamilton, 1980 . . . £15/£5
ditto, Houghton Mifflin (U.S.), 1980 . . £15/£5
The Turn of the Years, Russell, 1982 (150 signed copies) £150
The Shortest Day of the Year: A Christmas Fantasy, Sixth Chamber Press, 1986 (175 signed copies) £60
ditto, Sixth Chamber Press, 1986 (26 signed copies on handmade paper). £100
Sir Vidia's Shadow, Hamish Hamilton, 1998 £10/£5
ditto, Houghton Mifflin (U.S.), 1998 . . £10/£5

DYLAN THOMAS
(b.1914 d.1953)

Notorious fitzrovian poet and playwright, Thomas died after taking morphine and drinking around a dozen whiskies in the White Horse Tavern in Greenwich Village, New York.

18 Poems, The Sunday Referee/The Parton Bookshop, 1934 (first issue, c.250 copies, flat spine, no advertisment leaf between half title and title) .
. . . . £2,000/£600
ditto, The Sunday Referee/The Parton Bookshop, 1934 (second issue, c.250 copies, round-backed spine, with advertisment leaf between half title and title) .
. . . . £1,000/£300
Twenty-Five Poems, Dent, 1936 . . . £600/£150
The Map of Love: Verse and Prose, Dent, 1939 (first issue in mauve cloth with very smooth texture, gilt blocking, top edge stained) . . £300/£200
ditto, Dent, 1939 (second issue in plum-coloured cloth with course texture, gilt blocking, top edge stained) .
. . . . £200/£100
ditto, Dent, 1939 (third issue, blue blocking, top edge stained) . . . . £125/£75
ditto, Dent, 1939 (fourth issue, blue blocking, top edge unstained). . . . . £75/£25
The World I Breathe, New Directions (U.S.), 1939 .
. . . . £500/£100
Portrait of the Artist as a Young Dog, Dent, 1940 .
. . . . £300/£75
ditto, New Directions (U.S.), 1940 . . £200/£45
From In Memory of Ann Jones, Caseg Press, [1942], (500 copies, broadside) £300
New Poems, New Directions (U.S.), 1943 (paper boards, d/w) . . . . £200/£75
ditto, New Directions (U.S.), 1943 (wraps in d/w) .
. . . . £125/£75
Deaths and Entrances, Dent, 1946 . . . £250/£75
ditto, Gregynog Press, 1984 (250 copies, John Piper illustrated edition, in slipcase). . . £250/£100
ditto, Gregynog Press, 1984 (28 roman numbered copies, in slipcase). . . . . . £1,000/£900

Selected Writings of Dylan Thomas, New Directions (U.S.), 1946 . . . . £125/£25
Twenty-Six Poems, Dent/New Directions, [1950] (Nos I-X signed, numbered copies of 150, printed on Japanese vellum, in slipcase) £6,000
ditto, Dent/New Directions, [1950] (Nos 11-60 signed, numbered copies of 150, slipcase) . . . £2,000
ditto, Dent/New Directions, [1950] (Nos 61-147 signed, numbered copies of 150, slipcase). . £2,000
In Country Sleep and Other Poems, New Directions (U.S.), 1952 . . . . £200/£65
ditto, New Directions (U.S.), 1952 (100 signed, numbered copies, in slipcase) . £2,000/£1,750
Collected Poems, 1934-1952, Dent, 1952 . £75/£15
ditto, Dent, 1952 (65 signed, numbered copies) £2,000
ditto, New Directions (U.S.), 1953 . . . £65/£10
The Doctors and the Devils, Dent, 1953 . £25/£5
ditto, New Directions (U.S.), 1953 . . . £20/£5
Two Epigrams Of Fealty, privately printed for members of the Court of Redonda, 1947, (30 numbered copies, folded leaflet) £200
Galsworthy and Gawsworth, privately printed for members of the Court of Redonda (1953), (30 numbered copies, folded leaflet) £200
Under Milk Wood: A Play for Voices, Dent, 1954 . .
. . . . £100/£15
ditto, New Directions (U.S.), 1954 . . . £45/£10
Quite Early One Morning, Dent, 1954 . . £75/£15
ditto, New Directions (U.S.), 1954 . . . £35/£10
Conversation About Christmas, New Directions (U.S.), 1954 (wraps, in envelope) . . . £125/£95
Adventures in the Skin Trade and Other Stories, New Directions (U.S.), 1955 . . . . . £100/£20
ditto, Putnam , 1955 . . . . . . £100/£20
A Prospect of the Sea, Dent, 1955 . . . £35/£10
A Child's Christmas in Wales, New Directions (U.S.), 1954 [1955]. . . . . £65/£15
ditto, New Directions (U.S.), [1969] (100 copies, illustrated by Fritz Eichenberg, with signed portfolio)
. . . . £350/£200
ditto, New Directions (U.S.), [1969] (trade edition illustrated by Fritz Eichenberg). . . . £35/£10
ditto, Dent, 1978 (illustrated by Edward Ardizzone). .
. . . . £25/£10
Letters to Vernon Watkins, Dent/Faber, 1957 £25/£5
ditto, New Directions (U.S.), 1957 . . . £20/£5
The Beach of Falesa, Stein & Day (U.S.), 1963 (film script) . . . . £25/£5
ditto, Cape, 1964 . . . . £20/£5
Twenty Years A-Growing, Dent, 1964 (film script) .
. . . . £20/£5
Rebecca's Daughters, Triton, 1965 (film script with a foreword by Sidney Box) . . . . . £20/£5
ditto, Little, Brown (U.S.), 1965 . . . . £15/£5
Me and My Bike, McGraw Hill (U.S.), 1965 £45/£15
ditto, Triton, 1965 (film script) . . . £35/£10
ditto, Triton, 1965 (500 copies, in slipcase). £75/£50
The Doctor and the Devils and Other Scripts, New Directions (U.S.), 1966 . . . . . £15/£5

Selected Letters of Dylan Thomas, Dent, 1966 £20/£5
ditto, New Directions (U.S.), 1967 . . . £20/£5
The Notebooks of Dylan Thomas, New Directions
(U.S.), 1967 . . . . £20/£5
ditto, as *Poet in the Making: The Notebooks of Dylan
Thomas*, Dent, 1968 . . . . . . £20/£5
Twelve More Letters, Turret Books, 1969 (175 copies,
acetate d/w) . . . . £65/£55
ditto, Turret Books, 1969 (26 lettered copies, acetate
d/w) . . . . £125/£100
Dylan Thomas: Early Prose Writings, Dent, 1971 . .
. . . . £15/£5
ditto, New Directions (U.S.), 1972 . . . £15/£5
The Death of the King's Canary, Hutchinson, 1976
(with John Davenport) . . . . . £10/£5
ditto, Viking (U.S.), 1976 . . . . . £10/£5
*Drawings to Poems by Dylan Thomas by Ceri
Richards*, Enitharmon Press, 1980 (180 copies) £75
Collected Letters, Dent, 1985 . . . . £20/£5
ditto, Macmillan (U.S.), 1976 . . . £20/£5
Dylan Thomas: The Notebook Poems, 1930-1934,
Dent, 1989 . . . . £15/£5
Dylan Thomas: The Broadcasts, Dent, 1991 £10/£5
Dylan Thomas: The Filmscripts, Dent, 1995 £10/£5

EDWARD THOMAS
(b.1878 d.1917)

Not a 'war poet', although he did die in the First
World War, Thomas's love of nature comes through
in his best work.

Verse
Six Poems, Pear Tree Press, [1916] (pseud. 'Edward
Eastway', copies in boards of total edition of 100) .
. . . . £1,250
ditto, Pear Tree Press, [1916] (pseud. 'Edward
Eastway', copies in wraps of total edition of 100) .
. . . . £1,250
ditto, Pear Tree Press, 1927 . . . . . £250
Poems, Selwyn & Blount, 1917 (525 copies, pseud.
'Edward Eastway') £300
ditto, Holt (U.S.), 1917 (525 copies). . . £300
Last Poems, Selwyn & Blount, 1918 . . £150
Collected Poems, Selwyn & Blount, 1920 . £200/£75
ditto, Selwyn and Blount, 1920 (deluxe edition, 100
copies) £400
ditto, Seltzer (U.S.), 1921 . . . . . £150/£65
Augustan Books of Modern Poetry - Edward Thomas,
Benn, [1926] (wraps) £10
Selected Poems, Gregynog Press, 1926 (275 copies) .
. . . . £200
ditto, Gregynog Press, 1926 (25 specially bound
copies) £1,000
Two Poems, Ingpen & Grant, 1927 (85 copies) £400
Collected Poems, Ingpen & Grant, 1928 . £75/£25
The Last Sheaf, Cape, [1928] . . . . £45/£20

Others
The Woodland Life, Blackwood, 1897 (first issue, red
cloth) £350
ditto, Blackwood, 1897 (second issue, blue/green
buckram) £250
ditto, Blackwood, 1897 (second issue, smooth green
cloth) £200
Horae Solitaire, Duckworth, 1902 (300 copies) £200
ditto, Dutton (U.S.), [1902] £150
Oxford, A & C Black, [1903] £50
ditto, A & C Black, [1903] (deluxe edition, 300 copies)
. . . . £200
Rose Acre Papers, Langham, 1904 . . . . £100
Beautiful Wales, A & C Black, 1905 . . . £75
The Heart of England, Dent, 1906 . . . . £50
ditto, Dutton (U.S.), [1906] £40
Richard Jefferies, Hutchinson, 1909 . . . £50
ditto, Little, Brown (U.S.), 1909 . . . . £40
The South Country, Dent, 1909 . . . . £50
Rest and Unrest, Duckworth, 1910 . . . £45
ditto, Dutton (U.S.), 1910. . . . . . £45
Rose Acre Papers, Duckworth, 1910 . . . £35
Feminine Influence on the Poets, Secker, 1910 £45
ditto, John Lane (U.S.), 1911 . . . . . £35
Windsor Castle, Blackie & Son, 1910 . . . £45
The Isle of Wight, Blackie & Son, 1911. . . £45
Light and Twilight, Duckworth, 1911 . . . £30
Maurice Maeterlink, Methuen, [1911] . . . £30
Celtic Stories, Clarendon Press, 1911 . . . £75
The Tenth Muse, Secker, [1911]. £35
Algernon Charles Swinburne, Secker, 1912 . £35
George Borrow, Chapman & Hall, 1912 . . £25
Lafcadio Hearn, Houghton Mifflin (U.S.), 1912 £20
ditto, Constable, 1912 . . . . £20
Norse Tales, Clarendon Press, 1912 . . . . £45
The Icknield Way, Constable, 1913 . . . . £75
The Country, Batsford, [1913] £50
The Happy-Go-Lucky Morgans, Duckworth, [1913] .
. . . . £200
Walter Pater, Secker, 1913 . . . . . . £25
In Pursuit of Spring, Nelson, [1914] . . . £75
Four and Twenty Blackbirds, Duckworth, [1915] £40
The Life of the Duke of Marlborough, Chapman &
Hall, 1915 . . . . £20
Keats, Jack, 1916 . . . . £15
ditto, Dodge (U.S.), [1916] £15
A Literary Pilgrim in England, Dodd, Mead (U.S.),
1917 . . . . £25
ditto, Methuen, [1917] £20
Cloud Castle, Duckworth, [1922] . . . £100/£25
ditto, Dutton (U.S.), [1923] . . . . . £65/£15
Essays of Today and Yesterday, Harrap, [1926]
(wraps) £20
Chosen Essays, Gregynog Press, 1926 (350 copies) .
. . . . £75
The Childhood of Edward Thomas, Faber, 1938 £25
The Friend of the Blackbird, Pear Tree Press, 1938 .
. . . . £50

The Prose of Edward Thomas, Falcon Press, 1948 .
. . . . £30/£10
Letters from Edward Thomas to Gordon Bottomley,
O.U.P., 1968 . . . . £20/£5
Autumn Thoughts, Tragara Press, 1975 (190
numbered copies, wraps) £45
The Diary of Edward Thomas, Whittington Press,
1977 (575 copies, slipcase) . . . . £100/£75
Edward Thomas on the Countryside: A Selection,
Faber, 1977 . . . . £10/£5
Edward Thomas: A Centenary Celebration, Eric and
Joan Stevens, 1978 (75 copies signed by the artist) .
. . . . £75
Four Letters to Frederick Evans, Tragara Press, 1978
(150 numbered copies, wraps) £40
Reading out of Doors, Tragara Press, 1978 (110
numbered copies, wraps) £35
The Chessplayers, and other essays, Whittington
Press, 1981 (375 copies). £75
A Selection of Letters to Edward Garnett, Tragara
Press, 1981 (175 numbered copies, wraps) . £40
The Letters of Edward Thomas to Jesse Berridge,
Enitharmon, 1981 . . . . £25
The Fear of Death, Tragara Press, 1982 (95 numbered
copies, wraps) £45
A Sportsman's Tale, Tragara Press, 1983 (125
numbered copies, wraps) £40
A Handful of Letters: Edward and Helen Thomas,
Tragara Press, 1985 (wraps). £20

FLORA THOMPSON
(b.1877 d.1947)

Flora Thompson's autobiographical writings are
popularly collected together as *Lark Rise to
Candleford*. Her descriptions of countryside life are
precise and unsentimental.

Verse
Bog Myrtle and Peat, Allan, 1921 (wraps) . . £75

Prose
Guide to Liphook, Bramshott and Neighbourhood,
Williams, 1925 (wraps) £20
Lark Rise, O.U.P., 1939 . . . . . £65/£20
Over to Candleford, O.U.P., 1941 . . . £50/£15
Candleford Green, O.U.P., 1943 . . £50/£15
Lark Rise to Candleford, O.U.P., 1945 . £50/£20
ditto, Crown (U.S.), 1983 . . . . . £10/£5
Still Glides the Stream, O.U.P., 1948 . . £25/£5
ditto, Crown (U.S.), 1984 . . . . . £10/£5
A Country Calendar, O.U.P., 1979 . . . £10/£5
The Peverel Papers, Century, 1986 . . . £10/£5

COLIN THUBRON
(b.1939)

Popularly considered a travel writer, Thubron's
novels are also critical and commercial successes.

Travel
Mirror to Damascus, Heinemann, 1967. . £65/£15
ditto, Little, Brown (U.S.), 1968 . . . . £50/£10
The Hills of Adonis: A Quest In Lebanon, Heine-
mann, 1968 . . . . £25/£5
ditto, Little, Brown (U.S.), 1969 . . . £20/£5
Jerusalem, Heinemann, 1969 . . . . £25/£5
ditto, Little, Brown (U.S.), 1969 . . . £20/£5
Journey into Cyprus, Heinemann, 1975. . £40/£10
Istanbul, Time Life (Amsterdam), 1978 (with others) .
. . . . £25
The Venetians, Time Life (Amsterdam), 1980 (with
others) £10
The Ancient Mariners, Time Life (Amsterdam), 1981
(with others) £10
Among the Russians, Heinemann, 1983. . £30/£10
ditto, as *Where the Nights are Longest: Travels by Car
Through Western Russia*, Random House (U.S.),
1984 . . . . £20/£5
Behind the Wall: A Journey Through China,
Heinemann, 1987 . . . . . . £25/£10
ditto, Atlantic Monthly Press (U.S.), 1988 . £15/£5
*The Silk Road—China: Beyond the Celestial
Kingdom*, Pyramid, 1990 . . . . £45/£20
ditto, Simon & Schuster (U.S.), 1990 . . £45/£20
The Lost Heart of Asia, Heinemann, 1994 . £15/£5
ditto, HarperCollins (U.S.), 1994. . . . £10/£5
In Siberia, Chatto & Windus, 1999 . . £15/£5
ditto, HarperCollins (U.S.), 1999. . . . £10/£5

Novels
The God in the Mountain, Heinemann, 1977 £30/£10
ditto, Norton (U.S.), 1977. . . . . £10/£5
Emperor, Heinemann, 1978 . . . . £25/£10
A Cruel Madness, Heinemann, 1984 . . £15/£5
ditto, Atlantic Monthly Press (U.S.), 1985 . £10/£5
Falling, Heinemann, 1989 . . . . £10/£5
ditto, Atlantic Monthly Press (U.S.), 1990 . £10/£5
Turning Back the Sun, Heinemann, 1991 . £10/£5
ditto, HarperCollins (U.S.), 1992 . . . £10/£5
Distance, Heinemann, 1996 . . . . £10/£5

Others
The Royal Opera House, Covent Garden, Hamish
Hamilton, 1982 . . . . £10/£5

JAMES THURBER
(b.1894 d.1961)

An American short story writer and cartoonist whose best-known character, Walter Mitty, takes refuge in his daydreams from a confusing modern world

Fiction
Is Sex Necessary? Or Why Do You Feel the Way You Do?, Harper (U.S.), 1929 . . . . £1,000/£200
ditto, Heinemann, 1930 . . . . . £500/£100
The Owl in the Attic and Other Perplexities, Harper (U.S.), 1931 . . . . £750/£100
ditto, Harper, 1931 . . . . £400/£45
The Seal in the Bedroom and Other Predicaments, Harper (U.S.), 1932 . . . . . . £500/£75
ditto, Harper, 1932 . . . . £250/£35
My Life and Hard Times, Harper (U.S.), 1933 . . .
. . . . £250/£35
ditto, Harper, 1933 . . . . £100/£25
The Middle-Aged Man on the Flying Trapeze, Harper (U.S.), 1935 . . . . £250/£35
ditto, Harper, 1935 . . . . £100/£25
Let Your Mind Alone! And Other More or Less Inspirational Pieces, Harper (U.S.), 1937 . £250/£35
ditto, Hamish Hamilton, 1937 . . . . £100/£25
The Last Flower: A Parable in Pictures, Harper (U.S.), 1939 . . . . £150/£25
ditto, Hamish Hamilton, 1939 . . . . £75/£20
Cream of Thurber, Hamish Hamilton, 1939 £45/£15
Fables for Our Time and Famous Poems Illustrated, Harper (U.S.), 1940 . . . . . . £150/£25
ditto, Hamish Hamilton, 1940 . . . . £75/£20
My World–And Welcome To It, Harcourt Brace (U.S.), 1942 . . . . £250/£40
ditto, Hamish Hamilton, 1942 . . . . £125/£25
Men, Women and Dogs, Harcourt Brace (U.S.), 1943 .
. . . . £125/£25
ditto, Hamish Hamilton, 1943 . . . . £65/£15
The Thurber Carnival, Harper (U.S.), 1945 £100/£20
ditto, Hamish Hamilton, 1945 . . . . £50/£10
The Beast in Me and Other Animals, Harcourt Brace (U.S.), 1948 . . . . £45/£15
ditto, Hamish Hamilton, 1949 . . . . £25/£10
The Thurber Album: A New Collection of Pieces About People, Simon & Schuster (U.S.), 1952 . .
. . . . £45/£15
ditto, Hamish Hamilton, 1952 . . . . £25/£10
Thurber Country: A New Collection of Pieces About Males and Females, Simon & Schuster (U.S.), 1953 .
. . . . £35/£10
ditto, Hamish Hamilton, 1953 . . . . £20/£5
Thurber's Dogs, Simon & Schuster (U.S.), 1955 . .
. . . . £30/£5
ditto, Hamish Hamilton, 1955 . . . . £20/£5
A Thurber Garland, Hamish Hamilton, 1955 £25/£10
Further Fables for Our Time, Simon & Schuster (U.S.), 1956 . . . . £25/£5
ditto, Hamish Hamilton, 1956 . . . . £20/£5

Alarms and Diversions, Harper (U.S.), 1957   £25/£5
ditto, Hamish Hamilton, 1957 . . . . £20/£5
Lanterns and Lances, Harper (U.S.), 1961 . £25/£5
ditto, Hamish Hamilton, 1961 . . . . £20/£5
Credos and Curios, Harper (U.S.), 1962 . £25/£5
ditto, Hamish Hamilton, 1962 . . . . £20/£5
Thurber and Company, Harper (U.S.), 1966 £25/£5
ditto, Hamish Hamilton, 1967 . . . . £20/£5

Children's Books
Many Moons, Harcourt Brace (U.S.), 1943 (illustrated by Louis Slobodkin) . . . . . . £200/£45
ditto, Hamish Hamilton, 1944 . . . . £150/£40
ditto, Joseph & Roe (U.S.), 1958 (illustrated by Philip Reed, 250 copies signed by illustrator). . . £125
The Great Quillow, Harcourt Brace (U.S.), 1944 (illustrated by Doris Lee) . . . . £100/£25
The White Deer, Harcourt Brace (U.S.), 1945 (illustrated by Thurber and Don Freeman) . £50/£15
ditto, Hamish Hamilton, 1946 . . . . £40/£15
The Thirteen Clocks, Simon & Schuster (U.S.), 1950 (illustrated by Mark Simont) . . . £100/£15
ditto, Hamish Hamilton, 1951 . . . . £40/£15
The Wonderful O, Simon & Schuster (U.S.), 1957 (illustrated by Mark Simont) . . . . £45/£15
ditto, Hamish Hamilton, 1958 . . . . £40/£15

Plays
Many Moons, Ohio State Univ. (U.S.) 1922 (wraps) .
. . . . £350
The Male Animal, Random House (U.S.), 1940 (with Elliott Nugent) . . . . £125/£35
ditto, Hamish Hamilton, 1950 . . . . £35/£10

Non Fiction
Thurber on Humour, Ohioana Library Association (U.S.), 1953 (wraps) £45
The Years with Ross, Little, Brown (U.S.), 1959 . .
. . . . £25/£10
ditto, Hamish Hamilton, 1959 . . . . £25/£10

J. R. R. TOLKIEN
(b.1892 d.1973)

John Ronald Reuel Tolkien was born in South Africa but educated in Britain. He was appointed Professor of Anglo-Saxon at Oxford in 1925 and published a number of related academic works. He is best known for his novels dealing with the mythical land of 'Middle-Earth'.

Middle-Earth Novels
The Hobbit, Allen & Unwin, 1937 . £15,000/£1,000
ditto, Houghton Mifflin (U.S.), 1938 . £5,000/£750
The Fellowship of the Ring, being the First Part of 'The Lord of the Rings', Allen & Unwin, 1954 . .
. . . . £2,500/£125

ditto, Houghton Mifflin (U.S.), 1954 . . £500/£45
The Two Towers, being the Second Part of 'The Lord
of the Rings', Allen & Unwin, 1954 . £1,750/£150
ditto, Houghton Mifflin (U.S.), 1955 . . £350/£40
The Return of the King, being the Third Part of 'The
Lord of the Rings', Allen & Unwin, 1955 £1,000/£75
ditto, Houghton Mifflin (U.S.), 1956 . . £200/£35
The Lord of the Rings, Allen & Unwin, 1962 (first
combined edition, three books in grey box) £75/£50
ditto, Allen & Unwin, 1964 (deluxe combined edition,
three books bound in buckram, decorated box) . .
. . . . £125/£75
The Silmarillion, Allen & Unwin, 1977 (printed by
either Billing & Sons or William Clowes) . £25/£5
ditto, Houghton Mifflin (U.S.), 1977 . . £15/£5

History of Middle-Earth Titles
The Book of Lost Tales, Part 1, Allen & Unwin, 1983
. . . . £10/£5
ditto, Houghton Mifflin (U.S.), 1984 . . £10/£5
The Book of Lost Tales, Part 2, Allen & Unwin, 1984
. . . . £10/£5
ditto, Houghton Mifflin (U.S.), 1984 . . £10/£5
The Book of Lost Tales, Part 3: The Lays of
Beleriand, Allen & Unwin, 1985 . . . £10/£5
ditto, Houghton Mifflin (U.S.), 1985 . . £10/£5
The Book of Lost Tales, Part 4: The Shaping of
Middle-Earth, Allen & Unwin, 1986 . . £10/£5
ditto, Houghton Mifflin (U.S.), 1986 . . £10/£5
The Lost Road and Other Writings, Unwin Hyman,
1987 . . . . £10/£5
ditto, Houghton Mifflin (U.S.), 1987 . . £10/£5
The Return of the Shadow: The History of the Lord of
the Rings, Part 1, Unwin Hyman, 1988 . £10/£5
ditto, Houghton Mifflin (U.S.), 1988 . . £10/£5
Treason in Isengard: The History of the Lord of the
Rings, Part 2, Unwin Hyman, 1989 . . £10/£5
ditto, Houghton Mifflin (U.S.), 1989 . . £10/£5
The War of the Ring: The History of the Lord of the
Rings, Part 3, Unwin Hyman, 1990 . . £10/£5
ditto, Houghton Mifflin (U.S.), 1990 . . £10/£5
Sauron Defeated: The History of the Lord of the
Rings, Part 4, Unwin Hyman, 1992 . . £10/£5
ditto, Houghton Mifflin (U.S.), 1992 . . £10/£5

Other Middle-Earth Titles
The Adventures of Tom Bombadil and Other Verses
from 'The Red Book', Allen & Unwin, 1962 . . .
. . . . £100/£20
ditto, Houghton Mifflin (U.S.), 1963 . . £60/£15
The Road Goes Ever On: A Song Cycle, Houghton
Mifflin (U.S.), 1967 . . . . . . £35/£10
ditto, Allen & Unwin, 1968 . . . . . £35/£10
Bilbo's Last Song, Houghton Mifflin (U.S.), 1974 . .
. . . . £25/£5
ditto, Allen & Unwin, 1974 (poster) £10
Unfinished Tales, Allen & Unwin, 1980 . £15/£5
ditto, Houghton Mifflin (U.S.), 1980 . . £15/£5

Other Prose
Farmer Giles of Ham, Allen & Unwin, 1949 £200/£45
ditto, Houghton Mifflin (U.S.), 1950 . . £75/£15
Tree and Leaf, Allen & Unwin, 1964 . £100/£20
ditto, Houghton Mifflin (U.S.), 1965 . . £35/£10
The Tolkien Reader, Ballantine (U.S.), 1966 £25/£10
Smith of Wootton Major, Allen & Unwin, 1967 £35
ditto, Houghton Mifflin (U.S.), 1967 . £30/£10
The Father Christmas Letters, Allen & Unwin, 1976 .
. . . . £15/£5
ditto, Houghton Mifflin (U.S.), 1976 . £15/£5
Pictures by J.R.R. Tolkien, Allen & Unwin, 1979 . .
. . . . £25/£10
ditto, as **The Pictures of J.R.R. Tolkien**, Houghton
Mifflin (U.S.), 1979 . . . . £25/£10
Poems and Stories, Allen & Unwin, 1980 . £25/£5
ditto, Houghton Mifflin (U.S.), 1980 . £15/£5
Letters, Allen & Unwin, 1981 . . . . £10/£5
ditto, Houghton Mifflin (U.S.), 1981 . . £10/£5
Mr Bliss, Allen & Unwin, 1982 . . . . £10/£5
ditto, Houghton Mifflin (U.S.), 1983 . . £10/£5
Finn and Hengest: The Fragment and the Episode,
Allen & Unwin, 1983 . . . . . £10/£5
ditto, Houghton Mifflin (U.S.), 1983 . . £10/£5

Other Verse
Songs for the Philologists, privately printed, 1936 . .
. . . . £1,250
The Homecoming of Beorhtnoth, Allen & Unwin,
1975 . . . . £15/£5

Academic
A Middle English Vocabulary, O.U.P., 1922 (first
issue with ads dated October 1921, 186 ornaments in
cover design, wraps) £450
ditto, O.U.P., 1922 (second issue with ads dated
undated, 184 ornaments in cover design, wraps) £225
ditto, O.U.P. (U.S.), 1922 . . . . . . £75
Sir Gawain and the Green Knight, O.U.P., 1925 (with
errata slip) . . . . £200/£75
ditto, O.U.P. (U.S.), 1925 . . . . . . £75
Beowulf: The Monsters and the Critics, British
Academy, [1936] (wraps) £100
ditto, Folcroft Editions (U.S.), 1972 . . . . £10
Sir Gawain and the Green Knight, Pearl, and Sir
Orfeo, Allen & Unwin, 1975 . . . . £10/£5
ditto, Houghton Mifflin (U.S.), 1975 . . £10/£5

MARY TOURTEL
(b.1873 d.1948)

Rupert Bear was the best known creation of this British author and illustrator. Rupert first appeared in the Daily Express in 1920. Tourtel stopped working on the cartoon strip in 1935 due to failing eyesight. The very collectable series of Rupert Annuals began in the following year after the strip was taken over by Alfred Bestall. It is now drawn by John Harrold.

Rupert Annuals

1936, Daily Express, 1936 (with dustjacket)	£2,000
ditto, Daily Express, 1936 (without dustjacket) .	£350
1937, Daily Express, 1937	£300
1938, Daily Express, 1938	£300
1939, Daily Express, 1939	£350
1940, Daily Express, 1940	£350
1941, Daily Express, 1941	£450
1942, Daily Express, 1942 (wraps) . . .	£500
1943, Daily Express, 1943 (wraps) . . .	£350
1944, Daily Express, 1944 (wraps) . . .	£300
1945, Daily Express, 1945 (wraps) . . .	£250
1946, Daily Express, 1946 (wraps) . . .	£200
1947, Daily Express, 1947 (wraps) . . .	£200
1948, Daily Express, 1948 (wraps) . . .	£75
1949, Daily Express, 1949 (wraps) . . .	£75
1950-59, Daily Express, 1950-59 (boards) .	£75 each
1960-68, Daily Express, 1960-68 ('magic painting' pages not coloured in)	£100 each
1960-68, Daily Express, 1960-68 ('magic painting' pages coloured in)	£35 each
1969, Daily Express, 1969	£20
1970-89, Daily Express, 1970-89 . . .	£5
1990, Daily Express, 1990 (anniversary issue) .	£10
1991-97, Daily Express, 1991-97 . . .	£5 each

Rupert Annuals - Facsimiles

1936, Daily Express, 1985	£100/£45
1937, Daily Express, 1986	£80
1938, Daily Express, 1989	£100
1939, Daily Express, 1991	£30
1940, Daily Express, 1992	£15
1941, Daily Express, 1993 (in slipcase) .	£20/£10
1942, Daily Express, 1994 (in slipcase) . .	£50/£20

Monster Rupert Annuals

Monster Rupert, Sampson Low, [1931] (Rupert with wolf) £900
Monster Rupert, Sampson Low, [1932] (Rupert on log) £750
Monster Rupert, Sampson Low, [1933] (Rupert with bird) £750
Monster Rupert, Sampson Low, [1934] (Rupert with small boy in storeroom) £750
Monster Rupert, Sampson Low, [1948] (Rupert on log, with d/w) £35
Monster Rupert, Sampson Low, [1949] (Rupert with fox, with d/w) £35

Monster Rupert, Sampson Low, [1950] (Rupert helping boy out of hole, with d/w, with all cut-outs intact) £50
Monster Rupert, Sampson Low, [1953] (with all cut-outs intact) £40

'Rupert' Books

The Adventures of Rupert the Little Lost Bear, Nelson, [1921] £900
The Little Bear and the Fairy Child, Nelson, [1922] £1,000
Margot the Midget and Little Bear's Christmas, Nelson, [1922] £850
The Little Bear and the Ogres, Nelson, 1922 . £850
'Rupert Little Bear's Adventures', Sampson Low, 1924-25 (3 books) . . . . £800 each
'Rupert - Little Bear Series', Sampson Low, 1925-27 (6 books) . . . . £600 each
'Little Bear Library' titles, Sampson Low, [1928-1936] (numbered 1-46) . . . £150/£50 each
The Rupert Story Book, Sampson Low, [1938] £450
Rupert Little Bear: More Stories, Sampson Low, [1939] £450
Rupert Again, Sampson Low, [1940] . . . £450

'Adventure' Titles *(all in card covers)*

No. 1, Daily Express	£40
Nos. 2-9, Daily Express	£15 each
No. 10, Daily Express	£25 each
Nos. 11-30, Daily Express	£20 each
Nos. 31-40, Daily Express	£25 each
Nos. 41-45, Daily Express	£50 each
Nos. 46-48, Daily Express	£60 each
No. 49, Daily Express	£100
No. 50, Daily Express	£125

Daily Express Children's Annuals

Daily Express Children's Annual, 1930, Lane, 1930 . . . . £125
Daily Express Children's Annual, 1931, Lane, 1931 . . . . £125
Daily Express Children's Annual, 1932, Lane, 1932 . . . . £100
Daily Express Children's Annual, 1933, Lane, 1933 . . . . £100
Daily Express Children's Annual, 1934, Lane, 1934 . . . . £100
Daily Express Children's Annual, 1935, Lane, 1935 . . . . £125

Other Collectable Titles by Mary Tourtel

A Horse Book, Grant Richards 'Dumpy Books for Children' series No. 10, 1901, . . . £150
The Humpty Dumpty Book, Nursery Rhymes Told in Pictures, Treherne, [1902] £150
The Three Little Foxes, Grant Richards 'Dumpy Books for Children series No. 21, 1903 . . £150

WILLIAM TREVOR
(b.1928)

A novelist and short story writer, Trevor's work often deals with the corruption of innocence.

Novels

A Standard of Behaviour, Hutchinson, 1958 . . . . £600/£200
ditto, Sphere, 1967 (revised edition, wraps). . £10
The Old Boys, Bodley Head, 1964 . . . £150/£35
ditto, Viking (U.S.), 1964 . . . . £75/£15
The Boarding House, Bodley Head, 1965 . £125/£35
ditto, Viking (U.S.), 1965. . . . . . £65/£15
The Love Department, Bodley Head, 1966 £125/£35
ditto, Viking (U.S.), 1967. . . . . . £65/£15
Mrs Eckdorf in O'Neill's Hotel, Bodley Head, 1969 . . . . £65/£15
ditto, Viking (U.S.), 1970. . . . . . £45/£10
Miss Gomez and the Brethren, Bodley Head, 1971 . . . . £65/£15
Elizabeth Alone, Bodley Head, 1973 . £50/£15
ditto, as *Dreaming*, Stellar Press, 1973 (extract from *Elizabeth Alone*, 225 copies, wraps with d/w). . . . . £135/£100
ditto, Viking (U.S.), 1974. . . . . . £35/£10
The Children of Dynmouth, Bodley Head, 1976 . . . . £35/£10
ditto, Viking (U.S.), 1977. . . . . . £15/£5
Other People's Worlds, Bodley Head, 1980 . £20/£5
ditto, Viking (U.S.), 1981. . . . . . £10/£5
Fools of Fortune, Bodley Head , 1983 . . £20/£5
ditto, Bodley Head, 1983 (50 numbered, signed copies, bound by Kenny's of Galway, slipcase) . . £75
ditto, Viking (U.S.), 1983. . . . . . £10/£5
The Silence in the Garden, Bodley Head, 1988 £15/£5
ditto, London Limited Editions, 1988 (150 numbered, signed copies, glassine d/w). . . . . £75/£50
ditto, Viking (U.S.), 1988. . . . . . £10/£5
Two Lives, Viking (U.K.), 1991 . . . . £10/£5
ditto, Viking (U.S.), 1991. . . . . . £10/£5
Felicia's Journey, Viking (U.K.), 1994 . . £10/£5
ditto, Viking (U.S.), 1995. . . . . . £10/£5
Death in Summer, Viking (U.K.), 1998. . £10/£5
ditto, Viking (U.S.), 1998. . . . . . £10/£5

Short Stories

The Day We Got Drunk on Cake, Bodley Head, 1967. . . . . £500/£40
ditto, Viking (U.S.), 1968. . . . . . £75/£15
The Ballroom of Romance, Bodley Head, 1972 . . . . £125/£35
ditto, Viking (U.S.), 1972. . . . . . £45/£10
The Last Lunch of the Season, Covent Garden Press, 1973 (100 numbered, signed copies of 600, wraps) £75

ditto, Covent Garden Press, 1973 (500 copies of 600, wraps). £40
Angels at the Ritz and Other Stories, Bodley Head, 1975 . . . . £45/£15
ditto, Viking (U.S.), 1976. . . . . . £25/£10
Old School Ties, Lemon Tree Press, 1976 . £75/£20
Lovers of Their Time and Other Stories, Bodley Head, 1978 . . . . £30/£10
ditto, Stellar Press, 1973 (extract, 225 copies, wraps) £125
ditto, Viking (U.S.), 1978. . . . . . £20/£5
The Distant Past, Poolbeg Press (Dublin), 1979 (wraps) £20
Beyond the Pale, Bodley Head, 1981 . £20/£5
ditto, Viking (U.S.), 1982. . . . . . £10/£5
The News From Ireland and Other Stories, Bodley Head, 1986 . . . . £25/£5
ditto, Bodley Head, 1986 (50 numbered, signed copies, bound by Kenny's of Galway, slipcase) . . £125
ditto, Viking (U.S.), 1986. . . . . . £15/£5
Nights at the Alexandria, Hutchinson, 1987 £15/£5
ditto, Harper (U.S.), 1987. . . . . . £10/£5
Family Sins and Other Stories, Bodley Head, 1990 . . . . £10/£5
ditto, Viking (U.S.), 1990. . . . . . £10/£5
The Collected Stories, Viking (U.K.), 1990. £15/£5
ditto, Viking (U.K.), 1990, (100 signed copies). . . . . £150/£75
Marrying Damian, Colophon Press, 1995 (175 numbered signed copies, wraps) . . . £50
ditto, Colophon Press, 1994 (26 signed copies, slipcase) . . . . £125/£100
After Rain, Viking, 1996 . . . . . . £15/£5
ditto, Viking (U.S.), 1996. . . . . . £10/£5
Death of a Professor, Colophon Press, 1997 (200 numbered signed copies, wraps) . . . £30
ditto, Colophon Press, 1997 (26 signed copies, slipcase) . . . . £125/£100
Low Sunday, 1950, Colophon Press, 2000 (200 numbered signed copies, wraps) . . . £40
ditto, Colophon Press, 2000 (26 signed copies, slipcase) . . . . £125/£100

Plays

The Girl, French, 1968 (wraps) £25
The Old Boys, Poynter, 1971 (wraps) . . . £25
Going Home, French, 1972 (wraps). . . . £10
A Night With Mrs Da Tonka, French, 1972 (wraps) £10
Marriages, French, 1973 (wraps) £10
Scenes from an Album, Co-op Books (Dublin), 1981 (wraps) £15

Children's

Juliet's Story, O'Brien Press (Dublin), 1991 £25/£10
ditto, Bodley Head, 1992 . . . . . . £15/£5
ditto, Simon & Schuster (U.S.), 1992 . . £10/£5

Others

A Writer's Ireland, Viking (U.S.), 1984. . £15/£5
ditto, Thames & Hudson, 1984 . . . £15/£5
Excursions in the Real World, Hutchinson/Random
House, 1993 . . . . £15/£5
ditto, Knopf (U.S.), 1994 . . . . . £10/£5

ANTHONY TROLLOPE
(b.1815 d.1882)

Trollope's two most important series of novels are
based around the fictitious cathedral town of
Barchester. Arguably his greatest contribution to
society, however, was the introduction of the pillar-
box.

The Macdermots of Ballycoran, Newby, 1847 (3 vols)
. . . . £6,000
The Kellys and the O'Kelleys, Colburn, 1848 (3 vols)
. . . . £1,500
La Vendee, Colburn, 1850 (3 vols) . . . £2,000
The Warden, Longman, 1855 (first issue with ads
dated September 1854) £2,000
ditto, Longman, 1855 (later issue with ads dated March
1956 or no ads) £1,250
ditto, Longman, 1855 (later issue with ads dated
October 1959) £1,000
Barchester Towers, Longman, 1857 (first issue with
brick-red endpapers, some with ads dated 1857, 3
vols) £7,500
ditto, Longman, 1857 (second issue with brown
endpapers, ads dated 18603 vols) . . £4,500
The Three Clerks, Bentley, 1858 (3 vols) £2,000
Doctor Thorne, Chapman & Hall, 1858 (first edition
with 'mamma' on p.18, line 15, 3 vols) . £7,500
ditto, Chapman & Hall, 1858 (second edition with
'mommon' on p.18, line 15, 3 vols) . £650
The Bertrams, Chapman & Hall, 1859 (3 vols) £2,000
Castle Richmond, Chapman & Hall, 1860 (first issue
with 16 pages of ads dated February 1860, 3 vols) .
. . . . £2,500
ditto, Chapman & Hall, 1860 (second issue with 32
pages of ads dated May 1860, 3 vols) . . £1,000
Framley Parsonage, Smith Elder, 1861 (3 vols) £3,000
Tales of All Countries, Chapman & Hall, 1861 £500
Orley Farm, Chapman & Hall, 1862 (20 parts, wraps).
. . . . £6,000
ditto, Chapman & Hall, 1862 (2 vols) . . £3,000
Tales of All Countries: Second Series, Chapman &
Hall, 1863 . . . . £500
Rachel Ray, Chapman & Hall, 1863 (2 vols) £1,250
The Small House at Allington, Smith Elder, 1864 (2
vols) £2,000
Can You Forgive Her, Chapman & Hall, 1864 (2 vols)
. . . . £2,000
Miss Mackenzie, Chapman & Hall, 1865 (2 vols) . .
. . . . £2,000

The Belton Estate, Chapman & Hall, 1866 (3 vols) .
. . . . £2,500
Nina Balakta, Blackwood, 1867 (anonymous, 2 vols).
. . . . £2,000
The Last Chronicle of Barset, Smith Elder, 1866-67
(32 parts, wraps). £5,000
ditto, Smith Elder, 1867 (2 vols) £1,500
The Claverings, Smith Elder, 1867 (2 vols). . £750
Lotta Schmidt and Other Stories, Strahan, 1867 £350
Linda Tressel, Blackwood, 1868 (2 vols) . . £750
Phineas Finn, The Irish Member, Virtue, 1869 (2
vols) £500
He Knew He Was Right, Strahan, 1868-69 (32 parts,
wraps). £3,000
ditto, Strahan, 1869 (2 vols) £1,500
The Vicar of Bullhampton, Bradbury, Evans, 1869-70
(11 parts, wraps) £2,000
ditto, Bradbury, Evans, 1870 . . . . . £500
The Struggles of Brown, Jones and Robinson, Smith
Elder, 1870 . . . . £500
Sir Harry Hotspur of Humblethwaite, Hurst and
Blackett, 1871 . . . .£1,000
Ralph the Heir, Hurst and Blackett, 1871 (3 vols) . .
. . . . £2,000
The Golden Lion of Granpere, Tinsley, 1872 . £450
The Eustace Diamonds, Harpers (U.S.), 1872 (wraps)
. . . . £1,000
ditto, Chapman & Hall, 1873 (3 vols) . . . £750
Phineas Redux, Chapman & Hall, 1874 (2 vols) £450
Lady Anna, Chapman & Hall, 1874 (2 vols) £2,000
Harry Heathcote of Gangoil, Sampson Low, 1874 .
. . . . £450
The Way We Live Now, Chapman & Hall, 1875 (2
vols) £1,000
The Prime Minister, Chapman & Hall, 1877 (8 parts,
eraps or cloth) £1,250
ditto, Chapman & Hall, 1877 (4 vols) . . £1,000
The American Senator, Chapman & Hall, 1877 (3
vols) £1,500
Is He Popenjoy?, Chapman & Hall, 1878 (3 vols) £500
An Eye for an Eye, Chapman & Hall, 1879 (2 vols) .
. . . . £400
John Caldigate, Chapman & Hall, 1879 (first binding
grey cloth, 3 vols) £1,250
ditto, Chapman & Hall, 1879 (second binding dark
green cloth, 3 vols) £1,000
Cousin Henry, Chapman & Hall, 1879 (2 vols) £450
The Duke's Children, Chapman & Hall, 1880 (3 vols)
. . . . £750
Dr Wortle's School, Chapman & Hall, 1881 (2 vols) .
. . . .£1,000
Ayala's Angel, Chapman & Hall, 1881 (3 vols) £2,000
*Why Frau Frohmann Raised Her Prices and Other
Stories*, Ibister, 1882 (1 vol) £1,000
ditto, Ibister, 1882 (2 vols) £750
Kept in the Dark, Chatto & Windus, 1882 (2 vols). .
. . . .£1,000
Marion Fay, Chapman & Hall, 1882 (3 vols) .£1,500
The Fixed Period, Blackwood, 1882 (2 vols) .£1,000

Mr Scarborough's Family, Chatto & Windus, 1883 (3 vols) £1,250
The Landleaguers, Chatto & Windus, 1883 (3 vols) .
. . . . £1,450
An Old Man's Love, Blackwood, 1884 (2 vols volumes) £450
The Noble Jilt, Constable, 1923 . . . . . £250

Others
The West Indies and the Spanish Main, Chapman & Hall, 1859 . . . . £500
North America, Chapman & Hall, 1862 (2 vols) .
. . . . £1,000
Hunting Sketches, Chapman & Hall, 1863 . . £500
Travelling Sketches, Chapman & Hall, 1866 . £500
Clergymen of the Church of England, Chapman & Hall, 1866 . . . . £650
An Editor's Tales, Strahan, 1870 . . . . £450
The Commentaries of Caesar, Blackwood, 1870 £300
Australia and New Zealand, Chapman & Hall, 1873 (2 vols) £750
South Africa, Chapman & Hall, 1878 (2 vols) . £150
How the 'Mastiffs' Went to Iceland, Virtue, 1878 . .
. . . . £650
Thackeray, Macmillan, 1879 . . . . . . £600
The Life of Cicero, Chapman & Hall, 1880 (2 vols) .
. . . . £250
Lord Palmerston, Ibister, 1882 . . . . . £250
An Autobiography, Blackwood, 1883 (first issue with smooth red cloth, 2 vols) £600
ditto, Blackwood, 1883 (second issue with ribbed red cloth, 2 vols) £300
London Tradesmen, Mathews & Marrot, 1927 £75/£25

MARK TWAIN
(b.1835 d.1910)

A humourist, novelist and travel writer, Twain was the pen name of Samuel Langhorne Clemens.

The Celebrated Jumping Frog of Calaveras Country and Other Sketches, Webb (U.S.), 1867 (first issue with single leaf of ads on cream paper inserted before title page, last line on p.66 with 'life' unbroken, last line on p.198 with 'this' unbroken). . . £10,000
ditto, Webb (U.S.), 1867 (second issue with no ads and type broken or worn) £2,000
ditto, Routledge, 1867 (wraps) £3,000
The Innocents Abroad or The New Pilgrim's Progress, American Publishing Company (U.S.), 1868 (first issue, pp.xvii-xviii lacking page reference numbers; p.xviii with last entry reading 'Thankless Devotion - A Newspaper Valedictory'; p.129 with no illustration; p.643 reading Chapter XLI & p.654 reading 'Personal History') £1,000
ditto, Hotten, [1870] (2 vols) £750

ditto, as *Mark Twain's Pleasure Trip on the Continent*, Hotten, [1870] (1 vol.) £400
Mark Twain's (Burlesque) Autobiography & First Romance, Sheldon & Co. (U.S.), 1871 (first issue with no ad for Ball, Black & Co on verso title, wraps)
. . . . £450
ditto, Sheldon & Co. (U.S.), 1871 (first issue, cloth)
. . . . £300
ditto, Hotten, [1871] (cloth) £250
ditto, Hotten, [1871] (wraps) £200
Memoranda From the Galaxy, Backas (Toronto), 1871 . . . . £1,000
Eye Openers/Good Things, Hotten, [1871] (wraps and cloth) £175
Screamers/A Gathering, Hotten, [1871] (wraps and cloth) £175
Roughing It, Routledge, 1872 (2 vols) . . . £650
ditto, American Publishing Company (U.S.), 1872 . . .
. . . . £650
The Innocents at Home, Routledge, 1872 . . £600
A Curious Dream and Other Sketches, Routledge, [1872] £600
Mark Twain's Sketches, Routledge, 1872 . . £500
The Choice Humorous Works, Hotten, [1873] . £400
The Gilded Age, American Publishing Company (U.S.), 1874 (3 vols) £1,000
ditto, Routledge, 1874 (3 vols) £900
Sketches, New and Old, American Publishing Company (U.S.), 1875 . . . . . £300
Old Times on the Mississippi, Belford (Toronto), 1876
. . . . £400
Information Wanted and Other Sketches, Routledge (U.S.), 1876 . . . . £350
The Adventures of Tom Sawyer, Chatto & Windus, 1876 . . . . £6,000
ditto, American Publishing Company (U.S.), 1876 . . .
. . . . £10,000
A True Story, Osgood (U.S.), 1877 . . . £300
Punch, Brother, Punch, Slote, Woodman (U.S.), 1878 (wraps and cloth). £500
ditto, Livingston, 1878 (wraps) £400
A Tramp Abroad, American Publishing Company (U.S.), 1880 (first state with frontispiece captioned 'Moses') £750
ditto, American Publishing Company (U.S.), 1880 (second state with frontispiece captioned 'Titian's Moses') £250
ditto, Chatto & Windus, 1880 (2 vols) . . . £400
The Prince and the Pauper: A Tale for Young People of All Ages, Chatto & Windus, 1881 . . £1,000
ditto, Osgood (U.S.), 1882 . . . . . £1,000
The Stolen White Elephant, Chatto & Windus, 1882 (first state, list of books on verso half title does not mention *The White Elephant*) £300
ditto, Chatto & Windus, 1882 (second state, list of books on verso half title does mention *The White Elephant*) £150
ditto, Osgood (U.S.), 1882 . . . . . £150
Life on the Mississippi, Chatto & Windus, 1883 £500

ditto, Osgood (U.S.), 1883 . . . . . £1,000
The Adventures of Huckleberry Finn, Chatto &
Windus, 1884. . . . . £1,250
ditto, Webster (U.S.), 1885 (blue cloth) . . £4,500
ditto, Webster (U.S.), 1885 (green cloth) . £3,000
Mark Twain's Library of Humour, Chatto & Windus,
1888 . . . . £400
ditto, Webster (U.S.), 1888 . . . . . £500
A Connecticut Yankee in King Arthur's Court,
Webster (U.S.), 1889 . . . . . £1,000
ditto, as *A Yankee at the Court of King Arthur*, Chatto
& Windus, 1889 . . . . . . £250
Merry Tales, Webster (U.S.), 1892 . . . . £350
The American Claimant, Webster (U.S.), 1892 £200
ditto, Chatto & Windus, 1892 . . . £125
The $1,000,000 Bank Note, Webster (U.S.), 1893 .
. . . . £200
ditto, Chatto & Windus, 1893 . . . . £125
Tom Sawyer Abroad, Chatto & Windus, 1894 . £500
ditto, Webster (U.S.), 1894 . . . . . £650
Pudd'nhead Wilson, Chatto & Windus, 1894 . £300
ditto, American Publishing Company (U.S.), 1894 . ..
. . . . £400
*Tom Sawyer Abroad/Tom Sawyer, Detective/And
Other Stories*, Harper (U.S.), 1896 . . £1,000
Tom Sawyer, Detective, Chatto & Windus, 1897 £400
How to Tell a Story, Harper (U.S.), 1897 . . £250
Following the Equator, American Publishing
Company (U.S.), 1897 . . . . . . £200
ditto, as *More Tramps Abroad*, Chatto & Windus,
1897 . . . . £150
The Man That Corrupted Hadleyburgh, Harper
(U.S.), 1900 . . . . £150
ditto, Chatto & Windus, 1900 . . . . £100
To the Person Sitting in Darkness, Anti-Imperialist
League (U.S.), 1901 (wraps) £350
A Double Barrelled Detective Story, Harper (U.S.),
1902 . . . . £100
ditto, Chatto & Windus, 1902 . . . . £75
A Dog's Tale, National Anti-Vivesection Society, 1903
(wraps) £250
ditto, Harper (U.K. & U.S.), 1904 . . . . £100
Extracts from Adam's Diary, Harper (U.K. & U.S.),
1904 . . . . £100
King Leopold's Soliloquy, Warren (U.S.), 1905 £75
Eve's Diary, Harper (U.K. & U.S.), 1906 . . £100
The $30,000 Bequest, Harper (U.K. & U.S.), 1906 .
. . . . £75
What Is Man?, De Vinne Press (U.S.), 1906
(anonymous, 250 copies) £1,000
A Horse's Tale, S.P.C.A./Harper (U.K. & U.S.), 1907.
. . . . £50
Christian Science, Harper (U.K. & U.S.), 1907. £200

BARRY UNSWORTH
(b.1930)

Unsworth is not as widely known as he might be,
despite *Sacred Hunger* being jointly awarded the
1992 Booker Prize.

Novels
The Partnership, Hutchinson New Authors, 1966 . .
. . . . £275/£50
The Greeks Have a Word For It, Hutchinson, 1967 .
. . . . £75/£20
The Hide, Gollancz, 1970 . . . . . £75/£20
ditto, Norton (U.S.), 1996. . . . . . £10/£5
Mooncranker's Gift, Lane, 1973 . . . £45/£10
ditto, Houghton Mifflin (U.S.), 1974 . . £20/£5
The Big Day, Joseph, 1976 . . . . £25/£5
ditto, Mason/Charter (U.S.), 1976 . . £15/£5
Pascali's Island, Joseph, 1980 . . . £20/£5
ditto, as *The Idol Hunter*, Simon & Schuster (U.S.),
1980 . . . . £15/£5
The Rage of the Vulture, Granada, 1982 . £20/£5
ditto, Houghton Mifflin (U.S.), 1982 . . £15/£5
Stone Virgin, Hamish Hamilton, 1985 . . £20/£5
ditto, Houghton Mifflin (U.S.), 1986 . . £15/£5
Sugar and Rum, Hamish Hamilton, 1988 . £15/£5
Sacred Hunger, Hamish Hamilton, 1992 . £75/£10
ditto, Hamish Hamilton, 1992 (wraps) . . £10
ditto, Doubleday (U.S.), 1992 . . . . £15/£5
Morality Play, Hamish Hamilton, 1995 . . £15/£5
ditto, Doubleday (U.S.), 1995 . . . . £10/£5
After Hannibal, Hamish Hamilton, 1996 . £15/£5
ditto, Doubleday (U.S.), 1997 . . . . £10/£5
Losing Nelson, Hamish Hamilton, 1999 . £10/£5
ditto, Doubleday (U.S.), 1999 . . . . £10/£5

JOHN UPDIKE
(b.1932)

American novelist, short story writer and critic,
Updike has the reputation of a keen observer of
American life.

Verse
The Carpentered Hen and Other Tame Creatures,
Harper (U.S.), 1938 (first issue d/w with '...a wife
and two small children' on the rear inside flap) . .
. . . . £500/£45
ditto, as *Hoping for a Hoopoe*, Gollancz, 1959. . .
. . . . £150/£25
Telephone Poles, Knopf (U.S.), 1963 . . £65/£20
ditto, Deutsch, 1963 . . . . . . £40/£10
Dog's Death, Scott (U.S.), 1965 (100 signed copies,
broadside) £125
Bath After Sailing, Pendulum Press, 1968 (125 signed
copies, wraps) £350

Midpoint and Other Poems, Knopf (U.S.),1964 . .
. . . . £75/£15
ditto, Knopf (U.S.),1964 (350 signed copies in d/w) .
. . . . £150/£95
ditto, Deutsch, 1969 . . . . . . £45/£10
The Angels, King & Queen Press (U.S.), 1968 (150
copies, wraps in envelope) . . . . . £600/£500
On Meeting Authors, Wickford Press (U.S.), 1968
(250 copies, wraps) £500
Dance of the Solids, Scientific American (U.S.),
[1970] (wraps) £750
Seventy Poems, Penguin, 1971 (wraps) . . . £15
Six Poems, Aloe Editions (U.S.), 1973 (26 signed,
numbered copies, wraps) £450
ditto, Aloe Editions (U.S.), 1973 (100 signed,
numbered copies, wraps) £200
Cunts, Hallman (U.S.), 1974 (26 signed copies) £450
ditto, Hallman (U.S.), 1974 (250 signed copies) £175
Sunday in Boston, Rook Press (U.S.), 1975 (100
copies signed by author and illustrator, broadside) .
. . . . £125
ditto, Rook Press (U.S.), 1975 (100 copies signed by
author önly, broadside) £100
ditto, Rook Press (U.S.), 1975 (100 unsigned copies,
broadside) £65
Tossing and Turning, Knopf (U.S.), 1977 . £20/£5
ditto, Deutsch, 1977 . . . . . £15/£5
From the Journal of a Leper, Lord John Press (U.S.),
1983 (26 signed, lettered copies) £200
ditto, Lord John Press (U.S.), 1983 (300 signed,
numbered copies) £100
Sixteen Sonnets, Ferguson (U.S.), 1979 (250 signed,
numbered copies, wraps) £125
ditto, Ferguson (U.S.), 1979 (26 signed, lettered
copies) £200
The Beloved, Lord John Press (U.S.), 1978 (100
signed, numbered deluxe copies) £125
ditto, Lord John Press (U.S.), 1978 (300 signed,
numbered copies) £100
Facing Nature, Knopf (U.S.), 1985 . . £15/£5
ditto, Deutsch, 1986 . . . . . £10/£5
A Pear Like a Potato, Santa Susanna Press (U.S.),
1986 (broadside, 26 signed, lettered copies) . £75
ditto, Santa Susanna Press (U.S.), 1986 (broadside, 100
signed copies) £45
Two Sonnets, Northouse & Northouse (U.S.), 1987 (40
signed, Roman numbered copies) . . . £250
ditto, Northouse & Northouse (U.S.), 1987 . £40
Recent Poems, Eurographica (Helsinki), 1992 (350
signed, numbered copies, wraps) . . . £125
Collected Poems 1953-1993, Knopf (U.S.), 1993 .
. . . . £15/£5
ditto, Hamish Hamilton, 1993 . . . £15/£5
Down Time, Firefly Press (U.S.), 1997 (30 copies
signed by author and illustrator, broadside) . £150
ditto, Firefly Press (U.S.), 1997 (60 copies signed by
author, broadside) £125

Novels
The Poorhouse Fair, Knopf (U.S.), 1959 (first issue
d/w with one paragraph of copy only on back flap) .
. . . . £200/£35
ditto, Gollancz, 1959 . . . . . . £100/£15
Rabbit, Run, Knopf (U.S.), 1960 (first issue d/w with
16-line blurb on front flap) . . . . £500/£45
ditto, Knopf, 1961 . . . . . . £100/£15
The Centaur, Knopf (U.S.), 1963 . . £100/£20
ditto, Deutsch, 1963 . . . . . £45/£15
Of the Farm, Knopf (U.S.), 1965 . . £75/£10
ditto, Deutsch, 1973 . . . . . £50/£5
Couples, Knopf (U.S.), 1968 . . . £35/£5
ditto, Deutsch, 1968 . . . . . £25/£5
Rabbit Redux, Knopf (U.S.), 1971 . . £50/£10
ditto, Knopf (U.S.), 1971 (350 signed copies, slipcase,
clear d/w). . . . . £250/£200
ditto, Deutsch, 1972 . . . . . £30/£5
A Month of Sundays, Knopf (U.S.), 1975 . £25/£5
ditto, Knopf (U.S.), 1975 (450 signed, numbered
copies, slipcase, d/w) . . . . . £125/£75
ditto, Deutsch, 1975 . . . . . £20/£5
Marry Me, Knopf (U.S.), 1976 . . . £20/£5
ditto, Knopf (U.S.), 1976 (300 signed, numbered
copies, slipcase, d/w) . . . . . £100/£65
ditto, Franklin Library (U.S.), 1976 (signed copies) £50
ditto, Deutsch, 1977 . . . . . £15/£5
The Coup, Knopf (U.S.), 1978 . . . £15/£5
ditto, Knopf (U.S.), 1978 (350 signed, numbered
copies, slipcase, d/w) . . . . . £100/£65
ditto, Deutsch, 1979 . . . . . £10/£5
Rabbit is Rich, Knopf (U.S.), 1981 . . £30/£5
ditto, Knopf (U.S.), 1981 (350 signed copies, slipcase,
d/w) . . . . £200/£150
ditto, Deutsch, 1982 . . . . . £25/£5
Bech is Back, Knopf (U.S.), 1982 . . £15/£5
ditto, Knopf (U.S.), 1982 (500 signed, numbered
copies, slipcase, d/w) . . . . . £100/£65
ditto, Deutsch, 1983 . . . . . £10/£5
The Witches of Eastwick, Knopf (U.S.), 1984 £35/£10
ditto, Knopf (U.S.), 1984 (350 signed copies, glassine
d/w and slipcase). . . . . . . £125/£100
ditto, Franklin Library (U.S.), 1984 (signed copies) £45
ditto, Deutsch, 1984 . . . . . £25/£10
Roger's Version, Knopf (U.S.), 1986 . . £10/£5
ditto, Knopf (U.S.), 1986 (350 signed copies, glassine
d/w and slipcase) . . . . . . £125/£100
ditto, Franklin Library (U.S.), 1986 (signed copies) £35
ditto, Deutsch, 1986 . . . . . £10/£5
S, Knopf (U.S.), 1988 . . . . . . £10/£5
ditto, Knopf (U.S.), 1986 (350 signed copies, glassine
d/w and slipcase). . . . . . . £125/£100
ditto, Deutsch, 1988 . . . . . £10/£5
Rabbit at Rest, Knopf (U.S.), 1990 . . £20/£5
ditto, Knopf (U.S.), 1990 (350 signed copies, glassine
d/w and slipcase) . . . . . . £150/£125
ditto, Franklin Library (U.S.), 1990 (signed copies) £50
ditto, Deutsch, 1991 . . . . . £15/£5
Brazil, Knopf (U.S.), 1994 . . . . £15/£5

ditto, Franklin Library (U.S.), 1994 (signed copies) £35
ditto, Hamish Hamilton, 1994 . . . . £15/£5
In the Beauty of the Lilies, Knopf (U.S.), 1996 £15/£5
ditto, Franklin Library (U.S.), 1996 (signed copies) £35
ditto, Hamish Hamilton, 1996 . . . . £15/£5
Toward the End of Time, Knopf (U.S.), 1997 £10/£5
ditto, Franklin Library (U.S.), 1998 (signed copies) £35
ditto, Hamish Hamilton, 1998 . . . . £15/£5

Short Stories
The Same Door, Knopf (U.S.), 1959 . . £250/£30
ditto, Deutsch, 1962 . . . . . . £100/£20
Pigeon Feathers, Knopf (U.S.), 1962 . . £125/£20
ditto, Deutsch, 1962 . . . . . . £65/£15
The Music School, Knopf (U.S.), 1966 (first issue with
'The state' on p. 46, line 15) . . . £300/£250
ditto, Deutsch, 1967 . . . . . . £50/£15
Bech: A Book, Knopf (U.S.), 1970 . . £20/£5
ditto, Knopf (U.S.), 1970 (500 signed copies, slipcase)
. . . . £100/£65
ditto, Deutsch, 1970 . . . . . . £15/£5
Museums and Women and Other Stories, Knopf
(U.S.), 1972 . . . . £15/£5
ditto, Knopf (U.S.), 1972 (350 signed copies, slipcase)
. . . . £75/£50
ditto, Deutsch, 1973 . . . . . . £15/£5
Warm Wine: An Idyll, Albondocani Press (U.S.), 1973
(26 signed, lettered copies) £200
ditto. Albondocani Press (U.S.), 1973 (250 signed
copies, wraps) £100
Couples, Halty Ferguson, 1976 (26 signed, lettered
copies of 276) £200
ditto, Halty Ferguson, 1976 (250 signed, numbered
copies, wraps) £100
Problems and Other Stories, Knopf (U.S.), 1979 . .
. . . . £15/£5
ditto, Knopf (U.S.), 1979 (350 signed copies, glassine
d/w and slipcase) . . . . . . £100/£75
ditto, Deutsch, 1980 . . . . . . £10/£5
Too Far to Go: The Maples Stories, Fawcett (U.S.),
1979 (wraps) £15
Trust Me, Knopf (U.S.), 1987 . . . £10/£5
ditto, Knopf (U.S.), 1987 (350 signed, numbered
copies, slipcase, d/w) . . . . . £75/£50
ditto, Deutsch, 1987 . . . . . . £10/£5
The Afterlife, Sixth Chamber Press, 1987 (26 signed,
lettered copies, no d/w) £200
ditto, Sixth Chamber Press, 1987 (175 signed,
numbered copies, no d/w) £100
The Afterlife and Other Stories, Knopf (U.S.), 1994 .
. . . . £10/£5
ditto, Hamish Hamilton, 1994 . . . . £10/£5

Children's
The Magic Flute, Knopf (U.S.), 1962 (cloth, in d/w) .
. . . . £600/£250
ditto, Knopf (U.S.), 1962 (pictorial boards, no d/w) .
. . . . £500
A Child's Calendar, Knopf (U.S.), 1965 . £125/£40

Others
The Ring, Knopf (U.S.), 1964 . . . . £150/£45
Assorted Prose, Knopf (U.S.), 1965 . . . £35/£10
ditto, Knopf (U.S.), 1965 (signed copies, unspecified
number) . . . . £125/£100
ditto, Deutsch, 1965 . . . . . . £20/£5
*Bottom's Dream: Adapted from William
Shakespeare's 'A Midsummer Night's Dream'*,
Knopf (U.S.), 1969 . . . . £100/£30
A Good Place, Aloe Editions (U.S.), 1973 (26 signed,
lettered copies, wraps) £300
ditto, Aloe Editions (U.S.), 1973 (100 signed,
numbered copies, wraps) £200
Picked-Up Pieces, Knopf (U.S.), 1976 . . £20/£5
ditto, Knopf (U.S.), 1976 (250 signed, numbered
copies, slipcase) . . . . £125/£100
ditto, Deutsch, 1976 . . . . . . £15/£5
*Three Illuminations in the Life of an American
Author*, Targ Editions (U.S.), 1979 (350 signed,
numbered copies, glassine d/w). . . £125/£100
Hugging the Shore, Knopf (U.S.), 1983 . £15/£5
ditto, Deutsch, 1984 . . . . . . £15/£5
Self-Consciousness: Memoirs, Knopf (U.S.), 1989 .
. . . . £15/£5
ditto, Deutsch, 1989 . . . . . . £10/£5
Just Looking: Essays on Art, Knopf (U.S.), 1989 . .
. . . . £20/£5
ditto, Deutsch, 1989 . . . . . . £20/£5
Odd Jobs: Essays and Criticism, Knopf (U.S.), 1991
. . . . £10/£5
ditto, Deutsch, 1991 . . . . . . £10/£5
Memories of the Ford Administration, Knopf (U.S.),
1992 . . . . £10/£5
Golf Dreams, Knopf (U.S.), 1996 . . £10/£5
ditto, Knopf (U.S.), 1996 (500 signed large print
copies) . . . . £45/£25
ditto, Hamish Hamilton, 1996 . . . . £10/£5
More Matter: Essays and Criticism, Knopf (U.S.),
1999 . . . . £10/£5

Plays
Buchanan Dying, Knopf (U.S.), 1974 . . £25/£10
ditto, Deutsch, 1974 . . . . . . £20/£5

FLORENCE UPTON
(b.1873 d.1922)

Born in New York, Florence Upton moved to
England in her twenties. She illustrated the
'Golliwogg' stories (in verse and prose) written by
her mother, Bertha Upton. Thus started a whole
'Golliwogg' craze.

The Adventures of Two Dutch Dolls and a Golliwogg,
Longmans [1895] £500
The Golliwogg's Bicycle Club, Longmans, [1896]
. . . . £400

Little Hearts, Routledge, 1897 . . . . . £400	
The Vege-Men's Revenge, Longmans, [1897] . £400	
The Golliwogg at the Seaside, Longmans, 1898 £400	
The Golliwogg in War!, Longmans, 1899 . . £400	
The Golliwogg's Polar Adventures, Longmans, [1900]	
. . . . £450	
The Golliwogg's 'Auto-Go-Cart', Longmans, [1901] .	
. . . . £400	
The Golliwogg's Air-Ship, Longmans, [1902] . £400	
The Golliwogg's Circus, Longmans, [1903] . £400	
The Golliwogg in Holland, Longmans, [1904] . £400	
The Golliwogg's Fox-Hunt, Longmans, [1905] £400	
The Golliwogg's Desert Island, Longmans. [1906] .	
. . . . £400	
The Golliwogg's Christmas, Longmans, 1907 . £400	

The Adventures of Borbee and the Wisp: The Story of a Sophisticated Little Girl and an Unsophisticated Little Boy, Longmans, 1908. . . . . . £350
Golliwogg in the African Jungle, Longmans, 1909 .
. . . . £450

ALISON UTTLEY
(b.1884 d.1976)

An author of children's books which are not unlike those of Beatrix Potter, Uttley also wrote many volumes of essays and memoirs.

'Grey Rabbit' Books
The Squirrel, the Hare and the Little Grey Rabbit, Heinemann, 1929 . . . . . . £150/£35
How Little Grey Rabbit Got Back Her Tail, Heinemann, 1930 . . . . . . £125/£25
The Great Adventure of Hare, Heinemann, 1931 . .
. . . . £125/£25
The Story of Fuzzypeg the Hedgehog, Heinemann, 1932 . . . . £100/£25
Squirrel Goes Skating, Collins, 1934 . . £75/£25
Wise Owl's Story, Collins, 1935 . . . . £75/£25
Little Grey Rabbit's Party, Collins, 1936 . £75/£25
The Knot Squirrel Tied, Collins, 1937 . . £65/£20
Fuzzypeg Goes to School, Collins, 1938 . £50/£20
Little Grey Rabbit's Christmas, Collins, 1939 £65/£20
My Little Grey Rabbit Painting Book, Collins, 1940 .
. . . . £65/£20
Moldy Warp The Mole, Collins, 1940 . . £50/£20
Hare Joins the Home Guard, Collins, 1942 £50/£20
Little Grey Rabbit's Washing Day, Collins, 1942 . .
. . . . £45/£15
Water-Rat's Picnic, Collins, 1943 . . . £45/£15
Little Grey Rabbit's Birthday, Collins, [1944] £45/£15
The Speckledy Hen, Collins, [1945] . . . £40/£15
Little Grey Rabbit to the Rescue, Collins, 1946 .
. . . . £35/£10
Little Grey Rabbit and the Weasels, Collins, 1947 .
. . . . £35/£10

Grey Rabbit and the Wandering Hedgehog, Collins, 1948 . . . . £40/£10
Little Grey Rabbit Makes Lace, Collins, 1950 £40/£10
Hare and the Easter Eggs, Collins, 1952 . £40/£10
Little Grey Rabbit's Valentine, Collins, 1953 £40/£10
Little Grey Rabbit Goes to the Sea, Collins, 1954 . .
. . . . £40/£10
Hare and Guy Fawkes, Collins, 1956 . . £40/£10
Little Grey Rabbit's Paint-Box, Collins, [1958] . .
. . . . £40/£10
Grey Rabbit Finds a Shoe, Collins, [1960] . £40/£10
Grey Rabbit and the Circus, Collins, [1961] £40/£10
Three Little Grey Rabbit Plays, Heinemann, 1961 . .
. . . . £25/£5
Grey Rabbit's May Day, Collins, [1963] . £35/£10
Hare Goes Shopping, Collins, 1965 . . . £35/£10
Little Grey Rabbit's Pancake Day, Collins, 1967 . .
. . . . £35/£10
Little Grey Rabbit Goes to the North Pole, Collins, 1970 . . . . £35/£10
Fuzzypeg's Brother, Heinemann, 1971 . . £35/£10
Little Grey Rabbit's Spring Cleaning Party, Collins, 1972 . . . . £35/£10
Little Grey Rabbit and the Snow-Baby, Collins, 1973 .
. . . . £35/£10
Hare and the Rainbow, Collins, 1975 . . £35/£10

Other Children's Books
Moonshine and Magic, Faber, 1932. . . £100/£35
The Advenures of Peter and Judy in Bunnyland, Collins, [1935] . . . . £100/£35
Candlelight Tales, Faber, 1936 . . . . £75/£25
The Adventures of No Ordinary Rabbit, Faber, 1937 .
. . . . £65/£25
High Meadows, Faber, 1938 . . . . . £30/£10
Mustard, Pepper and Salt, Faber, 1938 . . £75/£25
A Traveller in Time, Faber, 1939 . . . £75/£25
Tales of the Four Pigs and Brock the Badger, Faber, 1939 . . . . £45/£10
The Adventures of Sam Pig, Faber, 1940 . £45/£10
Sam Pig Goes to Market, Faber, 1941 . . £35/£10
Six Tales of Brock The Badger, Faber, 1941 £25/£10
Six Tales of Sam Pig, Faber, 1941 . . . £35/£10
Six Tales of the Four Pigs, Faber, 1941. . £35/£10
Ten Tales of Tim Rabbit, Faber, 1941 . . £50/£15
Nine Starlight Tales, Faber, 1942 . . . £35/£10
Sam Pig and Sally, Faber, 1942 . . . . £35/£10
Ten Candlelight Tales, Faber, 1942 . . . £35/£10
Cuckoo Cherry-Tree, Faber, 1943 . . . £35/£10
Sam Pig at the Circus, Faber, 1943 . . . £35/£10
Mrs Nimble and Mr Bumble, James, 1944 £45/£15
The Spice Woman's Basket and Other Tales, Faber, 1944 . . . . £35/£10
Adventures of Tim Rabbit, Faber, 1945 . . £35/£10
Some Moonshine Tales, Faber, 1945 . . £25/£5
The Weather Cock and Other Stories, Faber, 1945 .
. . . . £35/£10
When All Is Done, Faber, 1945 . . . . £35/£10

John Barleycorn: Twelve Tales of Fairy and Magic,
Faber, 1948 . . . . £35/£10
Sam Pig in Trouble, Faber, 1948 . . . £35/£10
Snug and Serena Meet a Queen, Heinemann, 1950 .
. . . . £35/£10
Snug and Serena Pick Cowslips, Heinemann, 1950 .
. . . . £35/£10
The Cobbler's Shop and Other Tales, Faber, 1950 .
. . . . £15/£5
Going to the Fair, Heinemann, 1951 . . £35/£10
Toad's Castle, Heinemann, 1951. . . . £35/£10
Yours Ever, Sam Pig, Faber, 1951 . . . £35/£10
Christmas at the Rose and Crown, Heinemann, 1952 .
. . . . £35/£10
Mrs Mouse Spring Cleans, Heinemann, 1952 £35/£10
Snug and the Chimney-Sweeper, Heinemann, 1953 .
. . . . £35/£10
The Gypsy Hedgehogs, Heinemann, 1953 £35/£10
Little Red Fox and the Wicked Uncle, Heinemann,
1954 . . . . £75/£35
Sam Pig and the Singing Gate, Faber, 1955 £35/£10
The Flower Show, Heinemann, 1955 £35/£10
The Mouse Telegrams, Heinemann, 1955 £35/£10
Little Red Fox and Cinderella, Heinemann, 1956 . .
. . . . £75/£35
Magic in My Pocket: A Selection of Tales, Puffin,
1957 (wraps) £5
Mr Stoat Walks In, Heinemann, 1957 . . £35/£10
Snug and the Silver Spoon, Heinemann, 1957 £35/£10
Little Red Fox and the Magic Moon, Heinemann,
1958 . . . . £75/£35
Snug and Serena Count Twelve, Heinemann, 1959 .
. . . . £35/£10
Tim Rabbit and Company, Faber, 1959 . £35/£10
John at the Old Farm, Heinemann, 1960 £45/£15
Sam Pig Goes to the Seaside, Faber, 1960 £50/£10
Snug and Serena go to Town, Heinemann, 1961 . .
. . . . £25/£10
Little Red Fox and the Unicorn, Heinemann, 1962 .
. . . . £75/£30
*The Little Knife Who Did All The Work: Twelve Tales
of Magic*, Faber, 1962 . . . . £25/£10
Tim Rabbit's Dozen, Faber, 1964 . . . £20/£5
The Sam Pig Storybook, Faber, 1965 . £35/£10
Enchantment, Heinemann, 1966. . . . £20/£5
The Mouse, The Rabbit and the Little White Hen,
Heinemann, 1966 . . . . . £20/£5
Little Red Fox and the Big Tree, Heinemann, 1968 .
. . . . £75/£30
Lavendar Shoes: Eight Tales of Enchantment, Faber,
1970 . . . . £15/£5
*The Brown Mouse Book, Magical Tales of Two Little
Mice*, Heinemann, 1971 . . . . . £15/£5
Fairy Tales, Faber, 1975 . . . . . £20/£5
Stories for Christmas, Faber, 1977 . . . £20/£5
From Spring to Spring: Stories of the Four Seasons,
Faber, 1978 . . . . £20/£5
Foxglove Tales, Faber, 1984 . . . . £20/£5

Others
The Country Child, Faber, 1931 . . . . £75/£30
Ambush of Young Days, Faber, 1937 . . £50/£20
The Farm on the Hill, Faber, 1941 . . . £35/£10
Country Hoard, Faber, 1943 . . . . . £35/£10
*The Washerwoman's Child: A Play on the Life and
Stories of Hans Christian Andersen*, Faber, 1946 .
. . . . £35/£10
Country Things, Faber, 1946. . . . . £35/£10
Carts and Candlesticks, Faber, 1946 . . £35/£10
Buckinghamshire, Hale, 1950 . . . . £35/£10
Macduff, Faber, 1950 . . . . £35/£10
Plowmen's Clocks, Faber, 1952 . . . . £35/£10
The Stuff of Dreams, Faber, 1953 . . . £35/£10
Here's a New Day, Faber, 1956 . . . . £35/£10
A Year in the Country, Faber, 1957 . . . £35/£10
The Swan's Fly Over, Faber, 1959 . . . £35/£10
Something for Nothing, Faber, 1960 . . £35/£10
Wild Honey, Faber, 1962 . . . . . . £35/£10
Cuckoo in June, Faber, 1964. . . . . £35/£10
Recipes from an Old Farmhouse, Faber, 1966 . . .
. . . . £20/£10
A Peck of Gold, Faber, 1966 . . . . . £35/£10
The Button-Box and Other Essays, Faber, 1972 . .
. . . . £35/£10
A Ten O'clock Scholar and Other Essays, Faber, 1970
. . . . £35/£10
Secret Places and Other Essays, Faber, 1972 £35/£10
Country World: Memoirs of Childhood, Faber, 1984 .
. . . . £15/£5

JULES VERNE
(b.1828 d.1905)

Born in Nantes, France, Verne studied law in Paris
and began his literary career while working at the
Stock Exchange. Famous for his escapist adventure
novels and short stories, Verne also wrote opera
libretti and plays.

Fiction
Five Weeks in a Balloon, Appleton and Co. (U.D.),
1869 . . . . £500
ditto, Chapman & Hall, 1870 . . . . . £350
A Journey to the Centre of the Earth, Griffith &
Farran, 1872 [1871] £750
ditto, Scribners, Armstong & Co. (U.S.) 1874 [1873]
(with no address under publisher's imprint or ads) .
. . . . £600
ditto, Scribners, Armstong & Co. (U.S.) 1874 [1873]
(with address and ads) £300
Twenty Thousand Leagues Under the Seas, Sampson
Low, 1873 [1872] £750
ditto, Osgood (U.S.), 1873 (10-15 copies only, with
central gilt vignette on the top board of a school of
jellyfish) £7,500

ditto, George Smith (U.S.), 1873 (with central gilt vignette on the top board the image of Nemo with sextant) £1,000
From the Earth to the Moon Direct in 97 Hours, 20 Minutes, and a Trip Round it, Newark Publishing & Printing Co. (U.S.), 1870 (wraps, first book only) .
. . . . £400
ditto, Sampson Low, 1873 (complete edition) . £750
ditto, Scribners, Armstong & Co. (U.S.) 1874 . £500
Meridiana: The Adventures of Three Englishmen and Three Russians in South Africa, Sampson Low, 1873
. . . . £300
ditto, Scribners, (U.S.) 1873 . . . . . £300
The Fur Country, Sampson Low, 1874 [1873] £300
ditto, Osgood (U.S.), 1873 . . . . . £250
Around the World in Eighty Days, Osgood (U.S.), 1873· £350
ditto, Sampson Low, 1874 [1873] . . . £350
In Search of the Castaways, Lippincott (U.S.) 1873 .
. . . . £200
ditto, as *A Voyage Round the World*, Routledge, 1876-1877 (3 vols: *South America, Australia* and *New Zealand*) £400
A Floating City, and The Blockade Runners, Sampson Low, 1874 . . . . £250
ditto, Scribners, Armstong & Co. (U.S.) 1874 ('1875' also on some title pages) £250
Dr Ox's Experiment and Other Stories, Osgood (U.S.), 1874 . . . . £200
ditto, Sampson Low, 1875 . . . . . £200
The Mysterious Island, Sampson Low, 1875 (3 vols: *Dropped from the Clouds, Abandoned* and *The Secret of the Island*) £500
ditto, Scribners, Armstong & Co. (U.S.) 1875-1876 (3 vols) £500
The Adventures of Captain Hatteras: The English at the North Pole, Routledge, 1875 [1874] . . £300
ditto, Osgood (U.S.), 1875 [1874] (with *The Field of Ice*) £300
The Field of Ice, Routledge, 1876 . . . £300
The Chancellor: The Survivors of the Chancellor, Sampson Low, 1875 . . . . . . £450
ditto, Osgood (U.S.), 1875 (with *Martin Paz*) . £450
Martin Paz, Sampson Low, 1876 . . . . £200
A Winter Amid the Ice and Other Stories, Sampson Low, 1876 . . . . £75
Michael Strogoff, Frank Leslie's Publishing House (U.S.), 1876 (wraps) £400
ditto, Sampson Low, 1877 [1876] . . . £350
ditto, Scribners (U.S.) 1877 · £350
The Child of the Cavern, Munro (U.S.), 1877 (wraps).
. . . . £250
ditto, Sampson Low, 1877 . . . . . £250
Hector Servadac, Travels and Adventures through the Solar System, Munro (U.S.), 1877 (wraps) . £350
ditto, Sampson Low, 1878 . . . . . £350
ditto, Claxton, Remsen & Haffelfinger (U.S.) 1877 .
. . . . £350

Dick Sands; or A Captain at Fifteen, Munro (U.S.), 1877 (wraps) £250
ditto, as *Dick Sands, The Boy Captain*, Sampson Low, 1879 [1878] £250
500 Millions of the Begum, Munro (U.S.), 1879 (wraps, does not include 'Mutineers of the Bounty) .
. . . . £450
ditto, as *The Begum's Fortune*, Sampson Low, 1880 [1879]. £400
ditto, Lipincott (U.S.) 1879 . . . . . £400
The Tribulations of a Chinaman, Sampson Low, 1880
. . . . £300
ditto, Lee & Shepherd (U.S.), 1880 . . . . £200
ditto, Dutton (U.S.) 1880 . . . . . . £300
The Steam House, Munro (U.S.), 1880-1881 (2 vols, wraps). £400
ditto, Sampson Low, 1881 (2 vols: *Demon of Cawnpore* and *Tigers and Traitors*) . . £400
ditto, Scribners (U.S.) 1881 (2 vols) . . . £300
The Giant Raft, Sampson Low, 1881 (2 vols: *Down the Amazon* and *The Cryptogram*) . . . £500
ditto, Munro (U.S.), 1881-1882 (2 vols, wraps) £400
ditto, Scribners (U.S.) 1881-1882 (2 vols) . £500
Godfrey Morgan, A Californian Mystery, Sampson Low, 1883 . . . . £250
ditto, as *Robinson's School*, Munro (U.S.), 1883 (wraps) £200
ditto, Scribners (U.S.) 1883 . . . . . £250
The Green Ray, Sampson Low, 1883 . . . £350
ditto, Munro (U.S.), 1883 (wraps) £200
ditto, Arco (U.S.), 1965 . . . . . £25/£10
The Headstrong Turk, Munro (U.S.), 1883-1884 (2 vols: *The Captain of the Guidara* and *Scarpante the Spy*, wraps) £300
ditto, as *Keraban the Inflexible*, Sampson Low, 1884-5 (2 vols) £250
The Vanished Diamond, Sampson Low, 1885 . £300
ditto, as *The Southern Star or The Diamond Land*, Munro (U.S.), 1885 (wraps). £200
ditto, Arco (U.S.), 1966 . . . . . £25/£10
The Archipelago on Fire, Munro (U.S.), 1885 (wraps)
. . . . £200
ditto, Sampson Low, 1886 . . . . . £250
Mathias Sandorf, Munro (U.S.), 1885 (wraps) £250
ditto, Sampson Low, 1886 . . . . . £300
The Clipper of the Clouds, Sampson Low, 1887 £250
ditto, as *Robur the Conqueror or A Trip Round the World in a Flying Machine*, Munro (U.S.), 1887 (wraps) £200
Ticket No 9672, Munro (U.S.), 1886 (2 vols, wraps) .
. . . . £200
ditto, as *The Lottery Ticket*, Sampson Low, 1887 £250
The Flight to France, Toronto National Publishing Co. (Canada), 1888 . . . . . . £400
ditto, Sampson Low, 1888 . . . . . £300
ditto, Lovell (U.S.), 1888 (wraps) £200
Texan's Vengeance, or North Versus South, Munro (U.S.), 1887 (2 vols, wraps). £200

ditto, as *North Against South*, Sampson Low, 1888 .
. . . . £400
Adrift in the Pacific, Munro (U.S.), 1889 (wraps) £200
ditto, Sampson Low, 1889 . . . . . . £400
ditto, Bromfield & Co. (U.S.), 1889 . . . . £400
A Family Without a Name, Lovell (U.S.), 1889
(wraps) £200
ditto, Sampson Low, 1891 [1890] £300
The Purchase of the North Pole, Sampson Low, 1891
[1890] £300
ditto, as *Topsy Turvy*, Ogilvie (U.S.), 1890 . £1,000
ditto, Ogilvie (U.S.), 1890 (wraps) £200
Caesar Cascabel, Cassell (U.S.), 1890 . . . £250
ditto, Sampson Low, 1891 . . . . . £250
Mistress Branican, Cassell (U.S.), 1891 . . £250
ditto, Sampson Low, 1892 . . . . . £250
The Castle of the Carpathians, Sampson Low, 1893 .
. . . . £300
ditto, Merrian (U.S.), 1894 . . . . . £300
Claudius Bombarnac, Sampson Low, 1894 . £300
ditto, as *The Special Correspondent, Or the Adventures of Claudius Bombarnac*, The U.S. Book Co.
(U.S.), 1894 . . . . £300
Foundling Mick, Sampson Low, 1895 . . . £750
Captain Antifer, Sampson Low, 1895 . . . £300
ditto, Fenno (U.S.), 1895 (wraps) £200
ditto, Fenno (U.S.), 1895 . . . . . . £200
The Floating Island, Sampson Low, 1896 . . £300
ditto, Allison (U.S.), 1897 . . . . . £300
Clovis Dardentor, Sampson Low, 1897 . . £1,000
Facing the Flag, Tennyson Neely (U.S.), 1897 £300
ditto, as *For the Flag*, Sampson Low, 1897. . £300
An Antarctic Mystery, Sampson Low, 1898 . £600
ditto, Lippincott (U.S.), 1898 . . . . . £450
The Will of an Eccentric, Sampson Low, 1900. £100
The Chase of the Golden Meteor, Grant Richards,
1909 . . . . £75
ditto, as *The Hunt for the Meteor*, Arco (U.S.), 1965 .
. . . . £25/£10
Master of the World, Parke & Co (U.S.), 1911 (as vol
14 of the 15 volume *Works of Jules Verne*) . £100
ditto, Sampson Low, [1914] £75
The Lighthouse at the End of the World, Sampson
Hall, [1923] . . . . . . £400/£100
ditto, Watt (U.S.), 1924 . . . . . £400/£100
Second Patrie: Their Island Home, Sampson Low,
[1923] . . . . £100/£35
ditto, Watt (U.S.), 1924 . . . . £100/£35
The Castaways of the Flag, Sampson Low, [1923] .
. . . . £100/£35
The Barsac Mission: Into the Niger Bend, Arco
(simultaneous U.S. and U.K. editions), 1960 £25/£10
The City in the Sahara, Arco (U.S. and U.K.), 1960 .
. . . . £25/£10
The Survivors of the Jonathan: The Masterless Man,
Arco (U.S. and U.K.), 1962. . . . . £25/£10
The Unwilling Dictator, Arco (U.S. and U.K.), 1962 .
. . . . £25/£10

*The Golden Volcano: The Claim on Forty Mile
Creek*, Arco (U.S. and U.K.), 1962. . . £25/£10
Flood and Fame, Arco (U.S. and U.K.), 1962 £25/£10
The Secret of the Wilhelm Storitz, Arco (U.S. and
U.K.), 1964 . . . . £25/£10
The Village in the Treetops, Arco (U.S. and U.K.),
1964 . . . . £25/£10
Salvage from the 'Cynthia', Arco (U.S. and U.K.),
1964 . . . . £25/£10
Yesterday and Tomorrow, Arco (U.S. and U.K.), 1965
. . . . £25/£10
The Thompson Travel Agency: Package Holiday,
Arco (U.S. and U.K.), 1965 . . . £25/£10
End of the Journey, Arco (U.S. and U.K.), 1965 . .
. . . . £25/£10
Drama in Livonia, Arco (U.S. and U.K.), 1967 . .
. . . . £25/£10
The Danube Pilot, Arco (U.S. and U.K.), 1967 . .
. . . . £25/£10
The Sea Serpent, Arco (U.S. and U.K.), 1967 £25/£10
Backwards to Britain, Chambers (U.S. and U.K.),
1992 . . . . £20/£5
Adventures of the Rat Family, O.U.P. (U.S. and U.K.),
1993 . . . . £20/£5
Paris in the 20th Century, Random House (U.S. and
U.K.), 1996 . . . . £20/£5

Non Fiction
The Exploration of the World (B.C. 505 - A.D. 1700),
Sampson Low, 1879 . . . . . . £150
ditto, as *Famous Travels and Travellers*, Scribners
(U.S.), 1879 . . . . £150
The Great Navigators of the Eighteenth Century,
Sampson Low, 1880 . . . . . . £150
ditto, Scribners (U.S.), 1880 . . . . £150
The Great Explorers of the Nineteenth Century,
Sampson Low, 1881 . . . . . . £150
ditto, Scribners (U.S.), 1881 . . . . . £150

GORE VIDAL
(b.1925)

An acclaimed U.S. novelist and essayist, Vidal offers
a sharp insight into contemporary American life.

Novels
Williwaw, Dutton (U.S.), 1946 . . . . £500/£50
ditto, Heinemann, 1970 . . . . . £25/£10
In a Yellow Wood, Dutton (U.S.), 1947 . . £200/£25
The City and The Pillar, Dutton (U.S.), 1948 £150/£20
ditto, Lehmann, 1949 . . . . . . £35/£10
ditto, Dutton (U.S.), 1965 (revised edition) . £15/£5
ditto, Heinemann, 1966 (revised edition) . £15/£5
The Season of Comfort, Dutton (U.S.), 1949 £100/£15
A Search for The King, Dutton (U.S.), 1950 £100/£15
Dark Green, Bright Red, Dutton (U.S.), 1950 . . .
. . . . £100/£15

ditto, Lehmann, 1950 . . . . . . £45/£10
The Judgement of Paris, Dutton (U.S.), 1952 £75/£10
ditto, Heinemann, 1953 . . . . . £40/£10
Death in The Fifth Position, Dutton (U.S.), 1952
(pseud. 'Edgar Box') . . . . . £300/£35
ditto, Heinemann, 1954 . . . . . £65/£15
Death Before Bedtime, Dutton (U.S.), 1953 (pseud.
'Edgar Box') . . . . £300/£35
ditto, Heinemann, 1954 . . . . . £65/£15
Death Likes It Hot, Dutton (U.S.), 1954 (pseud. 'Edgar
Box') . . . . £300/£35
ditto, Heinemann, 1955 . . . . . £65/£15
Messiah, Dutton (U.S.), 1954 . . . £60/£15
ditto, Heinemann, 1955 . . . . . £50/£15
Julian, Little, Brown (U.S.), 1964 . . £40/£15
ditto, Heinemann, 1964 . . . . . £35/£10
Washington DC, Little, Brown (U.S.), 1967 £30/£5
ditto, Heinemann, 1967 . . . . . £25/£5
Myra Breckinridge, Little, Brown (U.S.), 1968 £30/£5
ditto, Blond, 1968 . . . . . . £25/£5
Two Sisters, Little, Brown (U.S.), 1970 . . £30/£5
ditto, Heinemann, 1970 . . . . . £25/£5
Burr, Random House (U.S.), 1973 . . £30/£5
ditto, Heinemann, 1974 . . . . . £25/£5
Myron, Random House (U.S.), 1974 . . £25/£5
ditto, Heinemann, 1975 . . . . . £20/£5
1876, Random House (U.S.), 1976 . . £25/£5
ditto, Random House (U.S.), 1976 (300 signed copies,
slipcase) . . . . £75/£50
ditto, Heinemann, 1976 . . . . . £20/£5
Kalki, Random House (U.S.), 1978 . . £20/£5
ditto, Franklin Library (U.S.), 1978 (signed copies) .
. . . . £45
ditto, Heinemann, 1978 . . . . . £20/£5
Creation, Random House (U.S.), 1981 . £20/£5
ditto, Random House (U.S.), 1981 (500 signed copies,
slipcase) . . . . £65/£50
ditto, Heinemann, 1981 . . . . . £20/£5
Duluth, Random House (U.S.), 1983 . £20/£5
ditto, Heinemann, 1983 . . . . . £20/£5
Lincoln, Random House (U.S.), 1984 . £20/£5
ditto, . Random House (U.S.), 1984 (350 signed,
numbered copies, slipcase) . . . . £75/£50
ditto, Franklin Library (U.S.), 1984 (signed copies)
. . . . £45
ditto, Heinemann, 1984 . . . . . £15/£5
Empire, Random House (U.S.), 1987 . . £15/£5
ditto, Random House (U.S.), 1987 (250 signed,
numbered copies, slipcase) . . . . £75/£50
ditto, Franklin Library (U.S.), 1987 (signed copies)
. . . . £45
ditto, Deutsch, 1987 . . . . . . £15/£5
Hollywood, Random House (U.S.), 1990 . £15/£5
ditto, Random House (U.S.), 1990 (200 signed,
numbered copies, slipcase) . . . . £75/£50
ditto, Deutsch, 1990 . . . . . . £15/£5
View from The Diner's Club, Random House (U.S.),
1991 . . . . £15/£5
ditto, Deutsch, 1991 . . . . . . £15/£5

Live from Golgotha, Random House (U.S.), 1992 .
. . . . £15/£5
ditto, Deutsch, 1992 . . . . . . £15/£5

Short Stories
A Thirsty Evil: 7 Short Stories, Zero Press (U.S.),
1956 . . . . £100/£20
ditto, Heinemann, 1958 . . . . . £30/£10
The Ladies in The Library and Other Stories,
Eurographica (Helsinki), 1985 (350 signed copies) .
. . . . £70

Plays
Visit to a Small Planet and Other Television Plays,
Little, Brown (U.S.), 1956 . . . . £50/£10
The Best Man, Little, Brown (U.S.), 1960 . £40/£10
Three Plays, Heinemann, 1962 . . . £35/£10
Romulus: A New Comedy, Dramatists Play Service
(U.S.), 1962 (wraps) £25
Weekend, Dramatists Play Service (U.S.), 1968
(wraps) £20
An Evening with Richard Nixon, Random House
(U.S.), 1972 . . . . £20/£5

Essays
Rocking The Boat, Little, Brown (U.S.), 1962 £50/£10
ditto, Heinemann, 1963 . . . . . £35/£10
Reflections Upon a Sinking Ship, Little, Brown (U.S.),
1969 . . . . £30/£5
ditto, Heinemann, 1969 . . . . . £25/£5
***Homage to Daniel Shays: Collected Essays 1952-
1972***, Random House (U.S.), 1972 . . . £20/£5
ditto, as ***Collected Essays 1951-1972***, Heinemann,
1974 . . . . £15/£5
Matters of Fact and Fiction: Essays, 1973-1976,
Random House (U.S.), 1977 . . . . £20/£5
ditto, Heinemann, 1977 . . . . . £15/£5
Armageddon? Essays 1985-1987, Deutsch, 1987 . .
. . . . £15/£5
ditto, as ***At Home***, Random House (U.S.), 1988 £15/£5
United States: Essays, 1951-92, Deutsch, 1993 £15/£5

Others
Great American Families, Norton (U.S.), 1977 (with
others). . . . . £15/£5
ditto, Times, 1977 . . . . £10/£5
Vidal in Venice, Weidenfeld, 1984 . . . £10/£5
ditto, Summit (U.S.), 1985 . . . . £10/£5
Screening History, Harvard Univ. Press (U.S.), 1992 .
. . . . £10/£5
ditto, Deutsch, 1992 . . . . . . £10/£5
Palimpsest, Random House (U.S.), 1995 £10/£5
ditto, Deutsch, 1995 . . . . . . £10/£5

KURT VONNEGUT
(b.1911)

An American novelist, Vonnegut's experiences as a prisoner of war in Dresden during World War Two have influenced much of his writing.

Novels
Player Piano, Scribner (U.S.), 1952 ('A' and publisher's seal on copyright page). . . £650/£75
ditto, Macmillan, 1953 . . . . . . £350/£50
The Sirens of Titan, Fawcett (U.S.), 1959 (wraps) £75
ditto, Houghton Mifflin (U.S.), 1961 . £1,000/£100
ditto, Gollancz, 1962 . . . . £500/£65
Mother Night, Fawcett (U.S.), 1962 (wraps) . £100
ditto, Harper &Row (U.S.), [1966] . . . £200/£30
ditto, Cape, 1968 . . . . £75/£15
Cat's Cradle, Holt Rinehart (U.S.), 1963 . £500/£65
ditto, Gollancz, 1963 . . . . £200/£35
God Bless You, Mr Rosewater, Holt Rinehart (U.S.), 1965 . . . . £300/£45
ditto, Cape, 1965 . . . . £200/£35
Slaughterhouse-Five, Delacorte (U.S.), 1969 £500/£25
ditto, Cape, 1970 . . . . £150/£20
ditto, Franklin Library (U.S.), 1978 (signed copies) £65
Breakfast of Champions, Delacorte (U.S.), 1973 . .
. . . . £25/£5
ditto, Cape, 1973 . . . . £25/£5
Slapstick, Delacorte (U.S.), 1976 . . . £25/£5
ditto, Delacorte (U.S.), 1976 (250 signed, numbered copies, slipcase) . . . . £200/£150
ditto, Franklin Library (U.S.), 1976 (signed copies) £35
ditto, Cape, 1976 . . . . £30/£5
Jailbird, Delacorte (U.S.), 1979 . . . . £20/£5
ditto, Delacorte (U.S.), 1979 (500 signed copies, slipcase) . . . . £135/£100
ditto, Franklin Library (U.S.), 1979 (signed copies) £35
ditto, Cape, 1979 . . . . £205/£5
Deadeye Dick, Delacorte (U.S.), 1981 . . £15/£5
ditto, Delacorte (U.S.), 1981 (350 signed copies, slipcase) . . . . £150/£125
ditto, Cape, 1983 . . . . £15/£5
Galapagos, Delacorte (U.S.), 1985 . . . £15/£5
ditto, Delacorte (U.S.), 1985 (500 signed copies, slipcase) . . . . £150/£125
ditto, Franklin Library (U.S.), 1985 (signed copies) £40
ditto, Cape, 1985 . . . . £15/£5
Bluebeard, Delacorte (U.S.), 1987 . . . £15/£5
ditto, Delacorte (U.S.), 1987 (500 signed copies, slipcase) . . . . £150/£125
ditto, Franklin Library (U.S.), 1987 (signed copies) £40
ditto, Cape, 1988 . . . . £15/£5
Hocus Pocus; Or, What's The Hurry Son?, Putnam (U.S.), 1990 . . . . £10/£5
ditto, Putnam (U.S.), 1990 (250 signed copies, slipcase) . . . . £150/£125
ditto, Franklin Library (U.S.), 1990 (signed copies) £40
ditto, Cape, 1990 . . . . £10/£5

Short Stories
Canary in a Cathouse, Fawcett (U.S.), 1961 (wraps) .
. . . . £65
Welcome to The Monkey House, Delacorte (U.S.), 1968 . . . . £300/£45
ditto, Cape, 1969 . . . . £125/£20

Plays
Happy Birthday, Wanda June, Delacorte (U.S.), 1971 (price at top on front flap of d/w) . . . £600/£30
ditto, Cape, 1973 . . . . £150/£20
Between Time and Timbuctoo, Delacorte (U.S.), 1972
. . . . £300/£65

Others
Wampeters, Foma, and Granfalloons: Opinions, Delacorte (U.S.), 1974 . . . . . . £40/£10
ditto, Cape, 1975 . . . . £25/£10
Palm Sunday, Delacorte (U.S.), 1981 . . £15/£5
ditto, Delacorte (U.S.), 1981 (500 signed copies, slipcase) . . . . £100/£75
ditto, Cape, 1981 . . . . £15/£5
Fates Worse Than Death: An Autobiographical Collage of The 1980's, Putnam (U.S.), 1991 £10/£5
ditto, Putnam (U.S.), 1991 (200 signed, numbered copies) £125
ditto, Cape, 1991 . . . . £10/£5

LOUIS WAIN
(b.1860 d.1939)

Highly successful British illustrator, well known for his drawings of cats.

Books Written and Illustrated by Louis Wain
Dreams by French Firesides, A & C Black, 1890 (pseud. 'Richard Leander') £350
Miss Lovemouse's Letters, Nelson, 1896 . . £250
Puppy Dogs' Tales, Nelson, 1896 . . . . £250
The Children's Tableaux: The Three Little Kittens, Nister, 1896 . . . . £250
The Dandy Lion, by Louis Wain and Clifton Bingham, Nister, [1900]. £500
Fun All The Way, Nister, 1900 . . . . £45
Cats, Sands, [1901] (pseud. 'Grimalkin') . . £450
Fun For Everyone, Nister, 1902. . . . . £45
Fun and Frolic, by Louis Wain and Clifton Bingham, Nister, [1902]. £1,000
Pa Cats, Ma Cats, and Their Kittens, Raphael Tuck, [1902] (pseud. 'Father Tuck') £1,000
The Louis Wain Nursery Book, Clarke, [1902] £200
Louis Wain's Cats and Dogs, Raphael Tuck, 1902 .
. . . . £350
Big Dogs, Little Dogs, Cats and Kittens, Raphael Tuck, [1903] £1,000
Comic Annuals ABC, by Louis Wain, Collins, [1903].
. . . . £500

Louis Wain's Baby's Picture Book, Clarke, 1903 £300
Louis Wain's Dog Painting Book, Raphael Tuck, 1903
. . . . £300
Louis Wain's Cat Painting Book, Raphael Tuck, 1903
. . . . £300
Louis Wain's Summer Book, Hutchinson, 1903 £300
The Louis Wain Kitten Book, Treherne, [1903]
(printed on one side of the page) . . . £1,000
Funny Animals and Stories About Them, Clarke,
1904 . . . . £400
In Animal Land with Louis Wain, Partridge, [1904] .
. . . . £750
Kits and Cats, Raphael Tuck, 1904 . . . £750
*Louis Wain's Animal Show: With Stories in Prose
and Verse*, Clarke, 1905. . . . . . £250
Louis Wain's Summer Book for 1906, King, 1906 .
. . . . £250
Animal Playtime, Clarke, 1908 . . . . £250
In Story Land with Louis Wain, Raphael Tuck, 1912 .
. . . . £1,000
Louis Wain's Painting Book, Shaw, 1912 . £300
Louis Wain's Father Christmas, Shaw, 1912 . £300
Animal Happyland, Clarke, 1913 . . . £300
Happy Hours with Louis Wain, Shaw, 1913 . £300
A Cat Alphabet and Picture Book for Little Folk,
Blackie & Sons, [1914] £350
Animal Picture-Land, Clarke, 1914 . . . £250
Daddy Cat, Blackie & Sons, [1915] . . . £750
Little Red Riding Hood and Other Tales, Gale &
Poleden, [1917] £250
Cinderella and Other Fairy Tales, Gale & Poleden,
1917 . . . . £250
Cats at Play, Blackie, 1917 . . . . . £750
The Story of Tabbykin Town in School and at Play,
Faulkner, [1920] (pseud. 'Kittycat') . . £1,000
Pussy Land, Geographia, [1920]. . . . £250
The Kitten's House, Valentine, 1922 . . . £750
Charlie's Adventures, Valentine, 1922 . . £750
Comical Kittens, Valentine, [1922] (painting book with
paints and brush). £125
Louis Wain's Children's Book, Hutchinson, [1923] .
. . . . £250
Souvenir of Louis Wain's Work, Louis Wain Fund,
1925 . . . . £125
ditto, as *Animals 'Xtra' and Louis Wain's Annual
1925*, Louis Wain Fund, [1925]. . . . £125
Louis Wain's Animal Book, Collins, 'Bumper Book',
[1928] £100
Louis Wain's Great Big Midget Book, Dean, 1934 .
. . . . £100

Annuals

Louis Wain's Annual, Treherne, 1901 . . £250
Louis Wain's Annual for 1902, Treherne, 1902 £250
Louis Wain's Annual 1903, Hutchinson, 1903 . £250
Louis Wain's Annual 1905, King, 1905 . . £200
Louis Wain's Annual for 1906, Shaw, 1906 . £200
Louis Wain's Annual 1907, Bemrose, 1907 . £200
Louis Wain's Annual 1908, Bemrose, 1908 . £200

Louis Wain's Annual 1909-10, Allen, 1909 . £175
Louis Wain's Annual 1910-11, Allen, 1910 . £175
Louis Wain's Annual 1911, Shaw, 1911 . . £175
Louis Wain's Annual 1911-12, Shaw, 1911 . £175
Louis Wain's Annual 1912, Shaw, 1912 . . £175
Louis Wain's Annual 1913, Shaw, 1913 . . £175
Louis Wain's Annual 1914, Shaw, 1914 . . £175
Louis Wain's Annual 1915, Shaw, 1915 . . £175
Louis Wain's Annual 1921, Hutchinson, 1921 . £175

Books Illustrated by Louis Wain

Madame Tabby's Establishment, by Kari, Macmillan,
1886 . . . . £1,500
Our Farm: The Trouble and Successes Thereof, by
F.W. Pattenden, Clarke, 1888 . . . . £400
Peter, A Cat O' One Tail: His Life and Adventures, by
Charles Morley, Pall Mall Gazette Extras, 1892 £750
Old Rabbit, The Voodoo and Other Sorcerers, by
M.A. Owen, Unwin, 1893 . . . . . £250
More Jingles, Jokes and Funny Folks, by Clifton
Bingham, Nister, 1898 . . . . . £400
The Monkey That Would Not Kill, by Henry
Drummond, Hodder & Stoughton, 1898 . . £65
*Pussies and Puppies: With Verses and Tales by
Various Writers*, Partridge, [1899] . . . £300
The Living Animals of The World, by C.J. Cornish,
[1901]. £150
All Sorts of Comical Cats, by Clifton Bingham, Nister,
1902 . . . . £1,000
Ping-Pong Calendar for 1903, by Clifton Bingham,
Raphael Tuck, [1903] £275
Kittenland, by Clifton Bingham, Collins, [1903] . .
. . . . £1,000
With Louis Wain to Fairyland, by Nora Chesson,
Raphael Tuck, [1904] £1,000
Funny Favourites, by Clifton Bingham, Nister, 1904 .
. . . . £750
*Claws and Paws: Stories and Pictures from Kittenland
and Puppyland*, by C. Bingham, Nister, [1904] . .
. . . . £1,000
Cat Tales, by W.L. Alden, Digby Long, 1905 . £750
The Adventures of Friskers and His Friends, by
Marian Hurrell, Culley, 1907 . . . £750
*Mephistopheles: The Autobiography and Adventures
of a Tabby Cat*, by C.Y. Stephens, Jarrold, 1907 £750
*The Kings and The Cats: Munster Fairy Tales for
Young and Old*, by John Hannon, Burns & Oates,
[1908]. £650
Cat's Cradle: A Picture Book for Little Folk, by May
Clariss Byron, Blackie, [1908] £650
Full of Fun, by Clifton Bingham, Nister, [1908] £650
Holidays in Animal Land, by A.W. Ridler, Clarke,
[1909]. £250
Two Cats at Large: A Book of Surprises, by S.C.
Woodhouse, Routledge, [1910]. . . . £750
The Merry Animal Picture Book, by A.W. Ridler,
Clarke, [1910] £250
The Happy Family, by Edric Vredenburg, Raphael
Tuck, 1910 . . . . £1,000

Such Fun with Louis Wain, by Norman Gale, Raphael Tuck, 1910 . . . . £300
To Nursery Land with Louis Wain, edited by Edric Vredenburg Raphael Tuck, 1910 . . . . £250
Cats at School, by S.C. Woodhouse, Routledge, [1911] £850
Animals in Fun-Land, by A.W. Rider, Clarke, 1911 . . . . £300
Merry Times in Animal-Land, by A.W. Rider, Clarke, 1912 . . . . £300
The Cat Scouts: A Picture Book for Little Folk, by Jessie Pope, Blackie, [1912] £1,000
Louis Wain's Happy Land, by A.W. Ridler, Shaw, 1912 . . . . £200
Tinker, Tailor, by Eric Vredenburg, Raphael Tuck, 1914 . . . . £1,000
Animal Fancy-Land, by A.W. Rider, Clarke, 1915 . . . . £300
Little Soldiers, by May Crommelin, Hutchinson, [1915]. £200
Merry Times with Louis Wain, by Dorothy Black, Raphael Tuck, 1916 . . . . £800
The Tales of Little Priscilla Purr, by Cecily M. Rutley, Valentine, 1920 . . . . £200
The Tale of Naughty Kitty Cat, by Cecily M. Rutley, Valentine, 1920 . . . . £200
The Tale of Peter Pusskin, by Cecily M. Rutley, Valentine, 1920 . . . . £200
The Tale of The Tabby Twins, by Cecily M. Rutley, Valentine, 1920 . . . . £200
The Teddy Rocker: Naughty Teddy Bear, by Cecily M. Rutley, Valentine, 1921 (shape book) . . £200
The Pussy Rocker: Polly Puss, by Cecily M. Rutley, Valentine, 1921 (shape book) £200

ALFRED WAINWRIGHT
(d.1907 d.1991)

Wainwright was the author and illustrator of numerous guides to the fells of England and Scotland.

A Pictorial Guide to the Lakeland Fells Titles
The Eastern Fells, Henry Marshall, 1955 (in 'second impression' d/w) . . . . £175/£150
The Far Eastern Fells, Henry Marshall, 1957 . . . . £165/£65
The Central Fells, Henry Marshall, 1958 . £150/£65
The Southern Fells, Henry Marshall, 1960 . £150/£65
The Southern Fells, Henry Marshall, 1962 . £150/£65
The North-Western Fells, Westmorland Gazette, 1964 . . . . £150/£65
The Western Fells, Westmorland Gazette, 1966 . . . . £150/£65

Lakeland Sketchbooks
A Lakeland Sketchbook, Westmorland Gazette, 1969 . . . . £75/£25

A Second Lakeland Sketchbook, Westmorland Gazette, 1970. . . . . £50/£20
A Third Lakeland Sketchbook, Westmorland Gazette, 1971 . . . . £30/£10
A Fourth Lakeland Sketchbook, Westmorland Gazette, 1972. . . . . £30/£10
A Fifth Lakeland Sketchbook, Westmorland Gazette, 1973 . . . . £30/£10

Scottish Mountain Drawings
The Northern Highlands, Westmorland Gazette, 1974 . . . . £50/£20
The North-West Highlands, Westmorland Gazette, 1976 . . . . £40/£15
The Western Highlands, Westmorland Gazette, 1976 . . . . £40/£15
The Central Highlands, Westmorland Gazette, 1977 . . . . £40/£15
The Eastern Highlands, Westmorland Gazette, 1978 . . . . £40/£15
The Islands, Westmorland Gazette, 1979 . £40/£15

Others
Fellwanderer, The Story Behind the Guidebooks, Westmorland Gazette, 1966. . . . £25/£10
Pennine Way Companion, Westmorland Gazette, 1968 . . . . £75/£25
Walks in Limestone Country, Westmorland Gazette, 1970 . . . . £50/£20
Walks on the Howgill Fells, Westmorland Gazette, 1972 . . . . £40/£15
A Coast to Coast Walk, St Bees Head to Robin Hood's Bay, Westmorland Gazette, 1973 . . £40/£15
The Outlying Fells of Lakeland, Westmorland Gazette, 1974. . . . . £40/£15
Westmorland Heritage, Westmorland Gazette, 1974 (1,000 signed copies) . . . . . £500/£200
ditto, Westmorland Gazette, 1988 . . . £15/£5
A Dales Sketchbook, Westmorland Gazette, 1976 . . . . £35/£15
Kendal in the Nineteenth Century, Westmorland Gazette, 1977. . . . . . . £75/£15
A Second Dales Sketchbook, Westmorland Gazette, 1978 . . . . £35/£15
A Furness Sketchbook, Westmorland Gazette, 1978 . . . . £35/£15
Walks from Ratty, Ravenglass and Eskdale Railway Co, 1978 . . . . £35/£15
A Second Furness Sketchbook, Westmorland Gazette, 1979 . . . . £35/£15
Three Westmorland Rivers, Westmorland Gazette, 1979 . . . . £35/£15
A Lune Sketchbook, Westmorland Gazette, 1980 . . . . £35/£15
A Ribble Sketchbook, Westmorland Gazette, 1980. . . . . £35/£15
An Eden Sketchbook, Westmorland Gazette, 1980 . . . . £35/£15

Lakeland Mountain Drawings, Westmorland Gazette,
1980 (5 vols) . . . . £35/£15 each
Welsh Mountain Drawings, Westmorland Gazette,
1981 . . . . £35/£15
A Bowland Sketchbook, Westmorland Gazette, 1981 .
. . . . £35/£15
A North Wales Sketchbook, Westmorland Gazette,
1982 . . . . £35/£15
A Wyre Sketchbook, Westmorland Gazette, 1982 . .
. . . . £35/£15
A South Wales Sketchbook, Westmorland Gazette,
1983 . . . . £35/£15
Wainwright in Lakeland, Abbott Hall Art Gallery,
1983 (1,000 signed copies) . . . . £450/£175
A Peak District Sketchbook, Westmorland Gazette,
1984 . . . . £35/£15
Fellwalking with Wainwright, Michael Joseph, 1984
(photographs by Derry Brabbs) . . . £15/£5
Old Roads of Eastern Lakeland, Westmorland
Gazette, 1985 . . . . £10/£5
Wainwright on the Pennine Way, Michael Joseph,
1985 (photographs by Derry Brabbs) . . £10/£5
A Pennine Journey, Michael Joseph, 1986 . £10/£5
Wainwright's Coast to Coast Walk, Michael Joseph,
1987 (photographs by Derry Brabbs) . . £10/£5
Ex-Fellwanderer, Westmorland Gazette, 1987 £10/£5
Wainwright in Scotland, Michael Joseph, 1988
(photographs by Derry Brabbs) . . . £10/£5
Fellwalking with a Camera, Westmorland Gazette,
1988 . . . . £10/£5
Wainwright on the Lakeland Mountain Passes,
Michael Joseph, 1989 (photographs by Derry Brabbs)
. . . . £10/£5
Wainwright in the Limestone Dales, Michael Joseph,
1991 (photographs by Ed Geldard) . . £10/£5
Wainwright's Favourite Lakeland Mountains,
Michael Joseph, 1991 (photographs by Derry Brabbs)
. . . . £10/£5
Wainwright in the Valleys of Lakeland, Michael
Joseph, 1992 (photographs by Derry Brabbs) £10/£5
Memoirs of a Fellwanderer, Michael Joseph, 1993 .
. . . . £10/£5
*Wainwright: His Tour of the Lake District,
Whitsuntide, 1931*, Michael Joseph, 1993
(photographs by Ed Geldard) . . . £10/£5
The Walker's Log Book, Michael Joseph, 1993 £10/£5

Other Titles Illustrated by Wainwright
Inside the Real Lakeland, by A.H. Griffin, Guardian
Press, 1961 . . . . £40/£15
Scratch and Co., by Molly Lefebure, Gollancz, 1968 .
. . . . £15/£5
The Hunting of Wilberforce Pike, by Molly Lefebure,
Gollancz, 1970 . . . . . . £10/£5
The Plague Dogs, by Richard Adams, Allen Lane,
1977 . . . . £10/£5
Guide to the View from Scafel Pike, Chris Jesty
Panoramas, 1978 . . . . . . £10/£5

A.E. WAITE
(b.1857 d.1942)

An occultist, poet, bohemian and mystic, Waite's
contribution to the literature of the occult is highly
regarded by devotees.

Principal Works
The Real History of The Rosicrucians, George
Redway, 1887 . . . . £150
A Handbook of Cartomancy, George Redway, 1889
(pseud. 'Grand Orient') £125
*The Interior Life from The Standpoint of The
Mystics*, 'Light', [1891] £200
The Occult Sciences, Kegan Paul, Trench, Trübner and
Co., 1891 . . . . £150
Azoth: or The Star in The East, Theosophical
Publishing Society, 1893 . . . . £200
Devil-Worship in France, George Redway, 1896 £125
The Book of Black Magic and Pacts, Redway, 1898
(500 copies) £250
The Life of Louis Claude de Saint-Martin, Philip
Wellby, 1901 . . . . £150
The Doctrine and Literature of The Kabalah,
Theosophical Publishing Society, 1902 . £200
Studies in Mysticism, Hodder & Stoughton, 1906 £100
The Hidden Church of The Holy Graal, Rebman Ltd,
1909 . . . . £125
The Key to The Tarot, William Rider & Son Ltd, 1910
. . . . £75
ditto, 1920 (new edition) £75
The Pictorial Key to The Tarot, William Rider & Son
Ltd, 1911 . . . . £75
The Book of Ceremonial Magic, William Rider and
Son Ltd, 1911 . . . . £75
The Secret Tradition in Freemasonry, Rebman Ltd,
1911 . . . . £75
The Secret Doctrine in Israel, William Rider & Son
Ltd, 1913 . . . . £100
The Way of Divine Union, William Rider & Son Ltd,
1915 . . . . £275
Deeper Aspects of Masonic Symbolism, privately
printed, 1915 . . . . £65
New Encyclopaedia of Freemasonry, William Rider &
Son Ltd, 1921 . . . . £125/£65
Robert Fludd and Freemasonry, offprint, (1922) £45
Raymond Lully, William Rider & Son Ltd, 1922 . .
. . . . £75/£45
Saint-Martin, William Rider & Son Ltd, 1922 . . .
. . . . £65/£35
Lamps of Western Mysticism, Kegan Paul, Trench,
Trübner and Co., 1923 . . . . £60/£35
The Brotherhood of The Rosy Cross, William Rider &
Son Ltd, 1924 . . . . £75/£25
Emblematic Freemasonry, William Rider & Son Ltd,
1925 . . . . £65/£35
The Secret Tradition in Alchemy, Kegan Paul, Trench,
Trübner and Co., 1926 . . . . . £75/£35

The Holy Kabbalah, William & Norgate Ltd, 1929 .
. . . . £50/£30
The Holy Grail, William Rider & Son Ltd, 1933 . .
. . . . £65/£35
The Secret Tradition in Freemasonry, Rider & Co.,
1937 . . . . £65/£35
Shadows of Life and Thought, Selwyn & Blount, 1938
. . . . £65/£30

Verse
An Ode to Astronomy and Other Poems, 1877?, (100
copies) £3,000
A Lyric of The Fairyland, Catty, 1879 . . .£2,000
A Soul's Comedy, George Redway, 1887 . . £100
Lucastra, James Burns, [1890] £100
A Book of Mystery and Vision, Philip Wellby, 1902 .
. . . . £65
ditto, Philip Wellby, 1902 (10 signed copies on
Japanese vellum). £350
Strange Houses of Sleep, Philip Wellby, 1906 (250
signed, numbered copies, with Arthur Machen) £125
The Collected Poems of Arthur Edward Waite, Rider,
1914 (2 vols) £65
The Book of The Holy Graal, J.M. Watkins, 1921 (500
copies) . . . . £75/£35
The Open Vision, Shakespeare Head Press, 1959 (500
copies) . . . . £30/£10

Fiction
Prince Starbeam, James Burns, 1889 . . . £100
The Golden Stairs, Theosophical Publishing Society,
1893 . . . . £100
Belle and The Dragon, James Elliot, 1894 . . £100
Steps to The Crown, Philip Wellby, 1906 . . £65
The Quest of The Golden Stairs, Theosophical
Publishing House Ltd, [1927] . . . . £50/£25

Others
Israfel, Letters, Visions and Poems, E.W. Allen, 1886
. . . . £75
ditto, James Elliot & Co., 1894 (enlarged edition) £65
The House of The Hidden Light, privately printed,
1904 (with Arthur Machen). £1,500
The Hermetic Text Society, Philip Wellby, 1907 £50

EDGAR WALLACE
(b.1875 d.1932)

Wallace's output of books was vast, and he made no
attempt to disguise the fact that it was popular rather
than critical success that he craved. In this ambition
he was incredibly successful.

Novels
The Four Just Men, Tallis Press, 1905 (numbered
competition slip) £125

ditto, Tallis Press, 1906 (includes chapter 12, a letter
from Manfred as solution) £30
ditto, Tallis Press, 1911 (includes full chapter 12) £20
ditto, Small Maynard (U.S.), 1920 . . . £75/£20
Angel Esquire, Arrowsmith, 1908 . . . . £40
ditto, Holt (U.S.), 1908 . . . . . . £40
The Council of Justice, Ward Lock, 1908 . . £100
Captain Tatham of Tatham Island, Gale & Polden,
1909 . . . . £175
ditto, as *The Island of Galloping Gold,* Newnes, 1916
. . . . £25
ditto, as *Eve's Island,* Newnes, 1926 [wraps] . £35
The Duke in the Suburbs, Ward Lock, 1909 . £100
The Nine Bears, Ward Lock, 1910 . . . £100
ditto, as *The Other Man,* Dodd, Mead (U.S.), 1911 £75
ditto, as *Silinski, Master Criminal,* World Syndicate,
1930 . . . . £20/£5
Private Selby, Ward Lock, 1912 . . . . £75
The People of the River, Ward Lock, 1912 . . £40
Grey Timothy, Ward Lock, 1913. . . . . £75
ditto, as *Pallard the Punter,* Ward Lock, 1914 (wraps)
. . . . £75
The River of Stars, Ward Lock, 1913 . . . £75
The Fourth Plague, Ward Lock, 1913 . . . £75
ditto, Doubleday Doran (U.S.), 1930 . £65/£15
The Admirable Carfew, Ward Lock, 1914 . . £30
Bosambo of the River, Ward Lock, 1914 . . £50
The Melody of Death, Arrowsmith, 1915 . . £75
ditto, Dial (U.S.), 1927 . . . . . £65/£25
1925: The Story of a Fatal Peace, Newnes, 1915
(wraps) £100
The Man Who Bought London, Ward Lock, 1915 £50
The Clue of the Twisted Candle, Small Maynard
(U.S.), 1916 . . . . £50
ditto, Newnes, 1917 . . . . £50
A Debt Discharged, Ward Lock, 1916 . . . £50
The Tomb of Ts'in, Ward Lock, 1916 . . . £300
The Just Men of Cordova, Ward Lock, 1917 . £50
ditto, Doubleday Doran (U.S.), 1929 . . £65/£15
The Secret House, Ward Lock, 1917 . . . £50
ditto, Small Maynard (U.S.), 1919 . . . £45
Kate Plus Ten, Small Maynard (U.S.), 1917 . £50
ditto, Ward Lock, 1919 . . . . . . £45
The Keepers of the King's Peace, Ward Lock, 1917 .
. . . . £50
Down Under Donovan, Ward Lock, 1918 . . £50
Those Folk of Bulboro, Ward Lock, 1918 . . £60
Lieutenant Bones, Ward Lock, 1918 . . . £50
Tam of the Scouts, Newnes, 1918 . . . . £50
ditto, as *Tam O' the Scoots,* Small Maynard (U.S.),
1919 . . . . £45
The Man Who Knew, Small Maynard (U.S.), 1918 £30
ditto, Newnes, 1919 . . . . £30
The Fighting Scouts, Pearson, 1919. . . . £30
The Green Rust, Ward Lock, 1919 . . . £40
ditto, Small Maynard (U.S.), 1920 . . . £150/£30
Jack O' Judgement, Ward Lock, 1920 . . £250/£40
ditto, Small Maynard (U.S.), 1921 . . . £125/£25
The Daffodil Mystery, Ward Lock, 1920 . £400/£75

ditto, as *The Daffodil Murder*, Small Maynard (U.S.),
1921. . . . . £250/£45
The Book of All Power, Ward Lock, 1921 . £200/£25
The Angel of Terror, Hodder & Stoughton, 1922 . .
. . . . £250/£50
ditto, Small Maynard (U.S.), 1922 . . . £125/£25
Sandi, The King-Maker, Ward Lock, 1922 £200/£50
Captains of Souls, Small Maynard (U.S.), 1922 . .
. . . . £150/£50
ditto, John Long, 1923 . . . . . £250/£50
The Flying Fifty-Five, Hutchinson, 1922 . £500/£50
The Crimson Circle, Hodder & Stoughton, 1922 . .
. . . . £200/£35
ditto, Doubleday Doran (U.S.), 1929 . £100/£20
Mr. Justice Maxell, Ward Lock, 1922 . £250/£50
The Valley of Ghosts, Odhams, 1922 . . £350/£75
ditto, Small Maynard (U.S.), 1923 . . £150/£30
The Clue of the New Pin, Hodder & Stoughton, 1923
. . . . £200/£35
ditto, Small Maynard (U.S.), 1923 . . . £100/£20
The Books of Bart, Ward Lock, 1923 . . £200/£30
The Green Archer, Hodder & Stoughton, 1923 . .
. . . . £200/£25
ditto, Small Maynard (U.S.), 1924 . . . £100/£15
Blue Hand, Small Maynard (U.S.), 1923 . £150/£20
ditto, Ward Lock, 1925 . . . . . £150/£20
The Fellowship of the Frog, Small Maynard (U.S.),
1923 . . . . £300/£45
ditto, Ward Lock, 1925 . . . . . £350/£50
The Missing Million, John Long, 1923 . £250/£75
ditto, as *The Missing Millions*, Small Maynard (U.S.),
1925 . . . . £125/£35
The Dark Eyes of London, Ward Lock, 1924 £200/£45
ditto, Doubleday Doran (U.S.), 1929 . . £100/£20
The Sinister Man, Hodder & Stoughton, 1924 . .
. . . . £100/£20
ditto, Small Maynard (U.S.), 1925. . . . £65/£15
Room 13, John Long, 1924 . . . . . £250/£50
The Three Oak Mystery, Ward Lock, 1924 £300/£65
Double Dan, Hodder & Stoughton, 1924 . £125/£25
ditto, as *Diana of Kara-Kara*, Small Maynard (U.S.),
1924 . . . . £75/£20
The Face in the Night, John Long, 1924 . £200/£50
ditto, Doubleday Doran (U.S.), 1929 . . £100/£25
Flat 2, Garden City (U.S.), 1924 (wraps) . . £65
ditto, John Long, 1927 . . . . . £45/£10
The Strange Countess, Hodder & Stoughton, 1925 .
. . . . £75/£15
ditto, Small Maynard (U.S.), 1926 . . £45/£10
A King by Night, John Long, 1925 . . £200/£45
ditto, Doubleday Page (U.S.), 1926 . . £100/£15
The Gaunt Stranger, Hodder & Stoughton, 1925 . .
. . . . £75/£15
ditto, as *The Ringer*, Doubleday Page (U.S.), 1926 .
. . . . £65/£16
The Three Just Men, Hodder & Stoughton, 1925 . .
. . . . £100/£15
ditto, Doubleday Doran (U.S.), 1929. . . £100/£15
The Man from Morocco, John Long, 1925 . £150/£35

ditto, as *The Black*, Doubleday Doran (U.S.), 1930 .
. . . . £65/£15
The Daughters of the Night, Newnes, 1925 (wraps) .
. . . . £75
The Hairy Arm, Small Maynard (U.S.), 1925 £75/£15
ditto, as *The Avenger*, John Long, 1926. . £150/£45
The Door with Seven Locks, Hodder & Stoughton,
1926 . . . . £35/£10
ditto, Doubleday Doran (U.S.), 1926 . . £35/£10
Sanders, Hodder and Stoughton, 1926 . . £50/£10
ditto, as *Mr. Commissioner Sanders*, Doubleday Doran
(U.S.), 1930 . . . . £45/£10
We Shall See, Hodder & Stoughton, 1926 . £50/£10
ditto, as *The Gaol-Breakers*, Doubleday Doran (U.S.),
1931 . . . . £45/£10
The Black Abbot, Hodder & Stoughton, 1926 £65/£15
ditto, Doubleday Page (U.S.), 1927 . . £50/£10
The Terrible People, Hodder & Stoughton, 1926 . .
. . . . £35/£10
ditto, Doubleday Page (U.S.), 1926 . . . £35/£10
The Day of Uniting, Hodder & Stoughton, 1926 . .
. . . . £45/£10
ditto, Mystery league (U.S.), 1930 . . £45/£10
Penelope of the Polyantha, Hodder & Stoughton, 1926
. . . . £50/£10
The Joker, Hodder & Stoughton, 1926 . . £35/£10
ditto, as *The Colossus*, Doubleday Doran (U.S.), 1932
. . . . £30/£10
The Square Emerald, Hodder & Stoughton, 1926 . .
. . . . £50/£10
ditto, as *The Girl from Scotland Yard*, Doubleday
Doran (U.S.), 1927 . . . . . £45/£10
The Yellow Snake, Hodder & Stoughton, 1926. . .
. . . . £30/£10
Barbara on Her Own, Newnes, [1926] . . £50/£10
The Million Dollar Story, Newnes, 1926 (wraps) £50
The Northing Tramp, Hodder & Stoughton, 1926 . .
. . . . £50/£10
ditto, Doubleday Doran (U.S.), 1929 . . £35/£10
The Hand of Power, John Long, 1926 . . £200/£45
ditto, Mystery League (U.S.), 1930 . . . £50/£10
The Traitor's Gate, Hodder & Stoughton, 1927 . .
. . . . £50/£10
ditto, Doubleday Page (U.S.), 1927 . . . £25/£5
The Man Who Was Nobody, Ward Lock, 1927 . .
. . . . £250/£50
The Feathered Serpent, Hodder & Stoughton, 1927 .
. . . . £75/£15
ditto, Doubleday Doran (U.S.), 1928 . . £35/£10
Terror Keep, Hodder & Stoughton, 1927 . £50/£10
ditto, Doubleday Page (U.S.), 1927 . . . £25/£5
Big Foot, John Long, 1927 . . . . . £75/£15
Number Six, Newnes, 1927 (wraps). . . . £65
The Squeaker, Hodder & Stoughton, 1927 . £45/£15
ditto, as *The Squealer*, Doubleday Doran (U.S.), 1928
. . . . £25/£5
The Forger, Hodder & Stoughton, 1927 . £50/£10
ditto, as *The Clever One*, Doubleday Doran (U.S.),
1928 . . . . £35/£10

The Double, Hodder & Stoughton, 1928 . £50/£10
ditto, Doubleday Doran (U.S.), 1928 . . £35/£10
The Twister, John Long, 1928 . . . £40/£10
ditto, Doubleday Page, 1929 . . . . £35/£10
The Flying Squad, Hodder & Stoughton, 1928. . .
. . . . £50/£10
ditto, Doubleday Doran (U.S.), 1928 . . £35/£10
The Gunner, Long, 1928 . . . . . . £45/£10
ditto, as *Gunman's Bluff*, Doubleday Doran (U.S.),
1929 . . . . £30/£10
Four Square Jane, Readers Library, 1929 . £40/£10
ditto, World Wide (U.S.), 1929 . . . . £35/£10
The India-Rubber Men, Hodder & Stoughton, 1929 .
. . . . £35/£5
ditto, Doubleday Doran, 1930 . . . . £20/£5
The Terror, Collins, 1929 . . . . . £25/£10
The Golden Hades, Collins, 1929 . . . £45/£10
The Green Ribbon, Hutchinson, 1929 . . £300/£45
ditto, Doubleday Doran, 1930 . . . £175/£25
White Face, Hodder & Stoughton, 1930 . £35/£10
ditto, Doubleday Doran (U.S.), 1931 . . £35/£10
The Calendar, Collins, 1930 . . . . . £75/£10
ditto, Doubleday Doran, 1931 . . . . £65/£10
The Clue of the Silver Key, Hodder & Stoughton, 1930
. . . . £35/£10
ditto, as *The Silver Key*, Doubleday Doran (U.S.), 1930
. . . . £35/£10
The Lady of Ascot, Hutchinson, 1930 . £50/£10
The Devil Man, Collins, 1931 . . . . £100/£25
ditto, Doubleday Doran (U.S.), 1931 . . £65/£15
On the Spot, John Long, 1931 . . . . £65/£15
ditto, Doubleday Doran (U.S.), 1931 . . £45/£10
The Man at the Carlton, Hodder & Stoughton, 1931 .
. . . . £35/£10
ditto, Doubleday Doran (U.S.), 1932 . . £35/£10
The Coat of Arms, Hutchinson, 1931 . . £75/£10
ditto, as *The Arranways Mystery*, Doubleday Doran
(U.S.), 1932 . . . . £65/£10
When the Gangs Came to London, John Long, 1932 .
. . . . £250/£75
ditto, Doubleday Doran (U.S.), 1932 . . £75/£20
King Kong, Grosset & Dunlap (U.S.), 1932 (with
Merian C. Cooper) . . . . . £1,500/£300
ditto, Corgi, 1966 (wraps). £5
The Frightened Lady, Hodder & Stoughton, 1932 . .
. . . . £40/£10
ditto, as *The Mystery of the Frightened Lady*,
Doubleday Doran (U.S.), 1933 . . . . £35/£5

Short Stories
Smithy, Tallis Press, 1905 (card covers). . . £100
Smithy Abroad, Hulton, 1909 (card covers). . £350
Sanders of the River, Ward Lock, 1911 . . £75
ditto, Doubleday Doran (U.S.), 1930 . . £35/£10
Smithy's Friend Nobby, Town Topics, 1914 . £250
ditto, as *Nobby*, Newnes, [1916] £20
Bones, Ward Lock, 1915 . . . . £45
Smithy and the Hun, Pearson, 1915 (card covers) £300

*Smithy, Not to Mention Nobby Clark and Spud
Murphy*, Newnes, 1915 (card covers) . . . £125
The Adventures of Heine, Ward Lock, 1919 . £50
Bones in London, Ward Lock, 1921. . . £250/£50
Law of the Four Just Men, Hodder & Stoughton, 1921
. . . . £250/£50
ditto, as *Again the Three Just Men*, Doubleday Doran
(U.S.), 1933 . . . . £65/£20
Chick, Ward Lock, 1923 . . . . . . £250/£50
Bones of the River, Newnes, [1923]. . . £50/£5
Educated Evans, Webster, [1924] . . . £50/£10
The Mind of Mr. J.G. Reeder, Hodder & Stoughton,
1925 . . . . £50/£10
ditto, as *The Murder Book of Mr. J.G. Reeder*,
Doubleday Doran (U.S.), 1929 . . . . £45/£10
More Educated Evans, Webster, [1926] . £50/£10
The Brigand, Hodder & Stoughton, 1927 . £35/£10
The Mixer, John Long, 1927 . . . . . £45/£10
Good Evans, Webster, [1927] . . . . £50/£10
Again the Three Just Men, Hodder & Stoughton, 1928
. . . . £25/£10
ditto, as *The Law of the 3 Just Men*, Doubleday Doran
(U.S.), 1931 . . . . £25/£10
Again Sanders, Hodder & Stoughton, [1928] £50/£10
ditto, Doubleday Doran (U.S.), 1929 . . £45/£10
The Orator, Hutchinson, 1928 . . . . £40/£10
Elegant Edward, Readers Library, [1928] . £25/£10
The Thief in the Night, Readers Library, 1928 £25/£10
Forty Eight Short Stories, Newnes, 1929 . £25/£10
Planetoid 127 and The Sweizer Pump, Readers
Library, 1929 . . . . £35/£10
Again the Ringer, Hodder & Stoughton, 1929 £25/£5
ditto, as *The Ringer Returns*, Doubleday Doran, 1931
. . . . £20/£5
The Cat Burglar, Newnes, 1929 (wraps) . . £20
Circumstantial Evidence, Newnes, 1929 (wraps) £25
ditto, as *Circumstantial Evidence and Other Stories*,
World Syndicate, 1934 . . . . . . £25/£5
Fighting Snub Reilly, Newnes, 1929 (wraps) . £20
ditto, as *Fighting Snub Reilly and Other Stories*,
World Syndicate (U.S.), 1934 . . . . £25/£5
*The Ghost of Down Hill, and The Queen of Sheba's
Belt*, Readers Library, 1929. . . . . £25/£10
The Little Green Man, Newnes, 1929 (wraps) . £20
The Prison-Breakers, Newnes, 1929 (wraps) . £20
Red Aces, Being Three Cases of Mr. Reeder, Hodder
& Stoughton, 1929 . . . . . . £50/£10
ditto, Doubleday Doran (U.S.), 1930 . . £45/£10
The Lone House Mystery, Collins, 1929 . £50/£10
The Black, Readers Library, 1929 . . . £25/£10
ditto, Digit Books, 1962 (wraps) £5
For Information Received, Newnes, 1929 (wraps). .
. . . . £100
The Governor of Chi-Foo, Newnes, 1929 (wraps) £20
ditto, as *The Governor of Chi-Foo and Other Stories*,
World Syndicate (U.S.), 1933 . . . . £25/£5
The Lady of Little Hell, Newnes, 1929 (wraps) £100
The Reporter, Readers Library, 1929 . . £25/£5
The Big Four, Readers Library, 1929 . . £25/£5

The Iron Grip, Readers Library, 1929 . . £25/£5
Killer Kay, Newnes, 1930 (wraps) £100
The Lady Called Nita, Newnes, 1930 (wraps) £150
Mrs William Jones and Bill, Newnes, 1930 (wraps) .
. . . . £100
The Guv'nor and Other Stories, Collins, 1932 £75/£15
ditto, as *Mr. Reeder Returns*, Doubleday Doran (U.S.),
1932 . . . . £45/£10
Sergeant Sir Peter, Chapman & Hall, 1932 £125/£25
ditto, Doubleday Doran (U.S.), 1933 . . £50/£10
The Steward, Collins, 1932 . . . . . £75/£15
Mr. J.G. Reeder Returns, Collins, 1934. . £15/£5
The Last Adventure, Hutchinson, 1934 . . £200/£35
The Woman from the East and Other Stories,
Hutchinson, 1934 . . . . £200/£35
The Undisclosed Client, Digit, 1963 (wraps) . £5

Verse
The Mission that Failed, T. Maskew Miller, 1898
(wraps) £350
Nicholson's Nek, Eastern Press, 1900 . . . £200
War and Other Poems, Eastern Press, 1900 . £200
Writ in the Barracks, Methuen, 1900 . . . £250

Others
Unofficial Dispatches, Hutchinson, [1901] . . £40
Famous Scottish Regiments, Newnes, 1914 (wraps) .
. . . . £125
Field Marshal Sir John French and His Campaigns,
Newnes, 1914 (wraps) £125
Heroes All, Gallant Deeds of the War, Newnes, 1914 .
. . . . £40
The Standard History of the War, Newnes, [1914-15]
(4 vols) £45
*Kitchener's Army and the Territorial Forces: The
Full Story of a Great Achievement*, Newnes, 1915 (6
vols, wraps) £75
War of the Nations, Newnes, 1915-17 (12 vols, wraps)
. . . . £75
The Real Shell-Man, John Waddington, 1919 (wraps)
. . . . £50
The Black Avons, George Gill, 1925, (4 paperbacks) .
. . . . £75
People: A Short Autobiography, Hodder & Stoughton,
1926 . . . . £25/£10
ditto, Doubleday Doran (U.S.), 1929 . . £25/£10
This England, Hodder & Stoughton, [1927] £40/£10
My Hollywood Diary, Hutchinson, [1932] . £20/£5

MINETTE WALTERS

A contemporary crime writer, Minette Walters owes
much of her popularity to highly successful television
adaptations of her books.

Novels
The Ice House, Macmillan, 1992 . . . £650/£45
ditto, Macmillan, 1992 (variant jacket, two heads under
the ice) . . . . £1,250/£45
ditto, St Martin's Press (U.S.), 1992 . . £200/£25
The Sculptress, Macmillan, 1993 . . . £60/£10
ditto, St Martin's Press (U.S.), 1992 . . £45/£5
The Scold's Bridle, Macmillan, 1994 . . £30/£5
ditto, Scorpion Press, 1994 (75 signed copies) . £100
ditto, Scorpion Press, 1994 (15 lettered copies) . £300
ditto, St Martin's Press (U.S.), 1994 . . . £25/£5
The Dark Room, Macmillan, 1995 . . . £15/£5
ditto, Putnam's (U.S.), 1996 . . . . . £15/£5
The Echo, Macmillan, 1997 . . . . . £15/£5
ditto, Putnam's (U.S.), 1997 . . . . . £10/£5
The Breaker, Macmillan, 1998 . . . . £15/£5
ditto, Putnam's (U.S.), 1999 . . . . . £10/£5
Shape of Snakes Macmillan, 2000 . . . £15/£5
ditto Macmillan, 2000 (600 signed copies of second
printing, slipcase) . . . . . . £50/£40
ditto, Putnam's (U.S.), 2000 . . . . . £10/£5

REX WARNER
(b.1905 d.1986)

A poet, novelist and translator, Warner is perhaps best
known for his Kafkaesque *The Aerodrome*.

Fiction
The Wild Goose Chase, Boriswood, 1937 . £65/£20
ditto, Knopf (U.S.), 1938 . . . . . £35/£10
The Professor, Boriswood, 1938. . . . £40/£10
ditto, Knopf (U.S.), 1939 . . . . . £25/£10
The Aerodrome, John Lane, 1941 . . . £125/£25
ditto, Lippincott (U.S.), 1946 . . . . £25/£10
Why Was I Killed? A Dramatic Dialogue, John Lane,
1943 . . . . £20/£5
ditto, as *Return of the Traveller*, Lippincott (U.S.),
1944 . . . . £15/£5
Men of Stones: A Melodrama, Bodley Head, 1949 .
. . . . £10/£5
ditto, Lippincott (U.S.), 1950 . . . . £10/£5
Escapade: A Tale of Average, Bodley Head, 1953 .
. . . . £10/£5
The Young Caesar, Collins, 1958 . . . £10/£5
ditto, Little, Brown (U.S.), 1958 . . . £10/£5
Imperial Caesar, Collins, 1960 . . . . £10/£5
ditto, Little, Brown (U.S.), 1960 . . . . £10/£5
Pericles the Athenian, Collins, 1963 . . £10/£5
ditto, Little, Brown (U.S.), 1963 . . . . £10/£5
The Converts, John Lane, 1967 . . . . £10/£5

ditto, Little, Brown (U.S.), 1967 . . . . £10/£5

Verse
Poems, Boriswood, 1937 . . . . . . £75/£25
ditto, Knopf (U.S.), 1938 . . . . . . £35/£10
ditto, as *Poems and Contradictions*, John Lane, 1945 .
. . . . £25/£10

Others
The Kite, Blackwell, 1936 . . . . . £100/£35
ditto, Hamish Hamilton, 1963 (revised edition). . .
. . . . £25/£10
English Public Schools, Collins, 1945 . . £15/£5
The Cult of Power: Essays, John Lane, 1946 £25/£10
ditto, Lippincott (U.S.), 1947. . . . . £25/£10
John Milton, Parrish, 1949 . . . . £15/£5
ditto, Chanticleer Press (U.S.), 1950 . . £10/£5
Views of Attica and Its Surroundings, Lehmann, 1950
. . . . £15/£5
E.M. Forster, Longmans, 1950 (wraps) . . . £10
ditto, Longmans, 1960 (revised edition, wraps). . £5
Men and Gods, MacGibbon & Kee, 1950 . £20/£5
ditto, Fararr Straus, Giroux (U.S.), 1959. . £15/£5
Ashes to Ashes: A Post-Mortem on the 1950-51 Tests,
MacGibbon & Kee, 1951 (with Lyle Blair) £10/£5
Greeks and Trojans, MacGibbon & Kee, 1951) £10/£5
Eternal Greece, Thames & Hudson, 1953 (photographs
by Martin Hurlimann) . . . . . £30/£10
The Vengeance of the Gods, MacGibbon & Kee, 1954
. . . . £10/£5
ditto, Michigan State (U.S.), 1955 . . . £10/£5
Athens, Thames & Hudson, 1956 . . . £10/£5
The Greek Philosophers, Michigan State (U.S.), 1958
. . . . £10/£5
Athens at War War: Retold from Thucydides History
of the Pelopennesian War, Bodley Head, 1970 . .
. . . . £10/£5
ditto, Dutton, (U.S.), 1971 . . . . £10/£5
Men of Athens, Bodley Head, 1972 . . . £10/£5
ditto, Viking, (U.S.), 1972 . . . . £10/£5
The Stories of the Greeks, Fararr Straus, Giroux
(U.S.), 1967 (includes *Men and Gods*, *Greeks and
Trojans*, *The Vengeance of the Gods*) . . £10/£5

Translations
The Medea of Euripides, John Lane, 1944 . £10/£5
ditto, Univ. of Chicago Press, (U.S.), 1955 (with
Euripides Alcestis, translated by Lattimore, *The
Heracleidae* translated by Ralph Gladstone,
Hippolytus translated by David Grene, etc.) £10/£5
Prometheus Bound, by Aeschylus, Bodley Head, 1947
. . . . £10/£5
The Persian Expedition, by Xenophon, Penguin, 1949
. . . . £5
Hippolytus, by Euripides, Bodley Head, 1949 £10/£5
Helen, by Euripides, Bodley Head, 1951 . £10/£5
The Peloponnesian War, by Thucydides. Penguin,
1954 . . . . £5
Fall of the Roman Republic. Martus, Sulla, Crassus,

Pompey, Caesar, Cicero: Six Lives, by Plutarch.
Penguin 1958. . . . . £5
ditto, Penguin 1972 (revised edition) . . . £5
Three Great Plays, New American Library, 1958
(contains *Medea, Hippolytus* and *Helen*) . £10/£5
Poems of George Seferis, 1960 . . . . £10/£5
War Commentaries of Caesar, New American Library,
1960 . . . . £10/£5
Confessions of St Augustine, New American Library,
1963 . . . . £10/£5
**On the Greek Style: Selected Essays in Poetry and
Hellentsm**, by George Seferis, Little, Brown (U.S.),
1966 (with Th. D. Frangopoulos) . . . £10/£5
ditto, Bodley Head, 1967 . . . . . . £10/£5
History of My Times, by Xenophon, Penguin 1966 £5
Moral Essays, by Plutarch, Penguin 1971 . . £5

SYLVIA TOWNSEND WARNER
(b.1893 d.1978)

A talented novelist, poet and short story writer,
Warner's concerns are often with the ordinary and
overlooked members of society. By examining the
detail of their lives she shows what extraordinary
people they often are.

Verse
The Espalier, Chatto & Windus, 1925 . . £200/£50
ditto, Dial Press (U.S.), 1925 . . . . . £150/£45
Time Importuned, Chatto & Windus, 1928 . £200/£50
ditto, Viking Press (U.S.), 1928 . . . . £150/£45
Opus 7, Chatto & Windus, 1931 . . . . £20/£10
ditto, Chatto & Windus, 1931 (110 signed, numbered
copies, glassine d/w and slipcase) . . £125/£100
ditto, Viking Press (U.S.), 1931 . . . . £25/£10
Rainbow, Borzoi (U.S.), 1932 (wraps, in envelope) .
. . . . £125/£100
Whether a Dove or Seagull, Viking Press (U.S.), 1933
(with Valentine Ackland) . . . . . £125/£40
ditto, Chatto & Windus, 1934 . . . . £125/£45
Boxwood, Monotype Corporation, 1957 (500 copies,
withdrawn) £100
ditto, Monotype Corporation, 1958 (500 copies). £75
ditto, Chatto & Windus, 1960 (enlarged edition) . .
. . . . £45/£15
King Duffus, privately printed, 1968 (wraps) . £125
Twelve Poems, privately circulated booklet, 1977
(duplicated sheets, stapled) £175
ditto, Chatto & Windus, 1980 (reissue) . . £15/£5
ditto, as *Azrael*, Libanus Press, 1978, (200 copies,
wraps) £95
Collected Poems, Carcanet Press/Viking Press (U.S.),
1982 . . . . £35/£15
Selected Poems, Carcanet Press, 1985 (wraps) £10

Novels
Lolly Willowes, Chatto & Windus, 1926 . £125/£20

ditto, Viking Press (U.S.), 1926 . . . . £125/£20
Mr Fortune's Maggot, Chatto & Windus, 1927 . .
. . . . £75/£15
ditto, Viking Press (U.S.), 1927 . . . £75/£15
The True Heart, Chatto & Windus, 1929 £75/£15
ditto, Viking Press (U.S.), 1929 . . . . £75/£15
Summer Will Show, Chatto & Windus, 1936 £45/£15
ditto, Viking Press (U.S.), 1936 . . . . £35/£10
After The Death of Don Juan, Chatto & Windus, 1938
. . . . £45/£10
ditto, Viking Press (U.S.), 1938 . . . . £35/£10
The Corner that Held Them, Chatto & Windus, 1948 .
. . . . £25/£10
ditto, Viking Press (U.S.), 1948 . . . . £25/£10
The Flint Anchor, Chatto & Windus, 1954 . £30/£10
ditto, Viking Press (U.S.), 1954 . . . . £25/£10

Short Stories
The Maze, Fleuron, 1928 (signed, wraps) . . £100
**Some World Far From Ours and 'Stay Corydon,
Thou Swain'**, Mathews & Marrot, 1929 (531
numbered, signed copies) . . . . £40/£25
Elinor Barley, Cresset Press, 1930 (350 numbered,
signed copies on mould made paper, slipcase)
. . . . £125/£100
ditto, Cresset Press, 1930 (30 numbered and signed
copies on hand made paper, extra set of engravings,
slipcase) . . . . £600/£500
A Moral Ending, W. Jackson, 1930 (550 numbered,
signed copies, glassine d/w with paper flaps) £75/£45
The Salutation, Chatto & Windus, 1932 . £75/£35
ditto, Viking Press (U.S.), 1932 . . . . £75/£35
More Joy in Heaven, Cresset Press, 1935 . £125/£45
The Cat's Cradle Book, Viking Press (U.S.), 1940 .
. . . . £65/£20
ditto, Chatto & Windus, 1960 . . . . £25/£10
A Garland of Straw, Chatto & Windus, 1943 £35/£15
ditto, Viking Press, 1943 . . . . . . £30/£15
The Museum of Cheats, Chatto & Windus, 1947 . .
. . . . £30/£10
ditto, Viking Press (U.S.), 1947 . . . . £25/£10
Winter in The Air Chatto & Windus, 1955 . £25/£10
ditto, Viking Press (U.S.), 1956 . . . £20/£5
A Spirit Rises, Chatto & Windus, 1962 . . £25/£10
ditto, Viking Press (U.S.), 1962 . . . . £20/£5
Sketches from Nature, privately printed, 1963 (wraps)
. . . . £125
A Stranger with a Bag, Chatto & Windus, 1966 . .
. . . . £25/£10
ditto, as **Swans on an Autumn River**, Viking Press
(U.S.), 1966 . . . . . . £20/£5
Two Conversation Pieces, privately printed, 1967
(wraps) £125
The Innocent and The Guilty, Chatto & Windus, 1971
. . . . £15/£5
ditto, Viking Press (U.S.), 1971 . . . £15/£5
Kingdoms of Elfin, Chatto & Windus, 1977 £15/£5
ditto, Viking Press (U.S.), 1977 . . . £15/£5
Scenes of Childhood, Chatto & Windus, 1981 £10/£5

ditto, Viking Press (U.S.), 1981 . . . . £10/£5
One Thing Leading to Another, Chatto & Windus,
1984 . . . . £10/£5
ditto, Viking Press (U.S.), 1984 . . . £10/£5
Selected Stories, Chatto & Windus, 1989 . £15/£5
ditto, Viking Press (U.S.), 1989 . . . . £15/£5
The Music at Long Verney, Counterpoint (U.S.) 2001
. . . . £15/£5

Translations
By Way of Saint-Beuve, by Marcel Proust, Chatto &
Windus, 1958. . . . . . . £40/£20
A Place of Shipwreck, by Jean Rene Huquenin, Chatto
& Windus, 1963 . . . . . . £40/£15

Other Works
Somerset, Paul Elek, 1949, (withdrawn). . £45/£20
Jane Austen, Longmans Green, 1941 (wraps) . £10
T.H. White, A Biography, Jonathan Cape, 1967 . .
. . . . £25/£10
ditto, Viking Press (U.S.), 1968 . . . . £25/£10
Letters, Chatto & Windus, 1982 . . . . £25/£10
The Diaries of Sylvia Townsend Warner, Chatto &
Windus, 1994. . . . . . . £20/£10
Sylvia and David, Sinclair Stevenson, 1994. £15/£5
I'll Stand by You, Pimlico, 1998 (wraps) . . £5
**The Element of Lavishness: Letters of Sylvia
Townsend Warner and William Maxwell, 1938-
1978**, Counterpoint (U.S.) 2001 . . . £15/£5

EVELYN WAUGH
(b.1903 d.1966)

Waugh is best known for his humorous, satirical
novels. He also wrote a number of travel books.

Verse
The World to Come: A Poem in Three Cantos,
privately printed, 1916 . . . . . £10,000

Novels
Decline and Fall, Chapman & Hall, 1928 £3,000/£250
ditto, Doubleday (U.S.), 1929 . . . £1,000/£100
ditto, Farrar (U.S.), 1929 . . . . . £500/£50
ditto, Chapman & Hall, 1937 (12 copies) . £2,500
Vile Bodies, Chapman & Hall, 1930. . £2,000/£200
ditto, Farrar (U.S.), 1930 . . . . . £500/£50
ditto, Chapman & Hall, 1937 (12 copies) . £2,500
Black Mischief, Chapman & Hall, 1932. £1,000/£150
ditto, Chapman & Hall, 1932 (250 signed copies) . .
. . . . £2,000/£1,000
ditto, Farrar (U.S.), 1932 . . . . . £500/£50
ditto, Chapman & Hall, 1937 (12 copies) . £2,500
A Handful of Dust, Chapman & Hall, 1934 . .
. . . . £1,500/£150
ditto, Farrar (U.S.), 1934 . . . . . £400/£75
ditto, Chapman & Hall, 1937 (12 copies) . £2,500

Scoop, Chapman & Hall, 1938 . . . . £650/£75
ditto, Little, Brown (U.S.), 1938 . . . . £225/£45
Put Out More Flags, Chapman & Hall, 1942 £350/£45
ditto, Little, Brown (U.S.), 1942 . . . £125/£30
Work Suspended, Chapman & Hall, 1942 (unfinished
novel, 500 copies) . . . . . . £200/£65
Brideshead Revisited, privately printed for the author,
1945 [1944] (50 copies, wraps) £4,000
ditto, Chapman & Hall, 1945 . . . . £650/£65
ditto, Little, Brown (U.S.), 1945 . . . £125/£25
ditto, Little, Brown (U.S.), 1945 (600 copies) . . .
. . . . £500/£150
Scott-King's Modern Europe, Chapman & Hall, 1947
. . . . £50/£15
ditto, Little, Brown (U.S.), 1949 . . . . £45/£10
The Loved One, Chapman & Hall, 1948 . £75/£25
ditto, Chapman & Hall, 1948 (250 signed, numbered
copies, glassine d/w) . . . . £750/£650
ditto, Little, Brown (U.S.), 1948 . . . £35/£10
Helena, Chapman & Hall, 1950 . . . . £35/£10
ditto, Chapman & Hall, 1950 (50 deluxe copies for
presentation) £1,750
ditto, Little, Brown (U.S.), 1950 . . . £25/£10
Men at Arms, Chapman & Hall, 1952 . £50/£15
ditto, Little, Brown (U.S.), 1952 . . . £35/£10
Love Among The Ruins, Chapman & Hall, 1953 . .
. . . . £35/£10
ditto, Chapman & Hall, 1953 (350 signed copies,
glassine d/w) . . . . £350/£275
Officers and Gentlemen, Chapman & Hall, 1955 . .
. . . . £50/£15
ditto, Little, Brown (U.S.), 1955 . . . £35/£10
The Ordeal of Gilbert Pinfold, Chapman & Hall, 1957
. . . . £35/£10
ditto, Chapman & Hall, 1957 (50 large copies for
presentation) £1,500
ditto, Little, Brown (U.S.), 1957 . . . £25/£10
Unconditional Surrender, Chapman & Hall, 1961 . .
. . . . £35/£10
ditto, as **The End of The Battle**, Little, Brown (U.S.),
1961 . . . . £15/£5
Basil Seal Rides Again, Chapman & Hall, 1963 (750
signed copies, glassine d/w) . . . . £400/£100
ditto, Chapman & Hall, 1963 . . . . £45/£15
ditto, Little, Brown (U.S.), 1963 . . . £45/£15
ditto, Little, Brown (U.S.), 1963 (1000 signed copies,
glassine d/w) . . . . £250/£225

Short Stories
Mr Loveday's Little Outing, Chapman & Hall, 1936 .
. . . . £1,000/£100
ditto, Little, Brown (U.S.), 1936 . . . £450/£45
Charles Ryder's Schooldays and Other Stories, Little,
Brown (U.S.), 1982 . . . . £15/£5

Essays
PRB: An Essay on The Pre-Raphaelite Brotherhood,
privately printed, 1926 . . . . £4,000

The Holy Places, Queen Anne Press, 1952 (50 signed
copies) . . . . £1,000/£750
ditto, Queen Anne Press, 1952 (900 copies) £150/£75

Travel
Labels, Duckworth, 1930 . . . . . . £300/£50
ditto, Duckworth, 1930 (110 signed copies, page of
manuscript laid in) £1,500
ditto, as **A Bachelor Abroad**, Farrar (U.S.), 1932 . .
. . . . £125/£25
Remote People, Duckworth, 1931 . . £250/£50
ditto, as **They Were Still Dancing**, Farrar (U.S.), 1932.
. . . . £125/£25
Ninety-Two Days, Duckworth, 1934. . . £250/£50
ditto, Farrar (U.S.), 1934 . . . . . . £125/£25
Waugh in Abyssinia, Longman, 1936 . £250/£50
ditto, Farrar (U.S.), 1936 . . . . . . £125/£25
Robbery Under Law, Chapman & Hall, 1939 £250/£50
ditto, as **Mexico: An Object Lesson**, Little, Brown
(U.S.), 1939 . . . . £150/£35
When The Going Was Good, Duckworth, 1946 . .
. . . . £150/£35
ditto, Little, Brown (U.S.), 1947 . . . £75/£20
A Tourist in Africa, Chapman & Hall, 1960 £45/£15
ditto, Little, Brown (U.S.), 1960 . . . £45/£15

Biography
Rosetti, Duckworth, 1928 . . . . . . £750/£100
ditto, Dodd (U.S.), 1928 . . . . . . £250/£65
Edmund Campion, Longman, 1935 . . £250/£50
ditto, Longman, 1935 (50 signed copies) . . £750
ditto, Sheed (U.S.), 1935 . . . . . . £125/£35
Ronald Knox, Chapman & Hall, 1959 . £25/£5
ditto, Little, Brown (U.S.), 1960 . . . £25/£5

Others
**An Open Letter to his Eminence the Cardinal
Archbishop of Westminster**, privately printed, 1933 .
. . . . £2,000
Wine in Peace and War, Saccone & Speed, [1947] .
. . . . £100/£35
A Little Learning, Chapman & Hall, 1964 . £25/£5
ditto, Little, Brown (U.S.), 1964 . . . £15/£5
Diaries, Weidenfeld, 1976 . . . . . £25/£5
ditto, Little, Brown (U.S.), 1976 . . . £15/£5
A Little Order, Methuen, 1977 . . . £20/£5
ditto, Little, Brown (U.S.), 1981 . . . £10/£5
The Letters of Evelyn Waugh, Weidenfeld, 1980 .
. . . . £10/£5
ditto, Ticknor & Fields (U.S.), 1980 . . £10/£5
The Essays, Articles and Reviews of Evelyn Waugh,
Methuen, 1983 . . . . £10/£5
ditto, Little, Brown (U.S.), 1984 . . . £10/£5

MARY WEBB

(b.1881 d.1927)

Webb only found success as a novelist after being championed by Stanley Baldwin, then Prime Minister. Her books are Hardyesque, with nature powerfully and beautifully described, and peopled by characters who battle grimly against fate.

Novels

The Golden Arrow, Constable, 1916 . . . £125
ditto, Dutton (U.S.), 1918. . . . . . . £45
Gone to Earth, Constable, 1917 (dark red cloth) £100
ditto, Dutton (U.S.), 1917. . . . . . . £40
The House in Dormer Forest, Hutchinson, [1920]. .
. . . . £125/£35
ditto, Doran (U.S.), 1921 . . . . . . £125/£30
Seven For A Secret, Hutchinson, 1922 . . £125/£30
ditto, Doran (U.S.), 1923 . . . . . £125/£30
Precious Bane, Cape, 1924 . . . . £200/£75
ditto, Modern Library (U.S.), 1926 . . . £25/£10
Armour Wherein He Trusted, Cape, 1929 . £30/£15
ditto, Dutton (U.S.), 1929. . . . . . £25/£10

Short Stories

The Chinese Lion, Rota, 1937 (350 copies, glassine d/w and slipcase). . . . . £50/£35

Verse

Poems and The Spring of Joy, Cape, 1928 £45/£15
ditto, Dutton (U.S.), 1929. . . . . . £35/£10
Fifty-One Poems, Cape, 1946 . . . . £20/£5
ditto, Dutton (U.S.), 1946. . . . . . £20/£5

Others

Spring of Joy: A Little Book of Healing, J.M. Dent & Sons, 1917 . . . . £50
A Mary Webb Anthology, Cape, 1935 (illustrated by Rowland Hilder and Norman Hepple) . . £15/£5
ditto, Dutton (U.S.), 1940. . . . . . £15/£5
The Essential Mary Webb, Cape, 1949 . . £15/£5

DENTON WELCH

(b.1915 d.1948)

Welch studied painting at Goldsmiths' School of Art, London, until a bicycle accident in 1935 severed his spine and left him temporarily paralysed and permanently ill. He took up writing as a career, producing three highly autobiographical books and numerous fragments.

Novels

Maiden Voyage, Routledge, 1943 . . . £200/£45
ditto, Fischer (U.S.), 1944 . . . . . £65/£20
In Youth is Pleasure, Routledge, 1944 [1945] £75/£25
ditto, Fischer (U.S.), 1946 . . . . . £65/£20

A Voice Through a Cloud, John Lehmann, 1950 . .
. . . . £50/£15
ditto, Dutton/Obelisk (U.S.), 1966 (wraps) . . £5

Short Stories/Miscellaneous

Brave and Cruel and Other Stories, Hamish Hamilton, 1948 [1949] . . . . £100/£15
A Last Sheaf, John Lehmann, 1951 . . . £65/£15
I Left My Grandfather's House, James Campbell, 1958 (150 copies) £75
ditto, The Lion & Unicorn Press, 1958 (20 deluxe copies of 200) £400
ditto, The Lion & Unicorn Press, 1958 (180 ordinary copies of 200) £75
Dumb Instrument, Enitharmon Press, 1976 (a selection of poems and fragments, 600 copies) . . . £65
The Denton Welch Journals, Hamish Hamilton, 1952 (edited by Jocelyn Brooke) . . . . £30/£10
The Journals of Denton Welch, Allison & Busby, 1984 (edited by Michael De-la-Noy) . . £15/£5
ditto, Dutton (U.S.), 1984. . . . . . £15/£5
A Lunch Appointment, Elysium Press (U.S.), 1993 (150 copies, bound in black silk) £100
ditto, Elysium Press (U.S.), 1993 (20 copies, bound in black silk), signed by Edmund White, with an extra signed etching by Le-Tan) £450

FAY WELDON

(b.1931)

A novelist and writer for television drama, Weldon's popular success was *The Life and Loves of a She Devil*.

Novels

The Fat Woman's Joke, MacGibbon & Kee, 1967
. . . . £100/£25
ditto, as *... and the Wife Ran Away*, McKay (U.S.), 1968 . . . . £50/£15
Down Among the Women, Heinemann, 1971 £25/£5
ditto, St Martin's Press (U.S.), 1972 . . . £15/£5
Female Friends, Heinemann, 1971 . . . £25/£5
ditto, St Martin's Press (U.S.), 1974 . . . £15/£5
Remember Me, Hodder & Stoughton, 1976. £15/£5
ditto, Random House (U.S.), 1976 . . . £15/£5
Little Sisters, Hodder & Stoughton, 1977 . £15/£5
ditto, as *Words of Advice*, Random House (U.S.), 1977
. . . . £15/£5
Praxis, Hodder & Stoughton, 1978 . . . £15/£5
ditto, Summit (U.S.), 1978 . . . . . £15/£5
Puffball, Hodder & Stoughton, 1980 . . £15/£5
ditto, Summit (U.S.), 1980 . . . . . £15/£5
The President's Child, Hodder & Stoughton, 1983 .
. . . . £15/£5
ditto, Doubleday (U.S.), 1983 . . . . £15/£5
The Life and Loves of a She Devil, Hodder & Stoughton, 1984 . . . . £15/£5

ditto, Pantheon (U.S.), 1984 . . . . . £10/£5
The Shrapnel Academy, Hodder & Stoughton, 1986 .
. . . . £10/£5
ditto, Viking (U.S.), 1987. . . . . . £10/£5
The Heart of the Country, Century Hutchinson, 1987 .
. . . . £10/£5
ditto, Viking (U.S.), 1988. . . . . . £10/£5
The Hearts and Lives of Men, Heinemann, 1987 . .
. . . . £10/£5
ditto, Viking (U.S.), 1988. . . . . . £10/£5
The Rules of Life, Century Hutchinson, 1987 £10/£5
ditto, Harper & Row (U.S.), 1987 . . . £10/£5
Leader of the Band, Hodder & Stoughton, 1988 . .
. . . . £10/£5
ditto, Viking (U.S.), 1989. . . . . . £10/£5
The Cloning of Joanna May, Collins, 1989 £10/£5
ditto, Viking (U.S.), 1989. . . . . . £10/£5
Darcy's Utopia, Collins, 1990 . . . £10/£5
ditto, Viking (U.S.), 1991. . . . . . £10/£5
Life Force, HarperCollins, 1992 . . . £10/£5
ditto, Viking (U.S.), 1992. . . . . . £10/£5
Growing Rich, HarperCollins, 1992 . . £10/£5
Affliction, Harper Collins, 1993 . . . £10/£5
ditto, as *Trouble*, Viking (U.S.), 1993 . . £10/£5
Splitting, HarperCollins, 1995 . . . £10/£5
ditto, Atlantic Monthly Press (U.S.), 1995 . £10/£5
Worst Fears, HarperCollins, 1996 . . . £10/£5
ditto, Atlantic Monthly Press (U.S.), 1996 . £10/£5
Big Girls Don't Cry, HarperCollins, 1997 . £10/£5
ditto, as *Big Women*, Atlantic Monthly Press (U.S.),
1997 . . . . £10/£5

Short Stories
Watching Me Watching You, Hodder & Stoughton,
1981 . . . . £15/£5
ditto, Summit (U.S.), 1981 . . . . £10/£5
Polaris, Hodder & Stoughton, 1985 . . . £10/£5
ditto, Penguin (U.S.), 1989 (wraps) . . . £10/£5
Moon Over Minneapolis, Collins, 1991 . . £10/£5
A Question of Timing, Colophon Press, 1992 (100
signed, numbered copies of 225, wraps) . . £20
Angel, All Innocence and Other Stories, Bloomsbury,
1995 . . . . £5
Wicked Women, HarperCollins, 1997 . . £10/£5
ditto, Atlantic Monthly Press (U.S.), 1997 . £10/£5
A Hard Time To Be A Father, HarperCollins, 1998 .
. . . . £10/£5
ditto, Bloomsbury (U.S.), 1999 . . . £10/£5

Children's Books
Wolf The Mechanical Dog, Collins, 1988 . £25/£5
Party Puddle, Collins, 1989 . . . . £25/£5
Nobody Likes Me, Bodley Head, 1997 . . £15/£5

Others
Letters to Alice, Michael Joseph/Rainbird Books, 1984
. . . . £15/£5
ditto, Taplinger (U.S.), 1985 . . . . £15/£5
Rebecca West, Penguin, 1985 . . . . £10/£5

Sacred Cows, Chatto & Windus, 1989 (wraps) . £5

H.G. WELLS
(b.1886 d.1946)

A versatile novelist whose work ranges from
innovative science fiction through to social realism,
Wells was also the author of works on politics,
society and history.

Novels
The Time Machine, Henry Holt (U.S.), 1895 ('H.S.
Wells' on title page) £500
ditto, Heinemann, 1895 (grey cloth) . . . £1,500
ditto, Heinemann, 1895 (red cloth) £200
ditto, Heinemann, 1895 (wrappers) £1,000
The Wonderful Visit, Dent, 1895 (front board blank) .
. . . . £400
ditto, Dent, 1895 (front board stamped with gilt angel)
. . . . £300
ditto, Macmillan (U.S.), 1895 . . . . £200
The Island of Doctor Moreau, Heinemann, 1896
(monogram blind-stamped on back board). . £650
ditto, Heinemann, 1896 (no monogram). . . £250
ditto, Stone & Kimball (U.S.), 1896 (black cloth) £200
The Wheels of Chance, Dent, 1896 . . . £150
ditto, Macmillan (U.S.), 1896 . . . . £75
The Red Room, Stone & Kimball (U.S.), 1896 (12
copies only) £10,000
The Invisible Man, Pearson, 1897 . . . £1,000
ditto, Arnold (U.S.), 1897. . . . . . £750
The War of The Worlds, Heinemann, 1898 (16 pages
of ads). £1,000
ditto, Heinemann, 1898 (32 pages of ads) . . £400
ditto, Harper (U.S.), 1898. . . . . . £200
When The Sleeper Wakes, Harpers, 1899 . . £150
ditto, Harper (U.S.), 1899. . . . . . £100
ditto, Thomas Nelson, 1910 (revised edition) . £25
Love and Mr Lewisham, Harpers, 1900 . . . £100
The First Men in The Moon, Bowen-Merrill (U.S.),
1901 . . . . £500
ditto, Newnes, 1901 (first issue in dark blue cloth,
black endpapers). £650
ditto, Newnes, 1901 (second issue in dark blue cloth,
white endpapers). £500
ditto, Newnes, 1901 (third issue in light blue cloth)
. . . . £300
ditto, Newnes, 1901 (fourth issue in blue/green cloth) .
. . . . £200
The Sea Lady: A Tissue of Moonshine, Methuen,
1902 . . . . £300
ditto, Appleton (U.S.), 1902 . . . . . £150
The Food of The Gods, Macmillan, 1904 . . £200
ditto, Scribners (U.S.), 1904 . . . . . £150
A Modern Utopia, Chapman & Hall, 1905 . . £125
ditto, Scribners (U.S.), 1905 . . . . . £100
Kipps, Macmillan, 1905 . . . . . . £75

ditto, Scribners (U.S.), 1905 . . . . . £50
In The Days of The Comet, Macmillan, 1906 . £150
ditto, Century (U.S.), 1906 . . . . . £125
The War in The Air, George Bell, 1908 (first issue, blue cloth with lettering and decorations in gilt) £300
The War in The Air, George Bell, 1908 (second issue with blue cloth blindstamped) £100
ditto, Macmillan (U.S.), 1908 . . . . £200
Tono-Bungay, Macmillan, 1909 (with ads dated '1.09'). £200
ditto, Macmillan, 1909 (with ads dated '2.09') . £75
ditto, Duffield (U.S.), 1909 . . . . . £100
Ann Veronica, T. Fisher Unwin, 1909 . . £75
ditto, Harper (U.S.), 1909. . . . . . £50
The History of Mr Polly, Thomas Nelson, 1910 £75
ditto, Duffield (U.S.), 1910 . . . . . £50
The New Machiavelli, Duffield (U.S.), 1910 (first issue with integral title page that does not have quotes by Lewes and James) £100
ditto, Duffield (U.S.), 1910 (second issue with cancel title page with quotes) £45
ditto, John Lane/Bodley Head, 1911. . . . £45
Marriage, Macmillan, 1912 . . . . . £45
The Passionate Friends, Macmillan, 1913 . £45
ditto, Harper (U.S.), 1913. . . . . . £45
The World Set Free, Macmillan, 1914 . . £35
ditto, Dutton (U.S.), 1914. . . . . . £30
The Wife of Sir Isaac Harman, Macmillan, 1914 £35
ditto, Macmillan (U.S.), 1914 . . . . £30
Boon, T. Fisher Unwin, 1915. . . . . £25
ditto, Doran (U.S.), 1915 . . . . . £25
Bealby, Methuen, 1915 . . . . . £20
ditto, Macmillan (U.S.), 1915 . . . . £20
The Research Magnificent, Macmillan, 1915 . £20
ditto, Macmillan (U.S.), 1915 . . . . £20
Mr Britling Sees It Through, Cassell, 1916. . £20
ditto, Macmillan (U.S.), 1916 . . . . £20
The Soul of a Bishop, Cassell, 1917. . . . £15
ditto, Macmillan (U.S.), 1917 . . . . £15
Joan and Peter, Cassell, 1918 . . . . £15
ditto, Macmillan (U.S.), 1918 . . . . £15
The Undying Fire, Cassell, 1919 . . . . £15
ditto, Macmillan (U.S.), 1919 . . . . £15
The Secret Places of The Heart, Cassell, 1922 . .
. . . . £100/£20
ditto, Macmillan (U.S.), 1922 . . . £100/£20
Men Like Gods, Cassell, 1923 . . . £100/£20
ditto, Macmillan (U.S.), 1923 . . . £100/£20
The Dream, Jonathan Cape, 1924 . . £100/£20
ditto, Macmillan (U.S.), 1924 . . . £100/£20
Christina Alberta's Father, Jonathan Cape, 1925 . .
. . . . £100/£15
ditto, Macmillan (U.S.), 1925 . . . £100/£15
The World of William Clissold, Ernest Benn, 1926 (3 vols) . . . . £125/£35
ditto, Ernest Benn, 1926 (218 deluxe signed copies, 3 vols, slipcase) . . . . £350/£300
ditto, Doran (U.S.), 1926 (2 vols, slipcase) . £100/£20
Meanwhile, Ernest Benn, 1927 . . . . £100/£15

ditto, Doran (U.S.), 1927 . . . . . . £75/£15
Mr Blettsworthy on Rampole Island, Ernest Benn, 1928 . . . . £65/£15
ditto, Doubleday Doran (U.S.), 1928 . . £65/£15
The King Who Was a King, The book of a film, Ernest Benn, 1929 . . . . £65/£15
ditto, Doubleday Doran (U.S.), 1929 . . £65/£15
The Autocracy of Mr Parham, Heinemann, 1930 . .
. . . . £50/£15
ditto, Doubleday Doran (U.S.), 1930 . . £50/£15
The Bulpington of Blup, Hutchinson, 1932 £40/£15
ditto, Macmillan (U.S.), 1933 . . . £40/£15
The Shape of Things to Come, The Ultimate Revolution, Hutchinson, 1933 . . . £75/£25
ditto, Macmillan (U.S.), 1933 . . . £65/£20
ditto, as *Things to Come: A Film Story*, Cresset Press, 1935 . . . . £45/£15
The Croquet Player, Chatto & Windus, 1936 £50/£15
ditto, Viking (U.S.), 1937. . . . . £50/£15
Man Who Could Work Miracles: A Film Story, Cresset Press, 1936 . . . . . £45/£15
ditto, Macmillan. (U.S.), 1936 . . . £45/£15
Star Begotten, Chatto & Windus, 1937 . £50/£20
ditto, Viking (U.S.), 1937. . . . . £50/£20
Brynhild, Methuen, 1937. . . . . £45/£15
ditto, Scribner. (U.S.), 1937 . . . £45/£15
The Camford Visitation, Methuen, 1937 £45/£15
The Brothers, Chatto & Windus, 1938 . . £45/£15
ditto, Viking (U.S.), 1938. . . . . £45/£15
Apropos of Dolores, Jonathan Cape, 1938 . £45/£15
ditto, Scribners (U.S.), 1938 . . . £45/£15
The Holy Terror, Michael Joseph, 1939. . £45/£15
ditto, Simon & Schuster. (U.S.), 1939 . £45/£15
The Final Men, Phantagraph Press, 1940 (wraps) £50
Babes in The Darkling Wood, Secker & Warburg, 1940 . . . . £45/£15
ditto, Alliance Book Corp. (U.S.), 1940 . . £45/£15
All Aboard for Ararat, Secker & Warburg, 1940 . .
. . . . £45/£15
ditto, Alliance Book Corp. (U.S.), 1941 . £45/£15
You Can't Be Too Careful, Secker & Warburg, 1941 .
. . . . £40/£15

Omnibus Editions
Three Prophetic Novels of H.G. Wells, Dover, 1960 (wraps) £10

Short Stories
Select Conversations with an Uncle, Lane, 1895 £250
ditto, Merriam (U.S.), 1895 . . . . . £200
The Stolen Bacillus and Other Incidents, Methuen, 1895 . . . . £650
The Plattner Story and Others, Methuen, 1897 £175
Thirty Strange Stories, Edward Arnold (U.S.), 1897 .
. . . . £500
Tales of Space and Time, Harpers, 1900 [1899] £300
ditto, Doubleday (U.S.), 1899 . . . . £250
Twelve Stories and a Dream, Macmillan, 1903 £250
ditto, Scribner (U.S.), 1905 . . . . . £150

The Country of The Blind, and Other Stories, Nelson, 1911 . . . . £125
ditto, privately printed. (U.S.), 1915 . . . . £125
ditto, Golden Cockerel Press, 1939, (30 signed copies) £1,000
ditto, Golden Cockerel Press, 1939, (280 signed copies) £450
The Door in The Wall and Other Stories, Mitchell Kennerley, 1911 (300 copies) £200
ditto, Mitchell Kennerley, 1915 (60 signed copies). £2,000
The Short Stories of H.G. Wells, Ernest Benn, 1927 . . . . £45/£20

Children's
Floor Games, Palmer, 1911 . . . . . . £175
ditto, Small, Maynard (U.S.), 1912 . . . . £175
Little Wars, Palmer, 1913. . . . . . . £200
ditto, Small, Maynard (U.S.), 1913 . . . . £200
The Adventures of Tommy, Harrap, 1929 . £125/£25
ditto, Amalgamated Press, 1929 (numbered copies for private circulation) £400
ditto, Stokes (U.S.), 1929 . . . . . . £125/£25

Others
Text-Book of Biology, W.B. Clive, 1893 (2 vols, with 47 two-page plates, first binding dark green cloth) £750
ditto, W.B. Clive, 1893 (2 vols, second binding brown cloth) £500
ditto, W.B. Clive, 1894 (revised edition of Part 1) £35
ditto, as *Text-Book of Zoology*, W.B. Clive, 1898 (revised edition) £25
Honours Physiography, Joseph Hughes, 1893 (with R.A. Gregory) £250
Certain Personal Matters, Lawrence & Bullen, 1898 [1897]. £100
Anticipations, Chapman & Hall, 1902 [1901] . £75
ditto, Harper (U.S.), 1902 . . . . £75
Mankind in The Making, Chapman & Hall, 1903 £25
ditto, Scribners (U.S.), 1904 . . . . . . £20
The Future in America, Chapman & Hall, 1906 £30
ditto, Harpers (U.S.), 1906 . . . . . . £20
Faults of The Fabian, Edward R. Pease, 1906 . £30
Socialism and The Family, Fifield, 1906 (hard covers) £30
ditto, Fifield, 1906 (paper covers) £30
Reconstruction of The Fabian Society, privately printed, 1906 . . . . £35
The So-Called Science of Sociology, Macmillan, 1907 . . . . £35
The Misery of Boots, The Fabian Society, 1907 £30
Will Socialism Destroy The Home?, Independent Labour Party, 1907 . . . . £35
New Worlds for Old, Constable, 1908 . . . £45
ditto, Macmillan (U.S.), 1908 . . . . . £40
First and Last Things, Constable, 1908. . . £40
ditto, Putnams (U.S.), 1908 . . . . . . £35
The Labour Unrest, Daily Mail, 1912 . . . £25

War and Common Sense, Daily Mail, 1913 . £25
Liberalism and It's Party, Good, 1913 . . . £25
An Englishman Looks at The World, Cassell, 1914 . . . . £25
The War That Will End War, Palmer, 1914 (wraps) £75
The Peace of The World, Daily Chronicle, 1915 (wraps) £35
What is Coming: A Forecast of Things after The War, Cassell, 1916 . . . . £30
ditto, Macmillan (U.S.), 1916 . . . . . £25
The Elements of Reconstruction, Nisbet, 1916. £25
War and The Future, Cassell, 1917 . . . . £25
God The Invisible King, Cassell, 1917 . . . £25
ditto, Macmillan (U.S.), 1917 . . . . . £20
In The Fourth Year: Anticipations of a World Peace, Chatto & Windus, 1918 . . . . £25
History is One, Ginn (U.S.), 1919 (pamphlet) . £30
The Outline of History, Newnes, [1919-1920] (24 parts, wraps) £100
ditto, Newnes, [1920] (2 vols) £45
Russia in The Shadows, Hodder & Stoughton, [1920]. . . . . £100/£30
The Salvaging of Civilisation, Cassell, 1921 £75/£25
ditto, Macmillan (U.S.), 1921 . . . . . £50/£15
University of London Election: An Electoral Letter, H. Finer, 1922 (wraps) £20
The Story of a Great Schoolmaster, Chatto & Windus, 1924 . . . . £60/£20
ditto, Macmillan (U.S.), 1924 . . . . . £50/£15
A Year of Prophesying, T. Fisher Unwin, 1924 £45
Mr Belloc Objects to 'The Outline of History', Watts, 1926 . . . . £40/£15
ditto, Doran (U.S.), 1926 . . . . . . £40/£15
Democracy Under Revision, Hogarth Press, 1927 . . . . £75/£25
The Way The World is Going, Ernest Benn, 1928 . . . . £100/£25
ditto, Doran (U.S.), 1929 . . . . . . £75/£20
The Open Conspiracy, Gollancz, 1928 . . £65/£20
The Common Sense of World Peace, Hogarth Press, 1929 . . . . £75/£30
The Science of Life, Amalgamated Press, [1930] (with Julian Huxley and G.P. Wells, 3 vols) . . £125/£50
ditto, Cassell, 1931 (1 vol.) . . . . . £50/£15
ditto, Doubleday Doran (U.S.), 1931 (750 signed copies, 4 vols) £250
ditto, Doubleday Doran (U.S.), 1931 (2 vols) . £250
The Problems of The Troublesome Collaborator, privately printed, 1930 (175 copies) . . . £125
Settlement of The Trouble Between Mr Thring and Mr Wells, A Footnote to The Problems of The Troublesome Collaborator, privately printed, 1930 (225 copies) £75
The Work, Wealth and Happiness of Mankind, Doubleday Doran (U.S.), 1931 (250 signed copies, 2 vols) £150
ditto, Heinemann, 1932, (1 vol.) . . . . £45/£20
After Democracy, Watts, 1932 . . . . . £50/£15

Experiment in Autobiography, Gollancz & Cresset
Press, 1936 (2 vols) . . . . £75/£30
ditto, Macmillan (U.S.), 1934 (1 vol.) . . £50/£15
The New America: The New World, Cresset Press,
1935 . . . . £50/£15
ditto, Macmillan (U.S.), 1935 . . . . £50/£15
The Idea of a World Encyclopaedia, Hogarth Press,
1936 (wraps) £45
The Anatomy of Frustration, Cresset Press, 1936 . .
. . . . £40/£10
ditto, Macmillan (U.S.), 1936 . . . . £40/£10
World Brain, Methuen, 1938. . . . . £45/£10
*Travels of a Republican Radical in Search of Hot
Water*, Penguin Special, 1939 (wrapper has title *In
Search of Hot Water*) £20
The Fate of Homo Sapiens, Secker & Warburg, 1939.
. . . . £50/£15
The New World Order, Secker & Warburg, 1940 . .
. . . . £45/£15
ditto, Knopf (U.S.), 1940 . . . . . . £45/£15
The Rights of Man, or What Are We Fighting For?
Penguin Special, 1940 . . . . . . £15
The Common Sense of War and Peace, Penguin, 1940
. . . . £15
Guide to The New World, Gollancz, 1941 . £35/£15
The Outlook for Homo Sapiens, Secker & Warburg,
1942 . . . . £30/£10
Phoenix, Secker & Warburg, 1942 . . . £40/£10
A Thesis on The Quality of Illusion, privately printed,
Watts, 1942 (wraps) £40
Crux Ansata, Penguin Special, 1943 (wraps) . . £5
'42 to '44, Secker & Warburg, 1944. . . £45/£10
Mind at The End of it's Tether and *The Happy
Turning*, Heinemann, 1945 . . . . . £40/£10
ditto, Didier (U.S.), 1946 . . . . . . £35/£10

MARY WESLEY
(b.1912)

Mary Wesley had her first novel published at the age
of 70, and continues to write, living rather a hermit-
like existence in Devon.

Novels
The Sixth Seal, Macdonald, 1969 . . . £75/£15
ditto, Stein & Day (U.S.), 1971 . . . . £45/£10
Jumping The Queue, Macmillan, 1983 . . £40/£10
ditto, Penguin (U.S.), 1988 . . . . . £10/£5
Haphazard House, Dent, 1983 . . . . £15/£5
The Camomile Lawn, Macmillan, 1984. . £30/£10
ditto, Summit (U.S.), 1985 . . . . . £10/£5
Harnessing Peacocks, Macmillan, 1985 . £15/£5
ditto, Scribner (U.S.), 1986 . . . . . £10/£5
The Vacillations of Poppy Carew, Macmillan, 1986 .
. . . . £15/£5
ditto, Penguin (U.S.), 1988 . . . . . £10/£5

Not That Sort of Girl, Macmillan, 1987. . £15/£5
ditto, Viking (U.S.), 1988. . . . . . £10/£5
Second Fiddle, Macmillan, 1988. . . . £15/£5
ditto, Viking (U.S.), 1989. . . . . . £10/£5
A Sensible Life, Bantam, 1990 . . . . £10/£5
ditto, Viking (U.S.), 1990. . . . . . £10/£5
A Dubious Legacy, Bantam, 1992 . . . £10/£5
ditto, Viking (U.S.), 1992. . . . . . £10/£5
An Imaginative Experience, Bantam, 1994 £10/£5
ditto, Viking (U.S.), 1995. . . . . . £10/£5
Part of the Furniture, Bantam, 1997 . . £10/£5
ditto, Viking (U.S.), 1997. . . . . . £10/£5

Collected Edition
The Mary Wesley Omnibus, Macmillan, 1992 £10/£5

REBECCA WEST
(b.1892 d.1983)

Throughout her many and diverse writings, West was
preoccupied with the idea of original sin. She was
made a Dame in 1959.

Novels
The Return of the Soldier, Century Publishing (U.S.),
1918 . . . . £50
ditto, Nisbet, 1918 . . . . £45
The Judge, Hutchinson, 1922 . . . . £125/£35
ditto, Doran (U.S.), 1922 . . . . . £75/£20
Harriet Hume, A London Fantasy, Hutchinson, 1929.
. . . . £100/£20
ditto, Doran (U.S.), 1929 . . . . . £75/£10
War Nurse, Cosmopolitan Book Co (U.S.), 1930
(anonymous) . . . . £100/£25
The Harsh Voice, Cape, 1935 . . . . £20/£5
ditto, Doubleday (U.S.), 1935 . . . . £15/£5
The Thinking Reed, Viking Press (U.S.), 1936 £25/£5
ditto, Hutchinson, [1936] . . . . . . £25/£5
The Fountain Overflows, Viking (U.S.), 1956 £15/£5
ditto, Macmillan, 1957 . . . . . . £15/£5
The Birds Fall Down, Macmillan, 1966. . £10/£5
ditto, Viking (U.S.), 1966. . . . . . £15/£5
This Real Night, Macmillan, 1984 . . . £15/£5
ditto, Viking (U.S.), 1985. . . . . . £10/£5
Cousin Rosamund, Macmillan, 1985 . . £10/£5
ditto, Viking (U.S.), 1986. . . . . . £10/£5
Sunflower, Virago, 1986 . . . . . . £10/£5
ditto, Viking (U.S.), 1987. . . . . . £10/£5

Others
Henry James, Nisbet, 1916 . . . . . £45
ditto, Holt (U.S.), 1916 . . . . . . £25
The Strange Necessity, Cape, 1928 . . . £35/£10
ditto, Doran (U.S.), 1928 . . . . . . £25/£10
Lions and Lambs, Cape, 1928 . . . . £40/£15
D.H. Lawrence, Secker, 1930 . . . . £35/£15

ditto as *Elegy*, Phoenix (U.S.), 1930 (250 signed copies, glassine d/w) . . . . . . £65/£50
Ending in Earnest: A Literary Log, Doubleday Doran (U.S.), 1931 . . . . £20
Arnold Bennett Himself, John Day (U.S.), 1931 (wraps) £15
St Augustine, Appleton (U.S.), 1933 . . £35/£10
ditto, Davies, 1933 . . . . . . £35/£10
A Letter to Grandfather, Hogarth Press, 1933 (wraps). £25
The Modern 'Rake's Progress', Hutchinson, 1934 .
. . . . £20
ditto, Hutchinson, 1934 (250 signed copies) . £45
Black Lamb and Grey Falcon, Viking Press (U.S.), 1941 (2 vols) . . . . £75/£35
ditto, Macmillan, 1942 (2 vols) . . . . £75/£5
The Meaning of Treason, Viking Press (U.S.), 1947 .
. . . . £15/£5
ditto, Macmillan, 1949 . . . . . . £15/£5
A Train of Powder, Macmillan, 1955 . . £15/£5
ditto, Viking (U.S.), 1955. . . . . . £15/£5
The Court and the Castle, Yale Univ. Press (U.S.), 1957 . . . . £15/£5
ditto, Macmillan, 1958 . . . . . . £15/£5
The Vassal Affair, Sunday Telegraph, 1963 (wraps) .
. . . . £10
McLuhan and the Future of Literature, The English Association, 1969 (wraps) £25
Rebecca West, A Celebration, Macmillan, 1977 £10/£5
ditto, Viking (U.S.), 1977. . . . . . £10/£5
1900, Weidenfeld & Nicolson, 1982. . . £10/£5
ditto, Viking (U.S.), 1982. . . . . . £10/£5
The Young Rebecca, Virago, 1982 . . . £10/£5
ditto, Viking (U.S.), 1982. . . . . . £10/£5
Family Memories, Virago, 1987. . . . £10/£5
ditto, Viking (U.S.), 1988. . . . . . £10/£5
The Only Poet and Short Stories, Virago, 1992 £10/£5

EDITH WHARTON
(b.1862 d.1937)

An American novelist and short story writer, with *The Age of Innocence* she became the first woman to be awarded the Pulitzer Prize.

Novels and Novellas
The Touchstone, Scribner's (U.S.), 1900 . . £150
ditto, as *A Gift from The Grave*, John Murray, 1900 .
. . . . £150
The Valley of Decision, Scribner's (U.S.), 1902 (2 vols) £150
ditto, John Murray, 1902. . . . . . . £75
Sanctuary, Scribner's (U.S.), 1903 . . . £125
ditto, Macmillan, 1903 . . . . £75
The House of Mirth, Scribner's (U.S.), 1905 . £75
ditto, Macmillan, 1905 . . . . £65

Madam de Treymes, Scribner's (U.S.), 1907 . £45
ditto, Macmillan, 1907 . . . . £45
The Fruit of The Tree, Scribner's (U.S.), 1907. £45
ditto, Macmillan, 1907 . . . . £45
Ethan Frome, Scribner's (U.S.), 1911 (first issue with top edge gilt and perfect type in last line of p.135) .
. . . . £450
ditto, Macmillan, 1911 . . . . . . £100
ditto, Scribner's (U.S.), 1922 (2,000 copies, new introduction, slipcase) . . . . . £65/£50
ditto, Limited Editions Club (U.S.), 1939 (1,500 signed copies, slipcase) . . . . . £45/£40
The Reef, D. Appleton & Co. (U.S.), 1912 . . £40
ditto, Macmillan, 1912 . . . . £35
The Custom of The Country, Scribner's (U.S.), 1913 .
. . . . £40
ditto, Macmillan, 1913 . . . . £35
Summer, Appleton & Co. (U.S.), 1917 . . . £45
ditto, Macmillan, 1917 . . . . £35
The Marine: A Tale of The War, Appleton & Co. (U.S.), 1918 . . . . £35
ditto, Macmillan, 1918 . . . . £25
The Age of Innocence, Appleton & Co., 1920 (first issue: 'burial', p.186, no mention of Pulitzer Prize on d/w) . . . . £3,000/£250
The Glimpses of The Moon, Appleton & Co., 1922 .
. . . . £175/£35
ditto, Chapman and Hall, 1922 . . . . £75/£15
A Son at The Front, Scribners (U.S.), 1923 £175/£35
ditto, Macmillan, 1923 . . . . . £150/£25
Old New York, Appleton & Co., 1924 (4 vols) . .
. . . . £450/£100
The Mother's Recompense, Appleton & Co., 1925 .
. . . . £150/£20
Twilight Sleep, Appleton & Co., 1927 . . £125/£15
The Children, Appleton & Co., 1928 . £125/£15
Hudson River Bracketed, Appleton & Co., 1929 . .
. . . . £125/£15
The Gods Arrive, Appleton & Co., 1932 . £125/£15
The Buccaneers, Appleton & Co., 1938 . £125/£15

Short Stories
The Greater Inclination, Scribners (U.S.), 1899 (first issue: 'Wharton' only on spine). . . . £250
ditto, John Lane, 1899. . . . . . . £125
Crucial Instances, Scribner's (U.S.), 1901 . . £125
ditto, John Murray, 1901 . . . . . . £75
The Descent of Man and Other Stories, Scribner's (U.S.), 1904 . . . . £100
ditto, Macmillan, 1904 . . . . £75
The Hermit and The Wild Woman, and Other Stories, Scribners (U.S.), 1908 . . . . . . £100
ditto, Macmillan, 1908 . . . . £75
Les Metteurs en Scene, (Paris), 1909 (in French) £50
Tales of Men and Ghosts, Scribners (U.S.), 1910 £100
ditto, Macmillan, 1910 . . . . £75
Xingu and Other Stories, Scribner's (U.S.), 1916 £35
ditto, Macmillan, 1916 . . . . £35
Here and Beyond, Appleton & Co., 1926 . £125/£25

Certain People, Appleton & Co., 1930 . . £125/£25
Human Nature, Appleton & Co., 1933 . . £125/£25
The World Over, Appleton & Co., 1936. . £125/£25
Ghosts, Appleton & Co., 1937 . . . . £125/£25
The Collected Short Stories of Edith Wharton,
Scribner's (U.S.), 1968 . . . . . . £45/£15
Quartet: Four Stories, Allen Press (U.S.), 1975 (140
copies) £300
The Ghost Stories of Edith Wharton, Constable, 1975
. . . . £25/£10
The Stories of Edith Wharton, Simon & Schuster,
1988 & 1989 (2 vols) . . . . . . £30/£10

Verse
Verses, privately printed (U.S.), 1908 (wraps; pseud.
'Edith Newbold Jones') £25,000
Artemis to Actaeon and Other Verses, Scribner's
(U.S.), 1909 . . . . £150
ditto, Macmillan, 1909 . . . . . . £75
Twelve Poems, The Medici Society, 1926 (130 signed
copies) . . . . £2,000/£1,000

Others
The Decoration of Houses, Scribner's (U.S.), 1897
(with Ogden Codman Jr.) £1,000
Italian Villas and Their Gardens, Century (U.S.),
1904 . . . . £500
ditto, John Lane, 1904. . . . . . . £400
Italian Backgrounds, Scribner's (U.S.), 1905 . £100
ditto, Macmillan, 1905 . . . . . . £75
A Motor-Flight through France, Scribner's (U.S.),
1908 . . . . £75
ditto, Macmillan, 1908 . . . . . . £65
Fighting France: From Dunkerque to Belfort,
Scribner's (U.S.), 1915 . . . . . . £65
ditto, Macmillan, 1915 . . . . . . £45
French Ways and Their Meaning, Appleton & Co.
(U.S.), 1919 . . . . £65
ditto, Macmillan, 1919 . . . . . . £45
In Morocco, Scribner's (U.S.), 1920. . . £125/£35
ditto, Macmillan, 1920 . . . . . £125/£30
The Writing of Fiction, Scribner's, 1925 . £125/£20
A Backward Glance, Appleton-Century, 1934 . . .
. . . . £125/£20
An Edith Wharton Treasury, Appleton-Century-Crofts
(U.S.), [1950]. . . . . £25/£10
The Letters of Edith Wharton, Simon & Schuster,
1988 . . . . £20/£5

DENNIS WHEATLEY
(b.1897 d.1977)

Wheatley's headstone describes him as the 'Prince of
Thriller Writers', and with worldwide sales of more
than 45 million copies few would argue with the
claim.

Duke de Richleau Titles
The Forbidden Territory, Hutchinson, [1933] £45/310
The Devil Rides Out, Hutchinson, [1935] £45/£10
The Golden Spaniard, Hutchinson, [1938] £25/£5
Three Inquisitive People, Hutchinson, [1940] £25/£5
Strange Conflict, Hutchinson, [1941] . £20/£5
Codeword - Golden Fleece, Hutchinson, [1946] £15/£5
The Second Seal, Hutchinson, 1950. . . £10/£5
The Prisoner in The Mask, Hutchinson, 1957 £10/£5
Vendetta in Spain, Hutchinson, 1961 . . £10/£5
Dangerous Inheritance, Hutchinson, 1965 £10/£5
Gateway to Hell, Hutchinson, 1970 . . . £10/£5

Gregory Sallust Titles
Black August, Hutchinson, [1934] . . £40/£5
Contraband, Hutchinson, [1936]. . . . £25/£5
The Scarlet Impostor, Hutchinson, [1940] £15/£5
The Black Baroness, Hutchinson, [1940] £15/£5
'V' for Vengeance, Hutchinson, [1942] . . £15/£5
Come into my Parlour, Hutchinson, [1946] £15/£5
Faked Passport, Hutchinson, [1949] . . £15/£5
The Island Where Time Stands Still, Hutchinson, 1954
. . . . £15/£5
Traitor's Gate, Hutchinson, 1958 . . £15/£5
The Used Dark Forces, Hutchinson, 1964 £20/£5
The White Witch of The South Seas, Hutchinson,
1968 . . . . £10/£5

Julian Day Titles
The Quest of Julian Day, Hutchinson, [1939] £25/£5
The Sword of Fate, Hutchinson, [1941]. . £15/£5
The Bill for The Use of a Body, Hutchinson, 1964 .
. . . . £10/£5

Roger Brook Titles
The Launching of Roger Brook, Hutchinson, [1947]
. . . . £20/£5
The Shadow of Tyburn Tree, Hutchinson, [1948] . .
. . . . £20/£5
The Rising Storm, Hutchinson, [1949] . . £20/£5
The Man Who Killed The King, Hutchinson, 1951 .
. . . . £15/£5
The Dark Secret of Josephine, Hutchinson, 1955 .
. . . . £15/£5
The Rape of Venice, Hutchinson, 1959 . . £15/£5
The Sultan's Daughter, Hutchinson, 1963 . £15/£5
The Wanton Princess, Hutchinson, 1966 . £15/£5
Evil in a Mask, Hutchinson, 1969 . . . £15/£5
The Ravishing of Lady Mary Ware, Hutchinson, 1971
. . . . £10/£5
Desperate Measures, Hutchinson, 1974. . £10/£5

Other Titles
Such Power is Dangerous, Hutchinson, [1933] £35/£5
The Fabulous Valley, Hutchinson, [1934] . £30/£5
The Eunuch of Stamboul, Hutchinson, [1935] £25/£5
They Found Atlantis, Hutchinson, [1936] . £25/£5
The Secret War, Hutchinson, [1937] . . £20/£5
Uncharted Seas, Hutchinson, [1938] . . £20/£5
Sixty Days to Live, Hutchinson, [1939] . £20/£5
The Man Who Missed The War, Hutchinson, [1945] .
. . . . £15/£5
The Haunting of Toby Jug, Hutchinson, [1948] . .
. . . . £15/£5
Star of Ill-Omen, Hutchinson, 1952 . . £15/£5
To The Devil - A Daughter, Hutchinson, 1953 £15/£5
Curtain of Fear, Hutchinson, 1953 . . . £15/£5
The Ka of Gifford Hillary, Hutchinson, 1956 £15/£5
The Satanist, Hutchinson, 1960 . . . . £15/£5
Mayhem in Greece, Hutchinson, 1962 . . £10/£5
Unholy Crusade, Hutchinson, 1967 . . . £10/£5
The Strange Story of Linda Lee, Hutchinson, 1972 .
. . . . £10/£5
The Irish Witch, Hutchinson, 1973 . . . £10/£5
The Deception Planners: My Secret War, Hutchinson,
1980 . . . . £10/£5

Short Stories
Mediterranean Nights, Hutchinson, [1942] £10/£5
Gunmen, Gallants and Ghosts, Hutchinson, [1943] .
. . . . £15/£5

Non Fiction
Old Rowley: A Private Life of Charles II, Hutchinson,
1933 . . . . £25/£5
Red Eagle: A Life of Marshal Voroshilov, Hutchinson,
1937 . . . . £15/£5
Total War, Hutchinson, [1941] . . . . £20/£5
The Seven Ages of Justerini's, Riddle Books, 1949 .
. . . . £10/£5
ditto, as *1749-1965: The Eight Ages of Justerini's'*,
Dolphin, 1965 . . . . £10/£5
Of Vice and Virtue, privately printed, 1950. . £75
Stranger than Fiction, Hutchinson, 1959 . £10/£5
Saturdays with Bricks and Other Days Under Shell-Fire, Hutchinson, 1961 . . . . . £10/£5
The Devil and All His Works, Hutchinson, 1971 . .
. . . . £15/£5

Autobiography
The Young Man Said: 1897-1914, Hutchinson, 1977 .
. . . . £20/£5
Officer and Temporary Gentleman: 1914-1919,
Hutchinson, 1978 . . . . . . £20/£5
Drink and Ink: 1919-1977, Hutchinson, 1979 £20/£5
The Time Has Come, Arrow, 1981 (wraps). . . £5

Crime Dossiers
Murder Off Miami, Hutchinson, [1936] (with J.G.
Links). £35

ditto, as *File on Bolitho Lane*, Morrow (U.S.), 1936 .
. . . . £35
Who Killed Robert Prentice?, Hutchinson, [1937]
(with J.G. Links). £35
ditto, as *File on Robert Prentice*, Greenburg (U.S.),
1937 . . . . £35
The Malinsay Massacre, Hutchinson, [1938] (with
J.G. Links) £35
Herewith The Clues!, Hutchinson, [1939] (with J.G.
Links). £35

PATRICK WHITE
(b.1912 d.1990)

An Australian novelist, short story writer and
dramatist, White won the Nobel Prize for Literature in
1973.

Novels
Happy Valley, Harrap, 1939 . . . . £2,000/£250
ditto, Viking (U.S.), 1940. . . . . £1,250/£200
The Living and the Dead, Viking (U.S.), 1941 . . .
. . . . £600/£75
ditto, Routledge, 1941. . . . . . £600/£75
The Aunt's Story, Routledge, 1948 . . . £500/£75
ditto, Viking (U.S.), 1948. . . . . £250/£45
The Tree of Man, Viking (U.S.), 1955 . . £75/£20
ditto, Eyre & Spottiswoode, 1956 . . . £50/£10
Voss, Viking (U.S.), 1957. . . . . . £40/£10
ditto, Eyre & Spottiswoode, 1957 . . . £40/£10
Riders in the Chariot, Viking (U.S.), 1961 . £35/£10
ditto, Eyre & Spottiswoode, 1961 . . . £35/£10
The Solid Mandala, Eyre & Spottiswoode, 1966 . .
. . . . £25/£10
ditto, Viking (U.S.), 1966. . . . . . £25/£10
The Vivesector, Cape, 1970 . . . . . £20/£5
ditto, Viking (U.S.), 1970. . . . . . £20/£5
The Eye of the Storm, Cape, 1973 . . . £20/£5
ditto, Viking (U.S.), 1974. . . . . . £20/£5
A Fringe of Leaves, Cape, 1976 . . . . £20/£5
ditto, Viking (U.S.), 1976. . . . . . £20/£5
The Twyborn Affair, Cape, 1979 . . . . £20/£5
ditto, Viking (U.S.), 1980. . . . . . £20/£5
Memoirs of Many in One, Cape, 1986 . . £15/£5
ditto, Viking (U.S.), 1986. . . . . . £15/£5

Short Stories
The Burnt Ones, Eyre & Spottiswoode, 1964 £35/£10
ditto, Viking (U.S.), 1964. . . . . . £25/£5
The Cockatoos, Cape, 1974 . . . . . £20/£5
ditto, Viking (U.S.), 1975. . . . . . £20/£5
Three Uneasy Pieces, Pascoe (Australia), 1987 (wraps)
. . . . £10
ditto, Cape, 1988 . . . . £15/£5
ditto, Viking (U.S.), 1988. . . . . . £15/£5

Verse
Thirteen Poems, privately printed, 1930 (wraps) . .
. . . . £2,500
The Ploughman and Other Poems, Beacon Press
(Australia), 1935 (200 copies) . . . £3,000/£500

Plays
Four Plays, Eyre & Spottiswoode, 1965 . £35/£10
ditto, Viking (U.S.), 1966. . . . . . £30/£10
The Night of the Prowler, Penguin/Cape, 1978 (wraps)
. . . . £10
Big Toys, Currency Press (Australia), 1978 (wraps) .
. . . . £10
Netherwood, Currency Press (Australia), 1983 (wraps)
. . . . £10
Signal Driver, Currency Press (Australia), 1983
(wraps) £10

Others
Flaws in the Glass, Cape, 1981 . . . £20/£5
ditto, Viking (U.S.), 1982. . . . . £15/£5
Patrick White Speaks, Primavera Press (Australia),
1989 . . . . £15/£5
ditto, Cape, 1990 . . . . £15/£5

T.H. WHITE
(b.1906 d.1964)

A novelist and children's writer, White's major
success was the re-telling of the Arthurian legends in
a series of novels which began with *The Sword in the
Stone*.

Novels
Dead Mr Nixon, Cassell, 1931 (with R. McNair Scott)
. . . . £600/£150
Darkness at Pemberley, Gollancz, 1932 £400/£100
ditto, Century (U.S.), 1933 . . . . £225/£45
They Winter Abroad, Gollancz, 1932 (pseud. 'James
Aston') . . . . £500/£125
ditto, Viking (U.S.), 1932. . . . . £250/£75
First Lesson, Gollancz, 1932 (pseud. 'James Aston') .
. . . . £450/£100
ditto, Knopf (U.S.), 1933 . . . . £250/£75
Farewell Victoria, Collins, 1933 . . . £250/£35
ditto, Smith & Haas (U.S.), 1934 . . £125/£20
Earth Stopped, Or Mr Marx's Sporting Tour, Collins,
1934 . . . . £225/£35
ditto, Putnam (U.S.), 1935 . . . . £125/£20
Gone to Ground, Collins, 1935 . . . £200/£35
ditto, Putnam (U.S.), 1935 . . . . £125/£20
The Elephant and The Kangaroo, Putnam (U.S.),
1947 . . . . £60/£15
ditto, Cape, 1948 . . . . £60/£15

Children's
The Sword in The Stone, Collins, 1938 . . £600/£50

ditto, Putnam (U.S.), 1939 . . . . . £150/£25
The Witch in The Wood, Putnam (U.S.), 1939 . . .
. . . . £350/£25
ditto, Collins, 1940 . . . . . . £500/£50
The Ill-Made Knight, Putnam (U.S.), 1940 . £125/£25
ditto, Collins, 1941 . . . . . . £400/£50
Mistress Masham's Repose, Putnam (U.S.), 1946 .
. . . . £45/£10
ditto, Cape, 1947 . . . . £45/£10
The Master, An Adventure Story, Cape, 1957 £50/£10
ditto, Putnam (U.S.), 1957 . . . . £45/£10
The Once and Future King, Collins, 1958 . £150/£25
ditto, Putnam (U.S.), 1958 . . . . £125/£20
The Book of Merlyn, Univ. of Texas Press (U.S.),
1977 . . . . £20/£5
ditto, Collins, 1978 . . . . . . £15/£5
The Maharajah and Other Stories, Putnam (U.S.),
1981 . . . . £15/£5
ditto, MacDonald, 1981 . . . . . £15/£5

Verse
*The Green Bay Tree, or The Wicked Man Touches
Wood*, Songs for Sixpence, No. 3, Heffer, 1929
(wraps) £250
Cambridge Poetry, No. 8, Hogarth Living Poets,
Hogarth Press, 1929 . . . . . . £250
Loved Helen and Other Poems, Chatto & Windus,
1929 . . . . £250/£50
ditto, Viking (U.S.), 1929. . . . . £250/£50
Verses, Shenval Press, 1962 (100 numbered copies) .
. . . . £750
A Joy Proposed, Bertram Rota, 1980 (500 numbered
copies) . . . . £25/£10
ditto, Univ. of Georgia Press (U.S.), 1983 £20/£5

Non Fiction
England Have My Bones, Collins, 1936 . £150/£25
ditto, Macmillan (U.S.), 1936 . . . . £75/£15
*Burke's Steerage, Or The Amateur Gentleman's
Introduction to Noble Sports and Pastimes*, Collins,
1938 . . . . £100/£20
ditto, Putnam (U.S.), 1939 . . . . £75/£15
The Age of Scandal, Cape, 1950. . . . £45/£10
ditto, Putnam (U.S.), 1950 . . . . £30/£10
The Goshawk, Cape, 1951 . . . . £65/£15
ditto, Putnam (U.S.), 1952 . . . . £45/£10
The Scandalmonger, Cape, 1952 . . . £30/£10
ditto, Putnam (U.S.), 1952 . . . . £20/£5
The Godstone and The Blackymor, Cape, 1959 . .
. . . . £25/£10
ditto, Putnam (U.S.), 1959 . . . . £15/£5
*America At Last, The American Journal of T.H.
White*, Putnam (U.S.), 1965. . . . £20/£5
The White/Garnett Letters, Cape, 1968 . . £20/£5
ditto, Viking (U.S.), 1968. . . . . £20/£5
*Letters to a Friend, The Correspondence Between
T.H. White and L.J. Potts*, Putnam (U.S.), 1982 .
. . . . £20/£5
ditto, Alan Sutton, 1984 (enlarged edition) . £20/£5

WALT WHITMAN
(b.1819 d.1892)

Whitman was not an immediate success in America. It was not until he was taken up by Rossetti, Swinburne and others in England that his importance was widely recognised.

Verse

Franklin Evans, or The Inebriate, Winchester (U.S.), 1842 (wraps) £5,000

Leaves of Grass, no publisher (U.S.), 1855 (first issue without adverts or reviews, with marbled endpapers, both front and back covers with triple gilt-stamped line, and frontis portrait on plain paper) . £20,000

ditto, Horsell, 1855 (copies with light yellowish-green or pink wrappers) £20,000

ditto, no publisher (U.S.), 1856 (second issue with a leaf of adverts by Fowler & Wells at end) . £2,000

Drum-Taps, Peter Eckler (U.S.), 1865 . . £1,000

Poems, Camden Hotten, 1868 (edited by W.M. Rossetti, first issue with no price on spine) . £275

Memoranda. Democratic Vistas, Redfield (U.S.) 1871 (first issue without author on tide-page, wraps) £500

ditto, Walter Scott, 1888 . . . . . . £100

After All, Not To Create Only, Pearson (U.S.), 1871 (11 folio sheets printed on one side only) . £1,750

ditto, Roberts Bros. (U.S.), 1871 . . . . £500

ditto, Roberts Bros. (U.S.), 1871 (wraps) . £350

Memoranda. During the War, Author's Publication (U.S.) 1875-6 (first issue with first page printed 'Remembrance Copy' and signed below) . £2,000

ditto, Author's Publication (U.S.) 1875-6 (second issue lacks portraits and the 'Remembrance Copy' leaf) .
. . . . £500

Two Rivulets, Author's Edition (U.S.) 1876 £3,000

Specimen Days and Collect, Rees, Welsh (U.S.) 1882-3 (cloth) £150

ditto, Rees, Welsh (U.S.) 1882-3 (wraps) . . £300

ditto, David McKay (U.S.) 1883 . . . . £100

November Boughs, David McKay (U.S.) 1888 . £200

ditto, David McKay (U.S.) 1888 (copies on large paper) £300

Complete Poems and Prose of Walt Whitman, Fergnson (U.S.) 11888-89 (600 signed copies) £2,500

Leaves of Grass with *Sands at Seventy*, Ferguson Bros (U.S.) 1889 (300 signed copies) . . £2,500

Good-bye My Fancy, David McKay (U.S.) 1891 £250

ditto, David McKay (U.S.) 1891 (copies on large paper) £300

Complete Prose Works, David McKay (U.S.) 1892 .
. . . . £200

Autobiographica, Webster (U.S.) 1892 . . £100

In Re Walt Whitman, David McKay (U.S.) 1893 £125

Calamus, Laurens Maynard (U.S.) 1897. . . £250

ditto, Laurens Maynard (U.S.) 1897 (35 numbered large paper copies) £500

ditto, Putnam, 1897 . . . . £150

Walt Whitman at Home, Critic Pamphlet No.2 (U.S.) 1898 (wraps) £75

The Wound Dresser, Small. Maynard (U.S.) 1898 . .
. . . . £150

ditto, Small. Maynard (U.S.) 1898 (60 large paper copies) £500

Notes and Fragments, Talbot & Co (U.S.) 1899 (250 copies) £200

When Lilacs Last in the Dooryard Bloomed, Essex House Press, 1900 (125 copies) £750

Letters ... To His Mother, Putnam (U.S.) 1902 (5 copies, wraps) £3,000

ditto, Goldsmith (U.S.), 1936 (325 copies) . . £125

The Complete Writings, Putnam (U.S.) 1902 (500 numbered sets, 10 vols) £400

The Half Breed and Other Stories, Columbia Univ. Press (U.S.) 1927 (155 copies) £100

ditto, Columbia Univ. Press (U.S.) 1927 (30 copies) .
. . . . £250

Pictures, The June House (U.S.) 1927 (700 copies) £65

Rivulets of Prose, Greenberg (U.S.) 1928 (499 copies)
. . . . £100

OSCAR WILDE
(b.1854 d.1900)

Known principally a playwright, Wilde was also a fine essayist, poet and novelist. Even today his public persona often overshadows his considerable literary achievements.

Verse

Ravenna, Thomas Shrimpton, 1878 (wraps) £1,000

Poems, David Bogue, 1881 (750 copies printed and issued as 3 editions) £1,000

ditto, Roberts Bros. (U.S.), 1881 . . . . . £250

ditto, Mathews and Lane, 1892 (220 signed copies) .
. . . . £3,000

The Sphinx, Mathews & Lane, 1894 (200 copies) . .
. . . . £4,000

ditto, Mathews & Lane, 1894 (25 large paper copies) .
. . . . £5,000

ditto, John Lane, The Bodley Head, 1910 (cheap edition) £25

ditto, John Lane, 1920 (1,000 copies, 10 illustrations by Alastair) £200

The Ballad of Reading Gaol, Leonard Smithers, 1898 (pseud 'C.3.3.') £1,000

ditto, Leonard Smithers, 1898 (30 numbered copies) .
. . . . £5,000

ditto, Leonard Smithers, 1898 (third edition, 99 signed copies) £3,500

ditto, Alfred Bartlett (U.S.), 1902 (550 copies) . £125

Short Stories

The Happy Prince and Other Tales, David Nutt, 1888
. . . . £1,000
ditto, David Nutt, 1888 (75 signed copies, large hand
made paper edition) £6,000
ditto, Roberts Bros. (U.S.), 1888 . . . . £400
ditto, Duckworth, 1913 (illustrated by Charles
Robinson). £75
ditto, Duckworth, 1913 (250 copies signed by artist, in
slipcase) . . . . £600/£500
Lord Arthur Saville's Crime and Other Stories,
Osgood, McIlvaine & Co., 1891 . . . . £650
ditto, Dodd, Mead (U.S.), 1891 . . . . £400
A House of Pomegranates, Osgood, McIlvaine & Co.,
1891 . . . . £750
L'Anniversaire de L'Enfant, Black Sun Press (Paris),
1928 (9 illustrations by Alastair) . . . £200
The Birthday of the Infanta, Black Sun Press (Paris),
1928 (100 copies, as above but text in English, 9
illustrations, slipcase) . . . £1,250/£1,000

Plays

Vera, or The Nihilists Ranken & Co., 1880 (grey
wraps). £12,500
ditto, privately printed (U.S.), 1882 (wraps). £10,000
The Duchess of Padua, privately printed (U.S.), 1883
(20 copies printed as manuscript) . . . £10,000
ditto, Methuen, 1908 . . . . £500
Salome, Drama en un Acte, Librairie de L'art
Independant/Elkin Mathews et John Lane, 1893 £450
ditto, Librairie de L'art Independant/Elkin Mathews et
John Lane, 1893 (50 tall copies on hand made paper)
. . . . £1,500
Lady Windermere's Fan, Elkin Mathews & John Lane,
1893 . . . . £750
ditto, Elkin Mathews & John Lane, 1893 (50 deluxe
copies on hand made paper) £1,500
Salome, Elkin Mathews & John Lane, 1894 (775
copies, illustrated by Beardsley) . . . £2,000
ditto, Lane & Mathews, 1894 (125 copies, on Japan
vellum, large paper issue) £10,000
ditto, Melmoth & Co., 1904 (250 numbered copies) .
. . . . £350
ditto, Melmoth & Co., 1904 (50 numbered copies). .
. . . . £500
ditto, G. Crès (Paris), 1922 (9 illustrations by Alastair)
. . . . £75
ditto, G. Crès (Paris), 1922 (100 copies on Imperial
Japon paper, 9 illustrations). £500
A Woman of No Importance, John Lane, 1894 £750
ditto, John Lane, 1894 (50 deluxe copies on hand made
paper) £1,500
The Importance of Being Earnest, Smithers, 1899 (by
the 'Author of Lady Windermere's Fan') . . £750
ditto, Smithers, 1899 (12 copies on Japanese vellum) .
. . . . £8,000
ditto, Smithers, 1899 (100 signed, deluxe copies) . .
. . . . £6,500
ditto, [Methuen], 1910 (1200 copies) . . . £75

An Ideal Husband, Smithers, 1899 (by the 'Author of
Lady Windermere's Fan') £750
ditto, Smithers, 1899 (12 copies on Japanese vellum) .
. . . . £6,500
ditto, Smithers, 1899 (100 signed, deluxe copies) . .
. . . . £4,000

Novel

The Picture of Dorian Gray, Ward, Lock, 1891 . . .
. . . . £1,500
ditto, Ward, Lock, 1891 (250 signed, numbered, large
paper copies). £6,000

Essays

Intentions, Osgood, McIlvaine & Co., 1891 . £350
ditto, Dodd, Mead (U.S.), 1891 . . . . . £200
The Soul of Man Under Socialism, Humphreys, 1895
(50 copies, brown paper wraps). . . . £450
ditto, Luce (U.S.), 1910 . . . . £100
The Portrait of Mr W.H., Smithers, 1904 (200 copies)
. . . . £250
Essays, Criticisms and Reviews, Wright & Jones, 1901
(300 numbered copies) £125
De Profundis, Methuen, [1905] (with ads dated
February) £150
ditto, Methuen, [1905] (with ads dated March) . £100
ditto, Methuen, [1905] (200 copies on hand-made
paper). £500
ditto, Methuen, [1905] (50 copies on Japanese vellum)
. . . . £2,000
ditto, Putnams (U.S.), 1905 . . . . . . £100
The Suppressed Portions of De Profundis, Paul
Reynolds (U.S.), 1913 (15 copies) . . . £1,500

Others

Phrases and Philosophies for The Use of The Young,
privately printed, A. Cooper, 1894 (wraps) . £250
Children in Prison and Other Cruelties of Prison Life,
Murdoch & Co., [1898] (wraps) . . . £1,000
Poems in Prose, Carrington, 1905 (50 copies on
Imperial Japanese vellum) £250
ditto, Carrington, 1905 (50 copies on Japanese vellum)
. . . . £250
*Wilde and Whistler: An Acrimonious Correspondence
in Art*, Smithers, 1906 (400 copies, wraps) . £200
After Reading, Letters of Oscar Wilde to Robert Ross,
Beaumont Press, 1921 (75 numbered copies on Japan
vellum of 475) £250
ditto, Beaumont Press, 1921 (400 numbered copies of
475) £75
After Berneval, Letters of Oscar Wilde to Robert Ross,
Beaumont Press, 1922 (75 copies on Japan vellum of
475) £200
ditto, Beaumont Press, 1922 (400 numbered copies of
475) £75
Some Letters from Oscar Wilde to Alfred Douglas,
1892-1897, privately printed (U.S.), 1924 (225
copies, slipcase) . . . . £250/£200
The Letters of Oscar Wilde, Hart-Davis, 1962 £75/£25

ditto, Harcourt Brace (U.S.), 1962 . . . £75/£25

Selected Work
Oscariana, privately printed by Humphreys, 1895 (50
copies in buff paper wraps) £200
ditto, Humphreys, 1910 (200 copies in Japanese vellum
wrappers). £250
ditto, Humphreys, 1910 (50 copies on Japanese vellum)
. . . . £300
Sebastian Melmoth, Humphries, 1904 . . . £65

CHARLES WILLIAMS
(b.1886 d.1945)

The author of many books on theological subjects,
Williams also wrote a number of supernatural thrillers
dealing with the conflict between good and evil.

Verse
The Silver Stair, Herbert & Daniel, [1912] . . £250
Poems of Conformity, O.U.P., 1917. . . . £100
Divorce, O.U.P., 1920. . . . . . £200/£65
Windows of Night, O.U.P., 1925. . . . £200/£65
Heroes and Kings, Sylvan Press, 1930 (300 copies) .
. . . . £200
Taliessin Through Logres, O.U.P., 1938 . £125/£30
The Region of The Summer Stars, Editions Poetry,
1944 . . . . £75/£25

Novels
War in Heaven, Gollancz, 1930 . . . . £175/£40
ditto, Pellegrini & Cudahy (U.S.), 1949 . £60/£15
Many Dimensions, Gollancz, 1931 . . . £150/£40
ditto, Pellegrini & Cudahy (U.S.), 1949 . £60/£15
The Place of The Lion, Gollancz, 1931 . £150/£40
ditto, Gollancz, 1931 (wraps). £65
ditto, Norton (U.S.), 1932. . . . . £125/£30
The Greater Trumps, Gollancz, 1932 . £125/£30
ditto, Pellegrini & Cudahy (U.S.), 1950 . £60/£15
Shadows of Ecstasy, Gollancz, 1933 . £125/£25
ditto, Pellegrini & Cudahy (U.S.), 1950 . £60/£15
Descent into Hell, Faber, 1937 . . . £125/£30
ditto, Pellegrini & Cudahy (U.S.), 1949 . £60/£15
All Hallows Eve, Faber, 1945 . . . £100/£25
ditto, Pellegrini & Cudahy (U.S.), 1948 . £60/£15

Drama
The Masque of The Manuscript, privately printed,
1927 (100 copies, wraps) £200
A Myth of Shakespeare, O.U.P., 1928 . £200/£75
The Masque of Perusal, privately printed, 1929 (100
copies, wraps) £200
Three Plays, O.U.P., 1931 (red glassine d/w with paper
flaps) . . . . £150/£50
Thomas Cranmer of Canterbury, H.J. Goulden, 1936
(wraps) £45
ditto, O.U.P., 1936. . . . . . . £75/£25

Judgement at Chelmsford, O.U.P., 1939 (wraps) £50
The House of The Octopus, Edinburgh House, 1945 .
. . . . £50/£15
Seed of Adam and Other Plays, O.U.P., 1948 £30/£10
Collected Plays, O.U.P., 1963 . . . . £25/£10

Biography
Bacon, Arthur Barker, 1933 . . . . . £125/£25
James I, Arthur Barker, 1934 . . . . £125/£25
Rochester, Arthur Barker, 1935 . . . . £125/£25
Queen Elizabeth, Duckworth, 1936 . . £100/£20
Henry VII, Arthur Barker, 1937 . . . £100/£20
Flecker of Dean Close, Canterbury Press, 1946 . .
. . . . £50/£10

Theology
He Came Down from Heaven, Heinemann, 1938 . .
. . . . £45/£10
The Descent of The Dove, Longmans, Green, 1939 .
. . . . £40/£10
Witchcraft, Faber, 1941 . . . . . £75/£20
The Forgiveness of Sins, Bles, 1942 . . £35/£10

Criticism
Poetry at Present, Clarendon Press, 1930 . £65/£20
The English Poetic Mind, Clarendon Press, 1932 .
. . . . £65/£20
Reason and Beauty in The Poetic Mind, Clarendon
Press, 1933 . . . . £65/£20
Religion and Love in Dante, Dacre Press, [1941]
(wraps) £25
The Figure of Beatrice, Faber, 1943 . . £75/£20
Arthurian Torso, O.U.P., 1948 (with C.S. Lewis) . . .
. . . . £75/£35
ditto, O.U.P. (U.S.), 1948. . . . . £75/£35
The Image of The City, O.U.P., 1958 . . £50/£10

TENNESSEE WILLIAMS
(b.1911 d.1983)

An American playwright, many of whose works have
been filmed. Most of Williams' plays show a
sympathy with lost, lonely and self-punishing
characters.

Plays
Battle of Angels, Pharos (U.S.), 1945 (wraps) . £400
The Glass Menagerie, Random House (U.S.), 1945 .
. . . . £650/£100
ditto, Lehmann, 1948 . . . . . . £75/£20
You Touched Me, French (U.S.), 1947 (with Donald
Windham) £300
ditto, French (U.S.), 1947 (grey wraps) . . . £100
A Streetcar Named Desire, New Directions (U.S.),
1947 . . . . £1,000/£100
ditto, Lehmann, 1949 . . . . . . £100/£25

American Blues, Dramatists Play Services (U.S.), 1948 (author's name misspelled on front cover: 'Tennesse', wraps) £200
Summer and Smoke, New Directions (U.S.), 1948 (first issue d/w lists three plays by Williams on inside back flap) . . . . £175/£15
ditto, Lehmann, 1952 . . . . . . £65/£15
The Rose Tattoo, New Directions (U.S.), 1951 (first binding rose cloth) . . . . . . £200/£75
ditto, New Directions (U.S.), 1951 (second binding tan cloth) . . . . £100/£15
ditto, Secker & Warburg, 1954 [1955] . . £60/£15
I Rise in Flame, Cried the Phoenix, A Play about D.H. Lawrence, New Directions (U.S.), 1951 (300 signed copies) . . . . . . £750/£700
ditto, New Directions (U.S.), 1951 (10 signed copies, slipcase) . . . . £2,000/£1,750
Camino Real, New Directions (U.S.), 1953 . £75/£15
ditto, Secker & Warburg, 1958 . . . . £50/£10
Cat on a Hot Tin Roof, New Directions (U.S.), 1955 .
. . . . £300/£45
ditto, Secker & Warburg, 1956 . . . . £200/£35
Suddenly Last Summer, New Directions (U.S.), 1958 .
. . . . £125/£25
A Perfect Analysis Given by a Parrot, Dramatic Play Services (U.S.), [1958] (wraps) £40
Orpheus Descending/Battle of Angels, New Directions, (U.S.), 1958 . . . . . £100/£20
Orpheus Descending, New Directions, (U.S.), 1959 .
. . . . £75/£15
ditto, Secker & Warburg, 1958 . . . . £75/£15
Garden District, Secker & Warburg, 1959 . £75/£15
Sweet Bird of Youth, New Directions (U.S.), 1959 .
. . . . £50/£15
ditto, Secker, 1961 . . . . £40/£10
Period of Adjustment/High Point over a Cavern/A Serious Comedy, New Directions (U.S.), 1960 . .
. . . . £50/£10
ditto, Secker, 1961 . . . . £35/£10
The Night of the Iguana, New Directions (U.S.), 1961
. . . . £75/£15
ditto, Secker, 1963 . . . . £60/£10
The Milk Train Doesn't Stop Here Anymore, New Directions (U.S.), 1964 (first issue, with pp. 19-22 integral and scene 2 staring at p.22) . £200/£100
ditto, New Directions (U.S.), 1964 (second issue, with pp. 19-22 tipped in and scene 2 staring at p.21) . .
. . . . £50/£15
ditto, New Directions (U.S.), 1964 (third issue, with pp.19-22 bound in) . . . . £30/£10
ditto, Secker, 1964 . . . . £45/£10
The Mutilated, Dramatists Play Service (U.S.), 1967 (wraps) £25
The Gnadiges Fraulein, Dramatists Play Service (U.S.), 1967 (wraps) £25
Kingdom of Earth: The Seven Descents of Myrtle, New Directions (U.S.), 1968 . . . . £35/£10

ditto, as *The Kingdom of Earth: The Seven Descents of Myrtle*, Dramatists Play Service (U.S.), 1969 (wraps) £15
The Two-Character Play, New Directions (U.S.), 1969
. . . . £25/£5
In The Bar of a Tokyo Hotel, Dramatists Play Service (U.S.), 1969 (wraps) £20
Small Craft Warnings, New Directions (U.S.), 1972 .
. . . . £25/£5
Vieux Carre, New Directions (U.S.), 1979 . £20/£5
A Lovely Sunday for Creve Coeur, New Directions (U.S.), 1980 . . . . £15/£5
Steps Must Be Gentle, Targ (U.S.), 1980 (350 signed copies, with plain d/w) . . . . £150/£100
Clothes for a Summer Hotel, A Ghost Play, Dramatists Play Service (U.S.), 1981 (wraps) . . . £10
It Happened the Day the Sun Rose, Sylvester & Orphanos (U.S.), 1981 (330 signed copies) . £200
The Remarkable Rooming-House of Mme Le Monde, Albondocani Press (U.S.), 1984 (26 of 176 copies) .
. . . . £100
ditto, Albondocani Press (U.S.), 1984 (150 of 176 copies, wraps) £50
The Red Devil Battery Sign, New Directions (U.S.), 1988 . . . . £25/£5
Not About Nightingales, Methuen, 1998 (wraps) £5

Novels
The Roman Spring of Mrs Stone, New Directions (U.S.), 1950 . . . . £75/£15
ditto, New Directions (U.S.), 1950 (500 signed copies in slipcase) . . . . £300/£250
ditto, Lehmann, 1950 . . . . . . £45/£15
Moise and the World of Reason, Simon & Schuster (U.S.), 1975 . . . . £45/£10
ditto, Simon & Schuster (U.S.), 1975 (350 signed copies) £200

Short Stories
One Arm and Other Stories, New Directions (U.S.), 1948 . . . . £50/£15
ditto, New Directions (U.S.), 1948 (50 signed copies, slipcase) . . . . £1,500/£1,300
ditto, New Directions (U.S.), 1948 (1,500 copies, slipcase) . . . . £150/£125
Hard Candy, A Book of Stories, New Directions (U.S.), 1954 . . . . £40/£15
ditto, New Directions (U.S.), 1954 (1,500 copies on laid paper, slipcase) . . . . . £150/£125
Man Brings This Up Road, Street & Smith (U.S.), 1959 . . . . £35/£10
Three Players of a Summer Game and Other Stories, Secker & Warburg, 1960 . . . . . £65/£15
Grand, House of Books (U.S.), 1964 (26 signed lettered copies, tissue d/w) . . . . £650/£600
ditto, House of Books (U.S.), 1964 (300 signed copies, tissue d/w) . . . . . . £300/£275
The Knightly Quest, A Novella and Four Short Stories, New Directions (U.S.), 1967 . . £35/£10

Eight Mortal Ladies Possessed, A Book of Stories, New Directions (U.S.), 1974 . . . . £25/£10
ditto, Secker & Warburg, 1975 . . . . £20/£5
Collected Stories, New Directions (U.S.), 1985 £15/£5

Screenplays
Baby Doll, The Script for a Film, New Directions (U.S.), 1956 . . . . £175/£50
ditto, Secker & Warburg, 1957 . . . . £150/£45
The Fugitive Kind, Signet (U.S.), 1960 (wraps) £10
Stopped Rocking and Other Screenplays, New Directions (U.S.), 1984 . . . . . . £15/£5

Poetry
In The Winter of Cities, New Directions (U.S.), 1956 .
. . . . £125/£25
ditto, New Directions (U.S.), 1956 (500 signed copies, slipcase) . . . . £750/£600
Androgyne, Mon Amour, New Directions (U.S.), 1977
. . . . £25/£5
ditto, New Directions (U.S.), 1956 (200 signed copies, slipcase) . . . . £250/£200

Other Titles
Lord Byron's Love Letter, An Opera in One Act, Ricordi (U.S.), [1955] . . . . . £45/£10
Memoirs, Doubleday (U.S.), 1975 . . . £35/£15
ditto, Doubleday (U.S.), 1975 (400 signed copies in slipcase) . . . . £250/£200
ditto, W.H. Allen, 1976 . . . . . . £25/£5
Tennessee Williams' Letters to Donald Windham, 1940-1965, Verona, 1976 . . . . £25/£5
ditto, Holt (U.S.), 1977 . . . . . . £25/£5
Where I Live, Selected Essays, New Directions (U.S.), 1976 . . . . £25/£5
Conversations with Tennessee Williams, Univ. Press of Mississippi (U.S.), 1986 . . . . £20/£5

HENRY WILLIAMSON
(b.1895 d.1977)

Williamson's most successful writings are considered to be his nature novels, such as *Tarka the Otter* and *Salar the Salmon*. It is generally acknowledged that these owe a debt to the 19th century naturalist Richard Jefferies. Williamson's right-wing political sympathies during the 1930s did much to damage his reputation.

A Chronicle of Ancient Sunlight Titles
The Dark Lantern, Macdonald, 1951 . . £50/£10
Donkey Boy, Macdonald, 1952 . . . . £50/£10
Young Phillip Maddison, Macdonald, 1953 £50/£10
How Dear is Life, Macdonald, 1954. . . £50/£10
A Fox Under My Cloak, Macdonald, 1955 . £65/£15
The Golden Virgin, Macdonald, 1957 . . £50/£10

Love and The Loveless: A Soldiers Tale, Macdonald, 1958 . . . . £45/£10
A Test To Destruction, Macdonald, 1960 . £40/£10
The Innocent Moon, Macdonald, 1961 . . £40/£10
It Was The Nightingale, Macdonald, 1962 £40/£10
The Power of The Dead, Macdonald, 1963 £40/£10
The Phoenix Generation, Macdonald, 1965 £35/£10
A Solitary War, Macdonald, 1966 . . . £35/£10
Lucifer Before Sunrise, Macdonald, 1967 . £35/£10
The Gale of The World, Macdonald, 1969 . £60/£15

Other Fiction
The Beautiful Years, Collins, 1921 . . £400/£150
ditto, Faber, 1929 (revised edition) . . . £65/£15
ditto, Faber, 1929 (200 signed copies, revised edition).
. . . . £150
ditto, Dutton, 1929 (revised edition). . . £65/£15
Dandelion Days, Collins, 1922 . . . . £100/£20
ditto, Faber, 1930 (revised edition) . . . £35/£10
ditto, Faber, 1930 (200 signed copies, revised edition).
. . . . £150
ditto, Dutton, 1930 (revised edition). . . £35/£10
The Dream of Fair Women, Collins, 1924 . £75/£15
ditto, Faber, 1931 (revised edition) . . . £35/£10
ditto, Faber, 1931 (200 signed copies, revised edition).
. . . . £150
ditto, Dutton, 1931 (revised edition). . . £35/£10
The Peregrin's Saga, Collins, 1923 (600 copies) £100
ditto, as *Sun Brothers*, Dutton (U.S.), 1925 . . £75
The Old Stag, Putnam, 1926 . . . . £100/£25
ditto, Dutton (U.S.), 1927. . . . . . £40/£15
Tarka The Otter, Putnams, 1927 (100 signed copies, privately printed for subscribers) £850
ditto, Putnam, 1927 (1000 copies) £200
ditto, Dutton (U.S.), 1928. . . . . £175/£30
The Pathway, Cape, 1928 . . . . . £65/£10
ditto, Faber, 1931 (200 signed copies) . . £150
ditto, Dutton (U.S.), 1929. . . . . . £50/£10
The Linhay on The Downs and The Firing Gatherer, Woburn Press, 1929 (530 copies) . . . £55/£35
ditto, Cape, 1934 (revised and enlarged edition) . .
. . . . £35/£10
The Patriot's Progress, Bles, 1930 . . . £40/£10
ditto, Bles, [1930] (350 signed copies, slipcase) . .
. . . . £200/£150
ditto, Dutton (U.S.), 1930. . . . . . £35/£10
The Star Born, Faber, 1933 . . . . . £40/£10
ditto, Faber, 1933 (70 signed copies) . . . £300
ditto, Faber, 1948 (revised edition) . . . £20/£5
The Gold Falcon or The Haggard of Love, Faber, 1933 (anonymous) . . . . £65/£25
ditto, Smith & Haas (U.S.), 1933. . . . £50/£15
ditto, Faber, 1947 (revised edition) . . . £20/£5
Salar The Salmon, Faber, 1935 . . . . £125/£20
ditto, Faber, 1935 (13 numbered copies signed and corrected by the author) £1,500
ditto, Little, Brown (U.S.), 1936 . . . £65/£15
The Sun in The Sands, Faber, 1945 . . . £25/£10
The Phasian Bird, Faber, 1948 . . . . £25/£10

ditto, Little, Brown (U.S.), 1950 . . . . £25/£10

Tales of Moorland and Estuary, Macdonald, 1953 .

. . . . £25/£10

Collected Nature Stories, Macdonald, 1970 £10/£5

The Scandaroon, Macdonald, 1972 . . . £20/£5

ditto, Macdonald, 1972 (250 signed copies, slipcase) .

. . . . £75/£50

ditto, Saturday Review Press (U.S.), 1973 . £20/£5

Omnibus Editions

The Flax of Dream, Faber, 1936. . . . £25/£10

ditto, Faber, 1936 (200 copies) £150

Children's

Scribbing Lark, Faber, 1948 . . . . . £25/£10

Non Fiction

The Lone Swallows, Collins, 1922 (500 copies) £65

ditto, Dutton (U.S.), 1926. . . . . £150/£35

ditto, Collins, 1928 (revised edition). . . £35/£10

The Wet Flanders Plain, Beaumont Press, 1929 (80 of 320 copies, signed copies on handmade parchment vellum) £400

ditto, Beaumont Press, 1929 (240 of 320 copies, numbered, on handmade paper) . . . £150

ditto, Faber, 1929 (revised edition) . . £65/£20

ditto, Dutton (U.S.), 1929. . . . . £50/£15

The Ackymals, Windsor Press (U.S.), 1929 (225 signed copies, slipcase) . . . . . £150/£125

The Village Book, Cape, 1930 . . . £35/£10

ditto, Cape, 1930 (504 signed copies) . . £175

ditto, Dutton (U.S.), 1930. . . . . £35/£10

The Wild Red Deer of Exmoor, Faber, 1931 (75 copies) £150

ditto, Faber, 1931 . . . . . . £45/£15

The Labouring Life, Cape, 1932. . . . £50/£15

ditto, Cape, 1932 (122 signed copies, acetate d/w) . .

. . . . £250/£175

ditto, as *As The Sun Shines*, Dutton, 1933 . £30/£10

On Foot in Devon, Maclehose, 1933 . . £50/£15

Devon Holiday, Cape, 1935 . . . . £40/£15

Goodbye West Country, Putnam, 1937 . . £40/£15

ditto, Little, Brown (U.S.), 1938 . . . £40/£10

The Children of Shallowford, Faber, 1939 . £70/£15

ditto, Faber, 1959 (revised edition) . . £15/£5

The Story of a Norfolk Farm, Faber, 1941 . £35/£10

Genius of Friendship - T.E. Lawrence, Faber, 1941 .

. . . . £75/£25

Norfolk Life, Faber, 1943 (with Lilias Rider Haggard)

. . . . £30/£10

Life in a Devon Village, Faber, 1945 . . £20/£5

Tales of a Devon Village, Faber, 1945 . . £20/£5

A Clear Water Stream, Faber, 1958 . . . £20/£5

ditto, Ives Washburn, (U.S.), 1958 . . . £20/£5

In The Woods, St Albert's Press, 1960 (50 numbered and signed copies, wraps) £75

ditto, St Albert's Press, 1960 (950 numbered copies, wraps). £35

A.N. WILSON
(b.1950)

A prolific writer, Wilson is at his best in his tragi-comic novels.

Novels

The Sweets of Pimlico, Secker & Warburg, 1977 . .

. . . . £200/£25

Unguarded Hours, Secker & Warburg, 1978 £100/£15

Kindly Light, Secker & Warburg, 1979 . . £50/£10

The Healing Art, Secker & Warburg, 1980 £35/£15

Who Was Oswald Fish?, Secker & Warburg, 1981 .

. . . . £20/£5

Wise Virgin, Secker & Warburg, 1982 . . £15/£5

ditto, Viking (U.S.), 1983. . . . . £15/£5

Scandal, Hamish Hamilton, 1983 . . . £15/£5

ditto, Viking (U.S.), 1984. . . . . £15/£5

Gentlemen in England, Hamish Hamilton, 1985 .

. . . . £10/£5

ditto, Viking (U.S.), 1986. . . . . £10/£5

Love Unknown, Hamish Hamilton, 1986 . £10/£5

ditto, Viking (U.S.), 1987. . . . . £10/£5

Incline Our Hearts, Hamish Hamilton, 1988 £10/£5

ditto, Viking (U.S.), 1989. . . . . £10/£5

A Bottle in The Smoke, Sinclair-Stevenson, 1989 . .

. . . . £10/£5

ditto, Viking (U.S.), 1990. . . . . £10/£5

Daughters of Albion, Sinclair-Stevenson, 1991 £10/£5

ditto, Viking (U.S.), 1991. . . . . £10/£5

Vicar of Sorrows, Sinclair-Stevenson, 1993 £10/£5

ditto, Norton (U.S.), 1994. . . . . £10/£5

Hearing Voices, Sinclair-Stevenson, 1995 . £10/£5

ditto, Norton (U.S.), 1996. . . . . £10/£5

A Watch in the Night, Sinclair-Stevenson, 1996 £10/£5

ditto, Norton (U.S.), 1996. . . . . . £10/£5

A Watch in the Night, Murray , 1998 . . £10/£5

ditto, Norton (U.S.), 1998. . . . . £10/£5

Biography

The Laird of Abbottsford: A View of Walter Scott, O.U.P., 1980 . . . . £25/£5

The Life of John Milton, O.U.P., 1983 . . £15/£5

Hilaire Belloc, Hamish Hamilton, 1984 . . £10/£5

ditto, Atheneum (U.S.), 1984. . . . . £10/£5

Tolstoy: A Biography, Hamish Hamilton, 1988 £10/£5

ditto, Norton (U.S.), 1988. . . . . £10/£5

Eminent Victorians, BBC, 1989 . . . . £10/£5

ditto, Norton (U.S.), 1990. . . . . £10/£5

C. S. Lewis; A Biography, Collins, 1990 . £10/£5

ditto, Norton (U.S.), 1990. . . . . £10/£5

Jesus, Sinclair-Stevenson, 1992 . . . £10/£5

ditto, Norton (U.S.), 1992. . . . . £10/£5

The Rise and Fall of the House of Windsor, Sinclair-Stevenson, 1993 . . . . . . £10/£5

ditto, Norton (U.S.), 1993. . . . . £10/£5

Paul: The Mind of the Apostle, Norton (U.S.), 1997 .

. . . . £10/£5

Verse
Lilibet: An Account in Verse of The Early Years of
The Queen Until The Time of Her Accession, Blond
& Briggs, 1984 . . . . £10

Essays
How Can We Know? An Essay on The Christian
Religion, Hamish Hamilton, 1985 . . . £10/£5
ditto, Atheneum (U.S.), 1985 . . . . £10/£5
The Church in Crisis, Hodder & Stoughton, 1986
(with Charles Moore and Gavin Stamp, wraps) £5
Penfriends from Porlock: Essay and Reviews, 1977-
1986, Hamish Hamilton, 1988 . . . £10/£5
ditto, Norton (U.S.), 1989 . . . . . £10/£5

Children's
Stray, Walker Books, 1987 . . . . . £15/£5
ditto, Orchard (U.S.), 1989 . . . . £10/£5
The Tabitha Stories, Walker Books, 1988 . £15/£5
ditto, as *Tabitha*, Orchard (U.S.), 1989 . £10/£5
Hazel The Guinea-pig, Walker Books, 1989 £10/£5

Others
Landscape in France, Elm Tree, 1987 . . £10/£5
ditto, St Martin's Press (U.S.), 1988 . . . £10/£5
God's Funeral, Norton, 1999 . . . . £10/£5

ANGUS WILSON
(b.1913 d.1991)

A novelist and short story writer, Wilson's critical
writings are highly regarded, particularly his studies
of Zola and Dickens.

Novels
Hemlock and After, Secker & Warburg, 1952 £30/£5
ditto, Viking (U.S.), 1952 . . . . . £15/£5
Anglo-Saxon Attitudes, Secker & Warburg, 1956 .
. . . . £25/£10
ditto, Viking (U.S.), 1956 . . . . . £15/£5
The Middle Age of Mrs Eliot, Secker & Warburg,
1958 . . . . £20/£5
ditto, Viking (U.S.), 1959 . . . . . £10/£5
The Old Men at The Zoo, Secker & Warburg, 1961 .
. . . . £20/£5
ditto, Viking (U.S.), 1961 . . . . . £10/£5
Late Call, Secker & Warburg, 1964 . . £20/£5
ditto, Viking (U.S.), 1965 . . . . . £10/£5
No Laughing Matter, Secker & Warburg, 1967 £10/£5
ditto, Viking (U.S.), 1967 . . . . . £10/£5
As if by Magic, Secker & Warburg, 1973 . £10/£5
ditto, Viking (U.S.), 1973 . . . . . £10/£5
Setting The World on Fire, Secker & Warburg, 1980 .
. . . . £10/£5
ditto, Viking (U.S.), 1980 . . . . . £10/£5

Stories
The Wrong Set and Other Stories, Secker & Warburg,
1949 . . . . £75/£20
ditto, Morrow (U.S.), 1950 . . . . £65/£10
Such Darling Dodos and Other Stories, Secker &
Warburg, 1950 . . . . £65/£20
ditto, Morrow (U.S.), 1951 . . . . £25/£10
A Bit Off The Map and Other Stories, Secker &
Warburg, 1957 . . . . £15/£5
ditto, Viking (U.S.), 1957 . . . . . £10/£5
Death Dance: 25 Stories, Viking (U.S.), 1969 £10/£5
Collected Stories, Secker & Warburg, 1987 £10/£5
ditto, Viking (U.S.), 1987 . . . . . £10/£5

Plays
The Mulberry Bush, Secker & Warburg, 1956 £30/£10

Others
Emile Zola, Secker & Warburg, 1952 . . £45/£15
ditto, Morrow (U.S.), 1952 . . . . £25/£10
For Whom The Cloche Tolls, Methuen, 1953 (with
Philippe Jullian) . . . . . . £25/£10
ditto, Curtis Books (U.S.), 1953 (wraps) . . £5
The Wild Garden: or, Speaking of Writing, Univ. of
California Press (U.S.), 1963 . . . . £10/£5
ditto, Secker & Warburg, 1963 . . . . £10/£5
Tempo: The Impact of Television on The Arts, Studio
Vista, 1964 . . . . £10/£5
ditto, Dufour (U.S.), 1966 . . . . . £10/£5
The World of Charles Dickens, Secker & Warburg,
1970 . . . . £10/£5
ditto, Viking (U.S.), 1970 . . . . . £10/£5
The Strange Ride of Rudyard Kipling, Secker &
Warburg, 1977 . . . . £15/£5
ditto, Viking (U.S.), 1978 . . . . . £10/£5
Diversity and Depth in Fiction: Selected Critical
Writings, Secker & Warburg, 1983 . . £10/£5
ditto, Viking (U.S.), 1983 . . . . . £10/£5
Reflections in a Writer's Eye, Secker & Warburg,
1986 . . . .
£10/£5
ditto, Viking (U.S.), 1986 . . . . . £10/£5

R.D. WINGFIELD
(b.?)

R.D. Wingfield is the creator of Inspector Jack Frost,
an unconventional policeman who nevertheless
manages to solve several crimes per book.

Verse
Frost at Christmas, Paperjacks (Canada), 1984 (wraps)
. . . . £250
ditto, Paperjacks (U.S.), 1987 (wraps) . . . £50
ditto, Constable, 1990 . . . . . . £150/£20
A Touch of Frost, Paperjacks (U.S.), 1987 (wraps) .
. . . . £200

ditto, Constable, 1990 . . . . . . £2,000/£200
ditto, Post Mortem Books, 1998 (350 signed copies) .
. . . . £65
Night Frost, Constable, 1992. . . . £500/£200
Hard Frost, Scorpion Press, 1995 (85 signed copies) .
. . . . £65
ditto, Constable, 1995 . . . . . . £30/£5
Winter Frost, Constable, 1999 . . . . £20/£5

JEANETTE WINTERSON
(b.1959)

A ·winner of numerous awards, Winterson's first
book, *Oranges Are Not The Only Fruit* remains the
classic.

Novels
Oranges Are Not The Only Fruit, Pandora Press, 1985
(wraps) £250
ditto, Atlantic Monthly Press (U.S.), 1987 (price of
$6.95, wraps). £25
ditto, Guild, 1990 . . . . £65/£10
Boating for Beginners, Methuen, 1985 . . £300/£35
ditto, Methuen, 1985 (wraps). £35
The Passion, Bloomsbury, 1987 . . . . £60/£20
ditto, Atlantic Monthly Press (U.S.), 1988 . £35/£5
Sexing The Cherry, Bloomsbury, 1989 . . £25/£5
ditto, Atlantic Monthly Press (U.S.), 1990 . £15/£5
Written on The Body, Cape, 1992 . . . £15/£5
ditto, Knopf (U.S.), 1993 . . . . . £15/£5
Art and Lies, Cape, 1994 . . . . . £10/£5
ditto, Knopf (U.S.), 1993 . . . . . £10/£5
Gut Symmetries, Granta, 1997 . . . . £10/£5
ditto, Knopf (U.S.), 1997 . . . . . £10/£5
The Powerbook, Cape, 2000 . . . . £10/£5
ditto, Knopf (U.S.), 2000 . . . . . £10/£5

Short Stories
The World and Other Places, Cape, 1998 . £10/£5
ditto, Knopf (U.S.), 1998 . . . . . £10/£5
The Dreaming Place, Ulysses, 1998 (150 signed
copies) £65

Others
Art Objects: Ecstasy and Effrontery, Cape, 1995 . .
. . . . £20/£5
ditto, Knopf (U.S.), 1996 . . . . . £15/£5
Fit for the Future, Pandora Press, 1986 . £150/£30
ditto, Pandora Press, 1986 (wraps) £75

WISDEN CRICKETERS' ALMANACKS

The cricketers' bible.

1864	£6,000
1865	£4,500
1866	£3,500
1867	£2,500
1868	£1,500
1869	£1,500
1870	£1,500
1871	£1,500
1872	£1,500
1873	£1,250
1874	£1,250
1875	£2,000
1876	£750
1877	£750
1878	£400
1879	£500
1880	£400
1881–1889	£300
1890–1895	£250
1896–1899	£750/£250
1900–1915	£750/£150
1916	£750/£600
1917–1919	£350/£150
1920–1930	£150/£100
1930–1940	£200/£125
1941	£400/£200
1942	£300/£150
1943	£350/£150
1944	£250/£120
1945	£120/£80
1946–1950	£80/£60
1950–1969	£25/£20
1970	£30/£20
1971	£35/£25
1972-present	£15/£10

P.G. WODEHOUSE
(b.1881 d.1975)

A prolific comic author, Wodehouse's world is light,
smart, superficial, and if you enjoy his humour,
highly addictive.

Jeeves and Wooster Novels
Thank You, Jeeves, Jenkins, 1934 . . . . £750/£100
ditto, Little, Brown (U.S.), 1934 . . . . £300/£45
Right Ho, Jeeves, Jenkins, 1934 . . . . . £750/£75
ditto, as **Brinkley Manor**, Little, Brown (U.S.), 1934 .
. . . . £300/£45
The Code of The Woosters, Jenkins, 1938 . £600/£45
ditto, Doubleday (U.S.), 1938 . . . . £300/£45

Joy in The Morning, Doubleday (U.S.), 1946 .   .   .
.   .   .   .   £125/£30
ditto, Jenkins, 1947 .   .   .   .   .   .   £100/£25
The Mating Season, Jenkins, 1949 .   .   .   £75/£20
ditto, Didier (U.S.), 1949 .   .   .   .   .   £75/£20
Ring for Jeeves, Jenkins, 1953 .   .   .   .   £75/£20
ditto, as *The Return of Jeeves*, Doubleday (U.S.), 1953
.   .   .   .   £75/£20
Jeeves and The Feudal Spirit, Jenkins, 1954 £100/£25
ditto, as *Bertie Wooster Sees It Through*, Simon &
Schuster (U.S.), 1955 .   .   .   .   .   £75/£20
Jeeves in The Offing, Jenkins, 1960.   .   .   £60/£15
ditto, as *How Right You Are, Jeeves*, Simon &
Schuster (U.S.), 1960 .   .   '   .   .   .   £60/£15
Stiff Upper Lip, Jeeves, Jenkins, 1963 .   .   £50/£15
ditto, Simon & Schuster (U.S.), 1963 .   .   £50/£15
Much Obliged, Jeeves, Barrie & Jenkins, 1971.   .   .
.   .   .   .   £25/£10
ditto, as *Jeeves and The Tie that Binds*, Simon &
Schuster (U.S.), 1971.   .   .   .   .   .   £25/£10
Aunts Aren't Gentlemen, Barrie & Jenkins, 1974 .   .
.   .   .   .   £25/£10
ditto, as *The Cat-Nappers*, Simon & Schuster (U.S.),
1974 .   .   .   .   £25/£10

Jeeves and Wooster Short Stories
The Man With Two Left Feet, Methuen, 1917 . £1,500
ditto, Burt (U.S.), 1933 .   .   .   .   .   £400/£75
My Man Jeeves, Newnes, 1919 (first printing by Butler
& Tanner). £450
The Inimitable Jeeves, Jenkins, 1923 .   £1,750/£75
ditto, as *Jeeves*, Doran (U.S.), 1923 .   . £1,250/£75
Carry On Jeeves, Jenkins, 1925 .   .   .   £750/£75
ditto, Doran (U.S.), 1927 .   .   .   .   .   £600/£50
Very Good, Jeeves, Jenkins, 1930 .   .   £600/£75
ditto, Doubleday (U.S.), 1930 .   .   .   £500/£50
A Few Quick Ones, Jenkins, 1959 .   .   £75/£15
ditto, Simon & Schuster (U.S.), 1959 .   .   £60/£15
Plum Pie, Jenkins, 1966 .   .   .   .   £60/£15
ditto, Simon & Schuster (U.S.), 1967 .   £50/£10

Jeeves and Wooster Omnibus Editions
Jeeves Omnibus, Jenkins, 1931 .   .   .   £500/£45
The World of Jeeves, Jenkins, 1967 .   .   £75/£25

Other Novels
The Pothunters, Black, 1902 (first binding with silver
loving cup on front board and spine, no ads) £2,500
ditto, Black, 1902 (secondary binding with frontis
illustration on front cover, 8pps of ads) .   .   £500
ditto, Macmillan (U.S.), 1924 .   .   £650/£100
A Prefect's Uncle, Black, 1903 .   .   .   £1,750
ditto, Macmillan (U.S.), 1924 .   .   .   £500/£75
The Gold Bat, Black, 1904 .   .   .   .   £1,250
ditto, Macmillan (U.S.), 1923 .   .   .   £500/£75
William Tell Told Again, A. & C. Black, 1904 (first
issue, off-white cloth lettered in gilt on spine and
front cover, top edge gilt, publisher's monogram on
title page, 2pps of ads) £1,000

ditto, A. & C. Black, 1904 (second issue with 12pps of
ads) £500
ditto, A. & C. Black, 1904 (third issue, tan/brown
cloth, gilt lettering on spine only, 2pps of ads, gilt on
cover). £350
ditto, A. & C. Black, 1904 (variant issue, buff cloth,
black lettering) £200
The Head of Kay's, A. & C. Black, 1905 .   £750
ditto, Macmillan (U.S.), 1922 .   .   .   £500/£75
Love Among The Chickens, Newnes, 1906.   . £3,000
ditto, Circle Publishing Co. (U.S.), 1909 .   £750
The White Feather, A. & C. Black, 1907 . £2,000
ditto, Macmillan (U.S.), 1922 .   .   £500/£75
Not George Washington, Cassell, 1907 (written with
H. Westbrook, 'Cassell & Company' on spine) .   .
.   .   .   .   £2,500
ditto, Cassell, 1907 ('Cassell' only on spine) .   £750
ditto, Continuum (U.S.), 1980 .   .   .   £25/£10
The Swoop, Alston Rivers, 1909 (wraps) .   £2,500
Mike, A. & C. Black, 1909 .   .   .   .   £2,000
ditto, Macmillan (U.S.), 1924 .   .   .   £500/£75
ditto, as *Enter PSmith*, Black, 1935 (re-issue of second
part of *Mike*).   .   .   .   .   .   .   £450/£65
ditto, as *Mike at Wrykyn*, Jenkins, 1953, and *Mike and
PSmith*, Jenkins, 1953 (2 vol. re-issue, novel revised)
.   .   .   .   £200/£35
A Gentleman of Leisure, Alston Rivers, 1910 . £1,000
ditto, as *The Intrusion of Jimmy*, Watt (U.S.) 1910 .
.   .   .   .   £400
PSmith in The City, A. & C. Black, 1910 .   £1,250
The Prince and Betty, Mills and Boon, 1912 £1,250
The Prince and Betty, Watt (U.S.), 1912 (different
from above) £600
ditto, as *PSmith Journalist*, A. & C. Black, 1915 .   .
.   .   .   .   £1,000
The Little Nugget, Methuen, 1913 .   .   £1,000
ditto, Watt (U.S.), 1914 .   .   .   .   .   £300
Something Fresh, Methuen, 1915 .   .   . £2,000
ditto, as *Something New*, Appleton (U.S.), 1915 £750
Uneasy Money, Appleton (U.S.), 1916 .   .   £300
ditto, Methuen, 1917 .   .   .   .   .   .   £1,750
Piccadilly Jim, Dodd, Mead (U.S.), 1917 .   £300
ditto, Jenkins, 1918 .   .   .   .   .   .   £750
A Damsel in Distress, Doran (U.S.), 1919 .   £250
ditto, Jenkins, 1919 .   .   .   .   .   .   £650
Their Mutual Child, Boni & Liveright (U.S.), 1919 .
.   .   .   .   £250
ditto, as *The Coming of Bill*, Jenkins, 1920.   .
.   .   .   .   £1,250/£150
The Little Warrior, Doran (U.S.), 1920 .   . £800/£200
ditto, as *Jill The Reckless*, Jenkins, 1921 £1,500/£350
The Girl on The Boat, Jenkins, 1922 . £1,500/£300
ditto, as *Three Men and a Maid*, Doran, 1922 (revised
version) .   .   .   . £600/£125
The Adventures of Sally, Jenkins, 1922 . £1,200/£250
ditto, as *Mostly Sally*, Doran (U.S.), 1923 £600/£125
Leave it to PSmith, Jenkins, 1923 .   . £1,000/£200
ditto, Doran (U.S.), 1923 .   .   .   .   £1,000/£200
Bill The Conqueror, Jenkins, 1924 .   . £1,000/£200

ditto, Doran (U.S.), 1925 . . . . . . £350/£100
Sam The Sudden, Methuen, 1925 . . . £750/£125
ditto, as **Sam in The Suburbs**, Doran (U.S.), 1925 .
. . . . £250/£50
The Small Bachelor, Methuen, 1927 . . £750/£125
ditto, Doran (U.S.), 1927 . . . . . . £250/£50
Money for Nothing, Jenkins, 1928 . . . £750/£125
ditto, Doran (U.S.), 1928 . . . . . £250/£50
Summer Lightning, Jenkins, 1929 . . . £750/£125
ditto, as **Fish Preferred**, Doubleday, 1929 £500/£100
Big Money, Doubleday (U.S.), 1931. . . £250/£50
ditto, Jenkins, 1931 . . . . . . £750/£100
If I Were You, Doubleday (U.S.), 1931 . . £250/£50
ditto, Jenkins, 1931 . . . . . . £500/£100
Doctor Sally, Methuen, 1932. . . . . £450/£100
Hot Water, Jenkins, 1932. . . . . . £450/£100
ditto, Doubleday (U.S.), 1932 . . . . £250/£50
Heavy Weather, Jenkins, 1933 . . . . £500/£125
ditto, Little, Brown (U.S.), 1933 . . . . £500/£125
The Luck of The Bodkins, Jenkins, 1935 . £300/£45
ditto, Little, Brown (U.S.), 1935 . . . . £250/£50
Laughing Gas, Jenkins, 1936 . . . . £400/£100
ditto, Doubleday (U.S.), 1936 . . . . £250/£50
Summer Moonshine, Doubleday (U.S.), 1937 . . .
. . . . £150/£45
ditto, Jenkins, 1938 . . . . . . £400/£100
Uncle Fred in The Springtime, Jenkins, 1939 . . .
. . . . £300/£65
ditto, Doubleday (U.S.), 1939 . . . . £150/£45
Quick Service, Jenkins, 1940. . . . . £150/£25
ditto, Doubleday (U.S.), 1940. . . . £100/£20
Money in The Bank, Doubleday (U.S.), 1942 . . .
. . . . £200/£50
ditto, Jenkins, 1946 . . . . . . £100/£20
Full Moon, Jenkins, 1947 . . . . £100/£25
ditto, Doubleday (U.S.), 1947 . . . . £100/£25
Spring Fever, Doubleday (U.S.), 1948 . £100/£25
ditto, Jenkins, 1948 . . . . . . £100/£25
Uncle Dynamite, Jenkins, 1948 . . . £100/£25
ditto, Didier (U.S.), 1948 . . . . . £100/£25
The Old Reliable, Jenkins, 1951 . . . £75/£15
ditto, Doubleday (U.S.), 1951 . . . . £75/£15
Barmy in Wonderland, Jenkins, 1952 . £75/£15
ditto, as **Angel Cake**, Doubleday (U.S.), 1952 £75/£15
Pigs Have Wings, Jenkins, 1952. . . . £75/£15
ditto, Doubleday (U.S.), 1952 . . . . £75/£15
French Leave, Jenkins, 1956. . . . . £50/£15
ditto, Simon & Schuster, 1959 . . . . £50/£15
Something Fishy, Jenkins, 1957 . . . £50/£15
ditto, as **The Butler Did It**, Simon & Schuster (U.S.),
1957 . . . . £50/£15
Cocktail Time, Jenkins, 1958. . . . £50/£15
ditto, Simon & Schuster (U.S.), 1958 . . £50/£15
The Ice in The Bedroom, Simon & Schuster (U.S.),
1961 . . . . £50/£15
ditto, as **Ice in The Bedroom**, Jenkins, 1961 £50/£15
Service with a Smile, Simon & Schuster (U.S.), 1961 .
. . . . £45/£10
ditto, Jenkins, 1962 . . . . . . £45/£10

Biffen's Millions, Simon & Schuster (U.S.), 1964 . .
. . . . £45/£10
ditto, as **Frozen Assets**, Jenkins, 1964 . . £45/£10
Galahad at Blandings, Jenkins, 1965 . . £40/£10
ditto, as **The Brinkmanship of Galahad Threepwood**,
Simon & Schuster (U.S.), 1967. . . . £30/£10
The Purloined Paperweight, Simon & Schuster (U.S.),
1967 . . . . £50/£15
ditto, as **Company for Henry**, Jenkins, 1967 £65/£20
Do Butlers Burgle Banks?, Simon & Schuster (U.S.),
1968 . . . . £65/£20
ditto, Jenkins, 1968 . . . . . . £75/£20
A Pelican at Blandings, Jenkins, 1969 . . £45/£10
ditto, as **No Nudes is Good Nudes**, Simon & Schuster
(U.S.), 1970 . . . . £30/£10
The Girl in Blue, Barrie & Jenkins, 1970 . £25/£10
ditto, Simon & Schuster (U.S.), 1971 . . £25/£10
Pearls, Girls and Monty Bodkin, Barrie & Jenkins,
1972 . . . . £25/£10
ditto, as **The Plot That Thickened**, Simon & Schuster
(U.S.), 1973 . . . . £25/£10
Bachelors Anonymous, Barrie & Jenkins, 1973 . .
. . . . £25/£10
ditto, Simon & Schuster (U.S.) ,1974 . . £25/£10
Sunset at Blandings, Chatto & Windus, 1977
(unfinished novel, finished by Richard Usborne) .
. . . . £25/£10
ditto, Simon & Schuster (U.S.), 1977 . . £25/£10
Sir Agravaine, Blandford, 1984 . . . . £25/£10

Other Short Stories
Tales of St Austin's, Black, 1903 . . . £750
ditto, Macmillan (U.S.), 1923 . . £650/£50
The Man Upstairs, Methuen, 1914 . . £1,500
Indiscretions of Archie, Jenkins, 1921 . £,1750/£125
ditto, Doran (U.S.), 1921 . . . . . £1,000/£65
The Clicking of Cuthbert, Jenkins, 1922 £1,500/£100
ditto, as **Golf Without Tears**, Doran (U.S.), 1924 .
. . . . £650/£50
Ukridge, Jenkins, 1924 . . . . . £1,500/£75
ditto, as **He Rather Enjoyed It**, Doran (U.S.), 1926 .
. . . . £650/£50
The Heart of a Goof, Jenkins, 1926 . . £1,500/£75
ditto, as **Divots**, Doran (U.S.), 1927 . . . £750/£50
Meet Mr Mulliner, Jenkins, 1927 . . . £750/£35
ditto, Doran (U.S.), 1928 . . . . . £350/£35
Mr Mulliner Speaking, Jenkins, 1929 . . £750/£35
ditto, Doubleday (U.S.), 1930 . . . . £350/£35
Mulliner Nights, Jenkins, 1933 . . . £750/£50
ditto, Doubleday (U.S.), 1933 . . . . £350/£45
Blandings Castle, Jenkins, 1935 . . . £650/£75
ditto, Doubleday (U.S.), 1935 . . . . £300/£65
Young Men in Spats, Jenkins, 1936 . . £600/£75
ditto, Doubleday (U.S.), 1936 . . . . £300/£45
Lord Emsworth and Others, Jenkins, 1937 . £600/£75
ditto, as **Crime Wave at Blandings**, Doubleday (U.S.),
1937 . . . . £300/£50
Eggs, Beans and Crumpets, Jenkins, 1940 . £400/£50
ditto, Doubleday (U.S.), 1940 . . . . £150/£30

Nothing Serious, Jenkins, 1950 . . . . £200/£35
ditto, Doubleday (U.S.), 1951 . . . . £125/£25

Other Omnibus Editions
Nothing but Wodehouse, Doubleday (U.S.), 1932 . .
. . . . £200/£40
Mulliner Omnibus, Jenkins, 1935 . . . £350/£65
Weekend Wodehouse, Jenkins, 1939 . . £350/£65
ditto, Doubleday (U.S.), 1939 . . . . £200/£25
Wodehouse on Golf, Doubleday (U.S.), 1940 £250/£65
The World of Mr Mulliner, Barrie & Jenkins, 1972 .
. . . . £15/£5
ditto, Taplinger (U.S.), 1974 . . . . . £10/£5
The Golf Omnibus, Barrie & Jenkins, 1973 £15/£5
ditto, Simon & Schuster (U.S.), 1974 . . £10/£5
The World of PSmith, Barrie & Jenkins, 1974 £15/£5
The World of Ukridge, Barrie & Jenkins, 1975 £15/£5
The World of Blandings, Barrie & Jenkins, 1975 . .
. . . . £15/£5
The Uncollected Wodehouse, Seabury Press (U.S.),
1976 . . . . £25/£5
Vintage Wodehouse, Barrie & Jenkins, 1977 £15/£5
Tales from The Drones Club, Hutchinson, 1982 . .
. . . . £15/£5
Wodehouse Nuggets, Hutchinson, 1983 . £15/£5
The World of Uncle Fred, Hutchinson, 1983 £10/£5
The World of Wodehouse Clergy, Hutchinson, 1984 .
. . . . £10/£5
The Hollywood Omnibus, Hutchinson, 1985 £10/£5
Wodehouse on Cricket, Hutchinson, 1987 . £10/£5
The Aunts Omnibus, Hutchinson, 1989 . . £10/£5

Autobiography
Performing Flea, Jenkins, 1953 . . . . £75/£20
ditto, as *Author! Author!*, Simon & Schuster (U.S.),
1962 . . . . £45/£15
Bring on The Girls, Simon & Schuster (U.S.), 1953
(with Guy Bolton) . . . . . . £50/£15
ditto, Jenkins, 1954 (differences from above) £50/£15
America I Like You, Simon & Schuster (U.S.), 1956
. . . . £50/£15
ditto, as *Over Seventy*, Jenkins, 1957 (revised) £50/£15

Others
The Globe By The Way Book, Globe, 1907 (written
with H. Westbrook, wraps) £6,000
Louder and Funnier, Faber, 1932 . . . £500/£100
The Parrot and Other Poems, Hutchinson, 1988 . .
. . . . £10/£5
Yours, Plum, Hutchinson, 1990 . . . . £10/£5

TOM WOLFE
(b.1930)

An American novelist and journalist, Wolfe
developed a 'new journalism', reporting hard facts
with a spectacular and emotional graphic style.

Essays
The Kandy-Kolored Tangerine Flake, Farrar Straus
(U.S.), 1965 . . . . £150/£25
ditto, as *Streamline Baby*, Cape, 1966 . . £100/£15
The Pump House Gang, Farrar Straus (U.S.), 1968 .
. . . . £25/£10
ditto, as *The Mid-Atlantic Man and Other New Breeds
in England*, Weidenfeld & Nicolson, 1969 £25/£10
The Electric Kool-Aid Acid Test, Farrar Straus (U.S.),
1968 . . . . £150/£25
ditto, Weidenfeld & Nicolson, 1968 . . . £75/£15
*Mauve Gloves and Madmen, Clutter and Vine and
Other Stories*, Farrar Straus (U.S.), 1976 . £20/£5
In Our Time, Farrar Straus (U.S.), 1980 . £10/£5
ditto, Picador, 1980 (wraps) £5

Journalism and Others
Radical Chic and Mau-Mauing The Flak Catchers,
Farrar Straus (U.S.), 1970 . . . . . £20/£5
ditto, Joseph, 1971. . . . . £20/£5
The Painted Word, Farrar Straus (U.S.), 1975 £15/£5
The Right Stuff, Farrar Straus (U.S.), 1979 £15/£5
ditto, Cape, 1979 . . . . £15/£5
From Bauhaus to Our House, Farrar Straus (U.S.),
1981 . . . . £20/£5
ditto, Farrar Straus (U.S.), 1981 (350 signed, numbered
copies, slipcase) . . . . £150/£125
ditto, Cape, 1982 . . . . £15/£5
A Man in Full, Farrar Straus (U.S.), 1998 . £10/£5
ditto, Farrar Straus (U.S.), 1998 (250 signed, numbered
copies, slipcase) . . . . £150/£125
ditto, Franklin Library (U.S.), 1998 (signed copies) £75
ditto, Cape, 1998 . . . . £10/£5
Hooking Up, Farrar Straus (U.S.), 2000 . £10/£5
ditto, Franklin Library (U.S.), 2000 (signed copies) £75

Fiction
The Purple Decades, Farrar Straus (U.S.), 1982 . .
. . . . £20/£10
ditto, Farrar Straus (U.S.), 1982 (450 signed copies,
slipcase) . . . . £75/£50
ditto, Cape, 1983 . . . . £10/£5
The Bonfire of The Vanities, Farrar Straus (U.S.),
1987 . . . . £30/£10
ditto, Farrar Straus (U.S.), 1987 (250 signed, numbered
copies, slipcase) . . . . £175/£125
ditto, Franklin Library (U.S.), 1987 (signed copies)
. . . . £175/£150
ditto, Cape, 1988 . . . . £25/£5

VIRGINIA WOOLF
(b.1882 d.1941)

Woolf's London home became the centre of the Bloomsbury Group. *To the Lighthouse* and *The Waves*, with their innovative stream-of-consciousness style, brought her to the forefront of Modernism.

Novels

The Voyage Out, Duckworth, 1915	£1,250
ditto, Doran (U.S.), 1920 (revised text)	£1,500/£150
ditto, Duckworth, 1920 (revised text)	£1,250/£150
Night and Day, Duckworth, 1919	£200
ditto, Doran (U.S.), 1920	£1,250/£150
Jacob's Room, Hogarth Press, 1922	£2,500/£500
ditto, Hogarth Press, 1922 (40 signed copies)	£5,000
ditto, Harcourt Brace (U.S.), 1923	£1,000/£250
Mrs Dalloway, Hogarth Press, 1925	£7,500/£750
ditto, Harcourt Brace (U.S.), 1925	£750/£100
To The Lighthouse, Hogarth Press, 1927	£7,500/£750
ditto, Harcourt Brace (U.S.), 1927	£750/£100
Orlando: A Biography, Crosby Gaige (U.S.), 1928 (861 numbered, signed copies)	£1,000
ditto, Hogarth Press, 1928	£750/£100
The Waves, Hogarth Press, 1931	£500/£65
ditto, Harcourt Brace (U.S.), 1931	£150/£25
Flush: A Biography, Hogarth Press, 1933	£200/£35
ditto, Harcourt Brace (U.S.), 1933	£75/£15
The Years, Hogarth Press, 1937	£250/£45
ditto, Harcourt Brace (U.S.), 1937	£75/£15
Between The Acts, Hogarth Press, 1941	£200/£25
ditto, Harcourt Brace (U.S.), 1941	£75/£15

Short Stories

Two Stories, Hogarth Press, 1917 (150 copies, wraps or paper-backed cloth)	£6,000
Kew Gardens, Hogarth Press, 1919 (150 copies, in wraps.)	£4,500
Monday or Tuesday, Hogarth Press, 1921 (1,000 copies)	£1,000
ditto, Harcourt Brace (U.S.), 1921 (cloth and boards)	£750
ditto, Harcourt Brace (U.S.), 1921 (full cloth)	£1,250
A Haunted House, Hogarth Press, 1943	£150/£20
ditto, Harcourt Brace (U.S.), 1944	£65/£15
Nurse Lugton's Golden Thimble, Hogarth Press, 1966 (glassine d/w)	£75/£65
Mrs Dalloway's Party, Hogarth Press, 1973	£30/£10
The Pargiters, Hogarth Press, 1977	£20/£5
ditto, Harcourt Brace (U.S.), 1977	£15/£5

Essays

Mr Bennett and Mrs Brown, Hogarth Press, 1924 (wraps)	£200
The Common Reader, Hogarth Press, 1925.	£1,000/£200
ditto, Harcourt Brace (U.S.), 1925	£350/£75
A Room of One's Own, Fountain Press (U.S.) /Hogarth Press, 1929 (492 signed copies)	£2,500/£1,750
ditto, Hogarth Press, 1929	£500/£75
ditto, Harcourt Brace (U.S.), 1929	£400/£35
Street Haunting, Westgate Press (U.S.), 1930 (500 signed copies, slipcase)	£650/£500
On Being Ill, Hogarth Press, 1930 (250 signed copies)	£1,500/£750
Beau Brummell, Rimington & Hooper (U.S.), (550 signed copies, glassine d/w, slipcase)	£750/£650
A Letter to A Young Poet, Hogarth Press, 1932 (wraps)	£35
The Common Reader: Second Series, Hogarth Press, 1932	£400/£50
ditto, Harcourt Brace (U.S.), 1932	£125/£35
Walter Sickert: A Conversation, Hogarth Press, 1934 (wraps)	£50
The Roger Fry Memorial Exhibition, Bristol, 1935 (125 copies)	£450
Three Guineas, Hogarth Press, 1938	£300/£65
ditto, Harcourt Brace (U.S.), 1938	£200/£40
Reviewing, Hogarth Press, 1939 (wraps)	£25
The Death of The Moth, Hogarth Press, 1942	£75/£20
ditto, Harcourt Brace (U.S.), 1942	£60/£15
The Moment and Other Essays, Hogarth Press, 1947	£50/£15
ditto, Harcourt Brace (U.S.), 1948	£45/£15
The Captain's Death Bed, Harcourt Brace (U.S.), 1950	£65/£20
ditto, Hogarth Press, 1950	£45/£15
Granite and Rainbow, Hogarth Press, 1958	£65/£20
ditto, Harcourt Brace (U.S.), 1958	£45/£15
Contemporary Writers, Hogarth Press, 1965	£25/£5
ditto, Harcourt Brace (U.S.), 1966	£20/£5
Collected Essays, Volume 1-4, Harcourt Brace (U.S.), 1967	£20/£5
Books and Portraits, Hogarth Press, 1977	£15/£5
ditto, Harcourt Brace (U.S.), 1977	£10/£5
The London Scene, Hogarth Press, 1982	£15/£5
ditto, Random House (U.S.), 1982	£10/£5
The Essays of Virginia Woolf, Volume I, Chatto & Windus, 1986.	£30/£10
ditto, Volume II, Chatto & Windus, 1987	£30/£10
ditto, Volume III, Chatto & Windus, 1988	£30/£10
ditto, Volume IV, Chatto & Windus, 1994	£30/£10

Biography

Roger Fry: A Biography, Hogarth Press, 1940.	£250/£35
ditto, Harcourt Brace (U.S.), 1940	£200/£30

Autobiography

Moments of Being, Sussex Univ. Press, 1976	£10/£5
ditto, Harcourt Brace (U.S.), 1976	£25/£5

Play

Freshwater, Hogarth Press, 1976	£25/£5
ditto, Harcourt Brace (U.S.), 1976	£25/£5

Others

A Writer's Diary, Hogarth Press, 1953	£75/£20

ditto, Harcourt Brace (U.S.), 1954 . . . £35/£20
Virginia Woolf and Lytton Strachey: Letters, Hogarth
Press, 1956 . . . . £40/£10
ditto, Harcourt Brace (U.S.), 1956 . . . £30/£10
*The Flight of The Mind: The Letters of Virginia
Woolf, 1888-1912*, Hogarth Press, 1975 . £25/£5
ditto, Harcourt Brace (U.S.), 1975 . . . £25/£5
*The Question of Things Happening: The Letters of
Virginia Woolf, 1912-1922*, Hogarth Press, 1976 .
. . . . £20/£5
ditto, Harcourt Brace (U.S.), 1976 . . . £20/£5
The Diary of Virginia Woolf, Volume 1, 1915-1919,
Hogarth Press, 1977 . . . . . . £15/£5
ditto, Harcourt Brace (U.S.), 1977 . . . £15/£5
*A Change of Perspective: The Letters of Virginia
Woolf, 1923-1928*, Hogarth Press, 1977 . £15/£5
ditto, Harcourt Brace (U.S.), 1977 . . . £15/£5
The Diary of Virginia Woolf, Volume II, 1920-1924,
Hogarth Press, 1978 . . . . . . £15/£5
ditto, Harcourt Brace (U.S.), 1978 . . . £15/£5
*A Reflection of The Other Person: The Letters of
Virginia Woolf, 1929-1931*, Hogarth Press, 1978 .
. . . . £15/£5
ditto, Harcourt Brace (U.S.), 1978 . . . £15/£5
*The Sickle Side of The Moon: The Letters of Virginia
Woolf, 1931-1935*, Hogarth Press, 1979 . £15/£5
ditto, Harcourt Brace (U.S.), 1979 . . . £15/£5
The Diary of Virginia Woolf, Volume III:, 1925-1930,
Hogarth Press, 1980 . . . . . . £15/£5
ditto, Harcourt Brace (U.S.), 1980 . . . £15/£5
*Leave The Letters Till We're Dead: The Letters of
Virginia Woolf, 1936-1941*, Hogarth Press, 1980 .
. . . . £15/£5
ditto, Harcourt Brace (U.S.), 1980 . . . £15/£5
The Diary of Virginia Woolf Volume IV, 1931-1935,
Hogarth Press, 1982 . . . . . . £15/£5
ditto, Harcourt Brace (U.S.), 1982 . . . £15/£5
The Diary of Virginia Woolf, Volume V, 1936-1941,
Chatto & Windus, 1984 . . . . . £15/£5
ditto, Harcourt Brace (U.S.), 1984 . . . £15/£5
Paper Darts: The Illustrated Letters, Collins & Brown,
1992 . . . . £15/£5

S. FOWLER WRIGHT
(b.1874 d.1965)

One of the key authors of science fiction in the U.K.,
Wright paid for the publication of his earliest books,
but soon found himself a bestseller with *Deluge*.

Poetry
Scenes from the Morte d'Arthur, Erskine Macdonald,
1919 (pseud. 'Alan Seymour') £45
Some Songs of Bilitis, Poetry, [1921] . . . £45
The Song of Songs and Other Poems, Merton Press,
[1925]. £45

ditto, Cosmopolitan Book Corp. (U.S.) 1929 £100/£30
The Ballad of Elaine, Merton Press, 1926 . . £45
The Riding of Lancelot: A Narrative Poem, Fowler
Wright, 1929 . . . . £45

Novels
The Amphibians, Swan Press, 1925 . . £1,500/£450
ditto, Merton Press, 1925 . . . . . £250/£45
Deluge, Fowler Wright, 1927 . . . . £175/£35
ditto, Cosmopolitan Book Corp. (U.S.) 1929 £75/£20
The Island of Captain Sparrow, Gollancz, 1928 .
. . . . £200/£25
ditto, Cosmopolitan Book Corp. (U.S.) 1928 £45/£15
The World Below, Collins, 1929 . . . . £200/£35
ditto, Longmans, Green & Co (U.S.), 1930. £200/£45
ditto, Shasta (U.S.), 1949 . . . . . £25/£10
ditto, Shasta (U.S.), 1949 (500 signed copies) £75/£45
Dawn, Cosmopolitan Book Corp. (U.S.) 1929 .
. . . . £100/£30
ditto, Harrap, 1930 . . . . . . £100/£30
Elfwin, Harrap, 1930 . . . . . . £100/£25
ditto, Longmans, Green & Co. (U.S.), 1930 £75/£25
Dream; or, The Simian Maid, Harrap, 1931 . . .
. . . . £100/£25
Seven Thousand in Israel, Jarrolds, 1931 . £100/£25
Red Ike, Hutchinson, [1931] (with J.M. Denwood) .
. . . . £45/£10
Beyond the Rim, Jarrolds, 1932 . . . . £100/£25
Lord's Right in Languedoc, Jarrolds, 1933 . £75/£20
Power, Jarrolds, 1933 . . . . . . £75/£20
David, Butterworth, 1934 . . . . . £45/£10
Prelude in Prague: A Story of the War in 1938,
Newnes, 1935 . . . . £45/£10
ditto, as *The War of 1938*, Putnam's (U.S.), 1936 . .
. . . . £45/£10
Four Days War, Hale, 1936 . . . . . £200/£45
Megiddo's Ridge, Hale, 1937 . . . . £200/£45
The Screaming Lake, Hale, [1937] . . . £200/£45
The Adventure of Wyndham Smith, Jenkins, 1938 .
. . . . £250/£65
The Hidden Tribe, Hale, 1938 . . . . £200/£45
Ordeal of Barrata, Jenkins, 1939 . . . £45/£10
The Siege of Malta, Muller, 1942 (2 vols) . £60/£20
The Throne of Saturn, Heinemann, 1951 . £45/£10
ditto, Arkham House (U.S.), 1949 . . . £40/£10
Spider's War, Abelard Press (U.S.), 1954 . £30/£10

Short Stories
The New Gods Lead, Jarrolds, 1932 . . . £100/£25
The Witchfinder, Books of Today, 1946 . £40/£10

Novels by 'Sidney Fowler'
The King Against Anne Bickerton, Harrap, 1930 . .
. . . . £75/£20
The Bell Street Murders, Harrap, 1931 . . £75/£20
ditto, Macaulay (U.S.), 1931 . . . . . £75/£20
By Saturday, Lane, 1931 . . . . . £75/£20
The Hanging of Constance Hillier, Jarrolds, 1931. .
. . . . £75/£20

The Hand-Print Mystery, Jarrolds, 1932 . £75/£20
ditto, as *Crime and Co*, Macaulay (U.S.), 1931. . .
. . . . £75/£20
Arresting Delia, Jarrolds, 1933 . . . . £75/£20
ditto, Macaulay (U.S.), 1933 . . . . . £75/£20
The Secret of the Screen, Jarrolds, 1933 . £75/£20
Who Else But She?, Jarrolds, 1934 . . . £75/£20
Three Witnesses, Butterworth, 1935. . . £75/£20
Vengeance of Gwa, Butterworth, 1935 (pseud.
'Anthony Wingrave'). . . . . . . £75/£20
ditto, as *The Vengeance of Gwa*, Books of Today,
1945 (by S. Fowler Wright) . . . . £75/£20
The Attic Murders, Temple, 1936 . . . £75/£20
Was Murder Done?, Butterworth, 1936. . £75/£20
Post-Mortem Evidence, Butterworth, 1936 . £75/£20
Four Callers in Razor Street, Temple, 1937 £75/£20
The Jordan's Murder, Jenkins, 1938 . . £75/£20
The Murder in Bethnal Square, Jenkins, 1938. . .
. . . . £75/£20
The Wills of Jane Kantwhistle, Jenkins, 1939 £75/£20
A Bout with the Mildew Gang, Eyre & Spottiswoode,
1941 . . . . £75/£20
The Rissole Mystery, Rich & Cowan, 1941 . £75/£20
A Second Bout with the Mildew Gang, Eyre &
Spottiswoode, 1942 . . . . £75/£20
Dinner in New York, Eyre & Spottiswoode, 1943 . .
. . . . £75/£20
The End of the Mildew Gang, Eyre & Spottiswoode,
1944 . . . . £75/£20
The Adventure of the Blue Room, Rich & Cowan,
1945 . . . . £75/£20
Too Much for Mr Jellipot, Eyre & Spotiswoode, 1945
. . . . £75/£20
Who Murdered Reynard?, Rich & Cowan, 1947 . .
. . . . £75/£20
With Cause Enough?, Harvill, 1954 . . £75/£20

Non Fiction
Police and Public: A Political Pamphlet, Fowler
Wright, 1929 . . . . £20
The Life of Sir Walter Scott: A Biography, Poetry
League, [1932] . . . . £35/£15
Should We Surrender Colonies?, Readers Library
Publishing Co., [1939] £15

Translation
*The Inferno From the Divine Comedy of Dante
Alighieri*, Fowler Wright, 1928. . . . £100/£45

JOHN WYNDHAM
(b.1903 d.1969)

Wyndham is the pen name used by John Wyndham
Parkes Lucas Beynon Harris, and he has written under
several other variations of his name. He is best known
for his peculiarly British science fiction novels.

Novels
The Secret People, Newnes [1935] (pseud. 'John
Beynon') . . . . £300/£75
ditto, Lancer (U.S.), 1964 (pseud. 'John Beynon
Harris', wraps) £10
Foul Play Suspected, Newnes [1935] (pseud. 'John
Beynon') . . . . £300/£75
Planet Plane, Newnes [1936] (pseud 'John Beynon') .
. . . . £250/£45
ditto, as *Stowaway to Mars*, Nova, 1953 (wraps) £20
Love in Time, Utopian Publications, 1945 (pseud.
'Johnson Harris'). . . . . £250/£45
The Day of The Triffids, Doubleday (U.S.), 1951 . .
. . . . £300/£45
ditto, Michael Joseph, 1951 . . . . . £300/£45
The Kraken Wakes, Michael Joseph, 1953 . £125/£25
ditto, Ballantine (U.S.), 1953 (cloth). . £150/£25
ditto, Ballantine (U.S.), 1953 (wraps) . . £20
Re-Birth, Ballantine (U.S.), 1955 (cloth) . £125/£25
ditto, Ballantine (U.S.), 1955 (wraps) . . £20
ditto, as *The Chrysalids*, Michael Joseph, 1955. . .
. . . . £100/£20
The Midwich Cuckoos, Michael Joseph, 1957 . . .
. . . . £100/£20
ditto, Ballantine (U.S.), 1957. . . . . £75/£15
Trouble with Lichen, Michael Joseph, 1960 £45/£10
ditto, Ballantine (U.S.), 1960 (wraps) . . £10
Chocky, Michael Joseph, 1968 . . . . £35/£10
ditto, Ballantine (U.S.), 1968 (wraps) . . £10
Web, Michael Joseph, 1979 . . . . £20/£5

Short Stories
Jizzle, Dennis Dobson, 1954 . . . . £125/£30
Seeds of Time, Michael Joseph, 1956 . £75/£15
Tales of Gooseflesh and Laughter, Ballantine (U.S.),
1956 (wraps) £10
The Outward Urge, Michael Joseph, 1959 (with 'Lucas
Parkes') . . . . £65/£15
ditto, Science Fiction Books Club, 1959 (1 extra story)
. . . . £30/£10
ditto, Ballantine (U.S.), 1959 (wraps) . . £10
Consider Her Ways, Michael Joseph, 1961 . £30/£10
The Infinite Moment, Ballantine (U.S.), 1961 (wraps)
. . . . £10
A John Wyndham Omnibus, Michael Joseph, 1964 .
. . . . £35/£10
The Best of John Wyndham, Sphere, 1973 (wraps) £5
ditto, as *The Man from Beyond*, Michael Joseph, 1975
. . . . £10/£5
Wanderers of Time, Coronet, 1973 (wraps) £5
ditto, Severn House, 1980. . . . . £10/£5

Sleepers of Mars, Coronet, 1973 (wraps) . . £5
ditto, Severn House, 1980. . . . . . £10/£5
Exiles on Asperus, Coronet, 1979 (wraps) . . £5
ditto, Severn House, 1979. . . . . . £10/£5

Others
Love in Time, Utopian Publications, 1946 (pseud. 'Johnson Harris'). £50

THE YELLOW BOOK

A literary and art periodical considered to be outrageous and decadent in its day. Many contributors went on to become major literary figures. It was Aubrey Beardsley's distinctive artwork that upset most commentators.

Volume 1, Matthews & Lane, April, 1894 . . £35
Volume 2, Matthews & Lane, July, 1894 . . £35
Volume 3, Lane/Bodley Head, October, 1894 . £35
Volume 4, Lane/Bodley Head, January, 1895 . £35
Volume 5, Lane/Bodley Head, April, 1895 . . £25
Volume 6, Lane/Bodley Head, July, 1895 . . £25
Volume 7, Lane/Bodley Head, October, 1895 . £25
Volume 8, Lane/Bodley Head, January, 1896 . £25
Volume 9, Lane/Bodley Head, April, 1896 . . £25
Volume 10, Lane/Bodley Head, July, 1896 . . £25
Volume 11, Lane/Bodley Head, October, 1896 . £25
Volume 12, Lane/Bodley Head, January, 1897 . £25
Volume 13, Lane/Bodley Head, April, 1897 . £25
Complete set, (evenly coloured spines) . . . £750

APPENDIX

CHINUA ACHEBE (b.1930)
Things Fall Apart, Heinemann, 1958 . . £150/£45
ditto, Obolensky (U.S.), 1959 . . . . £75/£20

W. HARRISON AINSWORTH (b.1805 d.1882)
The Tower of London, Bentley, 1840 (13 parts in 12,
wraps). £650
ditto, Bentley, 1840 . . . . £450

LOUISA MAY ALCOTT (b.1832 d.1888)
Little Women, Roberts Bros (U.S.), 1868-69 (2 vols) .
. . . . £10,000

RICHARD HARRIS BARHAM (b.1788 d.1845)
The Ingoldsby Legends, Bentley, 1840-42-47 (3 vols).
. . . . £650

WILLIAM BECKFORD (b.1759 d.1844)
An Arabian Tale, Johnson, 1786 (a.k.a. *Vathek*,
anonymous) £650

THOMAS BEWICK (b.1753 d.1828)
A General History of Quadrupeds, Bewick, Beilby &
Hodgson, 1790 . . . . £600

R.D. BLACKMORE (b.1825 d.1900)
Lorna Doone, Sampson Low & Marston, 1869 (3 vols)
. . . . £1,000

WILLIAM BLAKE (b.1757 d.1827)
Songs of Innocence and Experience, 1789 £200,000

ROLF BOLDREWOOD (b.1826 d.1915)
Robbery Under Arms, Remington, 1888 (3 vols) . .
. . . . £1,500

GEORGE BORROW (b.1803 d.1881)
Wild Wales, Murray, 1862 (3 vols) £250

JAMES BOSWELL (b.1740 d.1795)
The Life of Samuel Johnson, Baldwin, Dilly, 1791 (2
vols with 'gve' on p.235 of first volume) . £4,000

JOHN BUNYAN (b.1628 d.1688)
The Pilgrim's Progress, Nath. Ponder, Peacock, 1678 .
. . . . £75,000

FANNY BURNEY (b.1752 d.1840)
Evelina, or A Young Lady's Entrance into the World,
Lowndes, 1778 (anonymous, 3 vols) . £6,000
Cecilia, or Memoires of an Heiress, Payne & Cadell,
1782 ('By the Author of Evelina', 5 vols) . £1,000

ROBERT BURNS (b.1759 d.1796)
Poems, Chiefly in the Scottish Dialect, Wilson, 1786 .
. . . . £10,000

ROBERT BURTON (b.1577 d.1640)
The Anatomy of Melancholy, Lichfield & Short for
Henry Cripps, 1621 . . . . £20,000

SAMUEL BUTLER (b.1835 d.1902)
Erewhon or Over the Range, Trubner & Co, 1831
(anonymous) £150
The Way of All Flesh, Grant Richards, 1903 . £300

ERSKINE CHILDERS (b.1870 d.1922)
The Riddle of the Sands, Smith Elder, 1903 £1,000

SAMUEL TAYLOR COLERIDGE (b.1772
d.1834)
Lyrical Ballads, Longman, 1798 . . . . £10,000

WILLIAM CONGREVE (b.1670 d.1729)
The Way of the World, Tonson, 1700 . . . £2,000

STEPHEN CRANE (b.1871 d.1900)
The Red Badge of Courage, Appleton (U.S.), 1895 .
. . . . £2,000

W. H. DAVIES (b.1871 d.1940)
The Autobiography of a Super-Tramp, Fifield, 1908
. . . . £100

THOMAS DE QUINCEY (b.1785 d.1859)
Confessions of an English Opium Eater, Taylor &
Hessey, 1822 . . . . £1,000

CHARLES M. DOUGHTY (b.1843 d.1926)
Travels in Arabia Deserta, C.U.P., 1888 (2 vols) . .
. . . . £1,750

EDWARD FITZGERALD (b.1809 d.1883)
Rubáiyát of Omar Khayyám, Quaritch, 1859 £10,000

JOHN GAY (b.1685 d.1732)
The Beggar's Opera, Watts, 1728 . . . . £600

OLIVER GOLDSMITH (b.1730 d.1774)
The Vicar of Wakefield, Newbery, 1766 (2 vols,
anonymous) £2,000

NADINE GORDIMER (b.1923)
Face to Face, Silver Leaf Books (Johannesburg), 1949
. . . . £650/£65

KENNETH GRAHAME (b.1859 d.1932)
Wind in the Willows, Methuen, 1908 . . . £2,000

JOHN GRAY (b.1866 d.1934)
Silverpoints, Elkin Mathews & John Lane, 1893 (250 numbered copies) £1,000

GEORGE and WEEDON GROSMITH (b.1847 d.1912, and b.1854 d.1919,)
The Diary of a Nobody, Arrowsmith, 1892 . . £300

E. T. A. HOFFMANN (b.1776 d.1822)
The Devil's Elixir, Blackwood & Cadell, 1824 (2 vols)
. . . . £350
Hoffmann's Strange Stories from the German, Burnham Brothers (U.S.), 1855 . . . . . £350
Hoffmann's Fairy Tales, Burnham Brothers (U.S.), 1857 . . . . £350

HEINRICH HOFFMANN (b.1809 d.1894)
The English Struwwelpeter, or Pretty Stories and Funny Pictures for Little Children, Leipzig, 1848, (first English edition) £4,000

W.H. HUDSON (b.1841 d.1922)
The Purple Land, Sampson Low, 1885 . . £1,000

THOMAS HUGHES (b.1822 d.1896)
Tom Brown's Schooldays, Macmillan, 1857 . £500

SHIRLEY JACKSON (b.1916 d.1965)
The Haunting of Hill House, Viking (U.S.), 1959. .
. . . . £450/£50
ditto, Joseph, 1960. . . . . £125/£25

LIONEL JOHNSON (b.1867 d.1902)
Poems, Elkin Mathews/Copeland & Day, 1895 (25 signed copies) £4,000
ditto, Elkin Mathews/Copeland & Day, 1895 (750 copies) £500

SAMUEL JOHNSON (b.1709 d.1784)
A Dictionary of the English Language, various publishers, 1775 (2 vols) £7,500

BEN JONSON (b.1572 d.1637)
The Workes of Benjamin Jonson, [first volume], Will Stansby, 1616 . . . .£2,000
ditto, [second volume], Richard Meighen, 1640 £1,500

NIKOS KAZANTZAKIS (b.1885 d.1957)
Zorba the Greek, Lehman, 1952 . . . £200/£25
ditto, Simon & Schuster (U.S.), 1953 . £100/£15

CHARLES KINGSLEY (b.1819 d.1875)
The Water Babies, Macmillan, 1863 (first issue, containing 'L'Envoi') £600

CHARLES LAMB (b.1775 d.1834)
Tales From Shakespeare, Hodgkins, 1807 (2 vols) .
. . . . £1,500

MATTHEW GREGORY LEWIS (b.1775 d.1818)
The Monk, Bell, [March] 1796 (1st issue with 'In Three Volumes' *above* quotation on title page, 3 vols)
. . . . £3,000
ditto, Bell, [April] 1796 (2nd issue with 'In Three Volumes' *below* quotation on title page, 3 vols) . .
. . . .£1,750

ANITA LOOS (b.1893 d.1981)
Gentlemen Prefer Blondes, Boni & Liveright, (U.S.), 1925 (1st issue with 'Divine' for 'Devine' on contents page) . . . . £200/£25
ditto, Brentano's, 1926 . . . . . . £40/£15
ditto, Brentano's, 1926 (1,000 signed copies) . £100

EDWARD BULWER LYTTON (b.1803 d.1873)
The Last Days of Pompeii, Bentley, 1834 (anonymous, 3 vols) £500

RICHARD MARSH (b.1857 d.1915)
The Beetle, Skeffington, 1897 . . . . . £300

Rev. C.R. MATURIN (b.1782 d.1824)
Melmoth the Wanderer, Constable, 1820 (4 vols) . .
. . . . £1,750

HERMAN MELVILLE (b.1819 d.1891)
The Whale, Bentley, 1851 (3 vols) . . . £75,000
ditto, as *Moby Dick*, Harper (U.S.), 1851 . £15,000

JOHN MILTON (b.1608 d.1674)
Paradise Lost, Parker, 1667 . . . . . £30,000
Paradise Regain'd, Starkey, 1671 . . . £1,500

MICHAEL MOORCOCK (b.1939)
The Stealer of Souls, Neville Spearman, 1963 (orange boards) . . . . £125/£100
ditto, Neville Spearman, 1963 (green boards) £35/£10
Stormbringer, Herbert Jenkins, 1965 . . £150/£45
Caribbean Crisis, Fleetway Publications, 1962 (with Jim Cawthorne, pseud. 'Desmond Reid', wraps) £75

BILL NAUGHTON (b.1910 d.1992)
Alfie, MacGibbon & Kee, 1966 . . . . £50/£10

BARONESS ORCZY (b.1865 d.1947)
The Scarlet Pimpernel, Greening, 1905 . . . £200

JOHN POLIDORI (b.1795 d.1821)
The Vampyre, Sherwood, Neely & Jones, 1819 . .
. . . .£2,000

ALEXANDER POPE (b.1688 d.1744)
The Rape of the Lock, Lintott, 1714 (wraps) £4,500

MARIO PUZO (b.1920)
The Godfather, Putnam (U.S.), 1969 . . £200/£25
ditto, Heinemann, 1969 . . . . . . £45/£15

THOMAS PYNCHON (b.1937)
V, Lippincott (U.S.), 1963 (first issue d/w without reviews) . . . . £1000/£65
ditto, Cape, 1963 . . . . £200/£30

CHARLES READE (b.1814 d.1884)
The Cloister and the Hearth, Trubner, 1861 (4 vols) .
. . . . £1,000

SAMUEL RICHARDSON (b.1689 d. 1761)
Pamela, Rivington, 1741-1742 (4 vols) . . £5,000

CHRISTINA ROSSETTI (b.1830 d. 1894)
Goblin Market, Macmillan, 1862 . . . £1,000

DANTE GABRIEL ROSSETTI (b.1828 d. 1882)
Poems, privately printed, 1869 (wraps) . . £1,500
ditto, Ellis, 1870 . . . . £250

PHILIP ROTH (b.1933)
Goodbye Columbus and *Five Short Stories*, Houghton Mifflin (U.S.), 1959 . . . . . . £500/£50
ditto, Deutsch, 1959 . . . . . . £100/£20

SIR WALTER SCOTT (b.1771 d.1832)
Ivanhoe, Constable, 1820 (3 vols) £500

RONALD SEARLE (b.1920)
Hurrah for St Trinian's, Macdonald, 1948 . £45/£10
ditto, Macdonald (U.S.), 1948 . . . . £35/£10

PETER SHAFFER (b.1926)
Equus, Deutsch, 1973 . . . . . . £65/£15
ditto, Atheneum (U.S.), 1974 . . . . £35/£10

PERCY BYSSHE SHELLEY (b.1792 d.1822)
Queen Mab, privately printed, 1812 (with title page) .
. . . . £7,500
ditto, privately printed, 1812 (without title page) £650
Poetical Works, Kelmscott Press (1894-1895) (250 copies, 3 vols) £1,500

EDMUND SPENSER (b.1552 d.1599)
The Faerie Queen, Ponsonbie, 1590-1596 (2 vols) .
. . . . £15,000

LAURENCE STERNE (b.1713 d.1768)
The Life and Opinions of Tristram Shandy, Gentleman, Ravanat & Dodsley, 1760-67 (9 vols) .
. . . . £4,000

WALLACE STEVENS (b.1879 d.1955)
Harmonium, Knopf (U.S.), 1923 . . £2,500/£450
Idea of Order, Alcestis (U.S.), 1935 (135 signed copies, glassine d/w, slipcase) . . £1,500/£1,000
ditto, Knopf (U.S.), 1936 . . . . . . £500/£75

HARRIET BEECHER STOWE (b.1811 d.1896)
Uncle Tom's Cabin, Jewett (U.S.), 1852 (2 vols, wraps) £6,000
ditto, Cassell, 1852 . . . . . . £1,000

WILLIAM STYRON (b.1925)
Lie Down in Darkness, Bobbs-Merrill (U.S.), 1951
. . . . £200/£30

ELIZABETH TAYLOR (b.1912 d.1976)
At Mrs Lippincote's, Davies, 1945 . . . £100/£20
ditto, Knopf (U.S.), 1946 . . . . . £65/£15

COLIN WILSON (b.1931)
The Outsider, Gollancz, 1956 . . . . £75/£15
ditto, Houghton Mifflin (U.S.), 1956 . . £45/£15

LEONARD WOOLF (b.1880 d.1969)
The Village in the Jungle, Arnold, 1913 (U.S.), 1852
. . . . £200/£25
ditto, Harcourt Brace (U.S.), 1926 . . . £35/£10

WILLIAM BUTLER YEATS (b.1865 d.1939)
Poems, Unwin, 1895 . . . . £500
ditto, Unwin, 1895 (25 signed copies) . . £5,000
ditto, Copeland & Day (U.S.), 1895 . . . . £500